DATE DUE

FOLLETT

NOTABLE

SCIENTISTS

FROM 1900 TO THE PRESENT

NOTABLE
SCIENTISTS
FROM 1900 TO THE PRESENT

**VOLUME
5
T-Z
INDEXES**

Brigham Narins, Editor

While every effort has been made to ensure the reliability of the information presented in this publication, The Gale Group does not guarantee the accuracy of the data contained herein. Gale accepts no payment for listing; and inclusion in the publication of any organization, agency, institution, publication, service, or individual does not imply endorsement of the editors or publisher. Errors brought to the attention of the publisher and verified to the satisfaction of the publisher will be corrected in future editions.

∞™ This book is printed on acid-free paper that meets the minimum requirements of American National Standard for Information Sciences-Permanence Paper for Printed Library Materials, ANSI Z39.48-1984.

Contents

Introduction

Every year The Gale Group receives numerous requests from librarians for sources providing biographical information. *Notable Scientists: 1900 to the Present* has been designed specifically to fill a niche for scientific biographies. This set, which is the updated second edition of *Notable Twentieth-Century Scientists* and its accompanying volume, *Notable Twentieth-Century Scientists Supplement,* provides students, educators, librarians, researchers, and general readers with an affordable and comprehensive source of biographical information on approximately 1,600 scientists active in the twentieth century in all of the natural, physical, and applied sciences, including the traditionally studied subjects of astronomy, biology, botany, chemistry, earth science, mathematics, medicine, physics, technology, and zoology, as well as the more recently established and as yet sparsely covered fields of computer science, ecology, engineering, and environmental science. *Notable Scientists: 1900 to the Present* is international in scope, and its coverage ranges from the well-known scientific giants of the early twentieth century to contemporary scientists working on the latest advances in their fields.

Superior Coverage of Women, Minority, and Non-Western Scientists

Addressing the growing interest in and demand for biographical information on women, minority, and non-Western scientists, *Notable Scientists: 1900 to the Present* also seeks to bring to light the achievements of women scientists, Asian American, African American, Hispanic American, and Native American scientists, as well as scientists from countries outside North America and Western Europe. Due to the scarcity of published information on these scientists, information for many of the sketches on these listees has been obtained through telephone interviews and correspondence with the scientists themselves or with their universities, companies, laboratories, or families. Our hope is that in presenting these entries, we are providing a basis for future research on the lives and contributions of these important and historically marginalized segments of the scientific community.

Inclusion Criteria

A preliminary list of scientists was compiled from a wide variety of sources, including established reference works, history of science indexes, science periodicals, awards lists, and suggestions from organizations and associations. The advisory board evaluated the names and made suggestions for inclusion. Final selection of names to include was made by the editors on the basis of the following criteria:

■ Discoveries, inventions, overall contributions, influence, or impact on scientific progress in the twentieth century

■ Receipt of a major science award, including Nobel Prizes in Physics, Chemistry, and Physiology or Medicine, the Fields Medal (mathematics), Albert Lasker awards (medicine), the Tyler Prize (environmental science), the National Medal of Science, and the National Medal of Technology

■ Involvement or influence in education, organizational leadership, or public policy

■ Familiarity to the general public

Notable "first" achievements, including degrees earned, positions held, or organizations founded; several listees involved in the first space flights are also included

Entries Provide Easy Access to Information

Entries are arranged alphabetically by surname. The typical *Notable Scientists: 1900 to the Present* entry provides the following information:

Entry head—offers at-a-glance information: name, birth/death dates, nationality, and primary field(s) of specialization.

Biographical essay—ranges from 400 to 2500 words and provides basic biographical information, including date and place of birth, name(s) of spouse(s) and children, educational background and degrees earned, etc. The primary focus of the essay, however, is the subject's scientific endeavors and achievements, all of which are explained in prose accessible to high school students and readers who do not possess a scientific background. Headings within the essays highlight the significant events in the subject's life and career, allowing readers to easily find information they seek. Bold-faced names in the entries direct readers to other entries found in *Notable Scientists: 1900 to the Present.*

Selected Writings by the Scientist section—lists representative publications, including important papers, textbooks, research works, autobiographies, lectures, etc.

Further Reading section—provides citations of biographies, interviews, periodicals, obituaries, and other sources about the subject for readers seeking additional information.

Indexes Provide Numerous Points of Access

In addition to the complete list of scientists and the Chronology of Scientific Advancement found at the beginning of each volume, readers seeking more information can consult the four indexes at the end of Volume 5 for additional listings:

Field of Specialization Index—groups listees according to the scientific fields to which they have contributed.

Gender Index—provides lists of the women and men covered.

Nationality/Ethnicity Index—arranges listees by country of birth, citizenship, or ethnic heritage.

Comprehensive Subject Index—provides volume and page references for scientists and scientific terms used in the text. Includes cross references.

Photographs

Individuals in *Notable Scientists: 1900 to the Present* come to life in the 443 photos of the scientists.

Advisory Board

Contributors

Russell Aiuto, Ethan E. Allen, Julie Anderson, Olga K. Anderson, Denise Irene Arnold, Kenneth E. Ball, Nancy Bard, Dorothy J. Barnhouse, Jeffrey Bass, Karl Leif Bates, Madeleine D. Beckman, Matthew A. Bille, Maurice Bleifeld, Michael J. Boersma, Ervin Bonkalo, Janice Borzendowski, Barbara Boughton, Stephen Bowlsby, Barbara Branca, Barbara A. Branch, Hovey Brock, Michael Broder, Tammy J. Bronson, Valerie J. Brown, Leonard C. Bruno, Ray Bullock, Bryan H. Bunch, Margorie Burgess, Gerard Buskes, Joe Cain, Jill Carpenter, Chris Cavette, Katherine Chapin, Dennis W. Cheek, Kenneth Chiacchia, Miyoko Chu, Jacquelyn Coggin, Anne Compliment, Jane Stewart Cook, Kelly Cooper, Victor I. Cox, G. Scott Crawford, Thomas P. Crawford, Wendy Crooks-Frazier, Wilbur Cross, Michael T. Cruz, Antonella Cupillari, Karin M Deck, Lori DeMilto, Margaret DiCanio, Mindi Dickstein, Laurie DiMauro, Simon Dixon, Rowan L. Dordick, John Henry Dreyfuss, Thomas Drucker, Kala Dwarakanath, Marianne Fedunkiw, Martin R. Feldman, Eliseo Fernandez, George A. Ferrance, Jerome P. Ferrance, James R. Flanders, William Fletcher, David N. Ford, Fran Locher Freiman, Randall Frost, George L. Garrigues, Amanda de la Garza, Karyn Hede George, C. J. Giroux, Sheila Gray, Chris Hables Gray, Loretta Hall, Bridget K. Hall, Ernst P. Hamm, Betsy Hanson, Robert M. Hawthorne Jr., Carolyn Hemenway, Elizabeth Henry, Thomas A. Heppenheimer, Frank Hertle, Fran Hodgkins, Gillian S. Holmes, Dale (John) D. Hunley, Kelley Reynolds Jacquez, Roger Jaffe, Jessica Jahiel, Jeanne Spriter James, J. Sydney Jones, D. George Joseph, Mark J. Kaiser, Lee C. Katterman, Sandra Katzman, Janet Kieffer Kelley, Evelyn B. Kelly, Karen Susan Kelly, Roseann Kent, Roberta Klarreich, James Klockow, Susan Kolmer, Geeta Kothari, Jennifer Kramer, Marc Kusinitz, Steve LaRue, Roger D. Launius, Penelope Lawbaugh, Benedict A. Leerburger, Jeanne Lesinski, Linda Lewin, Paul Lewon, John E. Little, Pamela O. Long, Carol Lord, Anne Hladio Macios, Barbara Magalnick, Laura Mangan-Grenier, Gail B. C. Marsella, Liz Marshall, Renee Mastrocco, Patricia M. McAdams, William M. McBride, Mike W. McClure, Avril McDonald, Chris McGrail, Kim McGrail, Donald J. McGraw, William McPeak, Carla Mecoli-Kamp, Leslie A. Mertz, Robert Messer, Philip Metcalfe, Fei Fei Wang Metzler, George A. Milite, Tony Mitchell, Carol L. Moberg, Sally M. Moite, Patrick Moore, Paula M. Morin, Angie Mullig, J. Paul Myers, Miriam Nagel, Margo Nash, Laura Newman, David E. Newton, Joan Oleck, Donna Olshansky, Kristin Palm, Geriann P. Park, Nicholas Pease, Isleta L. Pement, Daniel Pendick, David A. Petechuk, Annette Petrusso, Tom K. Phares, Devera Pine, Karl Preuss, Rayma Prince, Pamela Proffitt, Barbara J. Proujan, Amy M. Punke, Lewis Pyenson, Jeff Raines, Mary B. Raum, Leslie Reinherz, John Rhea, Vita Richman, Jordan P. Richman, Larry Riddle, Marijke Rijsberman, Francis J. Rogers, Terrie M. Romano, Dan Rooney, Joshua Rosenbaum, Nancy Ross-Flanigan, Shari Rudavsky, Ted Rueter, Doris Runey, Kathy Sammis, Karen Sands, Neeraja Sankaran, Joel Schwarz, Philip Duhan Segal, Margaret M. Seiler, John A. Shanks, Susan Shelly, Alan R. Shepherd, Joel Simon, Michael Sims, Sankar Sitaraman, Doug Smith, Caroline B. D. Smith, Julian A. Smith, Linda Wasmer Smith, Lawrence Souder, Daniel A. Spatz, Dorothy Ann Spencer, John Spizzirri, David Sprinkle, Darwin H. Stapleton, Monica Stevens, Melissa A. Stewart, Sharon Fine Suer, Maureen L. Tan, Peter Hyde Taylor, David R. Teske, Melinda Jardon Thach, Sebastian Thaler, Brenda Tilke, Russell F. Trimble, Carol Turkington, Melissa Vaughn, Patricia M. Walsh, Cynthia Washam, Giselle Weiss, Wallace M. White, Katherine Williams, Nicholas Williamson, Philip K. Wilson, Rodolfo A Windhausen, Karen Withem, Alexandra M. Witze, Emily J. Yaghmour, Joshua Yoder, Cathleen M. Zucco.

Photo Credits

Photographs and illustrations appearing in *Notable Scientists* were received from the following sources. Every effort has been made to trace copyright, but if omissions have been made, please let us know.

Abraham, Edward, photograph. University of Oxford. Reproduced by permission. Ahlfors, Lars (pursed lips, saggy skin), Oberwolfach, Germany, 1988, photograph. Mathematisches Forschungsinstitut, Oberwolfach. Reproduced by permission. Aki, Keiiti, photograph. Reproduced by permission. Alfven, Hannes Olof Gosta, photograph. Nordisk Pressefoto/Archive Photos, Inc. Reproduced by permission. Alpher, Ralph A., photograph. Reproduced by permission. An Wang (posing next to a computer), photograph. Corbis-Bettmann. Reproduced by permission. Anderson, Carl D., photograph. AP/Wide World Photos. Reproduced by permission. Anderson, Dr. Gloria L., photograph. AP/Wide World Photos, Inc. Reproduced by permission. Anfinsen, Christian, photograph. AP/Wide World Photos, Inc. Reproduced by permission. Apgar, Virginia, photograph. The Mount Holyoke Archives and Special Collections. Reproduced by permission. Askey, Richard (standing in front of steps), Oberwolfach, Germany, 1977, photograph. Mathematisches Forschungsinstitut Oberwolfach. Reproduced by permission. Atanasoff, John, Ames, Iowa, 1983, photograph. AP/Wide World Photos, Inc. Reproduced by permission. Auger, Pierre (sitting with George P. Miller, and James A. Van Allen), photograph. UPI/Corbis-Bettmann. Reproduced by permission. Avery, Mary Ellen, photograph. Reproduced by permission. Avery, Oswald (with petri dish), photograph. AP/Wide World Photos, Inc. Reproduced by permission. Baade, Walter (smoking pipe), photograph. Corbis-Bettmann. Reproduced by permission. Babcock, Horace W. (wearing dark frame round glasses), photograph. Archive Photos, Inc. Reproduced by permission. Bakker, Dr. Robert (standing with Brontosaur bone), photograph by Francois Gohier. Photo Researchers, Inc. Reproduced by permission. Baltimore, David, 1975, photograph. AP/Wide World Photos, Inc. Reproduced by permission. Bardeen, John, photograph. AP/Wide World Photos. Reproduced by permission. Barghoorn, Else Sterren (sitting at side of desk), photograph. UPI/Corbis-Bettmann. Reproduced by permission. Beadle, George W., photograph. AP/Wide World Photos, Inc. Reproduced by permission. Bellow, Alexandra, photograph. Mathematisches Forschungsinstitut Oberwolfach. Reproduced by permission. Berners-Lee, Tim, photograph by Stephan Savoia. AP/Wide World Photos. Reproduced by permission. Bethe, Hans (at chalkboard), 1976, photograph. AP/Wide World Photos, Inc. Reproduced by permission. Bigeleisen, Dr. Jacob with T.J. Thompson, Dr. Albert Latter, Dr. Marshall Rosenbluth, and Glenn T. Seaborg, Ernest Orlando Lawrence Memorial Awards, photograph. AP/Wide World Photos. Reproduced by permission. Bird, R. Byron, photograph. University of Maryland. Reproduced by permission. Birkhoff, Garrett (tie with concentric circle design), photograph. Mathematisches Forschungsinstitut Oberwolfach. Reproduced by permission. Blobel, Gunter, Howard Hughes Medical Institute, Rockefeller University, New York, photograph. ©AFP/CORBIS. Reproduced by permission. Bloch, Konrad (seated at desk), photograph. AP/Wide World Photos, Inc. Reproduced by permission. Blodgett, Katharine Burr, photograph. General Electric Research and Development. Reproduced by permission. Blum, lenore (long, thick flowing dark hair), Berkeley, California, photograph. Mathematisches Forschungsinstitut Oberwolfach. Reproduced by permission. Blumberg, Dr. Baruch S., photograph. AP/Wide World Photos. Reproduced by permission. Bolin, Bert, 1997, photograph. AP/Wide World Photos. Reproduced by permission. Borlaug, Norman (standing in a field of wheat), photograph. AP/Wide World Photos. Reproduced by permission. Boyer, Paul, photograph. Reproduced by permission. Bragg, W.L., photograph. AP/Wide World Photos. Reproduced by permission. Brans, Carl, photograph. Reproduced by permission. Bremermann, Hans (open necked white shirt), Berekely, California, 1984, photograph. Mathematisches Forschungsinstitut Oberwolfach. Reproduced by permission. Bridges, Calvin B., photograph. National Academy of Sciences. Reproduced by permission. Bromley, D. Allan, photograph. Reproduced by permission. Bruce Ames (gesturing in front of a blackboard), photograph. AP/Wide World Photos. Reproduced by permission. Burbidge, Margaret, (head and shoulders) portrait. UPI/Corbis-Bettmann. Reproduced by permission. Burkitt, Denis (wearing tweed jacket), photograph. London Daily Express/Archive Photos, Inc. Reproduced by permission. Butenandt, Adolf, photograph. Deutche Presse/Archive Photos, Inc. Reproduced by permission. Cairns, John, portrait. AP/Wide World Photos. Reproduced by permission. Caldicott, Helen, photograph. AP/Wide World Photos. Reproduced by permission. Callender, Dr. Clive, 1987, photograph. AP/Wide World Photos. Reproduced by permission. Cannon, Annie J. (looking at photographic plates), photograph. UPI/Corbis-Bettmann. Reproduced by permission. Carothers, Wallace H., stretching rubber, photograph,. AP/Wide World Photos. Reproduced by permission. Carson, Dr. Ben (with model human brain), photograph. AP/Wide World Photos. Reproduced by permission. Carson, Rachel, 1971, photograph. AP/Wide World Photos. Reproduced by permission. Cartan, Elie Joseph (wearing shirt with pointed collar, his right side shadowed), 1920, photograph. Mathematisches Forschungsinstitut, Oberwolfach. Reproduced by permission. Cartan, Henri (with Mrs. D.J. Struik), photograph. UPI/Corbis-Bettmann. Reproduced by permission. Chadwick, James (standing next to a fireplace), photograph. AP/Wide World Photos. Reproduced by permission. Chandrasekhar, Subrahmanyan, 1983, photograph by Charlie Knoblock. AP/Wide World Photos, Inc. Reproduced by permission. Chandrasekhar, Subrahmanyan (seated), photograph. UPI/Corbis-Bettmann. Reproduced by permission. Chinn, May Edward, photograph. AP/Wide World Photos. Reproduced by permission. Chomsky, Noam (seated in chair), photograph. © Donna Coveney. Reproduced by permission. Chu Paul Ching-Wu, photograph. UPI/Bettmann. Reproduced by permission. Chu, Steven, photograph by L. A. Cicero. Stanford University News Service. Reproduced by permission. Clemence, Gerald M., (comparing illustrations of the moon), photograph. AP/Wide World Photos, Inc. Reproduced by permission. Cohen, Stanley, King Carl Gustav (Cohen receiving Nobel Prize from Gustav), photograph by Rolf Hamilton. Reuters/Archive Photos. Reproduced by permission. Cohen, Tannoudji Claude (in his laboratory), 1997, photograph. Agence France Presse/Corbis-Bettmann. Reproduced by permission. Colburn, Theo, photograph. Reproduced by permission. Commoner, Barry, (with a copy of his book "Making Peace With the Planet"), photograph. AP/Wide World Photos. Reproduced by permission. Condon, Edward U., photograph. National Academy of Sciences. Reproduced by permission. Cooley, Denton photograph. Archive Photos. Reproduced by permission. Cori, Gerty and Carl F. Cori, portrait. UPI/Bettmann Newsphotos. Reproduced by permission. Cousteau, Jacques (arms crossed in front of him), photograph. Corbis-Bettmann. Reproduced by permission. Cowings, Patricia, photograph. AP/Wide World Photos. Reproduced by permission. Cray, Seymour (jacket flung over shoulder), photograph. AP/Wide World Photos, Inc. Reproduced by permission. Crick, Francis, (sitting in front of a blackboard), photograph. The Bettmann Archive. Reproduced by permission. Crutzen, Paul, photograph. Agence France Presse/Corbis-Bettmann. Reproduced by permission. Curie, Marie, photograph. AP/Wide World Photos. Reproduced by permission. Curl, Robert (holding "buckyball"), photograph. Reuters/Andrees A. Latif/Archive Photos, Inc. Reproduced by permission. Dale, Henry, 1954, photograph. AP/Wide World Photos. Reproduced by permission. Dallmeier, Francisco, (holding a monkey), photograph. Courtesy of Francisco Dallmeier. Reproduced by permission. Darden, Christine Mann, photograph. AP/Wide World Photos. Reproduced by permission. de Forest, Dr. Lee and Shockley, Dr. William, photograph. AP/Wide World Photos. Reproduced by permission. DeBakey, Dr. Michael, photograph by Donna Carson. AP/Wide World Photos, Inc. Reproduced by permission. Diamond, Dr. Jared, photograph. AP/Wide World Photos. Reproduced by permission. Dicke, Robert H. (wearing tweed jacket, white shirt, striped tie), photograph. UPI/Corbis-Bettmann. Reproduced by permission. Doherty, Peter, photograph. Reuters/News Limited/Archive Photos, Inc. Reproduced by permission. Dolby, Ray (holding film up to light), photograph. The Gamma Liaison Network. © Liaison Agency. Reproduced by permission. Drew, Charles Richard (with microscope), photograph. AP/Wide World Photos. Reproduced by permission. Drickamer, Harry G., photograph. Reproduced by permission. Durrell, Gerald, monkey on back, photograph. AP/Wide World Photos, Inc. Reproduced by permission. Earle, Dr. Sylvia (diving outside the Aquarius underwater habitat), 1998, Florida Keys National Marine Sanctuary, Key Largo, Florida, photograph. AP/Wide World Photos. Reproduced by permission. Eckert, J. Presper, photograph. AP/Wide World Photos, Inc. Reproduced by permission. Eddington, Arthur (holding pipe), photograph. UPI/Corbis-Bettmann. Reproduced by permission. Edison, Thomas and George Eastman (showing first Kodak color movie film), Rochester, N.Y., 1928, photograph. AP/Wide World Photos, Inc. Reproduced by permission. Ehrlich, Paul (in field), photograph. AP/Wide World Photos. Reproduced by permission. Ehrlich, Paul with Dr. Anne Ehrlich, Dr. Richard Turco and Soviet scientist Dr. Georgiy Golitsyn, Scientists Against Nuclear Arms (SANA) conference on "Britain after Nuclear War," London, photograph. AP/Wide World Photos. Reproduced by permission. Eisenhower, Dwight, Walter H. Spinks, Charles C. Finucane, Mylon Merriam, Walter S. McAfee, Franklin D. Orth, (Eisenhower, meeting with grant recipients), 1956, photograph. UPI/Corbis-Bettmann. Reproduced by permission. Elion, Gertrude (in the laboratory), photograph. UPI/Corbis-Bettmann. Reproduced by permission. Erdos, Paul (close-up of face, open-necked shirt), photograph. Mathematisches Forschungsinstitut Oberwolfach. Reproduced by permission. Ewing, Maurice (seated in his office), photograph. AP/Wide World Photos. Reproduced by permission. Fabry, Charles (with Henri Abrahams), 1924, photograph. UPI/Corbis-Bettmann. Reproduced by permission. Fairbank, William M., 1965, photograph. UPI/Corbis-Bettmann. Reproduced by permission. Falconer, Etta, photograph. Reproduced by permission. Farnsworth, Philo (holding television tube), 1929, photograph. UPI/Corbis-Bettmann. Reproduced by permission. Fasenmyer, Sister Mary, photograph. A.K. Peters Ltd. Reproduced by permission. Fauci, Dr. Anthony S., photograph. AP/Wide World Photos. Reproduced by permission. Ferguson, Lloyd, photograph. Reproduced by permission. Flanagan, James L., 1974, photograph. UPI/Corbis-Bettmann. Reproduced by permission. Flory, Paul J., photograph. AP/Wide World Photos. Reproduced by permission. Folkers, Dr. Karl, photograph by Rudy Baum. Courtesy of C&EN News. Reproduced by permission. Fossey, Dian (surrounded by gorillas, holding camera in right hand), photograph. AP/Wide World Photos. Reproduced by permission. Fred Hoyle, photograph. UPI/Corbis-Bettmann. Reproduced by permission. Fredholm, Ivar (bushy grey mustache, white hair), photograph. Mathematisches Forschungsinstitut Oberwolfach. Reproduced by permission. Frisch, Dr. Karl, photograph. AP/Wide World Photos. Reproduced by permission. Fujita, Dr. Tatsuya and Sumiko Fujita, portrait. AP/Wide World Photos. Reproduced by permission. Fuller, Solomon Carter, photograph. Reproduced by permission. Gabor, Dr. Dennis (examining spool of film or tape), 1969, photograph. AP/Wide World Photos, Inc. Reproduced by permission. Galdikas, Dr. Birute (being embraced by two orangutans), Borneo, photograph. The Gamma Liaison Network. © Liaison Agency. Reproduced by permission. Gallo, Robert, photograph. Archive Photos, Inc. Reproduced by permission. Gates, Bill, photograph. Geiger, Hans Wilhelm (seated in laboratory), photograph. Corbis-Bettmann. Reproduced by permission. Gelfond, Aleksandr O. (head and shoulders), drawing. Mathematisches Forschungsinstitut Oberwolfach. Reproduced by permission. Gell-Mann, Murray (seated at desk), 1969, photograph. AP/Wide World Photos. Reproduced by permission. Ghiroso, Albert, teaching a class, photograph. AP/Wide World Photo. Reproduced by permission. Gilbert, Walter, photograph. AP/Wide World Photos. Reproduced by permission. Gilman, Alfred (standing in laboratory), photograph. AP/Wide World Photos, Inc. Reproduced by permission. Glenn, John, Astronaut, speaking at a news conference, photograph by Pat Sullivan. AP/Wide World Photo. Reproduced by permission. Godel, Kurt (white carnation in lapel), 1951, photograph. AP/Wide World Photos, Inc. Reproduced by permission. Gold, Thomas, photograph. AP /Wide World Photos. Reproduced by permission. Goldhaber, Dr. Maurice, photograph. AP/Wide World Photos. Reproduced by permission. Gould, Stephen; Christian Alfinson; and Francisco Ayala (standing, holding papers), photograph by Ron Bennett. UPI/Corbis-Bettmann. Reproduced by permission. Gould, Stephen Jay (seated, arms crossed over), photograph. AP/Wide World Photos. Reproduced by permission. Gourdine, Meredith, (working with research experiment), photograph. AP/Wide World Photos. Reproduced by permission. Grier, Herbert E., photograph. EG&G, Inc. Reproduced by permission. Groves, Major General Leslie, photograph. AP/Wide World Photos. Reproduced by permission. Guion Buford (in space shuttle simulator), photograph. AP/Wide World Photos. Reproduced by permission. Haber, Fritz, photograph. AP/Wide World Photos, Inc. Reproduced by permission. Harris, Wesley L., photograph. AP/Wide World Photos, Inc. Reproduced by permission. Hawking, Stephen (in wheelchair), photograph. AP/Wide World Photos. Reproduced by permission. Healy, Bernadine, photograph. American Heart Association. Reproduced by permission. Hermite, Charles (reading, holding book in both hands), photograph. Corbis-Bettmann. Reproduced by permission. Hilbert, David (his left hand on piece of paper), photograph. Corbis-Bettmann. Reproduced by permission. Hinton, Dr. William A., photograph. AP/Wide World Photos. Reproduced by permission. Ho, David, photograph. Reproduced by permission. Hodgkin, Dorothy Crowfoot, photograph. Hodgkin, Dorothy, photograph. Archive Photos, Inc./Express Newspapers. Reproduced by permission. Hollinshead, Dr. Ariel, photograph. Reproduced by permission. Hopper, Grace Murray (wearing Naval uniform, glasses), photograph. UPI/Corbis-Bettmann. Reproduced by permission. Hughes, John, photograph. Reproduced by permission. Huxley, Hugh, photograph. Brandeis University Photography Department. Reproduced by permission. Jarvik, Robert K., (holding artifical heart), photograph. AP/Wide World Photos. Reproduced by permission. Jeffreys, Alec with Hans-Eberhard Klein, photograph. AP/Wide World Photos, Inc. Reproduced by permission. Jemison, Mae C. (sitting in shuttle trainer cockpit), 1987, photograph. UPI/Bettmann. Reproduced by permission. Jencks, William, photograph. Brandeis University. Reproduced by permission. Jerne, Neils with King Carl Gustav (presenting Nobel Prize), photograph. AP/Wide World Photos, Inc. Reproduced by permission. Jobs, Steven (pointing with finger), 1992, photograph. Archive Photos/Reuters/Sell. Reproduced by permission. Johnson, Barbara Crawford, photograph. Reproduced by permission. Johnson, Virginia, photograph. AP/Wide World Photos. Reproduced by permission. Johnson, William S., photograph. AP/Wide World Photos, Inc. Reproduced by permission. Joliot-Curie, Irene, photograph. UPI/Bettmann Newsphotos. Reprinted by permission. Just, Ernest Everett, photograph. The Granger Collection Ltd. Reproduced by permission. Kandel, Eric, photograph. Reproduced by the permission of Mr. Kandel. Karle, Isabella L. (wearing scarf), photograph. AP/Wide World Photos. Reproduced by permission. Karp, Richard, photograph by Mary Levin. © 1996 Mary Levin/University of Washington. Reproduced by permission. Keen, Linda (seated, speaking on phone), Berkeley, California, from a color photograph by George Bergman. Mathematisches Forschungsinstitut, Oberwolfach. Reproduced by permission. Khorana, Har Gobind, photograph. AP/Wide World Photos. Reproduced by permission. Kimura, Motoo, photograph. Reproduced by permission. Kohler, Georg, photograph. AP/Wide World Photos, Inc. Reproduced by permission. Kohler, Georges J.F., standing holding a flute glass, photograph. UPI/Corbis-Bettmann. Reproduced by permission. Koshland, Daniel, Jr., photograph. University of California Berkeley. Reproduced by permission. Kouchner, Bernard, photograph. ©Baci/CORBIS. Reproduced by permission. Krim, Mathilde, photograph by T. Gates. Archive Photos, Inc. Reproduced by permission. Kurtz, Thomas E., photograph. Reproduced by permission. Kurzweil, Raymond, photograph. Reproduced by permission. Kusch, Polycarp, photograph. AP/Wide World Photos, Inc. Reproduced by permission. L^Esperance, Elise, Atkinson, Dr. Dorothy W, White, Dr. Priscilla, photograph. UPI/Corbis-Betrmann. Reproduced by permission. Langlands, Robert, receiving honorary degree from Nadine Forest, Paris, 1989, photograph. AP/Wide World Photos, Inc. Reproduced by permission. Laughlin, Robert B., 1998, photograph. The Gamma Liaison Network. © Liaison Agency. Reproduced by permission. Lawless, Theodore Kenneth (wearing dark color suit jacket, tie white shirt), photograph. Dillard University Library. Reproduced by permission. Leakey, Mary with Louise Robbins (holding plaster casts of footprints), 1979, photograph. AP/Wide World Photos. Reproduced by permission. Leavitt, Henrietta Swan, photograph. The Granger Collection, New York. Reproduced by permission. Lee, David (talking into microphones), photograph. Reuters/Bruce Young/Archive Photos, Inc. Reproduced by permission. Lee, Yuan T., photograph. AP/Wide World Photos. Reproduced by permission. Leeman, Susan (standing in front of an overhead projector), photograph. Reproduced by permission. Leevy, Carroll M., photograph. Leffall, Dr. Lasalle D. Jr. (finger pointing), photograph. AP/Wide World Photos. Reproduced by permission. Leloir, Luis F., photograph. UPI/Corbis - Bettmann. Reproduced by permission. LeMaitre, Abbe Georges (wearing clerical collar and round glasses), 1934, photograph. UPI/Corbis-Bettmann. Reproduced by permission. Leopold, Aldo, photograph. AP/Wide World Photos. Reproduced by permission. Levi-Strauss, Claude, photograph by Jerry Bauer. © Jerry Bauer. Reproduced by permission. Lewis, Gilbert N., photograph. Corbis-Bettmann. Reproduced by permission. Lewis, Professor Edward B., photograph. AP/Wide World Photos, Inc. Reproduced by permission. Lizhi, Fang, sitting in the garden of the Institute of Astronomy, photograph by Stringer/Andre de Wet. Corbis-Bettmann. Reproduced by permission. Lonsdale, Kathleen, photograph. AP/Wide World Photos. Reproduced by permission. Lorenz, Konrad, photograph. AP/Wide World Photos. Reproduced by permission. Lovejoy, Thomas, photograph. Smithsonian Institution. Reproduced by permission. Luria, Salvador E., photograph. Archive Photos, Inc. Reproduced by permission. Mandelbrot, Benoit, photograph © Hank Morgan. Photo Researchres, Inc. Reproduced by permission. Mayr, Ernst, photograph. AP/Wide World Photos. Reproduced by permission. McClintock, Barbara (seated at microscope), Long Island, New York, 1947, photograph. AP/Wide World Photos. Reproduced by permission. McDuff, (Margaret) Dusa, photograph. Reproduced by permission. Milstein, Cesar, photograph. Photo Researchers, Inc. Reproduced by permission. Min-Chueh Chang, Worcester Foundation for Experimental Biology, photograph. AP/Wide World Photos, Inc. Reproduced by permission. Minsky, Marvin, photograph. AP/Wide World Photos. Reproduced by permission. Mitchell, Peter (accepting Nobel Prize), photograph. AP/Wide World Photos, Inc. Reproduced by permission. Montagnier, Luc (close-up of face, reading glasses down on nose), 1990, photograph by Gareth Watkins. Reuters/Archive Photos, Inc. Reproduced by permission. Moore, Dr. Stanford, photograph. UPI/Corbis-Bettmann. Reproduced by permission. Mordell, Louis J. (buttoning rumpled suit, white hair), Nizza, 1970, photograph. Mathematisches Forschungsinstitut Oberwolfach. Reproduced by permission. Morgan, Ann Haven, photograph. Mount Holyoke College Archives and Special Collections. Reproduced by permission. Mossbauer, Rudolf, photograph. Archive Photos, Inc. Reproduced by permission. Mott, Nevill, photograph. AP/Wide World Photos, Inc. Reproduced by permission. Moulton, Dr. Barbara, 1960, photograph. UPI/Corbis-Bettmann. Reproduced by permission. Mullis, Kary (seated, legs crossed, two cameras filming him), photograph. Archive Photos, Inc. Reproduced by permission. Mundel, Robert A. with Walter Kohn (r), Stockholm, photograph. ©AFP/ CORBIS. Reproduced by permission. Nakanishi, Koji, photograph. Camera One. Reproduced by permission. Nash, John, 1994, photograph by Robert P. Matthews. Reproduced by permission. Nathans, Daniel, teaching a class, photograph. UPI/Corbis-Bettmann. Reproduced by permission. Neˆeman, Yuval, photograph. Archive Photos, Inc. Reproduced by permission. Needham, Joseph, photograph. Needham Research Institute. Reproduced by permission. Neufeld, Elizabeth (short curly hair, wearing dark striped blouse), photograph. AP/Wide World Photos. Reproduced by permission. Neumann, Hanna (wearing polka dot dress and wool coat), photograph. Mathematisches Forschungs-institut Oberwolfach. Reproduced by permission. Nicholson, Seth Barnes (seated at his spectroscope), 1929, photograph. AP/Wide World Photos. Reproduced by permission. Noether, Emmy (standing, looking down), photograph. Mathematisches Forschungsinstitut Oberwolfach. Reproduced by permission. Noether, Max (short grey hair, greying beard, oval glasses), photograph. Mathematisches Forschungs-institut Oberwolfach. Reproduced by permission. Noyce, Robert (semiconductor in hand), 1989, photograph. AP/Wide World Photos, Inc. Reproduced by permission. OˆNeill, Gerard K., photograph. Space Studies Institute. Reproduced by permission. Ochoa, Severo, photograph. AP/Wide World Photos, Inc. Reproduced by permission. Oeschger, Hans (seated at desk), photograph. AP/Wide World Photos. Reproduced by permission. Olah, George, photograph. Reuters/Fred Prouser/Archive Photos, Inc. Reproduced by permission. Oleinik, Olga (standing with Vekua at her left), 1976, photograph. Mathematisches Forschungsinstitut Oberwolfach. Reproduced by permission. Onsager, Lars (receiving Nobel Prize from King Gustaf Adolf), 1968, photograph. Archive Photo/Express News. Reproduced by permission. Osheroff, Douglas, photograph. Reuters/Bruce Young/Archive Photos, Inc. Reproduced by permission. Packard, David, 1969, photograph. AP/Wide World Photos, Inc. Reproduced by permission. Packard, David (standing in front of electronic equipment) 1958, photograph. AP/Wide World Photos. Reproduced by permission. Parker, Eugene N., photograph. © 1993 Matthew Gilson. Reproduced by permission. Patel, Kumar N., photograph. Reproduced by permission. Patrick, Jennie R. (wearing necklace and earrings), photograph. Reproduced by permission of Jennie R. Patrick. Patrick, Ruth, photograph. AP/Wide World Photos. Reproduced by permission. Paul, Wolfgang, photograph. AP/ Wide World Photos, Inc. Reproduced by permission. Pavlov, Ivan. Hulton-Deutsch Collection/Corbis-Bettmann. Reproduced by permission. Peierls, Rudolf, photograph by Norman McBeath. Reproduced by permission. Peirce, Charles S., photograph. Corbis-Bettmann. Reproduced by permission. Perl, Martin (standing in laboratory), photograph. AgenceFrance Presse/Corbis-Bettmann. Reproduced by permission. photograph. © Bettmann/CORBIS. Reproduced by permission. photograph. © Bettmann/CORBIS. Reproduced by permission. Pilbeam, David (holding fossilized bone), 1984, photograph. AP/Wide World Photos, Inc. Reproduced by permission. Plotkin, Mark J., photograph. Reproduced by permission. Ponnamperuma, Cyril, photograph. AP/Wide World Photos, Inc. Reproduced by permission. Pople, John, 1998, photograph. The Gamma Liaison Network. © Liaison Agency. Reproduced by permission. Press, Frank, photograph. Bachrach. Reproduced by permission. Progogine, Ilya, photograph. AP/Wide World Photos. Reproduced by permission. Prusiner, Dr. Stanley B. (close-up, laughing, in olive suit), 1997, photograph by Luc Novovitch. Reuters/Archive Photos, Inc. Reproduced by permission. Puck, Dr. Theodore T., 1954, photograph. AP/Wide World Photos. Reproduced by permission. Purcell, Edward, photograph. AP/Wide World Photos, Inc. Reproduced by permission. Ramanujan, Srinivasa, photograph. The Granger Collection. Reproduced by permission. Reed, Dr. Major Walter, photograph. AP/Wide World Photos. Reproduced by permission. Rice, Dr. Stuart A. (seated at desk), photograph. AP/Wide World Photos. Reproduced by permission. Rich, Dr. Alexander, 1973, photograph. AP/Wide World Photos. Reproduced by permission. Richter, Dr. Charles, photograph. AP/Wide World Photos. Reproduced by permission. Ride, Sally, photograph. AP/Wide World Photos. Reproduced by permission. Rita Levi-Montalcini, photograph. AP/Wide World Photos. Reproduced by permission. Rodbell, Dr. Martin, 1994, photograph. AP/Wide World Photos. Reproduced by permission. Roentgen, Wilhelm Konrad, photograph. Archive Photos, Inc. Reproduced by permission. Rubin, Vera (looking up at the stars and universe), photograph. © 1993 R.T. Nowitz. Photo Researchers, Inc. Reproduced by permission. Russell, Elizabeth S., 1972, photograph. AP/Wide World Photos, Inc. Reproduced by permission. Sabin, Florence Rena, photograph. The Granger Collection, New York. Reproduced by permission. Sagan, Carl, photograph. AP/Wide World Photos, Inc. Reproduced by permission. Sager, Ruth, photograph. AP/Wide World Photos, Inc. Reproduced by permission. Salam, Abdus (holding a pen), photograph. The Bettmann Archive/Newsphotos, Inc. Reproduced by permission. Salk, Jonas, Pittsburgh, Pennsylvania, 1955, photograph. A/P Wide World Photos. Reproduced by permission. Schick, Dr. Bela (center), with Mayor Robert Wagner and Catherine Schick, 1962, photograph. UPI/Corbis Images. Reproduced by permission. Schwarzschild, Dr. Martin, photograph. AP/Wide World Photos. Reproduced by permission. Simmons, Dr. Howard E. (wearing glen plaid suit), photograph. Archive Photos, Inc. Reproduced by permission. Sinclair, Clive (holding new pocket TV), photograph. UPI/Corbis-Bettmann. Reproduced by permission. Smale, Stephen, Moscow, 1966, photograph. AP/Wide World Photos, Inc. Reproduced by permission. Snyder, Solomon H., photograph. Reproduced by permission. Solomon, Susan, photograph. AP/Wide World Photos. Reproduced by permission. Spitzer, Lyman, photograph. AP/Wide World Photos, Inc. Reproduced by permission. Spitzer, Lyman, photograph. AP/Wide World Photos, Inc. Reproduced by permission. Stanley, Richard P., photograph. Reproduced by permission. Steptoe, Patrick, photograph. Archive Photos. Reproduced by permission. Stokes, Sir George Gabriel (thinning hair, bushy muttonchops), illustration. Archive Photos, Inc. Reproduced by permission. Stormer, Horst L. (smiling, disheveled hair, bushy eyebrows), Murray Hill, New Jersey, 1998, photograph by Mike Derer. AP/Wide World Photos. Reproduce by permission. Suomi, Verner (holding device in hands), photograph. AP/Wide World Photos, Inc. Reproduced by permission. 't Hooft, Gerardus, photograph. AP/Wide World Photos. Reproduced by permission. Tatum, Edward, photograph. Archive Photos, Inc. Reproduced by permission. Taussing, Helen, (helping a small girl find her heart with a stethoscope), photograph. AP/Wide World Photos. Reproduced by permission. Taussky-Todd, Olga, photograph. Reproduced by permission of the estate of Olga Taussky-Todd. Telkes, Maria, photograph. UPI/Corbis-Bettmann. Reproduced by permission. Tembaugh, Clyde W. (with homemade telescope), photograph. AP/Wide World Photos. Reproduced by permission. Thomson, Sir George, 1944, photograph. AP/Wide World Photos. Reproduced by permission. Tinbergen, Nikolaas, photograph. Mary Evans Picture Library. Reproduced by permission. Topchiev, Aleksandr (giving a speech), photograph. Archive Photos, Inc. Reproduced by permission. Torvalds, Linus, Las Vegas, Nevada, 1999, photograph. ©Reuters Newmedia Inc./CORBIS. Reproduced by permission. Tsui, Lap-Chee, photograph. Reproduced by permission of Lap-Chee Tsui. Turing, Alan, photograph. Photo Researchers, Inc. Reproduced by permission. Velez-Rodriguez, Argelia, photograph. Reproduced by permission. Veltman, Martinus J. G., 1999, photograph. AP/Wide World Photos. Reproduced by permission. Von Neumann, John, (testifying before the Atomic Energy Commission), photograph. AP/Wide World Photos. Reproduced by permission. Walker, John, photograph. Reuters/HO/Archive Photos, Inc. Reproduced by permission. Walton, Ernest T. S., photograph. AP/Wide World Photos. Reproduced by permission. Weber, Ernst, photograph. AP/Wide World Photos, Inc. Reproduced by permission. Wegener, Alfred, (head and shoulders), photograph. UPI/Corbis-Bettmann. Reproduced by permission. Weyl, Hermann (standing, from his right), 1954, photograph. AP/Wide World Photos, Inc. Reproduced by permission. Whitehead, Alfred North, photograph. AP/Wide World Photos. Reproduced by permission. Whittle, Frank, photograph. AP/Wide World Photos, Inc. Reproduced by permission. Widnall, Sheila, photograph. AP/Wide World Photos. Reproduced by permission. Wigner, Eugene, photograph. Archive Photos, Inc. Reproduced by permission. Wilmut, Ian, 1997, Washington, D.C., photograph. AP/Wide World Photos, Inc. Reproduced by permission. Wilson, Edward O., sitting at the table, with a insect sculpture in front of him, photograph by Jon Chase/Harvard. Reproduced by permission. Wilson, Robert, photograph. UPI/Corbis-Bettmann. Reproduced by permission. Wu, Chien-Shiung, photograph. UPI/Bettmann. Reproduced by permission. Wu, Chien-Shiung (sitting

Entry List

Blum, Lenore
Blumberg, Baruch Samuel
Bodmer, Walter Fred
Bohr, Aage
Bohr, Niels
Bolin, Bert
Bondar, Roberta Lynn
Bondi, Hermann
Booker, Walter M.
Borcherds, Richard Ewen
Bordet, Jules
Borel, Émile
Borlaug, Norman
Bormann, Frederick Herbert
Born, Max
Bosch, Karl
Bose, Satyendranath
Bothe, Walther
Bott, Raoul
Bovet, Daniel
Bowie, William
Boyer, Herbert W.
Boyer, Paul D.
Boykin, Otis
Brady, St. Elmo
Bragg, William Henry
Bragg, William Lawrence
Brans, Carl Henry
Branson, Herman
Brattain, Walter Houser
Braun, Karl Ferdinand
Breit, Gregory
Bremermann, Hans-Joachim
Brenner, Sydney
Breslow, Ronald C.
Bressani, Ricardo
Bridges, Calvin Blackman
Bridgman, Percy Williams
Brill, Yvonne Claeys
Brockhouse, Bertram Neville
Broecker, Wallace S.
Bromley, D. Allan
Bronk, Detlev Wulf
Brønsted, Johannes Nicolaus
Brooks, Ronald E.
Brouwer, Luitzen Egbertus Jan
Browder, Felix Earl
Brown, Herbert C.
Brown, Lester Russell
Brown, Michael S.
Brown, Rachel Fuller
Brown, Robert Hanbury
Browne, Marjorie Lee
Bucher, Walter Herman
Buchner, Eduard
Bullard, Edward
Bundy, Robert F.
Burbidge, E. Margaret
Burbidge, Geoffrey
Burger, Alfred
Burkitt, Denis Parsons
Burnet, Frank Macfarlane
Burton, Glenn W.
Bush, Vannevar

Butement, William Alan Stewart
Butenandt, Adolf

C

Cahn, John Werner
Cairns, John Jr.
Calderón, Alberto P.
Caldicott, Helen
Callender, Clive O.
Calvin, Melvin
Cambra, Jessie G.
Canady, Alexa I.
Cannon, Annie Jump
Cantor, Georg
Cardona, Manuel
Cardozo, W. Warrick
Cardús, David
Carlson, Chester
Carothers, E. Eleanor
Carothers, Wallace Hume
Carrel, Alexis
Carrier, Willis
Carruthers, George R.
Carson, Benjamin S.
Carson, Rachel
Cartan, Élie Joseph
Cartan, Henri
Cartwright, Dame Mary Lucy
Carver, George Washington
Castro, George
Cech, Thomas R.
Chadwick, James
Chain, Ernst Boris
Chamberlain, Owen
Chamberlin, Thomas Chrowder
Chance, Britton
Chandrasekhar, Subrahmanyan
Chang, Min-Chueh
Chang, Sun-Yang Alice
Chang, Te-Tzu
Chargaff, Erwin
Charnley, John
Charpak, Georges
Chase, Mary Agnes Mera
Chaudhari, Praveen
Cherenkov, Pavel A.
Chestnut, Harold
Chew, Geoffrey Foucar
Child, Charles Manning
Chinn, May Edward
Cho, Alfred Y.
Chomsky, Avram Noam
Chu, Paul Ching-Wu
Chu, Steven
Chung, Fan R. K.
Church, Alonzo
Clarke, Edith
Claude, Albert
Claude, Georges
Clay-Jolles, Tettje Clasina
Clay, Jacob
Clemence, Gerald Maurice
Cloud, Preston

Cobb, Jewel Plummer
Cobb, William Montague
Cockcroft, John D.
Cocke, John
Cohen, Joel Ephraim
Cohen, Paul
Cohen, Stanley Harold
Cohen, Stanley N.
Cohen-Tannoudji, Claude
Cohn, Mildred
Cohn, Zanvil
Coifman, Ronald R.
Colburn, Theodora E.
Colmenares, Margarita
Colwell, Rita R.
Commoner, Barry
Compton, Arthur Holly
Condon, Edward Uhler
Conway, Lynn Ann
Conwell, Esther Marly
Cooke, Lloyd M.
Cooley, Denton Arthur
Coolidge, William D.
Cooper, Leon N.
Corey, Elias James
Cori, Carl Ferdinand
Cori, Gerty T.
Cormack, Allan Macleod
Cornforth, John Warcup
Coster, Dirk
Coulomb, Jean
Courant, Richard
Cournand, André F.
Cousteau, Jacques
Cowings, Patricia S.
Cox, Elbert Frank
Cox, Geraldine V.
Cox, Gertrude Mary
Cram, Donald James
Cray, Seymour
Crick, Francis Harry Compton
Cronin, James W.
Crosby, Elizabeth Caroline
Crosthwait, David Nelson Jr.
Crutzen, Paul J.
Culler, Glen Jacob
Curie, Marie
Curie, Pierre
Curl, Robert Floyd Jr.
Cushman, David W.

D

Dale, Henry Hallett
Dalén, Nils
Dallmeier, Francisco
Dalrymple, G. Brent
Daly, Marie Maynard
Daly, Reginald Aldworth
Dam, Henrik
Daniels, Walter T.
Dansgaard, Willi
Dantzig, George Bernard
Darden, Christine

Dart, Raymond A.
Daubechies, Ingrid
Dausset, Jean
Davidson, Norman R.
Davis, Margaret B.
Davis, Marguerite
Davis, Raymond Jr.
Davisson, Clinton Joseph
DeBakey, Michael Ellis
de Broglie, Louis Victor
Debye, Peter J. W.
de Duve, Christian René
de Forest, Lee
de Gennes, Pierre-Gilles
de Sitter, Willem
Dehmelt, Hans
Deisenhofer, Johann
Delbrück, Max
Deligné, Pierre
Dennis, Jack Bonnell
d'Hérelle, Félix
Diacumakos, Elaine
Diamond, Jared M.
Diaz, Henry F.
Dicciani, Nance K.
Dick, Gladys Rowena Henry
Dicke, Robert Henry
Diels, Otto
Diener, Theodor Otto
Diggs, Irene
Dijkstra, Edsger W.
Dirac, Paul Adrien Maurice
Djerassi, Carl
Dobzhansky, Theodosius
Doherty, Peter C.
Doisy, Edward Adelbert
Dolby, Ray Milton
Dole, Vincent P.
Domagk, Gerhard
Donaldson, Simon
Douglas, Donald W.
Draper, Charles Stark
Dresselhaus, Mildred S.
Drew, Charles R.
Drickamer, Harry G.
Drucker, Daniel Charles
Dubois, Marie Eugène Francoise Thomas
Dubos, René
Dulbecco, Renato
Durand, William F.
Durrell, Gerald
du Vigneaud, Vincent
Dyson, Freeman J.

E

Eagle, Harry
Earle, Sylvia A.
Eastwood, Alice
Eccles, John Carew
Eckert, J. Presper
Eddington, Arthur Stanley
Edelman, Gerald M.
Edgerton, Harold

Edinger, Tilly
Edison, Thomas Alva
Edwards, Cecile Hoover
Edwards, Helen T.
Ehrenfest, Paul
Ehrenfest-Afanaseva, Tatiana
Ehrlich, Anne Howland
Ehrlich, Paul
Ehrlich, Paul Ralph
Eigen, Manfred
Eijkman, Christiaan
Einstein, Albert
Einstein-Maric, Mileva
Einthoven, Willem
Eisner, Thomas
El-Sayed, Mostafa Amr
Eldredge, Niles
Elion, Gertrude Belle
Elsasser, Walter M.
Elton, Charles
Emerson, Gladys Anderson
Enders, John Franklin
Engler, Adolph Gustav Heinrich
Enskog, David
Erdös, Paul
Erlang, Agner
Erlanger, Joseph
Ernst, Richard R.
Esaki, Leo
Esau, Katherine
Estes, William K.
Estrin, Thelma
Euler-Chelpin, Hans Karl Simon August
    von
Euler, Ulf von
Evans, Alice
Evans, James C.
Ewing, William Maurice

F

Faber, Sandra M.
Fabry, Charles
Fairbank, William
Falconer, Etta
Farman, Joseph C.
Farnsworth, Philo T.
Farquhar, Marilyn G.
Farr, Wanda K.
Fasenmyer, Sister Mary
Fauci, Anthony S.
Favaloro, René Geronimo
Fedoroff, Nina V.
Feigenbaum, Edward A.
Feigenbaum, Mitchell
Fell, Honor Bridget
Fenchel, Kate
Ferguson, Lloyd N.
Ferguson, Margaret Clay
Fermi, Enrico
Fersman, Aleksandr Evgenievich
Feynman, Richard P.
Fibiger, Johannes
Fieser, Louis F.

Fieser, Mary Peters
Fischer, Edmond H.
Fischer, Emil
Fischer, Ernst Otto
Fischer, Hans
Fisher, Elizabeth F.
Fisher, Ronald Aylmer
Fitch, Val Logsdon
Fitzroy, Nancy D.
Flanagan, James L
Fleming, Alexander
Fleming, John Ambrose
Flexner, Simon
Florey, Howard Walter
Flory, Paul
Flügge-Lotz, Irmgard
Fokker, Anthony H. G.
Folkers, Karl A.
Forbush, Scott Ellsworth
Ford, Henry
Forrester, Jay Wright
Forssmann, Werner
Fossey, Dian
Fowler, William A.
Fox, Sidney Walter
Fraenkel, Abraham Adolf
Fraenkel-Conrat, Heinz Ludwig
Franck, James
Frank, Il'ya
Franklin, Rosalind Elsie
Fraser-Reid, Bertram Oliver
Fréchet, Maurice
Fredholm, Ivar
Freedman, Michael H.
Freitag, Herta Therese
Frenkel, Yakov Ilyich
Friedman, Jerome
Friedmann, Aleksandr A.
Friend, Charlotte
Frisch, Karl von
Frisch, Otto Robert
Fujita, Tetsuya Theodore
Fukui, Kenichi
Fuller, (Richard) Buckminster
Fuller, Solomon

G

Gabor, Dennis
Gadgil, Madhav
Gadgil, Sulochana
Gagarin, Yuri A.
Gajdusek, D. Carleton
Galdikas, Birute
Gallo, Robert C.
Gamow, George
Gardner, Julia Anna
Garrod, Archibald
Gasser, Herbert Spencer
Gates, Bill
Gates, Sylvester James Jr.
Gaviola, Enrique
Gayle, Helene Doris
Geiger, Hans

Geiringer, Hilda
Gelfond, Aleksandr Osipovich
Gell-Mann, Murray
Geller, Margaret Joan
Gentry, Ruth
Ghiorso, Albert
Giacconi, Riccardo
Giaever, Ivar
Giauque, William F.
Gibbs, Josiah Willard
Gibbs, William Francis
Giblett, Eloise R.
Gilbert, Walter
Gilbreth, Frank
Gilbreth, Lillian
Gilman, Alfred Goodman
Glaser, Donald
Glashow, Sheldon Lee
Glenn, John Herschel, Jr.
Goddard, Robert H.
Gödel, Kurt Friedrich
Goeppert-Mayer, Maria
Goethals, George W.
Gold, Thomas
Goldberg, Adele
Goldhaber, Gertrude Scharff
Goldhaber, Maurice
Goldmark, Peter Carl
Goldreich, Peter M.
Goldring, Winifred
Goldschmidt, Richard B.
Goldschmidt, Victor
Goldstein, Avram
Goldstein, Joseph L.
Golgi, Camillo
Gomez-Pompa, Arturo
Good, Mary L.
Goodall, Jane
Gorer, Peter Alfred
Goudsmit, Samuel A.
Gould, Stephen Jay
Gourdine, Meredith Charles
Gourneau, Dwight
Govindjee
Gowers, William Timothy
Granit, Ragnar Arthur
Granville, Evelyn Boyd
Greatbatch, Wilson
Greenewalt, Crawford H.
Grier, Herbert E. Jr.
Griffith, Frederick
Grignard, François Auguste Victor
Gross, Carol
Grothendieck, Alexander
Groves, Leslie Richard
Guillaume, Charles-Edouard
Guillemin, Roger
Gullstrand, Allvar
Gutenberg, Beno
Guth, Alan
Guthrie, Mary Jane
Gutierrez, Orlando A.

H

Haagen-Smit, A. J.
Haber, Fritz
Hackerman, Norman
Hadamard, Jacques
Hahn, Otto
Haldane, John Burdon Sanderson
Hale, George Ellery
Hall, Lloyd Augustus
Hamburger, Viktor
Hamilton, Alice
Hammond, George S.
Hanafusa, Hidesaburo
Hannah, Marc R.
Hansen, James
Harden, Arthur
Hardy, Alister C.
Hardy, Godfrey Harold
Hardy, Harriet
Harmon, E'lise F.
Harris, Cyril
Harris, Wesley L.
Hartline, Haldan Keffer
Harvey, Ethel Nicholson Browne
Hassel, Odd
Hauptman, Herbert A.
Haus, Hermann A.
Hausdorff, Felix
Hawking, Stephen
Hawkins, W. Lincoln
Haworth, Walter
Hay, Elizabeth D.
Hay, Louise
Hayes, Ellen Amanda
Hazen, Elizabeth Lee
Hazlett, Olive Clio
Healy, Bernadine
Heezen, Bruce Charles
Heimlich, Henry Jay
Heinkel, Ernst
Heisenberg, Werner Karl
Hench, Philip Showalter
Henderson, Cornelius Langston
Henry, John Edward
Henry, Warren Elliott
Hermite, Charles
Herschbach, Dudley R.
Hershey, Alfred Day
Hertz, Gustav
Hertzsprung, Ejnar
Herzberg, Gerhard
Herzenberg, Caroline L.
Hess, Harry Hammond
Hess, Victor
Hess, Walter Rudolf
Hevesy, Georg von
Hewish, Antony
Hewitt, Jacqueline N.
Hewlett, William
Heymans, Corneille Jean-François
Heyrovský, Jaroslav
Hibbard, Hope
Hicks, Beatrice

Higgs, Peter Ware
Hilbert, David
Hill, Archibald V.
Hill, George William
Hill, Henry A.
Hill, Robert (Robin)
Hille, Bertil
Hinshelwood, Cyril N.
Hinton, William Augustus
Hitchings, George H.
Ho, David Da-I
Hobby, Gladys Lounsbury
Hodgkin, Alan Lloyd
Hodgkin, Dorothy Crowfoot
Hoffman, Darleane C.
Hoffmann, Roald
Hofstadter, Robert
Hogg, Helen Sawyer
Holdren, John Paul
Holley, Robert William
Hollinshead, Ariel Cahill
Holmes, Arthur
Hooft, Gerardus 't
Hopkins, Frederick Gowland
Hopper, Grace
Horn, Michael Hastings
Horstmann, Dorothy Millicent
Houdry, Eugene
Hounsfield, Godfrey
Houssay, Bernardo
Hoyle, Fred
Hrdlička, Aleš
Huang, Alice Shih-hou
Hubbard, Philip G.
Hubbert, M. King
Hubble, Edwin
Hubel, David H.
Huber, Robert
Huggins, Charles B.
Hughes, John
Hulse, Russell A.
Humason, Milton L.
Hunsaker, Jerome C.
Hutchinson, G. Evelyn
Huxley, Andrew Fielding
Huxley, Hugh Esmor
Huxley, Julian
Hyde, Ida H.
Hyman, Libbie Henrietta

I

Imes, Elmer Samuel
Ioffe, Abram F.
Isaacs, Alick
Itakura, Keiichi
Iverson, F. Kenneth

J

Jackson, Shirley Ann
Jacob, François
Janovskaja, Sof'ja Aleksandrovna
Jansky, Karl

Janzen, Dan
Jarvik, Robert K.
Jason, Robert S.
Jeffreys, Alec John
Jeffreys, Harold
Jeffries, Zay
Jemison, Mae C.
Jencks, William Platt
Jensen, Johannes Hans Daniel
Jerne, Niels K.
Jewett, Frank Baldwin
Jobs, Steven
Johannsen, Wilhelm Ludvig
Johnson, Barbara Crawford
Johnson, Clarence L.
Johnson, John B. Jr.
Johnson, Joseph Lealand
Johnson, Katherine Coleman Goble
Johnson, Marvin M.
Johnson, Virginia E.
Johnson, William Summer
Johnston, Harold S.
Joliot-Curie, Frédéric
Joliot-Curie, Irène
Jones, Fred
Jones, Mary Ellen
Jordan, Ernst Pascual
Josephson, Brian D.
Julian, Percy Lavon
Juran, Joseph M.
Just, Ernest Everett

K

Kadanoff, Leo Philip
Kamerlingh Onnes, Heike
Kan, Yuet Wai
Kandel, Eric R.
Kapitsa, Pyotr
Karle, Isabella
Karle, Jerome
Karlin, Samuel
Karp, Richard M.
Karrer, Paul
Kastler, Alfred
Kates, Robert W.
Kato, Tosio
Katz, Bernard
Katz, Donald L.
Kay, Alan C.
Keen, Linda
Keith, Arthur
Keller, Evelyn Fox
Kelsey, Frances Oldham
Kemeny, John G.
Kendall, Edward C.
Kendall, Henry W.
Kendrew, John
Kettering, Charles Franklin
Kettlewell, Bernard
Kety, Seymour S.
Khorana, Har Gobind
Khush, Gurdev S.
Kilburn, Thomas M.

Kilby, Jack St. Clair
Kimura, Motoo
King, Helen Dean
King, Louisa Boyd Yeomans
King, Reatha Clark
Kinoshita, Toichiro
Kinsey, Alfred
Kishimoto, Tadamitsu
Kistiakowsky, George B.
Kittrell, Flemmie Pansy
Klein, Christian Felix
Klug, Aaron
Knopf, Eleanora Bliss
Knudsen, William Claire
Knuth, Donald E.
Koch, Robert
Kocher, Theodor
Kodaira, Kunihiko
Koehl, Mimi A. R.
Köhler, Georges
Kohn, Walter
Kolff, Willem Johan
Kolmogorov, Andrey Nikolayevich
Kolthoff, Izaak Maurits
Konishi, Masakazu
Kontsevich, Maxim
Kornberg, Arthur
Korolyov, Sergei
Koshland, Daniel E., Jr.
Kossel, Albrecht
Kouchner, Bernard
Kountz, Samuel L.
Kouwenhoven, William Bennett
Kramer, Fred Russell
Krebs, Edwin G.
Krebs, Hans Adolf
Krieger, Cecilia
Krim, Mathilde
Krogh, August
Kroto, Harold Walter
Kuhlmann-Wilsdorf, Doris
Kuhn, Richard
Kuiper, Gerard Peter
Kuperberg, Krystyna
Kurchatov, Igor
Kurtz, Thomas Eugene
Kurzweil, Raymond
Kusch, Polycarp

L

L'Esperance, Elise Depew Strang
Ladd-Franklin, Christine
Lamb, Willis E., Jr.
Lancaster, Cleo
Lancefield, Rebecca Craighill
Land, Edwin H.
Landau, Edmund Georg Hemann
Landau, Lev Davidovich
Landsberg, Helmut E.
Landsteiner, Karl
Langevin, Paul
Langlands, Robert
Langmuir, Irving

Latimer, Lewis H.
Lattes, C. M. G.
Laub, Jakob Johann
Laue, Max von
Laughlin, Robert B.
Lauterbur, Paul C.
Laveran, Alphonse
Lawless, Theodore K.
Lawrence, Ernest Orlando
Le Beau, Désirée
Le Cadet, Georges
Leakey, Louis
Leakey, Mary Douglas Nicol
Leakey, Richard E.
Leavitt, Henrietta
Lebesgue, Henri
Leder, Philip
Lederberg, Joshua
Lederman, Leon Max
Ledley, Robert Steven
Lee, David M.
Lee, Raphael C.
Lee, Tsung-Dao
Lee, Yuan T.
Leeman, Susan E.
Leevy, Carroll Moton
Leffall, LaSalle D. Jr.
Lehmann, Inge
Lehmer, Emma Trotskaya
Lehn, Jean-Marie
Leloir, Luis F.
Lemaître, Georges
Lenard, Philipp E. A. von
Leopold, Aldo
Leopold, Estella Bergere
Leopold, Luna Bergere
Lester, William Alexander, Jr.
Levi-Civita, Tullio
Levi-Montalcini, Rita
Lévi-Strauss, Claude
Lewis, Edward B.
Lewis, Gilbert Newton
Lewis, Julian Herman
Lewis, Warren K.
Li, Ching Chun
Li, Choh Hao
Libby, Willard F.
Liepmann, Hans Wolfgang Leopold Edmund Eugene Victor
Likens, Gene Elden
Lillie, Frank Rattray
Lim, Robert K. S.
Lin, Chia-Chiao
Lindemann, Ferdinand von
Lipmann, Fritz
Lippmann, Gabriel
Lipscomb, William Nunn, Jr.
Little, Arthur D.
Litvinova, Elizabeta Fedorovna
Lizhi, Fang
Lloyd, Ruth Smith
Loeb, Jacques
Loewi, Otto
Logan, Myra A.

London, Fritz
Long, Irene D.
Lonsdale, Kathleen
Lorentz, Hendrik Antoon
Lorenz, Edward N.
Lorenz, Konrad
Lorius, Claude J.
Lovejoy, Thomas Eugene
Lovelock, James Ephraim
Lubchenco, Jane
Luria, Salvador Edward
Lwoff, André
Lynen, Feodor
Lynk, Miles Vandahurst

M

Maathai, Wangari
MacArthur, Robert H.
Macdonald, Eleanor Josephine
MacDonald, Gordon James Fraser
MacGill, Elsie Gregory
Macintyre, Sheila Scott
MacKinnon, Roderick
Macklin, Madge Thurlow
MacLane, Saunders
MacLeod, Colin Munro
Macleod, John James Rickard
MacPherson, Robert D.
Maddison, Ada Isabel
Maillart, Robert
Maiman, Theodore
Malone-Mayes, Vivienne
Maloney, Arnold Hamilton
Mandel'shtam, Leonid Isaakovich
Mandelbrot, Benoit B.
Manton, Sidnie Milana
Marchbanks, Vance H., Jr.
Marconi, Guglielmo
Marcus, Rudolph A.
Margulis, Gregori Aleksandrovitch
Margulis, Lynn
Marie-Victorin, Frère
Markov, Andrei Andreevich
Martin, A(rcher) J(ohn) P(orter)
Massevitch, Alla G.
Massey, Walter E.
Massie, Samuel P., Jr.
Masters, William Howell
Matthews, Alva T.
Matuyama, Motonori
Mauchly, John William
Maunder, Annie Russell
Maury, Antonia
Maury, Carlotta Joaquina
Maynard Smith, John
Mayr, Ernst
McAfee, Walter S.
McCarthy, John
McCarty, Maclyn
McCarty, Perry L.
McClintock, Barbara
McCollum, Elmer Verner
McConnell, Harden

McDuff, (Margaret) Dusa
McMillan, Edwin M.
McMullen, Curtis T.
Mead, George Herbert
Medawar, Peter Brian
Meitner, Lise
Mendenhall, Dorothy Reed
Meray, Hugues Charles Robert
Merrifield, R. Bruce
Merrill, Helen Abbot
Merrill, Winifred Edgerton
Meselson, Matthew
Metchnikoff, Élie
Mexia, Ynes
Meyerhof, Otto
Michel, Hartmut
Micheli-Tzanakou, Evangelia
Michelson, Albert
Midgley, Thomas, Jr.
Miller, Elizabeth C. & James Alexander
Miller, Stanley Lloyd
Millikan, Robert A.
Milne, Edward Arthur
Milnor, John
Milstein, César
Minkowski, Hermann
Minkowski, Rudolph
Minot, George Richards
Minsky, Marvin Lee
Mintz, Beatrice
Mitchell, Peter D.
Mittermeier, Russell
Mohorovičić, Andrija
Moissan, Henri
Molina, Mario
Moniz, Antonio Egas
Monod, Jacques Lucien
Montagnier, Luc
Moore, Charlotte E.
Moore, Raymond Cecil
Moore, Ruth Ella
Moore, Stanford
Morawetz, Cathleen Synge
Mordell, Louis Joel
Morgan, Ann Haven
Morgan, Arthur E.
Morgan, Garrett A.
Morgan, Thomas Hunt
Mori, Shigefumi
Morley, Edward Williams
Morrison, Philip
Moseley, Henry Gwyn Jeffreys
Mossbauer, Rudolf
Mott, Nevill Francis
Mottelson, Ben R.
Moulton Browne, Barbara
Moulton, Forest Ray
Muller, Hermann Joseph
Müller, K. Alex
Müller, Paul
Mulliken, Robert S.
Mullis, Kary
Munk, Walter
Murphy, William P.

Murray, Joseph E.

N

Nabrit, Samuel Milton
Nagata, Takesi
Nakanishi, Koji
Nambu, Yoichiro
Nash, John Forbes, Jr.
Nathans, Daniel
Natta, Giulio
Ne'eman, Yuval
Neal, Homer Alfred
Needham, Joseph
Néel, Louis-Eugène-Félix
Neher, Erwin
Nelson, Evelyn M.
Nernst, Walther
Neufeld, Elizabeth Fondal
Neumann, Hanna
Newell, Allen
Newell, Norman Dennis
Nice, Margaret Morse
Nichols, Roberta J.
Nicholson, Seth Barnes
Nicolle, Charles Jules Henri
Nier, Alfred O. C.
Nirenberg, Marshall Warren
Nishizawa, Jun-ichi
Nishizuka, Yasutomi
Noble, G. K.
Noddack, Ida Tacke
Noether, Emmy
Noether, Max
Noguchi, Hideyo
Nomura, Masayasu
Norrish, Ronald G. W.
Northrop, John Howard
Novikov, Sergei
Noyce, Robert
Nozoe, Tetsuo
Nüsslein-Volhard, Christiane

O

O'Neill, Gerard K.
Oberth, Hermann
Ocampo, Adriana C.
Ochoa, Ellen
Ochoa, Severo
Odum, Eugene Pleasants
Odum, Howard T.
Oeschger, Hans
Ogilvie, Ida H.
Olah, George A.
Olden, Kenneth
Oldham, Richard Dixon
Oleinik, Olga
Ondetti, Miguel A.
Onsager, Lars
Oort, Jan Hendrik
Oparin, Aleksandr Ivanovich
Oppenheimer, J. Robert
Osborn, Mary J.

Osheroff, Douglas D.
Osterbrock, Donald E.
Ostwald, Friedrich Wilhelm

 P

Packard, David
Palade, George Emil
Panajiotatou, Angeliki
Panofsky, Wolfgang Kurt Hermann
Papanicolaou, George
Pardue, Mary Lou
Parker, Arthur C.
Parker, Charles Stewart
Parker, Eugene Newman
Parsons, John T.
Patel, C. Kumar N.
Patrick, Jennie R.
Patrick, Ruth
Patterson, Claire
Patterson, Frederick Douglass
Paul, Wolfgang
Pauli, Wolfgang
Pauling, Linus
Pavlov, Ivan Petrovich
Payne-Gaposchkin, Cecilia
Peano, Giuseppe
Pearson, Karl
Peden, Irene Carswell
Pedersen, Charles John
Peebles, Phillip James Edwin
Peierls, Rudolf Ernst
Peirce, Charles S.
Pellier, Laurence Delisle
Pennington, Mary Engle
Penrose, Roger
Penry, Deborah L.
Penzias, Arno
Perey, Marguerite
Perl, Martin L.
Perrin, Jean Baptiste
Pert, Candace B.
Perutz, Max
Péter, Rozsa
Petermann, Mary Locke
Peterson, Edith R.
Pettersson, Hans
Phelps, Michael Edward
Phillips, William D.
Piasecki, Frank
Piccard, Auguste
Pierce, George Edward
Pierce, Naomi E.
Pilbeam, David Roger
Pimentel, David
Pinchot, Gifford
Pincus, Gregory Goodwin
Planck, Max
Pless, Vera
Plotkin, Mark
Pogue, William Reid
Poincaré, Jules Henri
Poindexter, Hildrus A.
Polanyi, John C.

Polubarinova-Kochina, Pelageya Yakov-
levna
Pólya, George
Ponnamperuma, Cyril
Pople, John A.
Porter, George
Porter, Rodney
Poulsen, Valdemar
Pound, Robert Vivian
Powell, Cecil Frank
Powless, David
Prandtl, Ludwig
Pregl, Fritz
Prelog, Vladimir
Press, Frank
Pressman, Ada I.
Prichard, Diana Garcia
Prigogine, Ilya
Profet, Margie
Prokhorov, Aleksandr
Prusiner, Stanley B.
Puck, Theodore T.
Punnett, R. C.
Purcell, Edward Mills

 Q

Qöyawayma, Alfred H.
Quarterman, Lloyd Albert
Quate, Calvin F.
Quimby, Edith H.
Quinland, William Samuel

R

Rabi, I. I.
Rainwater, James
Ramalingaswami, Vulimiri
Raman, C. V.
Ramanujan, S. I.
Ramart-Lucas, Pauline
Ramey, Estelle R.
Ramón y Cajal, Santiago
Ramsay, William
Ramsey, Frank Plumpton
Ramsey, Norman Foster
Randoin, Lucie
Rao, C. N. R.
Ratner, Sarah
Raven, Peter Hamilton
Ray, Dixy Lee
Reber, Grote
Reddy, Raj
Reed, Walter
Rees, Mina S.
Reichmanis, Elsa
Reichstein, Tadeus
Reid, Lonnie
Reines, Frederick
Revelle, Roger
Rice, Stuart A.
Rich, Alexander (a.k.a. Alan)
Richards, Dickinson Woodruff, Jr.
Richards, Ellen Swallow

Richards, Theodore William
Richardson, Lewis Fry
Richardson, Owen W.
Richardson, Robert C.
Richet, Charles Robert
Richter, Burton
Richter, Charles F.
Rickover, Hyman G.
Ride, Sally
Rigas, Harriett B.
Risi, Joseph
Ritchie, Dennis
Robbins, Frederick
Roberts, Lawrence
Roberts, Richard J.
Robinson, Julia
Robinson, Robert
Rock, John
Rockwell, Mabel M.
Rodbell, Martin
Roddy, Leon
Roelofs, Wendell L.
Rogers, Marguerite M.
Rohrer, Heinrich
Roman, Nancy Grace
Romer, Alfred Sherwood
Romero, Juan Carlos
Röntgen, Wilhelm Conrad
Rosenbluth, Marshall N.
Ross, John
Ross, Mary G.
Ross, Ronald
Rossby, Carl-Gustaf
Rothschild, Miriam Louisa
Rous, Peyton
Rowland, F. Sherwood
Rowley, Janet D.
Rubbia, Carlo
Rubin, Vera Cooper
Rudin, Mary Ellen
Runcorn, S. K.
Ruska, Ernst
Russell, Bertrand
Russell, Elizabeth Shull
Russell, Frederick Stratten
Russell, Henry Norris
Russell, Loris Shano
Rutherford, Ernest
Ružička, Leopold
Ryle, Martin

S

Sabatier, Paul
Sabin, Albert
Sabin, Florence Rena
Sacks, Oliver Wolf
Sagan, Carl
Sager, Ruth
Sakharov, Andrei
Sakmann, Bert
Salam, Abdus
Salk, Jonas
Samuelsson, Bengt

Sanchez, David A.
Sanchez, Pedro A.
Sandage, Allan R.
Sanford-Mifflin, Katherine Koontz
Sanger, Frederick
Satcher, David
Schafer, Alice T.
Schaller, George
Schally, Andrew Victor
Scharrer, Berta
Schawlow, Arthur Leonard
Schick, Bela
Schneider, Stephen H.
Schou, Mogens
Schrieffer, J. Robert
Schrödinger, Erwin
Schultes, Richard Evans
Schwartz, Melvin
Schwarz, John Henry
Schwinger, Julian
Scott, Charlotte Angas
Seaborg, Glenn Theodore
Segrè, Emilio
Seibert, Florence B.
Seitz, Frederick
Selberg, Atle
Semenov, Nikolai N.
Serre, Jean-Pierre
Shannon, Claude
Shapiro, Irwin
Shapley, Harlow
Sharp, Phillip A.
Sharp, Robert Phillip
Shaw, Mary
Sheldrake, Rupert
Shepard, Alan B., Jr.
Shepard, Roger N.
Sherrington, Charles Scott
Shockley, Dolores Cooper
Shockley, William
Shoemaker, Eugene M.
Shokalsky, Yuly Mikhaylovich
Shtokman, Vladimir Borisovich
Shull, Clifford Glenwood
Shurney, Robert E.
Siegbahn, Kai M.
Siegbahn, Karl M. G.
Sierpiński, Waclaw
Sikorsky, Igor I.
Silbergeld, Ellen Kovner
Simmons, Howard Ensign, Jr.
Simon, Dorothy Martin
Simon, Herbert Alexander
Simpson, George Gaylord
Sinclair, Clive Marles
Singer, I. M.
Singer, Maxine
Sioui, Richard H.
Skoog, Folke Karl
Skou, Jens C.
Slater, John Clarke
Slipher, Vesto M.
Slye, Maud
Smale, Stephen

Smalley, Richard Errett
Smith, Hamilton O.
Smith, Michael
Snell, George Davis
Snyder, Solomon Halbert
Soddy, Frederick
Solberg, Halvor
Solomon, Susan
Sommerfeld, Arnold
Sommerville, Duncan McLaren Young
Sorensen, Charles E.
Sørensen, Søren Peter Lauritz
Spaeth, Mary
Sparling, Rebecca H.
Spedding, Frank Harold
Spemann, Hans
Sperry, Elmer
Sperry, Roger W.
Spitzer, Lyman, Jr.
Stahl, Franklin W.
Stanley, Richard P.
Stanley, Wendell Meredith
Stark, Johannes
Starling, Ernest H.
Starr, Chauncey
Starzl, Thomas Earl
Staudinger, Hermann
Stefanik, Milan Ratislav
Stein, William Howard
Steinberger, Jack
Steinman, David B.
Steinmetz, Charles P.
Steitz, Joan Argetsinger
Steptoe, Patrick
Stern, Otto
Stevens, Nettie Maria
Stever, H. Guyford
Steward, Frederick Campion
Stewart, Thomas Dale, Jr.
Stibitz, George R.
Stock, Alfred
Stokes, George Gabriel
Stoll, Alice M.
Stommel, Henry Melson
Størmer, Fredrik
Stott, Alicia Boole
Strassmann, Fritz
Straus, William Levi, Jr.
Strutt, John William
Strutt, Robert
Stubbe, JoAnne
Sturtevant, A. H.
Sumner, James B.
Suomi, Verner E.
Sutherland, Earl, Jr.
Sutherland, Ivan
Sutton, Walter Stanborough
Svedberg, Theodor
Swaminathan, M. S.
Synge, Richard
Szego, Gabor
Szent-Györgyi, Albert
Szilard, Leo

Tamm, Igor
Tan, Jiazhen
Tapia, Richard A.
Tarski, Alfred
Tatum, Edward Lawrie
Taube, Henry
Taussig, Helen Brooke
Taussky-Todd, Olga
Taylor, Frederick Winslow
Taylor, Joseph H., Jr.
Taylor, Moddie
Taylor, Richard E.
Taylor, Stuart
Telkes, Maria
Teller, Edward
Temin, Howard
Tereshkova, Valentina
Terman, Frederick
Terzaghi, Karl
Tesla, Nikola
Tesoro, Giuliana Cavaglieri
Tharp, Marie
Theiler, Max
Theorell, Axel Hugo Teodor
Thom, René Frédéric
Thomas, E. Donnall
Thomas, Martha Jane Bergin
Thompson, D'Arcy Wentworth
Thompson, Kenneth
Thomson, George Paget
Thomson, J. J.
Thurston, William
Tien, Ping King
Tildon, J. Tyson
Timoshenko, Stephen P.
Tinbergen, Nikolaas
Ting, Samuel C. C.
Tiselius, Arne
Tishler, Max
Tizard, Henry
Todd, Alexander
Tombaugh, Clyde W.
Tomonaga, Sin-Itiro
Tonegawa, Susumu
Topchiev, Aleksandr Vasil'evich
Townes, Charles H.
Trotter, Mildred
Trump, John G.
Tsao, George T.
Tsiolkovsky, Konstantin
Tsui, Daniel Chee
Tsui, Lap-Chee
Tswett, Mikhail
Turing, Alan Mathison
Turner, Charles Henry
Tuve, Merle A.
Twort, Frederick William

U

Uhlenbeck, George
Uhlenbeck, Karen

Urey, Harold
Uvarov, Boris Petrovitch
Uyeda, Seiya

V

Vallée-Poussin, Charles Jean Gustave Nicolas de la
Vallois, Henri-Victor
Van Allen, James
Van de Graaff, Robert J.
Van de Kamp, Peter
van der Meer, Simon
van der Waals, Johannes Diderik
van der Wal, Laurel
van Straten, Florence W.
Van Vleck, John
Vane, John Robert
Varmus, Harold E.
Vassy, Arlette
Vedder, Edward Bright
Veksler, V. I.
Velez-Rodriquez, Argelia
Vernadsky, Vladimir Ivanovich
Vine, Frederick John
Virtanen, Artturi Ilmari
Vollenweider, Richard
Volterra, Vito
von Braun, Wernher
von Kármán, Theodore
von Klitzing, Klaus
von Mises, Richard
von Neumann, John
Voûte, Joan George Erardus Gijsbert
Vries, Hugo de

W

Waelsch, Salome
Wagner-Jauregg, Julius
Wahl, Arnold C.
Waksman, Selman
Wald, George
Walker, John E.
Wallach, Otto
Walton, Ernest
Wang, An
Wang, James C.
Wankel, Felix
Warburg, Otto
Washington, Warren M.
Watkins, Levi, Jr.
Watson-Watt, Robert
Watson, James D.
Weber-van Bosse, Anne Antoinette
Weber, Ernst
Weertman, Julia

Wegener, Alfred
Weidenreich, Franz
Weil, André
Weinberg, Robert A.
Weinberg, Steven
Weinberg, Wilhelm
Weiss, Mary Catherine Bishop
Weizsäcker, Carl F. Von
Weller, Thomas
Went, Frits
Werner, Alfred
West, Harold Dadford
Wetherill, George West
Wexler, Nancy
Weyl, Hermann
Wheeler, Anna Johnson Pell
Wheeler, John Archibald
Whinfield, John Rex
Whinnery, John R.
Whipple, Fred Lawrence
Whipple, George Hoyt
White, Augustus
White, Gilbert Fowler
White, Raymond L.
Whitehead, Alfred North
Whittaker, Robert Harding
Whittle, Frank
Wickenden, William E.
Widnall, Sheila E.
Wiechert, Emil
Wieland, Heinrich
Wien, Wilhelm
Wiener, Alexander
Wiener, Norbert
Wieschaus, Eric F.
Wiesel, Torsten
Wigglesworth, Vincent
Wigner, Eugene Paul
Wiles, Andrew J.
Wilkes, Maurice Vincent
Wilkins, J. Ernest, Jr.
Wilkins, Maurice Hugh Frederick
Wilkinson, Geoffrey
Williams, Anna W.
Williams, Cicely Delphin
Williams, Daniel Hale
Williams, Evan James
Williams, Frederic C.
Williams, Heather
Williams, Ozzie S.
Williamson, James S.
Willstätter, Richard
Wilmut, Ian
Wilson, C. T. R.
Wilson, Edmund Beecher
Wilson, Edward O.
Wilson, J. Tuzo

Wilson, Kenneth G.
Wilson, Robert Rathbun
Wilson, Robert Woodrow
Windaus, Adolf
Wirth, Niklaus
Witkin, Evelyn Maisel
Witten, Edward
Wittig, Georg
Wolman, Abel
Wood, Harland G.
Woodland, Joseph
Woodward, Robert B.
Woodwell, George M.
Wozniak, Stephen
Wright, Almroth Edward
Wright, Jane Cooke
Wright, Louis Tompkins
Wright, Sewall
Wright, Wilbur & Orville
Wu, Chien-Shiung
Wu, Y. C. L. Susan

X

Xide, Xie

Y

Yalow, Rosalyn Sussman
Yang, Chen Ning
Yau, Shing-Tung
Young, Grace Chisholm
Young, J. Z.
Young, Lai-Sung
Young, William Henry
Yukawa, Hideki

Z

Zadeh, Lotfi Asker
Zamecnik, Paul Charles
Zeeman, E. C.
Zeeman, Pieter
Zel'dovich, Yakov Borisovich
Zen, E-an
Zernike, Frits
Ziegler, Karl
Zinder, Norton David
Zinkernagel, Rolf M.
Zinn, Walter Henry
Zinsser, Hans
Zsigmondy, Richard
Zuse, Konrad
Zworykin, Vladimir

Chronology of Scientific Advancement

1895 Scottish physicist C.T.R. Wilson invents the cloud chamber

French physicist Jean Baptiste Perrin confirms the nature of cathode rays

1896 American agricultural chemist George Washington Carver begins work at the Tuskegee Institute

1897 English physicist J.J. Thomson discovers the electron

1898 Polish-born French radiation chemist Marie Curie and French physicist Pierre Curie discover polonium and radium

1900 German physicist Max Planck develops Planck's Constant

1901 Austrian American immunologist Karl Landsteiner discovers A, B, and O blood types

German geneticist Wilhelm Weinberg outlines the "difference method" in his first important paper on heredity

1902 English geneticist William Bateson translates Austrian botanist Gregor Mendel's work

1903 Polish-born French radiation chemist Marie Curie becomes the first woman to be awarded the Nobel Prize

German chemist Otto Diels isolates molecular structure of cholesterol

1904 English electrical engineer John Ambrose Fleming develops the Fleming Valve

Russian physiologist Ivan Petrovich Pavlov receives the Nobel Prize for digestion research

1905 German-born American physicist Albert Einstein publishes the theory of relativity

German chemist Fritz Haber publishes *Thermodynamics of Technical Gas Reactions*

German chemist Walther Nernst's research leads to the Third Law of Thermodynamics

1906 Danish physicist and chemist Johannes Nicolaus Brønsted publishes his first paper on affinity

English neurophysiologist Charles Scott Sherrington publishes *The Integrative Action of the Nervous System*

1907 Prussian-born American physicist Albert Michelson becomes the first American to receive the Nobel Prize for Physics

1908 American astrophysicist George Ellery Hale discovers magnetic fields in sunspots

1909 German bacteriologist and immunologist Paul Ehrlich discovers a cure for syphilis

American engineer and inventor Charles Franklin Kettering successfully tests the first prototypes of the electric automobile starter

1910 English American mathematician Alfred North Whitehead and English mathematician and philosopher Bertrand Russell publish the first volume of *Principia Mathematica*

American engineer and inventor Lee De Forest attempts the first live broadcast of radio

New Zealand-born English physicist Ernest Rutherford postulates the modern concept of the atom

1911 English mathematician Godfrey Harold Hardy begins his collaboration with J. E. Littlewood

Polish-born French radiation chemist Marie Curie becomes the first scientist to win a second Nobel Prize

1912 Danish physicist Niels Bohr develops a new theory of atomic structure

Austrian physicist Victor Hess discovers cosmic rays

English biochemist Frederick Gowland Hopkins publishes a groundbreaking work illustrating the nutritional importance of nutrients

German physicist Max von Laue discovers x-ray diffraction

Austrian physicist Lise Meitner becomes the first woman professor in Germany

German meteorologist and geophysicist Alfred Wegener proposes the theory of continental drift

1913 German bacteriologist and immunologist Paul Ehrlich gives an address explaining the future of chemotherapy

English physicist Henry Gwyn Jeffreys Moseley discovers atomic number of the elements

French physicist Jean Baptiste Perrin verifies German-born American physicist Albert Einstein's calculations of Brownian Motion

American astronomer and astrophysicist Henry Norris Russell publishes the Hertzsprung-Russell diagram

Russian-born American aeronautical engineer Igor I. Sikorsky designs the *Ilya Mourometz* bomber

German chemist Richard Willstätter and Arthur Stoll publish their first studies of chlorophyll

American geneticist A.H. Sturtevant develops gene mapping

1916 American chemist and physicist Irving Langmuir receives a patent for an energy-efficient, longer-lasting tungsten filament light bulb

American geneticist and embryologist Thomas Hunt Morgan publishes *A Critique of the Theory of Evolution*

German theoretical physicist Arnolde Sommerfeld reworks Danish physicist Niels Bohr's atomic theory

American anatomist Florence Rena Sabin publishes *The Origin and Development of the Lymphatic System*

1918 Daniel physical chemist Johannes Nicolaus Brønsted publishes his thirteenth paper on affinity

1919 New Zealand-born English physicist Ernest Rutherford determines that alpha particles can split atoms

1920 American astronomer Harlow Shapley convinces the scientific community that the Milky Way is much larger than originally thought and the Earth's solar system is not its center

1921 Canadian physiologist Frederick G. Banting and Canadian physiologist Charles Herbert Best discover insulin

1923 Danish physical chemist Johannes Nicolaus Brønsted redefines acids and bases

English astronomer Arthur Stanley Eddington publishes *Mathematical Theory of Relativity*

American astronomer Edwin Hubble confirms the existence of galaxies outside the Milky Way

American physicist Robert A. Millikan begins his study of cosmic rays

1924 French theoretical physicist Louis Victor de Broglie publishes findings on wave mechanics

English astronomer Arthur Stanley Eddington determines the mass-luminosity law

1925 German-born American physicist James Franck and German physicist Gustav Hertz prove Danish physicist Niels Bohr's theory of the quantum atom

Italian-born American physicist Enrico Fermi publishes a paper explaining Austro-Hungarian-born Swiss physicist Wolfgang Pauli's exclusion principle

English statistician and geneticist Ronald A. Fisher publishes *Statistical Methods for Research Workers*

1926 German-born English physicist Max Born explains the wave function

American physicist and rocker pioneer Robert H. Goddard launches the first liquid-propellant rocket

American geneticist Hermann Joseph Muller confirms that x rays greatly increase the mutation rate in Drosophila

Austrian physicist Erwin Schrödinger publishes his wave equation

1927 American physicist Arthur Holly Compton receives the Nobel Prize for x-ray research

English physiologist Henry Hallett Dale identifies the chemical mediator involved in the transmission of nerve impulses

German chemist Otto Diels develops a successful dehydrogenating process

German physicist Werner Karl Heisenberg develops the Uncertainty Principle

Belgian astronomer Georges Lemaître formulates the big bang theory

Hungarian American mathematical physicist Eugene Paul Wigner develops the law of the conservation of parity

American astronomer Edwin Hubble puts together the theory of the expanding universe, or Hubble's Law

1928 German chemist Otto Diels and German chemist Kurt Alder develop the Diels-Alder Reaction

Scottish bacteriologist Alexander Fleming discovers penicillin

Austro-Hungarian-born German physicist Hermann Oberth publishes a book explaining the basic principles of space flight

Indian physicist C. V. Raman discovers the Raman Effect

1929 American physicist Robert Van de Graaff constructs the first working model of his particle accelerator

Danish astronomer Ejnar Hertzsprung receives the Gold Medal Award for calculating the first intergalactic distance

Norwegian American chemist Lars Onsager develops the Law of Reciprocal Relations

German-born American mathematician Hermann Weyl develops a mathematical theory for the neutrino

Russian-born American physicist and engineer Vladimir Zworkin files his first patent for color television

1930 English statistician and geneticist Ronald A. Fisher publishes *The Genetical Theory of Natural Selection*

Austrian-born American mathematician Kurt Friedrich Gödel proves the incompleteness theorem

Austro-Hungarian-born Swiss physicist Wolfgang Pauli proposes the existence of the neutrino

1931 American engineer Vannevar Bush develops the differential analyzer with colleagues

American chemist Wallace Hume Carothers founds the synthetic rubber manufacturing industry with his research

South African-born American virologist Max Theiler's research leads to the production of the first yellow-fever vaccine

German biochemist Otto Warburg establishes the Kaiser Wilhelm Institute for Cell Physiology

1932 English atomic physicist John Cockcroft and Irish experimental physicist Ernest Walton split the atom

American physicist Carl David Anderson discovers the positron

English-born Indian physiologist and geneticist John Burdon Sanderson Haldane publishes *The Causes of Evolution*

American physicist Ernest Orlando Lawrence develops the cyclotron and disintegrates a lithium nucleus

1933   Canadian-born American biologist and bacteriologist Oswald Theodore Avery identifies DNA as the basis of heredity

English physicist Paul Adrien Maurice Dirac wins the Nobel Prize for his work on the wave equation

Italian-born American physicist Enrico Fermi proposes his beta decay theory

German inventor Felix Wankel successfully operates the first internal combustion, rotary engine

1934   French nuclear physicist Frédéric Joliot-Curie and French chemist and physicist Irène Joliot-Curie discover artificial radioactivity

American inventor Edwin H. Land develops a commercial method to polarize light

New Zealand-born English physicist Ernest Rutherford achieves the first fusion reaction

American chemist and physicist Harold Urey receives the Nobel Prize in Chemistry for his discovery of deuterium, or heavy hydrogen

1935   American seismologist Charles F. Richter and German American seismologist Beno Gutenberg develop the Richter(-Gutenberg) Scale

English physicist James Chadwick receives the Nobel Prize for the discovery of the neutron

1936   German experimental physicist Hans Geiger perfects the Geiger-Mueller Counter

Russian biochemist Aleksandr Ivanovich Oparin publishes his origin of life theory

English mathematician Alan Turing publishes a paper detailing a machine that would serve as a model for the first working computer

1937   Russian-born American biologist Theodosius Dobzhansky writes *Genetics and the Origin of Species*

Australian English pathologist Howard Walter Florey discovers the growth potential of polymeric chains

German-born English biochemist Hans Adolf Krebs identifies the workings of the Krebs Cycle

Hungarian American biochemist and molecular biologist Albert Szent-Györgyi receives the nobel Prize for isolating vitamin C

1938   German chemist Otto Hahn, Austrian physicist Lise Meitner, and German chemist Fritz Strassmann discover nuclear fission

American physicist Carl David Anderson discovers the meson

1939   Swiss-born American physicist Felix Bloch measures the neutron's magnetic movement

American chemist Wallace Hume Carothers founds the synthetic fiber industry with his research

French-born American microbiologist and ecologist René Dubos discovers tyrothricin

American chemist Linus Pauling develops the theory of complementarity

Russian-born American aeronautical engineer Igor I. Sikorsky flies the first single-rotor helicopter

1940   American physicist and inventor Chester Carlson receives a patent for his photocopying method

English experimental physicist George Paget Thomson forms the Maud Committee

1941   German-born English biochemist Ernst Boris Chain and Australian English pathologist Howard Walter Florey isolate penicillin

German-born American physicist Hans Bethe develops the Bethe Coupler

American biochemist Fritz Lipmann publishes "Metabolic Generation and Utilization of Phosphate Bond Energy"

1942 Hungarian American physicist and biophysicist Leo Szilard and Italian-born American physicist Enrico Fermi set up the first nuclear chain reaction

German-born American biologist Ernst Mayr proposes the theory of geographic speciation

American physicist J. Robert Oppenheimer becomes the director of the Manhattan Project

1943 German-born American molecular biologist Max Delbrück and Italian-born American molecular biologist Salvador Edward Luria publish a milestone paper regarded as the beginning of bacterial genetics

English physicist James Chadwick leads the British contingent of the Manhattan Project

French oceanographer Jacques-Yves Cousteau patents the Aqualung

Italian-born American molecular biologist Salvador Edward Luria devises the fluctuation test

1944 German American rocket engineer Wernher Von Braun fires the first fully operational V-2 rocket

Austrian-born American biochemist Erwin Chargaff discovers the genetic role of DNA

American nuclear chemist Glenn T. Seaborg successfully isolates large amounts of plutonium and develops the actinide concept

American paleontologist George Gaylord Simpson publishes *Tempo and Mode in Evolution*

Russian-born American microbiologist Selman Waksman develops streptomycin

1945 English physicist James Chadwick witnesses the first atomic bomb test

American biochemist Fritz Lipmann discovers coenzyme A

Hungarian American mathematician Johann Von Neumann publishes a report containing the first written description of the stored-program concept

American chemist Linus Pauling determines the cause of sickle-cell anemia

Austrian physicist Erwin Schrödinger publishes *What Is Life?*

1946 American geneticist Joshua Lederberg and American biochemist Edward Lawrie Tatum show that bacteria may reproduce sexually

English zoologist Julian Huxley becomes the first director-general of UNESCO

1947 French oceanographer Jacques-Yves Cousteau breaks the free diving record using his Aqualung

Hungarian-born English physicist Dennis Gabor discovers holography

American inventor Edwin H. Land demonstrates the first instant camera

American mathematician Norbert Wiener creates the study of cybernetics

1948 American physicist John Bardeen develops the transistor

American chemist Melvin Calvin begins research on photosynthesis

Russian-born American physicist George Gamow publishes "Alpha-Beta-Gamma" paper

American zoologist and sex researcher Alfred Kinsey publishes *Sexual Behavior in the Human Male*

American biochemist Wendell Meredith Stanley receives Presidential Certificate of Merit for developing an influenza vaccine

Swedish chemist Arne Tiselius receives the Nobel Prize for research in electrophoresis

1949 Hungarian-born American physicist Edward Teller begins developing the hydrogen bomb

American astronomer Fred Lawrence Whipple suggests the "dirty snowball" comet model

1950 American geneticist Barbara McClintock publishes the discovery of genetic transposition

1951

American chemist Katherine Burr Blodgett receives the Garvan Medal for women chemists

American biologist Gregory Goodwin Pincus begins work on the antifertility steroid the "pill"

Dutch-born English zoologist and ethologist Nikolaas Tinbergen publishes *The Study of Instinct*

1952

German-born American astronomer Walter Baade presents new measurements of the universe

French-born American microbiologist and ecologist René Dubos publishes a book linking tuberculosis with certain environmental conditions

American microbiologist Alfred Day Hershey conducts the "Blender Experiment" to demonstrate that DNA is the genetic material of life

Italian-born American molecular biologist Salvador Edward Luria discovers the phenomenon known as restriction and modification

American microbiologist Jonas Salk develops the first polio vaccine

English chemist Alexander Todd establishes the structure of flavin adenine dinucleotide (FAD)

1953

Russian theoretical physicist Andrei Sakharov and Russian physicist Igor Tamm develop the first Soviet hydrogen bomb

English molecular biologist Francis Crick and American molecular biologist James D. Watson develop the Watson-Crick model of DNA

English molecular biologist Rosalind Elsie Franklin provides evidence of DNA's double-helical structure

American physicist Murray Gell-Mann publishes a paper explaining the strangeness principle

American zoologist and sex researcher Alfred Kinsey publishes *Sexual Behavior in the Human Female*

French microbiologist André Lwoff proposes that "inducible lysogenic bacteria" can test cancerous and noncancerous cell activity

English biologist Peter Brian Medawar proves acquired immunological tolerance

American chemist Stanley Lloyd Miller publishes "A Production of Amino Acids under Possible Primitive Earth Conditions"

Austrian-born English crystallographer and biochemist Max Perutz develops method of isomorphous replacement

1955

English chemist Alexander Todd and English chemist and crystallographer Dorothy Crowfoot Hodgkin determine the structure of vitamin B12

American biochemist Sidney W. Fox begins identifying properties of microspheres

American microbiologist Jonas Salk's polio vaccine pronounced safe and ninety-nine percent effective

English biochemist Frederick Sanger determines the total structure of the insulin molecule

1956

American biochemist Stanley Cohen extracts NGF from a mouse tumor

American experimental physicist Leon Max Lederman helps discover the "long-lived neutral kaon"

1957

American biochemist Arthur Kornberg and Spanish biochemist Severo Ochoa use DNA polymerase to synthesize DNA molecules

1958

American physicist James Van Allen discovers Van Allen radiation belts

American geneticist George Wells Beadle receives the Nobel Prize for the One Gene, One Enzyme Theory

American population biologist Paul R. Ehrlich makes his first statement regarding the problem of overpopulation

German physicist Rudolf Mössbauer discovers recoilless gamma ray release

1959

American computer scientist Grace Hopper develops the COBOL computer language

German physicist Rudolf Mössbauer uses the Mössbauer Effect to test the theory of relativity

1960 English physicist and biochemist John Kendrew and Austrian-born English crystallographer and biochemist Max Perutz formulate the first three-dimensional structure of the protein myoglobin

American chemist Willard F. Libby receives the Nobel Prize for his development of radiocarbon dating

Russian-born American virologist Albert Sabin's oral polio vaccine is approved for manufacture in the United States

1961 French biologists François Jacob and Jacques Monod discover messenger ribonucleic acid (mRNA)

American chemist Melvin Calvin receives the Nobel Prize in Chemistry for his research on photosynthesis

American biochemist Marshall Warren Nirenberg cracks the genetic code

1962 American marine biologist Rachel Carson publishes *Silent Spring*

Russian theoretical physicist Lev Davidovich Landau receives the Nobel Prize for his research into theories of condensed matter

Hungarian-born American physicist Edward Teller becomes the first advocate of an "active defense system" to shoot down enemy missiles

New Zealand-born English biophysicist Maurice Hugh Frederick Wilkins shows the helical structure of RNA

1963 German American physicist Maria Goeppert-Mayer becomes the first woman to receive the Nobel Prize for theoretical physics

American chemist Linus Pauling becomes the only person to receive two unshared Nobel Prizes

1964 American psychobiologist Roger W. Sperry publishes the findings of his split-brain studies

1965 American geneticist A.H. Sturtevant publishes *The History of Genetics*

1967 English astrophysicist Antony Hewish and Irish astronomer Jocelyn Susan Bell Burnell discover pulsars

South African heart surgeon Christiaan Neethling Barnard performs the first human heart transplant

American primatologist Dian Fossey establishes a permanent research camp in Rwanda

1968 American physicist Luis Alvarez wins the Nobel Prize for his bubble chamber work

1969 American astronaut Neil Armstrong becomes the first man to walk on the moon

1970 Indian-born American biochemist Har Gobind Khorana synthesizes the first artificial DNA

American biologist Lynn Margulis publishes *Origins of Life*

1971 English ethologist Jane Goodall publishes *In the Shadow of Man*

1972 American evolutionary biologist Stephen Jay Gould and American paleontologist Niles Eldredge introduce the concept of punctuated equilibrium

American physicist John Bardeen develops the BCS theory of superconductivity

American inventor Edwin H. Land reveals the first instant color camera

1973 American radio engineer Karl Jansky receives the honor of having the Jansky unit adopted as the unit of measure of radiowave intensity

Austrian zoologist and ethologist Konrad Lorenz receives the Nobel Prize for his behavioral research

American biochemist and geneticist Maxine Singer warns the public of gene-splicing risks

1974 English astrophysicist Antony Hewish receives the first Nobel Prize awarded to an astrophysicist

1975 French oceanographer Jacques-Yves Cousteau sees his Cousteau Society membership reach 120,000

American zoologist Edward O. Wilson publishes *Sociobiology: The New Synthesis*

1976 American computer engineer Seymour Cray introduces the CRAY-1 supercomputer

1977 Russian-born Belgian chemist Ilya Prigogine receives the Nobel Prize in Chemistry for his work on nonequilibrium thermodynamics

1980 American biochemist Paul Berg receives the Nobel Prize for the biochemistry of nucleic acids

1981 American virologist Robert C. Gallo develops a blood test for the AIDS virus and discovers human T-cell leukemia virus

1982 American astronaut and physicist Sally Ride becomes the first American woman in space

1983 Italian-born American astrophysicist and applied mathematician Subrahmanyan Chandrasekhar receives the Nobel Prize for research on aged stars

American primatologist Dian Fossey publishes *Gorillas in the Mist*

French virologist Luc Montagnier discovers the human immunodeficiency virus (HIV)

American astronomer and exobiologist Carl Sagan publishes an article with others suggesting the possibility of a "nuclear winter"

1986 American physicist Richard P. Feynman explains why the space shuttle *Challenger* exploded

1987 Chinese American physicist Paul Ching-Wu Chu leads a team that discovers a method for higher temperature superconductivity

1988 English theoretical physicist Stephen Hawking publishes *A Brief History of Time: From the Big Bang to Black Holes*

English pharmacologist James Black receives the Nobel Prize for his heart and ulcer medication work

1989 German-born American physicist Hans Dehmelt and German physicist Wolfgang Paul share the Nobel Prize for devising ion traps

1990 American physicists Jerome Friedman, Henry W. Kendall, and Richard E. Taylor are awarded the Nobel Prize for confirming the existence of quarks

American surgeon Joseph E. Murray receives the Nobel Prize for performing the first human kidney transplant

1991 German physician and cell physiologist Bert Sakmann and German biophysicist Erwin Neher are awarded the Nobel Prize for inventing the patch clamp technique

1993 English biochemist Richard J. Roberts and American biologist Phillip A. Sharp share the Nobel Prize for their research on DNA structure American astrophysicists Russell A. Hulse and Joseph H. Taylor, Jr. receive the Nobel Prize for their work on binary pulsars

1994 American researchers Alfred G. Gilman and Martin Rodbell win the Nobel Prize for their discovery of the role of G-proteins in cellular communication

1995 American biologists Edward B. Lewis and Eric F. Wieschaus and German biologist Christiane Nusslein-Volhard are awarded the Nobel Prize for discoveries concerning the embryonic development of fruit flies

1996 American paleobiologist J. William Schopf determines that a Martian meteorite which struck Antarctica 16 million years ago did not contain evidence of life on Mars.

American medical researcher David Ho heads a research group that announces the results of a study in which nine HIV-infected men were treated with a combination of drugs that halted the progression of AIDS so that HIV was not detected in blood tests a year after treatment ended

1997 English embryologist Ian Wilmut at the Roslin Institute reports that a sheep named Dolly is the first mammal successfully cloned from adult tissue

American biologist Stanley Prusiner wins the Nobel Prize for his discovery of prions, cellular proteins capable of causing disease

 American Robert B. Laughlin, German-born American Horst L. Störmer, and Chinese American Daniel C. Tsui receive the Nobel Prize in Physics for their discovery of a new form of quantum fluid with fractionally charged excitations

English theoretical chemist John A. Pople and Austrian American physicist Walter Kohn receive the Nobel Prize in Chemistry for pioneering work in computational methods in quantum chemistry. Pople developed the computational methods, and Kohn developed density-functional theory

 Dutch physicists Gerardus 't Hooft and Martinus J.G. Veltman receive the Nobel Prize in Physics for elucidating the quantum structure of electroweak interactions in physics. They made particle physics theory more mathematically sound; in particular, the two showed how the theory may be used for precise calculations of physical quantities

German American medical researcher Günter Blobel receives the Nobel Prize in Physiology or Medicine for the discovery that proteins have intrinsic signals that govern their transport and localization in the cell

Igor Tamm
1895–1971
Russian physicist

Igor Tamm's work on nuclear physics and elementary particles covered a wide variety of topics, including relativity, quantum theory, cosmic rays, nuclear forces, plasma physics, and the properties of mesons. His discovery of "Tamm surface levels" in crystalline solids has had application in the development of solid-state devices. In the 1950s and 1960s Tamm became deeply interested in issues of science education and the peaceful use of nuclear energy. He is best known, however, for his theoretical explanation of the origin of Cherenkov radiation, discovered by colleague **Pavel Cherenkov** in about 1935. This theory, developed with **Il'ya Frank** during the period from 1937 to 1939, was recognized by the awarding of the 1958 Nobel Prize in physics to the three Russian physicists.

Igor Evgenievich (some sources cite middle name as Yevgenyevich) Tamm was born on July 8, 1895, in Vladivostok, Russia. His parents were Evgeny Tamm, a civil engineer, and the former Olga Davydova. When Tamm was six years old, his family moved to Elizavetgrad (later renamed Kirovograd), in the Ukraine. Tamm graduated from the Elizavetgrad Gymnasium in 1913, then spent a year at the University of Edinburgh. The end of his first year in Scotland coincided with the beginning of World War I, and Tamm returned to Russia. There he enrolled in the faculty of physics and mathematics at Moscow State University. His schooling was interrupted when the battle-front moved eastward, and in 1917 he became a member of the Elizavetgrad City Soviet of Workers and Soldier Deputies. When the war came to an end, he returned to his studies and was awarded his bachelor's degree in physics in 1918.

Begins Association with Mandel'shtam

Tamm's first teaching appointments were at the Crimean University from 1919 to 1921, and the Odessa Polytechnic Institute in Simferopol. At the latter institution, he made the acquaintance of **Leonid Mandel'shtam**, later to be called the father of Russian physics. Mandel'shtam was to have a critical and long-lasting influence on Tamm's professional career. One of Tamm's earliest research interests, for example, was crystal optics, a field in which Mandel'shtam had made important discoveries. Tamm also worked on the scattering of light (the Mandel'shtam-Brillouin effect or Rayleigh scattering), particularly on the scattering of light by crystals (the so-called Raman effect, discovered by Mandel'shtam and G. S. Landsberg in 1930).

In 1922 Tamm was offered a teaching post at the J. M. Sverdlov Communist University in Moscow, where he remained until 1925. During the same period he held appointments at the Second Moscow University (from 1923 to 1929) and Moscow State University (from 1924 to 1937). At Moscow State University he was promoted to professor of theoretical physics and made head of the department in 1930. He was granted his doctoral degree in 1933.

During the late 1920s and early 1930s, Tamm investigated a number of applications of quantum theory, which holds that energy exists in discrete units. Perhaps his best-known discovery concerned the properties of electrons on the surface of a crystalline solid. He found that these electrons are bonded in a unique way that gives a surface special properties. The discovery of these "Tamm surface levels" has had important applications in the development of solid-state devices, especially those containing semiconductors—solids whose electrical conductivity falls between that of an insulator and that of a conductor.

Another topic of interest to Tamm during the 1930s was the atomic nucleus. For example, in 1934 he predicted that the neutron, although uncharged, would have a magnetic moment with a negative sign. Although the idea did not meet with widespread approval at first, Tamm's prediction has since been shown to be correct. At about the same time, Tamm began a study of nuclear forces. He developed a theory that attributed beta decay (the spontaneous breakup of neutrons in the nucleus) to forces carried between nucleons (protons and neutrons) by means of electrons and neutrinos. He was incorrect in his choice of force carriers, but understood the general mechanism of intranuclear force transmission. In fact, **Hideki Yukawa** was to outline the correct theory for this phenomenon within a year of Tamm's own electron-neutrino hypothesis.

Explains Cherenkov Radiation

In the period from 1934 to 1936, Tamm's colleague, Pavel Cherenkov, discovered the phenomenon that now carries his name: Cherenkov radiation. The term "Cherenkov radiation" refers to the pale blue light emitted when gamma radiation passes through a (usually) liquid medium. Although Cherenkov determined a number of properties of this radiation, he was unable to develop a satisfactory theory explaining its origin.

That explanation came through the efforts of Tamm and Il'ya Frank in about 1936. Tamm and Frank found that although objects cannot travel faster than the speed of light in a vacuum, they can do so in other media. In the case of Cherenkov radiation, the passage of gamma rays through a medium results in the emission of electrons that do just that. Electrons emitted in this way form a wave that spreads out in a cone-shaped pattern in advance of the gamma ray in much the way that a sonic boom is produced by a supersonic aircraft. The blue glow is produced, then, when the wave velocity exceeds some given value. For this research, Tamm, Frank, and Cherenkov were jointly awarded the 1958 Nobel Prize in physics.

The last four decades of Tamm's life were spent at the P. N. Lebedev Physical Institute in Moscow, where he was named director of the theoretical section in 1934. After his work on Cherenkov radiation, Tamm returned to problems of nuclear physics and elementary particles. During the 1950s, he also carried out research on plasma physics, a topic critical to the development of controlled thermonuclear fusion reactions. Tamm was long interested in problems of science education and the peaceful applications of nuclear energy. In connection with the latter, he was active in the Pugwash movement for science and world affairs of the 1950s and 1960s.

In addition to the Nobel Prize in physics, Tamm was awarded two Orders of Lenin and the Order of the Red Badge of Labor. He was married to Natalie Shuiskaya on September 16, 1917. They had one daughter, Irene, and one son, Eugen. Among Tamm's writings are *Osnovy teorii elektrichestva* (title means "Principles of the Theory of Electricity"), *On the Magnetic Moment of the Neutrino,* and *Relativistic Interaction of Elementary Particles.* Tamm died in Moscow on April 12, 1971.

SELECTED WRITINGS BY TAMM:

Books

Osnovy teorii elektrichestva, (title means "Principles of the Theory of Electricity"), Nauka, 1966.

Periodicals

Nature, Exchange Forces Between Neutrons and Protons and Fermi's Theory, Volume 133, 1934, p. 981.
Nature, Nuclear Magnetic Moments and the Properties of the Neutron, Volume 134, 1934, p. 380.
Doklady Akademii Nauk SSSR, Kogerentnoe izluchenie bystrogo elektrona v srede, (title means "Coherent Radiation of Fast Electrons Passing through Matter") Volume 14, Number 3, 1937, pp. 107–112.

FURTHER READING:

Books

Biographical Encyclopedia of Scientists, Volume 2, Facts on File, 1981, p. 771.

Gillispie, Charles Coulson, editor, *Dictionary of Scientific Biography,* Volume 13, Scribner's, 1975, pp. 239–242.
Gillispie, Charles Coulson, editor, *McGraw-Hill Modern Scientists and Engineers,* Volume 3, McGraw-Hill, 1980, pp. 186–187.

Sketch by David E. Newton

Tan Jiazhen
1909–
Chinese biologist and geneticist

Tan Jiazhen's work in the field of genetics resulted in a distinguished scientific career in the United States and China. His broad-ranging intellect and abilities have served the scientific community of both countries through his work at many institutes of higher learning. For example, since 1984, he has been a senior research fellow at the Eleanor Roosevelt Institute for Cancer Research in Denver, Colorado. That same year, he also became director of the Genetics Institute at Fudan University in Shanghai, People's Republic of China, where he had held the post of vice president beginning in 1961. He has served in an advisory capacity as a member of the board of directors of the International Council for Development of Underutilized Plants, and he has held editorial and advisory positions at *The Scientist, Journal of Genetics,* and *Global Science Journal.* His work as president of the Genetics Society of China and as a member of various international science academies is well known. He capped off his affiliation with these prestigious scientific organizations by becoming, in 1991, a founding member of the World Institute of Sciences.

Tan was born on September 15, 1909, in Ningbo City, Zhejiang Province, the son of C. Y. and M. Y. Tan. He was educated at Suzhou University and obtained a biology degree in 1930. He continued his education at the California Institute of Technology, receiving a Ph.D. in genetics in 1936. A year later, he returned to China, serving as professor at Zhejiang University until 1952. During this period, he also taught for one year as visiting professor at Colorado University. He began work at Fudan University as a professor of genetics and vice president in 1961.

In the 1960s Tan experienced some difficulties given his position in China during the Cultural Revolution. Held in disgrace beginning in 1966, he went underground for a period of ten years, first surfacing in February 1978. He then began the road back to political and scientific legitimacy. First, he was elected deputy for Shanghai Municipality to the fifth National People's Congress, and in March of 1978, was elected as a member of the Standing

Committee of the fifth Chinese People's Political Consultative Conference. In June of 1978, his affiliation with Fudan University was once again recognized by the government. As political repression lessened even more, Tan gradually resumed a place of importance in his country's scientific community.

Tan has been the recipient of many honors from science peers throughout the world. He was granted the Distinguished Alumni Award from the California Institute of Technology in 1983. He was given honorary doctor of science degrees from York University in 1984 and from the University of Maryland in 1985. In 1986, he was made honorary president of Ningbo University, and in 1988 Shanghai Agricultural College presented him with that same distinction. He received the Medal of Merit from Konstanz Universität, Federal Republic of Germany, in 1989, and was made an honorary citizen of the State of California in 1990.

In 1932 Tan married M. Y. Fu, who is now deceased. His second marriage was to Dr. Y. F. Qiu in 1973. He has three sons and one daughter.

Sketch by Jane Stewart Cook

Richard A. Tapia
1939–
American mathematician

Richard A. Tapia is a nationally recognized educator who was named in 1990 one of the twenty most influential leaders in minority mathematics education. His four-day workshops on computational science have also received national attention by bringing secondary and middle school teachers from schools with high minority enrollments to Rice University to learn about opportunities in the computational sciences. As associate director for minority affairs in the Office of Graduate Studies at Rice, Tapia has been extremely successful in producing minority Ph.D.s.

Richard Alfred Tapia was born on March 25, 1939, in Santa Monica, California. The son of Mexican immigrant parents, Amado Tapia and Magda Tapia, he entered the University of California at Los Angeles after spending two preparatory years in junior college. He remained in that university, receiving his B.A. in 1961, his M.A. in 1966, and his Ph.D. in 1967. After graduate school, he taught at the University of Wisconsin as an assistant professor in its Mathematics Research Center from 1968 to 1970. That year he joined Rice University in Houston, Texas, as an assistant professor of mathematical science and has been there ever since. In 1972 he became an associate professor and then a full professor in 1976. Between 1978 and 1983, he was mathematical science department chair and was visiting professor at Baylor College and Stanford University. In 1989 he assumed his present position as associate director for minority affairs in Rice's Office of Graduate Studies.

Tapia has been concerned with the future role of mathematicians and mathematics in a world increasingly dominated by computers. As a member of the American Mathematics Society, he sits on its Strategic Planning Committee and has been able to lead the debate on this important issue. It is imperative, he believes, that mathematics shows itself to be relevant to the everyday world and be able to contribute to solving problems in engineering, medicine, and other applied disciplines.

Tapia's work resulted in his being named one of the twenty most influential leaders in minority mathematics education by the National Research Council of the National Science Foundation in 1990. That same year, he received the college level Education Award, one of the Society for Hispanic Professional Engineers' (SHPE) National Achievement Awards. Besides his membership in the American Mathematics Society, Tapia is a member of the Society for Industrial and Applied Mathematics, the Mathematical Association of America, the Mathematical Programming Society, and the Society for the Advancement of Chicanos and Native Americans in Science (SACNAS). He was also elected to the National Academy of Engineering. He is the author of over sixty technical papers as well as a textbook. He has been married to Jean Rodriguez since 1959, and they have two children, Richard and Rebecca.

SELECTED WRITINGS BY TAPIA:

Books

Nonparametric Probability Density Estimation, Johns Hopkins University Press, 1978.
Nonparametric Function Estimation, Modeling, and Simulation, Society for Industrial and Applied Mathematics, 1990.

FURTHER READING:

Periodicals

Mellado, Carmela C., *Hispanic Engineer,* Math Education in the Computer Age, Spring 1991, pp. 26–27.
Mellado, Carmela C., *Hispanic Engineer,* 1990 Award Winners, Conference Issue, 1990, pp. 66–67.

Sketch by Leonard C. Bruno

Alfred Tarski
1901–1983
American mathematician and logician

Alfred Tarski made considerable contributions to several areas of mathematics, including set theory and algebra, and his work as a logician led to important breakthroughs in semantics—the study of symbols and meaning in written and verbal communication. Tarski's research in this area yielded a mathematical definition of truth in language, and also made him a pioneer in studying models of linguistic communication, a subject that became known as model theory. Tarski's research also proved useful in the development of computer science, and he became an influential mentor to later mathematicians as a professor at the University of California at Berkeley.

Born Alfred Tajtelbaum in Warsaw, Poland (then part of Russian Poland) on January 14, 1901, Tarski was the elder of two sons born to Ignacy Tajtelbaum, a shopkeeper of modest means, and Rose (Iuussak) Tajtelbaum, who was known to have an exceptional memory. During his teens Tarski helped supplement the family income by tutoring. He attended an excellent secondary school, and although he was an outstanding student, he, surprisingly, did not get his best marks in logic. Biology was his favorite subject in high school, and he intended to major in this discipline when he first attended the University of Warsaw. However, as Steven R. Givant pointed out in *Mathematical Intelligence,* "what derailed him was success." In an early mathematics course at the university, Tarski was able to solve a challenging problem in set theory posed by the professor. The solution led to his first published paper, and Tarski, at the professor's urging, decided to switch his emphasis to mathematics.

Tarski received a Ph.D. from the University of Warsaw in 1924, the same year he met his future wife, Maria Witkowski. They got married on June 23, 1929, and later had two children, Jan and Ina. It is believed that the young mathematician was in his early twenties when he changed his name from Tajtelbaum to Tarski. His son, Jan, told interviewer Jeanne Spriter James that this step was taken because Tarski believed that his new Polish-sounding name would be held in higher regard at the university than his original Jewish moniker. When Tarski was married, he was baptized a Catholic, his wife's religion.

Early Struggles in Academia

Tarski served in the Polish army for short periods of time in 1918 and 1920. While working on his Ph.D. he was employed as an instructor in logic at the Polish Pedagogical Institute in Warsaw beginning in 1922. After graduating he became a docent and then adjunct professor of mathematics and logic at the University of Warsaw beginning in 1925. That same year he also took a full-time teaching position at

Zeromski's Lycee, a high school in Warsaw, since his income from the university was inadequate to support his family. Tarski remained at both jobs until 1939, despite repeated attempts to secure a permanent university professorship. Some have attributed Tarski's employment difficulties to anti-Semitism, but whatever the reason, his lack of academic prominence created problems for the young mathematician. Burdened by his teaching load at the high school and college, Tarski was unable to devote as much time to his research as he would have liked. He later said that his creative output was greatly reduced during these years because of his employment situation. The papers he did publish in this period, however, quickly marked Tarski as one of the premiere logicians of the century. His early work was often concentrated in the area of set theory. He also worked in conjunction with Polish mathematician **Stefan Banach** to produce the Banach-Tarski paradox, which illustrated the limitations of mathematical theories that break a space down into a number of pieces. Other research in the 1920s and 1930s addressed the axiom of choice, large cardinal numbers, the decidability of Euclidean geometry, and Boolean algebra.

Tarski's initial research on semantics took place in the early 1930s. He was concerned here with problems of language and meaning, and his work resulted in a mathematical definition of truth as it is expressed in symbolic languages. He also provided a proof that demonstrated that any such definition of truth in a language results in contradictions. A London *Times* obituary on Tarski noted the groundbreaking nature of his work in this area, proclaiming that the mathematician's findings "set the direction for all modern philosophical discussions of truth." Tarski expanded this early work in semantics over the ensuing years, eventually developing a new field of study—model theory—which would become a major research subject for logicians. This area of study examines the mathematic properties of grammatical sentences and compares them with various models of linguistic communication.

Additionally, Tarski pursued research in many other areas of math and logic during his career, including closure algebras, binary relations and the algebra of relations, cylindrical algebra, and undecidable theories. He also made a lasting contribution to the field of computer science. As early as 1930 he produced an algorithm that was capable of deciding whether any sentence in basic Euclidian geometry is either true or false. This pointed the way toward later machine calculations, and has also had relevance in determining more recent computer applications.

Outbreak of World War II leads to New Opportunities

In 1939 Tarski left Poland for a conference and speaking tour in the United States, intending to be gone for only a short time. Shortly after his departure, however, the German army invaded and conquered Poland, beginning World War II. Unable to return to his homeland, Tarski found himself stranded in the United States without money, without a job, and without his wife and children who had remained in Warsaw. The family would not be reunited until after the war, and in the meantime, Tarski set about finding work in America. He first served as a research associate in mathematics at Harvard University from 1939 to 1941. In 1940 he also taught as a visiting professor at the City College of New York. He had a temporary position at the Institute for Advanced Study at Princeton beginning in 1941, and in 1942 he obtained his first permanent position in the United States when he was hired as a lecturer at the University of California at Berkeley. The university would remain his professional home for the rest of his career.

Tarski became an associate professor at the university in 1945, was appointed to the position of full professor the following year, and was named professor emeritus in 1968. Tarski's contributions to mathematics and science were enhanced by his role as an educator. He established the renown Group in Logic and the Methodology of Science at Berkeley, and over his long tenure he taught some of the most influential mathematicians and logicians to emerge after World War II, including **Julia Robinson** and Robert Montague. His stature was further enhanced through his service as a visiting professor and lecturer at numerous U.S. and international universities. In 1973 Tarski ended his formal teaching duties at Berkeley, but he continued to supervise doctoral students and conduct research during the final decade of his life. He died in 1983 from a lung condition caused by smoking.

Tarski received many awards and honors throughout his career. He was elected to the National Academy of Sciences and the Royal Netherlands Academy of Sciences and Letters, and was also made a corresponding fellow in the British Academy. In 1966 he received the Alfred Jurzykowski Foundation Award, and in 1981 he was presented with the Berkeley Citation, the university's highest faculty honor. He also was awarded numerous fellowships and honorary degrees, and was a member in many professional organizations, including the Polish Logic Society, the American Mathematical Society, and the International Union for the History and Philosophy of Science.

SELECTED WRITINGS BY TARSKI:

Books

Introduction to Logic and to the Methodology of Deductive Sciences, Oxford University Press, 1941.
Logic, Semantics, Metamathematics: Papers from 1923 to 1938, Clarendon Press, 1956, revised edition, edited by J. Corcoran, Hackett Publishing, 1983.
Alfred Tarski: Collected Papers, 4 volumes, edited by Steven R. Givant and Ralph N. McKenzie, Stuttgart, 1986.
A Formalization of Set Theory without Variables, Colloquium Publications, 1987.

Periodicals

Philosophy and Phenomenological Research, The Semantic Conception of Truth and the Foundations of Semantics, Volume 4, 1944, pp. 341–375.

FURTHER READING:

Books

Dictionary of Scientific Biography, Volume 18, supplement II, Scribner, 1990, pp. 893–896.
Proceedings of the Tarski Symposium, An International Symposium to Honor Alfred Tarski on the Occasion of His Seventieth Birthday, Volume 25, American Mathematical Society, 1974.
Ulam, Stanislaw M., *Adventures of a Mathematician,* Scribner, 1976, pp. 29, 40, 114, 119, 122.

Periodicals

Addison, John W., *California Monthly,* December, 1983.
Addison, John W., *Chicago Tribune,* October 30, 1983.
Givant, Steven R., *Mathematical Intelligence,* A Portrait of Alfred Tarski, Volume 13, no. 3, 1991, pp. 16–32.
Givant, Steven R., *Journal of Symbolic Logic,* Volume 51, 1986; Volume 53, 1988.
Givant, Steven R., *Times,* (London), December 6, 1983, p. 16-G.
Givant, Steven R., *Washington Post,* October 29, 1983.

Other

Givant, Steven R., *Washington Post,* Tarski, Jan, interviews with Jeanne Spriter James conducted November 1, 2, 3, 4, and 21, 1993.

Sketch by Jeanne Spriter James

Edward Lawrie Tatum
1909–1975
American biochemist

Edward Lawrie Tatum's experiments with simple organisms demonstrated that cell processes can be studied as chemical reactions and that such reactions are governed by genes. With **George Beadle**, he offered conclusive proof in 1941 that each biochemical reaction in the cell is controlled via a catalyzing enzyme by a specific gene. The "one gene-one enzyme" theory changed the face of biology and gave it a new chemical expression. For the

Edward Lawrie Tatum

first time, the nature of life seemed within the grasp of science's quantitative methods. Tatum, collaborating with **Joshua Lederberg**, demonstrated in 1947 that bacteria reproduce sexually, thus introducing a new experimental organism into the study of molecular genetics. Spurred by Tatum's discoveries, other scientists worked to understand the precise chemical nature of the unit of heredity called the gene. This study culminated in 1953 with the description by **James Watson** and **Francis Crick** of the structure of DNA. Tatum's use of microorganisms and laboratory mutations for the study of biochemical genetics led directly to the biotechnology revolution of the 1980s. Tatum and Beadle shared the 1958 Nobel Prize in physiology or medicine with Joshua Lederberg for ushering in the new era of modern biology.

Tatum was born on December 14, 1909, in Boulder, Colorado, to Arthur Lawrie Tatum and Mabel Webb Tatum. He was the first of three children; a younger brother and sister would follow. Both of Edward's parents excelled academically. His father held two degrees, an M.D. and a Ph.D. in pharmacology. Edward's mother was one of the first women to graduate from the University of Colorado. Presumably an interest in science and medicine ran in the Tatum family: Edward would become a research scientist, his brother a physician, and his sister a nurse. As a boy, Edward played the French horn and trumpet; his interest in music lasted his whole life. He also enjoyed swimming and ice-skating.

In 1925, when Tatum was fifteen years old, his father accepted a position as a pharmacology professor at the University of Wisconsin. Tatum studied at the University of Chicago Experimental School and for two years at the University of Chicago before transferring and completing his undergraduate work at the University of Wisconsin. He almost became a geologist before deciding in his senior year to major in chemistry.

Tatum earned his A.B. degree in chemistry from the University of Wisconsin in 1931. In 1932 he earned his master's degree in microbiology. Two years later, in 1934, he received a Ph.D. in biochemistry for a dissertation on the cellular biochemistry and nutritional needs of a bacterium. Understanding the biochemistry of microorganisms such as bacteria, yeast, and molds would persist at the heart of Tatum's career.

After receiving his doctorate, Tatum remained at the University of Wisconsin for one year as a research assistant in biochemistry. He married the same year he completed his Ph.D. In Livingston, Wisconsin, Tatum wed June Alton, the daughter of a lumber dealer, on July 28, 1934. They eventually had two daughters, Margaret Carol and Barbara Ann.

From 1936 to 1937, Tatum studied bacteriological chemistry at the University of Utrecht in the Netherlands while on a General Education Board fellowship for post-graduate study. In Utrecht he worked in the laboratory of F. Kogl, who had identified the vitamin biotin. In Kogl's lab Tatum investigated the nutritional needs of bacteria and fungi. While Tatum was in Holland, he was contacted by geneticist George Beadle. Beadle, seven years older than Tatum, had done genetic studies with the fruit fly *Drosophila melanogaster* while in the laboratory of **Thomas Hunt Morgan** at the California Institute of Technology. Beadle, newly arrived at Stanford University, was now looking for a biochemist who could collaborate with him as he continued his work in genetics. He hoped to identify the enzymes responsible for the inherited eye pigments of *Drosophila*.

Upon his return to the United States in the fall of 1937, Tatum was appointed a research associate at Stanford University in the Department of Biological Sciences. There he embarked on the *Drosophila* project with Beadle for four years. The two men successfully determined that kynurenine was the enzyme responsible for the fly's eye color and that it was controlled by one of the eye-pigment genes. This and other observations led them to postulate several theories about the relationship between genes and biochemical reactions. Yet they realized that *Drosophila* was not an ideal experimental organism on which to continue their work.

Chooses Bread Mold Medium for Gene Experiments

Tatum and Beadle began searching for a suitable organism. After some discussion and a review of the literature, they settled on a pink mold that commonly grows on bread, known as *neurospora crassa*. The advantages to working with *neurospora* were many: it reproduced very quickly, its nutritional needs and biochemical pathways were already well known, and it had the useful capability of being able to reproduce both sexually and asexually. This last characteristic made it possible to grow cultures that were genetically identical and also to grow cultures that were the result of a cross between two different parent strains. With *neurospora*, Tatum and Beadle were ready to demonstrate the effect of genes on cellular biochemistry.

The two scientists began their *neurospora* experiments in March 1941. At that time, scientists spoke of "genes" as the units of heredity without fully understanding what a gene might look like or how it might act. Although they realized that genes were located on the chromosomes, they didn't know what the chemical nature of such a substance might be. An understanding of DNA (deoxyribonucleic acid, the molecule of heredity) was still twelve years in the future. Nevertheless, geneticists in the 1940s had accepted Gregor Mendel's work with inheritance patterns in pea plants. Mendel's theory, rediscovered by three independent investigators in 1900, states that an inherited characteristic is determined by the combination of two hereditary units (genes), one each contributed by the parental cells. A dominant gene is expressed even when it is carried by only one of a pair of chromosomes, while a recessive gene must be carried by both chromosomes to be expressed. With *Drosophila*, Tatum and Beadle had taken genetic mutants—flies that inherited a variant form of eye color—and tried to work out the biochemical steps that led to the abnormal eye color. Their goal was to identify the variant enzyme, presumably governed by a single gene, that controlled the variant eye color. This proved technically very difficult, and as luck would have it, another lab announced the discovery of kynurenine's role before theirs did. With the neurospora experiments, they set out to prove their one gene-one enzyme theory another way.

The two investigators began with biochemical processes they understood well: the nutritional needs of *neurospora*. By exposing cultures of *neurospora* to X rays, they would cause genetic damage to some bread mold genes. If their theory was right, and genes did indeed control biochemical reactions, the genetically damaged strains of mold would show changes in their ability to produce nutrients. If supplied with some basic salts and sugars, normal *neurospora* can make all the amino acids and vitamins it needs to live except for one (biotin).

This is exactly what happened. In the course of their research, the men created, with X-ray bombardment, a number of mutated strains that each lacked the ability to produce a particular amino acid or vitamin. The first strain they identified, after 299 attempts to determine its mutation, lacked the ability to make vitamin B_6. By crossing this strain with a normal strain, the offspring inherited the defect as a recessive gene according to the inheritance patterns described by Mendel. This proved that the mutation was a genetic defect, capable of being passed to successive generations and causing the same nutritional mutation in those offspring. The X-ray bombardment had altered the gene governing the enzyme needed to promote the production of vitamin B_6.

This simple experiment heralded the dawn of a new age in biology, one in which molecular genetics would soon dominate. Nearly forty years later, on Tatum's death, Joshua Lederberg told the *New York Times* that this experiment "gave impetus and morale" to scientists who strived to understand how genes directed the processes of life. For the first time, biologists believed that it might be possible to understand and quantify the living cell's processes.

Tatum and Beadle were not the first, as it turned out, to postulate the one gene-one enzyme theory. By 1942 the work of English physician **Archibald Garrod**, long ignored, had been rediscovered. In his study of people suffering from a particular inherited enzyme deficiency, Garrod had noticed the disease seemed to be inherited as a Mendelian recessive. This suggested a link between one gene and one enzyme. Yet Tatum and Beadle were the first to offer extensive experimental evidence for the theory. Their use of laboratory methods, like X rays, to create genetic mutations also introduced a powerful tool for future experiments in biochemical genetics.

Research Leads to Mass Production of Penicillin

During World War II, the methods Tatum and Beadle had developed in their work with pink bread mold were used to produce large amounts of penicillin, another mold. Their basic research, unwittingly, thus had a very important practical effect as well. In 1944 Tatum served as a civilian staff member of the U.S. Office of Scientific Research and Development at Stanford. Industry, too, used the methods the men developed to measure vitamins and amino acids in foods and tissues.

In 1945, at the end of the war, Tatum accepted an appointment at Yale University as an associate professor of botany with the promise of establishing a program of biochemical microbiology within that department. Apparently the move was due to Stanford's lack of encouragement of Tatum, who failed to fit into the tidy category of biochemist or biologist or geneticist but instead mastered all three fields. In 1946 Tatum did indeed create a new program at Yale and became a professor of microbiology. In work begun at Stanford and continued at Yale, he demonstrated that the one gene-one enzyme theory applied to yeast and bacteria as well as molds.

Discovers Sexual Reproduction of Bacteria

In a second extremely fruitful collaboration, Tatum began working with Joshua Lederberg in March 1946. Lederberg, a Columbia University medical student fifteen years younger than Tatum, was at Yale during a break in the medical school curriculum. Tatum and Lederberg began studying the bacterium *Escherichia coli*. At that time, it was believed that *E. coli* reproduced asexually. The two scientists proved otherwise. When cultures of two different mutant bacteria were mixed, a third strain, one showing characteristics taken from each parent, resulted. This discovery of biparental inheritance in bacteria, which Tatum called genetic recombination, provided geneticists with a new experimental organism. Again, Tatum's methods had altered the practices of experimental biology. Lederberg never returned to medical school, earning instead a Ph.D. from Yale.

In 1948 Tatum returned to Stanford as professor of biology. A new administration at Stanford and its Department of Biology had invited him to return in a position suited to his expertise and ability. While in this second residence at Stanford, Tatum helped establish the Department of Biochemistry. In 1956 he became a professor of biochemistry and head of the department. Increasingly, Tatum's talents were devoted to promoting science at an administrative level. He was instrumental in relocating the Stanford Medical School from San Francisco to the university campus in Palo Alto. In that year Tatum also was divorced from his wife June. On December 16, 1956, he married Viola Kantor in New York City. Kantor was the daughter of a dentist in Brooklyn. Owing in part to these complications in his personal affairs, Tatum left the West Coast and took a position at the Rockefeller Institute for Medical Research (now Rockefeller University) in January 1957. There he continued to work through institutional channels to support young scientists, and served on various national committees. Unlike some other administrators, he emphasized nurturing individual investigators rather than specific kinds of projects. His own research continued in efforts to understand the genetics of neurospora and the nucleic acid metabolism of mammalian cells in culture.

Contributions to Biology Recognized with Nobel Prize

In 1958, together with Beadle and Lederberg, Tatum received the Nobel Prize in physiology or medicine. The Nobel Committee awarded the prize to the three investigators for their work demonstrating that genes regulate the chemical processes of the cell. Tatum and Beadle shared one-half of the prize and Lederberg received the other half for work done separately from Tatum. Lederberg later paid tribute to Tatum for his role in Lederberg's decision to study the effects of X-ray-induced mutation. In his Nobel lecture, Tatum predicted that "with real understanding of the roles of heredity and environment, together with the consequent improvement in man's physical capacities and greater freedom from physical disease, will come an improvement in his approach to, and understanding of, sociological and economic problems."

Tatum had a marked interest in social issues, including population control. In 1965 and 1966 Tatum organized other Nobel laureates in science to make public endorsements of family planning and birth control. These included statements to Pope Paul VI, whose encyclical against birth control for Catholics was issued at this time.

Tatum's second wife, Viola, died on April 21, 1974. Tatum married Elsie Bergland later in 1974 and she survived his death the following year, on November 5, 1975. Tatum died at his home on East Sixty-third Street in New York City after an extended illness. In a memoir written for the *Annual Review of Genetics,* Lederberg recalled that Tatum's last years were "marred by ill health, substantially self-inflicted by a notorious smoking habit." Lederberg noted, too, that Tatum's "mental outlook" was scarred by the painful death of his second wife.

In addition to the Nobel Prize, Tatum received the Remsen Award of the American Chemical Society in 1953 for his work in biparental inheritance and sexual reproduction in bacteria. In 1952 he was elected to the National Academy of Sciences. He was a founding member of the *Annual Review of Genetics* and joined the editorial board of *Science* in 1957. Tatum's collected papers occupy twenty-five feet of space in the Rockefeller University Archives and span the years from 1930 to 1975.

SELECTED WRITINGS BY TATUM:

Books

An Introduction to Genetics, Saunders, 1939.

Periodicals

Proceedings of the National Academy of Sciences, Genetic Control of Biochemical Reactions in Neurospora, Volume 27, 1941, pp. 499–506.
Journal of Bacteriology, Gene Recombination in the Bacterium Escherichia coli, 1947.
Nobel Lectures in Molecular Biology 1933–1974, A Case History in Biological Search, (Nobel Lecture) Elsevier, 1977.

FURTHER READING:

Periodicals

Beadle, George W., *Annual Review of Biochemistry,* Recollections, Volume 43, 1973, pp. 1–13.
Beadle, George W., *Chemical and Engineering News,* May 18, 1953, p. 2099.
Kopp, Carolyn, *Journal of the History of Biology,* The J. H. B. Archive Report: The Edward Lawrie Tatum Papers at the Rockefeller University Archives, Volume 15, 1982, pp. 153–154, 1982.
Lederberg, Joshua, *Annual Review of Genetics,* Edward Lawrie Tatum, Volume 13, 1979, pp. 1–5.
Lederberg, Joshua, *New York Times,* November 7, 1975, p. 40.

Sketch by Liz Marshall

Henry Taube
1915–
American chemist

A Canadian-born American chemist and professor at Stanford, Henry Taube has dedicated over fifty years to research and teaching. In addition to conducting important research in the mechanics of electron transfer reactions in complex metals, Taube has contributed greatly to increase our understanding major concepts in inorganic chemistry with applications in the chemical industry. For his work in this field, Taube received the Nobel Prize in chemistry in 1983.

Taube, the youngest of four boys, was born on November 30, 1915, in Neudorf, Saskatchewan, Canada, to Samuel Taube and Albertina Tiledetzski. His parents were Ukrainian peasants, who moved from their home near Kiev to Saskatchewan in 1911 to escape the tyranny of the tsar. Although his parents were uneducated and poor, they were very astute and worked hard to develop a farm. Taube himself considered farm work and its lessons of perseverance a valuable part of his education. At the age of thirteen, Taube was sent to a Lutheran boarding school, from where he moved to the University of Saskatchewan. The depression brought difficult times to the Taube family, and as a result of some failed investments, Taube's father was no longer able to support the young boy at school. However, a chemistry teacher took an interest in Taube and arranged for him to help in the laboratory in order to continue his education. Although Taube received his best grades in chemistry, he loved English literature and wanted to become a writer.

Launches a Career in Chemistry

Taube received the bachelor of science degree in 1935 and the master of science degree in photochemistry in 1937. Regardless, it was not until he received an opportunity to attend the University of California, Berkeley, that Taube became deeply interested in chemistry. While at Berkeley, he won the Rosenberg prize and was considered one of the most promising students. He received the Ph.D. in 1940, following which the university employed him as an instructor. Wanting to return to Canada, Taube applied for jobs at the major universities, but the opportunities never came. Instead he received a job offer from Cornell University, which he accepted in 1941.

At Cornell Taube did not find much interest in the kind of research he wanted to pursue, and by 1946 he was ready for a change. When an opportunity arose to work at the University of Chicago, a hub of scientific activity and innovative research at the time, Taube accepted. He considered his experience at Chicago a highly productive part of his career. Chosen to develop a course in advanced inorganic chemistry, Taube found little in published textbooks. He researched widely and became interested in complex metal or coordination chemistry. In the course of these investigations, he realized that work he had done on substitution of carbon in organic reactions could be related to inorganic complexes. In 1952 he wrote a seminal paper published in *Chemical Reviews* on the rates of chemical substitution, relating them to electronic structure. Although his research is outdated in parts, Taube's work was tremendously useful to chemists in planning experiments that depend on the differential in substitution rates.

Awarded Nobel Prize for Electron Transfer Research

Taube chaired the Department of Chemistry at the University of Chicago form 1956 to 1959. However, he did not enjoy administrative work, and in 1961 he took a position at Stanford University that would allow him to concentrate on research. Seeking to extend his work on substitution rates, he launched into research on ruthenium and osmium, elements with an electronic structure that fascinated him. Ruthenium is a rare metallic chemical element of the platinum group first found in ores from the Ural Mountains in Russia. It has remarkable back-bonding properties with chemicals such as carbon monoxide. The element osmium has an even greater back-bonding capacity than ruthenium. As Taube investigated the way electrons were transferred between molecules in chemical reactions, he noted unexpected changes in the electrical charge and shape of the molecules. Taube's important discovery was that before the transfer of electrons occurs, molecules build a "chemical bridge." Previously, scientists had thought molecules simply exchanged electrons. Taube's work, identifying the intermediate step in electron exchanges, explained why some reactions among similar kinds of metals and ions occur at different rates.

Although inorganic reactions are important in developing principles of chemistry, interest in inorganic reactions had lagged behind the development of organic (carbon-based) chemistry. Taube's insights formed an important impulse for the further development of inorganic chemistry. For his work on the mechanisms of electron transfer, Taube won the 1983 Nobel Prize in chemistry, reversing the long-standing tradition of awarding achievements in organic chemistry.

In later work, Taube and several of his associates extended the scope of coordination chemistry with the study of ruthenium ammines and osmium, illuminating, for instance, the role of metals in catalysis. He was also able to show how the structure of the chemical bridge affects the electron transfer process in metals. In an interview with Richard Stevenson published in *Chemistry in Britain,* Taube described his work with chemistry as a love affair. "I'm a chemist and I wanted to know what happens when you mix things."

Taube is a member of fifteen societies, has received thirty-nine honors and awards, and became professor emeritus at Stanford in 1986. He has written over 330 scientific papers and articles. Taube married Mary Alice Wesche in 1952. They have two daughters and two sons. Until the mid–1960s he and his family continued to return to Saskatchewan during holidays to help with the family farm. Taube is semi retired and spends only part of his time at Stanford tutoring small groups. He also works part-time as a consultant to various firms, including Catalytica, Inc. and Hercules, a chemical manufacturer. In his leisure time, Taube is a collector of classical vocal records from vintage 1897 to the most recent recordings, and he loves gardening.

SELECTED WRITINGS BY TAUBE:

Periodicals

Science, Electron Transfer between Metal Complexes: Retrospective, 226, November 30, 1984, p. 1028.
Science, Use of Dihydrogen Osmium Complex, April 10, 1992.

FURTHER READING:

Periodicals

Bullen, Val, *Western People,* Work Can Be Fun, March 11, 1993, pp. 2–3.
Stevenson, Richard, *Chemistry in Britain,* Henry Taube: The Boy From the Prairie Who Made Good, November 1986.

Sketch by Evelyn B. Kelly

Helen Brooke Taussig
1898–1986
American pediatrician and cardiologist

Physician and cardiologist Helen Brooke Taussig spent her career as the head of the Children's Heart Clinic at Johns Hopkins University. In the course of her work with young children, she discovered that cyanotic infants—known as "blue-babies"—died of insufficient circulation to the lungs, not of cardiac arrest, as had been thought. She and colleague Dr. Alfred Blalock developed a surgical procedure, the Blalock-Taussig shunt, to correct the problem. First used in 1944, the Blalock-Taussig shunt has saved the lives of thousands of children. In 1961, after investigating reports of numerous birth defects in Germany, Taussig determined that the cause was use of the drug Thalidomide, and it was her intervention that prevented Thalidomide from being sold in the United States. She was the recipient of

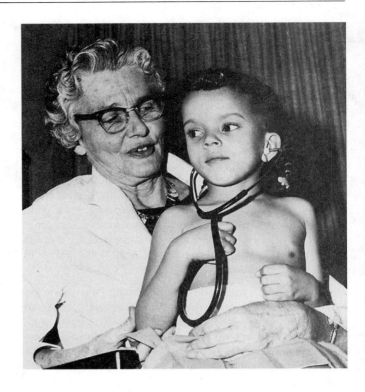

Helen Brooke Taussig

numerous honorary degrees and awards, including the Medal of Freedom in 1964 and the 1977 National Medal of Science.

Taussig was born on May 24, 1898, in Cambridge, Massachusetts, the youngest of four children of well-known Harvard economist Frank William Taussig. Her mother, Edith Guild Taussig, who had attended Radcliffe College and was interested in the natural sciences, died of tuberculosis when Helen was eleven years old. Like her mother, Taussig attended Radcliffe, where she played championship tennis. However, wishing to be further removed from the shadow of her well-known father, she transferred to the University of California at Berkeley, where she earned her B.A. in 1921.

Having decided on a career in medicine, Taussig's educational choices were limited by sex discrimination. Although she began her studies at Harvard University, the medical school did not admit women to its regular curriculum, and would not begin to do so until 1945. Taussig enrolled in Harvard's School of Public Health, where, like other women, she was permitted to take courses but not allowed to work toward obtaining a degree. She also was permitted to study histology as a special student in the medical school. After her studies at Harvard, Taussig took anatomy at nearby Boston University. There, her anatomy professor, Alexander Begg, suggested that she apply herself to the study of the heart, which she did. Also following Begg's advice, Taussig submitted her application to attend the medical school at Johns Hopkins University, where she was accepted.

During her four years of study at Johns Hopkins Medical School, Taussig worked at the Hopkins Heart Station. After receiving her M.D. in 1927, she spent another year there as a fellow, followed by an additional year and a half there as a pediatric intern. During this time, Taussig served as an attending physician at the recently established Pediatric Cardiac Clinic. The new chair of pediatrics, Edwards A. Park, recognized Taussig's abilities and became her mentor. Upon the completion of her pediatric internship in 1930, she was appointed physician-in-charge of the Pediatric Cardiac Clinic in the Harriet Lane Home, the children's division at Johns Hopkins. Taussig would spend her entire career at Johns Hopkins until her retirement in 1963. In 1946 she was appointed associate professor of pediatrics, and was promoted to full professor in 1959, the first woman in the history of the medical school to hold that title.

Groundbreaking Research on the Child's Heart

Taussig began her studies of congenital heart disease at the Pediatric Cardiac Clinic in 1930. Over the years she examined and treated hundreds of children whose hearts were damaged by rheumatic fever, as well as those with congenital heart disease. She developed new observational methods that led to a new understanding of pediatric heart problems. First Taussig became accomplished in the use of the fluoroscope, a new instrument which passed X-ray beams through the body and projected an image of the heart, lungs, and major arteries onto a florescent screen. Second, she used the electrocardiograph which makes a graphic record of the heart's movements. Third, she became expert at diagnosis through physical examination—made more complex in her case due to the fact that Taussig was somewhat deaf as a result of childhood whooping cough and unable to use a stethoscope, thereby necessitating her reliance on visual examination.

Taussig gradually realized that the blueness of cyanotic children was the result of insufficient oxygen in the blood. In the normal heart, bluish blood from the periphery of the body enters the right atrium (upper receiving chamber) of the heart and then goes to the right ventricle (the lower pumping chamber) to be pumped through a major artery to the lungs. In the lungs, the blood receives a new supply of oxygen that changes its color to bright red. Then it returns to the heart, entering the left atrium and descending to the left ventricle which pumps it to the rest of the body. The two sides of the heart are kept separate by a wall called the septum. Taussig discovered that the insufficient oxygen level of the blood of "blue-babies" was usually the result of either a leaking septum or an overly narrow artery leading from the left ventricle to the lungs. Although at that time surgeons were unable enter the heart to repair the septum surgically, Taussig believed that it might be possible either to repair the artery, or to attach a new vessel that would perform the same function.

She persuaded Dr. Alfred Blalock, the chairman of the Hopkins Department of Surgery, to work on the problem.

Blalock was a vascular surgeon who had done experimental research on an artificial artery with the assistance of long-time associate Vivian Thomas. Accepting Taussig's challenge, Blalock set Thomas to work on the technical problems. During the next year and a half, Thomas developed the technical procedures, using about two hundred dogs as experimental animals. In 1944, although earlier than Thomas had planned, the technique was tried on a human infant, a desperately ill patient of Taussig's named Eileen Saxon. With Taussig as an observer and Thomas standing by to give advice concerning the correct suturing of the artery, Blalock performed the surgery successfully. A branch of the aorta that normally went to the infant's arm was connected to the lungs. In the years that followed, the procedure, known as the Blalock-Taussig shunt, saved the lives of thousands of cyanotic children.

The fame of the Pediatric Cardiac Clinic grew rapidly. As they became flooded with patients, Blalock and Taussig developed team methods for dealing with the different phases of treatment. Their management methods became the model for many cardiac centers, as well as other kinds of medical care. Taussig's growing reputation also brought her numerous students. She trained a whole generation of pediatric cardiologists and wrote the standard textbook of the field, *Congenital Malformations of the Heart,* first published in 1947. In addition to her work in congenital heart disease, she carried out research on rheumatic fever, the leading cause of heart problems in children. Taussig is considered the founder of the specialty of pediatric cardiology. Neither her scientific and clinical acumen, nor her enormously demanding schedule, ever prevented Taussig from being a warm, compassionate physician to her many patients and their families. She followed her patients for years, even after her own retirement. She never found it necessary to distance herself from the critically ill children that she treated, or from their parents. Her warmth and ability to see and treat people as individuals has been recalled by many who knew her.

Influences U.S. Policy on a Dangerous Drug

In the 1950s Taussig served on numerous national and international committees. In 1962, a German graduate of her training program told her of the striking increase in his country of phocomelia, a rare congenital defect in which infants were born with severely deformed limbs. The defect was thought, but not yet proven, to be associated with a popular sedative called Contergan that was sold throughout Germany and other European countries and often taken by women to counteract nausea during early pregnancy. Taussig decided to investigate for herself and spent six weeks in Germany visiting clinics, examining babies with the abnormalities, and interviewing their doctors and mothers. She noted the absence of such birth defect in the infants of American soldiers living at U.S. military installations in Germany where the drug was banned. But there was one exception: a baby whose mother had gone off the post to obtain Contergan was born severely deformed. Taussig's testimony was instrumental in the U.S. Food and Drug Administration's rejection of the application from the William S. Merrell Company to market the drug they renamed Thalidomide in the United States.

Although Taussig formally retired in 1963, she remained deeply involved as a scientist, a clinician, and an activist in causes that affected the health of children. She fought for the right of scientists to use animals in experimental studies and advocated that women in the United States be able to choose to terminate their pregnancies through abortion. She was the author of a hundred major scientific publications, forty-one of which were written after her retirement. She occupied a home in Baltimore, often visited by guests and friends, and owned the cottage in Cape Cod where she had spent many happy childhood summers. Taussig enjoyed fishing, swimming, and gardening, as well as caring for her many pets. In the late 1970s she moved to a retirement community near Philadelphia. She became interested in the embryological causes of congenital heart defects and had begun a study of the hearts of birds when, on May 21, 1986, while driving some of her fellow retirees to vote in a primary election, she was killed in an automobile accident at the age of 87.

SELECTED WRITINGS BY TAUSSIG:

Books

Congenital Malformations of the Heart, Commonwealth Fund, 1947, second edition (two volumes), Commonwealth Fund/Harvard University Press, 1960.

Periodicals

Journal of the American Medical Association, The Surgical Treatment of Malformations of the Heart in which there is Pulmonary Stenosis or Pulmonary Atresia, Volume 128, May 19, 1945, pp. 189–202.
Scientific American, The Thalidomide Syndrome, Volume 207, August, 1962, pp. 29–35.

FURTHER READING:

Books

Baldwin, Joyce, *To Heal the Heart of A Child: Helen Taussig, M.D.,* (juvenile), Walker, 1992.
Nuland, Sherwin B., *Doctors: The Biography of Medicine,* Knopf, 1988, pp. 422–456.

Periodicals

Harvey, W. Proctor, *Medical Times,* A Conversation with Helen Taussig, Volume 106, November, 1978, pp. 28–44.

Sketch by Pamela O. Long

Olga Taussky–Todd
1906–1995
Austro-Hungarian-born American number theorist

Olga Taussky–Todd is best remembered for her research on matrix theory and algebraic number theory. Matrix theory is the study of sets of elements in a rectangular array that are subject to operations such as multiplication or addition according to specified rules. Number theory is the study of integers and their relationships. During a long, productive career, Taussky–Todd published over 200 research papers and other writings on a wide range of mathematical topics. In 1964 she was named "Woman of the Year" by the *Los Angeles Times*, and in 1970 she received the Ford Prize for an article on sums of squares. Taussky–Todd was also well known for her lectures. In 1981, she gave the **Emmy Noether** Lecture at the annual meeting of the Association for Women in Mathematics, taking as the subject of her talk the many aspects of Pythagorean triangles.

Taussky–Todd was born on August 30, 1906, in Olmütz, Austria–Hungary (now Olomouc, Czechoslovakia). She was the second of three daughters born to Julius David Taussky and Ida Pollach Taussky. Her father was an industrial chemist who also worked as a newspaper journalist. He encouraged his daughters to take their education seriously. Her mother was an intelligent person as well, but had little formal education. In an autobiographical essay published in *Mathematical People: Profiles and Interviews*, Taussky–Todd recalled of her mother: "She was rather bewildered about our studies and compared herself to a mother hen who had been made to hatch duck eggs and then felt terrified on seeing her offspring swimming in a pool." However, Taussky–Todd also noted that her mother was more willing than her father to accept the notion of girls actually using their educations later in life to earn a living.

Shortly before Taussky–Todd turned three, her family moved to Vienna. Midway through World War I, the family moved again, this time to Linz in upper Austria. Her father was manager of a vinegar factory there, and he often asked Taussky–Todd to help with such chores as calculating how much water to add to mixtures of various vinegars to achieve the right acidity. Taussky–Todd's best subjects in school were grammar and expository writing. As a girl in Linz, she began a lifelong hobby of writing poems.

First Forays into Number Theory

During Taussky–Todd's last year of high school, her father died, leaving the family without an income. Taussky–Todd took jobs tutoring and working at the vinegar factory. The next year she entered the University of Vienna, determined to prove that her plan to study mathematics was

Olga Taussky–Todd

a practical one. Among her professors was noted number theorist Philip Furtwängler. When the time came for Taussky–Todd to decide upon a thesis topic, Furtwängler suggested class field theory. In mathematics, a field is a set that has two operations—addition and multiplication. For each operation, the set is closed, associative, and commutative, and it has an identity element and inverses. As Taussky–Todd wrote in *Mathematical People*, "This decision had an enormous influence on my whole future . . . It helped my career, for there were only a very few people working in this still not fully understood subject. It was definitely a prestige subject."

In 1930, Taussky–Todd received her doctoral degree in mathematics. Based on her thesis, she was promptly offered a temporary post at the University of Göttingen in Germany, where she helped edit **David Hilbert**'s writings on number theory. She also edited Emil Artin's lectures on class field theory. By 1932, the growing political tensions in Germany made it unwise for Jews such as Taussky–Todd to stay there. She returned to Vienna, where she worked as a mathematics assistant. Among those she assisted was Hans Hahn, one of her former professors. Hahn had first introduced Taussky–Todd to functional analysis, the study of a particular type of function.

Travels to United States and England

Taussky–Todd applied for and received a three–year science fellowship from Girton College at Cambridge University in England. It was agreed that she could spend

the first year of the fellowship at Bryn Mawr College in Pennsylvania. Taussky–Todd took a few English lessons and embarked for the United States in 1934. At Bryn Mawr, she had the chance to work with Emmy Noether, whom she had earlier met at Göttingen. Noether, who was 24 years older than Taussky–Todd, was already an established figure in modern abstract algebra. Taussky–Todd enjoyed accompanying the older woman on her weekly trips to Princeton University whenever possible. However, she also found that Noether had a critical side. As Taussky–Todd recalled in *Mathematical People*, "She disliked my Austrian accent, my less abstract thinking, and she was almost frightened that I would obtain a [permanent] position before she would."

In 1935, Taussky–Todd traveled to Girton College at Cambridge, where she spent the last two years of her fellowship. The mathematical interests of her colleagues there did not quite match her own. However, she did get some much–needed practice at teaching in English. In 1937 she took a junior–level teaching position at one of the women's colleges at the University of London. The hours were arduous, but she still found time to attend professional seminars. It was at one such seminar that she met fellow mathematician John (Jack) Todd. The two were married in 1938.

Growing Interest in Matrix Theory

Soon thereafter World War II broke out, bringing not only political but also personal upheaval. The newlyweds moved 18 times during the war. For a while, the couple lived in Belfast, Ireland, where Taussky–Todd first began to focus on matrix theory while teaching at Queen's University. A year later Taussky–Todd returned to work at her London college, which had since been relocated to Oxford for safety reasons. In 1943, she took a research job in aerodynamics with the Ministry of Aircraft Production. There she joined a group that was studying flutter problems in combat aircraft. Flutter refers to the self–excited oscillations of part of an airplane such as the wings. A corresponding problem in mathematics involves the stability of certain matrices. As a result, this job just strengthened Taussky–Todd's growing fascination with matrix theory.

In 1947 Taussky–Todd's husband accepted an invitation to come to the United States for a year and work for the National Bureau of Standards. Taussky–Todd also joined the staff of the bureau field station at the University of California at Los Angeles. After this first year, the couple briefly went back to London. They soon returned to work again for the National Bureau of Standards, however, this time in Washington, D.C. Taussky–Todd's title at the bureau was mathematical consultant, and as she noted in *Mathematical People*, "this I truly was, because everybody dumped on me all sorts of impossible jobs, from refereeing every paper that was written by a member or visitor to the group, to answering letters from people . . . to helping people on their research."

Ends Personal Odyssey at Cal Tech

Taussky–Todd and her husband made one last major career move in 1957, accepting positions at the California Institute of Technology. In an autobiographical essay in *Number Theory and Algebra*, Taussky–Todd wrote: "It seemed to me as if an odyssey of 20 years (I left Cambridge, England, in 1937) had ended. I could at last work again with academic freedom and have Ph.D. students." Some of her students went on to play starring roles in the burgeoning of matrix theory that has occurred since the 1960s. In 1977, Taussky–Todd was made a professor emeritus at Cal Tech.

Taussky–Todd received a number of honors in the course of her prolific career. Upon her retirement, two journals, the *Journal of Linear Algebra* and the *Journal of Linear and Multilinear Algebra*, published issues dedicated to her. Going a step further, the *Journal of Number Theory* published an entire book, *Algebra and Number Theory*, dedicated to Taussky–Todd and two others. Taussky–Todd received the Gold Cross of Honor from the Austrian government in 1978. A decade later she was awarded an honorary D.Sc. degree by the University of Southern California.

Taussky–Todd died on October 7, 1995, at her home in Pasadena, California. An obituary by Myrna Oliver in the *Los Angeles Times* referred to her as "one of the most prominent women mathematicians in the United States." Indeed, a lifetime of contributions to both pure and applied mathematics across several specialty areas had earned her the respect of mathematicians of both genders and many nationalities.

SELECTED WRITINGS BY TAUSSKY–TODD:

Books

"Olga Taussky–Todd: An Autobiographical Essay." *Mathematical People: Profiles and Interviews*, edited by Donald J. Albers and G. L. Alexanderson, 1985, pp. 310–336.

FURTHER READING:

Books

Luchins, Edith H. "Olga Taussky–Todd." *Women of Mathematics: A Biobibliographic Sourcebook*. Edited by Louise S. Grinstein and Paul J. Campbell. Westport, CT: Greenwood, 1987, pp. 225–235.

"Olga Taussky–Todd." *Number Theory and Algebra: Collected Papers Dedicated to Henry B. Mann, Arnold E. Ross, and Olga Taussky–Todd*, edited by Hans Zassenhaus, New York: Academic Press, 1977, pp. xxxiv–xlvi.

Periodicals

Oliver, Myrna, "Olga Taussky–Todd: Noted Mathematician." *Los Angeles Times* (December 3, 1995): p. A44.

Other

Davis, Chandler, "Remembering Olga Taussky Todd," *Biographies of Women Mathematicians,* June 1997, http://www.scottlan.edu/lriddle/women/chronol.htm (July 22, 1997).

Sketch by Linda Wasmer Smith

Frederick Winslow Taylor
1856–1915
American efficiency engineer

Frederick Winslow Taylor pioneered the field of time studies and functional management in an effort to increase worker productivity in manufacturing and to promote harmony between management and labor. Through empirical studies, Taylor also advanced the techniques of steel manufacturing while at Midvale Steel Company and later as an engineering consultant to various firms, including Bethlehem Steel Company. Along with J. Maunsel White, Taylor developed a process heat treating steel used for tooling, which doubled the speed of metal-cutting machinery. Taylor is most noted for his work in scientific management, an effort to quantify human labor and eliminate wasted motion. He was a dominant force within the American Society of Mechanical Engineers, serving as vice president from 1904 until he was elected president in 1906. After retiring from active engineering at age forty-five, Taylor espoused scientific management from his estate near Philadelphia, Pennsylvania.

Taylor was born on March 20, 1856, in Germantown, Philadelphia, Pennsylvania, the second of three children. His father, Franklin, was a lawyer and a poet who had inherited great wealth based on the ownership of farms and other properties in Philadelphia and Bucks County. His mother, Emily Winslow Taylor, was a staunch abolitionist who worked with American reformer Lucretia Mott. Taylor's mother played a key role in instilling discipline and a work ethic in Taylor. Even as a child, Taylor was concerned with ordering and controlling his environment; a childhood friend recalled his obsessive desire to measure a rounders court to the last inch before a backyard game. Taylor also had frequent nightmares that he associated with sleeping on his back, so, when he was twelve, he developed a harness to wake him if he rolled onto his back.

Taylor's early schooling was at the Germantown Academy. At age thirteen, he went with his family to Europe and was tutored in France and Germany. After returning to the United States in 1872, Taylor enrolled at Phillips Exeter Academy, a college preparatory school in New Hampshire. Foreshadowing his later interest in scientific management, he was intrigued by a mathematics instructor's calculation of the number of problems an average student could complete for an assignment of a specified duration. Taylor's parents wanted him to attend Harvard University and pursue a legal career. Although he passed Harvard's entrance examination, Taylor left Exeter at the beginning of his senior year because of deteriorating eyesight and never attended the university. Both he and his parents were concerned that the extensive reading required in university studies might lead to blindness, though his decision to work as a machinist—a visually demanding profession—suggests that he actually stayed out of college in order to remain loyal to his strong work ethic. In 1874, Taylor began work as an apprentice machinist at the Enterprise Hydraulics Works, also known as Ferrell and Jones, which was partly owned by a family friend.

Rises from Laborer to Chief Engineer

Once he completed his apprenticeship, Taylor went to work for the Midvale Steel Company in Philadelphia. He rose from the position of laborer to machinist, then to superintendent of machine shops, assistant foreman, and foreman of the machine shops, and then to the position of chief draftsman in charge of new machinery and buildings. In June, 1883, as the result of a self-study program, Taylor received a degree in mechanical engineering from the Stevens Institute of Technology in Hoboken, New Jersey. In 1884, he was appointed chief engineer, serving in this position until 1890. As superintendent of the machine shops, Taylor had begun his campaign against "soldiering"—a term that described how workers would limit their production because they were being paid by the hour. After studying the capacity of both machines and machinists, Taylor developed his differential piece-rate policy, which paid ordinary wages (a lower rate per piece) to those workers who met a minimum output and very high wages to those who achieved maximum output. As chief engineer, Taylor supervised the forging of steel cannons for U.S. Navy warships. He developed a 25-ton steam hammer (the largest that had yet been built in the United States) that was used in the forging process. Taylor received a patent for the hammer in 1890, based on the ability of his design to maintain its alignment during use.

When the ownership of Midvale Steel changed in 1890, Taylor left to become the general manager of the Manufacturing Investment Company in Philadelphia, supervising paper mills in Maine and Wisconsin. In 1893, he embarked on a career as an industrial consultant specializing, according to his business card, in "systematizing shop management and manufacturing costs." Taylor and his associates provided services for various firms, including the

Simonds Rolling Machine Company, where he introduced piece work to the manufacture of ball bearings. In 1898, Taylor was hired by the Bethlehem Steel Company to reduce the cost of armor plate manufactured for the navy. Taylor—with the aid of Russell Davenport, Bethlehem's superintendent of manufacturing—went beyond his original mandate to reorganize the machine shop and tried to implement his "functional plan of organization" throughout the entire works. Starting with the machine shop, Taylor established what he called "functional foremanships": gang bosses, speed bosses, inspectors, and repair bosses. Taylor's functional plan had these foremen and their workers subordinated to five "planners": the superintendent in overall control; the "order-of-work-route man"; the "instruction-card man," who prepared detailed instructions for workers on how to perform their tasks; the "time-and-cost clerk;" and the "disciplinarian." The implementation of piece-rate pay brought about reduced production costs: the cost of moving shoveled material was reduced from 7.2 cents per ton on the day rate to 3.3 cents per ton on piece rate. The large size of the Bethlehem Iron Company and management's opposition to Taylor, however, made it difficult for Taylor to implement his plan throughout the works.

In 1898, Taylor and Bethlehem metallurgist J. Maunsel White began to develop stronger steel cutting tools for use in machining steel, specifically the hard steel used by the navy for the casings of armor-piercing shells. They claimed that heating steel close to its melting point produced superior steel for use in cutting tools. The Taylor-White process for the heat treatment of steel increased metal-cutting speed by at least 200 percent and was awarded a gold medal at the Paris Exposition in 1900. Taylor and White filed two patents for the process, both of which were granted in 1901, and they sold them to Bethlehem for $50,000 (the patents were voided in 1909; after five years of litigation, a judge ruled that they failed to define a unique process). A few months after Taylor and White received their first heat-treatment patent in February, 1901, Bethlehem executives opposed to Taylor's reorganization of the company terminated his contract. His official biographer, Frank B. Copley, wrote that Taylor retired from active work in 1901 to "serve the cause of science in management." According to recently uncovered court testimony, however, Taylor admitted that a nervous breakdown had prevented him from remaining active in business.

Becomes Foremost Spokesperson for Scientific Management

Taylor used his patent money from Bethlehem to construct Boxly, an eleven-acre estate in Chestnut Hill in northern Philadelphia. To present a more efficient environment for his visiting business clients, Taylor spent $17,000 to overhaul the gardens and removed a hill on the property to make way for a three-story colonial mansion. Boxly served as a center for Taylor's educational presentations on scientific management that were often updated by his associate, Morris L. Cooke.

Taylor wrote two books on scientific management, both published in 1911: *The Principles of Scientific Management* and *Shop Management.* The core of Taylor's managerial innovations for industry was a planning department; he believed this department should coordinate production by assigning production goals based on time-motion studies, measurements of machine capabilities, the standardization of worker tasks, routing of raw and processed materials, inventory control, centralized records, and cost accounting. In 1830, Antoine-Henri Jomini had attributed French emperor Napoleon Bonaparte's military success to an underlying science of warfare; in a similar manner, Taylor believed that business management could be reduced to an exact science. Just as Jomini's reductionism sought to simplify the chaotic dynamics of war, Taylor believed scientific management could engender harmonious relationships between management and labor. He sought to control the dynamics of the modern industrial sphere. The keys to his system were breaking the work process into the smallest components, specifying the duties of each component, employing the differential piece-rate to spur optimum production, and removing skill and creativity from the job, reserving them for management.

The belief that Taylor's scientific management offered the basis for efficiency and progress was reflected in its adoption throughout the Progressive Era, from public administration to economic theory. Progressive theorists viewed efficiency and expertise as positive components of the democratic experience and believed that scientific management, born in industry, had much to offer the nation. With the waning of Progressivism, scientific management returned to industry. The Society to Promote the Science of Management, later renamed the Taylor Society, pursued a policy of separation between management and administration within industrial firms. The view Taylorites had of the worker changed during the 1920s. Whereas Taylor himself had assumed that management and workers had a common interest in increasing prosperity, scientific managers of the 1920s saw labor not as individuals but as a group that required managerial expertise. Many economic and social planners of U.S. president Franklin Roosevelt's New Deal had been members of the Taylor Society during the 1920s.

Taylor married Louise M. Spooner in 1884. In 1901, they adopted the three youngest of four children who had survived the murder-suicide of their parents, William and Anna Aiken, distant relatives of Taylor's wife. In 1881, Taylor and his brother-in-law, Clarence M. Clark, were the first doubles champions of the U.S. Lawn Tennis Association. Taylor was also a golfer, ice skater, and cricket player, and among his forty-five patents were ones for a scoop-handled tennis racket and a two-handed putter. In 1910, Taylor's wife first manifested cyclic depression, which had a strong, adverse effect on him. During a lecture tour in Ohio in early 1915, Taylor caught a cold that developed into pneumonia; he died on March 21, 1915, after being hospitalized for nine days. He left an estate valued at approximately $1,000,000, none of which he had inherited. He was buried in Philadelphia and the epitaph on his tombstone reads, "Father of Scientific Management."

SELECTED WRITINGS BY TAYLOR:

Books

The Principles of Scientific Management, Harper and Brothers, 1911.
Shop Management, Harper and Brothers, 1911.
Scientific Management: Comprising Shop Management, The Principles of Scientific Management, and Testimony Before the Special House Committee, Greenwood Press, 1972.

Periodicals

Transactions of the American Society of Mechanical Engineers, A Piece-Rate System, Being a Step Toward Partial Solution of the Labor Problem, 1895, pp. 856–903.
Transactions of the American Society of Mechanical Engineers, On the Art of Cutting Metals, 1907, pp. 31–280.

FURTHER READING:

Books

Aitken, Hugh G. J., *Taylorism at the Watertown Arsenal,* Harvard University Press, 1960.
Copley, Frank B., *Frederick W. Taylor: Father of Scientific Management,* two volumes, Harper and Brothers, 1923.
Drury, Horace B., *Scientific Management: A History and Criticism,* Columbia University Press, 1918.
Haber, Samuel, *Efficiency and Uplift: Scientific Management in the Progressive Era, 1890–1920,* University of Chicago Press, 1964. Kakar, Sudhir.
Haber, Samuel, *Frederick W. Taylor: A Study in Personality and Innovation,* MIT Press, 1970.
Nelson, Daniel, *Frederick W. Taylor and the Rise of Scientific Management,* University of Wisconsin Press, 1980.
Schachter, Hindy L., *Frederick Taylor and the Public Administration Community,* State University of New York Press, 1989.
Wrege, Charles D., and Ronald G. Greenwood, *Frederick W. Taylor, The Father of Scientific Management: Myth and Reality,* Business One Irwin, 1991.

Periodicals

Wrege, Charles D., and Ronald G. Greenwood, *Transactions of the American Society of Mechanical En-*

gineers, Tributes to Frederick W. Taylor, 1915, pp. 1459–1496.

Sketch by William M. McBride

Joseph H. Taylor, Jr.
1941–
American astrophysicist

Joseph H. Taylor, Jr. is an astrophysicist who discovered the first binary pulsar—two extremely dense, collapsed stars in orbit around each other. He made this discovery in 1974 with **Russell A. Hulse**, who was then his graduate student at the University of Massachusetts. The two men used this binary pulsar to verify aspects of **Albert Einstein**'s general theory of relativity which scientists had not yet had an opportunity to test. Binary pulsars became what Taylor and Hulse describe in *Astrophysical Journal Letters* as "a nearly ideal relativity laboratory," and they have made particularly important contributions to the understanding of gravity. For their discovery of the binary pulsar and the application of their findings to the theory of relativity, Taylor and Hulse were awarded the 1993 Nobel Prize in physics.

Taylor was born in Philadelphia on March 29, 1941, the son of Joseph and Sylvia Evans Taylor. In 1959, Taylor entered Haverford College where he majored in physics. He graduated in 1963 with a B.A. degree and entered the doctoral program in astronomy at Harvard University. He was awarded his Ph.D. in 1968 and spent the next year as a research fellow and lecturer in astronomy at Harvard. In 1969 he joined the faculty at the University of Massachusetts in Amherst as an assistant professor of astronomy. In 1973, he was named an associate professor and four years later elevated to full professor. In the fall of 1980, Taylor left Massachusetts to become professor of physics at Princeton University; in 1986 he was named James S. McDonnell Distinguished University Professor of Physics.

Begins Search for Pulsars

While at the University of Massachusetts in 1970, Taylor was approached by one of his graduate students, Russell Hulse, in search of a thesis project. The pair agreed on an undertaking involving the use of the 300-meter diameter Arecibo telescope in Puerto Rico, the world's largest single-element radio telescope, to search the skies for the weak radio signals emitted by pulsars. Pulsars were first discovered in 1967 by **Susan Jocelyn Bell Burnell** and **Antony Hewish**. They are neutron stars whose diameter, in contrast with other stars, is very small, sometimes as small as ten kilometers. Their mass, on the other hand, is as great

or greater than that of the sun, and the gravitational field that surrounds them is extremely high. As a result of their strong gravitational pull, radio waves are released from pulsars only at the poles; the beams reach Earth in pulses as the star spins in space, and on a radio telescope the waves from a pulsar can resemble the beam from a lighthouse. In analyzing the results of a pulsar detected on July 2, 1974, Taylor and Hulse noticed an unexpected variation in the pulsar's period. The bursts were not perfectly regular like those of known pulsars, and the irregularity revealed that there were actually two pulsars, orbiting each other.

As a press release from the Royal Swedish Academy observes, "Hulse's and Taylor's discovery in 1974 of the first binary pulsar, called PSR 1913 + 16 . . . brought about a revolution in the field." Binary pulsars orbit at great speeds and at close range—approximately that of the distance from Earth to the Moon—and the discovery of these stars gave scientists an opportunity to study the effects of gravity outside the gravitational field of our solar system. Over a period of almost twenty years, Taylor and Hulse made detailed observations of the behavior of these stars in orbit. They discovered that the path the pulsars followed is changing: their orbit is contracting and the two stars are rotating at greater speeds as they grow closer to each other.

Their examination of the timing of the pulses provided the first evidence for the existence of what *Sky & Telescope* calls the "magnetic aspect of gravity." In 1916, Einstein predicted that two masses in orbit around each other would have certain properties similar to electromagnetism. He predicted that bodies would emit what he called gravitational waves and thus lose energy. The small changes Taylor and Hulse have detected are consistent with this prediction; even the rate of change very nearly matches the rate Einstein predicted it would follow.

For Taylor, this indirect confirmation of the gravitational waves is only part of the support binary pulsars can offer to the general theory of relativity. As Taylor told the *New York Times,* "Continued study of binary pulsars as they spin off energy over years is essential. We've measured three of the relativity effects on this pulsar to a high accuracy, and two other consequences to somewhat lower accuracy. But there are potentially about a dozen other relativity effects we hope to measure in the future." In 1985, Taylor and a graduate student discovered another binary pulsar. His work has raised the possibility of creating a new branch of astronomy, called gravitational wave astronomy, which would enable astronomers to gather evidence about a number of events in the universe that they currently cannot observe.

In addition to the Nobel Prize, Taylor received the Dannie Heineman Prize from the American Astronomical Society and American Institute of Physics in 1980, a MacArthur Fellowship in 1981, the National Academy of Sciences' Henry Draper Medal and Tomalla Foundation Prize in gravitation and cosmology in 1985, and the Wolf Prize in physics in 1992. He is a member of the National Academy of Sciences, the American Philosophical Society, and a fellow of the American Academy of Arts and Sciences. Taylor married Marietta Bisson on January 3, 1976. They have three children.

SELECTED WRITINGS BY TAYLOR, JR.:

Periodicals

Astrophysical Journal Letters, A Deep Sample of New Pulsars and Their Spatial Extent in the Galaxy, July 15, 1974.

Astrophysical Journal Letters, Discovery of a Pulsar in a Binary System, October 15, 1975.

Scientific American, Gravitational Waves from an Orbiting Pulsar, Volume 245, October, 1981, p. 66.

FURTHER READING:

Periodicals

Sky & Telescope, Binary Pulsar Reveals Magnetic Gravity, July, 1990. pp. 10–11.

Hewish, A., *Scientific American,* Pulsars, Volume 219, October, 1968, p. 25.

Kleppner, D., *Physics Today,* The Gem of General Relativity, Volume 46, April, 1993, p. 9.

Kleppner, D., *New York Times,* October 12, 1993, p. B9.

Sketch by Benedict A. Leerburger

Moddie Taylor
1912–1976
American chemist

Moddie Taylor gained distinction early in his career as an associate chemist on the U.S. Manhattan Project, which led to the development of the atomic bomb during World War II. A chemistry professor at Lincoln and later Howard Universities, Taylor published a chemistry textbook in 1960 and served as head of the chemistry department at Howard from 1969 to 1976.

Moddie Daniel Taylor was born in Nymph, Alabama, on March 3, 1912, the son of Herbert L. Taylor and Celeste (Oliver) Taylor. His father worked as a postal clerk in St. Louis, Missouri, and it was there that Taylor went to school, graduating from the Charles H. Sumner High School in 1931. He then attended Lincoln University in Jefferson City, Missouri, and graduated with a B.S. in chemistry in 1935 as valedictorian and as a summa cum laude student. He began

his teaching career in 1935, working as an instructor until 1939 and then as an assistant professor from 1939 to 1941 at Lincoln University, while also enrolled in the University of Chicago's graduate program in chemistry. He received his M.S. in 1939 and his Ph.D. in 1943. Taylor married Vivian Ellis on September 8, 1937, and they had one son, Herbert Moddie Taylor.

Joins Manhattan Project Team

It was during 1945 that Taylor began his two years as an associate chemist for the top-secret Manhattan Project based at the University of Chicago. Taylor's research interest was in rare earth metals (elements which are the products of oxidized metals and which have special properties and several important industrial uses); his chemical contributions to the nation's atomic energy research earned him a Certificate of Merit from the Secretary of War. After the war, he returned to Lincoln University until 1948 when he joined Howard University as an associate professor of chemistry, becoming a full professor in 1959 and head of the chemistry department in 1969.

In 1960, Taylor's *First Principles of Chemistry* was published; also in that year he was selected by the Manufacturing Chemists Association as one of the nation's six top college chemistry teachers. In 1972, Taylor was also awarded an Honor Scroll from the Washington Institute of Chemists for his contributions to research and teaching. Taylor was a member of the American Chemical Society, the American Association for the Advancement of Science, the National Institute of Science, the American Society for Testing Materials, the New York Academy of Sciences, Sigma Xi, and Beta Kappa Chi, and was a fellow of the American Institute of Chemists and the Washington Academy for the Advancement of Science. Taylor retired as a professor emeritus of chemistry from Howard University on April 1, 1976, and died of cancer in Washington, D.C., on September 15, 1976.

SELECTED WRITINGS BY TAYLOR:

Books

First Principles of Chemistry, Van Nostrand, 1960, revised edition, 1976.

FURTHER READING:

Books

Sammons, Vivian O., *Blacks in Science and Medicine,* Hemisphere, 1990, p. 227.

Periodicals

Sammons, Vivian O., *Jet,* May 26, 1960, p. 19.

Sammons, Vivian O., *Washington Post,* (obituary), September 18, 1976, p. D6.

Sketch by Leonard C. Bruno

Richard E. Taylor
1929–
American physicist

Richard E. Taylor's study of elementary particles with the use of Stanford University's Linear Accelerator Center (SLAC) led to the Nobel Prize-winning confirmation of the existence of quarks, which are thought to be the smallest and most fundamental particles in existence, and are the base substance of all matter.

Richard Edward Taylor was born in Medicine Hat, Alberta, Canada, on November 2, 1929. His father was Clarence Richard Taylor, the son of Scottish-Irish immigrants to Canada, and his mother was the former Delia Alena Brunsdale, the daughter of Norwegian immigrants. Taylor reports that his interest in science was inspired by the presence of military installations in the Medicine Hat area during World War II and by the explosion of the first atomic bombs in August 1945.

Taylor's undergraduate education took place at the University of Alberta, in Edmonton, where he earned a B.S. degree in mathematics and physics in 1950 and then a M.S. degree two years later. While working on the latter degree, Taylor married Rita Jean Bonneau, with whom he has one son, Norman Edward. After receiving his master's degree, Taylor moved to Stanford University. In 1954 Taylor accepted a job at Stanford's High Energy Physics Laboratory, where he began his long involvement in the study of elementary particles.

Taylor Begins Work with Friedman and Kendall at SLAC

Taylor's tenure at Stanford was interrupted for three years, from 1958 to 1961, a period during which he traveled to France to work on a new linear accelerator then being constructed at Orsay. Upon his return to the United States, Taylor completed his requirements for a Ph.D. degree, which was granted to him in 1962. He then began work, under the supervision of physicist **Wolfgang Kurt Panofsky**, on the design of Stanford's new two-mile-long linear accelerator (linac). Along with two colleagues, **Jerome I. Friedman** and **Henry W. Kendall**, Taylor initiated some of the first experiments to be carried out at the Stanford linac.

Those experiments were designed to be a continuation of work begun by physicist **Robert Hofstadter** at Stanford in the 1950s. Hofstadter had directed high-energy beams of electrons at a variety of elements and discovered that protons and neutrons have detailed structure that had previously been unanticipated. For this discovery, Hofstadter won the 1961 Nobel Prize in physics.

Taylor, Friedman, and Kendall Discover Quarks

In the early stages of their research, Taylor, Friedman, and Kendall did not anticipate making any revolutionary discoveries. They assumed that their work would refine and extend Hofstadter's discoveries, but not break any new ground. Two factors changed that expectation. First, the newly built particle accelerator had far more energy—twenty billion electron volts—than the accelerator that Hofstadter had used. Secondly, the team's colleague and theoretical physicist B. J. Bjorken made the important suggestion that they focus on inelastic, rather than elastic, collisions in their experiments. In elastic collisions (the kind Hofstadter had examined), electrons are diffracted by any atomic nucleus they pass close to. The angles at which electrons are diffracted and the energies they possess provide clues as to the structure and properties of nucleons (protons and neutrons) that cause the diffraction.

Instead of continuing that line of research, Bjorken advised that Taylor, Friedman, and Kendall should look for cases in which electrons have enough energy to actually collide with and blow apart an atomic nucleus, an inelastic collision. In such cases, the researchers might be able to collect some new and entirely different kinds of information about the structure of nuclei and nucleons.

When Taylor, Friedman, and Kendall redesigned their experiment along the lines recommended by Bjorken, they made a remarkable discovery: the detailed but fuzzy appearance of the nucleus and nucleons observed by Hofstadter was now seen clearly to consist of discrete granule-like particles. These particles were soon recognized to be the *quarks* that had been hypothesized by **Murray Gell-Mann** and, independently, by George Zweig, in the 1960s. The experiments provided confirmation of the view that protons and neutrons are not themselves discrete, fundamental particles, but are composed of even smaller units, quarks. For this discovery, Taylor, Friedman, and Kendall were jointly awarded the 1990 Nobel Prize in physics.

Long before he had received the Nobel Prize, Taylor had been promoted to associate professor (1968) and then full professor (1970) at Stanford. In 1982 he was made associate director of SLAC, a post he held until 1986. In addition to the Nobel Prize, Taylor has been awarded the Alexander von Humboldt Award in 1982 and an honorary degree from the Université de Paris-Sud in 1980. In 1989, he shared the American Physical Society's W. K. H. Panofsky Prize with Friedman and Kendall.

SELECTED WRITINGS BY TAYLOR:

Periodicals

Physical Review Letters, High-Energy Inelastic Electron-Proton Scattering at Six Degrees and Ten Degrees, Volume 23, 1969, p. 930.

Physical Review Letters, Observed Behavior of Highly Inelastic Electron-Proton Scattering, Volume 23, 1969, p. 935.

FURTHER READING:

Books

Nobel Prize Winners Supplement 1987–1991, H. W. Wilson, 1992, pp. 132–134.

Periodicals

Sutton, Christine, *New Scientist,* Nobel Trophy for the Hunters of the Quark, October 27, 1990, p. 14.

Waldrop, M. Mitchell, *Science,* Physics Nobel Honors the Discovery of Quarks, October 26, 1990, pp. 508–509.

Sketch by David E. Newton

Stuart Taylor

1937–

American biologist and cell physiologist

Stuart Taylor combined his background in physiology and biophysics to delve into the mechanism by which living muscle cells contract. Working at the Mayo Foundation, he built a high-speed supercomputer imaging system called CAMERA to study rapidly, and in three dimensions, the microscopic activity of muscle fibrils (or slender fibers). One of the findings of the CAMERA system has changed previous notions about the way in which the elements of muscle contract.

Stuart Robert Taylor was born on July 15, 1937, in Brooklyn, New York, to Rupert Robert Taylor, a physician, and Enid (Hansen) Taylor. He passed the entrance examination for the science-oriented Stuyvesant High School in Manhattan, and traveled there by subway for four years. At Cornell University, he majored in zoology and received his B.A. in 1958, returning to New York City to pursue a master's degree in zoology at Columbia University. Before receiving his degree in 1961, he served as a laboratory assistant, and then as a lecturer in the Department of Zoology. Taylor earned his Ph.D. in biology from New York University in 1966, with a dissertation entitled, "Electro-mechanical coupling in skeletal muscle," and served as a research assistant at the Institute for Muscle Disease.

In 1964, Taylor attended a lecture given by the British physiologist and Nobel Prize-winner, **Andrew Huxley**, at Columbia University. Huxley's remarks covered a range of topics dealing with muscle contraction, including the microscopic image of striated muscle (muscle tissue marked by alternating light and dark bands, including cardiac muscle and skeletal muscle), changes in striation pattern, and electrical activity during contraction. The lecture, Taylor later reported, strongly influenced his career "agenda," and in 1967 he was awarded a postdoctoral research fellowship in Huxley's laboratory at University College, London. Upon his return to the United States two years later, he was appointed an instructor, and then assistant professor of pharmacology, at the Downstate Medical Center in Brooklyn. Shortly thereafter, he left for the Mayo Foundation and, in 1971, he became a staff member in pharmacology, physiology and biophysics, and assistant professor of physiology at the University of Minnesota Graduate School. In 1980, he became a professor at Mayo Medical School and Graduate School of Medicine, where he stayed for over a decade until being appointed Distinguished Professor at Hunter College of the City University of New York.

His research at Mayo resulted in the development of the advanced cell-imaging computer called CAMERA (Computer-Assisted Measurements of Excitation-Response Activities). With this system, he was able to record the act of muscle contraction, obtaining views of up to 5,000 images per second. Previous attempts to use video cameras in imaging systems had yielded results limited to only thirty frames per second. Taylor felt that this was too slow to accurately show the effect, for example, of calcium stimulation on the individual sections of fibrils. Now, he reported in *MOSAIC,* he could see individual heart muscle cells on a "beat-to-beat basis." It has long been held that sarcomeres, the individual, contractile units of a muscle cell fibril, contract, relax, and then stretch back in unison to keep the muscle cell from tearing apart. While Taylor's research indicated similarities in certain cell response mechanisms, it also showed that adjacent sarcomeres differed in their reactions. Taylor and his colleagues concluded, as stated in *MOSAIC,* that there is some independence "between adjacent regions in a heart muscle cell, and that the links between regions are 'weak and very elastic.'" In other words, a muscle cell's twitch results from the average response of many sarcomeres, but it does not reflect the actions of individual sarcomeres. Taylor's continued use of CAMERA to further understand muscle contraction and the role of calcium in its activities has determined not only the role of calcium ions in initiating contraction, but also that there is a feedback mechanism between calcium and contraction. His CAMERA measurements also include other features of muscle cell contraction, such as changes of voltage across cell membranes, molecular rearrangements, and changes in resistance to stretching or compression.

Taylor was married in 1963, but later divorced. He has three children, Scott Carey, Nicole, and Mark Christopher. As his career developed, he gradually became an acknowledged authority on muscle cell contraction and, in 1987, was elected as a fellow of the American Association for the Advancement of Science for his research in the subject. As an African American scientist, he has become active in encouraging minority students to pursue science careers through special programs of the National Science Foundation, the Biophysical Society, and the National Institutes of Health. He has also served on the editorial board of science journals, and holds memberships in many scientific societies. Since 1967, he has received some twenty grants from the U.S. Department of Health, Education and Welfare, the National Institutes of Health, the National Science Foundation, National Aeronautics and Space Administration (NASA), and other agencies, to continue his investigations in muscle physiology.

SELECTED WRITINGS BY TAYLOR:

Books

Muscular Contraction: Andrew Huxley Festschrift, High-speed Digital Imaging Microscopy of Isolated Muscle Cells, edited by R. M. Simmons, Cambridge University Press, 1992. pp. 127–46.

Periodicals

Biophysics Journal, Non-uniform Volume Changes During Muscle Contraction, Volume 59, 1991, pp. 926–33.
Optical Engineering, High-speed Video Imaging and Digital Analysis of Microscopic Features in Contracting Muscle Cells, Volume 32, 1993, pp. 306–13.

FURTHER READING:

Periodicals

MOSAIC, fall, 1989, pp. 14–23.

Sketch by Maurice Bleifeld

Maria Telkes
1900–1995
Hungarian-born American physical chemist

Maria Telkes devoted most of her life to solar energy research, investigating and designing solar ovens, solar stills, and solar electric generators. She was responsible for the heating system installed in the first solar-heated home, located in Dover, Massachusetts. The importance of Telkes's work has been recognized by numerous awards and honors, including the Society of Women Engineers Achievement Award in 1952 (Telkes was the first recipient) and the Charles Greely Abbot Award from the American Section of the International Solar Energy Society.

Maria de Telkes, the daughter of Aladar and Maria Laban de Telkes, was born in Budapest, Hungary, on December 12, 1900. She grew up in Budapest and remained there to complete her high school and college education. Studying physical chemistry at Budapest University, she obtained a B.A. degree in 1920, then a Ph.D. in 1924. The following year, on a visit to her uncle in the United States, Telkes was hired as a biophysicist at the Cleveland Clinic Foundation investigating the energy associated with living things. Her studies looked at the sources of this energy, what occurs when a cell dies, and the energy changes which occur when a normal cell is transformed into a cancer cell. In 1937, the year she became an American citizen, Telkes concluded her research at the clinic and joined Westinghouse Electric as a research engineer. She remained at Westinghouse for two years, performing research and receiving patents on new types of thermoelectric devices, which converted heat energy into electrical energy.

In 1939, Telkes began working on solar energy, one of her greatest interests since her high school days. Joining the Massachusetts Institute of Technology Solar Energy Conversion Project, she continued her research into thermoelectric devices, with the heat energy now being supplied by the sun. She also researched and designed a new type of solar heating system which was installed in a prototype house built in Dover, Massachusetts, in 1948. Earlier solar heating systems stored the solar energy by heating water or rocks. This system differed in that the solar energy was stored as chemical energy through the crystallization of a sodium sulphate solution.

Telkes's expertise was also recruited by the United States government to study the production of drinking water from seawater. To remove salt from seawater, the water is vaporized to steam, then the steam is condensed to give pure water. Utilizing solar energy for vaporization of the water, she designed a solar still which could be installed on life rafts to provide water. This design was enlarged for use in the Virgin Islands, where the supply of fresh water was often a problem.

Maria Telkes

In 1953, Telkes moved to New York University and organized a solar energy laboratory in the college of engineering where she continued her work on solar stills, heating systems, and solar ovens. Transferring to the Curtiss-Wright company in 1958, she looked into the development of solar dryers and water heaters as well as the application of solar thermoelectric generators in space. Her position there, as director of research for the solar energy lab, also required her to design a heating and energy storage system for a laboratory building built by Curtiss-Wright in Princeton, New Jersey.

Working at Cryo-Therm from 1961 to 1963, Telkes developed materials for use in the protection of temperature sensitive instruments. Shipping and storage containers made of these materials were used for space and undersea applications in the Apollo and Polaris projects. In 1963, she returned to her efforts of applying solar energy to provide fresh water, moving to the MELPAR company as head of the solar energy application lab.

Telkes joined the Institute of Energy Conversion at the University of Delaware in 1969, where her work involved the development of materials for storing solar energy and the design of heat exchangers for efficient transfer of the energy. Her advancements resulted in a number of patents—both domestic and foreign—for the storage of solar heat. Her results were put into practical use in Solar One, an experimental solar-heated building at the University of Delaware.

In 1977, the National Academy of Science Building Research Advisory Board honored Telkes for her contributions to solar-heated building technology; previous honorees included Frank Lloyd Wright and Buckminster Fuller. In 1978, she was named professor emeritus at the University of Delaware, and retired from active research. She was, however, active as a consultant until about three years before her death. Telkes died on December 2, 1995, on a visit to Budapest in her native Hungary.

SELECTED WRITINGS BY TELKES:

Books

"Thermodynamic Basis for Selecting Heat Storage Materials," In *Solar Materials Science,* edited by L. E. Murr, Academic Press, 1980, pp. 405-38.

Periodicals

"Storing Solar Heat in Chemicals—a Report on the Dover House," *Heating and Ventilation* (November 1949): pp. 80-86.

"A Review of Solar House Heating," *Heating and Ventilation.* (September 1949): pp. 68-74.

"Fresh Water from Sea Water by Solar Distillation," *Industrial & Engineering Chemistry* 45 (1953): pp. 1108-15.

"Solar Thermoelectric Generators." *Journal of Applied Physics*, 25 (1954): pp. 765-77.

FURTHER READING:

Books

"Maria Telkes," *Current Biography 1950,* New York: H. W. Wilson, 1950, pp. 563-64.

O'Neill, Lois Decker, ed. *The Woman's Book of World Records and Achievements,* New York: Doubleday, 1979, p. 189.

Periodicals

"Maria Telkes Pioneering Researcher Built Early Solar Home," *Miami Herald* (15 August 1996): pp. B6.

Other

4 January 1994, Correspondence with Jerome P. Ferrance, University of Delaware Archives.

Sketch by Jerome P. Ferrance

Edward Teller
1908–
American physicist

Edward Teller

Trained as a theoretical physicist, Edward Teller became a leading authority on nuclear physics during the 1930s and was involved with the Manhattan Project during World War II. He was an early advocate of thermonuclear weapons, which are many times more powerful than the atomic bomb, and he is best known for the leading role he played in the development of the hydrogen bomb between 1949 and 1951. Beginning in the 1940s Teller figured prominently in policy discussions about America's nuclear arsenal, advising government officials at the highest levels and even testifying against **J. Robert Oppenheimer** at a Congressional hearing during the McCarthy era. By the 1980s a lifetime of advising politicians had given him a network of political contacts which included a friendship with President Ronald Reagan. Teller was instrumental in convincing Reagan that a system could be developed to shoot down incoming ballistic missiles. Many consider him responsible for the president's decision to support the Strategic Defense Initiate (SDI), popularly known as "Star Wars."

Teller was born in Budapest on January 15, 1908. His parents were Jewish but not orthodox, celebrating the sabbath and the high holidays. His father, Max Teller, was a lawyer from Hungarian Moravia. His mother, the former Ilona Deutch, was the daughter of a banker and a cotton-mill owner from a small town in the eastern part of the Austrian-Hungarian Empire. Teller did not speak until he was almost four years old, but once he began he spoke a great deal, and it became clear that he was quite precocious. He delighted in performing mathematical calculations in his head; when he was twelve, his father introduced him to Leopold Klug, a professor of mathematics at the University of Budapest, and Teller started seriously thinking of mathematics as a career. By the age of fourteen he was reading about **Albert Einstein** and his work on the special and general theories of relativity.

In 1925, when he was eighteen, Teller won first place in a prestigious mathematics contest for all Hungarian high school students. Still, his father worried that mathematics was not a dependable occupation, so Teller agreed to study engineering as well as mathematics in college. He studied first for a short time at the University of Budapest and then at the Institute of Technology in Karlsruhe, Germany. By 1928 he was enrolled in the University of Munich as a physics student.

The year he came to Munich, Teller fell while jumping off a streetcar and lost most of one foot when he slipped beneath its wheels. The amputation was so sudden that he did not even realize what had happened until he saw his boot, with his foot still in it, lying in front of him. What was

left of Teller's foot was reconstructed so he could walk without a prosthesis, which he was able to do after the accident, although he usually chose to use an artificial foot as well. Despite this injury, Teller never allowed the loss of his foot to stand in the way of his career or his life. Late that year he moved again to the University of Leipzig to study with **Werner Heisenberg**. Two years later, in 1930, he was awarded his doctorate; he had written his dissertation on experiments in which he used quantum mechanics to calculate energy levels in an excited hydrogen molecule.

Teller spent several years as an assistant at the University of Göttingen and then in 1934 he was awarded a Rockefeller Foundation fellowship. He used it to join **Niels Bohr** at the Copenhagen Institute for Theoretical Physics, where many of the great twentieth century physicists studied. On February 26, 1934, a few weeks after starting his Copenhagen fellowship, Edward married Augusta Maria Harkanyi, who he had known for over a decade. The couple spent a year in England, where Teller was a lecturer at the University of London, and then they moved to the United States, where he took a full professorship in the physics department at George Washington University.

Teller was twenty-six by this time and he had already published almost thirty papers, usually with coauthors. While at George Washinton University, he worked closely with **George Gamow**, a Russian exile; together they calculated the rules for one of the major forms of radioactivity, which became known as the Gamow-Teller selection rules for beta decay. During this early part of

Teller's career he worked on many different problems, including molecular vibrations, magnetic cooling processes, and the absorption of gases on solids. One of his specialties was the behavior of matter under unusual conditions, including the interior of stars.

Advocates the Development of the Hydrogen Bomb

At the end of 1938 two German chemists, **Otto Hahn** and **Fritz Strassmann**, succeeded in splitting the atom. Within months **Leo Szilard** and Walter H. Zinn had created a chain reaction at Columbia University and it had become clear that atomic weapons were possible. Teller was one of the physicists who lobbied President Franklin D. Roosevelt and his administration to attempt to build such a weapon, and he was involved in the Manhattan Project from the beginning. From 1940 to the end of the war, Teller worked on the atomic bomb, moving between Washington; New York; Chicago; and Los Alamos, New Mexico. In 1941, Teller and his wife became naturalized U.S. citizens; their son was born in 1943 and their daughter in 1946.

One of the tasks Teller was assigned on the Manhattan Project was calculating the possibility of a thermonuclear or hydrogen bomb, also then known among nuclear physicists as the "super." He initially concluded it was impossible, but he redid his figures with Emil Konopinski and realized he had been wrong. Once he understood that a hydrogen weapon was possible, convincing the government to research and build one became a major focus of his energies, although he did continue to offer advice on the atomic bomb. Teller continued to campaign for building the hydrogen bomb even after an atomic bomb was dropped on Hiroshima (an act which Teller opposed) and World War II ended.

There was initially little interest in the hydrogen bomb project, and in 1946 Teller left Los Alamos to teach at the University of Chicago. He focused on issues in theoretical physics, such as the relation of gravitational and electromagnetic forces over time and the origins of the elements and cosmic rays. But another arms race began in earnest when the Soviets exploded their atomic bomb in 1949; the development of the H-bomb became a priority for the United States and Teller returned to Los Alamos. It was at this juncture that Teller began to exert a strong influence on nuclear policy. He convinced Paul Nitze, who was then a key State Department official (and would later be President Reagan's top arms control advisor), that the H-bomb could be built. By 1951, Teller, Stanislaw M. Ulam, and Frederic de Hoffman had made a number of crucial breakthroughs, and the path to building a thermonuclear weapon was clear.

J. Robert Oppenheimer, one of the most influential nuclear physicists in the 1930s and the director of the laboratories at Los Alamos, publicly opposed the development of thermonuclear weapons. Over his objections, Teller used his growing influence in government and lobbied for a second nuclear weapons laboratory. It was established in July, 1952 at Livermore, California, and later named after the famous experimental physicist **Ernest Orlando Law-** rence, who had proposed the site. Teller was associate director of the Lawrence Livermore Laboratory from 1954 to 1958 and director from 1958 to 1960. In 1953, he was also appointed professor at the University of California; he was named university professor in 1960, a position he would hold until he retired in 1975. At the University of California's Davis campus, he played a major role in establishing the Department of Applied Sciences.

The political battles over the development of the H-bomb and the founding of a second nuclear weapons laboratory in Livermore, California, brought the tensions between Teller and Oppenheimer to a head. There was also a considerable amount of resentment in government circles against Oppenheimer for opposing thermonuclear weapons, and in 1953 the Atomic Energy Commission filed official charges against him, based primarily on his association with communists, including family members. He was denied his security clearance and requested a Congressional hearing. Though many scientists spoke in his favor, Teller appeared to testify against him. According to Daniel J. Kevles in *The Physicists: The History of a Scientific Community in Modern America,* Teller "considered Oppenheimer a Communist and an advocate of Soviet appeasement." At the hearing Teller testified, as quoted by Kevles, that "his actions frankly appeared to me confused and complicated . . . I would like to see the vital interests of this country in hands which I understand better and therefore trust more . . . I would feel personally more secure if public matters would rest in other hands." Though the committee did not find Oppenheimer disloyal, they decided not to restore his security clearance.

Teller's testimony alienated most of the nuclear physicists in the country and cost him many of his friendships among other scientists, but it strengthened his ties to military and political leaders. His influence on American strategic policy only increased during the 1950s. In 1956, Teller assured the navy that Livermore could build a warhead small enough to be fired from a submarine, and four years later the first Polaris submarine was armed with the warheads Teller had envisioned. He was less successful in fulfilling his promise that Livermore could build a "clean" nuclear weapon that would not produce dangerous radioactivity. It has never been made and many physicists believe it is impossible. During this period, Teller was also active in several other areas of nuclear policy, opposing nuclear test bans and advocating peaceful atomic projects such as power reactors and "plowshare" explosions for mining and canal digging. He was the first chairman of the Atomic Energy Commission's Advisory Committee on Reactor Safeguards, which oversaw the production of the first manual on technical aspects of reactor safety. He was especially fascinated by the prospect of nuclear fusion, where power is produced by merging atoms together, as opposed to the fission, or splitting, of atoms, and Livermore became a center for fusion research.

Argues for a Nuclear Defense System

All through the sixties and seventies Teller was an outspoken advocate of nuclear power and as early as 1962 he began advocating an "active defense system" to shoot down attacking enemy missiles. Teller became increasingly convinced that a nuclear shield could remove the threat of a retaliatory nuclear strike. Work at Lawrence Livermore National Laboratories suggested that giant X-ray lasers powered by nuclear blasts might possibly be an effective antimissile weapon; this was only a theory, however, and it was based on a number of assumptions which had not been proven and a number of scientific and technical breakthroughs which had not yet taken place.

When Teller retired from the University of California in 1975, he became a senior research fellow at Stanford University's Hoover Institute on War, Revolution, and Peace. He also continued to maintain his political contacts with policymakers both inside and outside of government. When his friend Reagan was elected president in 1980, Teller found himself with the most political influence he had ever had in his career, and he succeeded at last in his campaign to acquire government funding for an active nuclear defense system. Reagan supported the Strategic Defense Initiative (SDI) or "Star Wars," in large part because Teller convinced him it was possible.

Teller's conviction that such a defense system was possible turned out to be premature, if not entirely incorrect. His original plan for nuclear powered lasers was quickly rejected as infeasible; extensive research was done on burning small holes in the outer sheeting of enemy missiles, thereby causing them to break up in outer space. The necessary antimissile satellites for such a project were expected to be cheap but eventually turned out to be extremely costly; their effectiveness also depended upon complex computer technology.

Whatever the feasibility of the Strategic Defense Initiative, the proposal was at least partly designed to push the Soviets into an arms race they could not afford to pursue. Defense spending was already an enormous share of the Soviet Gross Domestic Product; an expensive antimissile system involving high technology items like lasars and computer tracking systems was simply beyond their means. Later commentators in both the West and Russia credit SDI with forcing the societal reforms which ended in the collapse of communism in Eastern Europe and the Soviet Union.

In *Physics Today*, Robert March writes that Teller is "best known to the public, and even to the generation of physicists educated after World War II, as the tireless and single-minded champion of the technological arms race." Teller's political influence has overshadowed many of his scientific contributions, but since World War II he has done important work in theoretical physics with **Enrico Fermi** and others. In 1962, he was given the Fermi Award, one of the highest honors in physics. In 1983, he was awarded the National Medal of Science for his research on stellar energy, fusion reaction, molecular physics, and nuclear safety. Among other awards Teller has received are the Priestley Memorial Award (1957), the Einstein Award (1959), the General Donovan Memorial Award (1959), the Robins

Award (1963), the Leslie R. Groves Gold Medal (1974), the Harvey Prize (1975), the Sylvanus Thayer Award (1986), the Presidential Citizen Medal (1989), and the Order of Banner with Rubies of the Republic of Hungary. Teller is a member of the National Academy of Science and a fellow of the American Nuclear Society, the American Physical Society, the American Academy of Arts and Science, and the American Association for the Advancement of Science.

In the 1990s, Teller remained active in both physics and public policy. "I am amusing myself with a number of problems from astrophysics and superconductivity," Teller told contributor Chris Hables Gray. He went on to describe his work organizing a conference among physicists on human health and radiation levels. On his political influence, he remarked: "I tried to contribute to the defeat of the Soviets. If I contributed one percent, it is one percent of something enormous." He added that it was a great pleasure, now that Eastern Europe is free, to be able to visit his native Hungary for the first time in fifty-six years.

SELECTED WRITINGS BY TELLER:

Books

The Structure of Matter, J. Wiley, 1949.
Our Nuclear Future: Facts, Dangers, and Opportunities, Criterion Books, 1958.
Power and Security, Lexington Books, 1976.
Fusion, Academic Press, 1981.
Better a Shield Than a Sword, Free Press, 1987.
Conversations on the Dark Secrets of Physics, Plenum Press, 1991.

FURTHER READING:

Books

Blumberg, Stanley A., and Louis G. Panos, *Edward Teller: Giant of the Golden Age of Physics,* Scribner, 1990.

Broad, William J., *Teller's War: The Top-Secret Story behind the Star Wars Deception,* Simon & Schuster, 1992.

Mark, Hans, and Sidney Fernbach, editors, *Properties of Matter under Unusual Conditions: In Honor of Edward Teller's 60th Birthday,* Interscience Publishers, 1969.

Hans, Mark, and Lowell Wood, editors, *Energy in Physics, War and Peace: A Festschrift Celebrating Edward Teller's 80th Birthday,* Kluwer Academic Publishers, 1988.

Kevles, Daniel J., *The Physicists: The History of a Scientific Community in Modern America,* Knopf, 1978.

Periodicals

Corn, David, *Nation,* Kudos for a Con Man, Volume 255, September 28, 1992, p. 316.

Davis, Burton H., *Chemtech,* B, E, & T: The Scientists behind the Surface Science, Volume 21, January 1991, p. 18.

March, Robert, review of, *Physics Today,* Conversations on the Dark Secrets of Physics, Volume 45, January 1992, p. 74.

Other

Teller, Edward, *Interview with Chris Hables Gray,* conducted January 29, 1994.

Sketch by Chris Hables Gray

Howard Temin
1934–1994
American virologist

Howard Temin is an American virologist who revolutionized molecular biology in 1965 when he found that genetic information in the form of ribonucleic acid (RNA) can be copied into deoxyribonucleic acid (DNA). This process, called reverse transcriptase, contradicted accepted beliefs of molecular biology at that time, which stipulated that DNA always passed on genetic information through RNA. Temin's research also contributed to a better understanding of the role viruses play in the onset of cancer. For this, he was featured on the cover of *Newsweek* in 1971, which hailed his discovery as the most important advancement in cancer research in sixty years. In addition, Temin shared the 1975 Nobel Prize in physiology or medicine for his work on the Rous sarcoma virus. His discovery of the reverse transcriptase process contributed greatly to the eventual identification of the human immunodeficiency virus (HIV). Temin's later research focused on genetic engineering techniques. A vehement antismoker, he took every opportunity to warn against the dangers of tobacco, even in his acceptance speech for the Nobel Prize.

Howard Martin Temin was born in Philadelphia on December 10, 1934, to Henry Temin, a lawyer, and Annette (Lehman) Temin. The second of three sons, Temin showed an early aptitude for science and first set foot in a laboratory when he was only fourteen years old. As a student at Central High School in Philadelphia, he was drawn to biological research and attended special student summer sessions at the Jackson Laboratory in Bar Harbor, Maine. After graduation from high school, Temin enrolled at Swathmore College in Pennsylvania where he majored and minored in biology in

the school's honors program. He published his first scientific paper at the age of eighteen and was described in his college yearbook as "one of the future giants in experimental biology."

After graduating from Swathmore in 1955, Temin spent the summer at the Jackson Laboratory and enrolled for the fall term at the California Institute of Technology in Pasadena. For the first year and a half, he majored in experimental embryology but then changed his major to animal virology. He studied under **Renato Dulbecco**, a renowned biologist in his own right, who worked on perfecting techniques for studying virus growth in tissue and developed the first plaque assay (a chemical test to determine the composition of a substance) for an animal virus. Temin received his Ph.D. in biology in 1959 and worked for another year in Dulbecco's laboratory. In 1960 he joined the McArdle Laboratory for Cancer Research at the University of Wisconsin—Madison, where he spent the remainder of his career as the Harold P. Rusch Professor of Cancer Research, and the Steenbock Professor of Biological Sciences.

Studies in Viral Research Stir Controversy

Temin began studying the Rous sarcoma virus (RSV) while still a graduate student in California. First identified in the early twentieth century by **Peyton Rous**, RSV is found in some species of hens and was one of the first viruses known to cause tumors. In 1958 Temin and Harry Rubin, a postdoctoral fellow, developed the first reproducible assay *in vitro* (outside of an organism) for the quantitative measuring of virus growth. Accepting an appointment as assistant professor of oncology at Wisconsin in 1960, Temin continued his research with RSV. Using the assay method he and Rubin developed, Temin focused on delineating the differences between normal and tumor cells. In 1965 he announced his theory that some viruses cause cancer through a startling method of information transfer.

Scientists at the time thought that genetic information could only be passed from DNA to RNA. DNA is a long molecule comprised of two chains of nucleic units containing the sugar deoxyribose. RNA is a molecule composed of a chain of nucleic units containing the sugar ribose. For years, many of Temin's colleagues rejected his theory that some viruses actually reverse this mode of transmitting genetic information, and they cited a lack of direct evidence to support it. Temin, however, was convinced that RNA sometimes played the role of DNA and passed on the genetic codes that made a normal cell a tumor cell.

It took Temin several years, however, to prove his theory. Despite making further inroads in gathering evidence implicating DNA synthesis in RSV infection, many of his colleagues remained skeptical. Finally, in 1970, Temin, working with Satoshi Mitzutani, discovered a viral enzyme able to copy RNA into DNA. Dubbed "a reverse transcriptase virus," this enzyme passed on hereditary information by seizing control of the cell and making a reverse transcript of the host DNA; in other words, the enzyme synthesized a DNA virus that contained all the genetic information of the RNA virus. This discovery was made simultaneously by biologist **David Baltimore** at his laboratory at the Salk Institute in La Jolla, California.

The work of Temin and Baltimore led to a number of impressive developments in molecular biology and recombinant DNA experimentation over the next twenty years, including characterizing retroviruses, a family of viruses that cause tumors in vertebrates by adding a specific gene for cancer cells. In 1975 Temin shared the Nobel Prize in physiology or medicine with his former mentor, Renato Dulbecco, and David Baltimore. These three scientists' research illustrated how separate avenues of scientific research could converge to produce significant advances in biology and medicine. Eventually, interdisciplinary research was to become a mainstay of modern science.

In 1987 Temin reflected on his discovery of viruses' roles in causing cancer. "I measure [my discovery's importance] by comparing what I taught in the experimental oncology course twenty-five years ago," said Temin in a University of Wisconsin press release, pointing out that the topic of viral carcinogenesis (the viral link to cancer) was rarely the focus of any lectures at that time. "Now, in the course we're teaching, between a third and half of the lectures are related directly or indirectly to viral carcinogenesis."

Research Leads to Understanding of AIDS

Temin's continuing work into the role viruses play in carcinogenesis had an important impact on acquired immunodeficiency syndrome (AIDS) research. Temin's discovery of reverse transcriptase provided scientists with the means to find and identify the AIDS virus. His interest in genetic engineering and the causes of cancer eventually led him to another exciting discovery. He found a way to measure the mutation rate in retroviruses (viruses that engage in reverse transcriptase), which led to insights on the variation of cancer genes and viruses, such as AIDS. Determining the speed at which genes and viruses change provided vital information for devising attempts to vaccinate or treat viral diseases. His discovery of reverse transcriptase also led to the development of standard tools used by biologists to prepare radioactive DNA probes to study the genetic makeup of viral and malignant cells. Another genetic engineering technique that arose from this research was the ability to make DNA copies of messenger RNA, which could be isolated and purified for later study.

Temin was also interested in such areas as gene therapy, which uses gene splicing techniques to "genetically improve" the host organism. As he began to apply genetic engineering techniques to his research, he recognized legitimate concerns about producing pathogens (microorganisms that carry disease) that could escape into the environment. He also served on a committee that drew up federal guidelines in human gene therapy trials.

Temin's research convinced him that science was making progress in the fight against cancer. Temin said in a 1984 United Press International release: "We know the names of some of the genes which are apparently involved in cancer. If past history is a guide, this understanding will lead to improvement in diagnosis, therapy, and perhaps prevention."

Throughout his career, Temin continued to teach general virology courses for graduates and undergraduates. He also worked with students in his laboratory. "I get satisfaction from a number of things—from discovering new phenomena, from understanding old phenomena, from designing clever experiments—and from seeing students and postdoctoral fellows develop into independent and outstanding scientists," he stated in a University of Wisconsin press release.

A scientist and family man who shunned the spotlight after winning the Nobel Prize (which he kept in the bottom drawer of a file cabinet), Temin was committed to quietly searching for clues into the mysteries of cancer-causing viruses. Temin married Rayla Greenberg, also a geneticist, in 1962, and the couple had two daughters, Miriam and Sarah. A familiar site on the Wisconsin-Madison campus, Temin bicycled to work every day on his mountain bike. Although he preferred not to attract attention so he could better concentrate on his work, Temin did not hesitate to speak out about his beliefs. For example, Temin said in an *On Wisconsin* article, "I enjoy teaching and believe I have gained a lot from doing it. As a researcher, I'm able to present to students the newest work in certain areas. I see that as a benefit." Because of this dedication to academics, he became upset when researchers started to leave the University of Wisconsin-Madison in 1984 because of a state employee wage freeze, even though his own salary was ensured through private and foundation support. Temin wrote the governor letters criticizing his lack of support for education and faculty researchers. Eventually, he reluctantly agreed to help the governor in developing salary proposals.

Temin also spoke out against cigarette smoking. During the award ceremonies for the Nobel Prize, he told the audience that he was "outraged" that people continued to smoke even though cigarettes were proven to contain carcinogens. He instructed that eighty percent of all cancers were preventable because they resulted from environmental factors, such as smoking. "It was the most important general statement I could make about human cancer," he said later in a *People* magazine interview. "And I realized the Nobel Prize would give me an opportunity to speak out that a person does not ordinarily have." Temin went on to testify before the Wisconsin legislature and congress in support of antismoking bills. His research efforts in AIDS led him to urge the federal government to increase funding for further research into the AIDS epidemic. Despite living a lifestyle designed to minimize the risk of cancer, Temin, who never smoked, developed lung cancer in 1992. His illness was a rare form of cancer called adenocarcinoma of the lung, which is not usually associated with cigarette smoking. He died of this disease on February 9, 1994. In addition to the

Nobel Prize, Temin received many other awards for his research, including the prestigious Albert Lasker Award in Basic Medical Research in 1974 and the National Medal of Science in 1992.

SELECTED WRITINGS BY TEMIN:

Periodicals

Scientific American, RNA-Directed DNA Synthesis, January 1972.

FURTHER READING:

Periodicals

Dorn, Patrick, *On Wisconsin,* Pursuit of Knowledge Constant Motivation for Temin, July 1989.

Dorn, Patrick, *People,* In Hospitals and Labs, 9 Researchers Wage War on the Elusive Enemy, Cancer, August 15, 1977.

Dorn, Patrick, *Science,* The 1975 Nobel Prize in Physiology or Medicine, Volume 190, 1975, pp. 650–713.

Other

Dorn, Patrick, *UW-Madison's Nobel Laureate Still Stalking Clues to Cancer,* press release, University of Wisconsin-Madison, January 29, 1987.

Dorn, Patrick, *Madison Nobel Winner Continues with Simple Life,* United Press International, October 8, 1984.

Sketch by David Petechuk

Valentina Tereshkova
1937–
Russian cosmonaut

Valentina Tereshkova was the first woman in space. Tereshkova took off from the Tyuratam Space Station in the Vostok VI in 1963, and orbited Earth for almost three days, showing women had the same resistance to space as men. She then toured the world promoting Soviet science and feminism, and served on the Soviet Women's Committee and the Supreme Soviet Presidium. Valentina Vladimirovna "Valya" Tereshkova was born on March 6, 1937, in the Volga River village of Maslennikovo. Her father, Vladimir Tereshkov, was a tractor driver; a Red Army soldier during World War II, he was killed when

Valentina was two. Her mother Elena Fyodorovna Tereshkova, a worker at the Krasny Perekop cotton mill, single-handedly raised Valentina, her brother Vladimir, and her sister Ludmilla in economically trying conditions; assisting her mother, Valentina was not able to begin school until she was ten.

Tereshkova later moved to her grandmother's home in nearby Yaroslavl, where she worked as an apprentice at the tire factory in 1954. In 1955, she joined her mother and sister as a loom operator at the mill; meanwhile, she graduated by correspondence courses from the Light Industry Technical School. An ardent Communist, she joined the mill's Komsomol (Young Communist League), and soon advanced to the Communist Party.

In 1959, Tereshkova joined the Yaroslavl Air Sports Club and became a skilled amateur parachutist. Inspired by the flight of **Yuri Gagarin**, the first man in space, she volunteered for the Soviet space program. Although she had no experience as a pilot, her 126-jump record gained her a position as a cosmonaut in 1961. Four candidates were chosen for a one-time woman-in-space flight; Tereshkova received an air force commission and trained for 18 months before becoming chief pilot of the Vostok VI. Admiring fellow cosmonaut Yuri Gagarin was quoted as saying, "It was hard for her to master rocket techniques, study spaceship designs and equipment, but she tackled the job stubbornly and devoted much of her own time to study, poring over books and notes in the evening."

At 12:30 P.M. on June 16, 1963, Junior Lieutenant Tereshkova became the first woman to be launched into space. Using her radio callsign Chaika (Seagull), she reported, "I see the horizon. A light blue, a beautiful band. This is Earth. How beautiful it is! All goes well." She was later seen smiling on Soviet and European TV, pencil and logbook floating weightlessly before her face. Vostok VI made 48 orbits (1,200,000 miles) in 70 hours, 50 minutes, coming within 3.1 miles of the previously launched Vostok V, piloted by cosmonaut Valery Bykovsky. Tereshkova's flight confirmed Soviet test results that women had the same resistance as men to the physical and psychological stresses of space.

Upon her return, she and Bykovsky were hailed in Moscow's Red Square. On June 22 at the Kremlin she was named a Hero of the Soviet Union and was decorated by Presidium Chairman Leonid Brezhnev with the Order of Lenin and the Gold Star Medal. A symbol of emancipated Soviet feminism, she toured the world as a goodwill ambassador promoting the equality of the sexes in the Soviet Union, receiving a standing ovation at the United Nations. With Gagarin, she travelled to Cuba in October as a guest of the Cuban Women's Federation, and then went to the International Aeronautical Federation Conference in Mexico.

On November 3, 1963, Tereshkova married Soviet cosmonaut Colonel Andrian Nikolayev, who had orbited the earth 64 times in 1962 in the Vostok III. Their daughter Yelena Adrianovna Nikolayeva was born on June 8, 1964, and was carefully studied by doctors fearful of her parents' space exposure, but no ill effects were found. After her flight, Tereshkova continued as an aerospace engineer in the space program; she also worked in Soviet politics, feminism, and culture. She was a Deputy to the Supreme Soviet between 1966 and 1989, and a People's Deputy from 1989 to 1991. Meanwhile, she was a member of the Supreme Soviet Presidium from 1974 to 1989. During the years from 1968 to 1987, she also served on the Soviet Women's Committee, becoming its head in 1977. Tereshkova headed the USSR's International Cultural and Friendship Union from 1987 to 1991, and subsequently chaired the Russian Association of International Cooperation.

Tereshkova summarized her views on women and science in her 1970 "Women in Space" article in the American journal *Impact of Science on Society:* "I believe a woman should always remain a woman and nothing feminine should be alien to her. At the same time I strongly feel that no work done by a woman in the field of science or culture or whatever, however vigorous or demanding, can enter into conflict with her ancient 'wonderful mission'—to love, to be loved—and with her craving for the bliss of motherhood. On the contrary, these two aspects of her life can complement each other perfectly."

SELECTED WRITINGS BY TERESHKOVA:

Periodicals

Impact of Science on Society, Women in Space, Volume 20, number 1, January–March, 1970, pp. 5–12.

FURTHER READING:

Books

Drexel, John, editor, *Facts on File Encyclopedia of the 20th Century,* Facts on File, 1991, pp. 884–885.

O'Neill, Lois Decker, *Women's Book of World Records and Achievements,* Farthest Out of All: The First Woman in Space, Anchor Books, 1979, pp. 739–740.

Sharpe, Mitchell, *"It is I, Sea Gull": Valentina Tereshkova, First Woman in Space,* Crowell, 1975.

Uglow, Jennifer S., editor, *The International Dictionary of Women's Biography,* Continuum, 1982, p. 461.

Periodicals

Uglow, Jennifer S., editor, *New York Times,* Soviets Orbit Woman Cosmonaut, June 17, 1963, pp. 1, 8.

Uglow, Jennifer S., editor, *New York Times,* 2 Russians Land in Central Asia after Space Trip, June 20, 1963, pp. 1, 3.

Sketch by Julian A. Smith

Frederick Terman
1900–1982
American electrical engineer and educator

During his fifty-year tenure at Stanford University, Frederick Terman was instrumental in transforming the school from what he described as an "underprivileged institution" to the cornerstone of the legendary Silicon Valley. An electrical engineer, he directed the nation's secret radar laboratory at Harvard University during World War II. The reference and text books he wrote are regarded as "bibles" of radio engineering.

Frederick Emmons Terman, an only child, was born on June 7, 1900, in English, Indiana, to Lewis and Anna Belle Minton Terman. In 1910 the elder Terman, a psychologist, joined the faculty at Stanford University, where he developed the Stanford-Binet intelligence quotient. The young Terman remained unenrolled in school until he was nine and a half because of his father's belief in natural education; he entered school at the third grade level and began a successful academic career. While in high school, he developed an interest in "ham" radio, and by age 16 he was operating his own transmitter.

Terman graduated at the top of his class when he received his bachelor's degree in chemical engineering at Stanford in 1920. Two years later, he earned an engineer's degree in electrical engineering at Stanford under Professor Harris J. Ryan, America's first professor of electrical engineering. Terman pursued his master's and doctoral degrees at the Massachusetts Institute of Technology, where he studied under Professor **Vannevar Bush**. He received his doctor of science degree in 1924 and was offered a teaching position at MIT.

Prior to beginning his new job, Terman left to visit his family in California, where he was stricken with millary tuberculosis. He was bedridden for a year at his family's Stanford campus home; he also suffered a ruptured appendix and developed eye trouble that would continue for years. Although he could not accept the faculty position at MIT, he was able to fulfill a half-time appointment in electrical engineering at Stanford in 1925. During that first year of teaching, Terman was out of bed only two hours a day. Throughout the rest of his life, he would take great care of his health, a strategy that enabled him to work 14-hour days seven days a week.

After a year, Terman was able to teach full time, and he became an assistant professor in 1927. The following year, he married Sibyl Walcutt, a graduate student in psychology. They had three sons, Frederick, Terence, and Lewis. Terman, who developed and taught Stanford's first course in electronics (then called radio engineering), headed the university's electronics laboratory and used his technical and administrative skills to encourage local industry. He suggested an idea for a marketable instrument to one of his students, **William Hewlett**, who turned the idea into an audio oscillator. Terman then helped Hewlett lure former student **David Packard** back from a General Electric job in New York. The business they started in a Palo Alto garage would grow into the huge Hewlett-Packard Company of computer manufacturing. In 1937, the year Terman became head of the electrical engineering department, the klystron tube (a vacuum tube that generates and amplifies microwave signals) was developed at Stanford by Russell Varian and William Hansen; the invention became the foundation for World War II radar devices, the Stanford Linear Accelerator, and clinical linear accelerators used in cancer treatment. Terman already enjoyed a national reputation, and in 1942 he became the first person working west of New York state to serve as president of the Institute of Radio Engineers (later known as the Institute of Electrical and Electronic Engineering).

That same year, Vannevar Bush, who was responsible for organizing American academic scientists and engineers for the wartime defense effort, asked Terman to head the covert Radio Research Laboratory at Harvard University. Terman assembled more than 800 people to develop countermeasures against enemy radar. One of their innovations, narrow strips of aluminum foil called chaff, reflected radar when strewn by airplanes; the country sacrificed its Christmas tree tinsel and chewing gum wrappers to help provide the 20 million pounds of chaff that Allied forces used during the war in Europe. The laboratory also made tunable receivers for detecting and analyzing enemy radar signals. By the end of the war, Terman's lab had developed 150 antiradar tools that reduced the effectiveness of German anti-aircraft efforts by 75 percent.

In 1945, Terman's achievements were recognized with an honorary doctorate from Harvard. The following year, he was elected to the National Academy of Sciences; he and his father thus enjoyed rare status as simultaneous members of that prestigious organization. He was awarded the king of England's special medal for service in the cause of freedom and, in 1948, the United States' Medal for Merit, the nation's highest civilian award.

Turns Stanford into Important Technological Research Center

Having accomplished his wartime assignment, Terman returned to Stanford in 1946 as dean of engineering. "Stanford emerged from World War II as an underprivileged institution," he was quoted as saying by Sandra Blakeslee in a Stanford News Service article. "It had not been significantly involved in any of the exciting engineering and scientific activities associated with the war." The government, whose previous support of basic research was limited to agricultural topics, showed a new interest in funding peacetime research. Terman seized the opportunity, negotiating contracts for Stanford in 1946 and 1947 that helped establish the framework for the way sponsored research would be implemented in university settings. He established a policy he called "steeples of excellence," by

which Stanford would pay top salaries to attract outstanding faculty members, reasoning that these experts would attract research contracts as well as quality junior faculty and promising graduate students. Under Terman's leadership, Stanford's reputation flourished and the university was sometimes referred to as "Terman Tech" because of his shaping influence. Terman envisioned universities as more than a place for learning, seeing them also as major economic influences in the nation's industrial life. Calling the idea of creating an industrial park on plentiful Stanford land "our secret weapon," he shaped the venture into a high-technology center. Klystron tube producers Varian Associates became the first tenant in 1951. By the late 1960s, 90 businesses would employ 26,000 workers at the Stanford Industrial Park.

In 1955, Terman was named provost at Stanford; in 1959, he took on additional duties as the school's vice president. Five years later, he helped organize the National Academy of Engineering, of which he became a founding member. His career achievements were commemorated in 1977 when Stanford University dedicated the $9.2-million Frederick Emmons Terman Engineering Center.

While at Harvard, Terman had written his famous *Radio Engineer's Handbook,* the fifth of his eight books. Not counting foreign publications in at least eight languages, his books had sold over 600,000 copies by the time he retired in 1965. His texts were readable, thorough, and practical; furthermore, Terman diligently updated each new edition to reflect current developments. Results of his personal research are documented in more than 50 articles he wrote for technical journals. In 1952, he summarized his vision of modern technology, as quoted by Blakeslee: "Through its ability to control, to amplify, and to convert between light, sound, and electricity, electronics provides a nervous system for our machine-age civilization."

Terman died in his sleep of cardiac arrest at his Stanford campus home on December 19, 1982.

SELECTED WRITINGS BY TERMAN:

Books

Radio Engineer's Handbook, McGraw-Hill, 1943.
Electronic and Radio Engineering, McGraw-Hill, 1955.

FURTHER READING:

Periodicals

Blakeslee, Sandra, *Stanford to Honor Fred Terman at Engineering Center Oct. 6,* Stanford News Service, October 5, 1977.
Blakeslee, Sandra, *Palo Alto Times,* December 12, 1945.
Blakeslee, Sandra, *San Jose Business Journal,* February 15, 1988, p. 19.

Other

Bloom, William, L. Kenneth Wilson, and Jane Morgan, *Audio Tapes of Interviews on the Occasion of the Silver Anniversary of Palo Alto,* Palo Alto, CA, 1969.

Sketch by Sandra Katzman

Karl Terzaghi
1883–1963
American engineer

Karl Terzaghi bridged the gap between geology and civil engineering by creating the field of soil mechanics. He developed the fundamental methods and tools used to investigate the nature and behavior of soils that are still employed by soil engineers today. His theories have greatly expanded how an understanding of the behavior of soils can be used in construction projects, and designs for the foundations of most major structures now depend on his work.

Terzaghi was born in Prague, Austria-Hungary (now Czechoslovakia), on October 2, 1883, to Anton Terzaghi von Pontenuovo and Amalia Eberle Terzaghi. His father, who died while Terzaghi was a boy, was an infantry commander. Terzaghi attended military school and then the technical high school in Prague. In 1900, he entered the Technische Hochschule, a university in Graz, Austria, where he studied mechanical engineering. He also discovered an interest in geology and was once encouraged to become a professional writer by a professor who had read some of his essays. Terzaghi served a year in the army after graduating from the Technische Hochschule, during which time he translated *Outlines of Field Geology* by Scottish geologist Archibald Geikei. His interest in geology increased; he agreed to serve as a geologist on a Greenland expedition in 1906, but a mountaineering accident forced him to back out.

Terzaghi's first job was as superintendent of construction at an engineering firm in Vienna. In 1908, he moved to Croatia on the Adriatic coast, where he remained until 1910, surveying the geology of the site for a proposed hydroelectric power facility. It was here that Terzaghi became interested in applying geology to engineering problems. After the project he addressed the subject in a paper he wrote on the origin of land forms and the underground conditions of the region. During this period, he began working in Russia, helping to complete a St. Petersburg construction project that had been halted due to structural hazards. In January 1912, he was awarded a doctorate of technical sciences from the Technische Hochschule with a thesis based on the unique design of one of his Russian construction projects.

Begins Work in Soil Mechanics

By 1912, Terzaghi had begun his search for a rational approach to foundation engineering and spent 1911 through 1913 in the United States traveling to dam sites, researching geological studies and looking for connections between them and his own construction experience. When World War I began in 1913, he returned to Austria to join the army, transferring to the newly formed Austrian air force and serving until 1916. In that year, he married Olga Byloff, with whom he would have one daughter. They were separated in 1922 and divorced in 1926.

After leaving the air force, Terzaghi accepted a position at the Imperial School of Engineers in Istanbul, Turkey, where he built his first soil mechanics laboratory. He used tools from the physics department and kitchen utensils to create a program for investigating the physical composition of clay soils. After World War I ended, Terzaghi accepted a teaching position at Roberts College, an American school in Istanbul. He developed his second soils laboratory there, remaining until 1925. Terzaghi's theories about soil mechanics advanced considerably during this period as he invented more tools and techniques for studying the behavior of soils. An example is Terzaghi's discovery that weight supported by clay soils is first carried by the liquid in the microscopic pores of the clay and then transferred over time into the clay itself. Terzaghi published a compilation of his works in 1925, which led to a visiting lectureship at the Massachusetts Institute of Technology (MIT).

During his four years at MIT, Terzaghi developed a program for teaching soil mechanics, improved his testing methods, and expanded his work to include investigations of pavement design and earth dams. Up until this time, Terzaghi had worked only in temperate climates. Curious about the effects of different climates on structures, he asked the United Fruit Company for the opportunity to study soil behavior at their Latin American locations. In 1928, he traveled to United Fruit facilities in Costa Rica, Panama, Spanish Honduras, and Guatemala, studying, among other things, the stability of sloped embankments and the flow of water through soils. After his return from Latin America, Terzaghi received a telephone inquiry about his work from Ruth Doggett, a doctoral student studying geology at Radcliffe College in Cambridge, Massachusetts. Their conversation led to courtship and then marriage in the summer of 1930. They would have a son and a daughter. The Terzaghis cooperated on several projects throughout their careers.

By 1930, Terzaghi had returned to Vienna to teach at the Technical University, which became, under his influence, the focal point of earthworks studies. For nine years, Terzaghi lectured and taught his laboratory techniques to engineers and students from as far away as Australia. He concentrated his research on developing new ways to measure the reactions of sand and clay to stresses such as the weight of buildings. During this period, the role of soil mechanics in engineering was becoming more widely understood by professionals; Terzaghi's role in the development of this field was recognized in 1936 when he returned to Boston, Massachusetts, for a special ceremony at Harvard University. There he was named the first president of the International Conference of Soil Mechanics and Foundation Engineering. He would remain the society's active president for twenty-one years and honorary president for several more.

Terzaghi lectured in many European cities, as well as North Africa and Central Asia. He was known for consulting on construction projects that had been interrupted by unexpected structural failures. An afternoon phone call to a place where he was staying in France once brought him to London that same evening to study a failure at an earthen dam project. This began a fruitful relationship with British engineers, and in 1939 he was invited to deliver the James Forrest Lecture to the Institution of Civil Engineers. Terzaghi was only the second non-British engineer to receive this honor since the institution was founded in 1890.

In 1938, Terzaghi accepted a visiting lectureship at Harvard University. He moved his family to the United States and settled in Winchester, Massachusetts. This developed into a very productive period of Terzaghi's career, during which he taught, consulted on a worldwide basis, and wrote two important books and almost one hundred papers. In 1946, Harvard made him Professor of the Practice of Civil Engineering. Terzaghi included adventure in his work as often as possible, such as studying the Sasumua dam site in Kenya in 1953 near the warring Mau Mau tribe. He also worked on famous projects and was chair of the Board of Consultants for the controversial High Aswan Dam in Egypt.

Terzaghi maintained a rigorous professional schedule and continued his teaching, consulting, and researching well into his seventies. His health remained excellent and he regularly out-paced much younger geologists on field investigations. Terzaghi retired from the Harvard faculty in 1956 at age seventy-three, but he still worked, and in the spring before his seventy-fifth birthday he traveled to fifteen cities throughout the United States and Europe. Over the next several years he wrote a textbook and worked with several leading engineering schools as a lecturer and research consultant. By the end of his career he had received six honorary doctoral degrees, the Norman Medal from the American Society of Civil Engineers three times, and the Frank B. Brown Medal of the Franklin Institute of Philadelphia. Terzaghi died on October 25, 1963, at his home in Winchester, Massachusetts.

SELECTED WRITINGS BY TERZAGHI:

Books

Erdbaumechanik auf bodenphysikalischer Grundlage, Deuticke (Vienna), 1925.

Principles of Soil Mechanics, McGraw-Hill, 1926.
Theoretical Soil Mechanics, Wiley, 1943.
Soil Mechanics in Engineering Practice, Wiley, 1948.
From Theory to Practice in Soil Mechanics: Selections from the Writings of Karl Terzaghi, with bibliography and contributions by L. Bjerrum, A. Casagrande, R. B. Peck, and A. W. Skempton, Wiley, 1960.

Periodicals

Engineering News Record, Large Retaining-Wall Tests I-V, February 1, 1934, pp. 136–140; February 22, 1934, pp. 259–262; March 8, 1934, pp. 316–318; March 29, 1934, pp. 403–406; April 19, 1934, pp. 503–508.
Proceedings of the International Conference on Soil Mechanics and Foundation Engineering, Stability of Slopes of Natural Clay, Volume 1, 1936, pp. 161–165.
Boston Society of Civil Engineers, Undisturbed Clay Samples and Undisturbed Clays, Volume 28, 1941, pp. 211–231.
Journal of the Boston Society of Civil Engineers, Permafrost, Volume 39, 1953, pp. 1–50.
Proceedings of the Canadian Soil Mechanics Conference, Egypt's Aswan High Dam, Volume 46, 1956, pp. 47–51.
Civil Engineering, Soil Mechanics in Action, Volume 29, 1959, pp. 69–70.

Sketch by David N. Ford

Nikola Tesla
1856–1943
American inventor and electrical engineer

The first person to prove and perfect the efficient use of alternating-current electricity, Nikola Tesla saw his polyphase system become the standard for power transmission throughout the world. He also pioneered research in such areas as artificial lightning, high-frequency and high-tension currents, and radio telegraphy. Before his death in 1943, Tesla had acquired more than one hundred patents for high-frequency generators, adjustable condensers, thermomagnetic motors, transformers, his famous Tesla coil, and other inventions that were to become integral elements in modern technology. Tesla was born on July 10, 1856, the son of Serbian parents in the Croatian village of Smiljan. The settlement was located near the town of Gospić in what was then a part of the Austro-Hungarian empire, an area that later became Yugoslavia. Tesla's father and mother, Milutin

Nikola Tesla

Tesla and Djuka Mandić, had expected their son to follow in his father's footsteps as a Greek Orthodox clergyman. But during his early school years in Smiljan and then in nearby Gospić, where his parents moved when he was six or seven years old, he excelled in math and science. Gradually it became clear that the young and independent-minded Tesla was no candidate for the seminary.

Early Achievements in Europe

In 1871, when Tesla was fifteen, he attended the higher secondary school at Karlovac, Croatia. After four years, Tesla moved to Graz, Austria, to attend the higher technical school or polytechnic institute in 1875. As before, he excelled in math and science, seemed to have a prodigious memory (he was reputed to have memorized Johann Wolfgang von Goethe's epic drama *Faust*), and showed particular interest in electrical engineering. While attending the technical school in Graz, Tesla commented on the unnecessary (and potentially dangerous) sparks that were emitted by a Gramme dynamo, a direct-current induction motor that was being demonstrated in the classroom. The sparks emerged from where the brushes came into contact with the commutator, and Tesla commented that these sparks could be eliminated by creating a motor without a commutator. The professor was skeptical of the young scientist's theory, and at that time nothing came of the idea. Over the coming years, however, Tesla would continue to work to overcome the problems of direct-current motors.

The details of this period of Tesla's life are unclear, but according to one of his biographers, Margaret Cheney in *Tesla: Man Out of Time,* Tesla's education was interrupted during these years by bouts of malaria and cholera. In any event, Tesla may have attempted to continue his university education at the University of Prague in 1880 (although Cheney indicates that there is no record of this). He was said to have gambled frequently in Prague, wagering for pleasure and in the often vain hope of augmenting his meager income. Tesla appears never to have completed his formal education at Prague, however, possibly because the death of his father forced him to become financially independent. As it was, Tesla may have merely audited classes and used the library without actually enrolling in the university.

Tesla's post-Prague years come into sharper focus. In January 1881 he moved to Budapest where he worked in the Hungarian government's new central telegraph office. During his brief tenure here, Tesla invented a telephone amplifier or loudspeaker, yet for reasons unknown he never patented the device. Tesla also continued to ruminate about the sparks created by the Gramme dynamo in the classroom in Graz, and about rotating magnetic fields, which would later become the basis for all polyphase induction motors. The following year, 1882, Tesla took a position with the Continental Edison Company in Paris.

Tesla's job here was to correct problems in the Edison plants in Germany and France. One of his trips took him to Strasbourg, where he earned local gratitude (but not a promised bonus) for having repaired the railroad station's lighting plant. While in Strasbourg, ever mindful of the sparking problem of direct-current motors, Tesla tried to interest the city's mayor and certain of his wealthy colleagues in his design for an alternating-current motor that would eliminate the need for a commutator. In response, the mayor and his friends rewarded Tesla with a few bottles of 1801 St. Estèphe wine but gave no financial support.

Seeks Opportunity with Edison in America

Tesla decided to try his luck in the United States where there were interesting developments in electrical engineering and presumably greater opportunities for funding. With a reference from the manager of the Edison company in Paris, Tesla secured a position in **Thomas Alva Edison**'s research laboratory in New York. Tesla embarked for the New World in 1884.

Thomas Edison had already made a reputation for himself as an electronics wizard, but he was committed to the use of direct-current electricity. When Tesla explained to Edison his plans for a motor based on alternating current, all he did was create the foundation for a difficult relationship with his unyielding new boss. Edison insisted that Tesla's designs for his new motor were impractical and dangerous. Edison hired Tesla, however, and for a year the new immigrant designed direct-current dynamos and motors for the Edison Machine Works in New York. The experience was limiting and unsatisfying for Tesla, who found that he was unable to overcome the personal and professional differences that separated him from Edison. These factors and a disagreement over compensation that Tesla felt was due to him caused the young Serb to strike out on his own.

In the ensuing year, some entrepreneurs persuaded Tesla to establish an electric company. He established the company's headquarters in Rahway, New Jersey, in 1885. In establishing his own company Tesla saw an opportunity for working out in a practical way his ideas for alternating current. His financial supporters, however, seemed mainly interested in providing arc lighting for streets and factories. Again, Tesla faced disappointment and was forced to work for at least part of 1886 as a common laborer. In his spare time, however, Tesla continued to work on his innovations. During this period he managed to acquire seven patents for his work with arc lighting. Growing interest in electrical innovations gradually worked to Tesla's advantage, and by 1887 he was able to establish the Tesla Electric Company.

Working within his own organization, Tesla was able to create the first efficient polyphase motor. This was achieved by designing a motor that incorporated several wire-taped blocks that surrounded the rotor. When alternating current is supplied to the wires, with the current to each block being slightly out of phase with the others, a rotating magnetic field is created. The movement of the rotor is achieved as it follows this revolving field. The practical effect of Tesla's invention was that it allowed strong electrical currents to be transmitted over long distances. Edison's direct current, on the other hand, was limited to local use and required many electrical relay stations to distribute the current throughout a given area such as a city. Tesla's invention undermined Edison's assertion that alternating current was impractical, and by 1891 Tesla had acquired forty patents having to do with this technology. His inventions attracted attention, and Tesla began giving lectures in the late 1880s. Perhaps the most notable of these lectures was the one he delivered to the American Institute of Electrical Engineers in May 1888, after which his reputation as a preeminent electrical engineer was firmly established.

George Westinghouse, inventor and manufacturer, bought one of Tesla's patents for the polyphase motor and hired the man to work in his Pittsburgh plant. In 1889 Tesla became an American citizen. He was now famous and his future seemed assured. During the ensuing years, Tesla continued to research and lecture to prestigious organizations across the United States and in Europe. In Britain he addressed the Institution of Electrical Engineers and the Royal Society, and in France, the Society of Electrical Engineers and the French Society of Physics. In these lectures Tesla discussed his work in the transmission of electrical power through radio waves. At the Columbian Exposition in Chicago in 1893, the first world's fair to have electricity, Westinghouse provided it using Tesla's system of polyphase alternating current. At the Exposition Tesla also gave lectures and demonstrations of his research.

Designs First Hydroelectric Generating Plant

It was also Tesla's partnership with Westinghouse that allowed Tesla the opportunity to design what may have been the scientist's greatest achievement, the world's first hydroelectric generating plant. The plant, located at Niagara Falls, distributed electrical current to the city of Niagara Falls and to Buffalo, New York, some twenty-three miles away. The Niagara power plant, completed late in 1895, destroyed forever Edison's objections to Tesla's polyphase system of alternating current and established the kind of power system that would eventually be used throughout the United States and the world.

Meanwhile, Tesla had turned his interests to the proposition that radio waves could carry electrical energy and in 1897 demonstrated wireless communication over some twenty-five miles. Tesla also demonstrated the idea of transmitting electrical energy in 1898 with several radio-controlled model boats that he had constructed. The Spanish-American War was underway at this time, however, distracting the public from this new revelation, and it's also possible that this type of remote-control system was too advanced for its usefulness to be fully appreciated. Many of Tesla's other inventions would later prove beneficial in a number of applications. His work with high-frequency currents yielded several generating machines that were forerunners of those used in radio communication, and his Tesla coil, a resonant air-core transformer, proved capable of producing currents at a great number of frequencies and magnitudes. In 1898, Tesla moved to the clear, dry air of Colorado Springs, Colorado, where he continued his experiments on electricity, but this time on a grander scale than model boats. As before, his interests focused on transmission of high energy, sending and receiving wireless messages, and related issues pertaining to high voltage electricity. The two hundred kilowatt transmitting tower that Tesla built in Colorado Springs could produce lightning bolts that were millions of volts in strength, so powerful they could overload the city's electrical generator. Indeed, during one experiment in creating artificial lightning, Tesla did just that, causing the municipal generator to catch fire and plunging the town into darkness.

Tesla's year of experimentation in Colorado Springs produced no immediate practical results. Tesla's work did provide the basis, however, for research by later scientists. Physicist Robert Golka, for example, modeled his research in plasma physics on material he gleaned from Tesla's often cryptic Colorado Springs notes that were housed at the Tesla Museum in Belgrade after World War II. Similarly, Soviet physicist **Pyotr Kapitsa**, who shared the 1978 Nobel Prize for his research on magnetism, acknowledged Tesla's work as a model for his own research. Richard Dickinson, a researcher at Cal Tech's Jet Propulsion Laboratory, who was involved in research on the transmission of wireless energy, also invoked Tesla's concepts as a guide to further research.

Tesla in Eclipse

Although Tesla's work had enduring qualities that inspired the research scientists of later generations, Tesla's influence in the scientific community of his contemporaries began to wane after his year in Colorado Springs. Although he had received royalties from his many patents, that income gradually diminished, due in part to a royalty agreement he had renegotiated with Westinghouse before alternating-current electricity attained prominence. As a result, Tesla realized only a fraction of the fortune that alternating current generated, and he was left with scant resources for his later research. In addition, it appeared at least to some minds that Tesla was beginning to lose his grasp on rigorous scientific inquiry. For example, Tesla had received radio signals while at Colorado Springs that he suggested were from intelligent life on Mars or Venus. Although radio signals from space are now a staple of astronomical research, they were not so in the early years of the twentieth century. And to suggest intelligent life as the source of these signals, without the benefit of corroborating evidence, undermined confidence in Tesla's credibility.

During the last four decades of his life Tesla became reclusive and lived alone in a hotel room in New York City. He continued to perform such experiments as he could with his limited resources, but he never recaptured the glory of his earlier years. Those past accomplishments continued to garner attention, however. Late in 1915 the press rumored that the Nobel Prize committee had listed Tesla and Edison as candidates to share the Nobel Prize in physics. Tesla became indignant because he would have to share the prize with his arch-rival, but for reasons never made clear, the Nobel Prize committee gave the award in physics to two other candidates. In 1917, a colleague recommended Tesla for the prestigious Edison Medal of the American Institute of Electrical Engineers. Again, because of the award's association with Edison, Tesla at first refused the honor. After he was finally induced to receive the medal and attend the banquet in his honor, he soon drifted from the crowd and was found outside feeding the pigeons.

As Tesla grew older his reclusive and eccentric behavior grew more intense. He was reportedly troubled by phobias—an aversion to pearl earrings and billiard balls, for example—and his ideas seemed ever more bizarre. On his seventy-eighth birthday he told an interviewer that he had plans for an invincible death beam with a potential for 50 million volts that could instantly destroy 10,000 airplanes or one million soldiers. He publicly offered to create such a death beam for the U.S. government, which he said he could create in three months for less than $2 million dollars.

Early in the morning of January 8, 1943, the maid at the Hotel New Yorker discovered Tesla's body in his room. He had been ill for the previous two years and had evidently died in his sleep on the evening of January 7 of a coronary thrombosis. He was 86 years old. In death he received much of the adulation that he did not receive during his lifetime. Scores of notable people—Franklin and Eleanor Roosevelt, New York mayor Fiorello H. LaGuardia, political figures from Yugoslavia, Nobel Prize winners, leaders in science—lauded Tesla as a visionary who provided the foundations for modern technology. Indeed, within a year of Tesla's death, the United States Supreme Court ruled that Nikola Tesla, and not Guglielmo Marconi, had invented the radio. Yugoslavia made him a national hero and established the Tesla Museum in Belgrade after World War II. In addition to honorary degrees from American and foreign universities (including Columbia and Yale in 1894), and the Edison Medal, Tesla was also recipient during his lifetime of the John Scott Medal. In 1975 Tesla became an inductee into the National Inventors Hall of Fame.

SELECTED WRITINGS BY TESLA:

Books

The Inventions, Researches and Writings of Nikola Tesla, originally published in The Electrical Engineer, 1894, reprinted by Barnes & Noble, 1992.
Lectures, Patents, Articles, originally published by the Nikola Tesla Museum, 1956, reprinted by Health Research, 1973.

Periodicals

Scientific American, Some Personal Recollections, June 1915.
Electrical Experimenter, My Inventions, May, June, July, and October 1919.

FURTHER READING:

Books

Cheney, Margaret, *Tesla: Man Out of Time,* Dorset Press, 1981.
Neidle, Cecyle S., *Great Immigrants,* New York, 1973.
Neidle, Cecyle S., *Nikola Tesla,* Édition de la Société pour la Foundation de l'Institut Nikola Tesla, 1936.
O'Neill, John J., *Prodigal Genius,* David McKay Co., 1944.
Ratzlaff, John T., and Leland I. Anderson, *Dr. Nikola Tesla Bibliography,* Ragusan Press, 1979.
Swezey, Kenneth M., *Dictionary of Scientific Biography,* Tesla, Nikola, Volume 13, Scribner's, 1976, pp. 286–287.

Periodicals

Hall, Stephen S., *Smithsonian,* Tesla: A Scientific Saint, Wizard or Carnival Sideman?, June 19, 1986, pp. 121–134.
Lawren, Bill, *Omni,* Rediscovering Tesla, March 1988, pp. 65–66, 68, 116–117.
Lawren, Bill, *New York Times,* Nikola Tesla Dies: Prolific Inventor, Jan. 8, 1943, p. 19.

Swezey, Kenneth M., *Science,* Nikola Tesla, May 16, 1958, pp. 1147–1159.

Sketch by Karl Preuss

Giuliana Cavaglieri Tesoro
1921–
American chemist

Giuliana Cavaglieri Tesoro has built an international reputation as an expert on polymers, compounds consisting of large molecules formed by repeating units of smaller molecules. In a productive career during which she has been granted about 120 patents, Tesoro has made several important contributions to the field of textile chemistry. Among her accomplishments have been the development of the first antistatic chemical for synthetic fibers, the improvement of the permanent press property of textiles, and the development of flame-resistant fabrics. In honor of this research, Tesoro received the Society of Women Engineers' Achievement Award in 1978.

Tesoro was born in Venice, Italy, on June 1, 1921, one of three children born to Gino and Margherita Maroni Cavaglieri. Although her father had trained as a civil engineer, he worked as the manager of a large insurance company. He died when Tesoro was only twelve. By the time she was ready to begin her higher education in 1938, the rise of fascism in her native land meant that she could not enroll in a university there because of her Jewish ancestry. To escape such oppression, Tesoro went to Switzerland, where she briefly pursued training in X-ray technology. She immigrated to the United States in 1939, just before Italy officially entered World War II.

Tesoro, still in her teens and new to America, nevertheless set her sights high: She wanted to enter the graduate program at Yale, despite having little more than the equivalent of a high school education. As she recalled in an interview with Linda Wasmer Smith: "I went to talk to the head of the chemistry department, and he said that I could enroll in the program if I could pass certain examinations. I studied, essentially on my own, for a number of months. Then the department head and a couple of chemistry professors gave me an oral exam, on the basis of which they decided that if I took some senior courses, I could enter the graduate school." This program was accelerated due to the war. In 1943, at the age of twenty-one, Tesoro completed her Ph.D.

Patents Organic Compounds and Textile Processes

Tesoro wasted no time establishing a solid track record in the chemical and textile industries. She worked first as a research chemist at American Cyanamid in Boundbrook, New Jersey. In 1944 she moved on to Onyx Chemical Company in Jersey City, New Jersey, where she served as chemical research director until 1955. From there, she moved again to a similar position at J. P. Stevens in Garfield, New Jersey, a job in which she remained from 1958 through 1968. After that came a year spent as a senior scientist at the Textile Research Institute. In 1969 Tesoro was named director of chemical research at Burlington Industries in Greensboro, North Carolina, a position she held for the next three years. During this period Tesoro became known as a prolific inventor of products and processes, and she was granted more than two dozen U.S. patents in 1970 alone. Her papers on applied topics ranging from antistatic finishes to flame retardants appeared in dozens of journals. In 1963 she was awarded the Olney Medal of the American Association of Textile Chemists and Colorists.

In 1973 Tesoro took a post as visiting professor at the Massachusetts Institute of Technology (MIT), and so embarked on a new phase of her career. She has since maintained ties with MIT, serving at various times in the roles of adjunct professor, senior research scientist, and senior lecturer. In 1982 she accepted a new appointment as research professor at Polytechnic University in Brooklyn, New York. As an academician, she has been able to pursue less pragmatic fields of study, and she revels in the change. "I enjoy basic science—not data gathering, but rather concepts and things that remain important over a period of time. That's an attitude I've tried to impart to my students at the university as well," Tesoro explained in an interview with Linda Wasmer Smith.

Tesoro was a member of three National Research Council committees—on fire safety of polymeric materials, chemical protective clothing systems, and toxicity hazards of materials used in railway vehicles—between 1979 and 1985. She also served a term as president of the Fiber Society, and she has been a columnist for *Polymer News.* Tesoro enjoys travel; she has delivered invited papers and lectures around the United States, as well as in Western Europe, Israel, and China. She is a member of such organizations as the American Association for the Advancement of Science and the American Chemical Society, as well as a fellow of the Textile Institute in Great Britain. She was married to Victor Tesoro on April 17, 1943, in New York City. The couple have two children, Claudia and Andrew. They make their home in Dobbs Ferry, New York.

SELECTED WRITINGS BY TESORO:

Books

Textile Flammability, MIT Press, 1976.
Fire Safety Aspects of Polymeric Materials, National Advisory Board Publication no. 318, ten volumes, Technomic Publishing, 1977–80.

Periodicals

Modern Textiles Magazine, An Effective New Anti-Static Finish, January 1957, pp. 47–48.

FURTHER READING:

Books

Manly, Robert H., *Durable Press Treatments of Fabrics,* Noyes Data Corporation, 1976.

Moussa, Farag, *Women Inventors,* Coopi, 1991.

O'Neill, Lois Decker, *The Women's Book of World Records and Achievements,* Doubleday, 1979.

Periodicals

Seymour, Raymond B., *Polymer News,* Polymer Science Pioneers: Giuliana Cavaglieri Tesoro, July 1989, pp. 207–208.

Other

Tesoro, Giuliana Cavaglieri, *Interview with Linda Wasmer Smith,* conducted February 9, 1994.

Tesoro, Giuliana Cavaglieri, *Interview with Linda Wasmer Smith,* Tesoro, Giuliana Cavaglieri, letter to Linda Wasmer Smith dated February 21, 1994.

Tesoro, Giuliana Cavaglieri, *Interview with Linda Wasmer Smith,* Tesoro, Giuliana Cavaglieri, letter to Emily McMurray dated January 22, 1994.

Sketch by Linda Wasmer Smith

Marie Tharp
1920–

American oceanographic cartographer and geologist

Marie Tharp is a mapmaker who charted the bottom of the ocean at a time when little was known about undersea geology. Her detailed maps showed features that helped other scientists understand the structure and evolution of the sea floor. In particular, Tharp's discovery of the valley that divides the Mid-Atlantic Ridge convinced other geologists that sea floor was being created at these ridges and spreading outward. The confirmation of "seafloor spreading" led to the eventual acceptance of the theory of continental drift, now called plate tectonics.

Tharp was born in Ypsilanti, Michigan, on July 30, 1920. Her father, William Edgar Tharp, was a soil surveyor for the United States Department of Agriculture's Bureau of Chemistry and Soils; he told his daughter to choose a job simply because she liked doing it. Marie's mother, Bertha Louise (Newton) Tharp, taught German and Latin. The family moved frequently because of William Tharp's mapping assignments across the country. Marie Tharp attended twenty-four different public schools in Iowa, Michigan, Indiana, Alabama (where she almost flunked out of the 5th grade in Selma), Washington, D.C., New York, and Ohio. In 1943 she received her bachelor's degree from Ohio University.

Since most young men were fighting in World War II at the time Tharp graduated, the University of Michigan opened the doors of its geology department to women for the first time. Tharp entered the masters program, which trained students in basic geology and then guaranteed them a job in the petroleum industry. Graduating in 1944, Tharp was hired as a junior geologist with Stanolind Oil & Gas in Tulsa, Oklahoma. Women were not permitted to search for oil in the field, so Tharp found herself organizing the maps and data for the all-male crews. While working for Stanolind, Tharp earned a B.S. in mathematics from the University of Tulsa in 1948.

The year of her second bachelor's degree, Tharp moved to Columbia University, where a group of scientists were about to revolutionize the study of oceanography. Hired as a research assistant by geologist Maurice Ewing, Tharp actually ended up helping graduate students with their data; she never told anyone that she had a graduate degree in geology. One student, Bruce Heezen, asked for help with his ocean profiles so often that after a while Tharp worked with him exclusively. Heezen and Tharp were to work closely together until his death in 1977. In 1950 the geophysical laboratory moved from Columbia University to the Lamont Geological Observatory in Palisades, New York.

Before the early 1950s, scientists knew very little about the structure of the ocean floor. It was much easier and cheaper to study geology on land. But without knowledge of the structure and evolution of the seafloor, scientists could not form a complete idea of how the entire earth worked. In the 1940s, most people believed that the earth was a shrinking globe, cooling and contracting from its initial hot birth. The work of Heezen, Tharp, and other geologists in the next decade—who gathered data on the sea floor using echo sounding equipment—helped replace that idea with the model of plate tectonics, where thin crustal "plates" shift around on the earth's mantle, colliding and grinding into each other to push up mountains and cause earthquakes.

The Mid-Atlantic Ridge, a mountainous bump that runs roughly parallel to and between the coastlines of the Americas and Africa, was one of the first topographical features on the sea floor to be identified. Initial studies were undertaken by those aboard the British ship *H.M.S. Challenger,* who discovered in the 1870s that the rise in the center of the Atlantic acted as a barrier between different water temperatures; and by those aboard the German ship *Meteor* who between 1925 and 1927 revealed the Mid-

Atlantic Ridge as rugged and mountainous. The *Meteor* staff also found several "holes" in the center of the Ridge, but did not connect these holes into the continuous rift valley that they were later discovered to be. In the 1930s, the British geologists Seymour Sewell and John Wiseman suspected that a rift valley split the Ridge, but World War II prevented an expedition to confirm this.

By 1950, when Tharp and Heezen moved to Lamont, the time was right for a series of discoveries. In 1952, the pair decided to make a map of the North Atlantic floor that would show how it would look if all the water were drained away. This type of "physiographic" diagram looked very different from the usual method of drawing contour lines for ocean floor of equal depth. Heezen and Tharp chose the physiographic method because it was a more realistic, three-dimensional picture of the ocean floor, and also because contours were classified by the U.S. Navy from 1952 to 1962.

Tharp assembled her first drawing of the North Atlantic ocean floor in 1952, after rearranging Heezen's data into six seafloor profiles that spanned the Atlantic. This initial map showed a deep valley dividing the crest of the Mid-Atlantic Ridge. Tharp pointed out the valley to Heezen. "He groaned and said, 'It cannot be. It looks too much like continental drift," Tharp wrote later in *Natural History*. The valley represented the place where newly formed rocks came up from inside the earth, splitting apart the mid ocean ridge. At the time, Heezen, like most scientists, thought that continental drift was impossible.

While Tharp was working on detailing and clarifying the first map, Heezen kept another assistant busy plotting the location of the epicenters of North Atlantic earthquakes. **Beno Gutenberg** and **Charles F. Richter** had already pointed out that earthquake epicenters followed the Mid-Atlantic Ridge quite closely. But Heezen's group found that the epicenters actually fell within the suspected rift valley. The association of topography with seismicity convinced Tharp that the valley was indeed real.

It took Heezen eight months to agree. By studying rift valleys in eastern Africa, Heezen convinced himself that the land in Africa was simply a terrestrial analogy to what was going on in the middle of the Atlantic: the earth's crust was splitting apart in a huge tensional crack. Heezen then began to wonder whether the earthquake epicenters that had been recorded in the centers of other oceans might also lie in rift valleys. Perhaps, he thought, all the mid ocean ridges could be connected into a huge 40,000-mile system.

Heezen told Maurice Ewing, director of Lamont, of the valley's discovery. For several years, only Lamont scientists knew of its existence. Heezen presented it to the scientific community in several talks during 1956. In 1959, most of the remaining skeptics were convinced by an underwater movie of the valley, made by French oceanographer **Jacques Cousteau** towing a camera across it. Today scientists understand how the rift valley represents the pulling apart of the seafloor as the new rock spreads outward from the ridge.

Heezen and Tharp printed their first edition of the North Atlantic map for a second time in 1959. By this time they knew that the Mid-Atlantic Ridge was cut by east-west breaks, now called transform faults. Heezen and Tharp had confirmed only one of these breaks, but they didn't know its exact length or direction. So in its place on the map they put a large legend to cover the space. In the following years, Tharp and Heezen improved their North Atlantic map and expanded their work to cover the globe, including the South Atlantic, Indian, Arctic, Antarctic, and Pacific Oceans. In 1977, three weeks before Heezen's death, they published the World Ocean Floor Panorama, based on all available geological and geophysical data, as well as more than five million miles of ocean-floor soundings. In 1978 Tharp and Heezen received the Hubbard Medal of the National Geographic Society.

After about fifteen years of work behind the scenes, Tharp finally went on research cruises herself, including trips to Africa, the Caribbean, Hawaii, Japan, New Zealand, and Australia. She retired from Lamont in 1983. Since then she has run a map distributing business in South Nyack, New York, and occasionally consults for various oceanographers. She also keeps Heezen's scientific papers and has written several articles on his life and work. Tharp enjoys gardening in her spare time.

SELECTED WRITINGS BY THARP:

Books

The Ocean Floor, Mapping the Ocean Floor 1947–1977, edited by R. A. Scrutton and M. Talwani, Wiley, 1982.

Periodicals

Natural History, Mappers of the Deep, October 1986, pp. 49–62.

Other

World Ocean Floor, (map), painted by H. C. Berann, Office of Naval Research, 1977.

FURTHER READING:

Periodicals

Oceanus, winter, 1973–74, pp. 44–48.

Sketch by Alexandra Witze

Max Theiler
1899–1972
American virologist

Max Theiler

Max Theiler (pronounced Tyler) was one of the leading figures in the development of the yellow-fever vaccine. His early research proved that yellow-fever virus could be transmitted to mice. He later extended this research to show that mice which were given serum from humans or animals that had been previously infected with yellow fever developed an immunity to this disease. From this research, he developed two different vaccines in the 1930s, which were used to control this incurable tropical disease. For his work on the yellow-fever vaccine, Theiler was awarded the Nobel Prize in medicine or physiology in 1951.

Theiler was born on a farm near Pretoria, South Africa, on January 30, 1899, the youngest of four children of Emma (Jegge) and Sir Arnold Theiler, both of whom had emigrated from Switzerland. His father, director of South Africa's veterinary services, pushed him toward a career in medicine. In part to satisfy his father, he enrolled in a two-year premedical program at the University of Cape Town in 1916. In 1919, soon after the conclusion of World War I, he sailed for England, where he pursued further medical training at St. Thomas's Hospital Medical School and the London School of Hygiene and Tropical Medicine, two branches of the University of London. Despite this rigorous training, Theiler never received the M.D. degree because the University of London refused to recognize his two years of training at the University of Cape Town.

Theiler was not enthralled with medicine and had no intention of becoming a general practitioner. He was frustrated by the ineffectiveness of most medical procedures and the lack of cures for serious illnesses. After finishing his medical training in 1922, the 23-year-old Theiler obtained a position as an assistant in the Department of Tropical Medicine at Harvard Medical School. His early research, highly influenced by the example and writings of American bacteriologist **Hans Zinsser,** focused on amoebic dysentery and rat-bite fever. From there, he developed an interest in the yellow-fever virus.

Yellow-Fever Work Generates Two Life-Saving Vaccines

Yellow fever is a tropical viral disease that causes severe fever, slow pulse, bleeding in the stomach, jaundice, and the notorious symptom, black vomit. The disease is fatal in 10% to 15% of cases, the cause of death being complete shutdown of the liver or kidneys. Most people recover completely, after a painful, extended illness, with complete immunity to reinfection. The first known outbreak of yellow fever devastated Mexico in 1648. The last major breakout in the continental U.S. claimed 435 lives in New Orleans in 1905. Despite the medical advances of the 20th century, this tropical disease remains incurable. As early as the 18th century, mosquitoes were thought to have some relation to yellow fever. Cuban physician Carlos Finlay speculated that mosquitoes were the carriers of this disease in 1881, but his writings were largely ignored by the medical community. Roughly 20 years later, members of America's Yellow Fever Commission, led by **Walter Reed,** the famous U.S. Army surgeon, concluded that mosquitoes were the medium that spread the disease. In 1901, Reed's group, using humans as research subjects, discovered that yellow fever was caused by a blood-borne virus. Encouraged by these findings, the Rockefeller Foundation launched a world-wide program in 1916 designed to control and eventually eradicate yellow fever.

By the 1920s, yellow-fever research shifted away from an all-out war on mosquitoes to attempts to find a vaccine to prevent the spread of the disease. In 1928, researchers discovered that the Rhesus monkey, unlike most other monkeys, could contract yellow fever and could be used for experimentation. Theiler's first big breakthrough was his discovery that mice could be used experimentally in place of the monkey and that they had several practical research advantages. When yellow-fever virus was injected into their brains, the mice didn't develop human symptoms. Instead, "when you give a mouse yellow fever, he gets not jaundice but encephalitis, not a fatal bellyache but a fatal headache," Theiler stated, according to Greer Williams author of *Virus Hunters.*

One unintended research discovery kept Theiler out of his lab and in bed for nearly a week. In the course of his experiments, he accidentally contracted yellow fever from one of his mice, which caused a slight fever and weakness. Theiler was much luckier than some other yellow-fever researchers. Many had succumbed to the disease in the course of their investigations. However, this small bout of yellow fever simply gave Theiler an immunity to the disease. In effect, he was the first recipient of a yellow-fever vaccine.

In 1930, Theiler reported his findings on the effectiveness of using mice for yellow fever research in the respected journal *Science*. The initial response was overwhelmingly negative; the Harvard faculty, including Theiler's immediate supervisor, seemed particularly unimpressed. Undaunted, Theiler continued his work, moving from Harvard University, where he was considered an upstart, to the Rockefeller Foundation in New York City. Eventually, yellow-fever researchers began to see the logic behind Theiler's use of the mouse and followed his lead. His continued experiments made the mouse the research animal of choice. By passing the yellow-fever virus from mouse to mouse, he was able to shorten the incubation time and increase the virulence of the disease, which enabled research data to be generated more quickly and cheaply. He was now certain that an attenuated live vaccine, one weak enough to cause no harm yet strong enough to generate immunity, could be developed.

In 1931, Theiler developed the mouse-protection test, which involved mixing yellow-fever virus with human blood and injecting the mixture into a mouse. If the mouse survived, then the blood had obviously neutralized the virus, proving that the blood donor was immune to yellow fever (and had most likely developed an immunity by previously contracting the disease). This test was used to conduct the first worldwide survey of the distribution of yellow fever.

A colleague at the Rockefeller Foundation, Dr. Wilbur A. Sawyer, used Theiler's mouse strain, a combination of yellow fever virus and immune serum, to develop a human vaccine. Sawyer is often wrongly credited with inventing the first human yellow-fever vaccine. He simply transferred Theiler's work from the mouse to humans. Ten workers in the Rockefeller labs were inoculated with the mouse strain, with no apparent side effects. The mouse-virus strain was subsequently used by the French government to immunize French colonials in West Africa, a hot spot for yellow fever. This so-called "scratch" vaccine was a combination of infected mouse brain tissue and cowpox virus and could be quickly administered by scratching the vaccine into the skin. It was used throughout Africa for nearly 25 years and led to the near total eradication of yellow fever in the major African cities.

Virus Work Leads to Nobel Prize

While he was somewhat pleased with the new vaccine, Theiler considered the mouse strain inappropriate for human use. In some cases, the vaccine led to encephalitis in a few

recipients and caused less severe side effects, such as headache or nausea, in many others. Theiler believed that a "killed" vaccine, which used a dead virus, wouldn't produce an immune effect, so he and his colleagues set out to find a milder live strain. He began working with the Asibi yellow-fever strain, a form of the virus so powerful that it killed monkeys instantly when injected under the skin. The Asibi strain thrived in a number of media, including chicken embryos. Theiler kept this virus alive for years in tissue cultures, passing it from embryo to embryo, and only occasionally testing the potency of the virus in a living animal. He continued making subcultures of the virus until he reached strain number 176. Then, he tested the strain on two monkeys. Both animals survived and seemed to have acquired a sufficient immunity to yellow fever. In March 1937, after testing this new vaccine on himself and others, Theiler announced that he had developed a new, safer, attenuated vaccine, which he called 17D strain. This new strain was much easier to produce, cheaper, and caused very mild side effects.

From 1940 to 1947, with the financial assistance of the Rockefeller Foundation, more than 28 million 17D-strain vaccines were produced, at a cost of approximately two cents per unit, and given away to people in tropical countries and the U.S. The vaccine was so effective that the Rockefeller Foundation ended its yellow-fever program in 1949, safe in the knowledge that the disease had been effectively eradicated worldwide and that any subsequent outbreaks could be controlled with the new vaccine. Unfortunately, almost all yellow-fever research ended around this time and few people studied how to cure the disease. For people in tropical climates who live outside of the major urban centers, yellow fever is still a problem. A major outbreak in Ethiopia in 1960–62 caused 30,000 deaths. The World Health Organization still uses Theiler's 17D vaccine and is attempting to inoculate people in remote areas.

The success of the vaccine brought Theiler recognition both in the U.S. and abroad and even from his former employer, Harvard University. Over the next ten years, he received the Chalmer's Medal of the Royal Society of Tropical Medicine and Hygiene (1939), the Lasker Award of the American Public Health Association, and the Flattery Medal of Harvard University (1945).

In 1951, Theiler received the Nobel Prize in medicine or physiology "for his discoveries concerning yellow fever and how to combat it." According to Williams (in *Virus Hunters*), when Theiler was asked what he would do with the $32,000 Nobel award, he remarked, "Buy a case of scotch and watch the ole Dodgers."

After developing the yellow-fever vaccine, Theiler turned his attention to other viruses, including some unusual and rare diseases, such as Bwamba fever and Rift Valley fever. His other, less exotic research focused on polio and led to his discovery of a polio-like infection in mice known as encephalomyelitis or Theiler's disease. In 1964, he retired from the Rockefeller Foundation, having achieved the rank of associate director for medical and natural sciences and director of the Virus Laboratories. In that same year, he accepted a position as professor of epidemiology and microbiology at Yale University in New Haven, Connecticut. He retired from Yale in 1967.

Theiler married Lillian Graham in 1938. They had one daughter. His nonscientific interests included reading (mostly history and philosophy but absolutely no fiction) and watching baseball games, especially those involving his beloved Brooklyn Dodgers. Although he immigrated to the U.S. in 1923 and remained in America for the rest of his life, he never applied for U.S. citizenship. Theiler died on August 11, 1972, at the age of 73.

SELECTED WRITINGS BY THEILER:

Books

The Arthropod-Borne Viruses of Vertebrates: An Account of the Rockefeller Foundation Virus Program, 1951–1970, Yale University Press, 1973.

FURTHER READING:

Books

Hill, R. N., *The Doctors Who Conquered Yellow Fever,* Random House, 1957.
Strode, G. K., editor, *Yellow Fever,* McGraw-Hill, 1951.
Williams, Greer, *Virus Hunters,* Alfred A. Knopf, 1959.

Periodicals

Bendinger, Elmer, *Hospital Practice,* Max Theiler: Yellow Jack and the Jackpot, June 1988, pp. 211–244.

Sketch by Tom Crawford

Axel Hugo Teodor Theorell
1903–1982
Swedish biochemist

A xel Hugo Teodor Theorell (also known as Hugo Theorell) spent the majority of his career studying the action of oxidation enzymes, proteins essential for the metabolic process in plants and animals. His isolation of the yellow enzyme in the mid–1930s was a breakthrough toward a clearer understanding of the transformation in the cell of food into energy, called cellular respiration. Theorell's discoveries provided basic knowledge for the eventual

creation of artificial life in the laboratory, and were essential to the study of such diseases as cancer and tuberculosis. In a related area of study, his work on the alcohol-burning enzymes led to a new method for testing the alcohol content in blood. He was the first to isolate myoglobin, a substance that gives certain muscles their red color. He also studied cytochrome c, a catalytic enzyme responsible for causing energy reactions in mitochondria, the cell's "powerhouse." Theorell was awarded the 1955 Nobel Prize in physiology or medicine for "his discoveries concerning the nature and mode of action of oxidation enzymes."

Theorell was born in Linköping, Sweden, on July 6, 1903, to Thure and Armida Bell Theorell. His father was a medical officer in the local militia and enjoyed singing; his mother was a gifted pianist. Young Axel absorbed their love of music, and developed an interest in his father's profession that led him to decide on a career in medicine. He received his bachelor of medicine degree (1924) and his doctor of medicine (1930) from the Karolinska Institute in Stockholm. He also studied at the Pasteur Institute in Paris. When a crippling attack of poliomyelitis made a career as a physician impractical, he decided instead to pursue research and teaching. His academic work while at Stockholm was an inquiry into the chemistry of plasma lipids (fatty acids) and their effect on red blood cells. A technique he developed at this time to separate the plasma proteins albumin and globulin was later to prove useful in his work on isolating enzymes (globular proteins) and coenzymes, which help to activate specific enzymes.

As professor of chemistry at Uppsala University from 1930 to 1936, Theorell expanded his research on plasma lipids to concentrate on myoglobin, a muscle protein whose oxygen-carrying capacities he compared to that of hemoglobin in the blood. By isolating (purifying) myoglobin, he was able to show its absorption and storage capacities, and to measure, using centrifugal force, its molecular weight. This determination of its physical properties showed that myoglobin was a separate protein from hemoglobin.

In 1933 Theorell received a grant from the Rockefeller Foundation that enabled him to further his study of enzymes with **Otto Warburg** at the Kaiser Wilhelm Institute (now the Max Planck Institute) in Berlin. Warburg had attempted without success to isolate the yellow enzyme. Using his own methods, Theorell accomplished the isolation. He further separated the yellow enzyme into two parts: the catalytic coenzyme and the pure protein apoenzyme. He also found that the main ingredient of the yellow enzyme is the plasma protein albumin. An important corollary to the research was Theorell's discovery of the chemical chain reaction necessary for cellular oxidation or respiration. These contributions brought a test-tube creation of life closer to reality, and advanced the study of the chemical differences between normal and cancerous cells.

Returning to Stockholm, Theorell became head of the biochemistry department at the Karolinska Institute, part of a Nobel Institute established for the purpose of providing Theorell with further research opportunities. Under his direction, the department acquired a reputation for excellence that attracted biochemists from all over the world. It was here that Theorell continued his research on cytochrome c, succeeding in his attempts to purify it by 1939. He furthered this study that same year in the United States with his colleague, **Linus Pauling**, who discovered the alpha spiral (protein molecules arranged in a twisted-atom chain).

After World War II, a collaboration with **Britton Chance** of the University of Pennsylvania elucidated steps in the oxidation (breakdown) of alcohol and gave the process a name—the Theorell-Chance mechanism. Theorell's study of the enzymes that catalyze the oxidation, alcohol dehydrogenases, provided a new method for determining the level of alcohol in the bloodstream—a technique that came to be used by Sweden and West Germany to test the sobriety of their citizens. From a different perspective, Theorell's alcohol enzyme research pinpointed several bacterial strains, knowledge of which was thought to be useful in the treatment of tuberculosis.

Theorell published accounts of his findings in many scientific journals throughout Europe and the United States. His professional affiliations included membership in the Swedish Chemical Association, the Swedish Society of Physicians and Surgeons, the Royal Swedish Academy of Sciences, the International Union of Biochemistry, and the American Academy of Arts and Sciences. In addition to the 1955 Nobel Prize, he was awarded the Paul Karrer Medal in Chemistry of the University of Zurich, the Ciba Medal of the Biochemical Society in London, the Legion of Honor (France), and the Karolinska Institute 150th Jubilee Medal. Honorary degrees were bestowed upon him from Belgium, Brazil, the United States, and France.

His love for music continued throughout his life and played an important part in his social and community life. He played the violin and was active in Stockholm musical societies. In 1931 he married Elin Margit Alenius, a professional musician. They became parents of three sons. Theorell retired from the Nobel Institute in 1970. Afflicted with a stroke in 1974, his health deteriorated over the following years. He died on August 15, 1982, while vacationing on an island off the coast of Sweden.

SELECTED WRITINGS BY THEORELL:

Books

The Enzymes, Catalases and Peroxidases, Academic Press, 1951, pp. 397–427.
Metabolic Regulation and Enzyme Action, Introduction to Mechanisms of Enzyme Actions, Academic Press, 1970, pp. 179–180.
Proteolysis and Physiological Regulation, My Life with Proteins and Prosthetic Groups, Academic Press, 1975, pp. 1–27.

Periodicals

Harvey Lectures, Function and Structure of Liver Alcohol Dehydrogenase, Volume 61, 1967, pp. 17–41.

FURTHER READING:

Books

Magill, Frank N., editor, *The Great Scientists,* Grolier, 1989, pp. 156–160.
Magill, Frank N., editor, *McGraw-Hill Modern Men of Science,* McGraw-Hill, 1966, pp. 474–475.
Wasson, Tyler, editor, *Nobel Prize Winners,* Wilson, 1989, pp. 1050–1053.

Sketch by Jane Stewart Cook

René Frédéric Thom
1923–
French mathematician

René Frédéric Thom is a French topologist and mathematical philosopher best known as the founder of catastrophe theory, which has received myriad applications in the exact and social sciences. Catastrophe theory provides models for the description of continuous processes that cause abrupt change.

Thom was born on September 2, 1923, at Montbéliard, France, to Gustav Thom, a pharmacist, and Louise Ramel. Thom's formal education took place at the Collège Cuvier at Montbéliard and in Paris at the Lycée Saint-Louis and the Ecole Normale Supérieure. After earning a master's degree in mathematics and a doctorate in science, Thom was Maître de Conférences at Grenoble from 1953 to 1954 and Strasbourg from 1954 to 1957. In 1957, he became a permanent professor (or chair) in the science department at Strasbourg, and since 1964 he has been a professor at the Institut des Hautes Études Scientifiques at Bures-sur-Yvette.

Develops Catastrophe Theory

Most of Thom's early work focused on the mathematics of sudden change, which eventually led to the formulation of catastrophe theory. Since its full presentation in 1972 in Thom's book *Stabilité structurelle et morphogénèse* (translated as *Structural Stability and Morphogenesis*), catastrophe theory has been used to study abrupt systems changes in such diverse fields as hydrodynamics, geology, particle physics, industrial relations, embryology, economics, linguistics, civil engineering, and medicine.

Thom's catastrophe theory is generally classified as a branch of geometry because variables and results are shown as curves or surfaces. It attempts to explain predictable discontinuities in output in systems characterized by continuous inputs. Contrary to the implications of the theory's name, the "catastrophes" studied are not necessarily negative in nature. Thom uses the word simply to describe dramatic change. The inflation of an everyday balloon, for instance, may provide a simple example of the behavior studied by catastrophe theory. As a balloon is steadily filled with air, it expands and changes shape. The change in shape occurs in a relatively uniform manner until the pressure on the balloon's interior reaches a critical value. Then the balloon undergoes a more abrupt, but predictable, change: it pops. More complex phenomena, such as the refraction of light through moving water, the amount of stress that can be placed on a bridge, and the synergistic effects of the ingredients in drugs can also be effectively studied using the catastrophe theory. The theory provides a universal method for the study of all jump transitions, discontinuities, and sudden qualitative changes.

Since its introduction, some scientists have hailed Thom's catastrophe theory as a tool more valuable to mankind than Newtonian theory, which considers only smooth, continuous processes. Catastrophe theory became something of a fad in the 1970s and 1980s and was used in applications that the theory does not support. As a result of such indiscriminate application, the theory has at times been criticized, unjustly, as a cultural phenomenon or a metaphysical view rather than a legitimate branch of mathematics. Although some popularizers have presented it in a metaphysical vein as proof of the deterministic nature of the universe, catastrophe theory does not purport to abolish the indeterminacy that is central to nuclear physics.

Work Recognized with Médaille Fields

In 1958, Thom was awarded the Médaille Fields (Fields Medal), the equivalent of a Nobel Prize in mathematics, and in 1974 he was awarded the Grand prix scientifique de la Ville de Paris. Thom became a member of the prestigious French Academy of Sciences in 1976, and has also been named a Chevalier de la Légion d'honneur (a Knight of the Legion of Honor).

He married Suzanne Heimlinger on April 9, 1949, and they have three children, Françoise, Elizabeth, and Christian.

SELECTED WRITINGS BY THOM:

Books

Stabilité structurelle et morphogénèse, (Structural Stability and Morphogenesis), W. A. Benjamin, 1972, translated edition, 1976.

Periodicals

Topology 8, Topological Models in Biology, 1969, pp. 313–335.

FURTHER READING:

Books

Arnol'd, V. I., *Catastrophe Theory,* 3rd edition, Springer-Verlag, 1992.

Periodicals

Zeeman, Christopher, *Scientific American,* Introduction to Catastrophe Theory, April 1976.

Sketch by Maureen L. Tan

E. Donnall Thomas
1920–
American physician

E Donnall Thomas has pioneered techniques for transplanting bone marrow, an operation that has been utilized to treat patients with cancers of the blood, such as leukemia. For proving that such transplants could save the lives of dying patients, Thomas was awarded the Nobel Prize in physiology or medicine in 1990, a commendation he shared with **Joseph E. Murray**, another American physician who has done important work in the area of transplants. Thomas has spent most of his career at the Fred Hutchinson Cancer Research Center in Seattle, Washington, which he built into the world's leading center for bone marrow transplants. The Hutchinson Center has also become an important training site for doctors learning to perform such operations, and transplant centers around the world are staffed by physicians who studied with Thomas in Seattle.

Thomas was born on March 15, 1920, in the small town of Mart, Texas, to Edward E. Thomas, a doctor, and Angie Hill Donnall Thomas, a school teacher. After graduating from a high school class of approximately fifteen students, Thomas entered the University of Texas at Austin in 1937. He received a B.A. in 1941 and continued on for a master's degree, which was awarded in 1943. In 1942 he married another University of Texas student, Dorothy Martin, who would later help him manage his research and write medical papers.

Medical Education Prepares Thomas for Early Research

After completing his master's degree, Thomas started medical school at the University of Texas Medical Branch in Galveston. After six months, however, he transferred to Harvard Medical School, where he received his M.D. in 1946. He became an intern and then a resident at Peter Bent Brigham Hospital in Boston and began to specialize in blood diseases. Thomas interrupted his formal medical training to serve as a physician in the United States Army from 1948 to 1950. He then returned to the Boston area and did research on leukemia treatments for a year as a postdoctoral fellow at the Massachusetts Institute of Technology. In 1953 he worked as an instructor at Harvard Medical School.

Thomas moved to New York in 1955 to take the position of physician-in-chief at the Mary Imogene Bassett Hospital in Cooperstown. The next year he became, in addition, an associate clinical professor of medicine at the College of Physicians and Surgeons at Columbia University. During the next eight years Thomas had the opportunity to develop and research his ideas about bone marrow transplants, and he applied these concepts to treating cancers of the blood.

Leukemia is a type of cancer in which certain blood cells, known generally as white blood cells, are produced in abnormally large numbers by the bone marrow. In other kinds of cancer, the diseased cells pile up into a tumor, which can often be treated by simply cutting out the lump. Leukemic blood cells, however, circulate throughout the body, making them much more difficult to eliminate. Furthermore, the white blood cells that become abnormal in leukemia are an important part of the body's immune system. Even if they could be destroyed by a means such as radiation, without them the patient would be vulnerable to infections.

In the 1950s, researchers showed that inbred laboratory mice could be irradiated, thus destroying the production of white blood cells by their bone marrow, and then saved from infection by a transplant of bone marrow taken from healthy mice. Inspired by these experiments, Thomas began similar studies on dogs, but he faced two important obstacles. First, the recipient animal's immune system had to be prevented from attacking and destroying the transplanted bone marrow—such immune rejection has long been a problem for bone marrow as well as organ transplant surgery. And second, if the bone marrow transplant was successful and the donated marrow began to produce white blood cells, these cells were likely to attack the recipient's other tissues, perceiving them as foreign. Both of these problems had been avoided in the earlier studies with inbred mice because the mice were genetically identical, and hence, have identical immune systems. People are not so similar genetically, with the exception of identical twins. All attempts to graft bone marrow between a donor and recipient who were not identical twins failed. In 1956, Thomas performed the first bone marrow transplant to a

leukemia patient from an identical twin. Although the patient's immune system did not reject the transplant, the cancer recurred.

Bone Marrow Transplants Succeed

Many researchers gave up working on organ transplants because the problems of immune rejection seemed insurmountable, but Thomas persisted. In 1963 he moved to Seattle to become a professor at the University of Washington Medical School. There he put together a team of expert researchers and began experimenting with new drugs that could suppress the recipient's immune system and thus prevent rejection of the new tissue. In the meantime, new methods were being developed by other researchers to identify people whose immune systems were similar, in order to match organ donors and recipients. The new methods of tissue typing were based on molecules known as histocompatibility antigens. Thomas's team performed the first bone marrow transplant to a leukemia patient from a matched donor in March 1969. During the 1970s they developed and perfected a comprehensive procedure for treating leukemia patients: first the patients receive radiation, both to kill cancer cells and to weaken the immune system so that it does not reject the transplant; then their bone marrow is replaced with marrow from a compatible donor. The patients also are given drugs that continue to suppress their immune systems. Many patients had been cured of leukemia using this technique by the late 1970s. Since then Thomas and his colleagues have improved their success rate from about 12 percent to about 50 percent. In addition to leukemia and other cancers of the blood, bone marrow transplants are used to treat certain inherited blood disorders and to aid people whose bone marrow has been destroyed by accidental exposure to radiation.

Thomas has received wide recognition for his work, including the American Cancer Society's National Award for Basic Science in 1980, and the National Medal of Science of the United States in 1990. The Nobel Prize that he received in 1990, however, came as a surprise. Thomas told reporters that the award is more often given to scientists who do basic research than to those that develop clinical treatments. Thomas shared the prize with Joseph Murray, who performed the first kidney transplant and whose research paved the way for the transplantation of other organs. As reported in *Time* magazine, both men were cited by the Nobel committee for discoveries "crucial for those tens of thousands of severely ill patients who either can be cured or given a decent life when other treatment methods are without success."

SELECTED WRITINGS BY THOMAS:

Periodicals

Journal of Clinical Investigation, Supralethal Whole Body Irradiation and Isologous Marrow Transplantation in Man, 38, October 1959, pp. 1709–1716.

Archives of Internal Medicine, Irradiation and Marrow Infusion in Leukemia: Observations in Five Patients with Acute Leukemia Treated by Whole Body Exposures of 1400 to 2000 Roentgens and Infusions of Marrow, 107, June 1961, pp. 829–845.

Canadian Medical Association Journal, Transplantation of Marrow and Whole Organs, 86, March 10, 1962, pp. 435–444.

FURTHER READING:

Periodicals

Kolata, Gina, *New York Times,* Two American Transplant Pioneers Win Nobel Prize in Medicine, October 9, 1990, p. C3.

Lemonick, Michael D., *Time,* A Pair of Lifesavers, October 22, 1990, p. 62.

Palca, Joe, *Science,* Overcoming Rejection to Win a Nobel Prize, 250, 1990, p. 378.

Sketch by Betsy Hanson

Martha Jane Bergin Thomas
1926–
American chemist and engineer

Martha Jane Bergin Thomas made significant contributions to the development of phosphors, solid materials that emit visible light when activated by an outside energy source. In a productive career, she achieved many firsts, becoming the first female director at GTE Electrical Products and the first woman to receive the New England Award for engineering excellence from the Engineering Societies of New England. She is the holder of twenty-three patents, ranging from innovations in electric light technology to improvements in lamp manufacturing methods.

Thomas was born on March 13, 1926, in Boston. Her parents, both teachers, were John A. and Augusta Harris Bergin. "Even as a girl, I had an intense interest in science," Thomas recalled in an interview with Linda Wasmer Smith. After high school, she pursued that interest at Radcliffe, where she graduated with honors in 1945 at the age of nineteen. Her bachelor's degree in chemistry was supposed to be the initial step toward a medical degree. But then she was offered a job at Sylvania—later GTE Electrical Products—in Danvers, Massachusetts. It was the first nonteaching position to come her way, and Thomas accepted. So began her forty-five-year association with the company, during which she rose from junior technician to director of the technical services labs.

Thomas did not abandon her educational goals, however. She attended graduate school at Boston University, where she received an A.M. degree in 1950 and a Ph.D. two years later. In 1980 she became a part-time student once again; motivated by her new responsibilities as a manager, she obtained a master's degree in business administration from Northeastern University. Thomas has since been honored as a distinguished graduate of every institution from which she earned a degree: Boston Girl's Latin School, Radcliffe, Boston University, and Northeastern.

Develops Phosphors for Fluorescent Lighting

Thomas's first patent was for a method of etching fine tungsten coils that was designed to improve telephone switchboard lights. She went on to establish two pilot plants for the preparation of phosphors—the powdery substances used to coat the inside of fluorescent lighting tubes. Among her accomplishments was the development of a natural white phosphor that allowed fluorescent lamps to impart daylight hues. She also developed a phosphor that raised mercury lamp brightness by 10 percent. These contributions were noted by the Society of Women Engineers in 1965, when it named Thomas Woman Engineer of the Year. Thomas also was named New England Inventor of the Year at a 1991 event sponsored by Boston's Museum of Science, the Inventors Association of New England, and the Boston Patent Law Association.

In addition to her applied research, Thomas taught evening chemistry classes at Boston University from 1952 through 1970. She also served as an adjunct professor at the University of Rhode Island. She is a member of the American Chemical Society and the Electrochemical Society, a fellow of the American Institute of Chemists, and the author of numerous technical papers. In her free time, Thomas enjoys traveling, spending time with her family, and dabbling in arts and crafts.

While still in graduate school, Thomas met her future husband, a fellow chemist. She married George R. Thomas in Millbury, Massachusetts, in 1955. The couple have four daughters: Augusta, Abigail, Anne, and Susan. Thomas accorded family the highest priority in life. Yet despite the cultural norms at the time she raised her children, Thomas was never tempted to give up her scientific career for the role of full-time homemaker. As she explained to Linda Wasmer Smith in an interview, "My career was very intense; it had to be. If you were a woman in science then, you had to stay with it unequivocally. And that's what I did." Commented her husband, "If her career as a scientist was intense, then her career as a wife and mother was absolutely ferocious."

SELECTED WRITINGS BY THOMAS:

Periodicals

Journal of the Electrochemical Society, Measurement of Particle Size Distribution of Phosphors, March 1954, Volume 101, pp. 149–154.

FURTHER READING:

Periodicals

Fowler, Elizabeth M., *New York Times,* Radcliffe Girl's Success Formula, August 4, 1965, pp. 43, 47.

Fowler, Elizabeth M., *Boston Globe,* Inventor of the Year, February 11, 1991, p. 45.

King, Mary Sarah, *Boston Evening Globe,* Women in Business—Martha Thomas, Amy Spear. Two Engineers, Two Different Approaches, July 19, 1972, p. 61.

King, Mary Sarah, *Electrical Products News,* Martha Thomas: A Lifetime of Achievement, (GTE), March/April 1990, p. 5.

Other

King, Mary Sarah, *Electrical Products News,* Martha Thomas: A Lifetime of Achievement, Thomas, George R., letter to Linda Wasmer Smith dated February 20, 1994.

Thomas, Martha Jane Bergin, *Interview with Linda Wasmer Smith,* conducted February 7, 1994.

Sketch by Linda Wasmer Smith

D'Arcy Wentworth Thompson
1860–1948
Scottish zoologist

Sir D'Arcy Wentworth Thompson combined extensive knowledge of natural history with insight into mathematics to develop a new approach to evolution and the growth of living things. His 1917 work, *On Growth and Form,* represented a significant departure from the zoology of his day and has since contributed to embryology, taxonomy, paleontology, and ecology, as well as influencing artists, engineers, architects, and poets. Thompson was also trained in the classics from a young age, and he applied his knowledge of ancient Greek culture, thought, and natural history to his *A Glossary of Greek Birds* and *A Glossary of Greek Fishes.*

Thompson was born in Edinburgh, Scotland, on May 2, 1860. His father, also named D'Arcy Wentworth Thompson, was a classical master at the Edinburgh Academy, and then a professor of Greek at Queens College, Galway. The elder Thompson wrote books expressing liberal ideas, and delivered the Lowell Institute Lectures in Boston in the late 1860s, in which he espoused the cause of women's rights. Thompson's mother, Fanny Gamgee, who died when he was born, came from a family that was active in medicine and science. Young D'Arcy thus received a scientific background from his maternal grandfather as he was growing up, and a classical education from his father. As a result, he could read, speak, and write Greek and Latin fluently.

Thompson attended Edinburgh Academy, and studied medicine at the University of Edinburgh. He showed a bent for natural history, and at the age of 19, published papers in science journals on hydroid taxonomy—or classification of invertebrate animals including corals, sea anemones, and jellyfishes—and on a Pleistocene fossil seal. He left Edinburgh for Trinity College, Cambridge, where he supplemented his finances by tutoring in Greek. While there, he translated Hermann Müller's German work, *Die Befruchtung der Blumen durch Insekten,* as *The Fertilisation of Flowers;* it was published with a preface by the naturalist Charles Darwin, about which Thompson later said, as quoted in *Science* magazine, "[It] is of peculiar interest as one of the very last of his writings."

Embarks on a Career as a Zoologist

In 1884, at the age of 24, Thompson was appointed professor of biology at University College in Dundee, where he established a teaching museum of zoology. When the college was united with the University of St. Andrews in 1897, he became the chair of natural history. He would hold that position until his death at the age of eighty-eight. Beginning in 1885, Thompson wrote scientific papers on a wide variety of zoological subjects, including the morphology of vertebrate limbs, classification of the chameleon, the nervous system and blood cells of cyclostomes (jawless fishes including hagfishes and lampreys), the newly discovered ear of the sunfish, and a fossil mammal thought to be related to whales, which he showed to be more similar to seals. He also continued to work on such varied subjects as the bones of the parrot's skull, a rare cuttlefish, the arrangement of feathers on the giant hummingbird, and a systematic survey of the sea spiders.

In 1896, when a dispute arose between Great Britain and the United States over the fur-seal fisheries in the Bering Sea, Thompson was sent to Alaska to investigate the situation. After expeditions to the Pribilof Islands, he represented Britain at the International Conference in Washington the following year. In recognition of the success of his undertaking, he was awarded the title of Companion of the Order of the Bath in 1898. In that year, he was appointed scientific adviser to the Fishery Board for Scotland, a position he held until the board was dissolved in

1939. Thompson issued a number of scientific reports in which he made biological, statistical, and hydrographical contributions. Starting in 1902, he began to serve as the British representative to the newly founded International Council for the Study of the Sea and regularly attended meetings in Copenhagen and elsewhere in Europe until 1947. During this time, he was chair of the statistical committee and editor of the *Bulletin Statistique,* writing many papers on oceanography and fishery statistics.

In 1895 Thompson drew upon his predilection for the classics and published his *A Glossary of Greek Birds.* Here, he revealed a learned understanding of ancient Greek literature, as well as medieval and modern ornithology. For many years afterward, he worked on a companion book, *A Glossary of Greek Fishes,* which was finally published in 1947, and which referred not only to fish mentioned in classic Greek literature, but also to other species listed under the heading of fish by the ancients, such as crabs, cuttlefish, and oysters. In both of these books, Thompson identified the bird or fish not only from a scientific point of view, but also classically, in terms of its interest to the poets and its relation to religion, folklore, and art. In 1910, he had issued an annotated translation of Aristotle's *Historia Animalium;* he delivered the Herbert Spencer Lecture, "On Aristotle as a Biologist," three years later. He continued to express his dual interest in these subjects in his presidential address to the Classical Association, entitled *Science and the Classics,* which was published in *Nature.* In this lecture he drew connections between the two disciplines: "Science and the classics—both alike continually enlarge our curiosity, and multiply our inlets to happiness."

Blazes a New Trail in Biology

In 1908, Thompson published a paper in *Nature,* "On the Shapes of Eggs and the Causes Which Determine Them," which indicated a new direction in his explanation of morphology using mathematical interpretations. He continued with this concept in 1911 in his presidential address to section D of the British Association, entitled "Magnalia Naturae; or the Greater Problems of Biology." He had now departed from standard zoology, and its occupation with comparative morphology and evolution, and was blazing a new trail in which mathematics and physics were the tools for interpreting biological phenomena. Thompson's influential book *On Growth and Form* appeared in 1917, presenting his unorthodox new principles and explaining them with numerous illustrative examples from ancient and modern texts. The book deals with the development of form and structure in living things and how physical forces influence them in their lifetime. He demonstrated some of his ideas by showing that various natural phenomena, such as the repeated six-sided shape of cells in a bee honeycomb, the spirals in the arrangement of seeds in a sunflower, the curve in snailshells, and even the flight of a moth attracted to light, follow mathematical principles. Thompson postulated that these and other geometrical patterns evolved as ideal adaptations in the development of the organisms. By means of graphs of grid coordinates based on logarithmic projections, he compared the changes in growth and shape of various organisms during their development. In one instance, with respect to the structure of bone, he showed that the trabeculae, or lattice-work, of calcium deposition, is aligned in the most efficient placement to cope with the stresses placed on the bone. He proved this point by comparing the metal cross structures of a hoisting crane with the internal structure of a femur.

Thompson married Maureen Drury in 1901, and they had three daughters. As his career progressed, he was received many honors. He was elected to the Royal Society in 1916, was its vice president from 1931 to 1933, and received the Darwin Medal in 1946. In 1928 he became president of the Classical Association of England and Wales, and from 1934 to 1939, he was president of the Royal Society of Edinburgh. Thompson was knighted in 1937, and a year later, the Linnean Society presented him with the Linnean gold medal. He delivered the Lowell Lectures in Boston in 1936, seventy-nine years after his father had had this honor. In 1946, he flew to India as a member of the Royal Society delegation to the Indian Science Congress at Delhi, but contracted pneumonia soon afterward and never recovered. Thompson died on June 21, 1948. He was remembered by his colleague, Robert Chambers, in *Science* magazine, as a "towering figure with massive sculptured head and [long] flowing beard," who had a ready sense of humor and a penchant for eloquent oratory.

SELECTED WRITINGS BY THOMPSON:

Books

Die Befruchtung der Blumen durch Insekten, 1873, as The Fertilisation of Flowers, Macmillan, 1883.
A Glossary of Greek Birds, Clarendon Press, 1895, new edition, 1936.
On Growth and Form, Cambridge University Press, 1917, new edition, 1942.
A Glossary of Greek Fishes, Oxford University Press, 1947.

Periodicals

Nature, On the Shapes of Eggs and the Causes Which Determine Them, 78, 1908, pp. 111–113.
Nature, Magnalia Naturae; or the Greater Problems of Biology, 87, 1911, pp. 325–328; reprinted in Smithsonian Institution Annual Report, 1911.
Nature, Science and the Classics, May 25, 1929.

FURTHER READING:

Books

Clark, W. E. LeGros and P. B. Medawar, editors, *Essays on Growth and Form,* Clarendon Press, 1945.

Periodicals

Chambers, Robert, *Science,* Sir D'Arcy Wentworth Thompson, C.B., F.R.S. (1860–1948), 109, 1949, pp. 138–139, 151.

Dobell, C., *Obituary Notices of Fellows of the Royal Society,* D'Arcy Wentworth Thompson, 6, 1949, pp. 599–617.

Hutchinson, G. E, *American Scientist,* In Memoriam, D'Arcy Wentworth Thompson, 36, 1948.

Sketch by Maurice Bleifeld

Kenneth Lane Thompson
1943–

American computer scientist

Kenneth Lane Thompson studied programming languages, operating systems, and computer games. He was one of the inventors of the UNIX operating system, perhaps the most widely used computer system in the world. He also invented the C programming language and co-developed several chess-playing machines.

UNIX is well known for its simplicity, generality, and portability. Thompson conceived of the system in the late 1960s, and together with **Dennis Ritchie**, a colleague working with him at Bell Laboratories, developed UNIX as an alternative to the old batch programming systems that dominated the industry at the time. Although Thompson created UNIX while working at Bell Labs, the system was developed independently by the two programmers. It was very unusual because it was not commercially marketed like other systems. Instead UNIX gained in popularity through a network of researchers long before it was released commercially, and it has had one of the longest gestation periods of any computer program. UNIX is now believed to be one of the most widely used systems in the world, supporting over twenty million dollars of equipment.

Kenneth Thompson was born on February 4, 1943 in New Orleans, Louisiana, the son of Lewis Elwood Thompson, a fighter pilot in the U.S. Navy, and Anna Hazel Lane Thompson. He majored in electrical engineering at the University of California, Berkeley, also working at the computer center as well as participating in a work-study program at the General Dynamics Corporation. Thompson received his B.S. in electrical engineering in 1965 and his M.S. in electrical engineering in 1966, both from Berkeley.

Though Thompson's formal education was in electronic hardware and he built a lot of computers, he was very accomplished in developing computer software, and this is what he pursued professionally. After receiving his master's degree, Thompson went to work for the Computing Science Research Center at Bell Laboratories in New Jersey. He married his wife Bonnie on July 2, 1967, and they had one son, Corey. Bell Labs was famous for its research productivity, and for the unconventional looks, dress, and work habits of some of its scientists. Thompson fitted in well—bearded, bespectacled, and long-haired, he wore a tee-shirt in one published picture. His work habits were also unusual, and he would sometimes put in thirty hours in a row without sleep while working on a project.

Inventing the Operating System UNIX

One of Thompson's greatest achievements at Bell Labs was inventing and then developing the UNIX with Ritchie. A computer operating system manages the housekeeping functions within a computer. By enabling the user to create, open, edit, and close data files, as well as move data from a disk to the screen or printer, and to store data on disks in addition to activating and using other programs, an operating system makes computers easy to run and fast. While at Bell Labs in the late 1960s, Thompson had been assigned to work on developing such a multitasking and multiuser system. Together with engineers from General Electric and the Massachusetts Institute of Technology (MIT), Thompson and other Bell Lab programmers began working on what was called Multics.

This multitasking and multiuser system would contrast in important ways with existing batch-operation computers. Batch computers required a user to create a stack of prepunched data cards which were then run through the computer at one time. During this process, the computer could only apply its programming abilities to the one user's stack of cards, requiring all other users to wait for their jobs to get done. After waiting an hour or longer a user would get a printout of results on paper. If users wanted to make any changes after seeing the results on the printouts, they would have to punch out another stack of cards and wait to resubmit them to the computer for processing. Getting the results from simple changes in a data request could take a long time.

On the other hand, multitasking, multiuser computer systems would be structured in such a way that the flow of data inside the computer would allow it to process many jobs at once for numerous users. The benefits were obvious: users could get their results back quickly and get much more work done. Also, if a computer screen terminal was used as an input and output device, users could key their requests into the terminal, and the computer could display its response to the requests on the screen. Changes and revisions could be made immediately, while the computer could still run other programs. Multitasking, multiuser computer systems like UNIX have replaced batch processing almost completely, and when Thompson invented the program at Bell Labs in 1969, he started the ball rolling to create that change. In late 1988, American Telephone & Telegraph (AT&T) licensed its millionth UNIX system.

The Cold War Adventures of a Chess-Playing Computer

In 1978 Thompson stopped working on UNIX and began other projects. Some of his later projects included another operating system called Plan 9, and computer chess. Chess had been one Thompson's boyhood hobbies, and he carried it into his adult years by making computers and computer programs that could play chess. One of these programs was so good that it became three-time American champion. Thompson also built a chess-playing computer, which he named "Belle." Besides programming, Thompson was also involved in teaching computing. During a 1975 sabbatical he taught upper division and graduate courses in computer science, including a seminar on the UNIX operating system, at the University of California at Berkeley. On another break in 1988, he taught computer science at the University of Sydney in Australia.

In 1993, after working for years on computer chess and another operating systems, Thompson began to work on digital audio encoding. He has received a number of awards for his contributions to computer programming, including the famous Turing award in 1983 from the Association for Computing Machinery, which he shared with Ritchie. The citation for the Turing award read as follows: "The success of the UNIX system stems from its tasteful selection of a few key ideas and their elegant implementation. The model of the UNIX system has led a generation of software designers to new ways of thinking about programming. The genius of the UNIX system is its framework, which enables programmers to stand on the work of others." Lane was elected to the National Academy of Sciences in 1985.

Lane is now a distinguished staff member at Lucent Technologies, the parent company of Bell Labs. Bell Labs is considered the most famous research and development and organization in the world.

SELECTED WRITINGS BY THOMPSON:

Periodicals

Communications of the ACM, The UNIX time-sharing system, Volume 17.7, July 1974, pp. 365–375.
Bell System Technical Journal, UNIX time-sharing system: UNIX implementation, Volume 57.6, 1978, pp. 1931–1946.

FURTHER READING:

Books

Slater, Robert, *Portraits in Silicon,* MIT Press, 1987.

Periodicals

Kolata, Gina, *Science,* Chess-Playing Computer Seized by Customs, Volume 216, June 25, 1982, p. 1392.

Kolata, Gina, *Communications of the ACM,* Dennis Ritchie and Ken L. Thompson: 1983 ACM A. M. Turing Award Recipients, Volume 27.8, August 1984, p. 757.
Rosenblatt, Alfred, *Electronics,* 1982 Award for Achievement: Dennis M. Ritchie and Ken Thompson, October 20, 1982, pp. 108–111.
Rosenblatt, Alfred, *Electronic Business,* The Outlook for UNIX, June 26, 1989, p. 30.

Other

Thompson, Kenneth, *Telephone interview with Patrick Moore conducted February 14,* 1994.

Sketch by Lori De Milto

George Paget Thomson
1892–1975
English experimental physicist

George Paget Thomson is known for providing direct experimental proof of French physicist **Louis Victor Broglie**'s theory of matter waves, which states that matter has wave-like properties in addition to characteristics associated with particles. For this discovery, Thomson was awarded the 1937 Nobel Prize in physics jointly with the American physicist **Clinton Davisson**, who had independently and coincidentally reached the same findings using different methods. Thomson is also recognized for his contribution to the study of neutrons and their use in nuclear chain reactions.

Thomson was born in Cambridge, England, on May 3, 1892, the only son of **J. J. Thomson**, a Nobel Prize-winning physicist, and Rose Paget, the daughter of Sir George Paget, a distinguished professor of medicine. Thomson's mother had met her husband while she was one of his students in the Cavendish Physical Laboratory. Not surprisingly, given the family tradition of learning, particularly in the physical sciences, Thomson showed an interest in science at a young age. His first recorded scientific inquiry is said to have concerned the twisting motion of a swing that hung in his nursery. Between the ages of nine and thirteen, Thomson was sent to the King's College Choir School, an experience that did not inculcate him with any deep-seated feeling for music. Instead, Thomson was interested in literature, ships (especially war ships), and model ship building.

At Perse School, where he was sent in 1895, he demonstrated a talent for rugby, but, although he was physically agile, he never particularly enjoyed team sports. When the time came for Thomson's graduation, his headmaster advised him to study classics, but Thomson

George Paget Thomson

decided on a career in physics. In 1910, he entered Trinity College, Cambridge, as a Scholar, taking mathematics and physics. There, he distinguished himself by becoming a Major Scholar and attaining first-class honors in mathematics at the end of his second year and the same in physics at the end of his third.

Works at Cavendish under His Father

Upon graduating, Thomson went to work at the Cavendish Physical Laboratory with his father. He researched radicals, the single replaceable atoms of an element's reactive atomic form, and also grew interested in aerodynamics. He became a fellow and mathematical lecturer of Corpus Christi College, Cambridge, in 1914. Though he held these positions through 1922, Thomson left Cambridge for the duration of World War I.

The war gave Thomson an opportunity to develop his interest in aerodynamics. He served in France as second lieutenant and was then transferred to the Royal Aircraft Factory in Farnborough, England. There, he did more aerodynamics work, which, along with his earlier work at Cavendish, earned him the 1916 Smith Prize. He also learned to fly while in Farnborough. For a brief period, he was transferred to the British War Mission in the United States.

When the war ended, Thomson worked for the Aircraft Manufacturing Co. He wrote his first book, *Applied Aerodynamics,* before returning to Cambridge in 1919.

There, he worked with positive and anode rays and discovered the existence of the two isotopes of lithium. Thomson left Cambridge in 1922 to accept an appointment as professor of natural philosophy at the University of Aberdeen. He found the college stimulating, both professionally and socially. The University's principal, Sir George Adam Smith, had a daughter, Kathleen, whom Thomson admired. They married and had four children: John, David, Clare, and Rose. Kathleen died prematurely in 1941.

At Aberdeen, Thomson continued his work with positive rays and also pursued a new direction of study. His presence at a 1926 meeting of the British Association for the Advancement of Science led him to consider the radical new matter waves theory being propounded by de Broglie. (Davisson, the physicist with whom Thomson would later share the Nobel Prize, was also at the gathering though the pair did not meet.) The meeting inspired Thomson to try to establish experimental proof of de Broglie's hypothesis.

Experimentally Proves Theory of Matter Waves

Thomson believed that he could use the same methods that had been used just three years previously to prove the wave character of X rays in order to demonstrate the same characteristic of matter. De Broglie had postulated that electrons have a wavelength proportional to their mass and velocity. In order to verify this, Thomson thought he could send a beam of electrons through a diffracting medium that would cause the electrons to bend or scatter, producing an interference pattern, if they did possess wave characteristics. However, because the wavelength that de Broglie predicted for electrons was extremely short, the diffraction apparatus required for the experiment would have to be minute. Thomson thought of using a film of metallic crystals: because crystals are composed of layers of atoms in parallel rows, they would act as a grate through which the electron beam could be shot. As he sent the electron beam through the crystal grate to a photographic plate beyond, Thomson was able to record a pattern extremely similar to that obtained from short-wave light under similar conditions. Calculating the electron's wavelength from this pattern, Thomson confirmed that it was precisely as de Broglie had predicted.

Thomson's reputation was sealed in 1930 when he was elected to London's Royal Society as a fellow. That same year, he was offered the post of professor of physics at London's Imperial College of Science and Technology. Thomson took an interest in the work of his department's various subdivisions, particularly its technical optics section, which sparked his interest in the recently invented electron microscope. He also worked hard to solidify the department's reputation for excellence by gathering about him some of the best minds in physics. Many of these individuals devoted themselves to continuing and extending Thomson's research into electron diffraction, using, for example, techniques of high voltage diffraction. Thomson summarized these developments in his textbook *Theory and Practice of Electron Diffraction,* which he wrote with

William Cochrane. In addition to guiding the work of the department, Thomson turned his attention to nuclear physics, which had been revolutionized by the recent discovery of neutrons, positrons, and artificial radioactivity.

With his colleague J. A. Saxton, Thomson bombarded positrons (positively charged particles possessing the same mass and magnitude of charge as an electron), hoping to produce radioactivity. He invented the apparatus that they used to separate positrons from negative beta-rays. Thomson also closely supervised a series of experiments conducted by P. B. Moon and J. R. Tillman to measure the velocity of neutrons. Before these experiments could be completed, war broke out and Thomson considered the possibility of a uranium chain reaction. As P. B. Moon quoted in *Biographical Memoirs of Fellows of the Royal Society,* Thomson noted: "The military possibilities were sufficiently obvious to make me ask . . . [the] Rector of Imperial College and . . . Chairman of the Committee for the Scientific Study of Air Defence, if we ought not to do something about it." Thomson obtained a ton of uranium oxide to undertake a series of experiments at Imperial College. With the uranium oxide, Thomson carried out experiments with slowed down neutrons. His conclusion that a nuclear chain reaction could not be achieved easily or rapidly was contained in a report submitted to the Air Ministry in 1940.

Heads Government's Maud Committee during War

In April of 1940, Thomson formed and headed the Maud Committee, which fostered relationships among nuclear scientists and was the first atomic energy committee in England. By the end of July, the committee had investigated the feasibility of making an atomic bomb and the potential of uranium as a source of power; they reported their findings to the Ministry of Aircraft. Thomson was given the title scientific liaison officer and sent to Canada to investigate the possibility of transferring the British atomic project to Ottawa. He recommended that the move should go ahead. The project was realized at Chalk River in Ottawa under the leadership of English atomic physicist **John D. Cockcroft**.

Back in England, Thomson was appointed deputy chair of the Radio Board and scientific advisor to the Air Ministry, a post that involved Thomson in work on a possible hydrogen bomb. He embarked on a series of experiments at his laboratory at Imperial College. The difficulty was determining a way to control the nuclear fusion reaction. Thomson took out a provisional patent covering his idea, which employed a ring discharge. Work began on developing the paper, but Thomson soon realized the difficulty of laboring in secret with a large group. In 1951, the project was transferred to the Aldermaston Court research laboratory of Associated Electrical Industries Ltd. for security reasons. Thomson continued working on the project and, according to Professor T. E. Allibone, the director of the laboratory, "his support was a tremendous help in boosting morale," quoted Moon. During this period, Thomson was also active in scientific societies. He was vice president of the Royal Society from 1949 to 1951 and chair of both the Sectional Committee for Physics and the Warren Research Fund.

Appointed Master of Corpus Christi College, Cambridge

In 1952, Thomson returned to Cambridge as master of his old alma mater, Corpus Christi College. He threw himself wholeheartedly into the job, overseeing major restorations of the campus, and took a keen interest in the college's finances. He was a genial and enthusiastic host who particularly enjoyed entertaining undergraduates. Moon quoted Michael McCrum, one of Thomson's colleagues and friends, on Thomson during this period: "[H]is well-stored practical memory, his wide-ranging, inquisitive mind combined with an insatiable zest for argument to make his table talk fascinating."

During his years as master, Thomson was also active on the lecture circuit, speaking to both specialist and general audiences on topics that included the relationship of physics to technology, the education of scientists, and nuclear power. He became more involved exploring the implications of the latter as a member of a committee of the Pugwash Group, a collection of scientists who met regularly to discuss various topics such as the easing of international tensions, the establishment of systems of mutual security, nuclear proliferation and disarmament, and the role of scientists in influencing debate.

In 1958, Thomson, who had been knighted in 1943, was elected president of the Institute of Physics, a position he held until 1960, when he was elected president of the British Association for the Advancement of Science at Cardiff. Thomson was also a member of the Royal Society (he received the Hughes Medal in 1939 and the Royal Medal in 1949), a foreign member of the American Academy of Arts and Sciences and of the Lisbon Academy, and a corresponding member of the Austrian Academy of Sciences. He was an honorary graduate of the University of Aberdeen; University College, Dublin; the University of Lisbon; the University of Sheffield; the University of Wales; the University of Reading; Cambridge University; and Westminster College. Thomson also was an honorary fellow at Trinity and Corpus Christi Colleges, Cambridge, and at Imperial College. He served as master of Corpus Christi until his retirement in 1962. He remained on at Cambridge and kept active both scientifically and socially. He died at the age of eighty-three on September 10, 1975.

SELECTED WRITINGS BY THOMSON:

Books

Applied Aerodynamics, Hodder and Stoughton, 1920.
Conduction of Electricity through Gases, Volumes I and II, Cambridge University Press, 1928, second edition, 1933.

The Atom, Holt, 1930, sixth edition, Oxford University
   Press, 1962.
The Wave Mechanics of the Free Electron, McGraw,
   1930.
Theory and Practice of Electron Diffraction, Macmillan,
   1939.
The Foreseeable Future, Cambridge University Press,
   1955, revised edition, Viking, 1960.
The Inspiration of Science, Oxford University Press,
   1961.
*J. J. Thomson and the Cavendish Laboratory in His
   Day,* Nelson, 1964, Doubleday, 1965, published as
   J. J. Thomson, Discoverer of the Electron, Double-
   day-Anchor, 1966.
The Electron, U.S. Atomic Energy Commission, Office
   of Information Services, 1972.

FURTHER READING:

Books

Biographical Memoirs of Fellows of the Royal Society,
   Volume 23, Royal Society (London), 1977, pp.
   529–556.
Cline, Barbara Lovett, *Men Who Made a New Physics:
   Physicists and the Quantum Theory,* University of
   Chicago Press, 1987, p. 184.
Cline, Barbara Lovett, *Modern Men of Science,* Volume
   I, McGraw, 1968, pp. 479–481.
Weber, Robert L., *Pioneers of Science: Nobel Prize
   Winners in Physics,* Institute of Physics, 1980.

Sketch by Avril McDonald

J. J. Thomson
1856–1940
English physicist

J. J. Thomson

A scientist of diverse interests, J. J. Thomson was
awarded the Nobel Prize in physics in 1906 for his
theoretical and experimental research on the behavior of
electricity in gases. As one consequence of that research,
Thomson discovered the electron in 1897. He also was
interested in a number of other topics, including optics,
magnetism, radioactivity, photoelectricity, and thermionics
(a branch of physics relating to the emission of charged
particles from an incandescent source).

Joseph John Thomson was born at Cheetham Hill, a
suburb of Manchester, England, on December 18, 1856. His
father was a bookseller and publisher who specialized in
antique volumes. J. J., as he was widely known, originally
planned to become an engineer, and arrangements were
made for him to apprentice with a friend of his father's.
When the senior Thomson died in 1870, however, the
family could no longer afford to pay the expense of J. J.'s
apprenticeship, and he enrolled at Owen's College, now the
University of Manchester. Thomson studied mathematics,
physics, and chemistry under a distinguished science
faculty, and with the encouragement of Thomas Baker, a
professor of mathematics, Thomson applied for and won a
scholarship to Baker's alma mater, Trinity College, Cambridge.

Fellowship Brings Thomson to Cambridge for a
Four-Decade Stay

Thomson entered Trinity College in 1876 and majored
in mathematics, beginning an affiliation with Cambridge
University that would last the rest of his life. Although some
of the most exciting and important physical and chemical
research was going on within a few steps of Thomson's
college, he made no attempt to find out about them.
However, his single-minded attention to mathematics was
rewarded when, in 1880, he earned a second place in the
college examination on that subject.

Thomson's first published work dealt with the research
of a fellow scholar at Cambridge whom he had never met,
James Clerk Maxwell. Maxwell had only recently devised
his mathematical theory of electromagnetism, and Thomson
became intrigued by some of its special implications. For
instance, when Thomson analyzed the properties that might

be expected of a charged sphere that is placed in motion, he discovered that the apparent mass of the sphere would increase as a result of its gaining electrical charge. Although Thomson did not pursue this line of research, the finding was clearly a preview of the concept of mass-energy equivalence that would be proposed by **Albert Einstein** a decade later.

In 1881 Thomson was awarded a fellowship that allowed him to stay on at Trinity College. The thesis he wrote in competition for that fellowship involved an analysis of some physical and chemical deductions that could be drawn from some very general mathematical laws, an approach Thomson used frequently in his research. He argued that it is sometimes useful simply to derive the physical implications of mathematical expressions without worrying about the physical reality that might be involved. One advantage of this approach, he said, was that new and unanticipated lines of research might be revealed.

Thomson did not disregard the role of physical reality in his research, however; he also argued that the best way to attack a problem may sometimes be to devise analogies or to construct models of the phenomenon under investigation. An example of this approach was an essay he wrote in 1882 for the Adams Prize competition. The subject of that competition was vortex rings, spinning cloud-like assemblies somewhat similar to smoke rings. Vortex rings were of great interest to scientists toward the end of the nineteenth century because many thought that atoms might consist of such arrangements. Thomson's essay won the prize but, probably more important, it eventually led him into a line of research—electrical discharges in gases—from which he was to produce his greatest accomplishments.

In 1884, Lord Rayleigh retired as Cavendish Professor of Physics—one of the most prestigious chairs of science in the English-speaking world—and he recommended that Thomson be appointed to replace him. Word of the recommendation caused an uproar within the Cambridge scientific community; numerous well-qualified and famous scholars wanted the position for themselves and were outraged that a young man of twenty-eight was being considered for the post. Critics of Thomson's candidacy perceived his background in experimental science as weak since most of his earlier studies and research had been in mathematics or theoretical science. Still, the selection committee, consisting of Lord Kelvin, George Gabriel Stokes, and George Howard Darwin, chose Thomson as Rayleigh's replacement and director of the world-famous Cavendish Laboratory at Cambridge.

Research on Electrical Discharge in Gases Reveals the Electron

The research field to which Thomson now turned was one related to the topic of his Adams Prize essay—electrical discharge in gases—which had become extremely popular among physicists during the preceding decade, largely as the result of the work of Julius Plücker, Johann Wilhelm Hittorf, William Crookes, Eugen Goldstein, and others.

Most experiments followed a common model: an electrical discharge is caused to pass through a gas under very low pressure in a glass tube. Under these circumstances, a glowing beam is observed to follow the electrical discharge from one end of the tube to the other. The beam, called a cathode ray, can be deflected by an electrical or magnetic field superimposed on the tube.

The primary question that remained in the mid–1890s concerned the nature of cathode rays. Were they streams of charged particles, as Crookes and others believed, or were they of the luminiferous ether as most German physicists thought? Thomson turned his attention to the resolution of this question. A key development in his approach to the problem was the development of better equipment; he was able to show, with better vacuums, a decrease in the ambiguous and contradictory results obtained by other researchers. Using improved equipment, Thomson accomplished the deflection of cathode rays by an electrical field, which was strong evidence that the rays did consist of particles.

Thomson then went one step further: he developed an experiment in which cathode rays were deflected by both magnetic and electrical fields. By measuring the angle at which the rays were deflected by such fields of any given magnitudes, he was able to calculate the ratio of the electrical charge to the mass (e/m) for the particles that made up the rays. He found that the value of e/m was the same for any gas used in the experiment (that is, whatever particle it was that made up the cathode rays occurred in all gases and was, therefore, a component of all of the different atoms of which those gases were made).

Thomson also extended his research to other phenomena caused by electrical discharges, such as the discharge from a negatively charged heated wire. He found an occurrence similar to that observed in the original glass tube experiments, in which particles with the same e/m ratio could be detected. He concluded that some fundamental particle with a constant e/m ratio was present in all of these experiments and, hence, was a component of all atoms. The term used by Thomson for these particles, *corpuscle*, was soon replaced by a name suggested earlier by G. J. Stoney, *electron*. Thomson's reports on his discoveries to the British Association in 1889 were so well documented that the existence of a new subatomic particle was almost immediately accepted by scientists worldwide.

Thomson's discovery raised a number of fundamental questions about atomic structure. For nearly a century, scientists had thought of the atom as some kind of indivisible, uniform particle or mass of material, but Thomson had shown that this view was untenable, and that the atom must consist of at least two parts, one of which was the newly discovered electron. To account for his discovery, Thomson proposed a new model of the atom, sometimes referred to as the "plum pudding" atom. In this model, the atom was thought to consist of a cloud of positive charge in which are embedded discrete electrons, much as individual plums are embedded in the traditional

English plum pudding. However, this model was never very successful, and, in the work of Thomson's successor, **Ernest Rutherford**, a better atomic picture would soon evolve.

In recognition of his research on electrical discharges in gases, Thomson was awarded the 1906 Nobel Prize in physics. Two years later, he was knighted for his accomplishments in science. By this time, however, Thomson had gone on to a new field of research, the study of the positively charged "canal" rays that are also produced during electrical discharge in gases. Thomson used a method similar to that with which he discovered the electron, the deflection of canal rays with magnetic and electrical fields. The instrument he developed to accomplish the procedure was the forerunner of today's mass spectrometer, in which particles of differing e/m ratios can be separated from each other.

Thomson's instrumentation eventually became so sophisticated that he was able to separate two isotopes of neon, neon–20 and neon–22, from each other. He was not able to completely interpret the results of this experiment, however, and he eventually turned the work over to one of his graduate students, **Francis Aston**. Aston's continuation of this work resulted not only in a more refined form of the spectrometer, but also in a confirmation that he and Thomson had indeed discovered the first isotopes of a stable element.

Career Concludes with Accomplishments in Teaching and Administration

The work on canal rays marked the end of Thomson's most creative years. His efforts after 1912 focused more on teaching and administration, although he did remain active in research to some extent. He was elected president of the Royal Society in 1915 and was appointed Master of Trinity College in 1918. He resigned as Cavendish professor in the following year, but was then appointed to an honorary chair which allowed him to maintain university privileges. Thomson was succeeded in the Cavendish chair by one of his greatest students, Ernest Rutherford.

Thomson's impact on science was just as notable for his skills as a teacher and administrator. He was responsible for the expansion of the Cavendish Laboratories (on two occasions) as well as for its efficient operation for thirty-five years. A tribute to his talent for finding, educating, and nurturing young researchers is the fact that no less than seven of his students eventually received Nobel Prizes in the sciences. A few years before Thomson's death, he was honored by a dinner given in his honor at Cambridge. The list of guests contained most of the leading figures in physical research of the day. At the dinner, Thomson was given a testimonial signed by more than two hundred friends, students, and colleagues. Thomson died in Cambridge on August 30, 1940, and was laid to rest in Westminster Abbey close to Isaac Newton and Charles Darwin.

SELECTED WRITINGS BY THOMSON:

Books

Treatise on the Motion of Vortex Rings, [London], 1883.
Applications of Dynamics to Physics and Chemistry, [London], 1888.
Notes on Recent Research in Electricity and Magnetism, [Oxford], 1893.
Conduction of Electricity through Gases, [Cambridge], 1903.
The Corpuscular Theory of Matter, [London], 1907.
Rays of Positive Electricity and their Application to Chemical Analysis, [London], 1913.
The Electron in Chemistry, [Philadelphia], 1923.
Recollections and Reflections, [London], 1936.

FURTHER READING:

Books

Jaffe, Bernard, *Crucibles: The Story of Chemistry,* Simon & Schuster, 1957, chapter 12.
Rayleigh, Lord John, *The Life of J. J. Thomson,* [Cambridge], 1943.
Thomson, G. P., *J. J. Thomson and the Cavendish Laboratory in His Day,* [New York], 1965.
Weber, Robert L., *Pioneers of Science: Nobel Prize Winners in Physics,* American Institute of Physics, 1980, pp. 29–30.

Periodicals

McCommack, R., *British Journal of the History of Science,* J. J. Thomson and the Structure of Light, (1967), pp. 362–387.

Sketch by David E. Newton

William Thurston
1946–
American mathematician

William Thurston has combined curiosity with a special ability to imagine higher-dimensional shapes to advance the field of topology. He has made a hypothesis, called Thurston's conjecture, concerning three-dimensional topological shapes and is a leader in what is known as experimental mathematics. His leadership in the new experimental approach to mathematics has opened up new avenues in topology and his efforts to understand higher-dimensional shapes have contributed to theories about the shape and movement of the universe. In 1982, he won the Fields Medal, the highest award in mathematics.

William Paul Thurston was born on October 30, 1946, in Washington, D.C., to Paul and Margaret Martt Thurston. As early as age five, he was fascinated with mathematics, especially by the abacus. As a teenager he loved geometrical puzzles, and at thirteen he discovered an unusual mathematical similarity among the solutions to a "connect-the-dot" game. He imagined that he would use this discovery as a Ph.D. dissertation topic until he learned that it was already a well-known theorem. Also as a teenager, he learned of a hypothesis that three billiard balls moving on an infinitely large, open table would collide not more than three times. Thurston, by visually imagining the table and the movement of the balls, discovered paths in which the balls collided four times and disproved the hypothesis.

Thurston attended New College in Sarasota, Florida, graduating with a degree in mathematics in 1967. He went on to earn his Ph.D. in mathematics from the University of California, Berkeley, in 1972. He spent a year at Princeton University's Institute for Advanced Study and was an assistant professor on a Sloan Fellowship at the Massachusetts Institute of Technology from 1973 to 1974. He then returned to Princeton to become a professor in the Department of Mathematics. He remained there until 1991, when he accepted a position at the University of California, Berkeley.

Topology is the branch of geometry that studies how the shapes of objects change by bending, twisting, and stretching. Objects are considered to be topologically equivalent when they remain mathematically alike even if their shapes are otherwise very different. Thurston specializes in imagining objects in four dimensions—that is, across time—instead of the three dimensions of length, width, and depth. Objects in this fourth dimension are called hypersurfaces. Topology and hypersurfaces are particularly relevant to physics and efforts to explain the shape and movement of the universe. American physicist **Albert Einstein** theorized that the future movement of the universe depends on its current shape and suggested that the universe is four-dimensional. If time is part of the shape of the universe, questions then arise about what kind of an object the universe might be. These are some of the questions topology is helping physics answer, and Thurston has made important contributions to speculations about four-dimensional objects.

Thurston made a conjecture—an unproven theory—that suggests a method for describing all three-dimensional topological shapes with the rigid structures of geometry. In 1980, Thurston presented surprising new evidence concerning the fundamental shapes of four-dimensional objects. Prior to his presentation, most mathematicians believed that four-dimensional hypersurfaces could not be described with the same shapes used for three-dimensional objects, but Thurston's work demonstrated that hypersurfaces can be described with the three fundamental shapes (elliptical,

hyperbolic, and flat) and five hybrids of these shapes. Thurston is also a leader in a new approach called experimental mathematics. Instead of using the classic approach of deducing mathematical proofs with step-by-step logic, experimental mathematics uses computers to run experiments. Thurston told *New Scientist* that computers are now powerful enough to be of use to mathematicians, and he believes computers allow them to address more complicated phenomena. He wants to see these mathematical experiments receive more scientific recognition, but many in the mathematics community continue to question the usefulness of this work.

In 1976, the American Mathematical Society presented Thurston with the Oswald Veblen Prize in Geometry. In 1979, he received the Alan T. Waterman Award by the National Science Foundation. In 1980 and 1981, he was Ulam Visiting Professor of Mathematics at the University of Colorado, Boulder. His contributions to mathematics were recognized in 1982 when he was awarded the Fields Medal (considered the equivalent of the Nobel Prize) by the International Mathematics Union. In 1992, he began directing the Mathematical Sciences Research Institute in Berkeley. He also acts as mathematics editor-in-chief for *Quantum Magazine*. Thurston married Rachel A. Findley on August 27, 1967. They have three children but were divorced in June of 1993.

SELECTED WRITINGS BY THURSTON:

Periodicals

Topology, A Generalization of the Reeb Stability Theorem, Volume 13, 1974, pp. 347–352.
Annals of Mathematics, Examples of Unknotted Curves which Bound Only Surfaces of High Genus within their Convex Hulls, Volume 105, 1977, pp. 527–538.
Advances in Mathematics, New Proofs of Some Results of Nielsen, Volume 56, 1985 pp. 203–247.
Memoirs of the American Mathematical Society, A Norm of the Homology of Three-Manifolds, Volume 339, 1986, pp. 99–130.

FURTHER READING:

Periodicals

Bown, William, *New Scientist,* New-Wave Mathematics, August 3, 1991, pp. 33–37.
Guillen, Michael, *Esquire,* The Shape of Things to Come, December 1984, pp. 100–103.

Sketch by David N. Ford

Ping King Tien
1919–
American electronic engineer

Ping King Tien has made a number of significant contributions to the fields of microwave technology and integrated optics. In recognition of his work in the latter area, he was awarded the Morris N. Liebmann Award by the Institute of Electrical and Electronic Engineers in 1979. Yet Tien's research during a long career at AT&T Bell Laboratories has touched on almost every branch of modern electronics, and other of his fundamental findings have dealt with acoustic wave phenomena, superconductivity, lasers, microfabrication, and high-speed integrated circuits.

Tien was born on August 2, 1919, in Shan-Yu, China, then a small village in the province of Chekiang. He was the youngest of three sons born to Neu-Shing Tien, a banker, and his wife, Chao-Sing Yun Tien. At the age of eight, Tien moved with his family to Shanghai. Of his later childhood, Tien recalled in a letter to Linda Wasmer Smith, "My father decided that one of the boys should be an engineer and sent me to l'Institut Technique Franco-Chinois in Shanghai for my middle school. I was not very good at the elementary school. Somehow, I did remarkably well at the Institut. I was ranked the first in the class for the entire middle school."

From there, Tien went to the National Central University at Chunking, where he began work on an electrical engineering degree. Of his college years, Tien wrote in his letter, "I would say I was inspired by science or mathematics, for the first time, in the class of the calculus of integration and differentiation. I was intrigued by the ways the differentials and the integrals are defined. They are so abstract and yet so accurate." Tien received his bachelor's degree in 1942.

In 1947 Tien immigrated to the United States to attend Stanford University; he later became a naturalized citizen. For his thesis, he invented a new mechanism for the amplification of microwave signals. He obtained an M.S. in electrical engineering in 1948 and a Ph.D. in 1951. As one version of Tien's later résumé proudly asserted, "At Stanford University, he met Miss Nancy N. Y. Chen and married her in 1952. They now have two daughters, Emily and Julia Tien. Their two daughters and sons-in-law studied at Stanford University. It is a Stanford University family."

Advances Microwave Technology and Integrated Optics

The year after his graduation, Tien joined the research division of the communication principles department at AT&T Bell Labs. His early work there focused primarily on microwaves, which are a relatively short kind of electromagnetic wave. One application of microwaves is the carrying of information for telephone systems. Tien made some critical calculations related to traveling-wave tubes, which are used to generate microwave signals. The practical theories that resulted from his esoteric calculations were basic to the development of improved microwave tubes.

In the ensuing years, it became apparent that light waves held even greater potential than microwaves as a telecommunications carrier. Tien's interests shifted accordingly. In the late 1960s and early 1970s, he became a pioneer in the emerging discipline of integrated optics. Until this time, research on lasers and their applications had been conducted on optical benches, where beams were sent through the air from component to component, and lenses and mirrors were used to change a beam's size or direction. This classical approach was not without its problems; results could be affected by such extraneous variables as temperature change and mechanical vibration. So the development of a miniature form of laser-beam circuitry represented an important advance. Tien was a co-organizer of the first topical meeting on integrated optics, held in 1974.

Waveguides are devices designed to confine and direct electromagnetic waves, including light waves. During the 1970s, Tien was one of the first scientists to recognize the potential of thin-film waveguides, devices built from a transparent material measuring only about one micrometer—less than a ten-thousandth of an inch thick. He also invented a prism coupler, a device that can be used to make the light from a laser beam travel within a thin-film waveguide. In all, Tien holds thirty-five patents and has published more than fifty papers in the course of a remarkably productive career.

Tien was awarded the Achievement Award of the Chinese Institute of Engineers in 1966. He has been elected a member of the National Academy of Sciences and the National Academy of Engineering, and he is a fellow of the Institute of Electrical and Electronic Engineers and the Optical Society of America. In 1983, he was honored with a chaired professorship at Shanghai Jiao Tong University in China, and he has traveled and lectured extensively in his native country. He currently maintains an office as an emeritus fellow at AT&T Bell Labs in Holmdel, New Jersey.

SELECTED WRITINGS BY TIEN:

Periodicals

Bell Laboratories Record, Integrated Optics: Wave of the Future, December 1980, pp. 371–378.
Bell Laboratories Record, Integrated Optics: The Components, January 1981, pp. 8–13.
Bell Laboratories Record, Integrated Optics: Putting It All Together, February 1981, pp. 38–45.

FURTHER READING:

Books

Millman, S., editor, *A History of Engineering and Science in the Bell System: Communications Sciences (1925–1980),* AT&T Bell Laboratories, 1984.

Other

Millman, S., editor, *A History of Engineering and Science in the Bell System: Communications Sciences (1925–1980),* AT&T Archives, résumé.

Millman, S., editor, *A History of Engineering and Science in the Bell System: Communications Sciences (1925–1980),* Tien, Ping King, letter to Linda Wasmer Smith dated March 1, 1994.

Sketch by Linda Wasmer Smith

J. Tyson Tildon
1931–

American biochemist

Discoverer of Coenzyme A Tranferase Deficiency, a disease of infants, J. Tyson Tildon and has also made major contributions to the establishment of the Sudden Infant Death Syndrome (SIDS) Institute at the University of Maryland School of Medicine. His research interests include developmental neurochemistry and the processes that control metabolism.

James Tyson Tildon was born April 7, 1931, in Baltimore, Maryland. He received his B.S. degree in chemistry from Morgan State College in 1954 and then worked for five years as a research assistant at Sinai Hospital, where he developed and used biochemical techniques to study vitamin deficiencies in humans and animal models. Subsequently, he spent a year as a Fulbright scholar at the Institut de Biologie Physico-Chimique in Paris and, upon his return, matriculated to the doctoral program in biochemistry at Johns Hopkins University. After receiving his Ph.D. in 1965, Tildon accepted a two-year postdoctoral fellowship at Brandeis University, where his studies included an examination of how cells assume specialized functions during development. Tildon returned to Baltimore in 1967 to assume the post of assistant professor in the Department of Chemistry at Goucher College. The following year, he became research assistant professor in the Department of Pediatrics at the University of Maryland School of Medicine, and, in 1969, assistant professor in the Department of Biological Chemistry. He has been a full professor of pediatrics since 1974 and a professor of biological chemistry since 1982. Tildon has also served as director of the Carter Clinical Laboratories for six years and director of pediatric research in the medical school's Department of Pediatrics for nine. In addition, he was a visiting scientist in the Laboratory of Developmental Biochemistry at the University of Groningen in the Netherlands, where he did research in the developmental neurobiology.

Among Tildon's contributions is the discovery of Coenzyme A (or CoA) Transferase Deficiency in infants. In his research, he demonstrated that the brains of infants use organic molecules called ketone bodies as an energy source during their first several weeks of life, disproving the previously held theory that glucose was the major energy source of the human brain at all ages of life. Tildon was also instrumental in establishing the SIDS Institute at the University of Maryland, one of the largest research programs dedicated to the study of SIDS, a disorder that causes an infant to abruptly stop breathing. Included in the discoveries made at the institute are those of researcher Robert G. Meny, who found that babies suffered bradycardia, or abnormally slow heartbeat, before they stopped breathing. This finding has stimulated new research into the role of the heart in SIDS.

Tildon's interests extend beyond medicine and biochemistry and into other realms of research. In his book *The Anglo-Saxon Agony,* he points out that members of Western civilization rely predominately on sight and hearing to gather information while ignoring the more personal senses of taste, smell, and touch. Rather than integrating all of the brain's responses to stimuli, Tildon suggests, the Anglo-Saxon approach is to separate thinking and feeling in an effort to be dispassionate. Yet, by excluding the emotional component, he writes, westerners fail to understand fully the human condition.

Among the many societies Tildon belongs to are Sigma Xi, the American Chemical Society, the Association for the Advancement of Science, the American Society for Biochemistry and Molecular Biology, and the Society for Experimental Biology and Medicine. He received the Maryland State Senate Citation for his work with SIDS in 1983, the City of Baltimore Citizen Citation in 1986, the Baltimore Chapter of the National Technical Association's Joseph S. Tyler, Jr. Award for Achievement in Science in 1986, the National Association of Negro Business and Professional Women's Club's Community Service Award in 1987, and the Humanitarian Award from the Associated Black Charities in 1991. In addition, he has served on several boards of directors, including those of the Mental Health Association of Metropolitan Baltimore, the Maryland Academy of Sciences, and the Associated Black Charities.

SELECTED WRITINGS BY TILDON:

Books

The Anglo-Saxon Agony, Whitmore Publishing Co., 1972.

Sudden Infant Death Syndrome, Academic Press, 1983.

Periodicals

Archives of Biochemistry and Biophysics, CoA Transfer-
    ase in the Brain and Other Mammalian Tissues,
    Volume 148, 1972, p. 382.
Journal of Clinical Investigation, Succinyl-CoA: 3-Keto-
    acid CoA-Transferase Deficiency—A Cause for Ke-
    toacidosis in Infancy, Volume 51, 1972, p. 493.

FURTHER READING:

Periodicals

Tildon, J. Tyson, *Interview with Marc Kusinitz,* con-
    ducted on April 5, 1994.

Sketch by Marc Kusinitz

Stephen P. Timoshenko
1878–1972
American mechanical engineer

Stephen P. Timoshenko was a specialist in theoretical
and applied mechanics whose research in the theory of
elasticity, vibration, structures, and strength of materials is
documented in a dozen textbooks. His works have been
published around the world in thirty-eight languages. An
effective teacher who coupled a thorough theoretical foundation with practical understanding of applications, he
personally instructed over ten thousand students during his
fifty-year career. After immigrating to America, he worked
to improve American engineering education by introducing
new topics into the stagnant curriculum. He was a member
of the Academy of Sciences of the United States, Russia, the
Ukraine, Poland, and France.

Stephen Prokofievitch Timoshenko was born in a small
Ukrainian town near Kiev on December 23, 1878. His
father, Prokop Timoshenko, had been a surveyor but
became a farmer so he could stay home with his family. His
mother, Josefina Jacovleva Sarnevskaja Timoshenko, was of
Polish extraction and had completed a gymnasium education, which was unusual for a woman. Inspired by yearly
trips to Kiev, his childhood dream was to build railroads.
Timoshenko was educated at home by private tutors until
the age of ten, when he entered the realschule in Romny, a
town twenty miles from his home. During the school year,
Timoshenko lived with his grandmother, but he spent his
summers on the farm. Although he learned easily and
helped explain material to his classmates, he was uncom-

fortable in class, fearing that he would fail to answer
correctly if called upon. He loved to read; one weekend he
read Jules Verne's *The Mysterious Island,* feigning illness
on Monday to finish it. When Timoshenko graduated in
1896, he applied for admission to the Institute of Engineers
of Ways of Communication in St. Petersburg. Despite
apprehension about the entrance exams, he scored among
the top forty of the seven hundred applicants and easily won
admission. When Timoshenko was fourteen, his father had
bought one of the farms he had been leasing, and the boy
helped plan and construct a new house for the family. The
experience, which even included making the bricks, proved
to be very useful during his summer work for a railroad in
1899 and 1900. In 1900, Timoshenko took the first of many
trips abroad when the institute allowed some students to
serve at its exhibit at the International Exposition in Paris.
During a six-week period, he traveled through Germany,
France, Switzerland, and Austria, and spent three weeks
working at a construction site he had learned about at the
exposition.

After graduating in 1901, Timoshenko spent the
following year in required military service, part of which
included a period of study in mathematics back at the
institute. Since he had volunteered for military service upon
graduation, he was extended privileges over draftees and
was free of much of the assigned work. In order to occupy
himself, he invented a bridge made of 3.5-inch poles and
telegraph wire that was light enough to be carried by two
men but could support the load of a twenty-five-member
platoon. Upon completing his military service in 1902,
Timoshenko married Alexandra Archangelskaja, a medical
student. Money was short, and they shared a three-room
apartment with his two brothers. He then took a job in the
institute's mechanics laboratory, testing cement and the
hardness and strength of railroad rails.

Timoshenko was hired in 1903 to organize a new
mechanics laboratory at the St. Petersburg Polytechnic
Institute and serve as a laboratory instructor. The following
summer, he took the first of several trips to study in
Germany, visiting the Munich Polytechnic Institute where
he learned to do original scientific research rather than
merely using laboratory equipment to repeat established
experiments. In 1905, Timoshenko took several classes at
the University of Göttingen, Germany, including a seminar
conducted by mathematician Felix Klein. He was assigned
to investigate the lateral stability of an I-beam and
succeeded in writing an equation for the beam's torsion
(twisting). He went on to examine the beam's stability; two
years later he used the results in his dissertation.

After another year of study in St. Petersburg, Timoshenko returned to Göttingen in the summer of 1906 and
studied under Ernst Zermelo and German physicist Wolde-
mar Voigt. That fall, Timoshenko was selected for a faculty
position in strength of materials at the Kiev Polytechnic
Institute, where he delivered the first lecture of his career in
January 1907, to over four hundred students. One of his
responsibilities was to supervise a laboratory for testing the
mechanical properties of building materials; he also devel-

oped a new program to ensure that students would learn to verify experimentally the theoretical results discussed in class. In 1909, he spent another summer at Göttingen, studying elasticity theory, hydrodynamics, and aerodynamics. Returning to Kiev, he was named dean of the Division of Structural Engineering.

That fall, Timoshenko began a year-long effort to create an entry for the Jourawski Medal competition, which was held every ten years to recognize the best work in structural mechanics. By late summer of 1911, when notified that his paper on elastic stability had won the prize, he was particularly grateful for the cash award. He had recently been fired from the institute for refusing to expel a number of Jewish students because their quota at the school had been exceeded. Moving back to St. Petersburg, Timoshenko was able to work unofficially at several schools for an hourly wage.

The following year, Timoshenko was hired as a consultant in the military shipyards; his earlier work on the stability of compressed plates was now being applied to the design of ships for the Russian navy. In 1913, his academic censure ended, and he joined the faculties at the Ways of Communication Institute and the Electrical Engineering Institute. His notable research results included the first mathematical description of the center of shear of a structural beam, and analysis of asymmetric buckling of a centrally compressed cylindrical shell.

In 1914, in the midst of World War I, Timoshenko was asked to work on the problem of strengthening the country's railroad tracks to carry wartime loads. Existing theory treated a rail as a beam supported by a series of elastic supports, which yielded an unsolvable differential equation; he simplified the theory by considering a beam on a continuous elastic foundation. This yielded a readily solvable equation showing how variation of a rail's weight affects the stresses in the rail and the rigidity of the track. He earned the Salov Prize for his solution. By 1917, wartime conditions were difficult in St. Petersburg, and Timoshenko's parents took his wife, his son Gregor, and his daughters Anna and Marine, to Kiev. At Christmas, Timoshenko visited them and was unable to leave when the Bolsheviks occupied the city. The following year, he was rehired as a professor at the Polytechnic Institute and served on a commission to organize a Ukrainian Academy of Sciences, in which he became a charter member. During the revolution, Timoshenko left the barely functioning institute to join the engineering division of the anticommunist White Army. As conditions worsened, he fled to Yugoslavia in 1920; seven months later, when the Poles occupied the Ukraine, he returned long enough to get his wife and children. Then he joined the faculty at the new Zagreb Polytechnic Institute.

In 1922, Timoshenko came to the United States to work for the Vibration Specialty Company in Philadelphia, Pennsylvania. The firm was financially insecure, and within a year, he found a better job at the Westinghouse Electric & Manufacturing Company in Pittsburgh, Pennsylvania. In

addition to supervising a laboratory, he taught strength of machine structures to the newly hired engineers. In 1927, the year Timoshenko became an American citizen, he left Westinghouse to occupy the University of Michigan's new chair of research in mechanics. He found the engineering education in America quite inferior to that in his homeland, and he strove to reorganize it. Under his leadership, mechanics education changed from the empirical to the scientific.

Timoshenko gave a month-long series of lectures at the University of California at Berkeley in early 1935. While there, he was invited to speak at Stanford University; the following fall, he accepted a professorship at Stanford. Again, he revised the curriculum, and he organized summer sessions to teach faculty from other schools. He retired in 1944, but continued as professor emeritus at Stanford until 1953.

In 1947, Great Britain's Institution of Mechanical Engineers awarded Timoshenko the James Watt International Medal, which was presented every five years to the most outstanding engineer. In 1957, he was honored as the first recipient of the Timoshenko Medal of the American Society of Mechanical Engineers. During his lifetime, he received honorary degrees from eight institutions in six countries.

Timoshenko was of the Greek Orthodox faith. He enjoyed hiking in the mountains and was interested in music, theater, art, travel, politics, economics, and world literature. In his later years, he lived with his daughter in Wuppertal, Germany, where he died on May 29, 1972, after a brief illness following kidney problems.

SELECTED WRITINGS BY TIMOSHENKO:

Books

Theory of Elasticity, McGraw, 1934.
Theory of Plates and Shells, McGraw, 1940.
Theory of Structures, McGraw, 1945.
History of Strength of Materials, Dover, 1953.
Engineering Education in Russian, McGraw, 1959.
As I Remember, (autobiography), Van Nostrand, 1968.

FURTHER READING:

Books

Biographical Memoirs of Fellows of the Royal Society, Volume 19, Royal Society (London), 1973.
National Cyclopedia of American Biography, Volume 57, White & Company, 1977, pp. 365–366.

Sketch by Sandra Katzman

Nikolaas Tinbergen
1907–1988
English zoologist and ethologist

Nikolaas Tinbergen

Nikolaas Tinbergen, a zoologist, animal psychologist, and pioneer in the field of ethology (the study of the behavior of animals in relation to their habitat), is most well known for his studies of stimulus-response processes in wasps, fishes, and gulls. He shared the 1973 Nobel Prize in physiology or medicine with Austrian zoologists **Karl Frisch** and **Konrad Lorenz** for his work on the organization and causes of social and individual patterns of behavior in animals.

The third of five children, Tinbergen was born April 15, 1907, in The Hague, the Netherlands, to Dirk Cornelius Tinbergen, a school teacher, and Jeanette van Eek. His older brother Jan studied physics but later turned to economics, winning the first Nobel Prize awarded in that subject in 1969. The Tinbergens lived near the seashore, where Tinbergen often went to collect shells, camp, and watch animals, many of which he would later formally research.

After high school, Tinbergen worked at the Vogel-warte Rossitten bird observatory and later began studying biology at the State University of Leiden, the Netherlands. For his dissertation, Tinbergen studied bee-killer wasps and was able to experimentally demonstrate that the wasps use landmarks to orientate themselves. Tinbergen first established the traditional routes of the wasps near their burrows, then altered the landscape to see how the wasps' behavior would be affected. Tinbergen was awarded his Ph.D. in 1932.

Tinbergen married Elisabeth Rutten in 1932 (they had five children together). Soon afterward, the Tinbergens embarked on an expedition to Greenland, where Tinbergen studied the role of evolution in the behavior of snow buntings, phalaropes, and Eskimo sled dogs. When he returned to the Netherlands in 1933, he became an instructor at the State University, where he organized an undergraduate course on animal behavior. Tinbergen's work had been recognized in the field of biology but it was not until after he met Lorenz—the acknowledged father of ethology—that his work began to form a directed body of research. Tinbergen took his family to Lorenz's home in Austria for a summer so the two men could work together. Although they published only one paper together, their collaboration lasted a number of years.

Begins Ethology Work

During 1936, Tinbergen and Lorenz began constructing a theoretical framework for the study of ethology, which was then a fledgling field. They hypothesized that instinct, as opposed to simply being a response to environmental factors, arises from an animal's impulses. This idea is expressed by the concept of a fixed-action pattern, a repeated, distinct set of movements or behaviors, which Tinbergen and Lorenz believed all animals have. A fixed-action pattern is triggered by something in the animal's environment. In some species of gull, for instance, hungry chicks will peck at a decoy with a red spot on its bill, a characteristic of the gull. Tinbergen showed that in some animals learned behavior is critical for survival. The oystercatcher, for instance, has to learn which objects to peck at for food by watching its mother. Tinbergen and Lorenz also demonstrated that animal behavior can be the result of contradictory impulses and that a conflict between drives may produce a reaction that is strangely unsuited to the stimuli. For example, an animal defending its territory against a formidable attacker, caught between the impulse to fight or flee, may begin grooming or eating.

Regarding his collaboration with Lorenz, Tinbergen is quoted in *Nobel Prize Winners* as saying: "We 'clicked' at once. . . . [Lorenz's] extraordinary vision and enthusiasm were supplemented and fertilized by my critical sense, my inclination to think his ideas through, and my irrepressible urge to check out 'hunches' by experimentation." Tinbergen and Lorenz's work was disrupted by World War II.

Receives Nobel Prize

Tinbergen spent much of the war in a hostage camp because he had protested the State University of Leiden's decision to remove three Jewish faculty members from the staff. After the war ended, he became a professor of experimental biology at the University. In 1949, Tinbergen traveled to Oxford University in England to lecture. He stayed at Oxford, establishing the journal *Behavior* with W. H. Thorpe and working in the university's animal behavior division. His 1951 book *The Study of Instinct* is credited with bringing the study of ethology to many English readers. The book summarized some of the newest insights into the ways signaling behavior is created over the course of evolution. In 1955, Tinbergen became an English citizen, and in 1966 he was appointed a professor and fellow of Oxford's Wolfson College. When the work of Tinbergen, Lorenz, and von Frisch, who had demonstrated that honeybees communicate by dancing, received the Nobel Prize in 1973, it was the first time the Nobel Committee recognized work in sociobiology or ethology.

It was Tinbergen's own hope that the ethologists' body of work would help in understanding of human behavior. "With von Frisch and Lorenz, Tinbergen has expressed the view that ethological demonstrations of the extraordinarily intricate interdependence of the structure and behavior of organisms are relevant to understanding the psychology of our own species," wrote P. Marler and D. R. Griffin in *Science*. "Indeed, [the Nobel Prize] might be taken . . . as an appreciation of the need to review the picture that we often seem to have of human behavior as something quite outside nature, hardly subject to the principles that mold the biology, adaptability, and survival of other organisms."

The ability of an organism to adapt to its environment is another element of Tinbergen's work. After he retired from Oxford in 1974, he and his wife attempted to explain autistic behavior in children to adaptability. The Tinbergens' assertion that autism may be caused by the behavior of a child's parents caused some consternation in the medical community. Tinbergen believed that much of the opposition to his work was caused by the unflattering view of human behavior it presented. "Our critics feel we degrade ourselves by the way we look at behavior," he is quoted as saying in *Contemporary Authors*. "Because this is one of the implications of ethology, that our free will is not as free as we think. We are determinists, and this is what they hate. . . . They feel that our ideas gnaw at the dignity of man."

Tinbergen was wrote a number of books and made many nature films during his lifetime. Among his publications were several children's books, including *Kleew* and *The Tale of John Stickle*. Among the numerous awards he received are the 1969 Italia prize and the 1971 New York Film Festival's blue ribbon, both for writing—with Hugh Falkus—the documentary *Signals for Survival*, which was broadcast on English television. Tinbergen died December 21, 1988, after suffering a stroke at his home in Oxford, England.

SELECTED WRITINGS BY TINBERGEN:

Books

Eskimoland, D. Van Sijn and Zonen (Rotterdam), 1934.

The Study of Instinct, Clarendon Press, 1951.
The Herring Gull's World: A Study of the Social Behavior of Birds, Collins, 1953, revised edition, Harper, 1971.
Social Behavior in Animals, With Special Reference to Vertebrates, Wiley, 1953, second edition, 1965.
Bird Life, Oxford University Press, 1954.

FURTHER READING:

Books

Contemporary Authors, Volume 108, Gale, 1983, pp. 489–90.
Nobel Prize Winners, H. W. Wilson, 1987, pp. 1059–61.

Periodicals

Newsweek, Learning from the Animals, October 22, 1973, p. 102.
Marler, P., and D. R. Griffin, *Science*, The 1973 Nobel Prize for Physiology or Medicine, November 2, 1973, pp. 464–467.

Sketch by James Klockow

Samuel C. C. Ting
1936–
American physicist

Samuel C. C. Ting is an American physicist who received the 1976 Nobel Prize for his discovery of the J/psi particle, which led to the detection of many new subatomic particles. Ting shared the prize with **Burton Richter**, who had made the same discovery almost simultaneously, using a different experimental technique. Ting is known as a confident, daring theorist, as well as a precise experimenter. He is a consummate practitioner of physics in the era of "big science," when research is conducted by large international teams using costly, complex experimental apparatus.

Ting was born in Ann Arbor, Michigan, on January 27, 1936, while his father, Kuan Hai Ting, was studying engineering at the University of Michigan. He completed his studies when Ting was two months old, and the family returned to mainland China, where his father became an engineering professor. His mother, Tsun-Ying Wang, was a psychology professor. As a child, Ting was cared for mostly by his maternal grandmother while both his parents worked. Although his grandmother emphasized the strong value of education, Ting was not able to begin school until he was twelve years old, because World War II intervened. After the war, the family moved to Taiwan, where Ting's father taught at the National Taiwan University.

In 1956, Ting enrolled at the University of Michigan, studying both mathematics and physics, and in 1959 he earned bachelor's degrees in both subjects. He married Kay Louise Kune, an architect, in 1960, with whom he would have two daughters. Ting received his Ph.D. in physics in 1962, and the next year he went to the European Center for Nuclear Research (CERN) in Geneva as a Ford Foundation fellow. He worked with Giuseppe Cocconi on the proton synchrotron, a device that accelerates protons (the nucleus of an atom) for analysis and measurement. In 1965 Ting joined the faculty of Columbia University, where he worked with **Tsung Lee** and **Chien-Shiung Wu**.

Ting became interested in the production of electron (negatively charged particles of an atom) and positron (positively charged particles of an atom) pairs by photon radiation after experiments conducted at Harvard raised questions regarding some of the predictions of quantum electrodynamic theory (the theory that deals with the interaction of matter with electromagnetic radiation). He took a leave of absence from Columbia and went to Hamburg, Germany, in 1966 to repeat the Harvard experiments at the German synchrotron facility. There his team built a double-arm spectrometer (an instrument used to analyze and measure particle emissions), which enabled them to measure the momentum of two particles simultaneously. It also recorded the angles of their deflection from the radiation beam. The researchers were able to calculate the masses of the particles and their combined energy, making identification of the particles easier and clarifying their interrelationships. Results of these experiments confirmed the accuracy of the quantum electrodynamic description of pair production.

Ting's work at Hamburg led him to ponder the nature of heavy photons (particles of radiation). After his return from Germany, he moved to the Massachusetts Institute of Technology (MIT), where he became full professor in 1969. In 1971, while still at MIT, Ting began a project to determine the properties of heavy photons at Brookhaven National Laboratory in Long Island, New York. Rather than the usual method of bombarding a beryllium target with photon beams, he used a proton beam of ten trillion protons per second in hopes of creating a heavy particle that would decay into pairs of electrons and positrons.

Because the search for heavy particles requires such high energy levels, Ting's MIT team redesigned the double-arm spectrometer to detect electron-positron pairs between 1.5 and 5.5 giga-electron volts (a giga equals one billion). The spectrometer also had to be capable of adding precise but small amounts of energy incrementally, as well as detecting their effects on the particle pairs. After several months of searching, the Ting team was rewarded in August 1974 by the appearance of a sharp spike of high-energy electron-positron pairs at 3.1 billion electron volts. This was

unexpected. Ting checked his measurements carefully and decided he was looking at evidence of a new particle that had not been predicted, the J/psi particle. It was heavier than known similar particles; it also occupied a very narrow range of energy states, and it lasted a relatively long time.

Ting reported his results to the Frascati Laboratory in Italy, where physicists were able to confirm his observations in only two days. Ting's paper and the results of the Frascati experiment were accepted for publication in *Physical Review Letters*. Just a few days after Ting discussed the paper with the review's editor, he attended a routine scheduling meeting at the Stanford Linear Accelerator Center; here he shared his results with Stanford's Burton Richter. Amazingly, Richter had made the same discovery at virtually the same time by creating collisions between positrons and electrons in an accelerator.

Ting and Richter shared the 1976 Nobel Prize for physics. The two-year period between discovery and award was probably the shortest interval on record and caused considerable comment at the time, because some scientists feared the discovery would not stand the test of time. However, it has since been the basis for a virtual explosion in the detection of many other fundamental particles.

The J/psi particle's lifespan was a thousand times longer than expected for such a heavy particle (three times heavier than a proton). It was believed that most subatomic particles were made up of combinations of even more fundamental particles called quarks, of which only three types were thought to exist before the discovery of the J/psi particle. The peculiarities of the J/psi particle (especially its long life) suggested the existence of a fourth type of quark, called charm. The J/psi particle was interpreted to be composed of a charmed quark and an antiquark, creating a property called "charmonium." Charm had been predicted in 1970 and its addition to the family of quarks was thought to unify the electromagnetic and weak forces, further encouraging physicists to believe in the possibility of a grand unifying theory in which the fundamental forces of nature would be shown to be equivalent at very high energies.

There are several stories of how the Ting-Richter particle received its name of J/psi, which is a combination of Ting's name for it (J) and Richter's (psi). Classical particles were traditionally assigned Greek letters for names, while newly discovered particles are labeled with capital letters. One story says Ting called his particle J because he had been working with electromagnetic currents carrying a J label. Another story says the J derives from the physical symbol for angular momentum. A third claims Ting chose the Chinese symbol for his name. In any case, the particle has retained the double label. A similar particle, called the psi-prime, was found by Richter's team within ten days of the first discovery.

Ting is a fellow of the American, European, and Italian physical societies as well as several academies of science, including the Academia Sinica. In addition to the Nobel Prize, Ting received the 1976 E. O. Lawrence Award.

SELECTED WRITINGS BY TING:

Books

The Search for Charm, Beauty, and Truth at High Energies, Plenum Press, 1984.

Periodicals

Physical Review, Timelike Momenta in Quantum Electrodynamics, Volume 145, 1966.

FURTHER READING:

Books

Close, Frank, et al., *The Particle Explosion,* Oxford University Press, 1987.

Periodicals

Close, Frank, et al., *Science,* Choosing Detectors for the SSC, December 21, 1990, pp. 1648–50.
Flam, Faye, *Science,* Community Asks: Has Sam Ting Found a New Particle? November 27, 1992, p. 1441.
Crease, Robert, *Science,* SSC Detectors: Yes, No, Maybe, January 4, 1991, p. 24.
Crease, Robert, *Science News,* 1976 Nobel Prizes: Clean Sweep for U.S., October 23, 1976, p. 260.

Sketch by Valerie Brown

Arne Tiselius
1902–1971
Swedish chemist

A rne Tiselius was awarded the 1948 Nobel Prize in chemistry for his research in electrophoresis (the movement of molecules based on their electric charge and their size) and for his investigations into adsorption, the inclination of certain molecules to cling to particular substances. Although the phenomenon of electrophoresis had been identified decades earlier, it did not become a useful technique for analyzing chemical compounds until Tiselius developed methods which delivered accurate results.

Arne Wilhelm Kaurin Tiselius was born in Stockholm, Sweden, on August 10, 1902, to Hans Abraham J. Tiselius, who was employed by an insurance company, and Rosa Kaurin Tiselius, the daughter of a Norwegian clergyman. Upon the death of Tiselius's father in 1906, Rosa relocated the family to Göteborg, Sweden, where Hans's family lived. Entering the gymnasium at Göteborg, Tiselius came under the tutelage of a chemistry and biology teacher who actively supported his student's interest in science. In 1921 Tiselius matriculated to the University of Uppsala—where his father had earned his degree in mathematics—and studied under the renowned physical chemist **Theodor Svedberg**. Earning his master's degree in chemistry, physics, and mathematics in 1924, Tiselius continued to work as Svedberg's research assistant in physical chemistry. Although Svedberg was interested in the electrophoretic properties of proteins, he turned the study of this over to his new assistant, and three years later Tiselius published his first paper jointly with Svedberg on the subject.

Tiselius would remain at Uppsala until his retirement in 1968, rising from researcher to full professor. His 1930 doctoral dissertation, which earned him a post as docent in the chemistry department, long stood as a standard in the field of electrophoresis. Sweden's first professorship in biochemistry was established for Tiselius at Uppsala in 1938. Besides his work in biochemistry, Tiselius had a strong interest in botany and ornithology and made frequent excursions into the Swedish countryside on photographic expeditions. On November 26, 1930, the year of his doctoral thesis, he married Ingrid Margareta Dalén, with whom he would have one son, Per, and a daughter, Eva.

Explores the Possibilities of Chromatography

Following his dissertation, Tiselius concentrated his attention in areas outside of chemistry. He expanded his research to include biochemical studies—not a typical element of the chemistry curriculum in those days—and became aware of the potential for exploiting the extremely specific electrical "signature" of proteins, as well as other substances. He became concerned, however, with the impurities in the substances under study, even those that had been carefully centrifuged, and turned to chromatography as a possible answer. In chromatographic analysis, light of a specific frequency is passed through a substance, and by using tables assembled over the course of many experiments, the "chromatic signature" of the particular sample can be detected. Tiselius applied this technique by looking into the properties of light diffusion through zeolite, a translucent mineral. While studying under Hugh S. Taylor from 1934 to 1935 at Princeton University's Frick Chemical Laboratory, Tiselius conceived of an accurate method to quantify the diffusion of water molecules through crystals of zeolite.

While at Princeton, Tiselius came to realize that a wealth of potential discoveries in the biochemical sciences awaited only the development of a method accurate enough to help separate and identify compounds. Returning to his original line of research, he completed a prototype of a new electrophoretic apparatus.

When Tiselius returned to Uppsala, he continued making improvements on his electrophoretic instrumentation. In one innovation, he filled a U-shaped tube with chemical solvents, added a solution containing the sample to be analyzed, then applied a charge to one end. As the elements migrated, they reached the solvents at different lengths along the tube. Tiselius constructed the tube so that test samples could be taken at various points along the path of migration and be analyzed to determine which of the original species had made it to that point. It was by using this technique that Tiselius was able to demonstrate that blood plasma contained a complex mix of different elements.

Tracking the movement of boundaries optically by a technique invented by August Toepler—the *Schlieren* method—Tiselius resolved the plasma into four distinct elements that showed up as separate bands in the tube. He was the first to isolate three of the blood proteins known as globulins, which he named *alpha, beta,* and *gamma.* These are important in many of the body's functions; the immunoglobulins, for example, are a critical factor in infection control. In the fourth band, located between those of *beta* and *gamma,* Tiselius discovered antibodies.

The method was a radical improvement but still dissatisfied Tiselius. At the time he was more interested in the breakdown products of polypeptides than in blood compounds. Peptides represent some of the most important proteins in the body and for a clear understanding of their function, it is essential to know their types. However, when the long chain of a polypeptide is broken down, the individual peptides are so similar in nature that even Tiselius's improved electrophoretic technique could not distinguish between them. Faced with this problem, he turned to adsorption methods of analysis, using the then-common column method. In this procedure, a mixture which contains a substance with a specific affinity for absorbing one peptide or another, is flushed through a column (a tube or cylinder). The peptides which had been in the original mix can then be determined by analyzing the eluate (the wash which passed through the column).

In 1943 Tiselius introduced a critical improvement in the process. Research to that point had been carried out using a "frontal analysis method," which revealed the concentration of the components in a mixture but was unable to separate them for further study. Elution could accomplish separation, but had a major setback, "tailing," which is the corruption of one part of a solution by molecules from the other. Tiselius demonstrated that a simple modification to the old technique could reduce tailing, and this new method became known as "displacement analysis."

Advises Government on Scientific Matters

Other important work came out of Tiselius's laboratory throughout the 1940s, such as research on paper electrophoresis and zone electrophoresis. However, increasing demands from other sources took over his time and, in the summer of 1944, Tiselius became an advisor to the Swedish government. His responsibilities included sitting on a committee established to help improve conditions for advancing scientific research, with a focus on basic research. This was the beginning of a long and distinguished relationship with the Swedish Parliament, an association that ended only when Tiselius suffered a heart attack following an important meeting in Stockholm. He died the next morning on October 29, 1971.

Up to his last day, Tiselius followed an active schedule. Having accepted the four-year chairmanship of the Swedish Natural Science Research Council in 1946, he was instrumental in the creation of the Science Advisory Council to the Swedish government. Tiselius was elected vice president of the Nobel Foundation with membership on the Nobel Committee for Chemistry in 1947, one year before he was awarded his own Nobel Prize. That same year, at the International Congress of Chemistry held in London, he was elected vice president in charge of the section for biological chemistry of the International Union of Pure and Applied Chemistry—a body which he led as president four years later.

Among other honors Tiselius received were the Bergstedt Prize of the Royal Swedish Scientific Society in 1926, the Franklin Medal of the Franklin Institute in 1956, and the Paul Karrer Medal in Chemistry from the University of Zurich in 1961. He was also presented with numerous honorary degrees from universities, including those of Stockholm, Paris, Glasgow, Madrid, California at Berkeley, Prague, Cambridge, and Oxford. Tiselius was always interested in fields beyond his own and was concerned with the environmental, social, and ethical implications of science and technology. As president of the Nobel Foundation in 1960, he established the Nobel Symposium, perceiving the foundation as the perfect vehicle for raising awareness of the need to promote science as a solution to mankind's problems. This organization gathered a mix of Nobel laureates to discuss the implications of their work during symposia in each of the five prize fields.

SELECTED WRITINGS BY TISELIUS:

Periodicals

Journal of the American Chemical Society, A New Method for Determination of the Mobility of Proteins, Volume 48, September 1926, pp. 2272–2278.

Journal of Physical Chemistry, Adsorption and Diffusion in Zeolite Crystals, Volume 40, February 1936, pp. 223–232.

Transactions of the Faraday Society, A New Apparatus for Electrophoretic Analysis of Colloidal Mixtures, Volume 33, 1937, pp. 524–31.

Biochemical Journal, Electrophoresis of Serumglobulin II: Electrophoretic Analysis of Normal and Immune Sera, Volume 31, July 1937, pp. 1464–77.

Science, Separation and Fractionation of Macromolecules and Particles, Volume 141, July 1963, pp. 13–20.

FURTHER READING:

Periodicals

Hjerten, S., *Journal of Chromatography,* Arne Tiselius, 1902–1971, Volume 65, 1972, pp. 345–348.

Sketch by Nicholas Williamson

Max Tishler
1906–1989
American chemist

Max Tishler is noted for taking the formulation of pharmaceutical chemicals out of the laboratory and onto the production floor. During his long career as an industrial research chemist, he received patents relating to more than 100 medicinal chemicals, vitamins, antibiotics, and hormones. In doing so he significantly improved human health and nutrition and laid the foundation for modern, large-scale process chemistry of complex compounds.

Tishler was born on October 30, 1906, in Boston, Massachusetts. His father's name was Samuel, and his mother's name was Anna Gray. He attended Tufts College in Medford, Massachusetts, where he earned a B.S. in chemistry in 1928. During his high school and college years, he worked part time in a pharmacy, where he first became interested in the use of pharmaceutical chemicals to treat health problems.

After graduation from Tufts, Tishler studied organic chemistry at Harvard University, where he was a teaching fellow from 1930 to 1934. He received an M.A. degree from Harvard in 1933 and a Ph.D. in 1934, both in organic chemistry. Shortly after he graduated, he married Elizabeth M. Verveer. They had two sons during their marriage, Peter Verveer Tishler, who went on to become a noted physician specializing in the genetics associated with diseases, and Carl Lewis Tishler.

Makes Significant Contributions to Process Chemistry

Tishler stayed on at Harvard, first as a research associate from 1934 to 1936 and then as an instructor in chemistry from 1936 to 1937. In 1937 George Merck, president of the pharmaceutical firm Merck and Company, persuaded Tishler to leave his teaching position at Harvard and become a research chemist at the company's laboratories in Rahway, New Jersey. One of Tishler's first assignments was to develop a method for making riboflavin, which would, in turn, allow economical production of vitamin B_2. His success in solving this problem led to processes for making other vitamins, such as vitamin A, vitamin K_1, and pantothenic acid.

In 1941 Tishler was named head of process development at Merck, and in 1944 he was promoted again to director of developmental research. During this period, Tishler continued to study complex chemical reactions and reduce them to definable processes for production in quantity. One of his investigations led to the development of a new drug, sulfaquinoxaline, which was used as a feed-additive to effectively combat parasite infections in poultry. This allowed a significant expansion of the poultry industry and opened up an entirely new field of pharmaceutical research specifically aimed at developing drugs to promote animal health.

In the late 1940s Tishler and his colleagues took on the difficult project of making the new therapeutic chemical, cortisone, in large quantities. In the laboratory the conversion of desoxcholic acid to cortisone was a complex process involving 42 separate steps which yielded less than one percent of the final product. By altering the chemical reactions, Tishler and his team at Merck were able to simplify the operations to work in a production environment, while at the same time increasing the product yield to 30 percent. Tishler's success proved that even the most sophisticated chemical process could be modified to work in a large-scale production facility, and his work made him one of the leaders in modern process chemistry.

In 1951 Tishler was awarded the Board of Directors' Scientific Award of Merck and Company, Inc. for his achievements. Tishler used the money from this award to establish the Max Tishler Visiting Lectureship at Harvard University and the Max Tishler Scholarship at Tufts University. In 1953 he was elected to the National Academy of Sciences.

Tishler was named vice president of scientific activities at Merck in 1954, and in 1956 he became president of the Merck laboratories. He held that position until 1969, when he took over as senior vice president of research and development until his retirement in 1970. During his 33 years at Merck, Tishler was responsible for the development of a wide range of new drugs for the treatment of infections, growth disorders, heart disease, hypertension, mental depression, and several inflammatory diseases, such as arthritis.

Tishler was honored for his contributions to industrial research when he was awarded the Industrial Research Institute Medal in 1961, and the Chemical Industry Award of the American Section of the Society of Chemical Industry in 1963. He received the Chemical Pioneer Award and the Gold Medal Award from the American Institute of Chemistry in 1968. In 1970 he was awarded the Priestley Medal, the highest award of the American Chemical Society.

Returns to the Academic World

After he retired from Merck in 1970, Tishler accepted a position as a professor of chemistry at Wesleyan

University in Middletown, Connecticut, where he taught and conducted research into the chemistry of various natural substances. Some of the chemical compounds he investigated were leukomycin and prumycin, which are natural antibiotics; and cerulenin, a microbe which inhibits the production of fats. Tishler took over as chairman of the chemistry department during 1973–1974, and was named professor of the sciences emeritus in 1975. Concurrent with his work at Wesleyan, Tishler held advisory and directory positions with the Weizmann Institute of Science, the American Cancer Society, and the Sloan Kettering Institute.

Among his many honors, Tishler received nine honorary doctorate degrees and numerous lecture awards. In 1987, he received the National Medal of Science "for his profound contributions to the nation's health and for the impact of his research on the practice of chemistry." Max Tishler died on March 18, 1989, at the age of 82.

SELECTED WRITINGS BY TISHLER:

Books

(With J. B. Conant) *Chemistry of Organic Compounds.* [publisher unknown], 1937.
(With S. A. Waksman) *Streptomycin.* [publisher unknown], 1949.
(Editor-in-chief) *Organic Synthesis*, vol. 39. [publisher unknown], 1959.

FURTHER READING:

Books

American Men and Women of Science, 16th edition. Reed Publishing, 1986.

Sketch by Chris Cavette

Henry Tizard
1885–1959
English physical chemist

Henry Tizard played a pivotal role in British military policy during World War II. He advised the government on a wide variety of military applications of scientific and technological innovations, including radar and the jet propulsion engine. His scientific education and military experience allowed him to communicate effectively with people in both areas.

Sir Henry Thomas Tizard was born on August 23, 1885, in Gillingham, Kent, to Captain Thomas Henry and Mary Elizabeth (Churchward) Tizard. The family was financially solid but not wealthy. As a navy hydrographer, his father had participated in extensive naval survey work around the world. He encouraged his son's early interest in science. The young Tizard looked forward to a naval career, but just before he was to enter naval school at 13, his left eye was damaged when a fly flew into it. His sight was impaired enough to bar him from naval service. He then enrolled at Westminster preparatory school, and later at Magdalene College, Oxford, where he studied physical chemistry. The day of his final examinations he was seriously ill with the influenza that would recur throughout his life, but he still managed to take first honors.

Early Experiences Influence Career

The center of physical chemistry research at the time was with **Walther Nernst** at the University of Berlin. Tizard enrolled there in 1908 to work toward a Ph.D. Although he stayed in Berlin only a year, Tizard had two experiences there that were to prove significant for Britain: he noted the powerful changes chemistry was bringing to Germany's technological (and therefore military) status, and he met Frederick Lindemann. Lindemann, a fellow chemistry student, was the son of an Alsatian who had become a naturalized Briton. In Berlin, Tizard and Lindemann studied together, practiced boxing at a gymnasium, and ice skated. This early friendship was to sour in the midst of the anxiety and political intrigue of World War II.

In 1911 Tizard became a fellow of Oriel College, Oxford, where he taught physical chemistry. In 1914 he embarked on a British Association tour of Australia, during which he met Cambridge's **Ernest Rutherford** (a noted physicist) and other eminent scientists. The onset of World War I cut the trip short, and Tizard returned to England to enlist in the Royal Garrison Artillery. He was soon transferred to the Royal Flying Corps, where he began a lifelong commitment to aviation technology. His training as a pilot during this period enabled Tizard to understand the practical problems of flying in a way that was rare among scientific advisers and much appreciated by the other aviators. It was also during this time (1915) that he married Kathleen Eleanor Wilson. They eventually had three sons, John, Richard, and David.

At the end of the war, Tizard became assistant deputy of the newly formed Royal Air Force and encountered Winston Churchill, then Minister of Munitions, for the first time. He never got along well with Churchill, who, like Lindemann, enjoyed the intricacies of political gamesmanship which Tizard disliked intensely. In 1919, partly at Tizard's urging, the professorship of experimental philosophy at Oxford went to Lindemann. The two men continued to see each other from time to time, but hostility was already flaring up between them. One colleague remembered them getting into a shouting match over the relatively trivial question of whether oranges should best be packed in symmetrical rows or in off-center layers.

Between the wars, Tizard consulted with the British petroleum industry. With Randall Pye, he studied adiabatic (heat neither lost nor gained) compression of gases, identifying the chemicals that were to prove most effective as fuel in internal combustion engines. Tizard also expanded his role as government adviser, working in the Department of Scientific and Industrial Research, where he hoped to encourage the application of scientific and technological discoveries. He found government and military leaders slow to assimilate new scientific knowledge, and this was to become a long-term frustration.

Politics and Science Combine for Tizard in World War II

By the early 1930s Hitler's aggression posed a threat to Europe, and the British began to worry about air attacks. They had no way to detect incoming planes which, in any effective defense strategy, would have to be intercepted at the coastlines. Various "death ray" ideas were discussed, but no technology presented itself clearly. Tizard became chair of a committee (the Tizard Committee) to investigate the possibilities, one of which was the reflection of radio waves off the atmosphere. Lindemann soon joined the committee, urging study of aerial mines and balloon intercepts, which Tizard believed were unlikely to be of much use. Lindemann also wanted to find a protection against night attacks, whereas Tizard believed the daylight threat was greater. Tension between the two men increased, as Lindemann was close to Churchill and Tizard's power was advisory rather than executive. As it turned out, Lindemann was right about the danger of night attacks. Tizard's mistake in this regard tended to obscure his foresight in pushing radar research. He was largely responsible for establishing the country's chain of radar stations that enabled Britain to survive the Battle of Britain in 1940. Credit for his role was slow in coming.

In 1939 Tizard was asked to evaluate the feasibility of an atomic bomb. He tried unsuccessfully to obtain the option for all the uranium available from the Belgian Congo, but he did manage to obtain some uranium to send to the United States, where it became the first nuclear fuel. Working as an unofficial adviser to Lord Beaverbrook (William Maxwell Aitken), Tizard served as a conduit for classified information passing between Britain and the United States. In 1940 he headed a mission to America for this purpose, taking along the cavity magnetron (called the "heart of radar"), which the British had developed but the Americans were to make practicable.

Political rivalry with Lindemann and frustration with the government's inability to set clear priorities and lines of authority led Tizard to curtail his active government service in the last years of the war. He opposed the government's policy of random bombing of German cities because he believed it would be less effective than bombing U-boats. He became president of Magdalene College, Oxford, in 1942 and retired from the Air Ministry in 1943. After the war, Tizard continued to support increased rigor in Britain's technological development, advising the government on science and military policy through the early 1950s. He received many honors, including the Order of the Bath, several honorary degrees, and membership in the Royal Society. Tizard died in Fareham, Hampshire, on October 9, 1959.

SELECTED WRITINGS BY TIZARD:

Books

Theoretical Chemistry, 3rd edition, Macmillan, 1911.

Periodicals

The Aeronautical Journal, Methods of measuring aircraft performance, Volume 21, 1917, pp. 108, 122.
Philosophical Magazine, Experiments on the ignition of gases for sudden compression, Volume 44, 1992, p. 79.

FURTHER READING:

Books

Clark, Ronald W., *Tizard,* MIT Press, 1965.

Sketch by Valerie Brown

Alexander Todd
1907–1997
English chemist

Alexander Todd was awarded the 1957 Nobel Prize in chemistry for his work on the chemistry of nucleotides. He was also influential in synthesizing vitamins for commercial application. In addition, he invesitgated active ingredients in cannabis and hashish and helped develop efficient means of producing chemical weapons.

Alexander Robertus Todd was born in Glasgow, Scotland, on October 2, 1907, to Alexander and Jane Lowrie Todd. The family, consisting of Todd, his parents, his older sister, and his younger brother, was not well to do. Todd's autobiography, *A Time to Remember,* recalls how, through hard work, his parents rose to the lower middle class despite having no more than an elementary education, and how determined they were that their children should have an education at any cost.

Alexander Todd

Education and Early Career

In 1918, Todd gained admission to the Allan Glen's School in Glasgow, a science high school; his interest in chemistry, which first arose when he was given a chemistry set at the age of eight or nine, developed rapidly. On graduation, six years later, he at once entered the University of Glasgow instead of taking a recommended additional year at Allan Glen's. His father refused to sign an application for scholastic aid, saying it would be accepting charity; because of superior academic performance during the first year, though, Todd received a scholarship for the rest of course. In his final year at university, Todd did a thesis on the reaction of phosphorus pentachloride with ethyl tartrate and its diacetyl derivative under the direction of T. E. Patterson, resulting in his first publication.

After receiving his B.Sc. degree in chemistry with first-class honors in 1928, Todd was awarded a Carnegie research scholarship and stayed on for another year working for Patterson on optical rotatory dispersion. Deciding that this line of research was neither to his taste nor likely to be fruitful, he went to Germany to do graduate work at the University of Frankfurt am Main under Walther Borsche, studying natural products. Todd says that he preferred Jöns Berzelius's definition of organic chemistry as the chemistry of substances found in living organisms to Gmelin's definition of it as the chemistry of carbon compounds.

At Frankfurt he studied the chemistry of apocholic acid, one of the bile acids (compounds produced in the liver and having a structure related to that of cholesterol and the

steroids). In 1931, he returned to England with his doctorate. He applied for and received an 1851 Exhibition Senior Studentship which allowed him to enter Oxford University to work under **Robert Robinson**, who would receive the Nobel Prize in chemistry in 1947. In order to ease some administrative difficulties, Todd enrolled in the doctoral program, which had only a research requirement; he received his D.Phil. from Oxford in 1934. His research at Oxford dealt first with the synthesis of several anthocyanins, the coloring matter of flowers, and then with a study of the red pigments from some molds.

After leaving Oxford, Todd went to the University of Edinburgh on a Medical Research Council grant to study the structure of vitamin B_1 (thiamine, or the antiberiberi vitamin). The appointment came about when George Barger, professor of medical chemistry at Edinburgh, sought Robinson's advice about working with B_1. At that time, only a few milligrams of the substance were available, and Robinson suggested Todd because of his interest in natural products and his knowledge of microchemical techniques acquired in Germany. Although Todd and his team were beaten in the race to synthesize B_1 by competing German and American groups, their synthesis was more elegant and better suited for industrial application. It was at Edinburgh that Todd met and became engaged to Alison Dale—daughter of Nobel Prize laureate **Henry Hallett Dale**—who was doing postgraduate research in the pharmacology department; they were married in January of 1937, shortly after Todd had moved to the Lister Institute where he was reader (or lecturer) in biochemistry. For the first time in his career, Todd was salaried and not dependent on grants or scholarships. In 1939 the Todds' son, Alexander, was born. Their first daughter, Helen, was born in 1941, and the second, Hilary, in 1945.

The Maturing of a Scientist

Toward the end of his stay at Edinburgh, Todd began to investigate the chemistry of vitamin E (a group of related compounds called tocopherols), which is an antioxidant—that is, it inhibits loss of electrons. He continued this line of research at the Lister Institute and also started an investigation of the active ingredients of the *Cannabis sativa* plant (marijuana) that showed that cannabinol, the major product isolated from the plant resin, was pharmacologically inactive.

In March of 1938, Todd and his wife made a long visit to the United States to investigate the offer of a position at California Institute of Technology. On returning to England with the idea that he would move to California, Todd was offered a professorship at Manchester, which he accepted, becoming Sir Samuel Hall Professor of Chemistry and director of the chemical laboratories of the University of Manchester. At Manchester, Todd was able to continue his research with little interruption. During his first year there, he finished the work on vitamin E with the total synthesis of alpha-tocopherol and its analogs. Attempts to isolate and identify the active ingredients in cannabis resin failed because the separation procedures available at the time were inadequate; however, Todd's synthesis of cannabinol involved an intermediate, tetrahydrocannabinol (THC), that had an effect much like that of hashish on rabbits and suggested to him that the effects of hashish were due to one of the isomeric tetrahydrocannabinols. This view was later proven correct, but by others, because the outbreak of World War II forced Todd to abandon this line of research for work more directly related to the war.

As a member, and then chair, of the Chemical Committee, which was responsible for developing and producing chemical warfare agents, Todd developed an efficient method of producing diphenylamine chloroarsine (a sneeze gas), and designed a pilot plant for producing nitrogen mustards (blistering agents). He also had a group working on penicillin research and another trying to isolate and identify the "hatching factor" of the potato eelworm, a parasite that attacks potatoes.

Late in 1943 Todd was offered the chair in biochemistry at Cambridge University, which he refused. Shortly thereafter he was offered the chair in organic chemistry, which he accepted, choosing to affiliate with Christ's College. From 1963 to 1978, he served as master of the college. As professor of organic chemistry at Cambridge, Todd reorganized and revitalized the department and oversaw the modernization of the laboratories (they were still lighted by gas in 1944) and, eventually, the construction of a new laboratory building.

Wins Nobel Prize for Work on Nucleotides

Before the war, his interest in vitamins and their mode of action had led Todd to start work on nucleosides and nucleotides. Nucleosides are compounds made up of a sugar (ribose or deoxyribose) linked to one of four heterocyclic (that is, containing rings with more than one kind of atom) nitrogen compounds derived either from purine (adenine and guanine) or pyrimidine (uracil and cytosine). When a phosphate group is attached to the sugar portion of the molecule, a nucleoside becomes a nucleotide. The nucleic acids (deoxyribonucleic acid, or DNA; and ribonucleic acid, or RNA), found in cell nuclei as constituents of the chromosomes, are chains of nucleotides. While still at Manchester, Todd had worked out techniques for synthesizing nucleosides and then attaching the phosphate group to them (a process called phosphorylating) to form nucleotides; later, at Cambridge, he worked out the structures of the nucleotides obtained by the degradation of nucleic acid and synthesized them. This information was a necessary prerequisite to **James Watson** and **Francis Crick**'s formulation of the double-helix structure of DNA two years later.

Todd had found the nucleoside adenosine in some coenzymes, relatively small molecules that combine with a protein to form an enzyme, which can act as a catalyst for a particular biochemical process. He knew from his work with the B vitamins that B_1 (thiamine), B_2 (riboflavin) and B_3 (niacin) were essential components of coenzymes involved in respiration and oxygen utilization. By 1949 he had succeeded in synthesizing adenosine—a triumph in itself—and had gone on to synthesize adenosine di- and triphosphate (ADP and ATP). These compounds are nucleotides responsible for energy production and energy storage in muscles and in plants. In 1952, he established the structure of flavin adenine dinucleotide (FAD), a coenzyme involved in breaking down carbohydrates so that they can be oxidized, releasing energy for an organism to use. For his pioneering work on nucleotides and nucleotide enzymes, Todd was awarded the 1957 Nobel Prize in chemistry.

Todd collaborated with **Dorothy Crowfoot Hodgkin** in determining the structure of vitamin B_{12}, the antipernicious anemia factor, which is necessary for the formation of red blood cells. Todd's chemical studies of the degradation products of B_{12} were crucial to Hodgkin's X-ray determination of the structure in 1955.

Another major field of research at Cambridge was the chemistry of the pigments in aphids. While at Oxford and working on the coloring matter from some fungi, Todd observed that, although the pigments from fungi and from higher plants were all anthraquinone derivatives, the pattern of substitution around the anthraquinone ring differed in the two cases. Pigment from two different insects seemed to be of the fungal pattern and Todd wondered if these were derived from the insect or from symbiotic fungi they contained. At Cambridge he isolated several pigments from different kinds of aphids and found that they were complex quinones unrelated to anthraquinone. It was found, however, that they are probably the products of symbiotic fungi in the aphid.

A Senior Scientist and Government Advisor

In 1952 Todd became chairman of the advisory council on scientific policy to the British government, a post he held until 1964. He was knighted in 1954 by Queen Elizabeth for distinguished service to the government. Named Baron Todd of Trumpington in 1962, he was made a member of the Order of Merit in 1977. In 1955 he became a foreign associate of the United States' National Academy of Sciences. He traveled extensively and had been a visiting professor at the University of Sydney (Australia), the California Institute of Technology, the Massachusetts Institute of Technology, the University of Chicago, and Notre Dame University.

A Fellow of the Royal Society since 1942, Todd served as its president from 1975 to 1980. He increased the role of the society in advising the government on the scientific aspects of policy and strengthened its international relations. Extracts from his five anniversary addresses to the society dealing with these concerns are given as appendices to his autobiography. In the forward to his autobiography, Todd reports that in preparing biographical sketches of a number of members of the Royal Society he was struck by the lack of information available about their lives and careers and that this, in part, led him to write *A Time to Remember*. Todd died on January 10, 1997, in his home city of Cambridge, England. He was 89.

SELECTED WRITINGS BY TODD:

Books

A Time to Remember: The Autobiography of a Chemist. Cambridge: Cambridge University Press, 1983.

Periodicals

"Chemistry of Nucleotides," *Proceedings of the Royal Society* A227 (1954): pp. 70-82.
"Chemical Structure of Nucleic Acids," *Proceedings of the National Academy of Sciences* 40 (1954): pp. 748-55.
"The Structure of Vitamin B_{12}," *Chemical Society Special Publication,* no. 3 (1955): pp. 109-23.

FURTHER READING:

Books

Current Biography 1958. New York: H. W. Wilson, 1958, pp. 437-39.
Nobel Lectures Including Presentation Speeches and Laureate's Biographies—Chemistry: 1942–1962. Elsevier, 1964, pp. 519–538.

Periodicals

Saxon, Wolfgang, "Lord Todd, 89, a Nobelist for Work on Nucleic Acids" (obituary), *New York TImes* (15 January 1997): pp. B7.

Sketch by R.F. Trimble

Clyde W. Tombaugh
1906–1997
American astronomer

Clyde W. Tombaugh, an astronomer and master telescope maker, spent much of his career performing a painstaking photographic survey of the heavens from Lowell Observatory in Flagstaff, Arizona. This led to the discovery of Pluto (1930), the ninth planet in the solar system. Although Tombaugh is best known for this early triumph, he went on to make other contributions, including his work on the geography of Mars and studies of the distribution of galaxies. Tombaugh also made valuable refinements to missile-tracking technology during a nine-year stint at the U.S. Army's White Sands Proving Grounds in New Mexico.

Clyde W. Tombaugh

Clyde William Tombaugh, the eldest of six children, was born on February 4, 1906, to Muron Tombaugh, a farmer, and Adella Chritton Tombaugh. He spent most of his childhood on a farm near Streator, Illinois. In 1922, the family relocated to a farm in western Kansas. Tombaugh glimpsed his first telescopic view of the heavens through his uncle Leon's three-inch (7.6-cm) refractor, a kind of telescope that uses a lens to gather faint light from stars and planets. In 1925, inspired by an article in *Popular Astronomy,* Tombaugh bought materials to grind an eight-inch light-collecting mirror for a reflecting telescope. He ground that first mirror by hand, using a fence post on the farm as a grinding stand.

The finished instrument, a seven-foot-long, rectangular wooden box, was equipped with wooden setting circles for aligning it to objects of interest in the sky. Tombaugh had not ground the mirror very accurately, and thus the telescope was unsuitable for the planetary observing he had in mind. However, it launched a lifetime of building, improving, and maintaining telescopes, tasks at which Tombaugh excelled. Tombaugh biographer and amateur astronomer, David H. Levy, estimated that Tombaugh ground some thirty-six telescope mirrors and lenses in his career. He continued to use a few of his early telescopes for decades after he first constructed them (for example, his nine-inch reflector, whose mechanical mounting included parts from a 1910 Buick).

Hired to Search for Ninth Planet

Tombaugh's nine-inch reflector, which he completed in 1928, led to a career as a professional observer as well as to sharper views of the planets and stars. After a 1928 hailstorm wiped out the Tombaughs' wheat crop and foiled Clyde's plans for college, the young observer turned his new telescope to Jupiter and Mars. Subsequently, he sent his best drawings of these planets to Lowell Observatory, which had been founded in the late nineteenth century by famed Mars watcher Percival Lowell.

Hoping only for constructive criticism of his drawings, Tombaugh instead received a job offer from the astronomers at Lowell. He accepted, and in January 1929 began his work on the search for the predicted ninth planet beyond the orbit of Neptune. Working full time as a professional observer (although lacking any formal education in astronomy), Tombaugh used Lowell's thirteen-inch telescope to systematically photograph the sky. He then used a special instrument, called a blink comparator, to examine the plates for telltale signs of moving bodies beyond the orbit of Earth. A blink comparator, or blink microscope, rapidly alternates—up to ten times per second—two photographic images, taken at different times, of the same field or area of the sky. Seen through a magnifying lens, moving bodies will appear to jump back and forth or "blink" as the images are switched.

Using his knowledge of orbital mechanics and his sharp observer's eye, Tombaugh was able to discern asteroids and comets from possible planets; a third "check" plate was then taken to confirm or rule out the existence of these suspected planets. On February 18, 1930, after ten months of concentrated, painstaking work, Tombaugh zeroed in on Pluto, fulfilling a search begun by Percival Lowell in 1905. The discovery of Pluto secured the twenty-four-year-old Tombaugh's reputation and his place in the history of astronomy, and he remained with the survey until 1943.

After his discovery, Tombaugh took some time off to obtain his formal education in astronomy. He left for the University of Kansas in the fall of 1932, returning to Lowell each summer to resume his observing duties. At college, he met Patricia Irene Edson, a philosophy major. They married in 1934, and subsequently had two children, Alden and Annette. Tombaugh paused only once more for formal education in science, taking his master's degree in 1938–39 at the University of Kansas. For his thesis work, he restored the university's twenty-seven-inch (68.6-cm) reflecting telescope to full health and studied its observing capabilities.

In 1943, Tombaugh taught physics at Arizona State Teachers College in Flagstaff; that same year, the U.S. Navy asked him to teach navigation, also at Arizona State. In what little spare time remained, Tombaugh struggled to continue the planet survey. The following year, he taught astronomy and the history of astronomy at the University of California in Los Angeles. Tombaugh's stint on the planet survey ceased abruptly in 1946. Citing financial constraints,

observatory director **Vesto M. Slipher** asked Tombaugh to seek other employment.

Tombaugh's contribution to the "planetary patrol" at Lowell proved enormous. From 1929 to 1945, he cataloged many thousands of celestial objects, including 29,548 galaxies, 3,969 asteroids (775 of them previously unreported), two previously undiscovered comets, one nova, and, of course, the planet Pluto. However, as Tombaugh pointed out to biographer David Levy, tiny Pluto cast a long and sometimes burdensome shadow over the rest of his career, obscuring subsequent astronomical work. For instance, in 1937, Tombaugh discovered a dense cluster of 1,800 galaxies, which he called the "Great Perseus-Andromeda Stratum of Extra-Galactic Nebula." This suggested to Tombaugh that the distribution of galaxies in the universe may not be as random and irregular as some astronomers believed at the time.

Tombaugh was also an accomplished observer of Mars. He predicted in 1950 that the red planet, being so close to the asteroid belt, would have impact craters like those on the moon. These craters are not easily visible from Earth because Mars always shows its face to astronomers fully or nearly fully lighted, masking the craters' fine lines. Images of the Martian surface captured in the 1960s by the *Mariner IV* space probe confirmed Tombaugh's prediction.

In 1946, Tombaugh began a relatively brief career as a civilian employee of the U.S. Army, working as an optical physicist and astronomer at White Sands Proving Grounds near Las Cruces, New Mexico, where the army was developing launching facilities for captured German V-2 missiles. Tombaugh witnessed fifty launchings of the forty-six-foot (14-m) rockets and documented their performance in flight using a variety of tracking telescopes. Armed with his observing skills and intimate knowledge of telescope optics, Tombaugh greatly increased the quality of missile tracking at White Sands, host to a number of important postwar missile-development programs.

Tombaugh resumed serious planetary observing in 1955, when he accepted a teaching and research position at New Mexico State University in Las Cruces. There, he taught astronomy, led planetary observation programs, and participated in the care and construction of new telescopes. From 1953 to 1958, Tombaugh directed a major search for small, as-yet-undetected objects near Earth—either asteroids or tiny natural satellites—that might pose a threat to future spacecraft. He and colleagues developed sensitive telescopic tracking equipment and used it to scan the skies from a high-altitude site in Quito, Ecuador. The survey turned up no evidence of hazardous objects near Earth, and Tombaugh issued a closing report on the program the year after the Soviet Union launched *Sputnik* (1957), the first artificial satellite.

Upon his retirement in 1973, Tombaugh maintained his links to New Mexico State University, often attending lunches and colloquia in the astronomy department that he helped to found. He also remained active in the local astronomical society and continued to observe with his cherished homemade telescopes. Indeed, asked by the Smithsonian Institution in Washington, D.C., to relinquish his nine-inch reflector to its historical collections, Tombaugh refused, explaining to *Smithsonian* magazine, "I'm not through using it yet!" He died on January 17, 1997 at his home in Las Cruces, New Mexico.

SELECTED WRITINGS BY TOMBAUGH:

Books

Out of Darkness: The Planet Pluto. Mechanicsburg, PA: Stackpole Books, 1980.

Periodicals

"Plates, Pluto, and Planet X," *Sky & Telescope* (April 1991): pp. 360-61.

FURTHER READING:

Books

Levy, David H., *Clyde Tombaugh: Discoverer of Planet Pluto.* Tucson: University of Arizona Press, 1991.

Periodicals

Dicke, William, "Clyde W. Tombaugh, 90, Discoverer of Pluto" (obituary), *New York Times* (20 January 1997): p. B8.
Levy, David H., "Clyde Tombaugh: Planetary Observer and Telescope Maker." *Sky & Telescope* (January 1987): pp. 88-89.
Searcey, Dionne, "Snatching Fame from the Heavens," *Chicago Tribune* (2 February 1997): Perspective 1.
Sheehan, William, "Clyde Tombaugh" (obituary), *Astronomy* 25, no. 4 (April 1997): p. 28.
Trefil, James, "Phenomena, Comments and Notes," *Smithsonian* (May 1991): pp. 32-36.

Sketch by Daniel Pendick

Sin-Itiro Tomonaga
1906–1979
Japanese physicist

Sin-Itiro Tomonaga was a pioneer in the field of quantum electrodynamics, a broad field that uses principles from quantum mechanics and special relativity to explain a wide variety of physical phenomena. He developed a theory about subatomic particles that was consistent

Sin-Itiro Tomonaga

with the theory of relativity, and he did so at about the time that **Richard P. Feynman** and **Julian Schwinger** independently reached similar solutions. The three were jointly awarded the 1965 Nobel Prize for their efforts in quantum theory.

Sin-Itiro (also transliterated as Sin-Ichiro) Tomonaga was born in Tokyo on March 31, 1906, to Sanjuro and Hide Tomonaga. When Sin-Itiro was a child, his family moved to Kyoto, where his father had been appointed professor of philosophy at the Kyoto Imperial University. Sin-Itiro enrolled at Kyoto's prestigious Third High School where he was a classmate of **Hideki Yukawa**, later to become Japan's first Nobel Prize winner (in the field of physics) in 1949. After graduation, Tomonaga and Yukawa both went on to Kyoto Imperial University, where both majored in physics and earned their bachelor's degrees in 1929. The two then stayed on as research assistants to Kajuro Tamaki.

In 1932, Tomonaga and Yukawa finally went their separate ways, with Tomonaga accepting a position as research assistant to Yoshio Nishina at the Institute of Physical and Chemical Research in Tokyo. After five years in this post, Tomonaga traveled to the University of Leipzig where he studied under physicist **Werner Heisenberg**. While at Leipzig, Tomonaga wrote a paper on the atomic nucleus that earned him a Ph.D. from Kyoto Imperial upon his return to Japan in 1939. In 1941 Tomonaga became professor of physics at Tokyo's Bunrika University (now Tokyo University of Education), a post he held until 1956, when he became president of the university. After leaving Tokyo University in 1962, Tomonaga served as president of the Science Council of Japan and director of the Institute for Optical Research.

Attacks Problems of Quantum Electrodynamics

The topic that dominated Tomonaga's research throughout most of his life was quantum electrodynamics (QED). QED arose during the 1920s when the successes of quantum theory and made it apparent that classical laws of physics were inadequate to explain the behavior of elementary particles. A number of theorists attempted to develop new equations that would take into consideration both quantum mechancis and relativity theory to explain the behavior of particles and their interaction with energy.

By the late 1920s, impressive progress had been made in dealing with this problem, especially as a result of the work of the English physicist **Paul Dirac**. Dirac's theory successfully predicted the qualitative properties of atomic particles and the way they interacted with energy. Over time, however, it became apparent that Dirac's theory was quantitatively inadequate. Among the most serious problems of the Dirac theory was the prediction that, under certain circumstances, particles would have infinite mass and infinite charge. The physical absurdity of these predictions, commonly known as "divergence difficulties," deeply troubled physicists, many of whom decided that a totally knew approach to QED would be needed.

Success with Quantum Electrodynamics Brings Nobel Prize

Tomonaga, however, took another view. He was convinced that techniques could be found that would allow the retention of Dirac's fundamental approach while resolving the "divergence difficulties" inherent within it. The mathematical technique he used, called renormalization, worked. Tomonaga was eventually able to demonstrate that infinite mass and charge are indeed a fundamental part of the Dirac theory, but that they apply to situations that would never be encountered in the real world.

Tomonaga's fundamental paper on QED was published in Japan in 1943. Because of the war, however, news and translation of the paper did not reach the rest of the world until 1947. At about the same time, similar papers dealing with QED written by Schwinger at Harvard and Feynman at the California Institute of Technology were also being published. When the 1965 Nobel Prize for Physics was announced, therefore, it was divided among the three physicists for the independent solutions of the "divergence difficulties" problem.

Tomonaga's prize-winning research had been carried out at Tokyo's Bunrika University of Science and Literature, where he had been appointed professor of physics in 1941. He remained in this post, after the university had been incorporated into the Tokyo University of Education, until 1949. He then accepted an invitation to become a visiting scholar at the Institute for Advanced Studies at Princeton, New Jersey. He returned to Tokyo in 1951 to become head

of the Institute for Scientific Research. Four years later, he was instrumental in the founding of the Institute for Nuclear Studies at the University of Tokyo and then, in 1956, became president of the university. Upon his retirement in 1962, Tomonaga accepted an offer to become president of the Science Council of Japan and director of the Institute for Optical Research, posts he held until 1969.

Tomonaga was married in 1940 to Ryoko Sekiguchi, daughter of the director of the Tokyo Metropolitan Observatory. They had two sons, Atsushi and Makoto, and a daughter, Shigeko. In addition to the Nobel Prize, Tomonaga was awarded the Japan Academy Prize in 1948, the Order of Culture of Japan in 1952, and the Lomonosov Medal of the Soviet Academy of Sciences in 1964. Tomonaga died in Tokyo on July 8, 1979.

SELECTED WRITINGS BY TOMONAGA:

Books

Quantum Mechanics, 2 volumes, Misuzu Publishing Company, 1949.
Scientific Papers of Tomonaga, 2 volumes, Misuzu Shobo Publishing Company, 1971–76.

FURTHER READING:

Books

McGraw-Hill Modern Scientists and Engineers, Volume 3, McGraw-Hill, 1980, pp. 224–225.
Wasson, Tyler, editor, *Nobel Prize Winners*, H. W. Wilson, 1987, pp. 1068–1071.
Williams, Trevor, editor, *A Biographical Dictionary of Scientists*, Wiley, 1974, pp. 610–611.

Periodicals

Dyson, Freeman J., "Tomonaga, Schwinger, and Feynman Awarded Nobel Prize for Physics," *Science*, October 29, 1965, pp. 588–589.

Sketch by David E. Newton

Susumu Tonegawa
1939–

Japanese molecular biologist

In 1987, Susumu Tonegawa became the first Japanese recipient of the Nobel Prize for physiology or medicine for his study of the immune system and his subsequent discovery of the causes of diversity—the ability of an antibody to resist infection from millions of different viruses and bacteria. Tonegawa provided direct evidence that a's ability to encode antibody is produced from separate, chain-like segments of DNA (deoxyribonucleic acid) which mutate to code for different antibodies. Since 1981, Tonegawa has worked at the Massachusetts Institute of Technology (MIT), and was honored as Howard Hughes Medical Institute Investigator in 1988.

Tonegawa was born in Nagoya, Japan, on September 5, 1939, the second of four children born to Tsutomu Tonegawa and the former Miyoko Masuko. Tonegawa's father was an engineer whose work required him to move frequently from town to town across the country. As a result, Tonegawa and his older brother were sent to Tokyo to live with an uncle. In Tokyo, the boys attended the prestigious Hibiya High School, where Tonegawa eventually developed an interest in chemistry. After graduation, he entered the University of Kyoto in 1959 to pursue a degree in chemistry. He earned his degree in 1963 and began graduate studies in a then-emerging branch of biology—molecular biology—which is the study of molecules that perform biological operations.

While he was still a student at Kyoto, Tonegawa learned about the field of molecular biology and decided that it was an area in which he wanted to specialize. In 1953, **James Watson** and **Francis Crick** had discovered the mechanism by which genetic information is stored in molecules. That discovery provided an exciting new way to understand biological phenomena in terms of atomic and molecular structure. Research in this promising new field developed very rapidly. In 1963, Tonegawa applied to the University of California at San Diego and began his graduate study in the Department of Biology under Masaki Hayashi. Tonegawa's research in genetic transcription in bacteriophages resulted in three scientific papers, published between 1966 and 1970 with Hayashi, and a Ph.D. in biology by 1968.

For his postdoctoral work, Tonegawa chose to stay in San Diego, working first with Hayashi from September 1968, to April 1969, and then moving to the Salk Institute in nearby La Jolla from May 1969, to December 1970. At the Salk Institute, Tonegawa studied genetic transcription in simian 40 (SV40), an important virus in genetic engineering, with **Renato Dulbecco**, who would go on to win a Nobel Prize in 1975.

Joins Institute of Immunology

In the fall of 1970, Tonegawa was confronted with a dilemma. His United States immigration visa was due to expire at the end of the year, and he had to decide where he was going to continue his studies. At that time, Tonegawa received a letter from Dulbecco notifying him of an opening for a molecular biologist at the Institute of Immunology in Basel, Switzerland. Tonegawa had no formal training in immunology, but applied for the position, and was accepted. By February 1971, Tonegawa found himself "surrounded by immunologists," as he was to point out in his Nobel Prize

lecture many years later as cited in *Bioscience Reports.* It was a challenging position, and he soon became deeply involved in the research for which he was to win the Nobel Prize.

Biologists had long known that an individual vertebrate has the ability to generate millions of different antibodies before it ever encounters an antigen that stimulates a specific defense. Biologists speculated on the mechanism by which the organism's immune system adapts with two theories. According to the first, named the "germ line" theory, all the genes needed to make an antibody are part of the genetic code. The problem was that it seemed impossible for a single gene to carry that much information. A second theory, "somatic," suggested that the antibody genes mutate readily, rearranging themselves in a variety of ways to code for different antibodies. According to this hypothesis, a relatively small number of genes would be able to generate a very large number of variants.

Solves the Antibody Diversity Puzzle

After half a decade of research, Tonegawa was able to report the first firm evidence on the antibody diversity debate. With Nobumichi Hozumi, a colleague, Tonegawa was able to prove that the somatic theory was correct. The biologists demonstrated that the parts of a DNA can rearrange themselves in many different ways—just as the fifty-two cards in a deck can be shuffled and rearranged—in response to an attack by a hostile organism. The antibody, which is thus selectively produced, then attacks the invader. As explained in a comment in *Nobel Prize Winners Supplement,* "DNA recombination and mutation could generate perhaps 10 billion different kinds of antibodies, more than enough to solve the diversity problem."

Among Tonegawa's contributions to is the discovery, with Hozumi, that the DNA segments which undergo rearrangement are separated by seemingly inactive (noncoding) strands of DNA, now known as introns. Additionally, Tonegawa's research into the immune system resulted in the breakthrough discovery of a control element "enhancer" in the intron. Jean L. Marx, writing in *Science,* observed that Tonegawa's work has far-reaching significance: "One unexpected consequence of the gene research was new information about the possible causes of cancer, especially the blood cancers known as lymphomas and leukemias."

Tonegawa stayed at Basel until 1981 when he was offered a position as professor of biology in the Center for Research and Department of Biology at MIT. In 1988, he was made Howard Hughes Medical Institute Investigator. In addition to the Nobel Prize in 1987, Tonegawa has received numerous honors and awards, including the Genetics Grand Prize of the Japanese Promotions Foundation in 1981, the V. D. Mattia Award of the Roche Institute of Molecular Biology in 1983, the Robert Koch Prize in 1986, the Albert and Mary Lasker Award for Basic Research in 1987, the Rabbi Shai Shacknai Memorial Prize in and Cancer Research in 1989, and Brazil's Order of the Southern Cross in 1991. In 1992, Tonegawa and his colleagues at MIT identified, for the first time, a specific gene which has an effect on the ability to learn. The *New York Times* reported that this research is "the first step toward discovering the entire repertoire of genes that affect function." Tonegawa was married to the former Mayumi Yoshinari on September 28, 1985. The couple has three children.

SELECTED WRITINGS BY TONEGAWA:

Periodicals

(With C. Steinberg, S. Dube, and A. Bernardini) "Evidence for Somatic Generation of Antibody Diversity," *Proceedings of the National Academy of Sciences, USA*, 1974, pp. 4027–31.

(With Steinberg) "Too Many Chains—Too Few Genes," *The Generation of Antibody Diversity: A New Look*, edited by A. Cunningham, Academic Press, 1976, pp. 175–82.

(With Richard Maki, John Kearney, and Christopher Paige) "Immunoglobulin Gene Rearrangement in Immature B Cells," *Science*, Volume 209, 1980, pp. 1366–69.

"The Molecules of the Immune System," *Scientific American*, October, 1985, pp. 122–31.

"Somatic Generation of Immune Diversity," *Bioscience Reports*, Volume 8, November 1, 1988, pp. 3–26.

FURTHER READING

Books

McGuire, Paula, editor, *Nobel Prize Winners Supplement 1987–1991*, Wilson, 1992, pp. 136–139.

Periodicals

Marx, Jean L., "Antibody Research Garners Nobel Prize," *Science*, October 23, 1987, pp. 484–85.

New York Times, July 14, 1992, p. C3.

Sketch by David E. Newton

Alexsandr Vasil'evich Topchiev
1907–1962

Russian organic chemist

Alexsandr Vasil'evich Topchiev was born in Russia in 1907. When Topchiev was 10 years old, the Russian Revolution began and soon led to the formation of the Union of Soviet Socialist Republics, or the Soviet Union, a

Alexsandr Vasil'evich Topchiev

profound change that was to affect Topchiev throughout his life. Like many scientists in the Soviet Union, Topchiev found that the road to success was through politics and cooperation with the national goals of his government.

Topchiev graduated from the Moscow Institute of Chemical Technology in 1930 and two years later joined the communist party, putting him in position to join the Soviet elite. He specialized in the economically important fields of food development and petroleum chemistry, and gained his initial reputation by the discovery of catalysts for obtaining usable chemicals, such as gasoline, from raw petroleum and for other processes used in treating petroleum. His services were especially important as Europe entered into World War II at the end of the 1930s, making production of fuel from petroleum vital to the war effort.

After World War II, development first of the atomic bomb and hydrogen bomb became an important priority, and Topchiev turned to nuclear chemistry, although he also stayed active in petroleum research. Because of the general secrecy of the Soviet research on fission and fusion weapons, not much is known in detail about Topchiev's activities in this field. He first went to England in 1955 for a conference on nuclear energy and was also a delegate at the opening of the world's first large-scale nuclear power plant in England in 1956. By 1958 he was able to deliver a paper on radioactive isotope s to the Geneva Congress on the Peaceful Uses of Atomic Energy. He also became involved in the Soviet space program of the 1950s, perhaps concerned with the chemistry of rocket fuel, but that too is shrouded in secrecy.

After World War II, Topchiev became a part of the Soviet government. He was the deputy Minister of Higher Education in the period from 1947 through 1949, and he continued as a deputy in the legislative body of Russia, known as the Supreme Soviet of the Russian Federation. After 1949, Topchiev suddenly became one of the members of the Soviet scientific elite, holding various posts in the Soviet Academy of Sciences, including the key one of scientific secretary of the academy. Consequently, he was generally addressed as "Academician Topchiev" instead of "Comrade Topchiev," the general way of speaking to a Soviet citizen. As Academician Topchiev, he was allowed to travel outside the U.S.S.R to international scientific conferences. During the post-Stalin period in the Soviet Union, Topchiev became involved with the political process known as de-Stalinization, but by 1958 his past caught up to him and he was ousted from his post as secretary of the academy. This did not, however, end his attendance at international conferences.

In 1957 Topchiev had been the first head of the Soviet delegations to the important series of scientific meetings on control of nuclear arms known as the Pugwash Conferences. These annual meetings were named after the location of the first such conference at Pugwash, Nova Scotia, the birthplace of Cyrus Eaton, an American multimillionaire who sponsored the early conferences. Although officially the scientists attending the conference were supposed to be individuals, the Soviet Union insisted on having a delegation and on naming a leader for it. The scientists from Western nations nicknamed the burly Russian "Top Chief" for his role in the conferences. He was known for his frequent speeches in favor of international peace and cooperation. Topchiev continued as delegation head through the 1962 conference. He died a few months later on December 27, 1962.

The Moscow Petroleum Institute, which he had headed since 1940, was later renamed the A.V. Topchiev Institute of Petrochemical Synthesis. During his life, Topchiev was awarded a Stalin Prize and on two occasions received the Order of Lenin.

SELECTED WRITINGS BY TOPCHIEV:

Books

(With L. S. Polak and R. H. Holroyd) *Radiolysis of Hydrocarbons,* Amsterdam, New York: Elsevier Publishing, 1964.
(With S. V. Zavgorodnii and V. G. Krychova) *Alkylation with Olefins,* Amsterdam, New York: Elsevier Publishing, 1964.
(With S. V. Zavgorodnii and Ya. M. Paushkin) *Boron Fluoride and its Compounds as Catalysts in Organic Chemistry.* (Translated by J. T. Greaves.) New York: Pergamon Press, 1959.

FURTHER READING:

Periodicals

Tomkeieff, S. I., "Academician A. V. Topchiev," *Nature* 4870 (March 2, 1963): p. 847.

Sketch by Bryan Bunch

Charles H. Townes
1915–
American physicist

Charles H. Townes was awarded a share of the 1964 Nobel Prize in physics for his discovery in 1951 of the maser, a device that can amplify microwaves for practical applications. About six years later, Townes speculated on the possibility of building a maser-like instrument using solid crystals instead of gasses. A device of this kind—the laser—was actually constructed two years afterwards by **Theodore Maiman**.

Charles Hard Townes was born in Greenville, South Carolina, on July 28, 1915. His father was Henry Keith Townes, an attorney, and his mother was the former Ellen Sumter Hard. Townes grew up in an intellectually stimulating environment in which both parents had an avid interest in natural history. He later told Shirley Thomas in a sketch for the book *Men of Space* that "there was always an inclination toward science" in his family. He was convinced that, had the opportunity been available, his father "would have become a very excellent scientist."

Townes's genius was obvious early on. His parents allowed him to skip seventh grade, and by age 16 he was ready to enter Furman University in his hometown of Greenville. Although he planned to major in science, he also took a full schedule of language classes. As a result, he was able to graduate in 1935 with a B.S. in physics and a B.A. in modern languages. He continued his mastery of French, German, Italian, Russian, and Spanish throughout his life. In addition to his demanding class work at Furman, Townes was also curator of the college museum and a member of the band, glee club, swimming team, and newspaper staff.

Townes entered Duke University in the fall of 1935 to work on his master's degree. In addition to his thesis research on van der Graaf generators, he continued his study of French, Italian, and Russian. Having completed his work at Duke (various biographers credit him with either an M.A. or an M.S., awarded in either 1936 or 1937), Townes headed for the California Institute of Technology (Cal Tech) in Pasadena, California. There he completed his doctoral research on the spin of the carbon–13 nucleus in 1939 and was awarded his Ph.D.

War Research Leads to Interest in Microwaves

An offer from Bell Laboratories to pay Townes a salary of $3,016 a year "astonished" him, according to Mary Ann Harrell in *Those Inventive Americans*. He could scarcely believe that a career in physics would be "so highly paid," and he accepted the Bell offer quickly. Townes found an apartment in New York City and began to take full advantage of the city's cultural opportunities. He took evening classes at the Julliard School of Music and, according to Harrell, "changed apartments every three months to explore the city thoroughly."

For most of his time at Bell, Townes worked on projects related to national defense. In particular, he was involved in the development of systems. At one point he warned the army against using a three-centimeter band radar wave detection system because he knew that water molecules absorb in this range and that the system would, therefore, be ineffective. Having ignored this advice, the army built three-centimeter radar devices anyway, only to find that they would not work.

As the pressures of war research receded, Townes turned his attention to a problem many scientists and engineers were thinking about: finding a way to amplify microwaves so that they could be used in practical applications, as were and radar waves. **Albert Einstein** had outlined a theoretical method for accomplishing this goal in 1917. He suggested using individual atoms as resonators rather than using macroscopic-sized objects. The problem was that, by 1950, no one had found a way to build a working device based on Einstein's principle.

Townes's breakthrough in this area came while he was sitting on a park bench in Washington D.C.'s Franklin Square in 1951, waiting for a restaurant to open so that he could have breakfast. As Harrell tells the story, "six years of work suddenly blossomed into insight: a way to make amonia molecules amplify . . . microwaves by the process Einstein had outlined." In classic storybook fashion, Townes outlined his ideas on the back of an old envelope he found in his pocket.

Producing a device that actually worked according to his theory, however, was no simple matter. Townes worked with two colleagues, James P. Gordon and H. J. Zeiger, for more than two years before they had success. Finally, in late 1953, the three produced a successful model of Townes's Franklin Square idea, a device that amplified an incoming microwave beam while maintaining the signal wave's phase. They gave to their invention the name maser (for microwave amplification by stimulated emission of radiaiton). For his discovery of the maser, Townes was awarded a share of the 1964 Nobel Prize in physics. He shared that prize with two Russian scientists, **N. G. Basov** and **Aleksandr Prokhorov**, who had independently and somewhat earlier come up with a similar method for using the Einstein principle to build a maser-like device, which they called a "molecular."

Outlines Laser Theory

By the time Townes announced the first working in 1954, he had already been at Columbia University for six years, having been appointed full professor there in 1954. He continued to teach and do research at Columbia until 1961, when he resigned to become professor of and provost at the Massachusetts Institute of Technology (MIT). While still at Columbia, he developed a theory with his brother-in-law **Arthur L. Schawlow** that described a method by which a maser-like device could be built that would operate with visible light instead of microwaves. Theodore Maiman's laser provided proof of Townes and Schawlow's theory some two years later.

In 1966 Townes left MIT to become University Professor of Physics at the University of California at Berkeley, where he remained until his retirement in 1986. Townes was married on May 4, 1941, to the former Francis H. Brown, and they raised four children. Townes has received many honors and awards in addition to his 1964 Nobel Prize in physics. These include the Liebmann Memorial Prize of the Institute of Radio Engineers, the Sarnoff Award of the Institute of Electrical Engineers, the Comstock Medal of the National Academy of Sciences, the Ballantine Medal of the Franklin Institute, the Distinguished Public Service Medal of the National Aeronautics and Space Administration, and the National Medal of Science from the National Science Foundation.

SELECTED WRITINGS BY TOWNES:

Books

(With A. L. Schawlow) *Microwave Spectroscopy*, McGraw-Hill, 1955.
(Editor) *Quantum Electronic: A Symposium,* Columbia University Press, 1960.

Periodicals

(With J. P. Gordon and H. J. Zeiger) "Molecular Microwave Oscillator and New Hyperfine Structure in the Microwave Spectrum of NH_3XN," *Physical Review*, July 1, 1954, pp. 282–84.

FURTHER READING:

Books

Current Biography 1963, H. W. Wilson, 1963, pp. 423–425.
Harrell, Mary Ann, in *Those Inventive Americans*, National Geographic Society, 1971, pp. 218–227.
McGraw-Hill Modern Scientists and Engineers, Volume 10, McGraw-Hill, 1980, pp. 227–228.

Thomas, Shirley, *Men of Space*, Volume 5, Chilton
    Books, 1962, pp. 221–251.
Weber, Robert L., *Pioneers of Science: Nobel Prize
    Winners in Physics*, American Institute of Physics,
    1980, pp. 195–196.

Periodicals

Gordon, J. P., "Research on Maser-Laser Principal
    Wins Nobel Prize in Physics," *Science*, November
    13, 1964, pp. 897–899.

Sketch by David E. Newton

Mildred Trotter
1899–1991
American anatomist

Mildred Trotter was an anatomist and physical anthropologist whose pioneering bone studies contributed to a wide range of disciplines, including medicine, forensics, engineering, and aeronautics. "She has been responsible for the largest single increase in our knowledge of bone, both as a tissue and as the primary locus of the mineral mass of the human body," observed Dr. Stanley M. Garn, professor of nutrition at the University of Michigan. Her method for using the length of certain bones to estimate the height of their owners in life has been a primary tool of forensic experts and physical anthropologists since its formulation in 1952. Also, her studies of human hair have disproved many popular myths and contributed to the understanding of hypertrichosis, or excessive hair growth.

Trotter was born on February 3, 1899, to farmers of German and Irish extraction. James R. and Jennie (nee Zimmerley) Trotter also produced two other daughters, Sarah Isabella and Jeannette Rebecca, and a son, Robert James. Trotter's parents were active Presbyterians and Democrats, and, in addition to farming, her father served for a time as community school director. Trotter attended grammar school in a one-room facility, graduating in 1913. She completed high school in nearby Beaver, Pennsylvania, where, as her hometown paper would report in a career retrospective, the principal objected to her choice of geometry over home economics as a subject for study.

Trotter enrolled at Mt. Holyoke College where she majored in zoology. While there she found role models in female professors and the zoology department head. In an interview late in life, Trotter recalled that she "never even thought, let alone worried, about being a woman in science" as a result of their influence. Upon graduating, Trotter rejected a better-paying job as a high school biology teacher to work as a research assistant to Dr. C. H. Danforth, an associate professor of anatomy at Washington University in St. Louis, Missouri. Danforth had received funding to study hypertrichosis from an anonymous donor whose wife and daughters suffered from excessive facial hair. Trotter's work on the subject earned her credit toward a masters degree in anatomy, which she received in 1921. After the donor pledged more funds, she continued her study of hair, using it as the basis of her doctoral thesis in 1924. As a result of her analysis, Trotter determined that hair follicles keep to fixed patterns of growth, resting, and shedding; she also discovered that women have as much facial hair as men. In addition she disproved such common myths as the belief that sun exposure cures baldness or that shaving thickens hair. Trotter's collected papers on hair were published serially, then in book form by the American Medical Association in 1925 under Danforth's name.

Farmer's Daughter Turns "Bone Detective"

Upon completing her studies, Trotter was made an instructor at Washington University. Not long afterwards, she accepted a National Research Council Fellowship to study physical anthropology at Oxford for the year 1926. Although she had planned to continue her research on hair, she was asked instead to study bones, specifically museum specimens from ancient Egypt and Roman-era Britain. During the course of her stay at Oxford, Trotter discovered that she "liked studying skeletons better than studying hair." When she received yet another fellowship, the head of Washington's anatomy department offered her a promotion to assistant professor, which she accepted over the grant. Her career stalled, however, despite a steadily increasing workload, and she did not receive another promotion until sixteen years later when she straightforwardly asked the department chair to explain why she had been passed over. He responded by convening a review committee, and in 1946 Trotter became the first woman to attain full professorship at Washington University's Medical School. In all, Trotter spent over fifty-five years on the university's staff, during which time she published numerous papers on the human skeleton, including studies of growth cycles, sexual and racial differences, and changes in mineral mass and density occurring with age.

In 1948 Trotter, growing restless in her position at the university, took an unpaid sabbatical to volunteer as director of the Central Identification Laboratory at Schofield Barracks, Oahu, Hawaii. For the next fourteen months she and her team identified the skeletal remains of war dead found in the Pacific theater. During this time she also secured permission from the U.S. Army to conduct allometric studies using the long limb bones of identified dead, one of the first times that war casualties were used for scientific research. From these studies Trotter then devised a formula for estimating the stature of a person based upon the relative length of the long bones. Published in 1952, her update of nineteenth-century French stature estimation tables was described in a 1989 *Journal of Forensic Sciences* article as "a landmark study in physical anthropology."

Trotter returned to Washington University in 1949. Soon after, the new department chair eliminated the adjective "gross" from her title Professor of Anatomy—an important distinction to Trotter who had fought to be accepted as an equal in a field dominated by microscopic research. During the 1950s and 1960s Trotter began attracting national and international attention for her work. In 1955 she was asked to serve as president of the American Association of Physical Anthropologists, an organization she helped found in 1930. A year later she became the first female recipient of the Wenner-Gren Foundation's Viking Fund Medal. She was asked by the editors of *Encyclopedia Britannica* to contribute entries on the skin and exoskeleton for their 1953 and 1956 editions. In addition she gathered material for reference books in her field, such as a lab guide, an anatomical atlas, and a dictionary of Latin nomenclature. Trotter also served as a consultant to the Rockefeller Foundation, lecturing in London and Washington, D.C., and as a visiting professor to Uganda's Makerere University College.

Along with her academic responsibilities, Trotter also sat on the St. Louis Anatomical Board and Missouri State Anatomical Board, serving as president of the latter from 1955 to 1957. St. Louis detectives regularly consulted with Trotter on missing persons and "John Doe" cases as well as on partial, sometimes nearly obliterated, physical evidence. For example, when police recovered a handful of blackened bones from a furnace, Trotter identified them as being from a human infant, not a small animal as originally suspected. She was also instrumental in passing legislation that enabled Missourians to donate their bodies to universities for medical research. When asked in 1980 about her practical approach to such morbid subjects, Trotter observed, "the attitude of our culture toward death is silly. We all know we have to die."

Coaches Nobel Laureates

Trotter's work as an instructor proved as important as her research. During her forty-one-year career as a full-time professor at Washington University, Trotter's students totaled into the thousands. Hundreds went on to careers as medical school faculty, prepared by her rigorous coursework. As Dr. John C. Herweg recalled in 1975, "we learned because we admired and respected her and because, to an extent, we feared her. After we had passed Gross Anatomy, we grew to love her as a friend." Her belief that students should learn not from books but from observing nature guided Trotter's instruction. "Learning to observe is one of the chief benefits of studying anatomy," she asserted during an interview in 1975. Two of Trotter's students, **Earl Sutherland** and **Daniel Nathans**, went on to win Nobel Prizes in medicine.

Upon her retirement in 1967, Trotter was named professor emeritus and lecturer in anatomy and neurobiology. She continued to publish scientific papers, and eight years later she became the first female faculty member to be honored by the medical school with a lectureship in her name. Trotter, who never married, spent leisure time in later years knitting, gardening, or auditing classes at the university until she suffered a disabling stroke. Upon her death on August 23, 1991, her body was donated to the Washington University School of Medicine.

SELECTED WRITINGS BY TROTTER:

Books

Laboratory Guide for Gross Anatomy, 2nd ed., Bardgett Printing and Publishing Co., 1957.
Personal Identification in Mass Disasters, Estimation of Stature from Intact Long Limb Bones, edited by T. D. Steward, Smithsonian Institution, 1970, pp. 71–83.
Encyclopedia of Microscopy and Microtechnique, Hair, pp. 233–234, edited by Peter Gray, Van Nostrand Reinhold Co., 1973.

Periodicals

American Journal of Physical Anthropology, Estimation of Stature from Long Limb Bones of American Whites and Negroes., no. 10, 1952.
American Journal of Physical Anthropology, Corrigenda to 'Estimation of Stature from Long Limb Bones of American Whites and Negroes,' American Journal of Physical Anthropology, 1952, no. 47, 1977.

FURTHER READING:

Periodicals

Kerley, Ellis R., *Trial,* Forensic Anthropology: Increasing Utility In Civil and Criminal Cases, January 1983, pp. 66–111.
Wood, W. Raymond and Lori Ann Stanley, *Journal of Forensic Sciences,* Recovery and Identification of World War II Dead: American Graves Registration Activities in Europe, Volume 34, 1989, pp. 1365–1373.

Other

Wood, W. Raymond and Lori Ann Stanley, *Journal of Forensic Sciences,* Recovery and Identification of World War II Dead: American Graves Registration Activities in Europe, Trotter Papers, Resource & Research Center for Beaver County & Local History, Inc., Carnegie Free Library, Beaver Falls, PA.
Wood, W. Raymond and Lori Ann Stanley, *Journal of Forensic Sciences,* Recovery and Identification of World War II Dead: American Graves Registration Activities in Europe, Trotter Papers, Washington University School of Medicine Library Archives, St. Louis, MO.

Sketch by Jennifer Kramer

John G. Trump
1907–1985
American electrical engineer

John G. Trump is best remembered for introducing key advances in radiation therapy for cancer. At the Massachusetts Institute of Technology (MIT), he worked closely with **Robert Van de Graaff** and adapted the latter's high-voltage electrostatic system for use as a generator of energetic X-ray beams. These beams offered the basis for Trump's cancer treatments. Initial clinical tests in the late 1930s showed promise, and Trump and Van de Graaff went on to found High Voltage Engineering Corporation, which built and sold such X-ray systems commercially.

John George Trump was born in New York City on August 21, 1907, the son of Frederick and Elizabeth (Christ) Trump. He received a B.S. in electrical engineering from Brooklyn Polytechnic Institute in 1929, followed by an M.A. in physics from Columbia University in 1931. He continued onward to MIT, where the dean of engineering, **Vannevar Bush**, suggested that he talk to Van de Graaff about a topic for a Ph.D. dissertation. Van de Graaff had invented an electrostatic accelerator, a machine capable of sustaining very high voltages using static electricity. In turn, these voltages could accelerate beams of electrons and other particles, for research in nuclear physics. Trump worked with him and won a D.Sc. in 1933, in electrical engineering.

Launches New Initiatives against Cancer

As a disease, cancer dates to antiquity; its name comes from Hippocrates. In the 1930s, the only effective treatment lay in surgery. X-ray systems of the era could generate beams with as much as 200,000 volts of energy, but such beams could not be focused on a tumor, particularly if it lay deep within a patient's body. Instead, the rays would scatter throughout adjacent tissues, damaging these tissues while doing little harm to the cancer.

Trump appreciated that the Van de Graaff system offered a route toward X-ray beams of much higher energy. Its high voltage could produce a particularly energetic electron beam, which would produce X-rays when this beam struck a target of heavy metal. In turn, energetic X-rays could penetrate the body with ease, delivering their energy to the tumor while producing much less damage to nearby tissues. Working with colleagues from Harvard Medical School, Trump built a million-volt X-ray source at Boston's Huntington Memorial Hospital. The first cancer patient was treated with the equipment in March 1937. Trump, meanwhile, was pursuing research that showed how to raise the voltage of such a system while reducing its size. This led to development of a far more compact X-ray source of 1.25

million volts. It entered clinical use at Massachusetts General Hospital in the spring of 1940.

World War II then intervened, with Trump taking an active role in the development and use of radar. He served as chairman of the radar division of the National Defense Research Committee. In 1944 he became director of the British branch of MIT's Radiation Laboratory, the nation's principal center for radar development. He also served as a member of a specialist group advising General Carl Spaatz, who led the Eighth Air Force, the nation's main force of heavy bombers in the war against Germany. Returning to MIT after the war, he took over the directorship of that university's High Voltage Research Laboratory, a post he held until 1980. Also in 1946, he cofounded the firm of High Voltage Engineering. Its purpose lay in taking the Van de Graaff generator out of the esoteric world of physics research, selling these systems commercially for use in treating cancer. Trump's firm faced competition from General Electric (GE) and from Allis-Chalmers, which also were entering this field. But Trump proposed to offer a 2-million-volt unit for $75,000, about $50,000 less than a similar system from GE. This allowed him to win start-up funding from a Boston venture capital firm, American Research and Development. Trump also introduced the technique of rotating the patient. This permitted the X-ray beam to strike the tumor from all directions, while delivering minimal doses to surrounding tissues. In 1949 the first patients received this treatment at Boston's Lahey Clinic.

Radiation therapy combined with rotation did not offer a magic bullet against cancer—indeed, no such bullet exists to this day—but it offered a valuable new treatment that could stand alongside the standard approach of surgery. Radiation could combat many inoperable or hard-to-reach tumors, as in the pituitary gland, which lies below the brain. At times radiation could also open the way to successful surgery, by stopping the spread of a malignancy and reducing the size of the primary tumor. Hugh Hare, head of the Department of Radiology at the Lahey Clinic, told *Collier's* magazine in 1953 that "this is the most promising method evolved so far of treating deep tumors susceptible to radiation, including many cases previously considered inaccessible."

Honored Repeatedly for Achievements

For his work in both war and peace, Trump received a number of high distinctions during his career. In 1946 the king of England, George VI, presented him with His Majesty's Medal for contributions to the Allied victory. Two years later, President Harry Truman awarded Trump a Presidential Citation. His work with cancer won him the Gold Medal of the American College of Radiology. This 1982 award was particularly noteworthy because it is generally bestowed on physicians, whereas Trump was an electrical engineer.

In 1935 Trump married Elora Gordon Sauerbrun. They had three children: John Gordon, Christine Elora, and Karen

Elizabeth. He was also the uncle of Donald Trump, the real-estate magnate. Trump died in Winchester, Massachusetts, on February 21, 1985, following a long illness. A month later the White House cited him anew, presenting him posthumously with the National Medal of Science.

SELECTED WRITINGS BY TRUMP:

Periodicals

Technology Review, Roentgen Rays against Cancer, December 1947, reprinted in Annual Report of the Board of Regents of the Smithsonian Institution, 1948, pp. 209–16.

FURTHER READING:

Periodicals

Cantwell, J. L., H. R. Stewart, and J. G. Trump, *Electrical Engineering,* John G. Trump: 1960 Lamme Medalist, August 1961, pp. 596–600.
Ratcliff, J. D., *Collier's,* The X-Ray Cannon and the Rotating Chair, January 3, 1953, pp. 36–38.
Robinson, Denis M., *Physics Today,* John George Trump, September, 1985, pp. 90, 92.
Robinson, Denis M., *Fortune,* Supervoltage Machines, April 1950, pp. 113–124.

Sketch by T.A. Heppenheimer

George T. Tsao
1931–
American chemical engineer

As director of the Laboratory of Renewable Resources Engineering at Purdue University, George T. Tsao has been in the forefront of research in biomass conversion—the process of extracting new energy sources from organic waste material. His studies in the development of alcohol fuels—such as gasahol—from cellulose materials, including urban organic garbage and agricultural waste, have won him international respect as well as helped to create viable alternatives to the burning of petroleum products in order to meet rising world energy demands.

Tsao was born on December 4, 1931, in Nanking, China, and received his early education in Taiwan. He earned his B.S. from National Taiwan University in 1953, and then travelled to the United States for graduate studies, completing his M.S. in 1956 at the University of Florida,

and his Ph.D. in chemical engineering in 1960 at the University of Michigan. After graduation, Tsao held a one-year assistant professorship in physics at Olivet College, and then worked as a chemical engineer for Merck & Company for another year before becoming research chemist for the Tennessee Valley Authority. Tsao's career continued to alternate between industry and academia for the next several years: From 1962 to 1965, he worked for Miles Labs in the research department, specializing in hydrolysis and fermentation; in 1966 he accepted a position at Iowa State University, first as an associate professor of chemical engineering, and then as a full professor; and in 1977 he moved to Purdue University as a professor of chemical engineering and agricultural engineering, eventually becoming the director of Purdue's Laboratory of Renewable Resources Engineering (LORRE).

Focuses on Biomass Conversion

At Purdue, Tsao set himself a formidable task: to convert cellulose—the primary carbohydrate substance in plants—into glucose, a type of sugar. By converting cellulose waste materials such as garbage and grain stalks into glucose, Tsao could then ferment the sugar into ethanol, a burnable fuel alcohol. Others before Tsao had tackled this problem with little success. Not only does cellulose have a strong crystalline structure, it is also protected by a layer of lignin, a substance that binds the cellulose fiber together. As Tsao said in *Pioneers of Alcohol Fuels,* "The structure of a piece of cellulosic material resembles that of a reinforced concrete pillar with cellulose fibers being the metal rods, and lignin the natural cement." The problem, then, was not only to break down the crystalline structure of cellulose, but also to somehow tear apart the lignin shield.

Tsao's solution was to use sulfuric acid in a multistep process by which crop waste is converted into three usable by–products: glucose; lignin; and hemicellulose, a carbohydrate containing several sugars that occurs in plants and that is more easily hydrolyzed or decomposed than cellulose. The glucose, which is the primary by–product, is fermented into ethanol; the lignin is dried and then processed into a coal-like substance for fuel; and the hemicellulose is processed to extract sugars that can be made into plastic. In effect, Tsao came up with a biomass conversion process that would not only produce ethanol at approximately eighty cents per gallon, but also would—as a result of the secondary products—pay for the energy it used in the conversion process. Yet Tsao's work was far from done. He spent much time during the next several years testifying before Congress and campaigning for sufficient funds to support the project.

In addition to his work in biomass conversion, Tsao has also studied industrial carbohydrates, enzyme engineering, and the utilization of agricultural and natural products, as well as waste disposal. He is a member of the American Chemical Society, the American Institute of Chemical Engineers, and the American Society of Engineering Educators.

SELECTED WRITINGS BY TSAO:

Books

Research in the General Field of the Mechanism of Cellulose Synthesis and Degradation, University of Florida, 1955.

Treatment of Aqueous Agricultural Wastes for Clean Water and for Microbial Protein Production, Iowa State University, 1971.

Investigations on Mixing, Flow, and Fluidization in Systems of Cereal Starches and Flours, Iowa State University, 1975.

Conversion of Biomass from Agriculture into Useful Products, U.S. Department of Energy, 1978.

Periodicals

ASPAC Technical Bulletin, Ethanol and Chemicals from Cellulosics, December 1984, pp. 1–9.

Biological Wastes, Methane Generation from Chemically Pretreated Cellulose by Anaerobic Fluidized-Bed Reactors, Volume 29, 1989, pp. 201–210.

Biotechnology and Bioengineering, Some Considerations for Optimization of Desorption Chromatography, January 5, 1991, pp. 65-70.

Process Biochemistry, Hydrolysis of Maltose and Corn-starch by Glucoamylase Immobilized in Porous Glass Fibres and Beads, May 1992, pp. 177–181.

Biotechnology and Bioengineering, An Energetic Model for Oxygen-Limited Metabolism, December 1993, pp. 1270–1276.

FURTHER READING:

Books

Burns, Paul, and others, *Pioneers of Alcohol Fuels,* Volume 1, Citizens' Energy Project, 1981, pp. 29–32.

Sketch by J. Sydney Jones

Konstantin Tsiolkovsky
1857–1935
Russian aerospace engineer

Konstantin Tsiolkovsky

Konstantin Tsiolkovsky was almost entirely self-educated, yet became one of the greatest Russian scientists of the early twentieth century. He studied and wrote about a wide range of scientific topics, but is best known for his pioneering work in astronautics. As early as the 1890s he had begun preliminary calculations on the mathematics and physics of space flight, which he saw as the first step in the colonization of space by humans. When the Soviet Union was prepared to launch the world's first artificial satellite, *Sputnik 1,* it attempted to do so on the one-hundredth anniversary of Tsiolkovsky's birth. It failed to meet that precise deadline, but the flight was still dedicated as a memorial to Tsiolkovsky's life and work. Throughout his life, Tsiolkovsky saw himself as far more than a scientist working on abstract problems; his goal was to work for the betterment of life for all humans.

Konstantin Eduardovich Tsiolkovsky was born on September 17, 1857, in the Russian village of Izhevskoye in the province of Ryazan. His mother was the former Maria Yumasheva and his father, Eduard Tsiolkovsky, a forester, teacher, and minor government official. The Tsiolkovsky family moved frequently while Konstantin was young, and their financial situation was often very difficult.

Until the age of ten, Tsiolkovsky led a childhood that was typical for the time. His biographer V. N. Sokolsky says that "he liked games, went skating in winter, sent up kites, climbed fences, and dreamt of becoming strong and agile." Then disaster struck. Tsiolkovsky was taken seriously ill in 1867, which caused him to lose his hearing.

For a period of time, Tsiolkovsky was despondent about his misfortune. He later wrote in his autobiography that the three years that followed his illness "was the saddest time of my life." Gradually, however, he worked his way through this difficult period. He began to develop an intense interest in science, teaching himself at every step along the way. Once again in his autobiography, Tsiolkovsky explained that "there were very few books, and I had no teachers at all. . . . There were no hints, no aid from anywhere; there was a great deal that I couldn't understand in those books and I had to figure out everything by myself."

In 1873 Tsiolkovsky's father found enough money to send his son to Moscow. There Tsiolkovsky continued his self-education, albeit in an intellectually richer surrounding. He built himself an trumpet that allowed him to attend lectures, but could not afford to enroll in any formal college or university program. At the end of three years in Moscow, Tsiolkovsky returned to his home town where he continued to teach himself science, build models of all kinds of machines, and carry out original experiments.

Early Studies

In 1879 Tsiolkovsky passed the examination for a school teaching license and took a job as instructor of arithemtic and geometry at the Borovsk Uyzed School in Kaluga. Simultaneously he continued his own research and in 1880 wrote his first scientific paper, "The Graphical Depiction of Sensations." The paper was an attempt to express human sensations in strict mathematical formulas.

A year later, in 1881, Tsiolkovsky wrote his second paper, "The Theory of Gasses." The paper is extraordinary in that it outlines a theory very similar to one developed two decades earlier by James Clerk Maxwell. Tsiolkovsky, however, had not heard of Maxwell's work nor was he familiar with any of the studies that Maxwell had used as the basis of his theory, including those of Rudolf Clausius, Ludwig Boltzmann, and **Johannes van der Waals**. The Russian Physico-Chemical Society, to which Tsiolkovsky sent his paper, greatly admired his work and offered its support for his future research, but decided that the paper did not qualify for publication.

Tsiolkovsky's next paper, written in 1882–83, was "On the Theoretical Mechanics of a Living." In that paper Tsiolkovsky analyzed the ways in which natural forces, such as gravity, affect the structure and movement of human beings. This paper was not published either, although it impressed the Physico-Chemical Society sufficiently to elect Tsiolkovsky as one of its members.

Tsiolkovsky's interest in flight can be traced at least to the age of fifteen, when he posed for himself the problem "what size a balloon should be to carry people aloft if made of a shell of a definite thickness." More than a decade later he wrote his first paper on this subject, "The Theory and Experiment of a Horizontally Elongated Balloon." In 1887 he was invited to lecture to a meeting of the Society of Lovers of Natural Science on his ideas. He continued to work on lighter-than-air machines for more than a decade, but failed to obtain funding with which to build working models of his ideas. Those who controlled the purse strings

for scientific research could see no practical utility for the metal dirigible that Tsiolkovsky envisioned."

By the mid-1880s, Tsiolkovsky had also begun to think about heavier-than-air craft. One of his first papers on the subject, written in 1890, was entitled "On the Problem of Flying by Means of Wings." In it, Tsiolkovsky completed one of the earliest mathematical studies of the forces operating on the wings and body of an aircraft. The 1890 paper was followed by other studies on the shape of aircraft fuselages, the cantilevering of wings, the use of internal engines in aircraft, the shape of wings, and other important features of heavier-than-air machines. His research was essentially unaffected by his acceptance of a high-school teaching job in Kaluga in 1892.

Constructs the First Wind Tunnel

Tsiolkovsky was well aware of the fact that most of his ideas were theoretical speculations that needed to be tested in actual experiments. To that end, he designed the first wind tunnel to be built in Russia. The wind tunnel, first put to use in Kaluga in 1897, produced a stream of air that could be forced over aircraft bodies and wings of various size, shape, and design. Tsiolkovsky described the preliminary results of his wind tunnel experiments in an 1897 paper on "Air Pressure on Surfaces Introduced into an Artificial Air Flow." Encouraged by his success, Tsiolkovsky appealed to the Russian Academy of Sciences for a grant that would allow him to continue and to extend his wind tunnel experiments. He was successful in getting an award of 470 rubles (worth about $235 at the time) to build a larger wind tunnel. The grant was apparently the only financial assistance that Tsiolkovsky ever received while Russia was ruled by czarist governments. In May 1900, construction on the larger wind tunnel began, and experiments in it were started before the end of the same year.

For all his many achievements, Tsiolkovsky will probably best be remembered for his accomplishments in the field of astronautics or travel. He first began to wonder about this subject during his three-year stay in Moscow from 1873 to 1876. In a 1904 article, he wrote that his first thoughts on space travel dazzled him. "I was excited, even staggered," he wrote, "to such an extent that I could not sleep all night; I wandered about Moscow and kept thinking of the great consequences of my discovery."

By the late 1870s, Tsiolkovsky's ideas about spacecraft and space travel were pouring forth at an astonishing rate. They dealt with virtually every aspect of the subject. In about 1879, for example, he designed an instrument for measuring the effects of gravitational acceleration on the human body. Four years later he outlined the mechanism by which a jet rocket could carry an object into space. In the early 1890s he was writing about space travel to the moon, other planets, and beyond. His 1895 article "Dreams of the Earth and Sky and the Effects of Universal Gravitation" first set forth the concept of an artificial Earth, which he describes as "something like the Moon, but arbitrarily close to our planet, just outside its atmosphere." By 1896,

Tsiolkovsky was also deriving the mathematical formulas needed to describe the movement of a space craft. A year later he worked out the fundamental relationship among the velocity and mass of a rocket and the exhaust velocity of the propellant used to send it into space. That formula is now known as the basic rocket equation.

One of the consequences of Tsiolkovsky's research was his realization that the most efficient way of placing rockets into space is to arrange them in packets, or "cosmic rocket trains" as he called them in a 1929 article. These trains made use of the concept of "staging," as it is known today, in which a series of rocket engines are fired successively to put an object into space.

Argues for the Colonization of Space

In his work on astronautics, Tsiolkovsky investigated virtually every technical question that bears on the subject. He worked intensively, for example, on the kinds of fuels that would work best as rocket propellants, eventually settling on a mixture of liquid hydrogen and liquid oxygen as the best choice. In 1903, he completed a historic paper, "Investigations of Outer Space by Reaction Devices," that summarized his work in a variety of fields. That paper did not actually appear in print until it was published in the journal *Vestnik vozdukhoplavaniya* (*Herald of Aeronautics*) in 1911–12. This paper also provided an outline of Tsiolkovsky's views on the colonization of space. He argued that space travel should not be viewed as some abstract scientific experiment, but as a way of creating new human communities outside the Earth. "In all likelihood," he wrote in the paper, "the better part of humanity will never perish but will move from sun to sun as each one dies out in succession" In 1920, Tsiolkovsky wrote a popular exposition of his ideas about space travel in a book called *Beyond the Earth.* The book was an attempt to describe to nonscientists what space traveland living in space would be like.

The first sixty years of Tsiolkovsky's life were extremely difficult, not only because of the suffocating poverty in which he lived, but also because of the indifference of his colleagues to his work. He once wrote that "it is hard to work by oneself many years and under unfavorable conditions and not experience any gratification or support at all."

The October Revolution of 1917 brought about a remarkable change in Tsiolkovsky's life, however. He was elected a member of the Socialist Academy and was given a pension by the Council of the Peoples' Commissariats of the Russian Federation. For the first time in his life, Tsiolkovsky could concentrate on his scientific research with some degree of comfort. An indication of the impact this pension made on Tsiolkovsky's productivity is the fact that about one-quarter of his five-hundred-plus papers were written in the six decades between 1857 and 1917, and the remaining three-quarters in the last two decades of his life.

During the late 1920s, Tsiolkovsky began to spend more time on problems of aeronautics. Typical of the papers written during this period were "A New Airplane" and "Reactive Airplane," as well as studies of issues further removed from air and space travel, including "A Common Alphabet for the Human Race," "The Future of Earth and Man," "Auto-Trailer on Tracks," "Solar Energy and Its Applications," and "The Elasticity of Solids."

On September 13, 1935, in an effort to gain a pension for his family, Tsiolkovsky bequeathed all of his books and papers to the Communist Party and the Soviet government. He died of at his home in Kaluga six days later. His home was later made into a museum that was badly damaged during World War II. After the launching of *Sputnik 1* in 1957, the home-museum became a popular sightseeing stop for visitors.

SELECTED WRITINGS BY TSIOLKOVSKY:

Books

Kosmicheskaia raketa: opytnaia podgotovka, Gostipografiia, 1927.
Atlas dirizhablia iz volnistoi stali, Mosoblpoligraf, 1931.
Reaktivnye letatel'nye apparaty, Nauka, 1964.
The Will of the Universe. Intellect Unknown. Mind and Passiona, Pamiat', 1992.

Periodicals

"Free Space," unpublished manuscript, 1883.
"The Aeroplane or Bird-Like (Aviation) Flying Machine," *Nauka i zhizn*, Volume 46, 1894.
"Investigation of World Spaces by Reactive Vehicles," *Vestnik vozdukhoplavaniya*, Volume 9, 1912.

SOURCES:

Books

Dictionary of Scientific Biography, Volume 13, Scribner's, 1975, pp. 482–484.
Sharpe, Mitchell R., "Tsiolkovsky," in *The McGraw-Hill Encylcopedia of World Biography*, Volume 11, McGraw-Hill, 1973, pp. 8-10.
Sokolsky, Volume N., compiler, *K. E. Tsiolkovsky: Selected Works*, translated by G. Yankovsky, Mir, 1968

Sketch by David E. Newton

Daniel Chee Tsui
1938–
American physicist

Daniel Chee Tsui's research in solid state physics has laid important groundwork for the development of superconductors, which are substances that can conduct an electric current with no resistance (or loss of energy) and which can also create powerful magnetic fields. Tsui was the first scientist to measure energy levels in the surface space charge layer of a semiconductor at the quantum, or subatomic level.

Tsui was born February 28, 1938, in Henan, China. Receiving his bachelor of arts degree from Augustana College in 1961, he went on to the University of Chicago, where he earned both his master's degree and Ph.D. in 1967. After graduation, Tsui remained at the university as a research fellow from 1967 to 1968. He then joined the technical staff at Bell Labs in Murray Hill, New Jersey, where he and his colleagues began studying the two-dimensional electron gas that is present at semiconductor interfaces. Examining the far infrared wavelengths of this gas through spectroscopy—a method by which the electromagnetic spectra can be observed—they were able to note the localization of the gas as well as the lack of a mobility edge in such a two-dimensional system. In 1981, Tsui and his colleagues discovered the fractional quantum Hall effect, which addresses the movement of electrons in a conductor at the quantum level.

In 1982, Tsui joined the faculty of Princeton University's electrical engineering department as the Arthur LeGrand Doty Professor. He is also a member of the associated faculty in physics at Princeton. Tsui's research there has concentrated on the electronic properties of metals (including cadmium and nickel), the surface properties of superconductors, and low-temperature superconductors. He is particularly interested in conduction in ultra-small structures, and quantum physics of electronic materials in strong magnetic fields and low temperatures. Tsui has published more than two hundred forty scientific papers.

A member of the National Academy of Sciences since 1987, Tsui has been married since 1964 and has two children. In recognition of his work in solid state physics, particularly for the discovery of the fractional quantized Hall effect, Tsui received the American Physical Society's Oliver E. Buckley Prize in 1984. Sharing the prize with him that year were H. L. Stormer and A. C. Gossard of Bell Laboratories. Since discovering the effect, Tsui has continued to research it.

SELECTED WRITINGS BY TSUI:

Periodicals

IEEE Journal of Quantum Electronics, The Fractional Quantum Hall Effect, Volume 22, 1986.

FURTHER READING:

Periodicals

Bulletin of the American Physical Society, Awards of Prizes by the American Physical Society, Volume 29, March 1984.

Sketch by F. C. Nicholson

Lap-Chee Tsui
1950–
Chinese-born Canadian molecular geneticist

Lap-Chee Tsui (pronounced "choy") is best known for his lead role in the discovery of the gene that causes cystic fibrosis. This inherited disease affects about 1 out of every 2,500 Caucasian children in the world. It can lead to a host of problems, including lung infections and digestive symptoms. Until recently, most people with cystic fibrosis died by age 30. In 1989, Tsui and his collaborators announced their landmark discovery of the cystic fibrosis gene in the journal *Science.* In an accompanying editorial, **Daniel E. Koshland, Jr.,** described the finding as "a milestone of major importance." Among other things, it was a crucial step in the search for a cure for this devastating disease.

Tsui was born in Shanghai, China, on December 21, 1950. He was the eldest of four children born to Jing-Lue Hsue, a salesman, and Hui-Ching (Wang) Hsue, a housewife. Tsui was raised and educated in Hong Kong. As a boy, he dreamed of being an architect. His love of drawing persists to this day, and he still creates his own diagrams and sketches. Young Tsui also liked to explore ponds with his friends, catching tadpoles and fish. One of his favorite pastimes was to buy silkworms, then feed the worms mulberry leaves. He later recalled getting into trouble for stripping the leaves from a neighbor's mulberry bush.

Explores the Nature of Diseases

Tsui went on to study biology at the Chinese University in Hong Kong, where he received a bachelor's degree in 1972 and a master's degree in 1974. By this point in his career, Tsui was already interested in studying the nature of diseases. His doctoral dissertation looked at the structure and early developmental stages of bacteriophage lamba, a virus that infects bacteria. It was not until after he had earned a Ph.D. from the University of Pittsburgh in 1979, however, that Tsui first began to focus on genetic research.

For a short time after completing his Ph.D., Tsui trained in the biology division of Oak Ridge National

Lap-Chee Tsui

Laboratory in Tennessee. Then, in 1981, he moved to the Hospital for Sick Children in Toronto. Initially a postdoctoral fellow at the hospital, Tsui became a staff scientist there two years later. Today he continues to do research at the hospital, where he now holds the title of geneticist-in-chief. At the same time, he is a professor of molecular and medical genetics at the University of Toronto.

Finds the Cystic Fibrosis Gene

When Tsui first arrived at the Hospital for Sick Children, scientists were just developing new ways to identify defective genes. Tsui and his coworkers were looking for a genetic marker; in other words, a variation in deoxyribonucleic acid (DNA) that is associated with the defective gene that causes cystic fibrosis. Tsui, together with Manuel Buchwald and other scientists, identified the first such marker in 1985. Four years later, Tsui led a team of scientists that found the defective gene that causes cystic fibrosis and defined the main defect involved. The gene, which sits on the long arm of human chromosome 7, was dubbed the Cystic Fibrosis Transmembrane Regulator. This discovery marked the culmination of seven years of painstaking work, much of it done in Tsui's cramped, cluttered lab at the hospital.

Having found the defective gene, Tsui and his coworkers set about determining what was wrong with it. There are 150,000,000 base pairs, or units, of DNA on chromosome 7. The mutation Tsui found involves a deletion of just three base pairs. While this is the main defect involved in cystic

fibrosis, hundreds of other mutations have since been linked to the disease as well. To advance the study of such mutations, Tsui organized an information exchange among 150 research labs in 35 countries. The success of this group effort, the first of its kind, has served as a model for the study of other genetic diseases. In more recent work, Tsui and his colleagues identified a modifier gene that can affect the severity of cystic fibrosis.

Thanks to Tsui, scientists now have a much clearer picture of how cystic fibrosis does its harm. Tsui and his coworkers found that the DNA sequence with the main mutation is part of the instructions for making a particular protein. This protein, in turn, is part of the cell membrane in certain mucus-producing cells that line organs such as the lungs and pancreas. All proteins are composed of long chains of amino acids. Of the 1,480 amino acids making up this particular protein, it turns out that people with cystic fibrosis are missing a single, critical one. As a result, their bodies produce abnormally thick, sticky mucus that can clog the lungs and lead to fatal infections. The thick mucus can also block the pancreas, interfering with normal digestion.

Maps Human Chromosome 7

In addition to the cystic fibrosis work, Tsui and his colleagues have been striving to create a complete map of human chromosome 7. This map should make it easier to identify other disease-causing genes located on the chromosome. In the process, Tsui and his coworkers have developed a number of new chromosome mapping techniques. Another line of current research is a study aimed at identifying the defective gene responsible for Tourette's syndrome. This severe neurological disorder typically leads to facial and body tics and uncontrollable verbal outbursts. Tsui also manages the DNA sequencing facility for the Canadian Genetic Disease Network and a physical mapping facility for the Canadian human genome project.

Tsui has published over 250 scientific papers. He has received a number of awards for his research, including the Paul di Sant'Agnese Distinguished Scientific Achievement Award from the Cystic Fibrosis Foundation, the Award of Excellence from the Genetic Society of Canada, the Gairdner International Award, the Starstedt Research Prize, and the Medal of Honor from the Canadian Medical Association. In 1991, Tsui was presented the Order of Canada. He has also received honorary doctoral degrees from universities in Canada, Hong Kong, and the United States. Tsui is a senior scientist in the Medical Research Council of Canada and a fellow in the Royal Societies of Canada and London.

Past Mentors and Future Directions

"Great Canadian Scientists," a site on the World Wide Web, contains a page devoted to Tsui. On this page, Tsui identifies mentors who have influenced his work. They include K. K. Mark, who taught him "how to concentrate on a single thing, and be good at it;" Roger Hendricks, who taught him "how to encourage independent thinking" in students; Manuel Buchwald, who taught him "how to be critical and look at the broad perspective;" and Han Chang, who taught him "how to be flexible [and] adaptive" and helped him to understand "the Western (American) way of thinking."

Tsui married Ellen Lan Fong on February 11, 1977. The couple has two sons, Eugene and Felix. Tsui travels widely, giving lectures to scientists, physicians, and students around the world. He devotes much of his spare time to volunteer work within the Chinese community. Tsui especially enjoys good food and wine. His other leisure interests range from basketball to the music of Puccini.

In 1989, *Maclean's* magazine named Tsui to its "honor roll." Writing in the magazine, D'Arcy Jenish and Brian Willer observed that "if Tsui and his fellow researchers or others solve the mysteries of cystic fibrosis, doctors may eventually be able to administer drugs to correct the genetic defect and eliminate the symptoms. . . .The dedication of scientists such as Tsui gives victims of that disease—and of other genetic disorders—new reasons to have hope." Tsui himself is optimistic about the future of cystic fibrosis research. Writing to contributor Linda Wasmer Smith, he notes that his team's recent progress in finding modifiers of disease severity "has generated renewed excitement in disease gene research."

SELECTED WRITINGS BY TSUI:

Books

(Editor with Giovanni Romeo, Rainer Greger, and Sergio Gorini) *The Identification of the CF Cystic Fibrosis Gene: Recent Progress and New Research Strategies.* New York: Plenum Press, 1991.

Periodicals

(With Johanna M. Rommens, Michael C. Iannuzzi, Bat-Sheva Kerem et al.) "Identification of the Cystic Fibrosis Gene: Chromosome Walking and Jumping," *Science* (September 8, 1989): pp. 1059-1065.
(With John R. Riordan, Johanna M. Rommens, Bat-Sheva Kerem et al.) "Identification of the Cystic Fibrosis Gene: Cloning and Characterization of Complementary DNA," *Science* (September 8, 1989): pp. 1066-1073.
(With Bat-Sheva Kerem, Johanna M. Rommens, Janet A. Buchanan et al.) "Identification of the Cystic Fibrosis Gene: Genetic Analysis," *Science* (September 8, 1989): pp. 1073-1080.

FURTHER READING:

Books

Biographical Encyclopedia of Scientists, 2nd edition. Bristol: Institute of Physics Publishing, 1994, p. 891.

Periodicals

Jenish, D'Arcy and Brian Willer, "Discoveries of Hope at the Heart of Human Life: Lap-Chee Tsui," *Maclean's* (December 25, 1989): pp. 22-23.
Koshland, Daniel E., Jr. "The Cystic Fibrosis Gene Story," *Science* (September 8, 1989): p. 1029.

Other

"Lap-Chee Tsui: Molecular Geneticist," http://www.science.ca/scientists/Tsui/tsui.html (October 14, 1997).

Sketch by Linda Wasmer Smith

Mikhail Tswett
1872–1919
Russian chemist and botanist

Although recognized only belatedly, Mikhail Tswett (sometimes spelled Tsvet) was the first to lay out in detail the methods of the separation technique called chromatography. Tswett himself regarded chromatography only as a tool in his chemical and biological studies; his purpose was to separate and identify the many different pigments in leaves and other plant parts, and he considered it merely an improvement on existing techniques such as acid-extraction, base-extraction, and fractional crystallization. Since he first described this process, many kinds of chromatography have been developed, and no laboratory is considered complete without a number of chromatographic instruments.

Mikhail Semyonovich Tswett was born May 14, 1872, in Asti, in the northwest part of Italy, about seventy miles from the Swiss border. His parents were Semyon Nikolaevich and Maria de Dorozza Tswett. His father was a Russian civil servant and his mother, who was very young, died soon after his birth. His father returned to Russia after her death, and left his son with a nurse in Lausanne. Tswett was educated in Lausanne and Geneva, becoming multilingual in the process. He received his secondary education at the Collège Gaillard in Lausanne and the Collège de St. Antoine in Geneva; he entered the University of Geneva in 1891, studying chemistry, botany, and physics. His baccalaureate in both physical and natural sciences was awarded in 1892. He began plant research during his undergraduate years, earning the Davy Prize while a doctoral student with a paper on plant physiology that was subsequently published. In 1896 he defended his thesis, "Études de physiologie cellulaire," and received his doctoral degree.

Thereafter he moved to Russia, and in 1897 he began working at the laboratory of plant anatomy and physiology at the Academy of Sciences and the St. Petersburg Biological Laboratory. His academic horizon was limited by the fact that foreign degrees were not recognized in tsarist Russia, and he set to work earning another master's degree in botany at Kazan University. He finished in 1901, with a thesis in Russian whose title is translated "The Physicochemical Structure of the Chlorophyll Grain." In 1902 Tswett became an assistant in the laboratory of plant anatomy and physiology at the University of Warsaw, which was under Russian control at that time, where he became a full professor in 1903. In 1907 he took on the additional task of teaching botany and microbiology at the Warsaw Veterinary Institute; a year later he was also teaching at the Warsaw Technical University. He resigned his teaching post at the University of Warsaw but took a second doctorate there in 1910 with a dissertation on plant and animal chromophils. This apparently led to his only book, published in the same year, whose title is translated as "The Chromophils in the Animal and Vegetable Kingdoms." The book itself has never been translated. By 1914 Tswett's brief, brilliant research career was essentially at an end. The German invasion of Poland in 1915 forced the Technical University to move to Moscow, and then to Nizhni Novgorod in 1916. Tswett's time was largely consumed with organizing the work of the botanical laboratories after each of these moves. In 1917 he accepted a position at the University at Yuryev in Estonia, but that too was overrun by the German army a year later. The university moved to Voronezh in 1918, but Tswett's health, never robust, failed quickly, and he died of a heart ailment at age forty-seven, on June 26, 1919.

Tswett's strength as a scientist lay in how well he understood both chemistry and botany. He had always been interested in the internal molecular structures of plants, often inquiring what their purpose might be, and the work he did on chlorophyll was one of his most important research efforts. He had long doubted the contention, which was widely accepted at the time, that chlorophyll was a compound that actually existed in plants. He decided this belief was the result of a misunderstanding; he hypothesized that chemists had been confused either because chlorophyll was combined nearly inseparably with other molecules within the leaf or because a compound recovered by a particular separation technique might in fact be an artifact of the technique. He was able to demonstrate all of these misunderstandings in the work of others, both by his deployment of the chemical separation methods of the time (fractional solution and precipitation, diffusion, differential solution) and by the adsorption methods he developed, culminating in chromatography.

Develops Chromatography Process

"Adsorbent" means holding molecules on the surface of the material, not in the body, and chromatography is a process which employs substances which have this property.

It is a separation technique in which a very finely powdered adsorbent material is held in a vertical tube or "column." The mixture to be separated is placed on the top of the column, dissolved in as small an amount of solvent as possible, so that it forms a narrow band of adsorbed mixture; then more solvent is allowed to flow through the column, top to bottom. The molecules in the mixture are more or less strongly held by the adsorbent; those weakly held are washed down the column most rapidly, and those strongly held move less rapidly. After a suitable development time, the components of the mixture separate into a series of bands spaced along the column. The plug of wet adsorbent is blown out of the column onto a plate, where the bands can be cut apart and the components recovered separately. As the mixtures separated in these early experiments were colored, and the bands absorbed light in the visible spectrum, Tswett named the process *chromatography* ("color-writing"), and the developed separation he called a *chromatogram*. Even though most mixtures are not colored, this terminology is retained; the components must be detected by some means other than the eye. Many sophisticated varieties of chromatography are in use today: paper, thin-layer, gas-liquid, and ion exchange, to name but a few. Still, Tswett's column method has not been totally displaced.

Tswett used this technique to demonstrate that chlorophyll indeed does not exist in the plant as a free molecule but is complexed with albumin. He named this complex "chloroglobin," by analogy with the heme complex of the blood, hemoglobin. There was, however, widespread skepticism of his research methods, and this finding was sharply criticized. Tswett next analyzed the plant pigments themselves, which were understood at the time to be only two: green chlorophyll and yellow xanthophyll. Using not chromatography but the standard chemical methods of the time, he demonstrated that there are two chlorophylls: xanthophyll and carotene. This finding was hotly disputed, partly because chlorophyll passed the test of a single pure compound: it could be crystallized. Tswett was able to show that the "crystallizable chlorophyll" formed by lengthy extraction with hot ethanol was in fact another compound; it is known today as an ethyl ester formed by transesterification of one of chlorophyll's ester groups.

During the course of his pigment work Tswett had found that, when he ground the plant leaves with powdered calcium carbonate to neutralize acids, all but carotene were adsorbed on the solid carbonate. He used this as a method to separate carotene. It is not clear that this led to his devising column chromatography, but once he had developed this technique he found that, in addition to two chlorophylls, there were four xanthophylls and, of course, carotene. These findings came to be accepted later, but mainly through the work of the German chemist **Richard Willstätter**.

The technique of column chromatography was not widely used in Tswett's lifetime, being regarded by his most vocal opponent, L. Marchlewski, as no more than a "filtration experiment." It was only later in the century that his work was reevaluated and his status as one of the originators, though probably not the sole inventor, of chromatography, was confirmed. This is his legacy today, although some would consider the plant pigment work to be at least as important.

SELECTED WRITINGS BY TSWETT:

Books

Michael Tswett's First Paper on Chromatography, (translated by Gerhard Hesse and Herbert Weil from 1903 Russian paper), M. Woelm, 1954.

Periodicals

Journal of Chemical Education, Adsorption Analysis and Chromatographic Methods; Application to the Chemistry of the Chlorophylls, (translated by Harold H. Strain and Joseph Sherma from 1906 German paper) Volume 44, 1967, pp. 238–242.

FURTHER READING:

Books

Heftmann, E., editor, *Chromatography,* Elsevier, 1983.

Periodicals

Dhere, C., *Candollea,* Michel Tswett, Volume 10, 1943, pp. 23–63.

Robinson, Trevor, *Journal of Chemical Education,* Michael Tswett, Volume 36, 1959, pp. 144–147.

Robinson, Trevor, *Chymia,* Michael Tswett, Volume 6, 1960, pp. 146–161.

Strain, Harold H., and Joseph Sherma, *Journal of Chemical Education,* Michael Tswett's Contributions to Sixty Years of Chromatography, Volume 44, 1967, pp. 235–237.

Sketch by Robert M. Hawthorne Jr.

Alan Turing
1912–1954
English mathematician

Mathematician Alan Turing is recognized as a pioneer in computer theory. His classic 1936 paper, "On Computable Numbers, with an Application to the Entscheidungs Problem," detailed a machine that served as a model for the first working computers. During World War II, Turing took part in the top-secret ULTRA project and

Alan Turing

helped decipher German military codes. During this same time, Turing conducted groundbreaking work that led to the first operational digital electronic computers. Another notable paper was published in 1950 and offered what became known as the "Turing Test" to determine if a machine possessed intelligence.

Alan Mathison Turing was born on June 23, 1912, in Paddington, England, to Julius Mathison Turing and Ethel Sara Stoney. Turing's father served in the British civil service in India, and his wife generally accompanied him. Thus, for the majority of their childhoods, Alan and his older brother, John, saw very little of their parents. While in elementary school, the young Turing boys were raised by a retired military couple, the Wards. At the age of 13, Turing entered Sherbourne school, a boys' boarding school in Dorset. His record at Sherbourne was not generally outstanding; he was later remembered as untidy and disinterested in scholastic learning. He did, however, distinguish himself in mathematics and science, showing a particular facility for calculus. Turing also developed an interest in competitive running while at Sherbourne.

Produces Prophetic Paper

Turing twice failed to gain entry to Trinity College in Cambridge, but was accepted on scholarship at King's College (also in Cambridge). He graduated in 1934 with a master's degree in mathematics. In 1936 Turing produced his first, and perhaps greatest, work. His paper "On Computable Numbers, with an Application to the Entscheidungs Problem," answered a logical problem staged by German mathematician **David Hilbert.** The question involved the completeness of logic—whether all mathematical problems could, in principle, be solved. Turing's paper, presented in 1937 to the London Mathematical Society, proved that some could not be solved. Turing's paper also contained a footnote describing a theoretical automatic machine, which came to be known as the Turing Machine, that could solve any mathematical problem—provided it was give the proper algorithms, or problem-solving equations or instructions. Although it may not have been Turing's intent at the time, his Turing Machine defined the modern computer.

After graduating from Cambridge, Turing was invited to spend a year in the United States studying at Princeton University. He returned to Princeton for a second year—on a Proctor Fellowship—to finish his doctorate. While there, he worked on the subject of computability with **Alonso Church** and other mathematicians. Turing and his associates worked with binary numbers (1 and 0), and Boolean Algebra developed by George Boole, to develop a system of equations called logic gates. These logic gates were useful for producing problem-solving algorithms such as would be needed by an automatic computing machine. From the initial paper exercise, it was a simple matter to develop logic gates into electrical hardware, using relays and switches, which could—theoretically, and in huge quantities—actually perform the work of a computing machine. As a sideline, Turing put together the first three or four stages of an electric multiplier, using relays he constructed himself. After receiving his doctorate, Turing had an opportunity to remain at Princeton, but decided to accept a Cambridge fellowship instead. He returned to England in 1938.

Helps Crack German War Codes

Cryptology, the making and breaking of coded messages, was greatly advanced in England after World War I. The German high command, however, had modified a device called the Enigma machine that mechanically enciphered messages. The English found little success in defeating this method. The original Enigma machine was not new, or even secret; a basic Enigma machine had been in operation for several years, mostly used to produce commercial codes. The Germans' alterations, though, greatly increased the number of possible letter combinations in a message. The Allies were able to duplicate the modifications, but it was a continual cat-and-mouse game; each time Allied analysts figured out a message, the Germans' changes made all of their work useless.

In the fall of 1939, Turing found himself in a top-secret installation in Bletchley, where he played a critical role in the development of a machine that deciphered the Enigma's messages by testing key codes until it found the correct combinations. This substitution method was uncomplicated, but impractical to apply because possible combinations could range into the tens of millions. Here Turing was able

to put his experience at Princeton to good use; no one else had bridged the gap between abstract logic theory and electric hardware as he had with his electric multiplier. Turing helped construct relay-driven decoders (which were called Bombes, after the ticking noise of the relays) that shortened the code-breaking time from weeks to hours. The Bombes helped uncover German movements, particularly the U-boat war in the Atlantic, for almost two years. Eventually, however, the Germans changed their codes and the new level of complexity was too high to be solved practically by electrical decoders. British scientists agreed that, although a Bombe of sufficient size could be made for further deciphering work, the machine would be slow and impractical.

Yet other advances would prove advantageous for the decoding machine. Vacuum tubes used as switches (the British called them thermiotic valves) used no moving parts and were a thousand times faster than electrical relays. A decoder made with tubes could do in minutes what it took a Bombe several hours to accomplish. Thus work began on a device which was later named Collosus. Based on the same theoretical principles as earlier Bombes, Collosus was the first operational digital electronic computer. It used 1800 vacuum tubes, proving the practicality of this approach. Much information concerning Collosus remained classified by the British government in the early 1990s. Some claimed that Turing supervised the construction of the first Collosus.

Many stories were circulated about Turing during the war; mostly surrounding his eccentricity. Andrew Hodges noted in his book *Alan Turing, The Enigma,* "With holes in his sports jacket, shiny grey flannel trousers held up with an ancient tie, and hair sticking out at the back, he became the cartoonist's 'boffin'—an impression accentuated by his manner of practical work, in which he would grunt and swear as solder failed to stick, scratch his head and make a strange squelching noise as he thought to himself." Unconvinced of England's chances to win the war, Turing converted all of his funds to two silver bars, buried them, and was later unable to locate them. He was horrified at the sight of blood, was an outspoken atheist, and was a homosexual. Still, for his unquestionably vital role in the British war effort, he was later awarded the Order of the British Empire, a high honor for someone not in the combat military.

In the waning months of the war, Turing turned his thoughts back to computing machines. He conceived of a device, built with vacuum tubes, that would be able to perform any function described in mathematical terms and would carry instructions in electronic symbols in its memory. This universal machine, clearly an embodiment of the Turing machine described in his 1936 paper, would not require separate hardware for different functions, only a change of instructions. Turing was not alone in his ambition to construct a computing machine. A group at the University of Pennsylvania had built a computer called ENIAC (Electronic Numerical Integrator and Computer) that was similar to, but more complex, than Colossus. In the process, they had concluded that a better machine was possible.

Turing's design was possibly more remarkable because he was working alone out of his home while they were a large university research group with the full backing of the American military. The American group published well before Turing did, but the British government subsequently took a greater interest in Turing's work.

Postwar Work

In June of 1945 Turing joined the newly formed mathematics division of the National Physical Laboratory (NPL). Here he finalized plans for his Automatic Computing Engine (ACE). The rather archaic term "engine" was chosen by NPL management as a tribute to Charles Babbage's Analytical Engine (and also because it made a pleasing acronym). Turing, however, was unprepared for the inertia and politics of a bureaucratic government foundation. All of his previous engineering projects had been conducted during wartime, when time was of the essence and no budget constraints existed. More than a year after the ACE project was approved, though, no engineering work had been completed and there was little cooperation between participants. A scaled-down version of the ACE was finally completed in 1950. But Turing had already left NPL in 1948, frustrated at the slow pace of the computer's development.

In 1950 Turing produced a widely read paper titled "Computing Machinery and Intelligence". This classic paper expanded on one of Turing's interests—if computers could possess intelligence. He proposed a test called the "Imitation Game," still used today under the name "Turing Test." In the test, an interrogator was connected by teletype (later, by computer keyboard) to either a human or a computer at a remote location. The interrogator is allowed to pose any questions and, based on the replies, the interrogator must decide whether a human or a computer is at the other end of the line. If the interrogator cannot distinguish between the two in a statistically significant number of cases, then artificial intelligence has been achieved. Turing predicted that, within fifty years, computers could be programmed to play the game so effectively that after a five-minute question period the interrogator would have no more than a seventy-percent chance of making the proper identification.

Personal Troubles Mount

Turing's personal life deteriorated in the early 1950s. After leaving NPL he took a position with Manchester College as deputy director of the newly formed Royal Society Computing Laboratory. But he was not involved in designing or building the computer on which they were working. By this time, Turing was no longer a world-class mathematician, having for too long been sidetracked by electronic engineering, nor was he engineer: The scientific world seemed to be passing him by.

While at Manchester, Turing had an affair with a young street person named Arnold Murray, which led to a burglary at his house by one of Murray's associates. The investigating police learned of the relationship between Turing and Murray; in fact Turing did nothing to hide it. Homosexuality was a felony in England at the time, and Turing was tried and convicted of "gross indecency" in 1952. Because of his social class and relative prominence, he was sentenced to a year's probation and given treatments of the female hormone estrogen in lieu of serving a year in jail.

Turing committed suicide by eating a cyanide-laced apple on June 7, 1954. His death puzzled his associates; he had been free of the hormone treatments for a year, and, although a stigma remained, he had weathered the incident with his career intact. He left no note, nor had he given any hint that he had contemplated this act. His mother tried for years to have his death declared accidental, but the official cause of death was never seriously questioned.

SELECTED WRITINGS BY TURING:

Periodicals

Proceedings of the London Mathematical Society, On Computable Numbers, with an Application to the Entscheidungs Problem, Volume 42, 1937, pp. 230–265.
Mind, Computing Machinery and Intelligence, Volume 59, 1950, pp. 433–460.

FURTHER READING:

Books

Carpenter, B. S., and R. W. Doran, editors, *A. M. Turing's ACE Report of 1946 and Other Papers,* MIT Press, 1986.
Hodges, Andrew, *Alan Turing, The Enigma,* Simon and Schuster, 1983.
Shurkin, Joel, *Engines of the Mind,* W. W. Norton, 1984.
Slater, Robert, *Portraits in Silicon,* MIT Press, 1987.
Turing, Sara, *Alan M. Turing,* Heffers, 1959.

Sketch by Joel Simon

Charles Henry Turner
1861–1923
American entomologist

Charles Henry Turner, an African American scientist, made major contributions to the field of entomology during the early years of the twentieth century. Through meticulous analytical research and untiring observation, he proved conclusively that insects can hear and distinguish pitch and that roaches learn by trial and error. In 1910 he discovered that the common honey bee can distinguish color and is drawn to flowers not just by odor but by sight as well. He was the first person to note that ants are guided back to their colony by light rays, not odors. He showed that wasps use visual landmarks to find their way back to their nests, disproving the long-held assumption that their homing skills resulted from an instinctual sixth sense. He also demonstrated that invertebrates often display certain "turning" behaviors when stimulated by light (in ants, the behavior is now known as Turner's circling). His research led to many journal publications, all of which advanced existing knowledge about ants, bees, wasps, and other insects.

Turner was born in Cincinnati, Ohio, on February 3, 1861 (one source says 1867), to Thomas and Addie Campbell Turner. His father was a church custodian and his mother worked as a practical nurse. The education-minded Turners owned a library containing several hundred volumes and instilled a love of reading in their son. At an early age, he decided to pursue a career in science. He received both his bachelor of science (1891) and master of science (1892) degrees from the University of Cincinnati.

From 1892 to 1893, Turner held an assistant professorship in biology at the University of Cincinnati. With the help of Booker T. Washington, he received an appointment as professor of biology at Clark College in Atlanta. From 1894 to 1897, he pursued a doctoral degree at the University of Chicago. He received his Ph.D. (magna cum laude) in 1907; his dissertation was entitled "The Homing of Ants: An Experimental Study of Ant Behavior." That same year, he began his long affiliation with Sumner High School in St. Louis, where he taught biology and psychology. He died in Chicago on February 14, 1923.

Constrained throughout his professional life by a lack of facilities and equipment, Turner made clever use of tools and techniques. He used his window shades to prove that wasps use landmarks (and not instinct) in finding their way. Colored disks and colored boxes filled with honey were used in experiments that showed that sight as well as odor leads bees to flowers. He observed death feinting in ant lions, and a "turning" activity of some invertebrates in response to sensory excitation—the scuttling away of roaches when the lights go on, for instance. A particular kind of movement in ants came to be known as Turner's circling. Turner published numerous papers on his work between 1911 and 1923, and he also wrote a book on nature for children and a collection of poems.

FURTHER READING:

Periodicals

Ferguson, Charles, *Journal of Negro Education,* Charles Henry Turner and His Contributions, Volume 10, October 1940.

Books

Hudson, G. H., *American Black Scientists and Inventors,* Charles Henry Turner, National Science Teachers Association, 1975.

Sketch by Tom Crawford

Merle A. Tuve
1901–1982
American physicist

Merle A. Tuve left his mark on a number of fields of scientific research, beginning as a graduate student with his confirmation of the existence of the ionosphere, which led directly to the development of radar. He later explored the structure of the atomic nucleus, discovering the existence of the strong force and developing the particle accelerator as a tool in conducting nucleus research. During World War II, he was largely responsible for the development of a new and more efficient system of detonating bombs, the proximity fuse. After the war, he used surplus weapons to study the structure and composition of Earth's interior. Beginning in the 1950s, Tuve turned his attention to astronomy, developing systems for greatly improving the sensitivity of observational devices.

Merle Antony Tuve was born in Canton, South Dakota, on June 27, 1901. His parents were Anthony E. and Ida Marie Larsen Tuve. Coincidentally, another man destined to earn international fame as a scientist, **Ernest O. Lawrence**, was also born in the small town of Canton, just two months after Tuve. Tuve and Lawrence played together as children and on one occasion constructed a telegraph between their homes. When Lawrence moved away, the two boys continued to communicate—by ham radio.

After completing his secondary education at the Augustana Academy in Canton, Tuve enrolled in the University of Minnesota, where he planned to major in chemistry. Those plans changed, however, and he received his bachelor's degree in electrical engineering in 1922. During his undergraduate years, Tuve came into contact with John T. Tate, a theoretical physicist, and became convinced that it was physics, not engineering, that interested him most. Accordingly, he entered the master's program in physics at Minnesota and began a study of the microwave radiation produced in vacuum tubes. For this research, he received his master's degree in 1923.

Doctoral Research Reveals Ionosphere

After graduation, Tuve was offered a teaching position at Princeton University but transferred after a single year to

Johns Hopkins University, where he entered the doctoral program in physics in 1924. It was at Johns Hopkins that Tuve made his first important discovery. Scientists had known for many years that radio signals can be transmitted over long distances. The explanation for this phenomenon at the time was that radio waves generated at one location on Earth's surface pass into the upper atmosphere, where they are reflected off a layer of charged particles. Those waves then return to Earth's surface, where they can be detected at some distant location. For his doctoral research, Tuve and colleague **Gregory Breit** developed a method for generating very short radio-wave pulses that could be directed into the atmosphere. By measuring the time it took for these pulses to be received at a detection station, Tuve and Breit were able to calculate the height of the atmospheric reflecting layer, a region later named the ionosphere. This process of measuring reflected pulses was later utilized in the development of radar. Upon completion of this research, Tuve was awarded his Ph.D. in 1926.

In the same year, Tuve accepted a position as staff researcher at the Carnegie Institute in Washington, D.C. He was to remain at Carnegie for the next four decades, becoming director in 1946 and distinguished service member in 1966, the year of his retirement. Tuve was joined at Carnegie in 1926 by Breit, and the two physicists then began a research project designed to study the forces that exist within the atomic nucleus. By the 1920s, it had become apparent that the only charged particles present in the nucleus are positively charged protons. The question that arose, therefore, was how the nucleus was able to remain stable when it seemed that electrostatic forces of repulsion would tend to drive it apart.

To study this question, Tuve, working initially with Breit and later with Lawrence R. Hafstad and Odd Dahl, developed devices for the acceleration of particles to very high speeds. At first, they adapted Tesla coils for thier particle accelerator but then found Van de Graaff generators more effective. Their goal was to cause a stream of rapidly moving protons to collide with a stationary mass of protons (hydrogen gas) and observe the results of these collisions. After a decade of study with increasingly more powerful machines, Tuve and his colleagues eventually made an important discovery. They found that there exists within the nucleus a force far stronger than the electrostatic force, indeed, the most powerful force yet discovered. That force was eventually given the apt name "the strong force."

Just prior to World War II, Tuve learned of the discovery of atomic fission by **Otto Hahn** and **Fritz Strassmann** and immediately confirmed their findings in his own laboratory at Carnegie's Department of Terrestrial Magnetism. He served briefly on the uranium committee appointed to study the application of atomic fission to the construction of nuclear weapons. He soon decided, however, to devote his wartime efforts to the problems of more conventional weapons. In particular, he worked on the development of a new device for explosive detonation.

At the time, detonation of explosives was accomplished by one of two methods: a bomb could be set off either by means of a timing device or by impact with another object. Neither mechanism was adequately effective against rapidly moving objects, such as the high-speed "buzz bombs" being used by the Germans. Tuve's solution to this problem was the proximity fuse, an instrument that transmitted radio waves as an explosive device traveled through the air. The reflection of the waves emanating from an intended target could be used to measure the distance between bomb and target and, at a certain point, facilitate detonation.

Turns Attention to Earth's Interior

Tuve did not return to nuclear physics after World War II but instead became interested in the structural characteristics of Earth's crust. He was able to obtain war surplus land mines and depth charges that could be used to generate shock waves. By timing and tracking the passage of these shock waves through the crust, Tuve was able to determine properties of the crust to a depth of about 125 miles. In one application of this work, Tuve supervised the establishment of a network of seismic stations in the Andes plateau as part of the 1957 International Geophysical Year.

From the 1950s on, Tuve become involved in astronomical research. He and his colleagues developed devices to improve the collection and analysis of telescopic data. He also became interested in the study of radio-wave emission by hydrogen clouds located between galaxies.

Tuve married Winifred Gray Whitman, a medical doctor, in 1927. The Tuves had two children—Trygve Whitman, who was to become a health care administrator, and Lucy Winifred, who became a cell biologist. Tuve died of heart disease in Bethesda, Maryland, on May 20, 1982.

SELECTED WRITINGS BY TUVE:

Books

Velocity Structures in Hydrogen Profiles: A Sky of Neutral Hydrogen Emission, Carnegie Institution of Washington, 1973.

FURTHER READING:

Books

Steinhart, John S., editor, *The Earth Beneath the Continents: A Volume of Geophysical Studies in Honor of Merle A. Tuve,* American Geophysical Union, 1966.

Periodicals

Cornell, Thomas D., *Physics Today,* Merle Antony Tuve: Pioneer Nuclear Physicist, January, 1988, pp. 57–64.

Sketch by David E. Newton

Frederick Twort
1877–1950
English bacteriologist

As a pioneering bacteriologist, Frederick Twort was responsible for several important advances in his field. He discovered what would be known asbacterio-phages, bacteria-attacking viruses. This discovery led to the advent of molecular biology. Twort was the first scientist to grow the organism that caused Jöhne's disease, a deadly cattle infection, and his efforts contributed to its elimination. Twort also discovered a nutritional element later identified as vitamin K.

Frederick William Twort was born in Camberley, Surrey, England, on October 22, 1877. His father, William Henry Twort, was a doctor. Frederick was the oldest of ten siblings. He studied medicine in London at St. Thomas's Hospital Medical School. He became qualified and licensed in 1900, though he never actually practiced clinically. Soon after graduation Twort began his work as an assistant to Louis Jenner in London's St. Thomas's Hospital, working in their clinical laboratory. In 1902, Twort found work with William Bullock as an anatomy instructor in London Hospital. It was here that his first work in bacteriology began. He spent several years familiarizing himself with the bacteriology of hospitals and soon began his own experimentation.

Twort married Dorothy Nony Banister, who helped him with his work, and with her had a son and three daughters. His son, Antony, also became a doctor as well as his father's biographer.

Devotes Life to Research

Twort's own research work became of primary importance to him in 1907. In that year, he published one of his earliest significant papers on bacteria. In it, he outlined how bacteria adapted and mutated. Two years later, in 1909, he published on bacterial growth and related growth agents. In what became a common occurrence, Twort's results were basically ignored at the time, and found to be important only decades later.

In that same year Twort was named superintendent of the Brown Institution at the University of London, an animal hospital. While working here, Twort was able to devote all his time to research. His work was limited, however, by funding and support problems, which plagued him throughout his career. Still, Twort pushed ahead with his theories. His work was considered remarkable and original from the beginning. He believed that all pathogenic, or disease-causing, bacteria developed from organisms that lived freely, while most of his contemporary bacteriologists believed pathogens originated in the body.

Scrutinizes Jöhne's Disease

Twort's first important achievement was his in-depth study, with G. L. Y. Ingram, of Jöhne's disease, the results of which were published in the early 1900s. Twort did the earliest cultures of the organism that caused the disease. He believed that there was a connection between tuberculosis and Jöhne's disease, so he derived what he called his "essential substance" from dead tubercle bacilli. These bacilli, when incorporated in a culture medium, proved ideal for growing Jöhne's bacillus. Twort's study of Jöhne's disease directly led to the development of the Jöhnin test. His discovery also eventually proved important to biochemistry, specifically in the study of bacteria and their nutritional needs.

Discovers Bacteriophages

In 1915, Twort discovered what came to be known as bacteriophages. Twort's discovery was something of an accident. He spent several years using artificial media to grow viruses. Twort noticed that the bacteria infecting his plates kept becoming transparent. This was the earliest recorded proof of bacteriophages, though Twort called his discovery "transmissible lytic agent."

Twort published his results, but he was not certain about what he discovered. He made several guesses in his articles, but did not commit to any specific one, a hallmark of his career that lessened his findings in the eyes of his peers. Twort's experiments in this area were also overshadowed by World War I; he served in the Royal Army Medical Corps from 1915 to 18.

In 1917, Canadian bacteriologist **Felix d'Hérelle** made the same discovery, independent of Twort. D'Hérelle gave his findings their now-common name, bacteriophages, which translates as bacteria eater. After d'Hérelle announced his findings, there was some controversy over who made the discovery first and when, in part because of Twort's published uncertainties. The results eventually carried both their names, and became known as the Twort-d'Hérelle phenomenon. Both scientists shared a life-long obsession with their discovery, and both wanted to use it to fight diseases plaguing humans.

Before antibiotics were developed, scientists were searching for ways to fight disease. Twort and d'Hérelle thought bacteriophages might be an answer, but the viruses did not work when used on human patients. The importance of the discovery of bacteriophages did not emerge until after Twort and d'Hérelle had died. In recent years, the idea has again come to light, as bacteria continues to develop resistance to antibiotics. In 1984, it was learned that illnesses in livestock and human illnesses such as meningitis can be curbed with bacteriophages.

Based on his many accomplishments, Twort was accorded some honors. Among other distinctions, he was appointed professor of bacteriology at the University of London in 1919 and in 1929, he was elected a fellow of the Royal Society. Twort's peers found him a difficult and remote man, which perhaps limited the acceptance of him and his ideas. Still, his rather unique ability to work independently and at a high level of technical aptitude contributed to his capacities as a scientific explorer.

Abrupt End to Research

As Twort's research progessed, he became obsessed with proving, in more specific terms, that bacteria evolved from viruses, and that these viruses had evolved from more primary cellular forms. Though he spent years on this idea, he did not publish anything of consequence. Twort's research was permanently interrupted in 1944 when the Brown Institution was destroyed by enemy fire during World War II. His laboratories and specimens were completely decimated. Twort spent his last years suffering greatly from this loss.

Twort died in the city of his birth, Camberley, on March 20, 1950. Posthumously, he was remembered for his scientific accomplishments, as well as his uncompromising belief that scientific funding should not be controlled by the government. His obituary in the leading journal *The Lancet* states: "An outstanding representative of the independent research-worker, he had made valuable contributions to bacteriology, but he felt himself increasingly uneasy in the closer relationship of research and the State."

Leaves a Complicated Legacy

There was more to Frederick Twort than his scientific accomplishments and related attitudes. In a review of his biography, *In Focus, Out of Step: A Biography of Frederick William Twort* written by son Antony Twort, Bernard Dixon describes the elder Twort as "a multifaceted man, who at various times made violins and began to design a more efficient internal combustion engine, who entered the Daily Mail contest for the biggest and best sweet pea in England, threw vegetables and meat each day into a large cooking pot of stew kept continually on the hob, and later developed considerable skills as an amateur radio constructor." This giant of science was a very complicated man, working, as the title of his biography so succinctly states, in his own focus and quite out of step with his times.

SELECTED WRITINGS BY TWORT:

Periodicals

"The Fermentation of Glucosides by Bacteria of the Typhoid-coli Group and the Aquisition of New Fermentings Powers by *Bacillus dysenteriae* and other Micro-Organisms, Preliminary Communication," *Proceedings of the Royal Society*, B series (1907): pp. 329-36.

FURTHER READING:

Books

Clarke, Edwin, *Dictionary of Scientific Biography*, ed. Charles Coulston Gillispie, Vol. 8. New York: Charles Scribner Sons, 1976, pp. 519-21.
Daintith, John et al, eds., *A Biographical Encyclopedia of Scientists*, Vol. 2. New York: Facts on File, Inc., 1981, pp. 797-98.
Muir, Hazel, ed., *Larousse Dictionary of Scientists*, New York: Larousse, 1994, p. 519.
Williams, Trever, ed., *A Biographical Dictionary of Scientists*, 2nd ed. New York: Halsted Press, 1971, pp. 521-22.
Twort, Antony, *In Focus, Out of Step: A Biography of Frederick William Twort FRS, 1877-1950*, Gloucestershire, UK: Alan Sutton Publishing, 1993.

Periodicals

Dixon, Bernard, "Attack of the Phages: Bacteriophages," *American Association for the Advancement of Science* 84 (June 1984): p. 66.
"Obituaries, Frederick William Twort," *The Lancet* (April 1, 1950): pp. 648-49.
"Obituaries, Prof. F. W. Twort, F.R.S.," *Nature* (June 3, 1950): p. 874.
Radetsky, Peter, "The Good Virus; the use of Bacteriophages to Fight Antibiotic Resistant Bacterial Diseases," *Discover* (November 1996): p. 50.

Sketch by Annette Petrusso

George Uhlenbeck
1900–1988
American physicist

Geroge Uhlenbeck made the discovery for which he became famous, electron spin, while still a graduate student at the University of Leiden studying under the eminent physicist **Paul Ehrenfest**. His collaborator in that work was another graduate student, **Samuel Goudsmit**. Many scholars believe that the failure of the Nobel Prize committee to award Uhlenbeck and Goudsmit a physics prize for this discovery has been one of its greatest errors of omission.

George Eugene Uhlenbeck was born on December 6, 1900, in Batavia, Java (now Djakarta, Indonesia), part of what was then the Dutch East Indies. He came from a prominent Dutch family with roots in Germany. A paternal ancestor, Johannes Wilhelmus Uhlenbeck, had served in the army of Frederick the Great of Prussia, fled the country after a duel, and joined the Dutch East India Company in Ceylon (now Sri Lanka). That episode marked the beginning of the Dutch line of Uhlenbecks. George's father, Eugenius Marius Uhlenbeck, was born on the island of Sumatra and later joined the Dutch East Indian Army. George's mother was the former Annie Beegers, daughter of a major general in the Dutch East Indian Army.

Uhlenbeck's education began in the town of Padang-pandjang on Sumatra, but was interrupted by his family's return to Holland in 1907. He then completed his elementary and secondary schooling in The Hague. His interest in physics was first aroused by a three-year course at the higher burgher school he attended.

Encounters Paul Ehrenfest

Upon graduation from high school in 1918, Uhlenbeck entered the Technische Hogeschool at Delft. He would have preferred to attend the University of Leiden, but national regulations required a university student to be proficient in Latin and Greek, which Uhlenbeck was not. Only a few months into his first semester at Delft, however, those regulations were changed, and Uhlenbeck found it possible to transfer to Leiden.

As a graduate student at Leiden, Uhlenbeck came into contact with the man who was to become the most influential force in his life, Paul Ehrenfest. Abraham Pais

writes in *Physics Today* that "in all the years I knew Uhlenbeck, in Utrecht, in Ann Arbor, and in New York, a single picture always stood on his desk: a small photograph of a warmly smiling Ehrenfest." Uhlenbeck obtained his first teaching job, in fact, as a result of Ehrenfest's influence. That job was as a private tutor to a son of the Dutch ambassador to Italy, stationed in Rome.

Begins Work with Goudsmit

During his three years in Rome, from September 1922 to June 1925, Uhlenbeck returned to Holland during the summers to continue his studies at Leiden. By September 1923, he had completed the requirements for the degree of doctorandus, the equivalent of a master's degree. Two years later, he resigned from his job in Rome and returned to Leiden to work on his Ph.D. The summer and fall of 1925 were a momentous period for Uhlenbeck. In June, Ehrenfest had introduced Uhlenbeck to Samuel A. Goudsmit, another of his graduate students, and suggested that the two work on the problem of line spectra. The topic on which they were to concentrate in particular was doublet lines, the splitting of lines in a spectrum when subjected to an external magnetic field.

This phenomenon had been known for some time, but no satisfactory explanation as to its cause had been developed. From June to October, Uhlenbeck and Goudsmit worked on the problem, finally arriving at a solution. Suppose, they said, that one imagines the electron as a tiny spinning sphere. As such, it would generate its own magnetic field that, depending on its alignment, could either oppose or reinforce the external magnetic field. These two positions would have similar, but not identical, energies that could account for the formation of doublet lines.

The Uhlenbeck-Goudsmit discovery came only months after **Wolfgang Pauli** had concluded that a fourth quantum number was needed to explain existing data on atomic structure. Pauli had no idea as to how the new quantum number could be interpreted physically, but knew that it could have only one of two values. Uhlenbeck and Goudsmit showed that the numerical value associated with electron spin could be either +1/2 or –1/2, values that satisfied Pauli's theoretical constraints for the fourth quantum number.

Uhlenbeck was awarded his Ph.D. in physics from Leiden in 1927, two years after the discovery of electron spin. In the same year, he immigrated to the United States, where he took a position teaching physics at the University of Michigan in Ann Arbor. He became professor of theoretical physics in 1939, and Henry Carhart Professor of

Physics in 1954. During World War II, Uhlenbeck was head of the theoretical division at the Radiation Laboratory of the Massachusetts Institute of Technology. He married Else Ophorst in 1947, and together they had one son, Olke. In 1961, he was offered an opportunity to establish a new Department of Theoretical Physics at the Rockefeller Medical Research Center of the State University of New York, later Rockefeller University. He remained at Rockefeller until his retirement in 1974. Among the honors he received during his lifetime were the Research Corporation Award in 1953, the Oersted Medal of the American Association of Physics Teachers in 1955, the Max Planck Medal in 1964, the Lorentz Medal of the Royal Netherlands Academy of Science in 1970, and the National Medal of Science in 1977. Uhlenbeck died in Boulder, Colorado, on October 31, 1988.

FURTHER READING:

Periodicals

Pais, Abraham, *Physics Today,* George Uhlenbeck and the Discovery of Electron Spin, December 1989, pp. 34–40.

Sketch by David E. Newton

Karen Uhlenbeck
1942–
American mathematician

Karen Uhlenbeck is engaged in mathematical research that has applications in theoretical physics and has contributed to the study of instantons, models for the behavior of surfaces in four dimensions. In recognition of her work in geometry and partial differential equations, she was awarded a prestigious MacArthur Fellowship in 1983.

Karen Keskulla Uhlenbeck was born in Cleveland, Ohio, on August 24, 1942, to Arnold Edward Keskulla, an engineer, and Carolyn Windeler Keskulla, an artist. When Uhlenbeck was in third grade, the family moved to New Jersey. Everything interested her as a child, but she felt that girls were discouraged from exploring many activities. In high school, she read American physicist **George Gamow**'s books on physics and English astronomer **Fred Hoyle**'s books on cosmology, which her father brought home from the public library. When Uhlenbeck entered the University of Michigan, she found mathematics a broad and intellectually stimulating subject. After earning her B.S. degree in 1964, she became a National Science Foundation Graduate Fellow, pursuing graduate study in mathematics at Brandeis

University. In 1965, she married Olke Cornelis Uhlenbeck, a biophysicist; they later divorced.

Uhlenbeck received her Ph.D. in mathematics from Brandeis in 1968 with a thesis on the calculus of variations. Her first teaching position was at the Massachusetts Institute of Technology in 1968. The following year she moved to Berkeley, California, where she was a lecturer in mathematics at the University of California. There she studied general relativity and the geometry of space-time, and worked on elliptic regularity in systems of partial differential equations.

In 1971, Uhlenbeck became an assistant professor at the University of Illinois at Urbana-Champaign. In 1974, she was awarded a fellowship from the Sloan Foundation that lasted until 1976, and she then went to Northwestern University as a visiting associate professor. She taught at the University of Illinois in Chicago from 1977 to 1983, first as associate professor and then professor, and in 1979 she was the Chancellor's Distinguished Visiting Professor at the University of California, Berkeley. An Albert Einstein Fellowship enabled her to pursue her research as a member of the Institute for Advanced Studies at Princeton University from 1979 to 1980. She published more than a dozen articles in mathematics journals during the 1970s and was named to the editorial board of the *Journal of Differential Geometry* in 1979 and the *Illinois Journal of Mathematics* in 1980.

In 1983, Uhlenbeck was selected by the John D. and Catherine T. MacArthur Foundation of Chicago to receive one of its five-year fellowship grants. Given annually, the MacArthur fellowships enable scientists, scholars, and artists to pursue research or creative activity. For Uhlenbeck, winning the fellowship inspired her to begin serious studies in physics. She believes that the mathematician's task is to abstract ideas from fields such as physics and streamline them so they can be used in other fields. For instance, physicists studying quantum mechanics had predicted the existence of particle-like elements called instantons. Uhlenbeck and other researchers viewed instantons as somewhat analogous to soap films. Seeking a better understanding of these particles, they studied soap films to learn about the properties of surfaces. As soap films provide a model for the behavior of surfaces in three dimensions, instantons provide analogous models for the behavior of surfaces in four-dimensional space-time. Uhlenbeck co-wrote a book on this subject, *Instantons and 4-Manifold Topology,* which was published in 1984.

After a year spent as a visiting professor at Harvard, Uhlenbeck became a professor at the University of Chicago in 1983. Her mathematical interests at this time included nonlinear partial differential equations, differential geometry, gauge theory, topological quantum field theory, and integrable systems. She gave guest lectures at several universities and served as the vice president of the American Mathematical Society. The Alumni Association of the University of Michigan named her Alumna of the Year in 1984. She was elected to the American Academy of Arts and Sciences in 1985 and to the National Academy of

Sciences in 1986. In 1988, she received the Alumni Achievement award from Brandeis University, an honorary doctor of science degree from Knox College, and was named one of America's one hundred most important women by *Ladies' Home Journal*.

In 1987, Uhlenbeck went to the University of Texas at Austin, where she broadened her understanding of physics in studies with American physicist **Steven Weinberg**. In 1988, she accepted the Sid W. Richardson Foundation Regents' Chair in mathematics at the University of Texas. She also gave the plenary address at the International Congress of Mathematics in Japan in 1990.

Concerned that potential scientists were being discouraged unnecessarily because of their sex or race, Uhlenbeck joined a National Research Council planning group to investigate the representation of women in science and engineering. She believes that mathematics is always challenging and never boring, and she has expressed the hope that one of her accomplishments as a teacher has been communicating this to her students. "I sometimes feel the need to apologize for being a mathematician, but no apology is needed," she told *The Alcalde Magazine*. "Whenever I get a free week and start doing mathematics, I can't believe how much fun it is. I'm like a 12-year-old boy with a new train set."

SELECTED WRITINGS BY UHLENBECK:

Books

Instantons and 4-Manifold Topology, Springer Verlag, 1984.

FURTHER READING:

Periodicals

Benningfield, Damond, *The Alcalde Magazine,* Prominent Players, September/October, 1988, pp. 26–30.

Other

Uhlenbeck, Karen, *Some Personal Remarks on My Partly Finished Life,* unpublished manuscript.

Sketch by C. D. Lord

Harold Urey
1893–1981
American chemist and physicist

In 1934 Harold Urey was awarded the Nobel Prize in chemistry for his discovery of deuterium, an isotope—or species—of hydrogen, in which the atoms weigh twice as much as those in ordinary hydrogen. Also known as heavy hydrogen, deuterium became profoundly important to future studies in many scientific fields, including chemistry, physics, and medicine. Urey continued his research on isotopes over the next three decades, and during World War II his experience with deuterium proved invaluable in efforts to separate isotopes of uranium from each other in the development of the first atomic bombs. Later, Urey's research on isotopes also led to a method for determining the earth's atmospheric temperature at various periods in past history. This experimentation has become especially relevant because of concerns about the possibility of global climate change.

Harold Clayton Urey was born in Walkerton, Indiana, on April 29, 1893. His father, Samuel Clayton Urey, was a schoolteacher and lay minister in the Church of the Brethren. His mother was Cora Reinoehl Urey. Urey's father died when Harold was only six years old, and his mother later married another Brethren minister. Urey had a sister, Martha, a brother, Clarence, and two half-sisters, Florence and Ina.

After graduating from high school, Urey hoped to attend college but lacked the financial resources to do so. Instead, he accepted teaching jobs in country schools, first in Indiana (1911–1912) and then in Montana (1912–1914) before finally entering Montana State University in September of 1914 at the age of 21. Urey was initially interested in a career in biology, and the first original research he ever conducted involved a study of microorganisms in the Missoula River. In 1917 he was awarded his bachelor of science degree in zoology by Montana State.

Early Job Experience Leads to Career in Chemistry

The year Urey graduated also marked the entry of the United States into World War I. Although he had strong pacifist beliefs as a result of his early religious training, Urey acknowledged his obligation to participate in the nation's war effort. As a result, he accepted a job at the Barrett Chemical Company in Philadelphia and worked to develop high explosives. In his Nobel Prize acceptance speech, Urey said that this experience was instrumental in his move from industrial chemistry to academic life.

At the end of the war, Urey returned to Montana State University where he began teaching chemistry. In 1921 he decided to resume his college education and enrolled in the doctoral program in physical chemistry at the University of

Harold Urey

California at Berkeley. His faculty advisor at Berkeley was the great physical chemist **Gilbert Newton Lewis**. Urey received his doctorate in 1923 for research on the calculation of heat capacities and entropies (the degree of randomness in a system) of gases, based on information obtained through the use of a spectroscope. He then left for a year of postdoctoral study at the Institute for Theoretical Physics at the University of Copenhagen where **Niels Bohr**, a Danish physicist, was researching the structure of the atom. Urey's interest in Bohr's research had been cultivated while studying with Lewis, who had proposed many early theories on the nature of chemical bonding.

Upon his return to the United States in 1925, Urey accepted an appointment as an associate in chemistry at the Johns Hopkins University in Baltimore, a post he held until 1929. He interrupted his work at Johns Hopkins briefly to marry Frieda Daum in Lawrence, Kansas, on June 12, 1926. Daum was a bacteriologist and daughter of a prominent Lawrence educator. The Ureys later had four children, Gertrude Elizabeth, Frieda Rebecca, Mary Alice, and John Clayton.

Discovery of Deuterium Leads to Nobel Prize

In 1929, Urey left Johns Hopkins to become associate professor of chemistry at Columbia University, and in 1930 he published his first book, *Atoms, Molecules, and Quanta,* written with A. E. Ruark. Writing in the *Dictionary of Scientific Biography,* Joseph N. Tatarewicz called this work "the first comprehensive English language textbook on atomic structure and a major bridge between the new quantum physics and the field of chemistry." At this time he also began his search for an isotope of hydrogen. Since **Frederick Soddy**, an English chemist, discovered isotopes in 1913, scientists had been looking for isotopes of a number of elements. Urey believed that, if an isotope of heavy hydrogen existed, one way to separate it from the ordinary hydrogen isotope would be through the vaporization of liquid hydrogen. Since heavy hydrogen would be more dense than ordinary hydrogen, Urey theorized that the lighter hydrogen atoms would vaporize first, leaving behind a mixture rich in heavy hydrogen. Urey believed that, if he could obtain enough of the heavy mixture through a process of slow evaporation, spectroscopic readings would show spectral lines that differed from that of ordinary hydrogen.

With the help of two colleagues, Ferdinand Brickwedde and George M. Murphy, Urey carried out his experiment in 1931. The three researchers began with four liters of liquid hydrogen which they allowed to evaporate very slowly. Eventually, only a single milliliter of liquid hydrogen remained. This sample was then subjected to spectroscopic analysis which showed the presence of lines in exactly the positions predicted for a heavier isotope of hydrogen. This was deuterium.

The discovery of deuterium made Urey famous in the scientific world, and only three years later he was awarded the Nobel Prize in chemistry for his discovery. Since his wife was pregnant at the time, he declined to travel to Stockholm and was allowed to participate in the award ceremonies the following year. Urey's accomplishments were also recognized by Columbia University, and in 1933 he was appointed the Ernest Kempton Adams Fellow. A year later he was promoted to full professor of chemistry. Urey retained his appointment at Columbia until the end of World War II. During this time he also became the first editor of the new *Journal of Chemical Physics,* which became one of the principal periodicals in the field.

During the latter part of the 1930s, Urey extended his work on isotopes to other elements besides hydrogen. Eventually his research team was able to separate isotopes of carbon, nitrogen, oxygen, and sulfur. One of the intriguing discoveries made during this period was that isotopes may differ from each other chemically in very small ways. Initially, it was assumed that, since all isotopes of an element have the same electronic configuration, they would also have identical chemical properties. Urey found, however, that the mass differences in isotopes can result in modest differences in the *rate* at which they react.

Work on Isotopes Proves of Value during World War II

The practical consequences of this discovery became apparent all too soon. In 1939, word reached the United States about the discovery of nuclear fission by the German scientists **Otto Hahn** and **Fritz Strassmann**. The military consequences of the Hahn-Strassmann discovery were apparent to many scientists, including Urey. He was one of the first, therefore, to become involved in the U.S. effort to build a nuclear weapon, recognizing the threat posed by such a weapon in the hands of Nazi Germany. However, Urey was deeply concerned about the potential destructiveness of a fission weapon. Actively involved in political topics during the 1930s, Urey was a member of the Committee to Defend America by Aiding the Allies and worked vigorously against the fascist regimes in Germany, Italy, and Spain. He explained the importance of his political activism by saying that "no dictator knows enough to tell scientists what to do. Only in democratic nations can science flourish."

As World War II drew closer, Urey became involved in the Manhattan Project to build the nation's first atomic bomb. In 1940, he became a member of the Uranium Committee of the project, and two years later he was appointed director of the Substitute Alloys Materials Laboratory (SAML) at Columbia. SAML was one of three locations in the United States where research was being conducted on methods to separate two isotopes of uranium. As a leading expert on the separation of isotopes, Urey made critical contributions to the solution of the Manhattan Project's single most difficult problem, the isolation of uranium–235 from its heavier twin.

At the conclusion of World War II, Urey left Columbia to join the Enrico Fermi Institute of Nuclear Studies at the University of Chicago. In 1952 he was named Martin A. Ryerson Distinguished Service Professor there. The postwar period saw the beginning of a flood of awards and honorary degrees that was to continue for more than three decades. He received honorary degrees from more than two dozen universities, including doctorates from Columbia (1946), Oxford (1946), Washington and Lee (1948), the University of Athens (1951), McMaster University (1951), Yale (1951), and Indiana (1953).

The end of the war did not end Urey's concern about nuclear weapons. He now shifted his attention to work for the control of the terrible power he had helped to make a reality. Deeply conscious of a sense of scientific responsibility, Urey was opposed to the dropping of an atomic bomb on Japan. He was also aggressively involved in defeating a bill that would have placed control of nuclear power in the United States in the hands of the Department of Defense. Instead, he helped pass a bill creating a civilian board to control future nuclear development. In later years Urey explored peaceful uses of nuclear energy, and in 1975 he petitioned the White House to reduce production in nuclear power plants. He was also a member of the Union of Concerned Scientists.

More Applications of Isotope Research Uncovered

Urey continued to work on new applications of his isotope research. In the late 1940s and early 1950s, he explored the relationship between the isotopes of oxygen and past planetary climates. Since isotopes differ in the rate of chemical reactions, Urey said that the amount of each oxygen isotope in an organism is a result of atmospheric

temperatures. During periods when the earth was warmer than normal, organisms would take in more of a lighter isotope of oxygen and less of a heavier isotope. During cool periods, the differences among isotopic concentrations would not be as great. Over a period of time, Urey was able to develop a scale, or an "oxygen thermometer," that related the relative concentrations of oxygen isotopes in the shells of sea animals with atmospheric temperatures. Some of those studies continue to be highly relevant in current research on the possibilities of global climate change.

In the early 1950s, Urey became interested in yet another subject: the chemistry of the universe and of the formation of the planets, including the earth. One of his first papers on this topic attempted to provide an estimate of the relative abundance of the elements in the universe. Although these estimates have now been improved, they were remarkably close to the values modern chemists now accept.

Urey also became involved in a study of the origin of the solar system. For well over 200 years, scientists had been debating the mechanism by which the planets and their satellites were formed. From his own studies, Urey concluded that the creation of the solar system took place at temperatures considerably less than those suggested by most experts at the time. He also proposed a new theory about the origin of the earth's moon, claiming that it was formed not as a result of being torn from the earth, but through an independent process of a gradual accumulation of materials.

Urey's last great period of research brought together his interests and experiences in a number of fields of research to which he had devoted his life. The subject of that research was the origin of life on Earth. Urey hypothesized that Earth's primordial atmosphere consisted of reducing gases such as hydrogen, ammonia, and methane. The energy provided by electrical discharges in the atmosphere, he suggested, was sufficient to initiate chemical reactions among these gases, converting them to the simplest compounds of which living organisms are made, amino acids. In 1951, Urey's graduate student **Stanley Lloyd Miller** carried out a series of experiments to test this hypothesis. In these experiments, an electrical discharge passed through a glass tube containing only reducing gases resulted in the formation of amino acids.

In 1958 Urey left the University of Chicago to become Professor at Large at the University of California in San Diego at La Jolla. At La Jolla, his interests shifted from original scientific research to national scientific policy. He became extremely involved in the U.S. space program, serving as the first chairman of the Committee on Chemistry of Space and Exploration of the Moon and Planets of the National Academy of Science's Space Sciences Board. Even late in life, Urey continued to receive honors and awards from a grateful nation and admiring colleagues. He was awarded the Johann Kepler Medal of the American Association for the Advancement of Science (1971), the Priestley Medal of the American Chemical Society (1973), National Aeronautics and Space Administration (NASA) Exceptional Scientific Achievement Award (1973), and the

200th Anniversary Plaque of the American Chemical Society (1976). Urey died of a heart attack in La Jolla on January 5, 1981, at the age of 87.

SELECTED WRITINGS BY UREY:

Books

Atoms, Molecules, and Quanta, McGraw-Hill, 1930.
The Planets: Their Origins and Development, Yale University Press, 1952.
Nuclear Geology, The Origin of the Earth, edited by Henry Faul, Wiley, 1954, pp. 355–71.
America's Race for the Moon, Earth's Daughter, Sister, or Uncle?, edited by W. Sullivan, Random House, 1962.

Periodicals

Physical Review, On the Relative Abundances of Isotopes, Volume 38, 1931, pp. 718–24.
Angewandte Chemie, Some Thermodynamic Properties of Hydrogen Deuterium, Volume 48, 1935, pp. 315–20.
Science, A Hypothesis Regarding the Origin of the Movement of the Earth's Crust, October 28, 1949, pp. 445–46.
Yearbook of the Physical Society, Meteorites and the Origin of the Solar System, New York, 1957.
Forbes, As I See It, July 15, 1969, pp. 44–48.

FURTHER READING:

Books

Holmes, Frederic L., editor, *Dictionary of Scientific Biography,* Volume 18, Supplement II, Scribner, 1990.
Schoenebaum, Eleanora W., *Political Profiles: The Truman Years,* Facts on File, 1978, pp. 571–72.

Periodicals

Brickwedde, Ferdinand G., *Physics Today,* Harold Urey and the Discovery of Deuterium, September 1982, pp. 34–39.
Brush, Stephen G., *Science,* Nickel for Your Thoughts: Urey and the Origin of the Moon, Volume 217, 1982, pp. 891–98.
Garfield, Eugene, *Current Comments,* A Tribute to Harold Urey, December 3, 1979, pp. 5–9.
Sagan, Carl, *Icarus,* Obituary, Harold Clayton Urey, 1893–1981, Volume 48 1981, pp. 348–52.

Sketch by David E. Newton

Boris Petrovich Uvarov
1889–1970
Russian-born English entomologist

Boris Uvarov's enormous love of scientific inquiry and its practical applications, coupled with his intense sense of purpose, allowed him to become the world's leading expert on locust and grasshopper research. Not only did he contribute to the taxonomy of 284 genera and over 900 species and subspecies of Orthoptera, but he single-handedly organized and activated a worldwide cooperation to combat and control locust swarms.

Boris Petrovich Uvarov was born on November 11, 1889, in Uralsk, Russia. His father, Petr P. Uvarov was a bank cashier employed by the State Bank. His mother's name was Alexandra. He was the youngest of three sons. As a child, Uvarov enjoyed collecting bugs, and he took this interest with him to the University of St. Petersburg, where he graduated with a degree in biology in 1910. After graduation, he married Anna Federova Prodanjuk; they had one son.

As a young adult in a turbulent Russia, Uvarov held several positions in the country's agricultural department. In 1911, he was stationed in the Northen Caucasus, where he was to begin his lifelong study of locust. The next year, when he was 23 years old, he was appointed director of the Entomological Bureau at Stavropol. It was during this time that Uvarov developed his theory on locust swarming and nonswarming tendencies.

At the time, it was believed that swarming and nonswarming locusts were two different species because their physical and behavioral characteristics appeared to be vastly different. Through scientific observation and data collection, Uvarov proved that swarming and nonswarming locusts were indeed the same species that were engaged in apparently different phases. Such a discovery was startling because it meant that the gross agricultural devastation caused by swarming locust could in fact be controlled by deploying a management plan. Uvarov's phase theory had monumentous effects worldwide.

In 1915, he was appointed to director of the Tiflis Bureau of Plant Protection. In 1919, he became Professor of Zology at the State University of Tiflis and Keeper of Entomology and Zoology in the State Museum of Georgia. By 1919, Russia had gone through its revolution and broken up into republics. Tiflis was now the capital of Georgia, which was experiencing militant nationalism. Understandably, Uvarov was uncomfortable with the new instability and was having difficulties performing his duties. It was at this time that he met Patrick A. Buxton, a medical entomologist accompanying the British troops stationed in the area. It was through his friendship with Buxton that Uvarov was able to accept a position at the Imperial Bureau of Entomology in London. Even though it occupied but a small corner of the British Museum, the bureau, renamed the Commonwealth Institute of Entomology, would become the world headquarters for locust research and plague control under Uvarov's 25-year tenure.

During the 1920s, Uvarov focused primarily on identifying and classifying insects within the British Commonwealth. In 1928, Uvarov published his book *Locusts and Grasshoppers*, which became the reference work on the subject for the next 30 years. After several major locust outbreaks in Asia and Africa, Uvarov was asked to head the Locust Committees of the Economic Advisory Council in Africa. At once, Uvarov recognized the need for a global antilocust plan. He organized antilocust conferences, monitored investigations into locust plagues, and eventually developed an international plan to research and contain locust populations. World War II inhibited full rollout of Uvarov's methodology, however his plan was successfully implemented in break-out areas of Africa.

At the end of the World War II in 1945, the Commonwealth Institute realigned itself under the Colonial Office and was named the Anti-Locust Research Centre. Uvarov actively developed the center's laboratory by inspiring younger researchers, while at the same time encouraging global cooperation in locust control by traveling extensively. He retired as director of the center in 1959 and spent the next three years serving as president of the Royal Entomological Society of London.

Uvarov's scientific career spanned over 50 years, and in that time he received many accolades. The highest honor bestowed upon him by England was a knighthood in 1961. This was possible because Uvarov was naturalized in 1943. Other honors include an honorary doctorate in science at the University of Madrid in 1935, commandeur de l'Ordre Royal de Lion in 1948, and Fellow of the Royal Society in 1950.

Uvarov spent the 1960s revising a new edition of *Locusts and Grasshoppers*. The updated first volume was completed in 1966. In 1968, his wife of 58 years died. Uvarov passed away at his home in Ealing on March 18, 1970. At the time of his death, Uvarov was approaching completion of his updated second volume of his 1928 publication. It was eventually completed by colleagues and published in 1977.

SELECTED WRITINGS BY UVAROV:

Books

Locusts and Grasshoppers, 1928.
Insect Nutrition and Metabolism, 1928.
Insects and Climate, 1931.

FURTHER READING:

Books

Oxbury, H., ed., *Great Britons: 20th Century Lives*, 1985.

Wigglesworth, V. B., *Dictionary of Notable Biographies 1961–1970*.

Periodicals

Obituary. *The New York Times* (March 19, 1970).

Sketch by Jacqueline L. Longe

Seiya Uyeda
1929–
Japanese geophysicist

Geophysicist Seiya Uyeda became an expert on tectonics—the study of the earth's crust and its motions—through his studies of the Japanese island arc. Using this knowledge, he demonstrated the relationship between terrestrial heat flow around Japan and earthquake and volcanic activity. He also developed, with D. Forsyth, a theory explaining the motion of the earth's tectonic plates. Uyeda was born in Tokyo on November 28, 1929, to Seiichi, a government official, and Hatsuo (Okino) Uyeda. He attended the University of Tokyo, majoring in geophysics. He was awarded his bachelor of science in 1952 and his D.Sc. in 1958. In 1952 Uyeda married Mutsuko Kosaka; they have three children, Taro, Makiko and Naoko.

For his doctoral research, Uyeda studied the phenomenon of the self-reversal of magnetism in some rock minerals. This means that the direction of the magnetism of some rocks was exactly opposite of that of the earth's geomagnetic field. The reversal of magnetism in some minerals indicated that in the geological past, the earth's magnetic field had experienced reversals. This area of study was very important at the start of Uyeda's career, as it corresponded with the continental drift theory. Originally proposed in 1912 by **Alfred Wegener**, the theory was experiencing a revival in the scientific community. It proposed that the earth's continents were not fixed in place, which contradicted the earlier theory that the surface of the earth was rigid and unchanging.

Wegener's continental drift theory claimed that all of the current continents were once one large land mass. Although now discounted, that theory was connected to the related theories of sea-floor spreading and plate tectonics. According to plate tectonics, the ocean floor was created at the mid-oceanic trenches, then spread horizontally and finally ended in the deep trenches. Plate tectonics posit that the earth's surface was made of fifteen rigid blocks or plates. The collisions and other interactions of these plates explain the appearance of the earth's crust.

Researches Plate Tectonics and Heat Flow

Plate tectonics can explain the current appearance of island arcs, the area of study that Uyeda pioneered in association with other scientists. Island arcs are the series of island chains along the northern and western edges of the Pacific. Named for their typical arc shape, they have trenches which are more than six thousand meters (twenty thousand feet) deep, usually lying on the ocean side of each arc. From 1957 to 1964, Uyeda was a research associate at the Earthquake Research Institute at the University of Tokyo, where he studied the distribution of terrestrial heat flow over the Japanese island arc and its surrounding seas. He found that the flow was low on the ocean side of the arc and high on the continental side; the heat flow in the Sea of Japan was always higher than that of the Japan Trench and the Pacific on the east of Japan. Uyeda's research demonstrated that the distribution of heat flow was related to the distribution of volcanoes and earthquakes. These findings were used as the basis of a theory of typical heat flow for island arcs.

Uyeda's research on island arcs led to his discovery, with colleagues, of magnetic lineations in the Pacific Ocean. From this finding, he posited that the Pacific floor had undergone a major northward move sometime in the geological past. Uyeda also co-originated, with Forsyth in 1975, a theory based on a pulling at the trenches of plates that explained the origin of plate motions.

Uyeda became an associate professor at the Geophysical Institute in 1964, where he remained until he returned to the Earthquake Research Institute as a professor from 1969 to 1990. Since 1990, he has served as both a professor in the Department of Marine Science and Technology at Tokai University in Simizu, Japan, and a professor at the Texas A & M University College Station. Throughout his career Uyeda also has spent many years as a visiting scientist at prestigious institutions. He has taught at Cambridge and Oxford Universities, the Scripps Institution of Oceanography, Stanford University, the Massachusetts Institute of Technology, the Lamont-Doherty Geological Observatory, and the California Institute of Technology.

Uyeda has received numerous prizes and honors, including the Tanakadte Prize of the Society of Terrestrial Magnetism and Electricity in 1955, the Agassiz Medal of the U.S. National Academy of Sciences in 1972, the Academy Prize of the Japanese Academy in 1987, and the G. P. Woollard Award of the Geological Society of America in 1989. Uyeda is a foreign associate of the National Academy of Science, and an associate member of the Societé Géologique de France.

SELECTED WRITINGS BY UYEDA:

Books

Island Arcs: Japan and its Environs, Elsevier, 1973.
The New View of the Earth: Moving Continents and Moving Oceans, W. H. Freeman, 1978.

FURTHER READING:

Books

McGraw-Hill Modern Scientists and Engineers, Volume 3, McGraw-Hill, 1980, pp. 241–242.

Sketch by Terrie M. Romano

Charles Jean Gustave Nicolas de la Vallée–Poussin
1866–1962
Belgian number theorist

Charles Jean Gustave Nicolas de la Vallée–Poussin was responsible for proving the prime number theorem. A prime number is a number that can be divided by only one and itself without producing a remainder, and de la Vallée–Poussin—like many others—set out to prove the relationship between prime numbers. In an article for *MAA Online* dated December 23, 1996, Ivars Peterson asserts: "In effect, [the prime number theorem] states that the average gap between two consecutive primes near the number x is close to the natural logarithm of x. Thus, when x is close to 100, the natural logarithm of x is approximately 4.6, which means that in this range, roughly every fifth number should be a prime." De la Vallée–Poussin was additionally known for his writings about the zeta function, Lebesgue and Stieltjes integrals, conformal representation, algebraic and trigonometricpolynomial approximation, trigonometric series, analytic and quasi–analytic functions, and complex variables. His writings and research, which were—and are—considered clear, stylish, and precise, were highly respected by his peers in academia and other well–placed individuals in Western society.

Despite the historical confusion posed by de la Vallée–Poussin's name (it is often rendered as Charles–Jean–Gustave–Nicolas, Charles–Jean Gustave Nicolas, Charles–Joseph, Vallée Poussin, etc.), the facts surrounding his origins are well known. De la Vallée–Poussin was born on August 14, 1866, in Louvain, Belgium. A distant relative of the French painter Nicolas Poussin, de la Vallée–Poussin's father was, like himself, an esteemed teacher at the University of Louvain. (The elder de la Vallée–Poussin, however, specialized in geology and mineralogy.) De la Vallée–Poussin's family was well–off, and, as a child, he found encouragement and inspiration in fellow mathematician Louis–Philippe Gilbert (some sources identify him as Louis Claude Gilbert), with whom he would eventually work.

De la Vallée–Poussin enrolled at the Jesuit College at Mons in southwestern Belgium, where it is said he originally intended to pursue a career in the clergy. He ultimately, however, obtained a *diplôme d'ingenieur* and began to pursue a career in mathematics. In 1891, like his father and Gilbert, he became employed at the University of Louvain, where he initially worked as Gilbert's assistant. Gilbert's death the following year created an academic opening to which de la Vallée–Poussin was appointed in 1893, thereby earning him the title of professor of mathematics.

Although de la Vallée–Poussin was gaining recognition as early as 1892, when he won a prize for an essay on differential equations, he earned his first widespread fame four years later. In 1896, de la Vallée–Poussin capitalized on the ideas set forth by earlier mathematicians, notably Karl Friedrich Gauss, Adrien Marie Legendre, Leonhard Euler, Peter Gustav Lejeune Dirichlet, Pafnuty Lvovich Chebyshev, and Georg Friedrich Bernhard Riemann, and proved what is now known as the prime number theorem. (De la Vallée–Poussin shares this honor with **Jacques Hadamard**, who revealed his finding in the same year. Historians note, however, that de la Vallée–Poussin's and Hadamard's achievements were performed independently and that, although both mathematicians used the Riemann zeta function in their work, they came to their conclusions in different ways.)

De la Vallée–Poussin revealed much of his ground-breaking work in a series of celebrated books and papers. His two–volume *Cours d'analyse infinitésimale* went through several printings, and the work was consistently edited between printings to offer updated information. Initially, the book was directed toward both mathematicians and students, and de la Vallée–Poussin used different fonts and sizes of types to differentiate between the audiences to whom a particular passage was directed. In the 1910s, de la Vallée–Poussin was preparing the third edition of this work, but this was destroyed by German forces, who invaded Louvain during World War I. De la Vallée–Poussin subsequently dedicated his 1916 *Intégrales de Lebesgue fonctions d'ensemble, classes de baire* to the Lebesgue interval to compensate for the material destroyed by the Germans. De la Vallée–Poussin continued to publish well into his eighties, and, like *Cours d'analyse infinitésimale,* many of his writings went through various reprintings and revisions. Almost all of de la Vallée–Poussin's writing have been praised for their originality and the clarity of his writing style.

De la Vallée–Poussin, who married a Belgian woman whom he met while vacationing in Norway in the late 1890s, died on March 2, 1962, in the city of his birth. During his lifetime, he was accorded many honors. In addition to the celebrations commemorating his thirty-fifth and fiftieth anniversaries as chair of mathematics at the University of Louvain, he was elected to various prestigious institutions including the French Académie Royales des Sciences, the International Mathematical Union, the London Mathematical Society, the Belgian Royal Academy, and the Legion of Honor. In 1928, the king of Belgium also awarded him the title of baron in recognition of his years of academic tenure and his professional achievements.

SELECTED WRITINGS BY DE LA VALLÉE–POUSSIN:

Books

Cours d'analyse infinitésimale. 2 volumes, 1903–1906. (Much of de la Vallée–Poussin's works was revised and reprinted. This work, in particular, was heavily revised, with each new edition offering substantive changes and new information.)

Intégrales de Lebesgue fonctions d'ensemble, classes de baire, 1916.

Leçons sur l'approximation des fonctions d'une variable réelle, 1919.

Leçons de mécanique analytique, 1924.

Les nouvelles méthodes de la théorie du potentiel et le problème généralisé de Dirichlet: Actualités scientifiques et industrielles, 1937.

Le potentiel logarithmique, balayage et représentation conforme, 1949.

FURTHER READING:

Books

Burkhill, J. C. "Charles–Jean–Gustave–Nicolas de la-Vallée–Poussin," in *Dictionary of Scientific Biography.* Volume XIII. Edited by Charles Coulston Gillispie. New York: Charles Scribner's Sons, 1976, pp. 561–62.

Young, Laurence. *Mathematicians and Their Times: History of Mathematics and Mathematics of History.* Amsterdam: North–Holland Publishing Company, 1981, p. 306.

Periodicals

Bateman, Paul T, and Harold G. Diamond, "A Hundred Years of Prime Numbers." *The American Mathematical Monthly* 103, no. 9 (November 1996): pp. 729–41.

Burkill, J. C., "Charles–Joseph de la Vallée Poussin," *Journal of the London Mathematical Society* 39 (1964): pp. 165–75.

Other

Peterson, Ivars, "Ivars Peterson's MathLand: Prime Theorem of the Century," *MAA Online* (December 23, 1996), http://www.maa.org.

Sketch by C. J. Giroux

Henri-Victor Vallois
1889–1981
French anatomist and paleontologist

Henri-Victor Vallois was one of the major proponents of the presapiens theory of human evolution, one of a number of theories which attempted to determine the evolutionary position of the fossilized remains of an early form of human known as the Neanderthal.

Born in Nancy, France, in 1889, Vallois received degrees in medicine and natural science and joined the faculty of medicine in Toulouse in 1922. In 1933 he became director of the laboratory of the École Pratique des Hautes Études. A prolific writer, Vallois published more than four hundred works between 1908 and 1980. He served as professor at the Musée d'Histoire Naturelle, held the post of director of the Institut de Paléontologie Humaine in Paris from 1942, and was Marcellin Boule's successor as director of the Musée de l'Homme from 1950 to 1959.

As was common in the early part of the twentieth century, Vallois's research concerned the origin of the racial differences recognized in modern humans, and he established a system of classification of humans by racial type. He identified twenty-seven races, distinguished by such features as size, skin color, and head shape, which he grouped into four major categories: the australoid, the leucoderme, the melanoderm, and the xanthoderm. This classification was substantially criticized by other scientists; however, it produced two influential books, *Les races de l'empire français* (1943) and *Les races humaines* (1944).

His most significant work, however, concerned the development of the modern human, *Homo sapiens,* from earlier forms now known as *Homo erectus.* Vallois was the first to critique the three most prevalent theories of human origin, each of which is identified by the position attributed to the Neanderthal in the sequence of human evolution. The Neanderthal-phase hypothesis holds that humans developed in a relatively linear manner, from the earliest forms through *Homo erectus,* the Neanderthals, and *Homo sapiens,* that is, placing modern humans in a direct line from the Neanderthals. The presapiens theory maintains that the Neanderthal was too primitive a form of human living too late in the sequence to have been a direct ancestor of modern humans; rather, a more advanced type of human had already developed, and with their superior tools and more advanced culture, these humans eventually displaced the more primitive Neanderthals. The pre-Neanderthal hypothesis offers a compromise, accepting the premise that the European Neanderthals (the "classic" Neanderthals) were too primitive to have been direct ancestors of modern humans, but suggesting that another branch of Neanderthal had been the intermediate stage between *Homo erectus* and modern *Homo sapiens.*

Vallois first organized these theories in his 1958 monograph on the fossil remains found at Fontéchevade in France. He rejected the Neanderthal-phase theory, associated with the ideas of **Franz Weidenreich** and **Aleš Hrdlička**, believing, on the basis of certain anatomical indexes derived from analysis of Neanderthal remains, that the species was too specialized to fall within the evolutionary sequence. Vallois also believed that two nearly contemporaneous human forms, the Neanderthal and the more modern-appearing Cro-Magnon, or Aurignacian, were too different morphologically to have been part of the same line of descent; he maintained that modern humans were descended from the Aurignacian, who, he theorized, had originated in Western Asia independent of the Neanderthals and migrated into Europe between glacial periods.

Vallois criticized the pre-Neanderthal theory, concluding that the fossils grouped together as pre-Neanderthals were too different from each other to form a coherent type, and he believed that the Neanderthals as a group exhibited relatively little interindividual variation. In his view, some of the so-called pre-Neanderthal fossils were morphologically too close to modern humans—especially in their lack of a prominent brow ridge—to be ancestral to the Neanderthals.

Vallois's main evidence in support of the presapiens theory, which was upheld by such paleoanthropologists as **Arthur Keith** and **Louis Leakey**, came from European sites, notably Fontéchevade, with corroborating evidence taken from skull fragments found in Swanscombe, England. Although these fossils lacked the portion of the skull on which the brow ridge would have appeared or were of immature individuals who would not yet have developed such a ridge, Vallois's reconstruction of the skulls led him to conclude that these provided evidence of a modern human species predating the Neanderthals and the pre-Neanderthals as well, and provided the link between ancient and modern humans. The theory held that anatomically modern humans could be very ancient, in fact developing earlier than some more primitive types. Additional evidence from the fossil remains found at Piltdown, England, was quickly discarded when it was found to be fraudulent, but the presapiens theory was already losing support. Even by the time of publication of his monograph in 1958, few scholars supported Vallois's view. Further research into the Fontéchevade and Swanscombe remains led an increasing number of scholars to the conclusion that these were actually ancestral to the Neanderthals, and the pre-Neanderthal theory gained prominence. Vallois retired in 1961 and died in 1981.

SELECTED WRITINGS BY VALLOIS:

Books

La paléontologie et l'origine de l'homme, Paris, 1950.
Fossil Men, Dryden, 1957.

Social Life of Early Man, The Social Life of Early Man: The Evidence of Skeletons, edited by Sherwood L. Washburn, Aldine, 1961.

Periodicals

L'anthropologie, Les preuves anatomiques de l'origine monophyletique de l'homme, Volume 39, 1929, pp. 77–101.
American Journal of Physical Anthropology, The Fontéchevade Fossil Man, Volume 7, 1949, pp. 339–362.
Journal of the Royal Anthropological Institute, Neanderthals and Presapiens, Volume 84, 1954, pp. 111–130.

FURTHER READING:

Books

Smith, Fred H., and Frank Spencer, *The Origins of Modern Humans: A World Survey of the Fossil Evidence,* Liss, 1984.
Trinkaus, Erik, and Pat Shipman, *The Neanderthals: Changing the Image of Mankind,* Knopf, 1993.

Periodicals

Delmas, André, tribute in, *L'anthropologie,* December 1981.

Sketch by Michael Sims

James Van Allen
1914–
American physicist

James Van Allen is best known for his discovery of bands of high-level radiation surrounding the earth. Popularly known as the Van Allen radiation belts, these belts are part of the earth's magnetosphere. Although Van Allen's discovery of the belts has been the highlight of his career, he has also been associated with other significant scientific research. During World War II Van Allen made his first significant scientific contribution by creating the radio proximity fuse, a small tracking device that triggered weapons when they were close to the target. The knowledge and skills Van Allen developed in weapons research and miniaturization later proved useful in his studies of the atmosphere using rockets and satellites.

James Alfred Van Allen was born in Mount Pleasant, Iowa, on September 7, 1914. He was the second of four sons of Alfred M. Van Allen, an attorney, and Alma E. (Olney) Van Allen. His interest in science developed early, and when he was twelve, he and a brother built their own electrostatic generator. The boys used their machine to produce bolts of artificial lightning. By the time Van Allen reached high school, physics had become a passion for him. According to biographer D. S. Halacy, Jr., in *They Gave Their Names to Science,* "Teachers sometimes had to forcibly eject him from laboratories after the day was over!"

After graduating from high school, Van Allen entered Wesleyan College in his hometown. At Wesleyan he was strongly influenced by Thomas Poulter, later to become director of the Stanford Research Institute at Stanford University. In 1935 Van Allen received his bachelor of science degree from Wesleyan and entered the State University of Iowa at Iowa City for graduate study. He earned his master of science degree in 1936 and his Ph.D. in 1939.

Van Allen's work at the State University of Iowa caught the attention of the Carnegie Institute in Washington, D.C., and he was offered a position as research fellow there in the Department of Terrestrial Magnetism. After three years at Carnegie, he moved on to the Applied Physics Laboratory at Johns Hopkins University in 1942.

War Brings New Opportunities

By 1942, however, World War II had become the dominant factor in Van Allen's life. He left Johns Hopkins to accept a commission in the U.S. Navy, where he served until 1946. Van Allen's first important scientific accomplishment—the radio proximity fuse—came as a result of his war research. The fuse was a device consisting of a radio transmitter and receiver that was attached to weapons. Signals sent out and received by the fuse indicated when the weapon was close to the target, allowing it to explode before actual impact. This greatly increased the effeciency of the missiles, as it eliminated the need for a direct hit.

Van Allen's work on the fuse was to shape his future scientific career in unexpected ways. At the end of World War II, American scientists inherited about one hundred V–2 rockets built by German scientists. Far more advanced than anything produced by Americans at the time, these rockets promised to be valuable for scientists studying the earth's atmosphere. As a result of his research on the fuse, Van Allen had become a leading authority on the miniaturization of instruments, a skill crucial in rocket research. The U.S. Army therefore appointed him to administer and coordinate rocket-based research, and in 1946 Van Allen took charge of the V–2 research program based at the White Sands Proving Ground in New Mexico. His primary responsibilities were to design payloads to be sent into the atmosphere and to select projects to be used in the rocket research. From 1947 to 1958 he also served as chairman of the committee overseeing this research, originally called the V–2 Rocket Panel and, later, the Rocket and Satellite Research Panel.

This change of name reflected a change in actual rocket research itself. With a limited number of V–2 rockets available, scientists soon began to explore alternative instruments. Although American scientists could not produce an equivalent of the V–2, under Van Allen's direction they eventually constructed an acceptable substitute, the Aerobee. The Aerobee carried smaller payloads than the V–2, and although it reached altitudes of only sixty miles, compared to the German rocket's one hundred miles, it became a research workhorse for American scientists over the next decade.

The Return to Iowa

In 1951 Van Allen returned to his native state of Iowa as professor of physics and head of the Department of Physics and Astronomy at the State University of Iowa, positions he held until 1985. Shortly after this move, Van Allen developed a new approach for the study of the atmosphere. For over a century, balloons had been the most effective way to accumulate information about the atmosphere. Instruments were carried aloft in balloons to heights of up to fifteen miles and then parachuted back to earth with their data.

Van Allen combined ballooning techniques with modern rocket technology to make a "rockoon,"which consisted of a balloon carrying a rocket. When the balloon reached its maximum altitude, the rocket was fired off by remote control. It traveled straight upward, through the balloon itself, another 50–70 miles into the atmosphere. Readings obtained from such rockoon launchings provided better information about the outer atmosphere than ever before.

Information from two rockoons sent up in 1953 produced data that puzzled Van Allen. He discovered that levels of radiation at an altitude of 30 miles were much higher than had been expected. These results made Van Allen curious about what he might find at even higher altitudes. At this time scientists were discussing the next stage in rocket development: an artificial Earth satellite that would remain in long-term orbit around the planet. As part of the International Geophysical Year planned for 1957–58, the U.S. government had made a commitment to finance such a satellite. The first satellite in that program, *Explorer I,* was launched on January 31, 1958. Results obtained from the satellite were intriguing; the levels of cosmic radiation in the upper atmosphere were much higher than had been anticipated. Instruments on *Explorer II* and *Explorer III* gave similar results.

By May of 1958, Van Allen was ready with an explanation for these results. He hypothesized the existence of two belts of radiation, one at an altitude of 600–3000 miles, the other at an altitude of 9,000–15,000 miles. Later research confirmed this hypothesis and proved that the belts consist of high-velocity protons and electrons spiraling around the earth's magnetic lines of force. These are the Van Allen radiation belts. In scientific terms, these belts form part of Earth's magnetosphere, an area of space around the planet dominated by charged particles that are held there by Earth's magnetic field. For his discovery of the belts and other contributions to science, Van Allen has received many scientific awards and honors, including the Space Flight Award of the American Astronautical Society, the John A. Fleming Award of the American Geophysical Union, and the Elliott Cresson Medal of the Franklin Institute.

Van Allen married Abigail Fithian Halsey on October 13, 1945. They have five children, Cynthia (Schaffner), Margot (Cairns), Sarah (Trimble), Thomas, and Peter.

SELECTED WRITINGS BY VAN ALLEN:

Books

Scientific Uses of Earth Satellites, University of Michigan Press, 1956.
Pioneer: First to Jupiter, Saturn, and Beyond, National Aeronautics and Space Administration, 1980.
Origins of Magnetospheric Physics, Smithsonian Institution Press, 1983.

FURTHER READING:

Books

Halacy, D. S., Jr., *They Gave Their Names to Science,* Putnam's, 1967.

Sketch by David E. Newton

Robert J. Van de Graaff
1901–1967
American physicist

Robert J. Van de Graaff invented a particle accelerator named for him that tremendously advanced research in nuclear physics. He devoted his life to the improvement and commercial construction of his Van de Graaff accelerator, which has found widespread application in nuclear research, medicine, and industry around the world. At the time of his death, he was immersed in an effort to further extend the capabilities of his accelerator. Robert Jemison Van de Graaff was born and raised in Tuscaloosa, Alabama. His mother was Minnie Cherokee Hargrove, and his father was Adrian Sebastian Van de Graaff, a jurist. He was educated in Tuscaloosa's public schools, and then attended the University of Alabama, from which he received his B.S. degree in 1922 and his M.S. degree in 1923, both in mechanical engineering. After graduation, Van de Graaff worked for the Alabama Power Company for a year as a research assistant, continuing his studies of the conversion of heat into mechanical energy.

The young engineer's desire to understand the physical forces that drive natural phenomena—rather than work only with practical methods to harness and use those forces—led him to the study of physics. He began with studies at the Sorbonne in Paris from 1924 to 1925 and while there attended **Marie Curie**'s lectures on radiation. In 1925 he went to Oxford University in England as a Rhodes Scholar, where he received another B.S. degree, this time in physics in 1926, followed by his Ph.D. in physics in 1928 for work on ion mobility. He stayed at Oxford for one more year on a fellowship. While at Oxford, Van de Graaff absorbed **Ernest Rutherford**'s 1927 address to the Royal Society expressing that pioneer nuclear experimenter's hope that particles could someday be accelerated to speeds sufficient to disintegrate nuclei. Study of a nucleus as it disintegrated and scatterd would reveal much about the nature of individual atoms. Only very high-speed particles would have enough force to smash apart an atomic nucleus, and nature does not supply enough of these: hence the need for an acceleration machine.

Develops New Atom Smasher

Van de Graaff realized the importance of research on atomic nuclei, and, impressed by Rutherford's address, worked out the principle of a device to accelerate elementary particles to high energies, drawing on his mechanical engineering background. He based his design on the oldest kind of electricity known: static electricity, the kind that causes small effects like static cling and large effects like lightning. Van de Graaff decided to generate high voltages using a direct-current electrostatic method. A moving belt would carry an electric charge inside an insulating tube into an insulated metal sphere, which would store the accumulated electricity on its surface. High-voltage discharges of this electricity into an acceleration tube would provide the required particle acceleration. From his engineering background, Van de Graaff knew that a polished and rounded surface for the electric terminal would greatly reduce the possibility of electric stress and breakdown.

In 1929 Van de Graaff returned to the United States, joining Princeton University's Palmer Physics Laboratory as a National Research Fellow. That fall, he verified his particle acceleration principles by constructing the first working model of his device, which developed 80,000 volts. It was not sophisticated, consisting as it did of a silk ribbon, a tin can, and a small motor. E. Alfred Burrill in *Physics Today* wrote that, in order to construct this elementary model, Van de Graaff searched through Princeton's local millinery shops for pure silk, going so far as to set at least one sample on fire—in the shop—to be sure of its purity. More working models followed, and Van de Graaff introduced his invention to fellow physicists in September 1931 at a meeting of the American Physical Society. He followed with a demonstration in November 1931 at the inaugural dinner of the American Institute of Physics, producing over a million volts.

Particle Accelerator Makes Dramatic Debut

Fellow physicist Karl T. Compton encouraged Van de Graaff in his work at Princeton. When Compton became president of the Massachusetts Institute of Technology (MIT) in 1931, Van de Graaff accepted Compton's invitation to come to MIT as a research associate and further developed his accelerator. In 1932 and 1933, Van de Graaff constructed his first large generator, in an aircraft hangar at Round Hill, on the shore of Buzzard's Bay in South Dartmouth, Massachusetts. The machine was truly enormous. It consisted of two polished aluminum spheres each fifteen feet in diameter mounted on cylindrical insulating columns twenty-five feet high and six feet in diameter. The columns were mobile, mounted on trucks operating on a railway track which boosted the spheres to forty-three feet above ground level. This machine had its debut performance on November 28, 1933, with spectacular effects choreographed for half an hour by Van de Graaff as he directed the switches controlling the generator's current. The spheres, acting as voltage terminals, sent out seven-million-volt bolts of blue lightning between each other and between themselves and the hangar's walls and floor. Observers could feel their hair rise from the static force. The *New York Times,* reporting on the demonstration on November 29, 1933, headlined its story "Man Hurls Bolt of 7,000,000 Volts," and went on to describe the "brilliance and the savage fury of [the generator's] unleashed power," the "magic wands which spat out flaming streaks of blue, liquid fire," and the "snakelike tongues of violet, pink and lavender flames [that] lashed out" as the participating scientists calmly monitored their switches. Operating the generator in the hangar caused problems, so the machine was moved to a pressurized enclosure at MIT in 1937. A vacuum tube to contain the current was added. By 1940, a modified version was producing voltages of 2.75 MV, and, after its productive years as a tool of nuclear and radiography research ended, it became a permanent "atom smasher" exhibit at the Boston Museum of Science.

The Van de Graaff accelerator was an immediate success, as its advantages over existing machines were immediately apparent. **John D. Cockcroft** and **Ernest Walton** of the Cavendish Laboratory in England had built a successful particle accelerator in 1932, which used voltage-multiplier circuits to produce the required high voltages. This machine was bulky and complicated, however, and maximum voltages were limited. The Van de Graaff device, in contrast, was extremely simple and (ultimately) compact, based as it was on electrostatic generation, employing a simple belt rather than multiple transformers. Because its voltage was relatively easy to stabilize, it permitted precisely controllable particle acceleration, which the Cockcroft-Walton accelerator did not, and it achieved significantly higher energies. The simplicity of Van de Graaff's principle is made apparent by the fact that it is possible to

produce a small, homemade Van de Graaff generator—and many science students and laboratory assistants do so with, for example, loaf pans (for the base and dome), a plastic fruit-juice mixer (for the insulating tube), a rubber belt, and a toy motor.

Guided by Compton and by **Vannevar Bush**, MIT's vice president, Van de Graaff toiled through the writing of his patent application and was rewarded with a patent for his invention in 1935. Through the 1930s and 1940s Van de Graaff worked with **John G. Trump**, a professor of electrical engineering at MIT, and William W. Buechner, a professor in MIT's physics department, to modify and improve his particle accelerator, aiming for higher voltages, vertically mounted and more compact designs, and steadier, more homogeneous particle beams. With Trump, Van de Graaff adapted his design into a machine that could treat cancerous tumors with precisely penetrating X rays. The medical Van de Graaff machine was first used clinically in 1937 at Harvard Medical School's Huntington Memorial Hospital.

Launches Commercial Production of the Accelerator

During World War II, Van de Graaff remained at MIT as director of the High Voltage Radiographic Project, sponsored by the Office of Scientific Research and Development. Working with Buechner, he directed the adaptation of the electrostatic generator to precision radiographic examination of U.S. Navy ordnance. This opened up the possibility of industrial applications for the Van de Graaff accelerator. After the war, a 1945 Rockefeller Foundation grant funded the development of an improved accelerator at MIT, which involved Van de Graaff in continued nuclear research and experimentation. On December 19, 1946, Trump and Van de Graaff formed the High Voltage Engineering Corporation (HVEC) in Burlington, Massachusetts, for the commercial production of particle accelerators. Denis M. Robinson, a professor of electrical engineering from England, became president. Trump was technical director. Van de Graaff was chief physicist and a board member; he acted in the capacity of consultant while retaining his post as associate professor of physics at MIT.

Under the direction of these three men, HVEC produced a series of ever more technologically advanced Van de Graaff particle accelerators. Soon the company was the leading supplier of electrostatic generators, which were used in cancer therapy, in industry for radiography, and in studies of nuclear structure in both chemistry and physics. In 1951 **Luis W. Alvarez** at the University of California in Berkeley rediscovered the tandem principle of particle acceleration first invented by Willard Bennett in 1937. Van de Graaff became very involved in efforts at HVEC to develop a tandem Van de Graaff accelerator, which uses the same high voltage twice to accelerate the particles twice, resulting in particle energies double the machine's voltage. The first of these machines was purchased for use in 1956 by the Chalk River Laboratories of Atomic Energy of

Canada and put into use in 1959. HVEC's tandem Van de Graaff accelerators became very successful.

Pursues Further Innovations

Van de Graaff solved other difficult and limiting problems inherent with the electrostatic generator. His uniform-field electrode configuration and inclined field tubes overcame problems in the insulating tubes that could inhibit acceleration. His insulating-core transformer of the late 1950s generated high-voltage direct current via magnetic flux rather than by the electrostatic charging belt, thereby permitting higher dc voltages than previously attainable with electrostatic machines. This invention had important applications in high-voltage electric power utilities and industrial processes, and the inspiration for it came from a magnetic circuit Van de Graaff had observed in an Alabama Power company hydroelectric generator decades earlier. Van de Graaff also devised many methods of controlling particle beams after their acceleration so they could be adapted to precise and individual research requirements. Using Van de Graaff accelerators, experimenters accumulated a vast amount of information on nuclear disintegrations and reactions, which led directly to very sophisticated theories of nuclear structure.

Toward the end of his life, Van de Graaff was absorbed with adapting his insulating-core concept to produce triple tandem accelerators powerful enough to accelerate heavy ions, which in turn could smash the nuclei of even the heaviest atoms—in particular, uranium. He envisioned the possibility of creating new elements if a uranium nucleus bombarded by a high-speed proton captured the proton rather than disintegrating. He also was excited by the powerful nuclear reaction that would result if two uranium nuclei could be induced to fuse. His goal for particle acceleration was to be able to produce and use precisely controlled charged-particle beams of any element, including heavy ones. In the fall of 1966, shortly before his death, Van de Graaff launched an intensive research program at HVEC bombarding uranium nuclei with uranium ions, thereby producing highly charged uranium atoms and yielding valuable data on heavy particle motion.

In 1936, Van de Graaff married Catherine Boyden; they had two sons, John and William. He was an associate professor of physics at MIT from 1934 until 1960, when he resigned to devote himself to his ever-increasing involvement with HVEC. In 1966, he was awarded the Tom W. Bonner Prize by the American Physical Society "for his contribution to and continued development of the electrostatic accelerator, a device that has immeasurably advanced nuclear physics." (The prize was named for a scientist who had used Van de Graaff particle accelerators to achieve the results of his fundamental research.) Van de Graaff also advanced physics in his role as a teacher and mentor, producing many proteges who themselves advanced particle accelerator technology and basic nuclear knowledge. Van de Graaff was courteous and unassuming, but nevertheless was inspirational and effective as a teacher and research leader because he was able to communicate his ideas clearly, visually, and with excitement. He published many articles in scientific journals, often coauthored with colleagues, and was granted many patents, including those for the electrostatic generator and the insulating-core transformer. He received honorary doctorates from several universities and many honors and awards, including the 1947 Duddell Medal of the Physical Society of Great Britain. Van de Graaff died of a heart attack on the morning of January 16, 1967, in Boston at the age of sixty-five. At the time of his death, over five hundred Van de Graaff particle accelerators were in use in more than thirty countries.

SELECTED WRITINGS BY VAN DE GRAAFF:

Periodicals

Physical Review, A 1,500,000 Volt Electrostatic Generator, Volume 38, 1931, pp. 1919–1920.

Progress in Physics, Electrostatic Generators for the Acceleration of Charged Particles, Volume 11, 1948, pp. 1–18.

Journal of Applied Physics, Irradiation of Biological Materials by High-Energy Roentgen Rays and Cathode Rays, Volume 19, 1948, pp. 599–604.

Nuclear Instruments and Methods, Tandem Electrostatic Accelerators, Volume 8, 1960, pp. 195–202.

Bulletin, American Physical Society, Electrostatic Acceleration of Very Heavy Ions, with Resulting Possibilities for Nuclear Research, August 29, 1966.

FURTHER READING:

Books

Livingston, M. Stanley, *Particle Accelerators: A Brief History,* Harvard University Press, 1969.

Rosenblatt, J., *Particle Acceleration,* Methuen, 1968.

Wilson, Robert R., and Raphael Littauer, *Accelerators: Machines of Nuclear Physics,* Doubleday, 1960.

Periodicals

Burrill, E. Alfred, *Physics Today,* Van de Graaff, the Man and His Accelerators, February 1967, pp. 49–52.

Huxley, L. G. H., *Nature,* Dr. R. J. Van de Graaff, April 8, 1967.

Huxley, L. G. H., *New York Times,* Man Hurls Bolt of 7,000,000 Volts, November 29, 1933, p. 14.

Rose, P. H., *Nuclear Instruments and Methods,* In Memoriam: Robert Jemison Van de Graaff, 20 December 1901—16 January 1967, Volume 60, 1968.

Sketch by Kathy Sammis

Peter van de Kamp
1901–1995
Dutch-born American astronomer

Peter van de Kamp devoted his career to the study of planets that exist outside of our own solar system. He is perhaps best known for his controversial assertion that two planets orbit nearby Barnard's Star, a claim questioned by many astronomers. Yet, despite this debate, van de Kamp is credited with advancing the study of extrasolar planets with his pioneering work and inspiring other astronomers to pursue the existence of worlds outside of our own.

Born in the Netherlands on December 26, 1901, Peter van de Kamp studied at the University of Utrecht, where he earned his doctoral degree in 1922. He emigrated to the United States in 1923 and joined the staff of the University of Virginia. In 1924, he left for a position at the Lick Observatory, but returned to the university a year later.

Joins Swathmore College and the Sproul Observatory

In 1937, van de Kamp became professor of astronomy at Swathmore College in Pennsylvania and director of the Sproul Observatory, a post he held until he retired in 1972. At the observatory, he used the twenty-four-inch (fifty-three-centimeter) telescope to conduct extensive studies of the movement of Barnard's Star. This red dwarf star is named for E. E. Barnard, who first observed in 1916 that it had some peculiarities. It has a proper motion of 10.3 seconds of arc per year—very large when compared to most stars, and giving it the highest-known apparent motion of all stars. In addition, Barnard's Star is a virtual neighbor to our system, being less that six light-years away from Earth (only the Centuri system lies closer).

Over the years, as he made and compared thousands of photographic plates, van de Kamp noticed that Barnard's Star seemed to wobble very slightly. In 1969, he attributed this motion to a companion body which could not been seen via a telescope; the gravitational pull of an astronomical body can effect the motion of another, thereby creating a wobble, or sinusoidal motion. Through mathematical calculations, van de Kamp estimated that the invisible companion of Barnard's Star was too small to be another star—it had a mass roughly one and a half times that of the planet Jupiter, he maintained, and circled the Barnard's Star once every 24 years in an elliptical orbit. He decided that, given the relatively small mass, the companion body had to be a planet. He published his results in March 1969, in a paper in the *Astronomical Journal*.

Van de Kamp, after further calculations, revised his theory that same year. In the August issue of the journal, he stated that there was not only one planet orbiting Barnard's Star, but two, each about the mass of Jupiter, one with the orbital period of 12 years, the other, 26. Six years later, he published another paper that analyzed the data he had collected from 1950 to 1974. He estimated the sizes of one of the companions to be four-tenths the size of Jupiter, with an orbital period of 22 years. The other he maintained to be about the same size as Jupiter, with orbital period of 11.5 years.

Others Question his Observations

Other researchers, however, disagreed with van de Kamp regarding the companions of Barnard's Star. George Gatewood and Heinrich Eichhorn, working with the Van Vleck Observatory's 20-in (51-cm) refractor telescope and the Allegheny Observatory's 30-in (76 cm) Thaw refractor, were unable to discern any wobbling in Barnard's Star. They published their results in 1973, a year after van de Kamp's retirement from Sproul and Swathmore. Doubts were further cast upon the companion planets by researchers Robert Harrington of the U.S. Observatory and Laurence Frederick of the McCormick Observatory, both of whom recorded no wobbles with their instruments.

In 1973, another astronomer at the Sproul Observatory, John Hershey, used the same plates that van de Kamp had analyzed in his own study. He looked at 12 stars, including Barnard's, and noticed that all of them seemed to wobble. Such an observation raised an interesting question: could all the stars have companion planets, or was the Sproul telescope in some way not correct? Could the installation of new parts, first in 1949, then in 1957, and the subsequent readjustment of the scope, be the cause of the discrepancy in star positions that Hersey noted on plates made between 1949 and 1956, and those made after 1957?

Defends his Observations

Van de Kamp defended his work throughout his lifetime, maintaining that his observations had taken place over a much longer period of time and involved many more photographic plates than did any other study of Barnard's Star. In 1982, he published his last paper on the subject. Involving the analysis of thousands of plates taken between 1938 and 1982, the article reconfirmed van de Kamp's belief in the existence of two companions, one about seven-tenths and the other about half the size of Jupiter, orbiting Barnard's Star in period of 12 and 20 years, respectively. Their orbits were circular, he maintained.

Other researchers have as yet been unable to confirm or fully deny the existence of planets around Barnard's Star. Some are quite pessimistic, while others suggest that planets smaller than Jupiter may indeed be in orbit around the star. Harrington's and Gatewood's work have largely ascertained that no near-Jupiter-sized planet or larger orbits Barnard's Star.

Leaves a Legacy of Research

Despite these controversies, Peter van de Kamp's lifelong devotion to the search for extrasolar planets was by no means in vain. He was among the first to suggest that planets could be orbiting other stars, and he inspired other astronomers to search for them. Because of him, planets have been detected in orbit around the stars Peg 51, Rho 1 Canceri, Rho Cornoae Borealis, Tau Bootis, Upsilon Andromedae, 47 Ursae Majoris, and 70 Virginis. Many other stars are also believed to have planets, although the presence of the planets has not yet been confirmed. Scientists have also found planets around pulsars as well.

Besides his scientific work, van de Kamp was well known on campus as a composer and musician. He directed the college's orchestra for 10 years, from 1944 to 1954. He also played the piano at campus screenings of silent movies, many of them Charlie Chaplin films from his own collection.

Peter van de Kamp died May 18, 1995, in Middenbeemster, the Netherlands.

SELECTED WRITINGS BY VAN DE KAMP:

Periodicals

"Alternate Dynamical Analysis of Barnard's Star," *Astronomical Journal*, 74:(2): March 1969, pp. 238-240,

"Astrometric Study of Barnard's Star from Plates Taken with the Sproul 61-cm Refractor," *Astronomical Journal*, 80(8): August 1975, pp. 658-661.

"The Planetary System of Barnard's Star," *Vistas in Astronomy*, 26: 1982, pp. 141-157.

FURTHER READING:

Periodicals

Black, David, "Worlds Around Other Stars," *Scientific American*, 264:1, January 1991, pp. 76-81.

Schilling, Govert, "Peter van de Kamp and His 'Lovely Barnard's Star,'" *Astronomy*, 13 (December 1985): pp. 26, 28.

Stoudt, David, "Peter van de Kamp, Astronomer and Musician at Swathmore, 93," *New York Times*, May 23, 1995, p. B10.

Other

Bell, George H., "The Search for Extrasolar Planets: A Brief History of the Search, the Findings and the Future Implications," On the Arizona State University web site, URL: http://www.lib.asu.edu/noble/space/exoplnt.htm

Sketch by Fran Hodgkins

Simon van der Meer
1925–
Dutch physicist

Simon van der Meer is one of the world's authorities on particle accelerator engineering. Beginning in 1968, he worked out a technique for accumulating nonoverlapping bunches of particles in an accelerator with a system he invented known as stochastic cooling. He utilized this technique in a series of experiments carried out in the early 1980s that led to the discovery of the W and Z bosons, force-carrying particles by which the electroweak force is transmitted. For his contributions to this discovery, van der Meer shared with **Carlo Rubbia** the 1984 Nobel Prize in physics.

Van der Meer was born on November 24, 1925, in The Hague, the Netherlands, the only son of Pieter van der Meer, a teacher, and Jetske Groeneveld. Van der Meer graduated from the local gymnasium in 1943 and hoped to enter college, but the colleges had been closed by the German army, which occupied Holland. As a result, he remained at the gymnasium for an additional two years; in 1945, he was finally able to enroll at the technical college at Delft to study physics. He graduated in 1952 with an engineering degree.

Van der Meer took a job that same year with the Phillips Research Laboratory in Eindhoven. Over the next four years, his work dealt primarily with the development of electron microscopy and high voltage equipment. He left Phillips in 1956 for a job at the European Center for Nuclear Research (CERN) in Geneva, where he has remained ever since. CERN had been established two years earlier as a thirteen-nation, intergovernmental research institute for the study of elementary particles and has become one of the leading particle research laboratories in the world.

At CERN, van der Meer worked on the design of the new proton synchrotron (PS). The technical challenge of this work was daunting. The plan was to produce masses of charged particles and then accelerate them to speeds near that of light in a smaller accelerator before injecting them into the larger accelerator, the PS, where they would be given even more energy. The primary engineering challenge involved in the PS was to design the electrical and magnetic fields so they would be imposed on the revolving particles in such a way as to keep them in a very precise path; these fields had to prevent the particles from drifting away from the center of the accelerator tube and getting lost in collisions with each other and with the tube itself.

Develops Stochastic Cooling

By the 1970s, a major focus of research at CERN had become the search for W and Z bosons. Electromagnetism and the so-called weak force are two of the forces in nature recognized by quantum theory. In the 1960s, hypotheses that would explain both these theories were developed by American physicist **Sheldon L. Glashow**, Pakistani physicist **Abdus Salam**, and American physicist **Steven Weinberg**. Essential to their theory was the existence of the force-carrying W and Z bosons. In 1976, van der Meer joined a project led by Rubbia, a scientist at CERN and professor of physics at Harvard University, who had made it his goal to discover the hypothesized bosons.

To accomplish this task, Rubbia proposed to redesign CERN's PS accelerator. He suggested rebuilding the machine so that two beams of particles, one consisting of protons and one of antiprotons, would be accelerated in opposite directions. Then, at various positions in the accelerator ring, the two beams would be allowed to collide. These collisions would release enough energy, Rubbia predicted, to allow the formation of W and Z bosons. The proton-antiproton colliding beam was extremely difficult to design and build, however; antiprotons—a form of antimatter—have a tendency to interact with ordinary forms of matter and change into energy. A critical problem involved the injection of antiprotons into the accelerator as well as maintaining a sufficient supply of them within the accelerator tubes.

It was van der Meer's solution to this problem that made the discovery of the W and Z bosons possible. For more than a decade, he had been developing stochastic cooling, which involves an elegant statistical technique for compressing many bunches of particles into a relatively small region, thus cooling them. In most instances, bunches of particles introduced into an accelerator have a tendency to overtake each other, causing the loss of the preceding bunch. Van der Meer was able to design an electrical system that prevented the "bunching up" of antiprotons, even when their density became quite high within the accelerator tubes. Using van der Meer's design, the CERN PS was converted to a Super Proton Synchrotron (SPS). The SPS began operation in early 1983 and, within a short period of time, the first W bosons were observed. Less than a year later, Z bosons were also detected.

For his share in this work, van der Meer was awarded the 1984 Nobel Prize in physics with Rubbia. Van der Meer also has been given honorary doctorates by the universities of Amsterdam, Geneva, and Genoa. He is a member of the Royal Netherlands Academy of Arts and Sciences and the American Academy of Arts and Sciences. Van der Meer married Catharina M. Koopman on April 26, 1966. They have a daughter and a son.

SELECTED WRITINGS BY VAN DER MEER:

Periodicals

Lawrence Berkeley Laboratory Report LBL–7574, Stochastic Cooling Theory and Devices, 1978, pp. 93–97.

IEEE Transactions in Nuclear Science, Antiproton Production and Collection for the CERN Antiproton Accumulator, Part I, 1983, pp. 2778–80.

FURTHER READING:

Books

Nobel Prize Winners, H. W. Wilson, 1987, pp. 689–691.

Periodicals

Lederman, Leon M., and Roy F. Schwitters, *Science,* The 1984 Nobel Prize in Physics, January 11, 1985, pp. 131–134.

Sketch by David E. Newton

Johannes Diderik van der Waals
1837–1923
Dutch physicist

Johannes Diderik van der Waals received his doctorate in physics from the University of Leiden at the relatively late age of thirty-six. His doctoral dissertation, "On the Continuity of Gaseous and Liquid States," quickly became known among his colleagues and made his reputation almost immediately. The Nobel Prize in physics, awarded him in 1910, recognized the line of work begun in his dissertation, eventually resulting in a famous equation of state relating the pressure, volume, and temperature of a gas. He also demonstrated why a gas cannot be liquified above its critical temperature. Van der Waals also investigated the weak nonchemical bond forces between molecules that now carry the name *van der Waals forces.*

Van der Waals was born in Leiden in the Netherlands on November 23, 1837. His parents were Jacobus van der Waals, a carpenter, and the former Elisabeth van den Burg. Van der Waals attended local primary and secondary schools and then took a job teaching elementary school in his hometown. In 1862 he began taking courses at the University of Leiden and, two years later, received the credentials necessary to teach high school physics and mathematics. He then accepted a job teaching physics in the town of Deventer and, a year later, in 1866, became headmaster of a secondary school in The Hague.

During his year at Deventer, van der Waals married Anna Magdalena Smit, who bore him three daughters—

Anne Madeleine, Jacqueline Elisabeth, and Johanna Diderica—and one son, Johannes Diderik. Biographers note that Anna Magdalena died while the children were still very young; Van der Waals never remarried.

While in The Hague, van der Waals continued to attend the University of Leiden on an informal basis. Since he had never studied Greek and Latin in high school, he was not allowed by federal law to enroll in a doctoral program. When that regulation was abolished in the late 1860s, van der Waals was admitted as a regular graduate student at Leiden. For his dissertation he chose to study the nature and behavior of the particles that make up gases and liquids.

Studies Relationship of Gases and Liquids

Van der Waals' choice of topics, he later said, was strongly influenced by a paper written by the German physicist Rudolf Clausius in 1857. In that paper Clausius had argued that the molecules of a gas can be considered tiny points of matter in constant motion. From this initial premise, Clausius was able to derive theoretically a law relating gas pressure and volume originally stated empirically by Robert Boyle in 1662. It occurred to van der Waals that the molecules of both gases and liquids might be considered in the same way, as tiny points of matter. In such a case, according to van der Waals, there might be no fundamental difference between gases and liquids, the latter being only compressed gas at a low temperature.

It was this concept that van der Waals explored in detail in his doctoral thesis, presented to the faculty at Leiden in 1873. He pointed out that two fundamental assumptions of earlier gas laws were not valid. In the first place, such laws had assumed that the particles of which a material is made had no effective size. Van der Waals argued that they did have measurable volume and that such volume affected the behavior of a gas. A second assumption of gas laws was that gas particles do not interact with each other. Van der Waals argued instead that particles do indeed exert forces on each other.

Given these modifications in starting assumptions, van der Waals was able to develop an equation that more closely matches the actual behavior of gases. Laws such as those of Robert Boyle and J. A. C. Charles had been regarded as correct for "ideal" gases, but always failed to some extent when applied to any real gas. Under van der Waals's formulation, the revised gas law applied with remarkable precision to any real gas. Van der Waals' work earned him almost instantaneous fame among his colleagues. His thesis was translated into German, English, and French, and gained him notice in the science world. Van der Waals was elected to the Royal Dutch Academy of Sciences in 1877, and two years later he was appointed professor of physics at the newly created University of Amsterdam. He remained in that post for three decades, retiring in 1907, to be succeeded by his son.

Develops Concepts of Binary Solutions and Pseudoassociation

Van der Waals continued to work on the relationship between gases and liquids for the rest of his career. In 1890 he suggested the notion of binary solutions—states in which a substance exists as both a gas and a liquid at the same time. The calculations that van der Waals made on binary solutions later proved crucial in the fledgling field of cryogenics, specifying the conditions under which a gas can be converted to a liquid. One of the pioneers of this field, **Heike Kamerlingh Onnes**, acknowledged his debt to van der Waals in an article in Eduard Farber's book, *Great Chemists,* in which he said, "How much I was under the influence of its great importance as much as forty years ago may be best judged by my taking it then as a guide for my own researches."

For many students of science, van der Waals may be best known for the weak intermolecular forces that now carry his name. Originally called by him "pseudoassociation," these forces were hypothesized by van der Waals to explain the aggregation of particles in liquid solutions that occurred, for example, during the formation of binary solutions. Today, van der Waals forces are invoked to describe a host of situations in which rapidly shifting electron distributions in a molecule result in the formation of weak, but nonzero, transient attractions between molecules.

During the last ten years of his life, van der Waals gradually grew frail; he died in Amsterdam on March 8, 1923. Van der Waals had been elected to membership in the French Academy of Sciences, the British Chemical Society, the U.S. National Academy of Sciences, the Royal Academy of Sciences of Berlin, and the Russian Imperial Society of Naturalists.

SELECTED WRITINGS BY VAN DER WAALS:

Books

Over de Continuiteit van den Gasen-Vloeistoftoestand, A. W. Sijthoff, 1873.

De Relativiteitstheorie, F. Bohn, 1923.

Lehrbuch der Thermostatik, das Heisst, des Thermischen Gleich Gewichtes Materieller Systeme, J. A. Barth, 1927.

FURTHER READING:

Books

Gillispie, Charles Coulson, editor, *Dictionary of Scientific Biography,* Volume 14, Scribner's, 1975, pp. 109–111.

Kamerlingh Onnes, Heike, *Great Chemists,* Johannes Diderik van der Waals, edited by Eduard Farber, Interscience, 1961, pp. 751–755.

Periodicals

Oesper, R. E., *Journal of Chemical Education,* Johannes Diderik van der Waals, Volume 31, 1954, p. 599.

Sketch by David E. Newton

Laurel van der Wal
1924–

American aeronautical engineer and space biologist

Laurel van der Wal spent a large part of her career in the fields of aeronautical and aerospace engineering, including the design of missiles, rocket systems, and manned spacecraft. But she is also known for her research into the physical effects of spaceflight on mice. This pioneering work in space biology, known as Project MIA (Mouse-In-Able), later led to the scientist's work on life support systems in space craft for human passengers.

Van der Wal was born in Spokane, Washington, on September 22, 1924, to the former Lillian Gerischer and Richard van der Wal. As a teenager during World War II, van der Wal was drawn to the field of aviation. This interest carried over into her career; in 1944 she began working at the Hamilton Air Force Base in California as an aircraft engine mechanic. She began training to become a woman air services pilot, or WASP, and left California for Nevada to acquire the required number of flying hours. After she had completed her hours, however, the war ended and the program was terminated. Van der Wal decided to pursue engineering because she realized that the opportunities for female pilots were limited at that time.

She enrolled at the University of California at Berkeley where she studied mechanical engineering and carried out research on wind tunnel operation. In 1949 van der Wal graduated with a bachelor of science degree and an option in aeronautics. From 1950 to 1951 she was a laboratory research analyst for the guided missiles division of the Douglas Aircraft Company in Santa Monica, California. In 1953 the scientist moved briefly to the East Coast to take up a position as associate engineer for Reaction Motors, Inc. in New Jersey. There she investigated the starting time of turbopump-rocket systems. She returned to California the same year, accepting a position as a design engineer at the Rheem Manufacturing Company, where she was responsible for the design and test of fuse components for fast-burning rockets. During her three years at Rheem, she also worked in the Aircraft Engineering Department, analyzing the aerodynamics of the design, performance, and operation of various aircraft and missiles. Van der Wal moved in 1956 to the Ramo-Wooldridge Corporation, where she worked on the design of missile and space-probe systems in the Guided Missiles Research Division.

In 1958, van der Wal took a position with Space Technology Laboratories, Inc., where she carried out the research for which she is most noted. She was first hired to work on missile programs, but after discussions with some of the bioengineering scientists there she became curious about the problems associated with manned spaceflight. She developed the idea of putting mice into the missile nosecones that were being tested. By simply adding the animal tests onto already existing experiments to determine the viability of the missiles on reentry into the atmosphere, the mice experiments were done at almost zero cost. Van der Wal eventually became the head of the company's Bioastronautics Group. In this position she focused on designing space systems to accommodate the life support requirements of human (or other living) beings. Her research group was responsible for experiments providing information about the environmental, mechanical, physical, and biomedical requirements of manned space systems.

While at Space Technology Laboratories, van der Wal had been appointed an airport commissioner for the city of Los Angeles and had become interested in transport. After taking a break from engineering in the period when her two sons were born, she worked for Rand Corporation on domestic transportation systems from 1967 to 1974. She briefly moved to Nigeria with her children to work on domestic transport systems, but was forced to return to the United States when a coup d'etat in the African nation made it impossible for her to take up the position. On her return she worked for the Community Redevelopment Agency in Los Angeles on a proposed people mover. Van der Wal's final professional post was with the Southern California Association of Governments.

During her career, van der Wal received many honors, including a National Research Council Fellowship in aeronautics. In 1961 she was doubly honored; van der Wal was chosen by the Society of Women Engineers for their annual Achievement Award and by the Los Angeles Times as one of its women of the year.

SELECTED WRITINGS BY VAN DER WAL:

Periodicals

American Rocket Society Journal, Project MIA (Mouse-In-Able), Experiments on Physiological Response to Spaceflight, October 1959.

FURTHER READING:

Books

Significant Achievements in Space Bioscience, 1958–1964, United States National Aeronautics and Space Administration Scientific and Technical Information, 1966.

Other

van der Wal, Laurel, *Interview with Terrie M. Romano*, conducted March 29, 1994.

Sketch by Terrie M. Romano

Florence W. van Straten
1913–
American physicist and meteorologist

Florence W. van Straten worked for many years with the U.S. Navy researching the causes of weather patterns and investigating the possibility of human weather modification. She served as the head of naval tests in cloud seeding to create and dissipate clouds, as well as an educator and writer.

Florence Wilhelmina van Straten was born on November 12, 1913, in Darien, Connecticut, the daughter of Jacques and Rosette (Roozeboom) van Straten, Dutch immigrants. Her father was an executive for Metro-Goldwyn-Mayer, and she thus grew up in various cities in North America and Europe. From an early age, van Straten wanted to be a writer. Influenced by her practical father, she agreed to take chemistry classes in addition to English at New York University, and it was the chemistry that won out. She earned her B.S. in 1933, the M.A. in 1937, and a Ph.D. in chemistry in 1939. From her senior year in college, she had been an instructor of freshman chemistry courses. After graduation, she accepted a teaching fellowship at New York University. With the advent of World War II she joined the Waves, becoming a specialist in meteorology and doing postgraduate work at the Massachusetts Institute of Technology.

Researches Weather Modification

After the war, van Straten continued working for the Navy in a civilian capacity, becoming director of its Technical Requirements Branch of the U.S. Naval Weather Service. During the war she had already begun researching a problem meteorologists had been looking at for generations: how to control and modify the weather so as to stop a hurricane or end rain in flooded areas. In her view, rain was often caused by atmospheric events in tropical areas, for which the standard model involving subfreezing temperatures in the tops of clouds would not hold. Finally, van Straten developed the theory that rain is dependent upon evaporation rates within a cloud. She concluded that she could create or dissipate clouds by 'seeding' them with some material that could change temperatures by absorbing light. In 1958 van Straten had a chance to test these theories,

seeding carbon particles into clouds and successfully dissipating seven clouds, marking the conclusion of fifteen years of theorizing.

In 1962 van Straten left the Naval Weather Service and made her home near Washington, D.C., but remained a consultant in atmospheric physics as well as a lieutenant commander in the reserves. She was awarded for her researches in weather modification with the Meritorious Service Award of the U.S. Department of the Navy in 1958 and the Woman of the Year award from the Aerospace Medical Association in 1959. Retirement brought van Straten the time she had always lacked to devote to her first love—writing. She authored a popular study of weather, short stories, and pamphlets on radar and radioactive fallout.

SELECTED WRITINGS BY VAN STRATEN:

Books

Radar as a Meteorological Tool, U.S. Government Printing Office, 1957.
Weather or Not, Dodd, 1966.

FURTHER READING:

Periodicals

New York Times, Does Something about It: Florence Wilhelmina van Straten, September 24, 1958, p. 52.

Sketch by J. Sydney Jones

John Van Vleck
1899–1980
American physicist

John Van Vleck was one of the United States' first theoretical physicists, specializing in problems of chemical physics, magnetism, quantum theory, and spectroscopy. Some of his work has had important practical applications in such devices as the atomic clock, lasers, and transistors. He shared the 1977 Nobel Prize in physics for his "fundamental theoretical investigations of the electronic structure of magnetic and disordered systems."

John Hasbrouck Van Vleck was born in Middletown, Connecticut, on March 13, 1899, into a prosperous family with a history of notable intellectual accomplishments. His paternal grandfather had been a professor of astronomy at Connecticut's Wesleyan College, and his father, Edward

Burr Van Vleck, was professor of mathematics at Wesleyan at the time of his son's birth. Van Vleck's mother was the former Hester Lawrence (also given as Laurence) Raymond. It has been noted that his parents' overbearing manner may have been responsible for their only child's shyness as a youngster. When Van Vleck was seven years old his father accepted an appointment at the University of Wisconsin. John attended public schools in Madison and then entered the University of Wisconsin, graduating in 1920 with a bachelor's degree in physics. For his graduate work, Van Vleck chose to attend Harvard University, where his father was serving as visiting professor of mathematics.

Chooses a Career in Theoretical Physics

At Harvard, Van Vleck decided to concentrate on theoretical physics, a field with little tradition in American science at the time. In fact, when he received his doctorate in 1922, his thesis was one of the first, if not actually *the* first, in America based on a purely theoretical subject—the ionization energy of a particular model of the helium atom. Upon completing his degree, Van Vleck was invited to stay on at Harvard as an instructor in physics.

In 1923, based largely on his doctoral work, the University of Minnesota offered Van Vleck a job in its physics department; he accepted and remained at Minnesota until 1928. During his tenure there, Van Vleck worked on problems involving the application of quantum mechanical theory to a variety of physical phenomena. His magnum opus during this period was his first book, *Quantum Principles and Line Spectra,* published in 1926. Though the book came out just as major modifications in quantum theory were being made, much of what he had written remained valid and the book was an unexpected commercial success.

Begins Work on Magnetism

Van Vleck's years at Minnesota were also marked by his first venture into the field for which he is best known, the quantum explanation of magnetic effects. He tried to find a way in which modern developments in quantum theory could be used to explain the various forms of magnetism—efforts which resulted in the publication of *The Theory of Electric and Magnetic Susceptibilities* in 1932. The work on magnetism was by no means the only topic Van Vleck researched at Minnesota, but it would prove to be the most important, earning him both a share of the 1977 Nobel Prize in physics and the title "father of modern magnetism."

Van Vleck was married to Abigail June Pearson on June 10, 1927. The following year he moved to the University of Wisconsin, where he accepted a post as professor of physics. He was attracted to Wisconsin, in part, by the university's visiting scholars program. Each semester, an outstanding authority in some field was invited to be in residence on the Madison campus. Van Vleck knew that the program would be an excellent way for him to stay in touch with developments in modern physics, a field in which American scientists were woefully deficient. In 1934, Van Vleck was offered an opportunity to return to Harvard, one that he accepted. He remained at Harvard until his retirement in 1969, serving the last eighteen years of his tenure there as Hollis Professor of Mathematical and Natural Philosophy, the oldest endowed science chair in North America.

One of Van Vleck's areas of interest at Harvard was crystal field theory. He again used quantum theory to evaluate the relationship between electron and ion energy levels in bound systems such as crystals. Understanding these relationships is critical in solid-state theories and in their applications in devices such as lasers and semiconducting devices.

At the beginning of World War II, Van Vleck was asked to serve on a committee evaluating the feasibility of building an atomic bomb. That committee's favorable decision eventually led to the creation of the Manhattan Project, under which the world's first nuclear weapons were designed and built. For the majority of the war years, however, Van Vleck worked on the development of radar at the Radio Research Laboratory in Cambridge, Massachusetts.

Van Vleck worked on a host of other problems on his return to Harvard after the war, including nuclear magnetic resonance, molecular spectra, and the cohesive energy of metals. In addition to the Nobel Prize, he was awarded the title of Chevalier in the French Legion of Honor, and was the recipient of the Irving Langmuir Award of the General Electric Foundation in 1965, the National Medal of Science in 1966, and the Lorentz Medal of the Royal Netherlands Academy of Science in 1974, among others. Van Vleck died in Cambridge on October 27, 1980.

SELECTED WRITINGS BY VAN VLECK:

Books

Quantum Principles and Line Spectra, National Research Council, 1926.
The Theory of Electric and Magnetic Susceptibilities, Oxford University Press, 1932.

Periodicals

Physical Review, Quantum Theory of the Specific Heat of Hydrogen. I. Relation to the New Mechanics, Band Spectra, and Chemical Constants, Volume 28, 1926, pp. 980–1021.
Nature, Magnetic Susceptibilities and Dielectric Constants in the New Quantum Mechanics, Volume 118, 1927, pp. 226–27.
Chemical Reviews, The New Quantum Mechanics, Volume 5, 1928, pp. 467–507.

FURTHER READING:

Books

Dictionary of Scientific Biography, Volume 18, Scribner, 1982, pp. 949–57.

McGraw-Hill Modern Scientists and Engineers, Volume 3, McGraw, 1980, pp. 251–52.

Nobel Prize Winners, H. W. Wilson, 1987, pp. 1086–88.

Weber, Robert L., *Pioneers of Science: Nobel Prize Winners in Physics,* American Institute of Physics, 1980, pp. 249–50.

Weber, Robert L., *World of Scientific Discovery,* Gale, 1994.

Sketch by David E. Newton

John R. Vane
1927–
English pharmacologist

John R. Vane's research on prostaglandins, hormone-like substances produced by the body, has had enormous consequences for the research and treatment of such illnesses as heart disease, strokes, ulcers and asthma. Through his studies, first at the Royal College of Surgeons and then at the Wellcome pharmaceutical company, Vane was able to discover how these previously little-known secretions function. For these contributions to medicine and to how the body works, he shared the 1982 Nobel Prize in medicine or physiology.

John Robert Vane was born March 29, 1927, in Tardebigge, Worcester, the son of Maurice Vane and the former Frances Fisher. Vane's father, the son of Russian immigrants, owned a small manufacturing company; his mother came from a family of farmers. Their Christmas gift of a chemistry set sparked Vane's interest in science when he was twelve, and his home became the site of numerous experiments. However, upon entering the University of Birmingham in 1944, he found that the work given him was not as challenging as he anticipated. At the advice of a professor, he decided to go to Oxford University to study pharmacology under Harold Burn after receiving his B.S. in chemistry from Birmingham in 1946. Vane became a fellow on Oxford's Therapeutic Research Council for the next two years. He obtained a B.S. in pharmacology from Oxford in 1949, a year after marrying Elizabeth Daphne Page, and earned his doctorate in 1953. Vane and his wife eventually had two daughters, Nicola and Miranda. After leaving Oxford, Vane came to America to teach at Yale University as an instructor and assistant professor of pharmacology. He returned to England in 1955 as a senior lecturer in pharmacology at the Royal College of Surgeons, at its Institute of Basic Medical Sciences.

Vane became interested in prostaglandins in the late 1950s. Discovered in the 1930s, they were originally thought to be secreted by the prostate gland, which is how they got their name. Prostaglandins are natural compounds, developed from fatty acids, which control many bodily functions. Different prostaglandins regulate blood pressure and coagulation, allergic reactions to substances, the rate of metabolism, glandular secretions, and contractions in the uterus.

For many years after the discovery of prostaglandins, scientists were unaware of how they were produced and how they functioned. In the early 1960s Vane expanded upon the procedure known as biological assay (bioassay), by which the strength of a substance is measured by comparing its effects on an organism with those of a standard preparation. Vane developed the dynamic bioassay, which allows scientists to measure more than one substance in blood or body fluids. This method enabled Vane and his colleagues at the Royal College to prove that prostaglandins are produced by many tissues and organs in the body. Further research led the scientists to discover that, unlike hormones, certain prostaglandins are effective only in the areas where they were formed.

In 1966 Vane advanced to professor of experimental pharmacology at the Institute for Basic Medical Sciences and continued his studies. An experiment he conducted in 1969 resulted in the discovery of the methods by which aspirin alleviates pain and reduces inflammation. Using the lung tissue of guinea pigs, Vane found that aspirin inhibited the production of a certain prostaglandin that causes inflammation. He published the results in a June 1971, issue of *Nature New Biology,* a science magazine.

Leaves Academia to Head Pharmaceutical Research

In 1973 Vane resigned his post at the Institute to enter the business world as director of research and development at the Wellcome Foundation, a pharmaceutical company. Following up on research by the Swedish chemist **Bengt Samuelsson** (who found that a type of prostaglandin was responsible for allowing blood to clot), Vane discovered the existence of a prostaglandin with the opposite quality, which inhibits clot formation. With the assistance of the Upjohn Chemical Corporation, Vane isolated the secretion, which he named prostacyclin. This discovery proved to be of great assistance in dissolving clots blocking the blood supply in stroke and heart attack victims and is also useful for keeping blood from clotting during surgery. Scientists have discovered even more uses for prostaglandins, including the treatment of ulcers, alleviating pain from menstruation and gallstones, and stimulating contractions for childbirth.

Vane, along with Samuelsson and Swedish chemist **Sune Bergström**, was given the Albert Lasker Basic

Medical Research Award in 1977 for his work on prostaglandins. Five years later the Nobel Committee gave the trio the Nobel Prize for medicine or physiology. After receiving the award, Vane predicted that future research on prostaglandins would create major breakthroughs in the areas of medicine. "In the next twenty years we should see a substantial attack on the disease process," *Time* quoted him as saying. "We will be able to find new drugs that have effects on cardiovascular disease, on asthma, on heart attack," and even health problems associated with old age, the magazine reported.

During the 1980s Vane embarked on a crusade for greater research on new drugs to fight both new diseases (such as acquired immunodeficiency syndrome, known as AIDS) and drug-resistant strains of old diseases, such as malaria. In articles for scientific and medical journals, he stressed the need for greater international cooperation in the search for a cure or vaccine for AIDS and advocated the creation of an Institute for Tropical Diseases to research new drugs to battle disease in the tropics.

Vane's professional activities also include memberships in the British Pharmacological Society and the American Academy of Arts and Sciences. A popular lecturer, he has received more than a dozen awards for his accomplishments. In addition to the many hours he devotes to his work, Vane finds time for his hobbies of photography, travel, snorkeling, and waterskiing.

SELECTED WRITINGS BY VANE:

Books

Adrenergic Mechanisms, Little, Brown, 1960.
Prostaglandin Synthetase Inhibitors—Their Effects on Physiological Functions and Pathological States, Raven Press, 1974.
Anti-Inflammatory Drugs, Springer Verlag, 1979.
Prostacyclin, Raven Press, 1979.
Prostacyclin in Health and Disease, Royal College of Physicians, 1982.

Periodicals

Nature New Biology, Inhibition of Prostaglandin Synthesis as a Mechanism of Action for Aspirin-like Drugs, June 23, 1971.
World Health, TDR and the Drug Industry, May, 1985.

FURTHER READING:

Books

Butt, Wilfred, *Hormone Chemistry,* Van Nostrand, 1967.
Connor, Julius, *Exploring the Heart—Heart Diseases and High Blood Pressure,* Norton, 1983.

Connor, Julius, *Current Biography,* H. W. Wilson, 1986, pp. 575–78.
Connor, Julius, *Nobel Prize Winners Biographical Dictionary,* H. W. Wilson, 1987, pp. 1082–84.

Periodicals

Miller, J. A., *Science News,* Nobel Prize in Medicine for Prostaglandin Discoveries, October 16, 1982, p. 245.
Miller, J. A., *Time,* Sharing the Nobel Prize, October 25, 1982, p. 84.

Sketch by Francis Rogers

Harold E. Varmus
1939–
American microbiologist and virologist

When Harold E. Varmus was appointed director of the National Institutes of Health (NIH) in November 1993, he was already famous throughout the world for his investigations into cancer-causing genes and other fundamental areas of biology, including the complex mechanisms of viruses. Varmus, who helped prove that there is a genetic component to cancer, was the corecipient of a 1989 Nobel Prize for his research into oncogenes (genes with the capacity to turn normal cells into cancerous ones). Varmus's title of director of the NIH carries with it immense responsibilities, including the managing of a ten billion-dollar-plus NIH budget and the determination of grant awards for many types of medical research.

Harold Eliot Varmus was born in Oceanside, New York, on December 18, 1939, to Frank and Beatrice (Barasch) Varmus. He attended Amherst College, graduating with a B.A. degree in 1961 (twenty-three years later, Amherst would award him with an honorary doctorate). Varmus went on to perform graduate work at Harvard University, receiving an M.A. degree in 1962, then he studied medicine at Columbia University, receiving an M.D. in 1966.

Varmus practiced medicine as an intern and resident at the Presbyterian Hospital of New York City between 1966 and 1968. He then worked as a clinical associate at the National Institutes of Health in Bethesda, Maryland, from 1968 to 1970. Moving to California, Varmus served as a lecturer in the Department of Microbiology at the University of California in San Francisco, becoming an associate professor in 1974—the same year that he was named associate editor of *Cell and Virology*—then, in 1979, he was promoted to full professor of microbiology, biochemistry and biophysics. During the 1980s, Varmus began to accumulate a number of prestigious honors for his research, including the 1982 California Academic Scientist of the Year award and the 1983 Passano Foundation award; he was also the corecipient of the Lasker Foundation award. In 1984, Varmus received both the Armand Hammer Cancer prize and the General Motors Alfred Sloan award, and the American Cancer Society made him an honorary professor of molecular virology. These honors were followed by the Shubitz Cancer prize and, in 1989, the Nobel Prize in physiology or medicine.

Cancer Gene Research Wins Nobel Prize for Medicine

Varmus and **J. Michael Bishop**, his colleague from the University of California at San Francisco, were awarded the Nobel Prize in honor of their 1976 discovery which showed that normal cells contain genes that can cause cancer. Varmus and Bishop, working with Dominique Stehelin and Peter Vogt, helped to prove the theory that cancer has a genetic component, demonstrating that oncogenes are actually normal genes that are altered in some way, perhaps due to carcinogen-induced mutations. Their research focused on Rous sarcoma, a virus which can produce tumors in chickens by attaching to a normal chicken gene as it duplicates within a cell. Since then, research has identified a number of additional "proto-oncogenes" which, when circumstances dictate, abandon their normal role of overseeing cell division and growth and turn potentially cancerous. Varmus's and Bishop's oncogene studies had a tremendous impact on the efforts to understand the genetic basis of cancer. The results of their work quickly found practical applications, especially in cancer diagnosis and prognosis.

Director of the National Institutes of Health

Varmus was nominated by U.S. president Bill Clinton to the directorship of the NIH and was confirmed in November 1993. The director of the NIH plays a vital part in setting the course for biomedical research in the United States. Varmus's nomination was strongly supported by biomedical scientists, but there was some opposition from AIDS activists. They—as well as others who were concerned with the health of women and members of minority groups—were concerned that Varmus would be more interested in basic biomedical research than in applied studies and feared that the medical research related to their specific concerns might be neglected. Varmus has argued that basic research in science, especially investigations of the fundamental properties of cells, genes, and tissues, could eventually lead to cures for many diseases, such as AIDS and cancer. As director, Varmus is also interested in revitalizing the intramural research program at NIH. He believes that science education in the United States needs to be improved and that students should be exposed to a science curriculum sooner, in smaller classes, by better-informed teachers.

A licensed physician in the state of California, Varmas is a member of numerous professional and academic associations, including the National Academy of Sciences, the American Society of Microbiologists, the American Society of Virologists, and the American Academy of Arts and Sciences. He married Constance Louise Casey on October 25, 1969, and they have two sons, Jacob Carey and Christopher Isaac.

SELECTED WRITINGS BY VARMUS:

Books

Cells, Development, and the Biology of Cancer, Freeman, 1992.
Genes and the Biology of Cancer, Scientific American Library, 1993.

Periodicals

Annual Review of Genetics, The Molecular Genetics of Cellular Oncogenes, Volume 18, 1984, pp. 513–612.
Scientific American, Reverse Transcription, Volume 257, September 1987, pp. 56–59.
Science, Oncogenes and Transcriptional Control, Volume 238, December 4, 1987, pp. 1337–1339.
Science, Retroviruses, Volume 240, June 10, 1988, pp. 1427–35.
Science, Science and the New Administration, Volume 259, January 22, 1993, pp. 444–446.

FURTHER READING:

Periodicals

Angier, Natalie, *New York Times,* Out of the Lab and Into the Bureaucracy, November 23, 1993, p. C1.
Campbell, Neil A., *American Biology Teacher,* A conversation with . . . Michael Bishop and Harold Varmus, Volume 54, November/December 1992, pp. 476–481.

Sketch by Jessica Jahiel

Arlette Vassy
1913–
French atmospheric physicist

Arlette Vassy is a leading authority on ozone in the atmosphere. As one of France's premier atmospheric physicists, she undertook a series of positions that made use of both her laboratory and field study skills. In this work she examined the role of ozone gas, a triatomic form of oxygen formed by photochemical reactions that, while extant in lower areas, makes up a layer in the high atmosphere that protects the earth from harmful ultraviolet lights. In connection with her atmospheric studies, Vassy also participated in France's early space exploration, acting as a scientific advisor on numerous rocket launches.

Vassy was born in St-Nexans (Dordogne) to Pierre Tournaire and the former Jeanne Vitrac. Her father was a physics teacher and had passed the rigorous state pedagogical licensing procedure known as the *agrégation*. Entering higher education herself, Vassy matriculated into her father's career. In 1934 she took a *licence* in physics at the University of Paris, known since medieval times as the Sorbonne. She then received a *diplôme d'études supérieures* in physics in 1935. (These diplomas correspond in a formal sense to B.S. and M.S. degrees, although they represent a more sophisticated mastery of material than was then typical in North America.) The following year, 1936, Vassy married fellow physicist Etienne Vassy, with whom she would collaborate on much of her work.

Begins Work in Atmospheric Physics

Vassy and her husband dedicated themselves to upper-atmospheric physics, a field in which the French were leaders. In 1937 the couple spent five months studying the absorption of light in the atmosphere at a newly opened geophysical station in Ifrane, located in the mountains of Morocco. This and related work led to Sorbonne doctoral dissertations—Etienne in 1937 and Arlette in 1941.

Vassy's career was carried out within the Centre National de la Recherche Scientifique (CNRS). This national research organization, created in 1939, was the result of nearly twenty years of experimentation with the administration of scientific research. At its debut, the CNRS acted as a central authority for funding laboratories and employing scientists. In a notable innovation (already anticipated in the national German laboratories of the Kaiser-Wilhelm Gesellschaft and those of diverse foundations like the Solvay, Nobel, and Carnegie), researchers had no teaching responsibilities. Vassy received predoctoral funding from the CNRS and then obtained an appointment as a scientist there. She rose to senior scientist (*maître de recherche*) in 1954 and, in 1968, became director of a CNRS laboratory devoted to atmospheric ozone.

Atmospheric ozone and its related problems required both laboratory analysis and observations in the field. Vassy's research ideally suited her for playing an active role in the inception of France's space program. Beginning in 1954 she participated in nearly forty rocket launches; from 1963 to 1967 she directed the scientific side of France's high-altitude ballistic rocket research. In 1959 Vassy became an officer in the Order of Academic Palms—France's national society of merit; in 1988 she received the gold medal of the Society for the Encouragement of Progress.

SELECTED WRITINGS BY VASSY:

Books

Fondements théoriques de la photographie, Editions de la Revue d'optique, 1953.

Colloque sur la sensibilité des cristaux et des émulsions photographiques, Editions de la Revue d'optique, 1953.

Advances in Geophysics, Atmospheric Ozone, Volume 2, Academic Press, 1965, pp. 115–73.

La Luminescence nocturne, Springer, 1976.

Sketch by Lewis Pyenson

Edward Bright Vedder
1878–1952
American bacteriologist

Edward Bright Vedder made invaluable contributions to early twentieth century medicine. He discovered the causes of beriberi and scurvy; both are diseases stemming from vitamin deficiencies. He also contributed to knowledge about leprosy, syphilis, and amoebic dysentery.

Vedder was born in New York, New York, on June 28, 1878, the son of Baptist clergyman Henry Clay Vedder and his wife, Minnie Lingham Vedder. Vedder attended public schools on Long Island and then graduated from the University of Rochester in New York in 1898. He earned his M.D. degree at the University of Pennsylvania in 1902. While working on his master's degree in science (which he obtained in 1903), he studied with Simon Flexner, investigating the bacteria that causes dysentery.

In 1903 Vedder joined the army and became first lieutenant and assistant surgeon for the medical corps. After attending the Army Medical School and contributing to experiments on the typhoid vaccine, he graduated in 1904. He would then serve in cities in the United States and the Philippines until 1910, even working in the Philippines under General Pershing during the guerilla war against the Moros from 1904 to 1906. Starting in 1910, he studied tropical diseases as a member of the army's scientific board in the Philippines and became an instructor in bacteriology in 1913 at the Army Medical School, where he served until 1919.

It was while he was in the Philippines that Vedder did his most important work. While studying the disease beriberi, he deduced that it was a deficiency disease associated with the Philippine custom of eating polished rice. He had the idea of substituting half-polished rice, instead, which successfully cured the disease. Later, scientists found the disease came from a deficiency of vitamin B_1.

Vedder's groundbreaking study on beriberi was so impressive that he won the Cartwright Prize of the College of Physician and Surgeons of Columbia University in 1913. He then moved on to investigate the causes of scurvy, which he found to be a deficiency of vitamin C. Vedder celebrated his discovery of vitamin C with a paper called "Study of the Antiscorbutic Vitamin," which won him the Wellcome prize in 1932.

Vedder also added to knowledge about the treatment of leprosy and syphilis. In 1911 he showed the effectiveness of emetine in the treatment of amoebic dysentery. His study of this medicine led to its widespread use.

After leaving the Philippines, he led the Southern Department Laboratory in Fort Sam, Texas, from 1920 until 1922. Then Vedder entered a new field of research, chemical warfare. From 1922 until 1925, he was chief of medical research at the Edgewood Arsenal, Maryland, where he delved into the basics of chemical warfare. From there, he moved back to the Philippines to become a senior member of the Army's Board of Medical Research in 1926. That same year, he was promoted to the rank of colonel.

In 1928 Vedder became the Army Medical School's commandant, and then during 1931 started research on poison gas at Edgewood Arsenal.

After retiring from the army in 1933, he was appointed professor of experimental medicine at George Washington University in Washington D.C. In 1942 he moved to the San Francisco Bay area of California to become director of medical education at the Alameda County Hospital and director of the Highland County Hospital's laboratory in Oakland. He retired in 1947.

Vedder wrote a number of noteworthy books including *Beriberi* (1913), *Sanitation for Medical Officers, War Manual* (1917), *Syphilis and Public Health* (1918), *The Medical Aspects of Chemical Warfare* (1925), and *Medicine: Its Contribution to Civilization* (1929), as well as many articles which appeared in respected scientific journals of the time. In 1924 he received an honorary Sc.D. degree from the University of Rochester.

Vedder was a Baptist and a Republican who enjoyed walking and playing tennis. On June 22, 1903, he married his wife Lily Sheldrake in Philadelphia. She was the daughter of a Philadelphia manufacturer, Henry Edward Norton. They had two children, Sibyl Norton, and Henry Clay, as well as three grandchildren.

The scientist died in Walter Reed General Hospital in Washington D.C. on January 30, 1952. Vedder was 73.

SELECTED WRITINGS BY VEDDER:

Books

Sanitation for Medical Officers, Philadelphia: Lea and Febiger, 1917.

Syphilis and the Public Health, Philadelphia: Lea and Febiger, 1918.

FURTHER READING:

Periodicals

"Col. E. B. Vedder, 73, Noted as Scientist," *The New York Times* (Febuary 2, 1952): p. 13.
"Deaths," *Journal of the American Medical Association* (April 5, 1952): p. 1236.
"Obituary," *British Medical Journal* (February 23, 1952): p. 441.

Sketch by Barbara Boughton

V. I. Veksler
1907–1966
Russian physicist

Physicist V. I. Veksler's early research covered a variety of topics, including X rays, cosmic radiation, nuclear physics, and particle detection devices. He is best known for his development of the principle of phase stability of particles in accelerators. This principle, discovered independently and concurrently in the United States by **Edwin M. Mc Millan**, became the basis for a whole new class of particle accelerators that included the synchrocyclotron in the United States and the synchrophasotron in the Soviet Union.

Vladimir Iosifovich Veksler was born in Zhitomir, Russia, on March 4, 1907, according to the Julian calendar in use in Russia at the time. His father, Iosif Lvovich Veksler, was an engineer. Veksler took his first job as an assembler in a factory before entering the Moscow Energetics Institute, where he received his diploma in electrical engineering in 1931. A year earlier he had taken a job with the All-Union Electrotechnical Institute, where he worked primarily on X rays. He continued his studies at the Institute of Energetics over the next decade, eventually earning both his candidate of physico-mathematical sciences degree (similar to a master's degree) in 1934 and his doctorate in 1940.

Moves to the Lebedev Institute

In 1936, Veksler moved from the All-Union Institute to a new post at the P. N. Lebedev Institute of Physics in Moscow. During his twenty years in this position he carried out extensive studies of cosmic radiation, conducting much of that work in the Pamir Mountain range of Central Asia.

As a means of providing science with a more comprehensive understanding of the the atomic nucleus, Veksler began devising methods for increasing the effectiveness of existing particle accelerators. **Ernest Orlando Lawrence**'s invention of the cyclotron in the early 1930s had made available to physicists a powerful new tool for the investigation of the atomic nucleus. In a cyclotron, subatomic particles, such as protons and electrons, are accelerated by a changing electrical field at opposite sides of the cyclotron. The particles are then forced into a spiral path by a fixed magnetic field perpendicular to the plane of the particles' path. An instrument of this design can accelerate particles to velocities close to the speed of light.

At such velocities, however, technical problems begin to accumulate. Raising the energy of particles can no longer be accomplished by increasing their speed since, according to **Albert Einstein**'s theory of relativity, they can never go faster than the speed of light; further increases in speed can only result in an increase in the particles' mass. This so-called relativistic mass increase creates serious problems in cyclotron design, since the heavier particles take longer than expected to reach the point at which they are supposed to receive their next "push" from the electrical field.

Solves the Problem of Relativistic Mass Increase

In 1944, Veksler proposed a method by which this problem could be resolved. He showed how particles can be treated in "bunches" and accelerated in orbits that remain stable, even during relativistic mass increases. An almost identical proposal to Veksler's was developed shortly thereafter by Edwin M. McMillan at the University of California at Berkeley. Phase stability was incorporated almost immediately into the design of a whole new generation of particle accelerators that had energy capacities significantly greater than any that had previously been possible. Those machines included the synchrocyclotrons used in the United States, and the corresponding synchro-phasotrons built in the Soviet Union. For their independent development of the concept of phase stability in particle accelerators, Veksler and McMillan were jointly awarded the sixth Atoms for Peace Award in 1963.

Veksler was elected an associate member of the U.S.S.R.'s Academy of Science in 1946, becoming a full member in 1958. In 1956, Veksler moved on to a new assignment as director of the high-energy laboratory at the Joint Institute of Nuclear Research at Dubna, where he directed the construction of the ten billion-electron-volt synchrotron that was, at that time, the most powerful particle accelerator in the world.

Veksler died of a heart attack in Moscow on September 22, 1966. In his obituary in *Physics Today*, McMillan described him as "a quiet, modest man with a gentle sense of humor [who] was known as a strong proponent of international amity among scientists." In addition to the Atoms for Peace Award, Veksler also received both the Lenin and State Prizes of the U.S.S.R.

SELECTED WRITINGS BY VEKSLER:

Books

Eksperimentalnye Metody Yadernoy Fiziki, [Moscow-Leningrad], 1940.
Ionizatsionnye Metody Issledovania Izlucheny, [Moscow], 1950.

Periodicals

Doklady Akademii Nauk SSR, Novy Metod Uskorenia Relyativistskikh Chastis, Volume 43, number 8, 1944, p. 346.
Atomnaya Energiya, Kogerentny Metod Uskoremia Zaryazhennykh Chastis, Volume 11, number 5, 1957, p. 427.

FURTHER READING:

Books

Daintith, John, editor, *A Biographical Encyclopedia of Scientists,* Facts on File, 1981, p. 808.
Gillispie, Charles Coulson, editor, *Dictionary of Scientific Biography,* Volume 13, Scribner, 1975, pp. 600–01.
Turkevich, John, *Soviet Men of Science,* Van Nostrand, 1963, p. 409–10.

Periodicals

Turkevich, John, *Physics Today,* Atoms for Peace Award, September 1963, p. 94.
McMillan, Edwin M., *Physics Today,* Vladimir Iosifovich Veksler, November 1966, pp. 103–04.
Walkinshaw, W., *Nature,* Academician Volume I. Veksler, November 12, 1966, p. 674.

Sketch by David E. Newton

Argelia Velez–Rodriguez
1936–
Cuban-born American mathematics educator

Since leaving her native Cuba shortly after completing her Ph.D., Argelia Velez–Rodriguez has devoted her career to mathematics and physics education. She has been involved with math education programs of the National Science Foundation (NSF) since 1970 and became director of the Minority Science Improvement Program at the U.S. Department of Education in 1980.

Argelia Velez–Rodriguez

FURTHER READING:

Other

"Argelia Velez–Rodriguez," *Biographies of Women Mathematicians,* June 1997. http://www.scottlan.edu/lriddle/women/chronol.htm (July 22, 1997).
Velez–Rodriguez, Argelia, interview with Karl Leif Bates, conducted June 17, 1997.

Sketch by Karl Leif Bates

After showing promise in mathematics as a girl, Velez–Rodriguez earned a bachelor's degree in 1955 from the Marianao Institute of Cuba and a Ph.D. in 1960 from the University of Havana. Her doctoral dissertation concerned the use of differential equations in figuring astronomical orbits. Her father, Pedro Velez, had worked in the Cuban Congress under Fulgencio Batista, the leader ousted by Fidel Castro in 1959.

Velez–Rodriguez's first teaching position in the United States was at Texas College, where she began teaching mathematics and physics in 1962. In 1972, she became a professor of math and served as the department's chair at Bishop College in Dallas. Velez–Rodriguez's research at the time focused on differential equations and classical analysis, and it was at Bishop that she first became involved with the NSF programs for improving science education. Velez–Rodriguez has also studied teaching strategies, with a particular focus on helping minorities and disadvantaged students learn mathematics. She directed and coordinated several NSF programs for high school and junior high school mathematics teachers.

Velez–Rodriquez was married to Raul Rodriguez in 1954 in Cuba and they had two young children when the family fled the country in 1962. "I had just finished my Ph.D.," she told contributor Karl Bates in an interview. Her son is now a surgeon, and her daughter is an engineer with a Harvard MBA. She and Rodriguez are divorced, and she is a naturalized citizen of the United States.

Vladímir Ivanovich Vernadsky
1863–1945
Russian mineralogist, geochemist, and biogeochemist

In a life that spanned two centuries, eight decades, and dozens of Russian and Soviet regimes, Russian geologist Vladímir Ivanovich Vernadsky successfully combined mineralogy with chemistry and biology, using this new approach to investigate evolution. Vernadsky's biosphere theory—the concept that living matter and the atmosphere's essential gases exist in a mutual relationship—lay the groundwork for modern environmentalism.

Vernadsky's ability to meld the scientific and the political can be traced back to his childhood and early adolescence. He was born on March 12, 1863, in St. Petersburg, Russia. His father, Ivan, was a professor of political economy and edited a liberal journal that barely escaped the Tsarist regime's censorship. Vladímir's mother, Anna Petrovna Konstantinovich, was a teacher of singing who was neither as intellectual nor as politically inclined as her husband. When Vernadsky was five, the family moved to the more provincial town of Kharkov, where he received an introduction to nature and astronomy from his uncle. At the age of 13, Vernadsky moved with his family back to St. Petersburg, where he attended a classical gymnasium. Because a classical Russian education in this era did not include the sciences, Vernadsky and his friends were forced to form a study group of their own.

In 1881 Vernadsky entered the physics and math departments at St. Petersburg University. Although it was the custom for men of his class to study abroad, Vernadsky remained close to home to help care for his father, who had suffered a stroke the previous spring. At St. Petersburg, Vernadsky studied with Dmitri Ivanovich Mendeleev, who derived the periodic table of the elements, chemist Aleksandr Butlerov, and mineralogist V. V. Dokuchaev. He published two scientific articles during his undergraduate years, one on mineral analysis and the other on the prairie rodent. Vernadsky's undergraduate thesis on isomorphism so impressed his professors that they urged him to pursue an academic career. That same year he joined an underground committee on literacy, which wrote and distributed reading materials for the common people. Through the committee, Vernadsky met Natalia Egorovna Staritskaya, who was three years his senior. Though their age difference concerned Natalia, the two began courting. When Vernadsky was appointed curator of the university's mineralogical collection in 1886, he persuaded her to accept his offer of marriage.

But Vernadsky was not to enjoy the peaceful existence of the newlywed for long. Russia in the late 1880s was in turmoil and few places were more tumultuous than the university campuses. After a group of students there were found guilty of a plot to kill Alexander III, the Tsarist government considered St. Petersburg University a hotbed of radicalism. Administrators at the state-run university targeted students and faculty suspected of rebellious feelings towards the autocracy. The 25-year-old Vernadsky was among the suspects, not because of any radical activities but because of his decision not to study abroad, a decision which, according to administrators, branded him an avowed rabble-rouser. Vernadsky's father-in-law, a well-respected government official, appealed his ouster and the government decided to allow Vernadsky to continue his association with the university as long as he now sought that international education. As soon as his first child, George (later a Russian historian) was born, Vernadsky began studying at the University of Naples.

Undertakes Research on Polymorphism

Soon after his arrival in Italy, Vernadsky realized that the Naples department no longer led the field, so he transferred to Munich to study with the German crystallographer Paul Groth. Although in letters to his wife Vernadsky poked fun at the German professor's pedantic lecturing style, he also admitted that he learned how to observe and experiment in practical mineralogy in Germany. In 1889 Vernadsky transferred to Paris's Mining Academy, where, under the guidance of Henri Le Châtelier, he chose polymorphism—the ability of some chemical compounds to assume different forms—as the topic for his master's thesis. Whereas it was previously believed that the aluminosilicate minerals which make up most of the earth's crust were silicic acid salts, Vernadsky showed them to have a different structure, with aluminum that is chemically analogous to silicon. He proposed the theory of the kaolin nucleus, a structure which is made up of two aluminum, two silicon, and seven oxygen atoms, and which forms the basis of many minerals. The theory has since been confirmed, and is considered essential to an understanding of minerals.

Vernadsky started lecturing at Moscow University in 1891, the year he received his master's degree. Like many intellectuals of his time and place, he found himself balancing academic interests with political ones. In 1897,

Vernadsky earned a doctoral degree with his dissertation on crystalline matter, qualifying him for a full professorship. The following year his daughter Nina (later a psychiatrist) was born.

The first decade of the twentieth century proved a productive one for Vernadsky. His new approach of combining geologic interests with other scientific fields, such as chemistry and biology, attracted supporters. By 1901, when he created the Mineralogical Circle at Moscow University, he had a devoted cadre of students and colleagues who formed a scientific school that was heavily influenced by the latest theories in chemistry and evolutionary biology. He also maintained an interest in politics, helping to found the Union of Liberation, a group that sought to end the Russian autocracy peacefully. In 1902 he published a summary of his political views, disguised as science, in *On a Scientific World View*. The next year, he published his first scientific book, *Fundamentals of Crystallography*. When the universities again erupted in turmoil in 1905, Vernadsky operated a lab until the university closed. Caught up in the fervor of the times, he helped organize the Constitutional Democratic party, the largest opposition party to pose candidates for the nation's newly created Duma. His political work did not deter him from amassing scientific honors, however. In 1906 Vernadsky was elected as an adjunct member of the Academy of Sciences and appointed director of St. Petersburg's Mineralogical Museum; two years later he melded his interests with his appointment to the Agrarian Commission of the State Council.

After the university riots of 1905, the campus situation calmed down somewhat, allowing the faculty to return to teaching and research. For Vernadsky, that meant expanding the field of mineralogy to include evolutionary concerns. As he explained in volume 2 of *Izbrannye sochinenia* his version of mineralogy held that "mineralogy, like chemistry, must study not only the products of chemical reactions but also the very processes of reaction." He was particularly interested in paragenesis, or the way in which essential minerals formed. By studying the many layers of the earth's crust in this manner, Vernadsky hoped to be able to piece together some of the planet's evolutionary history. In 1911 strikes interrupted his work once more. In retaliation for the liberal faculty's support of miscreant students, the government fired three professors. Twenty-eight percent of the faculty—including Vernadsky—resigned in protest. Soon after resigning, Vernadsky was expelled from the state council.

Introduces Theory of the Biosphere

Loss of both these positions translated into free time for Vernadsky to pursue his scientific interests. He moved to St. Petersburg, where he took a job as a scientific administrator and continued research on the distribution of rare elements such as cesium, rubidium, scandium, and indium. He made one expedition per year to remote areas in the Russian empire to catalog the nation's resources. During

World War I, Vernadsky spearheaded a movement to conserve Russian natural resources, culminating in the formation of the Commission for the Study of the Natural Productive Forces of Russia in 1915. When the Tsarist regime collapsed in 1917, Vernadsky became involved in politics again, joining a campaign to persuade Russians to take pride in and preserve their culture. Vernadsky served briefly as the government's assistant minister in charge of universities and institutions, until the October revolution, which ushered in a government whose politics did not mesh with Vernadsky's. In 1919, he moved to Kiev to found and become president of the Ukrainian Academy of Sciences. When the Red Terror of 1919 drove him into hiding, Vernadsky spent his time in isolation, developing the blueprints for a new field he called biogeochemistry. As he saw it, this new discipline studied the nexus between geology, chemistry, and biology, determining how prevalent life was, the rates at which different forms of life multiply, and the processes and speed of adaptation.

Vernadsky left Russia in 1921 for France, where he worked with the grande dame of radiation physics, **Marie Curie**. During this period, he coalesced his thoughts on the interconnection of all living and nonliving beings on Earth into a book entitled *The Biosphere*. After four years in the West, Vernadsky's wife lobbied to move there permanently, rather than returning to Soviet Russia. But the government was eager to attract prominent scholars such as Vernadsky and offered him a chair in the academy with the promise of time and funding for his own work, an offer that no Western institution matched. In 1926 he founded and headed the Commission on the History of Knowledge of the Academy of Sciences of the U.S.S.R. and lay the basis for the organization that later became the Vernadsky Institute of Geochemistry and Analytical Chemistry.

During the Stalin years, Vernadsky continued working, relatively uninterrupted. His earlier years of protest against the Tsar, combined with his image as an elder statesman of science, protected him from the government persecution that many of his colleagues experienced. In 1935 he began writing philosophical essays on the nature of the world. In 1940 his years of interest in radioactivity culminated in the creation of the Uranium Institute. During World War II, he argued for Russia to develop its atomic energy program. His wife of 56 years died in 1943 while the couple was evacuated from their home. Vernadsky passed away two years later on January 6, 1945, a few months after suffering a cerebral hemorrhage.

SELECTED WRITINGS BY VERNADSKY:

Books

Izbrannye sochinenia, (title means "Selected Works"), six volumes, [Moscow], 1954-1960.
Biosfera, (title means "The Biosphere"), [Leningrad], 1926, [Moscow], 1967.

Izbrannye sochinenia, (title means "selected works"), 6 volumes, [Moscow], 1954–1960.

FURTHER READING:

Books

Bailes, Kendall, *Science and Russian Culture in an Age of Revolutions: V. I. Vernadsky and His Scientific School, 1863–1945,* Indiana University Press, 1990.
Balandin, R. K., *Outstanding Soviet Scientists: Vladímir Vernadsky,* translated by Alexander Repyev, Mir Publishers (Moscow), 1982.

Sketch by Shari Rudavsky

Frederick John Vine
1939–
English geophysicist

The creation of the theory of plate tectonics cannot be ascribed to any one person or year, unlike most of the other overarching theories of science. But acceptance of the theory by most geologists stems from the convincing argument and evidence of Frederick John Vine, first developed in 1963 and presented in full form in 1966. After 1966 leading geologists around the world came to believe that the ocean floor was created at the mid-ocean ridges and slowly spread apart as large individual plates. These plates move with respect to each other, with some plate edges plunging under others to form great ocean trenches. Action of the plates accounts for chains of mountains and for patterns of earthquake or volcanic activity. Plate tectonics also produces the movement of continents with respect to each other, which is known as continental drift.

Vine's work in the 1960s did more than establish the theory of plate tectonics. It also connected that theory to evidence for periodic reversals of Earth's magnetic field and established the validity of that idea.

Vine was born in Chiswick, England, a suburb of west London. His parents were Frederick Royston Vine, an accountant, and Ivy Grace (Bryant) Vine, a personal secretary. Vine attended school in London before going to St. John's College at Cambridge University to study for a degree in natural sciences and for a Ph.D. in marine geophysics with Drummond Matthews. In 1967 he came to the United States to teach and do research in geophysics at Princeton University in New Jersey, but in 1970 returned to England to work in the environmental sciences department at the University of East Anglia in Norwich. He is currently Dean of Environmental Sciences at that university. In 1964 he married Susan Alice McCall. They have a daughter and a son.

Vine was a graduate student at St. John's in 1962 and already a firm believer in continental drift since the age of 14 when, like so many others before him, he was struck by the fit between the great gulf of West Africa and the bulge of Brazil. In 1962 his supervisor at Cambridge, Drummond Matthews, traveled on *H.M.S. Owen* to the northwest part of the Indian Ocean to map the trapped magnetic pattern in the sea floor near that part of the Mid-Ocean Ridge System, which locally is termed the Carlsberg Ridge. The resulting map was not the first to observe that the magnetism of the ocean floor consists of a series of stripes. These had also been observed off the coast of California in the Pacific Ocean and near Iceland in the Atlantic Ocean. Now the magnetic banding appeared in the Indian Ocean as well. The individual stripes can be as much as 20 miles (30 km) wide. A magnetometer towed through the sea shows these as regular changes from band to band in the intensity of Earth's magnetic field.

Vine and Matthews had given considerable thought to the then-new hypothesis of sea-floor spreading, just published that year by **Harry Hammond Hess** but widely circulated among oceanographers since 1960 (the name "sea-floor spreading" was coined by Robert J. Dietz in 1961). Vine and Matthews recognized that previous interpretations of the magnetic variations on the ocean floor had overlooked an important clue. Although the magnetometer recorded the changes from band to band as variations in intensity, the same effect on the magnetometer would be produced by variations in polarity (the direction of the magnetic field; that is, which pole is observed as north). They reinterpreted their data with this in mind. If trapped magnetic fields in one band show the north magnetic pole in its expected location near the north geographic pole, a few kilometers east or west will be a band that appears to show the north magnetic pole near the south geographic pole.

This interpretation of the stripes as variations in polarity would not make much sense unless there were some mechanism that could account for the changes, but Vine and Matthews recognized that sea-floor spreading could account for the changes, provided that one also accepted another new idea that was being advanced in the early 1960s. This idea, largely the work of several young Americans led by Allan Cox, Richard Doell, and Brent Dalrymple, was based on measurements of magnetism trapped in continental rocks. Their work showed that every hundred thousand years or so something causes Earth's magnetic field to reverse its polarity. Few in the early 1960s accepted Cox, Doell, and Dalrymple's theory on geomagnetic reversals any more than they believed Hess and Dietz on sea-floor spreading.

Vine and Matthews saw how the two new concepts could work together. If the sea floor were stable, as previously believed by geologists, polarity reversals of Earth's magnetic field would place rocks of one magnetic direction on top of another, like a layer cake. But if the sea floor is being created at mid-ocean ridges and new crust is spreading away from the ridges, the polarity reversals would appear as stripes instead of as layers. Furthermore, one could expect that the stripes on each side of the ridge would be symmetrical. If the third stripe from the ridge on the east is a wide one with a north magnetic pole near the north geographic pole, then the third stripe on the west should also be wide with the same polarity. This pattern could be observed in the intensity map—not the polarity, of course, but the comparative widths.

About the same time as Vine and Matthews, a Canadian geophysicist also had this idea but could not get it published because he did not have the data to back it up, and the idea was rejected as worthy only of conversation interest. Vine and Matthews had the data and were published in *Nature* in September 1963. Combined with other data supporting sea-floor spreading, magnetic reversals of the ocean floor became the convincing evidence that led to the theory of plate tectonics. This did not happen at once, since few believed in any of the theories or even in some of the evidence in 1963.

In 1965 a chance meeting with Brent Dalrymple on a trip to the United States led Vine to forge another link in the chain of reasoning. Dalrymple told Vine in private conversation in some detail of an unannounced discovery of a previously unrecognized geomagnetic reversal, this one less than a million years ago, an eye blink in geological time. The rock that revealed the reversal was located near Jamarillo Creek in Mexico. A few months later, Vine visited the Lamont Geological Observatory (now Lamont-Doherty Earth Observatory) in New York, where he was shown new data from the South Pacific floor that also showed a geomagnetic reversal at exactly the same time as the Jamarillo event. Vine could easily see that the two were the same. Indeed, the two magnetic records were identical. It was too good a match to have occurred unless the reversals were real events, and not some effect that occurred as a result of chance local conditions. But if the reversals were real, then so would sea-floor spreading be real, and indeed would create a whole new view of Earth.

The exact date that plate tectonics became the accepted and orthodox theory of Earth's crustal history among geologists is difficult to pin down. There is no single moment like the 1858 presentations of the theory of evolution by Darwin and Wallace. But a case can be made for a meeting of the Geological Society of America in San Francisco in December 1966, when Vine presented a paper titled "Proof of Ocean-Floor Spreading." Following that meeting, most geologists came to believe in that explanation of the apparent continental drift first proposed by **Alfred Wegener** in 1912 and mostly derided since that time. Two years later, a series of ocean cores revealed that the ages of the different stripes on the sea floor matched the ages of the geomagnetic reversals observed on continental rocks. No one could doubt the reality of sea-floor spreading after that.

Subsequently and notably, with Eldridge Moores, Vine has worked on a rock formation in the Troodos Mountains of southern Cyprus that is thought to be an upthrust slice of ocean floor. Their project is to elucidate further details of the structure and physical properties of oceanic crust formed by sea-floor spreading. Vine's other work includes studies of the form of Earth's magnetic field in the past and of the electrical conductivity of the continental crust.

SELECTED WRITINGS BY VINE:

Books

(With Philip Kearey) *Global Tectonics, 2nd ed.,* London: Blackwell Science, 1996.

Periodicals

(with D. H. Matthews) "Magnetic anomalies over oceanic ridges," *Nature* (1963), 199: pp. 947-949.

"Spreading of the ocean floor; new evidence," *Science* (1966), 154: pp. 1405-1415.

"The continental drift debate." *Nature* (1977), 266: pp. 19-22.

FURTHER READING:

Books

Miller, Russell, *Continents in Collision,* Alexandria, VA: Time-Life Books, 1983.

Weiner, Jonathan, *Planet Earth,* New York and Toronto: Bantam Books, 1986.

Sketch by Bryan Bunch

Artturi Ilmari Virtanen
1895–1973
Finnish biochemist

Artturi Ilmari Virtanen was a Finnish biochemist who discovered many of the nutritionally important components of plants, including vitamins and amino acids. His most important discovery, a method of preserving green fodder and silage, led to an improved understanding of the mechanism of plant decay. For his biochemical investigations in agriculture and nutrition he received the 1945 Nobel Prize in chemistry.

Virtanen was born January 15, 1895, in Helsinki, Finland, to Serafina (Isotalo) and Kaarlo Virtanen. He began his education at the Classical Lyceum in Viipuri (now Vyborg, Russia). Upon graduation, he entered the University of Helsinki to study biology, chemistry, and physics.

Virtanen received his master of science degree in 1916 and worked briefly as an assistant chemist in the Central Industrial Laboratory of Helsinki. That same year he returned to the University to continue his studies and in 1919 he received his doctorate. Interested in a broad range of scientific subjects, Virtanen traveled extensively to pursue his studies. In 1920 he left for Zurich, Switzerland, to undertake postgraduate work in physical chemistry. The next year he had moved to Stockholm, Sweden, to study bacteriology, and in 1923 he worked on enzymology with **Hans Euler-Chelpin**. At this time Virtanen discovered the subject that would become his life work, biochemistry.

Career and Discoveries in Agricultural Chemistry

In 1921 Virtanen was appointed laboratory director of the Finnish Cooperative Dairies Association in Valio, where he was responsible for controlling the manufacture of dairy products such as cheese and butter. A decade later, in 1931, he was appointed the director of the Biochemical Research Institute in Helsinki. In that same year, he began teaching as professor of biochemistry at the Finland Institute of Technology. Late in 1939 he became professor of biochemistry at the University of Helsinki.

Virtanen was interested in both the theoretical and practical aspects of biochemistry. His first important study was an investigation of the fermentation reactions of some biologically important acids. His research showed how enzymes were necessary for bacterial fermentation. Enzymes, the complex organic catalysts of living cells, were thought to speed up chemical reactions without being chemically changed. Virtanen, who believed that enzymes were composed of proteins, began an exhaustive study of the protein content and enzyme activity of plants.

Proteins are rich in nitrogen, an essential element in both human and animal nutrition. Virtanen realized that nitrogen was plentiful in the atmosphere but almost completely unavailable to most plants and animals. He began to study legumes (peas, clover, and soybeans), which are able to convert atmospheric nitrogen into nitrogen compounds suitable for plant growth. Virtanen became interested in what happened to plants after they were cut and stored for cattle fodder. It was found that fodder stored as silage could lose one-quarter to one-half of its nutrients to bacterial decay. Animals consuming this silage produced poor quality butter, milk, and cheese. After study and experimentation, Virtanen discovered that the addition of a simple mixture of dilute hydrochloric and sulfuric acids to stored silage could slow down bacterial decay and prevent the destruction of nutritionally important vitamins and proteins.

Virtanen fed his acid-treated silage to dairy cows and tested the milk to determine the safety and effectiveness of his method. He discovered that milk remained rich in protein, carotene, and vitamin C, and that the milk cows remained healthy and strong. The method Virtanen devised for treating silage—called the Artturi Ilmari Virtanen (AIV) method—was first used in Finland in 1929.

Although most of Virtanen's scientific investigations had practical agricultural applications, his later work was more theoretical. He studied how bacteria in the root nodules of legumes synthesize nitrogen compounds, and how plant cells assimilate simple molecules into large complex vitamins. He discovered a red pigment in plant cells similar in structure and function to hemoglobin, the molecule that transports life-giving oxygen in human blood. He also studied the composition of plants, discovering many important amino acids—the building blocks of proteins. For his work on the AIV method of silage preservation and for his research in agricultural chemistry Virtanen received the 1945 Nobel Prize in chemistry.

After winning the Nobel Prize, Virtanen remained actively engaged in research. He published a book on animal and human nutrition and served on the editorial boards of several leading biochemical journals. He represented Finland on a United Nations Commission on Nutrition, and in 1948 he was elected president of Finland's State Academy of Science and Arts. Virtanen, remembered as one of Finland's leading scientists, died November 11, 1973, in the city of his birth, Helsinki.

SELECTED WRITINGS BY VIRTANEN:

Books

Cattle Fodder and Human Nutrition with Special Reference to Biological Nitrogen Fixation, Cambridge, 1938.

FURTHER READING:

Books

Dictionary of Scientific Biography, Volume XIV, Scribner, 1976.
Nobel Prize Winners, H. W. Wilson, 1987.

Sketch by Mike McClure

Richard Vollenweider
1922–
Canadian limnologist

Richard Vollenweider is best known for his innovative research in eutrophication (nutrient enrichment and its effects) which advanced the fields of modern limnology, the study of the properties of fresh waters, and lake management. Eutrophication is generally seen as a problem of the middle and late stages of the twentieth century, a consequence of society's urban, industrial, and agricultural use of plant nutrients and their disposal. The term eutrophication describes the biological effects of an increase in concentration of plant nutrients, usually nitrogen and phosphorous, but can also include silicon, potassium, calcium, iron, or manganese, on aquatic systems. Vollenweider was the first to recognize phosphorus as the primary element in lake production, a discovery which laid the foundation for the restoration of the Great Lakes and for eutrophication control models employed internationally.

Richard Albert Vollenweider was born in Zurich, Switzerland, on June 27, 1922. He grew up in Lucerne where he finished high school and obtained a teacher's diploma in 1942. He attended the University of Zurich where he earned a diploma in biology in 1946, and completed a Ph.D. in biology in 1951, with a thesis on "Experimental Studies on Phytoplankton Ecology." He was awarded an honorary doctorate of science from McGill University in Montreal in 1986.

Vollenweider devoted much of his career to education. He taught in undergraduate schools in Lucerne, Switzerland from 1949 to 1954, followed by two fellowships studying limnology. The first fellowship took him to the Italian Hydrobiological Institute in Palanza, Italy, from 1954 to 1955, and the second to the Swedish Research Council in Uppsala, Switzerland, from 1955 to 1956.

From 1957 to 1959 he worked as a field expert in limnology and fisheries for the United Nations Educational, Scientific and Cultural Organization (UNESCO) Department of Agriculture in Egypt. He then returned to the Italian Hydrobiological Institute to work as a research associate from 1959 to 1966, followed by a position as a water pollution consultant for the Organization for Economic Cooperative development in Paris from 1966 to 1968. He served as chief limnologist and head of the Fisheries Research Board for the Canadian Centre for Inland Waters (CCIW), Burlington, Ontario, from 1968 to 1970, followed by a position as chief of the National Water Research Institute Lakes Research Division from 1970 to 1973. Vollenweider's final professional position was as a senior scientist with the Canadian Centre of Inland Waters from 1973 to 1988, which he held concurrently with a position as professor of biology at McMaster University in Hamilton, Ontario, from 1978 to 1988.

While head of the Fisheries Research Board laboratories at CCIW, Vollenweider administered a research staff of 140 scientists and technicians. In this capacity he was responsible for organizing and developing the early research activities on the Laurentian Great Lakes and other limnological studies in Canada. CCIW created the position of senior scientist for Vollenweider to allow him to continue his own research as well as to serve as chair of the centre's Scientific Committee for Research Coordination.

Water Purification Research Earns International Recognition

Vollenweider's primary contribution to the study of limnology began at the theoretical stage when he designed a mathematical model for measuring the levels of phosphorus in the Great Lakes. This model determined the appropriate level of reduction of phosphorus necessary to stabilize the aquatic environments. His prior research, as well as that of others, concluded that the dumping of massive quantities of phosphorous had resulted in the destructive overgrowth of algae in these lakes. Vollenweider's theory of maximum tolerable levels of phosphorus in the lakes became the accepted standard among scientists and extended to the political arena when it formed the basis of the 1972 Great Lakes Water Quality Agreement between Canada and the United States. This recognition of the work of a single scientist within international law is an unusual distinction. Vollenweider's experiment to reduce phosphorous in the Great Lakes, begun in 1972, has proved successful and has stimulated similar projects around the world.

Vollenweider studied the primary production of Swiss, Italian, Swedish, and Egyptian lakes using oxygen techniques and radioactive carbon, and developed mathematical models for calculating integral photosynthesis. He also explored the relationship between primary production and absorption characteristics and the spectral correlation of underwater light over a broad range of lakes. This early line of research became the frame for later efforts to resolve the question about eutrophication. Further, he discovered the acidification process of lakes due to industrial ammonia pollution.

In addition to his research work in Canada, Vollenweider served as a consultant to many United Nations organizations and the governments of Italy, Argentina, Venezuela, Japan, and Ecuador. He has been instrumental in helping these countries develop programs to deal with major water management issues and in supporting purification projects. Vollenweider also served as a consultant to the Pan American Health Organization for Venezuela from 1977 to 1980, Italy in 1977, Argentina in 1980, Ecuador in 1982, and Brazil and Mexico in 1983. He worked for the International Lake Environment Commission and the World Health Organization in 1985.

Vollenweider has published more than ninety scientific papers in current scientific and technical journals, two books, and authored and/or coauthored numerous other scientific and technical reports in the fields of aquatic primary production, algal nutrition, optical conditions in lakes, water chemistry, freshwater and marine eutrophication, and modelling. In addition to several papers on these topics, the primary outcome from Vollenweider's studies was the International Biological Programme (IBP) handbook on "Methods for Measuring Primary Production in the Aquatic Environment," of which he was the primary contributor.

Vollenweider's honors and awards include the International Award, Premio Cervia/Ambiente in 1978; the International Tyler Prize for Global Environmental Achievement in 1986; and the Societas Internationalis Limnologiae Naumann-Thienemann Medal in 1987. He has been a member of the Italian Association of Ecology, the Italian Association

of Theoretical and Applied Limnology, and the Royal Society of Canada.

In recognition of his scientific leadership and public involvements for the environmental safeguard of the Adriatic Sea from eutrophication and pollution, Vollenweider has been conferred honorary citizenship of the city of Cesenatico, Italy. He has been a frequent guest on Italian television regarding Adriatic pollution, and his activities have been reported in many Italian daily newspapers. He currently divides his time between Canada and Italy.

The annual R. A. Vollenweider Lectureship in Aquatic Sciences was established in his honor by the National Water Research Institute upon his retirement in 1988 to commemorate his global contribution to the advancement of the aquatic sciences. At the time of his retirement, Vollenweider was the National Water Research Institute's senior scientist.

Vollenweider was married in 1965 and has no children.

SELECTED WRITINGS BY VOLLENWEIDER:

Books

Water Management Research; Scientific Fundamentals of the Eutrophication of Lakes and Flowing Waters, with Particular Reference to Nitrogen and Phosphorus as Factors in Eutrophication, Organization for Economic Cooperation and Development (OECD), Paris, 1968.

A Manual on Methods for Measuring Primary Production in Aquatic Environments, 2nd edition, Blackwell Scientific Publishers, 1974.

Periodicals

Journal of the Fisheries Research Board of Canada, A Comparative View of Phytoplankton and Primary Production in the Laurentian Great Lakes, Volume 31, 1974.

Input-Output Models with Special Reference to the Phosphorous Loading Concept in Limnology, Schweizische Zeitshrift fuer Hydrologie, Volume 37, 1975.

FURTHER READING:

Other

Vollenweider, Richard A., *Interview with Kelly Otter Cooper,* conducted December 3, 1993.

Sketch by Kelly Otter Cooper

Vito Volterra
1860–1940
Italian mathematician and physicist

Vito Volterra has been called a modern Renaissance man for the extraordinary variety of his interests, his great scientific curiosity, and his love of art, literature, and music. In a scientific career that spanned fifty-nine years, Volterra made his most important contributions in the areas of higher analysis, mathematical physics, celestial mechanics, the mathematical theory of elasticity, and mathematical biometrics. His name is most often associated with the creation of the theory of functionals and with the theory of integral and integro-differential equations.

Volterra was born in Ancona, Italy, on May 3, 1860, the only child of Abramo Volterra, a cloth merchant, and Angelica Almagià. After the death of his father in 1862, Volterra and his mother went to stay with her brother, Alfonso Almagià, who raised Volterra as his own son. Volterra spent most of his childhood in Florence and considered himself a native of that city. From a very early age, Volterra demonstrated an aggressive curiosity and an uncanny talent in mathematics and science. At the age of thirteen, inspired by Jules Verne's novel *From the Earth to the Moon,* Volterra tried to determine the trajectory of a projectile in the combined gravitational fields of the earth and moon. To solve this restricted version of the so-called three-body problem, he divided passing time into sufficiently small intervals to allow the forces operating on the projectile to be treated as constant in each interval. Volterra used this technique again and again over the years as he attacked such problems as differential linear equations, the theory of functionals, and linear substitutions.

Volterra attended the Scuola Tecnica Dante Alighieri and the Instituto Tecnico Galileo Galilei in Florence, Italy, graduating in 1878. Over the opposition of his mother and uncle, he enrolled at the University of Florence, where he was offered the position of assistant in the Physical Laboratory. He studied mineralogy and geology as well as mathematics and physics. In 1878, he transferred to the University of Pisa, and in 1880 won a competition to become a resident student at the Scuola Normale Superiore, where he remained for three years. While there, he wrote his first original paper on the theory of aggregates and the functions of a real variable. In 1882, Volterra was awarded a doctorate in physics for a thesis in the area of hydrodynamics.

In 1883, at the age of twenty-three, Volterra won the competition for a professorship of mechanics at the University of Pisa and went on to become the chair of mathematical physics. In 1892, he was appointed professor of mechanics at the University of Turin. Eight years later, in 1900, he became the chair of mathematical physics at the

University of Rome. He was a gifted teacher and lectured in many different European countries in the course of his life.

From his first paper in 1881 to a 1940 paper in *Acta* of the Pontifical Academy of Sciences, Volterra demonstrated a keen intelligence and a curiosity about many areas. Beyond his seminal work on the theory of functionals and on the theory of integro-differential equations, Volterra made important scientific contributions in many areas of applied science, including elasticity, physics, astronomy, mathematical biology, and hereditary phenomena. One of his most important achievements in applied science was his work on the mathematics of population growth, which took this field of inquiry beyond the Malthusian approach that any given environment can only sustain a strictly limited population. Volterra argued that cooperation among human beings would allow for increases in the food supply and thus accommodate a greater increase in population. He developed a mathematical model of population growth that takes these considerations into account.

Career Interrupted by World War II

In March 1905, at the comparatively young age of forty-five and in recognition of his scientific achievements, Volterra was made a senator of the Kingdom of Italy. The Italian government also appointed him chairman of the Polytechnic School at Turin. Although Volterra would have preferred to pursue a career of pure science, politics and war disrupted his plans. Throughout his life, Volterra was touched by these forces. When Volterra was three months old, he was nearly killed by a bomb that destroyed his cradle during a siege by the Italian army. In 1914, at the outbreak of World War I, Volterra was among those who urged his government to join the Allies. When Italy entered the war on the Allied side in 1915, Volterra enlisted in the army (at the age of fifty-five) and joined the air force. For more than two years he worked to perfect a new type of airship and developed a system for firing a gun from it. He was the first to propose the use of helium as a substitute for hydrogen, which is highly explosive, and he organized the manufacture of the slightly heavier gas. He also experimented with early aircraft designs and published mathematical works relating to aerial warfare. In 1917, he established the Office for War Inventions and, as its chairman, worked successfully to promote scientific and technical collaboration among the Allies. He was decorated with the War Cross and mentioned in dispatches for his work.

Forced from Homeland by Fascism

At war's end, Volterra returned to his research and teaching. But in 1922, at a time when he was generally recognized as the most eminent man of science in Italy, his academic life was again disrupted by politics. From the beginning, Volterra opposed fascism, especially objecting to changes in the educational system that deprived the Italian middle schools of their liberty. At great personal risk, Volterra and a small group of his fellow senators opposed the "laws of national security." In 1931, one year after the Italian parliamentary system had been abolished, Volterra refused to take the Oath of Allegiance imposed by the fascist government and was forced to leave the University of Rome, where he had taught and studied for more than thirty years. In 1932, he was compelled to resign from all Italian scientific academies and, from that time on, lived mostly abroad.

Despite the political disruptions, Volterra's life was generally happy and productive. He was much honored and well recognized for the excellence of his scientific work. He was a member of almost every major scientific and mathematical society, including the Royal Society, which he joined in 1910. In 1936, he was elected to the Pontifical Academy of Sciences after being nominated by Pope Pius XI. He was a Grand Officer of the French Legion of Honor. In 1921, he received an honorary knighthood from George V of England. He was also awarded honorary doctorates by many universities, including Cambridge, Oxford, and Edinburgh. In 1900, Volterra married Virginia Almagià, a distant cousin. They had six children. In 1938, Volterra developed phlebitis but continued his academic pursuits until his death on October 11, 1940, in Rome.

SELECTED WRITINGS BY VOLTERRA:

Books

Opere Matematiche. Memorie e Note, (collected works), five volumes, [Rome], 1954–1962.

FURTHER READING:

Books

American Philosophical Society Yearbook, 1940, Lancaster Press, 1941, pp. 448–451.
Manheim, J., *The Genesis of Point Set Topology,* Macmillan, 1964.
Manheim, J., *Obituary Notices of Fellows of the Royal Society,* Volume 3, Morrison & Gibb, 1939–41, pp. 691–729.

Sketch by Maureen L. Tan

Wernher von Braun
1912–1977
American rocket engineer

Wernher von Braun was the most famous rocket engineer of his time as well as a scientist and noted promoter of spaceflight. Teams under his direction designed the V–2, Redstone, Jupiter, and Pershing missiles, as well as the Jupiter C, Juno, and Saturn launch vehicles that carried most of the early U.S. satellites and spacecraft beyond the earth's atmosphere and ultimately to the moon. He became both a celebrity and a national hero in the United States, winning numerous awards, including the first Robert H. Goddard Memorial Trophy in 1958, the Distinguished Federal Civilian Service Award (presented by President Dwight D. Eisenhower) in 1959, and the National Medal of Science in 1977. As President Jimmy Carter stated at the time of von Braun's death: "To millions of Americans, [his] name was inextricably linked to our exploration of space and to the creative application of technology. He was not only a skillful engineer but also a man of bold vision; his inspirational leadership helped mobilize and maintain the effort we needed to reach the Moon and beyond."

The second of three children (all male), Wernher Magnus Maximilian von Braun was born on March 23, 1912, in the east German town of Wirsitz (later, Wyrzysk, Poland). He was the son of Baron Magnus Alexander Maximilian von Braun—then the principal magistrate (*Landrat*) of the governmental district and later (1932 to early 1933) the minister of nutrition and agriculture in the last two governments of the Weimar Republic before Hitler rose to power in Germany—and of Emmy (von Quistorp) von Braun, a well-educated woman from the Swedish-German aristocracy with a strong interest in biology and astronomy. She inspired her son's interest in spaceflight by supplying him with the science fiction works of Jules Verne and H. G. Wells and by giving him a telescope as a gift upon his confirmation into the Lutheran church in his early teens instead of the customary watch or camera. Despite these influences, the young von Braun was initially a weak student and was held back one year in secondary school because of his inability in math and physics. Due to his interest in astronomy and rockets, he obtained a copy of space pioneer **Hermann Oberth**'s book *Die Rakete zu den Planeträumen* ("Rockets to Planetary Space") in 1925. Appalled that he could not understand its complicated mathematical formulas, he determined to master his two weakest subjects. Upon completion of secondary school, von Braun entered the Berlin-Charlottenburg Institute of Technology, where he earned a bachelor of science in mechanical engineering and aircraft construction in 1932.

Begins Career in Rocketry

In the spring of 1930 von Braun found time to work as part of the German Society for Space Travel, a group founded in part by Hermann Oberth which experimented with small, liquid-fueled rockets. Although Oberth returned to a teaching position in his native Romania, von Braun continued working with the society. When the group ran short of funds during the depression, von Braun, then twenty, reluctantly accepted the sponsorship of the German military. In 1932 he went to work for the German army's ordnance department at Kummersdorf near Berlin, continuing to develop liquid-fueled rockets. Entering the University of Berlin about this same time, he used his work at

Wernher von Braun

Kummersdorf as the basis for his doctoral dissertation and received his Ph.D. in physics in 1934.

Von Braun's staff at Kummersdorf eventually grew to some eighty people, and in early 1937 the group moved to Peenemünde, a town on the Baltic coast where the German army, together with the air force, had constructed new facilities. Before the move, engineers at Kummersdorf had begun developing ever larger rockets, and in 1936 they completed the preliminary design for the A–4, better known as the V–2. This was an exceptionally ambitious undertaking, since the missile was to be 45 feet long, deliver a 1-ton warhead to a target some 160 miles distant, and employ a rocket motor that could deliver a 25-ton thrust for 60 seconds, compared to the 1.5 tons of thrust supplied by the largest liquid-fueled rocket motors then available. Von Braun's team encountered numerous difficulties—perfecting the injection system for the propellants, mastering the aerodynamic properties of the missile, and especially in developing its guidance and control system. Thus, even with the assistance of private industry and universities, the first successful launch of the A–4 did not occur at Peenemünde until October 3, 1942. Despite this success, failed launches continued to plague the project, and as a result the first fully operational V–2s were not fired until September 1944. Between then and the end of the war, approximately 6,000 rockets were manufactured at an underground production site named *Mittelwerk,* using the slave labor of concentration camp inmates and prisoners of war. Although several thousand V–2s struck London, Antwerp, and other allied targets, they were not strategically significant in the German war effort. Their importance lies in the technological advances they brought to the development of rocketry.

This fact and von Braun's later importance in the American spaceflight effort often overshadows the issue of his ethical responsibility for the suffering and loss of life associated with the V–2. Although the youthful, blond, blue-eyed, von Braun always gave credit to his whole team for the technical success of this and other programs, he clearly played a key role in the development of the missile. Thoroughly familiar with its technical details, he also had a remarkable ability to express ideas clearly, to resolve problems, and to promote a sense of belonging to and functioning as a team. He and his army superior, General Walter Dornberger, were also notably successful in obtaining funding and other support for the V–2. While he had no direct responsibility for production at *Mittelwerk,* von Braun was aware of conditions in the concentration camp that provided the factory's labor. Moreover, he had joined the Nazi party on May 1, 1937, and became an officer in the elite SS on May 1, 1940. (The SS started as Hitler's bodyguards, but under Heinrich Himmler it came to control military police activities, Nazi intelligence, and the administration and maintenance of the death camps.) While more research is needed on this subject, available American records support his claim that he had joined both organizations only because failure to do so would have forced him to abandon his work on rocketry. He further stated that his motivation in building army missiles was their ultimate use in space travel and scientific endeavors and that his own arrest by Nazis in 1944 resulted from this concern for the future, and lack of interest in the immediate uses of the V–2. Underneath the ethical and moral issues, it is clear that von Braun was a remarkable individual with a wide range of accomplishments beyond his role as a space pioneer. A musician who played the piano and cello, he loved the music of Mozart, Chopin, and Puccini. At the same time, he was an ardent outdoorsman who enjoyed scuba diving, fishing, hunting, sailing, piloting an airplane, and sail planing.

Is Brought to America

As the war drew to a close in Europe in the early months of 1945, von Braun organized the move of hundreds of his staff from Peenemünde to Bavaria so they could surrender to the Americans rather than the Soviets. Subsequently, about 120 of them went to Fort Bliss near El Paso, Texas, as part of a military operation called Project Paperclip (under the auspices of which the United States military employed and protected numerous Nazi scientists and intelligence agents). They worked on rocket development and employed captured V–2s for high altitude research at the nearby White Sands Proving Ground in New Mexico. In the midst of these efforts, von Braun returned to Germany to marry his second cousin, Maria Louise von Quistorp, on March 1, 1947, returning with her to Texas after the wedding. In 1950, the von Braun team transferred to the Redstone Arsenal near Huntsville, Alabama, where between April 1950 and February 1956 it developed the Redstone medium-range ballistic missile under his technical direction. Deployed in 1958, the Redstone was basically an offshoot of the V–2 but featured several modifications including an improved inertial guidance system. The Redstone also served as a launch vehicle, placing Alan B. Shephard and Virgil I. "Gus" Grissom in suborbital flight in May and July 1961, respectively. Meanwhile, in February 1956 von Braun became the director of the development operations division of the newly established Army Ballistic Missile Agency (ABMA) in Huntsville. While located there, he and his wife raised three children—Iris Careen (born in 1948), Margrit Cecile (1952), and Peter Constantine (1960)—and von Braun himself became a U.S. citizen on April 14, 1955.

The next missile designed by von Braun and his team was the Jupiter intermediate range ballistic missile. Unlike the Redstone and the V–2, which used liquid oxygen and an alcohol-water mixture as propellants, the Jupiter employed liquid oxygen and kerosene. Following development, it was assigned to the air force for deployment after 1958. In the meantime, von Braun's engineers had developed the Jupiter C, which consisted of three parts or "stages." Its first stage was a modified Redstone missile, while the second and third stages were derived from the Sergeant missile, initially developed by the Jet Propulsion Laboratory. In its third launch, on August 8, 1957, the Jupiter C carried a nose cone that became the first man-made object to be recovered from outer space. It also proved the feasibility of a new technique to carry off the excessive heat produced by friction upon the nose cone of a missile or spacecraft during reentry into the atmosphere. In addition, the von Braun team developed the Pershing—a two-stage, solid-fuel ballistic missile that had its first test launch in February 1960. Another group of rockets developed under von Braun was the Juno series. Juno I, a four-stage version of Jupiter C, launched America's first satellite, Explorer I, on January 31, 1958. Juno II, using the Jupiter missile as its first stage and Jupiter C upper stages, launched a number of satellites in the Pioneer and Explorer series, including Pioneer IV that went past the moon and entered solar orbit following launch on March 3, 1959.

Transfers to NASA

Undoubtedly the greatest claim to fame of von Braun and his team was the powerful Saturn family of rockets, which propelled Americans into lunar orbit and landed twelve of them on the moon between July 1969 and January 1971. Development of these launch vehicles began under ABMA and was completed during the decade after July 1, 1960, when von Braun and over four thousand ABMA personnel transferred to the National Aeronautics and Space Administration (NASA), forming the George C. Marshall Space Flight Center, which von Braun directed until February 1970. The Saturn I and Ib were developmental rockets leading to the massive Saturn V that actually launched the astronauts of the Apollo program. Propelled by

liquid oxygen and kerosene in its first stage, and liquid oxygen and liquid hydrogen for the two upper stages, the Saturn V stood 363 feet high, six stories above the level of the Statue of Liberty. Its first stage constituted the largest aluminum cylinder ever produced; its valves were as large as barrels, its fuel pumps larger than refrigerators.

As von Braun repeatedly insisted, he and his team were not alone responsible for the success of the Saturn and Apollo programs. In fact, the engineers at Marshall often urged more conservative solutions to problems occurring in both programs than NASA ultimately adopted. To von Braun's credit, he invariably accepted and supported the more radical approaches once he was convinced they were right. One example involved the debate over all-up versus step-by-step testing of Saturn V. Having experienced numerous rocket system failures going back to the V–2 and beyond, the German engineers favored testing each stage of the complicated rocket. At NASA headquarters, however, administrator George Mueller preferred the air force approach, which relied much more heavily on ground testing. He therefore insisted upon testing Saturn V all at once in order to meet President John F. Kennedy's ambitious goal of landing an American on the moon before the end of the decade. Ever cautious, von Braun hesitated but finally concurred in the ultimately successful procedure.

Beyond his role as an engineer, scientist, and project manager, von Braun was also an important advocate for spaceflight, publishing numerous books and magazine articles, serving as a consultant for television programs and films, as well as testifying before Congress. Perhaps most important in this regard were his contributions, with others, to a series of *Collier's* articles from 1952 to 1953 and to a Walt Disney television series produced by Ward Kimball from 1955 to 1957. Both series were enormously influential and, along with the fears aroused by the Soviet space program, galvanized American efforts to conquer space. As von Braun said to Kimball in late 1968 after the Apollo 8 orbit of the moon: "Well, Ward, it looks like they're following our script."

In March 1970, NASA transferred von Braun to its headquarters in Washington, D.C., where he became deputy associate administrator. He had hoped to renew interest in the space program, but a much smaller NASA budget, as he said, "reduced my function in Washington eventually to one of describing programs which I knew could not be funded for the next 10 years anyway." Consequently, he resigned from the agency effective July 1, 1972, to become vice president for engineering and development with Fairchild Industries of Germantown, Maryland. Besides his work for that aerospace firm, he continued his efforts to promote human spaceflight, helping to found the National Space Institute in 1975 and serving as its first president. On June 16, 1977, he died of cancer at a hospital in Alexandria, Virginia.

SELECTED WRITINGS BY VON BRAUN:

Books

Across the Space Frontier, with J. Kaplan and others, Viking Press, 1952.
Man on the Moon, Sidgwick and Jackson, 1953.
The Mars Project, University of Illinois Press, 1953.
Exploration of Mars, with Willy Ley, Viking Press, 1956.
The History of Rocket Technology, The Redstone, Jupiter, and Juno, Eugene M. Emme, editor, Wayne State University Press, 1964, pp. 107–121.
History of Rocketry and Space Travel, with F. I. Ordway III, Crowell, 1966.

Periodicals

Colliers, Man on the Moon—The Journey, October 18, 1952, pp. 52–60.
Colliers, Baby Space Station, with Cornelius Ryan, June 27, 1953, pp. 33–40.
Colliers, Can We Get to Mars?, with Cornelius Ryan, April 30, 1954, pp. 22-28.

FURTHER READING:

Books

Bergaust, Erik, *Wernher von Braun,* National Space Institute, 1976.
Bilstein, Roger E., *Stages to Saturn: A Technological History of the Apollo/Saturn Launch Vehicles,* NASA SP–4206, 1980.
Hunt, Linda, *Secret Agenda: The United States Government, Nazi Scientists, and Project Paperclip, 1945 to 1990,* St. Martin's Press, 1991.
Huzel, Dieter K., *Peenemünde to Canaveral,* Prentice-Hall, Inc., 1962.
Kennedy, Gregory P., *Vengeance Weapon 2: The V–2 Guided Missile,* Smithsonian Institution Press, 1983.
Neufeld, Michael J., *Science, Technology and National Socialism,* The Guided Missile and the Third Reich: Peenemünde and the Forging of a Technological Revolution, Monika Renneberg and Mark Walker, editors, Cambridge University Press, 1993.
Stuhlinger, Ernst and Frederick I. Ordway III, *Wernher von Braun: Crusader for Space,* Volume I, A Biographical Memoir, Krieger, 1994.

Periodicals

Biddle, Wayne, *New York Times,* Science, Morality and the V–2, October 2, 1992, p. A31.
Hutchins, Timothy, *Washington Star,* Space Hero Von Braun Dead at 65, June 17, 1977, pp. 9–10.
Wilford, John Noble, *New York Times,* Wernher von Braun, Space Pioneer, Dies, June 18, 1977, pp. 16–18.

Other

Agent Report on Von Braun, Wernher Magnus Maximilian, prepared by Milton F. Gidge, 10 April 1953, available in, *Wernher von Braun,* biographical files, NASA Historical Reference Collection, Washington, D.C.
Agent Report on Von Braun, Wernher Magnus Maximilian, prepared by Milton F. Gidge, 10 April 1953, available in, *Wernher von Braun,* Letter, Thomas J. Ford, Colonel, GSC, Director, to Commanding General, United States Forces, European Theater, Attention: G–2, subject: Request for Information on German Scientist [Wernher von Braun], 3 March 1947, available in biographical files, NASA Historical Reference Collection, Washington, D.C.
Agent Report on Von Braun, Wernher Magnus Maximilian, prepared by Milton F. Gidge, 10 April 1953, available in, *Wernher von Braun,* National Aeronautics and Space Administration Biographical Data, Dr. Wernher von Braun, February 1971.

Sketch by J. D. Hunley

Theodore von Kármán
1881–1963
Hungarian aerodynamicist

Often referred to as "the father of aerodynamics," Theodore von Kármán's studies of aerodynamics resulted in a number of important and fundamental discoveries, including the existence of Kármán vortex streets, a characteristic flow of air that has passed over a cylindrical surface. These discoveries had significant applications in the design of aircraft frames, bridges, and other structures subject to winds and other types of air flow. Von Kármán, who lived both in Europe and the United States, was very active in developing the practical applications of his scientific discoveries. Equally interested in dealing with the political implications of these discoveries, he served as consultant and advisor to a number of private corporations and governmental agencies. Von Kármán died in Germany in 1963.

Theodore von Kármán was born in Budapest, Hungary, on May 11, 1881. His father was Moritz von Kármán, founder of the modern Hungarian system of secondary education and professor of education at the University of Budapest. His mother was the former Helen Konn, a member of a distinguished Bohemian-Jewish family that included many teachers and rabbis. For his secondary education, von Kármán attended the Minta Gymnázium in

Budapest, a demonstration school established by his father. He showed an interest in mathematics and science at an early age and decided to major in mechanical engineering at the Technical University of Budapest, where he was awarded an engineering degree with high honors in 1902. After serving a year of compulsory military service, von Kármán returned to the university as an assistant professor of hydraulics. He also began his long consulting career while working with the manufacturing firm of Granz and Company.

Becomes Interested in Aerodynamics

In 1906, von Kármán was awarded a two-year fellowship by the Hungarian Academy of Sciences. He chose to use the fellowship at the University of Göttingen, then home to a number of first-rate scholars in science. Among these was the German physicist **Ludwig Prandtl**, who would later carry out many of the earliest fundamental experiments in the field of aerodynamics. Von Kármán's own research at Göttingen, however, was directed toward other topics. His doctoral thesis dealt with the stability of structures under various conditions of stress. He also worked with his friend, a German physicist named **Max Born**, on problems concerning the theory of specific heats.

Eventually, von Kármán increasingly concentrated on aerodynamics and, in 1911, he made the discovery for which he is most famous. It had been known that air, or fluid, moving over a cylindrical surface, creates a particular pattern of vortices in its wake. In considering that flow, von Kármán was the first to use a mathematical approach to understanding the distribution of vortices in an alternating double row, now recognized as a Kármán vortex street. Under certain conditions, a Kármán vortex street can have disastrous consequences for the object with which it is associated. The collapse of the Tacoma Narrows bridge in 1940, for example, was later found to have resulted from the formation of Kármán vortices, when winds reached a velocity of forty-two miles per hour over the bridge.

In 1912 von Kármán left Göttingen to become professor of the theory of machines at the College of Mining Engineering in Selmecbánya, Hungary. However, that same year he was offered an opportunity to organize the new Aeronautical Institute at the Technical University of Aachen. He accepted the offer and became professor of aerodynamics and mechanics as well as director of the new institute. Von Kármán retained his affiliation with Aachen until 1930, interrupted briefly by a leave of absence during the first world war.

Turns to Issues of Aircraft Design

During World War I, von Kármán was assigned work on the design of aircraft parts for the newly created Austro-Hungarian air force. That experience apparently solidified his interest in airfoil design that had been aroused some years earlier. His military tasks included finding a solution for the problem of synchronizing machine gun fire with rapid propeller rotation and designing improvements in helicopter design. After the war, von Kármán returned to Aachen and the task of building up the aeronautical institute there. He also became active as a consultant to various aircraft manufacturers, including the Junkers Aeroplane Works and Luftschiffbau Zepplin in Germany, Handley-Paige Limited in England, and Kawanishi Aircraft Company in Japan.

Von Kármán's first visit to the United Sates came in 1926, when he was asked to consult on the design of the recently endowed Guggenheim Aeronautical Laboratory and its accompanying wind tunnel at the California Institute of Technology (Cal Tech). He made a strong impression on **Robert A. Millikan**, then president of Cal Tech, and was eventually persuaded to leave Aachen for a permanent position as director of the Guggenheim Laboratory. He retained an affiliation with Cal Tech until 1949, although that connection became increasingly tenuous in the latter years.

Von Kármán exerted a powerful influence on the science of aerodynamics at the Guggenheim Laboratory because of the many specialists he helped to train. His establishment of the Jet Propulsion Laboratory at Cal Tech, which he directed from 1938 to 1945, would also prove critical in the development of future U.S. space programs. However, as von Kármán became increasingly involved with the military applications of aerodynamic research, he gradually withdrew from Cal Tech. In 1938 he became consultant to the U.S. Army Ballistic Research Laboratory, and in the following year he was appointed as a consultant to the U.S. Army Air Corps. After the war, he became even more involved in a number of governmental activities with the objective of garnering scientific cooperation on an international level. He conceived of an aeronautical collaboration between European scientists through the North Atlantic Treaty Organization (NATO) Advisory Group for Aeronautical Research and Development, for which he served as chair from its conception in 1952 until his death a decade later.

Von Kármán also expanded his activities into the private sector. Disappointed by the lack of willingness among established industries to explore the potential applications of rockets, von Kármán was instrumental in the formation of the Aerojet Engineering Corporation in 1942. Aerojet was later reorganized as Aerojet-General Corporation, a subsidiary of General Tire and Rubber Company. In *Biographical Memoirs of Fellows of the Royal Society,* S. Goldstein points out that, by 1951, von Kármán's many government-related activities had caused him to establish his "main headquarters" in Washington, D.C., although he maintained a residence in Pasadena until his death. Von Kármán never married, but lived most of his life with his mother, and his sister, Josephine. Among the many awards and honorary doctorates he received were the U.S. Medal for Merit in 1946, the Franklin Gold Medal of the Franklin Institute in 1948, and the National Medal of Science in 1963. Von Kármán died on May 7, 1963, in Aachen, while on a projected four-month visit to Europe in connection with the NATO advisory group.

SELECTED WRITINGS BY VON KÁRMÁN:

Books

Mathematical Methods in Engineering, McGraw-Hill, 1940.

Aerodynamics: Selected Topics in the Light of Their Historical Development, Cornell University Press, 1954.

Collected Works of Dr. Theodore von Kármán, Butterworths, 1956.

From Low-Speed Aerodynamics to Astronautics, Pergamon Press, 1961.

FURTHER READING:

Books

Biographical Memoirs, Volume 38, National Academy of Sciences, 1965.

Biographical Memoirs of Fellows of the Royal Society, Volume 12, Royal Society (London), 1966.

Sketch by David E. Newton

Klaus von Klitzing
1943–
German physicist

Klaus von Klitzing was awarded the 1985 Nobel Prize in physics for his discovery of the quantized Hall effect, a variation on an electrical phenomenon first observed by the American physicist Edwin Hall in about 1880. Von Klitzing's discovery has had a number of profound effects in both theoretical and practical fields of physics, exhibiting one of the first instances in which quantum effects had been observed on a macroscopic scale. In addition, it made possible the establishment of an entirely new international standard for the ohm, the unit of measure of electrical resistance.

Von Klitzing was born on June 28, 1943, in Schroda, Germany, close to the Polish border, to Bogislav von Klitzing, a forester, and Anny Ulbrich. As World War II turned against Germany, the von Klitzing family decided to stay ahead of the advancing Soviet army and moved westward to the town of Lutten. Three years later, in 1948, they moved again to Oldenburg and finally, in 1951, to the northern town of Essen. Von Klitzing eventually completed his secondary education at the Artland Gymnasium in Quakenbrück.

Begins His Studies of Semiconductors

In 1962, von Klitzing entered the Technical University of Braunschweig, intending to major in physics. He was awarded his baccalaureate degree in 1969 for a dissertation on the electrical properties of indium antimonide, a compound of two semiconducting elements, indium and antimony. Von Klitzing then moved to the University of Würzburg for his doctoral studies, planning to continue his work on semiconductors there. He also accepted a job at the University teaching physics to premedical students. At Würzburg, von Klitzing became particularly interested in the effects of strong magnetic fields on the conducting properties of semiconductors. In 1971, he published his first scientific paper on this topic, "Resonance Structure in the High Field Magnetoresistance of Tellurium," with G. Landwehr, one of his instructors, and was awarded his Ph.D. the following year for this line of research.

A key feature of von Klitzing's ongoing research was the need for stronger and stronger magnetic fields. He spent the 1975 academic year at Oxford University because of the powerful superconducting magnets being manufactured there and, in 1979, continued his research at the High-Field Magnet Laboratory of the Institute Max von Laue-Paul Langevin in Grenoble, France. It was at Grenoble that von Klitzing made the discovery that earned him the Nobel Prize.

Observes Quantization of the Hall Effect

The Hall effect is a three-dimensional phenomenon in which an electrical current is passed in one direction through a conducting material while a magnetic field is applied at right angles to the current. The accumulation of electrons along one edge of the conductor results in a potential difference along the face of the material that is called the Hall voltage. The Hall resistance, then, is the Hall voltage divided by the current in the conductor. Under these conditions, von Klitzing observed a totally unexpected effect. As the magnetic field on the sample was strengthened, the Hall resistance also increased as a linear function over a certain range, and then levelled off. Further increases in the magnetic field had no effect on the Hall resistance over another range, but then the Hall resistance began to increase again. After another period, the Hall resistance again levelled off. The final results of the experiment appear graphically as a series of steps. Under conventional experimental conditions, however, the Hall resistance is a continuous, linear function of the imposed magnetic field.

To analyze his contradictory findings, von Klitzing devised an experiment with a number of conditions. Most important was his use of a very thin sheet of silicon that constrained the movement of electrons to two dimensions rather than the three normally allowed. In addition, the experiment was carried out in a powerful magnetic field at temperatures close to absolute zero. In this manner, von Klitzing demonstrated that the Hall effect is quantized; changes in the external magnetic field only induce electrical changes in the silicon in certain steps and not continuously. Von Klitzing found that all the possible quantum steps had a value of a fundamental constant divided by an integer number. That constant, 25,813 ohms, is significant because it is the ratio of two fundamental constants of nature, the square of an electron's electrical charge and Planck's constant. In fact, an effect of this type had been foreseen in 1975 by three Japanese theoretical physicists, T. Ando, Y. Matsumoto, and Y. Uemura. The theory did not predict, however, the high degree of precision that von Klitzing had found.

Von Klitzing's discovery is a significant one for physics. It is one of the few instances in which quantum effects have been observed directly in the laboratory; such effects are normally important only at the level of individual particles such as the electron or atom. In addition, the high precision of von Klitzing's results means that a new and more exact standard for the ohm, the unit of electrical resistance, may be possible.

In 1971, von Klitzing married Renate Falkenberg, with whom he had two sons and a daughter. In addition to the Nobel Prize, von Klitzing was awarded the Walter-Schottley Prize of the German Physical Society in 1981 and the Hewlett Packard Prize of the European Physical Society in 1982.

SELECTED WRITINGS BY VON KLITZING:

Periodicals

Solid State Communications, Resonance Structure in the High Field Magnetoresistance of Tellurium, Volume 9, 1971, pp. 1251–54.
Physical Review Letters, New Method for High-Accuracy Determination of the Fine-Structure Constant Based on Quantized Hall Effect, Volume 45, 1990, p. 494.

FURTHER READING:

Books

Nobel Prize Winners, H. W. Wilson, 1987, pp. 558–60.

Periodicals

Halperin, Bertrand I., *Science,* The 1985 Nobel Prize for Physics, February 21, 1986, pp. 820–22.
Halperin, Bertrand I., *Scientific American,* 1985 Nobel Prize Winners: Physics, December 1985, pp. 75–76.

Schwarzschild, Bertram, *Physics Today,* Von Klitzing Wins Nobel Physics Prize for Quantized Hall Effect, December 1985, pp. 17–20.

Sketch by David E. Newton

Richard von Mises
1883–1953
American mathematician and aerodynamicist

Richard von Mises was an aerodynamicist and applied mathematician who made significant contributions to the theory of probability and statistics. A student of logical positivism, he believed in solving problems through rational reasoning. Although his mathematical theories have been widely explored, they have not been universally accepted.

Richard Martin Edler von Mises was born on April 19, 1883, in Lemberg, Austria (now Lvov, Ukraine). His father, Arthur Edler von Mises, was an engineer with the Austrian railway system, who held a doctorate of technical sciences. His mother, Adele Landau von Mises, hailed from a family of literary scholars. He had a younger brother who died in infancy, and an older brother, Ludwig, who became an economist. Although his family was Jewish, von Mises converted to Catholicism as a young man.

Except for occasional temporary relocations for his father's work assignments (including an 1883 stay in Lemberg), von Mises lived in Vienna. During his teenage years, he studied the classics and the humanities at Vienna's Akademische Gymnasium, graduating with distinction in Latin and mathematics in 1901. Shortly thereafter, von Mises entered the Vienna Technical University, where he studied mechanical engineering and published his first mathematical paper. Following graduation, von Mises enrolled in the German Technical University in Brünn at the beginning of 1906, working part time in a factory while completing his doctoral dissertation. He received his doctorate from the University of Vienna in 1907 and lectured the following year at Brünn. In 1909 von Mises took the post of professor of applied mathematics at the University of Strassburg in Germany (now Strasbourg, France).

Shaped the Development of Flight Mechanics

Von Mises began his career investigating fluid mechanics. Dramatic advances in heavier-than-air flying machines drew his attention to aerodynamics and aeronautics. After learning to fly, he taught a summer class in 1913 that apparently was the first university course in the mechanics of powered flight. His own contributions to the field included improvements in boundary layer flow theory and refinements in airfoil design, and he also worked on problems of elasticity, plasticity, and turbulence.

When World War I began in 1914, von Mises returned to his homeland to volunteer for military service, becoming an officer in the new Flying Corps of the Austro-Hungarian Army. He was first given a field assignment, but later assigned to teach at the Fliegerarsenal in Aspern. While there he led a team that devised, built, and tested a 600-horsepower military airplane featuring a new wing profile of his own design. His booklet on flight, published in Vienna in 1916, formed the basis of his work *Theory of Flight,* which von Mises published with English colleagues in 1945. At his own request, he returned to field duty in 1918.

After World War I ended, von Mises returned to Strassburg. The war had cost him his university position as well as much of his personal property. He moved to Germany and worked as a lecturer in mathematics at the University of Frankfurt. In 1919 von Mises took the position of full professor of mechanics at the Technical University in Dresden.

In 1920 von Mises became a professor of applied mathematics and director of the Institute for Applied Mathematics at the University of Berlin. He published nearly 150 technical works throughout his career and was particularly proud of having founded the journal *Zeitschrift für angewandte Mathematik und Mechanik* in 1921, serving as its editor for the first 12 years. While in Berlin, von Mises met **Hilda Geiringer**, a student from Vienna. She became his assistant, then his collaborator, and eventually his wife. After his death, she edited and completed several of his unfinished manuscripts.

Formalized the Frequency Theory of Probability

Von Mises explored topics ranging from the philosophy of science to practical computational techniques, viewing applied mathematics as the crucial link between theory and scientific observation. He saw the field of statistics as fundamentally important: repetitions of an experiment yield a set of different measurements, which must be analyzed to obtain a single result for comparison with theoretical predictions. Statistics, in turn, are intimately related to probability, especially as von Mises developed the concept.

Recognizing that the existing theory of probability was vague and nonrigorous, von Mises developed a formal, axiomatic treatment of the subject. Pierre-Simon Laplace's original definition of the probability of an event, formulated in 1820, held that the ratio of the number of favorable outcomes to the number of possible outcomes, assuming each outcome to be equally likely. This worked adequately for artificial applications such as games of chance, but failed when applied to naturally occurring events (such as expressing the probability of rain on a given day). Half a century later, John Venn and others proposed defining the probability of an event as the relative frequency with which the event would actually occur "in the long run" (i.e., after

an unlimited number of trials). This approach seemed promising, but it was not developed with sufficient precision to validate it.

In 1919 von Mises proposed two axioms which probability must satisfy. His axiom of convergence states that as a sequence of trials is extended, the proportion of favorable outcomes tends toward a definite mathematical limit; such a limit must exist in order to define the probability of an event as the long-term relative frequency of its occurrence. The axiom of randomness was von Mises' most important new concept. It states that the limiting value of the relative frequency must be the same for all possible infinite subsequences of trials chosen solely by a rule of place selection within the sequence (i.e., the outcomes must be randomly distributed among the trials).

With probability clearly defined as a relative frequency, statistics comprises the system of strategies and tools for designing and evaluating experiments to determine the probability of a specific event. Von Mises' 1928 book, *Probability, Statistics and Truth,* offers an interesting explanation of the subject for the lay reader.

Various mathematicians have identified inconsistencies in von Mises' treatment of probability, which implies that the observation of any finite number of trials is insufficient to determine the probability of an event. Nonetheless, von Mises' contributions have significantly affected the development of modern theories of probability and its relationship to statistics.

When Adolph Hitler became chancellor of Germany in 1933, von Mises moved to Turkey and taught at the University of Istanbul. In 1939 he left for the United States and joined the faculty at Harvard University in Boston.

Throughout his life, von Mises was a scholar with wide-ranging interests. He studied German literature and published eight articles and books on Rainer Rilke's life and poetry; he amassed the largest privately owned collection of Rilke's works, which is now housed at Harvard University. Von Mises even developed a hobby of bookbinding during his years in Berlin. Besides German, he was also fluent in several other languages, including Turkish and English. During a 1951–52 leave of absence from Harvard to lecture on statistics in Rome, he looked forward to teaching in Italian and was reportedly disappointed at being asked to use French instead. In 1944 von Mises was named Gordon McKay Professor of Aerodynamics and Applied Mathematics at Harvard, a position he filled until his death from cancer on July 14, 1953.

SELECTED WRITINGS BY VON MISES:

Books

Selected Papers of Richard von Mises, two volumes, American Mathematical Society, 1963.
Positivism: A Study in Human Understanding, Dover, 1968.

Probability, Statistics, and Truth, Dover, 1981.

FURTHER READING:

Books

Abbott, David, editor, *The Biographical Dictionary of Scientists: Mathematicians,* Blond Educational, 1985, pp. 130–131.

Gillispie, Charles Coulston, editor, *Dictionary of Scientific Biography,* Volume IX, Charles Scribner's Sons, 1974, pp. 419–420.

Magill, Frank N., editor, *Great Events from History II,* Volume 2, 1991, pp. 664–668.

Sketch by Loretta Hall

John von Neumann

John von Neumann
1903–1957
American mathematician

John von Neumann, considered one of the most creative mathematicians of the twentieth century, made important contributions to quantum physics, game theory, economics, meteorology, the development of the atomic bomb, and computer design. He was known for his problem-solving ability, his encyclopedic memory, and his ability to reduce complex problems to a mathematically tractable form. Von Neumann served as a consultant to the United States government on scientific and military matters, and was a member of the Atomic Energy Commission. According to mathematician Peter D. Lax, von Neumann combined extreme quickness, very broad interests, and a fearsome technical prowess; the popular saying was, "Most mathematicians prove what they can; von Neumann proves what he wants." The Nobel Laureate physicist **Hans Albrecht Bethe** said, "I have sometimes wondered whether a brain like von Neumann's does not indicate a species superior to that of man."

Max and Margaret von Neumann's son Janos was born in Budapest, Hungary, on December 28, 1903. As a child he was called Jancsi, which later became Johnny in the United States. His father was a prosperous banker. Von Neumann was tutored at home until age ten, when he was enrolled in the Lutheran Gymnasium for boys. His early interests included literature, music, science, and psychology. His teachers recognized his talent in mathematics and arranged for him to be tutored by a young mathematician at the University of Budapest, Michael Fekete. Von Neumann and Fekete wrote a mathematical paper which was published in 1921.

Von Neumann entered the University of Budapest in 1921 to study mathematics; he also studied chemical engineering at the Eidgenössische Technische Hochschule in Zurich, receiving a diploma in 1925. In those same years, he spent much of his time in Berlin, where he was influenced by eminent scientists and mathematicians. In 1926 he received a Ph.D. in mathematics from the University of Budapest, with a doctoral thesis in set theory. He was named *Privatdozent* at the University of Berlin (a position comparable to that of assistant professor in an American university), reportedly the youngest person to hold the position in the history of the university. In 1926 he also received a Rockefeller grant for postdoctoral work under mathematician **David Hilbert** at the University of Göttingen. In 1929 he transferred to the University of Hamburg. By this time, he had become known to mathematicians through his publications in set theory, algebra, and quantum theory, and was regarded as a young genius.

Extends Theory in Pure Mathematics and Quantum Physics

In his early career, von Neumann focused on two research areas: first, set theory and the logical foundations of mathematics; and second, Hilbert space theory, operator theory, and the mathematical foundations of quantum mechanics. During the 1920s, von Neumann published seven papers on mathematical logic. He formulated a rigorous definition of ordinal numbers and presented a new system of axioms for set theory. With Hilbert, he worked on a formalist approach to the foundations of mathematics, attempting to prove the consistency of arithmetic. In about 300 B.C., Euclid's *Elements of Geometry* had proved mathematical theorems using a limited number of axioms. Between 1910 and 1913, **Bertrand Russell** and **Alfred North Whitehead** had published *Principia Mathematica,* which showed that much of the newer math could similarly be derived from a few axioms. With Hilbert, von Neumann worked to carry this approach further, although in 1931 **Kurt Gödel** proved that no formal system could be both complete and consistent.

Hilbert was interested in the axiomatic foundations of modern physics, and he gave a seminar on the subject at Göttingen. The two approaches to quantum mechanics—the wave theory of **Erwin Schrödinger** and the particle theory of **Werner Karl Heisenberg**—had not been successfully reconciled. Working with Hilbert, von Neumann developed a finite set of axioms that satisfied both the Heisenberg and Schrödinger approaches. Von Neumann's axiomatization represented an abstract unification of the wave and particle theories.

During this period, some physicists believed that the probabilistic character of measurements in quantum theory was due to parameters that were not yet clearly understood and that further investigation could result in a deterministic quantum theory. However, von Neumann successfully argued that the indeterminism was inherent and arose from the interaction between the observer and the observed.

In 1929 von Neumann was invited to teach at Princeton University in New Jersey. He accepted the offer and taught mathematics classes from 1930 until 1933, when he joined the elite research group at the newly established Princeton Institute for Advanced Study. The atmosphere at Princeton was informal yet intense. According to mathematician Stanislaw Ulam, writing in the *Bulletin of the American Mathematical Society,* the group "quite possibly constituted one of the greatest concentrations of brains in mathematics and physics at any time and place." During the 1930s von Neumann developed algebraic theories derived from his research into quantum mechanics. These theories were later known as von Neumann algebras. He also conducted research into Hilbert space, ergodic theory, Haar measure, and noncommutative algebras. In 1932 he published a book on quantum physics, *The Mathematical Foundations of Quantum Mechanics,* which remains a standard text on the subject. After becoming a naturalized citizen of the United States, von Neumann became a consultant to the Ballistics Research Laboratory of the Army Ordnance Department in 1937. After the attack on Pearl Harbor in 1941, he became more involved in defense research, serving as a consultant to the National Defense Research Council on the theory of detonation of explosives, and with the Navy Bureau of Ordnance on mine warfare and countermeasures to it. In 1943 he became a consultant on the development of the atomic bomb at the Los Alamos Scientific Laboratory in New Mexico.

Develops Design for Stored-Program Computer

At Los Alamos, von Neumann persuaded **J. Robert Oppenheimer** to pursue the possibility of using an implosion technique to detonate the atomic bomb. This technique was later used to detonate the bomb dropped on Nagasaki. Simulation of the technique at the Los Alamos lab required extensive numerical calculations which were performed by a staff of twenty people using desk calculators. Hoping to speed up the work, von Neumann investigated using computers for the calculations and studied the design and programming of IBM punch-card machines. In 1943 the army sponsored work at the Moore School of Engineering at the University of Pennsylvania, under the direction of **John William Mauchly** and **J. Presper Eckert**, on a giant calculator for computing firing tables for guns. The machine, called ENIAC (Electronic Numerical Integrator and Computer), was brought to von Neumann's attention in 1944. He joined Mauchly and Eckert in planning an improved machine, EDVAC (Electronic Discrete Variable Automatic Computer). Von Neumann's 1945 report on the EDVAC presented the first written description of the stored-program concept, which makes it possible to load a computer program into computer memory from disk so that the computer can run the program without requiring manual reprogramming. All modern computers are based on this design.

Von Neumann's design for a computer for scientific research, built at the Princeton Institute for Advanced Study between 1946 and 1951, served as the model for virtually all subsequent computer applications. Those built at Los Alamos, the RAND Corporation, the University of Illinois, and the IBM Corporation all incorporated, besides the stored program, the separate components of arithmetic function, central control (now commonly referred to as the central processing unit or CPU), random-access memory (or RAM) as represented by the hard drive, and the input and output devices operating in serial or parallel mode. These elements, present in virtually all personal and mainframe computers, were all pioneered under von Neumann's auspices.

In addition, von Neumann investigated the field of neurology, looking for ways for computers to imitate the operations of the human brain. In 1946 he became interested in the challenges of weather forecasting by computer; his meteorology project at Princeton succeeded in predicting the development of new storms. Because of his role in early computer design and programming techniques, von Neumann is considered one of the founders of the computer age.

Formulates Game Theory and Its Application to Economics

While in Germany, von Neumann had analyzed strategies in the game of poker and wrote a paper presenting a mathematical model for games of strategy. He continued his work in this area while he was at Princeton, particularly considering applications of game theory to economics.

When the Austrian economist Oskar Morgenstern came to Princeton, he and von Neumann started collaborating on applications of game theory to economic problems, such as the exchange of goods between parties, monopolies and oligopolies, and free trade. Their ambitious 641-page book, *Theory of Games and Economic Behavior,* was published in 1944. Von Neumann's work opened new channels of communication between mathematics and the social sciences.

Von Neumann and Morgenstern argued that the mathematics as developed for the physical sciences was inadequate for economics, since economics seeks to describe systems based not on immutable natural laws but on human action involving choice. Von Neumann proposed a different mathematical model to analyze strategies, taking into account the interdependent choices of "players." Game theory is based on an analogy between games and any complex decision-making process, and assumes that all participants act rationally to maximize the outcome of the "game" for themselves. It also assumes that participants are able to rank-order possible outcomes without error. Von Neumann's analysis enables players to calculate the consequences or probable outcomes of any given choice. It then becomes possible to opt for those strategies that have the highest probability of leading to a positive outcome. Game theory can be applied not only to economics and other social sciences but to politics, business organization, and military strategy, to mention only a few areas of its usefulness.

Serves as Advisor to Government and Military

After the war, von Neumann served as a scientific consultant for government policy committees and agencies such as the CIA and National Security Agency. He advised the RAND Corporation on its research on game theory and its military applications, and provided technical advice to companies such as IBM and Standard Oil. Following the detonation of an atomic bomb by the Soviets in 1949, von Neumann contributed to the development of the hydrogen bomb. He believed that a strong military capacity was more effective than a disarmament agreement. As chairman of the nuclear weapons panel of the air force scientific advisory board (known as the von Neumann committee), his recommendations led to the development of intercontinental missiles and submarine-launched missiles. Herbert York, the director of the Livermore Laboratory, said, "He was very powerful and productive in pure science and mathematics and at the same time had a remarkably strong streak of practicality [which] gave him a credibility with military officers, engineers, industrialists, and scientists that nobody else could match."

In 1954 President Eisenhower appointed von Neumann to the Atomic Energy Commission. Von Neumann was hopeful that nuclear fusion technologies would provide cheap and plentiful energy. According to the chairman of the commission, Admiral Lewis Strauss, "He had the invaluable faculty of being able to take the most difficult problem, separate it into its components, whereupon every-

thing looked brilliantly simple, and all of us wondered why we had not been able to see through to the answer as clearly as it was possible for him to do." He received the Enrico Fermi Science Award in 1956, and in that same year the Medal of Freedom from President Eisenhower.

Von Neumann has been described as a genius, a practical joker, and a raconteur. Laura Fermi, wife of the associate director of the Los Alamos Laboratory, wrote that he was "one of the very few men about whom I have not heard a single critical remark. It is astonishing that so much equanimity and so much intelligence could be concentrated in a man of not extraordinary appearance."

Von Neumann married Mariette Kovesi, daughter of a Budapest physician, in 1929. Their daughter, Marina, was born in 1935. Mariette obtained a divorce in 1937. The following year, von Neumann married Klara Dan, from an affluent Budapest family. In 1955, von Neumann was diagnosed with bone cancer. Confined to a wheelchair, he continued to attend Atomic Energy Commission meetings and to work on his many projects. He died in 1957 at the age of fifty-three.

SELECTED WRITINGS BY VON NEUMANN:

Books

Mathematische Grundlagen der Quanton-mechanik, (title means "Mathematical Foundations of Quantum Mechanics.") [Berlin], 1932.
The Theory of Games and Economic Behavior, Princeton University Press, 1944.
The Collected Works of John von Neumann, edited by A. H. Traub, Macmillan, 1963.

FURTHER READING:

Books

Aspray, William, *John von Neumann and the Origins of Modern Computing,* MIT Press, 1990.
Glimm, James, John Impagliazzo, and Isadore Singer, editors, *The Legacy of John von Neumann: Proceedings of Symposia in Pure Mathematics,* Volume 50, American Mathematical Society, 1990.
Heims, Steve J., *John von Neumann and Norbert Wiener: From Mathematics to the Technologies of Life and Death,* MIT Press, 1980.
Macrae, Norman, *John von Neumann,* Pantheon, 1992.
Poundstone, William, *Prisoner's Dilemma,* Doubleday, 1992.

Periodicals

Ulam, Stanislaw, *Bulletin of the American Mathematical Society,* John von Neumann, May, 1958, pp. 1–49.

Sketch by C. D. Lord

Joan George Erardus Gijsbert Voûte
1879–1963
Dutch astronomer

I n spite of an unorthodox career, Joan George Erardus Gijsbert Voûte became a significant figure in mid-twentieth-century astronomy as a result of his observations at Bosscha Observatory on Java, Indonesia. Over a period of almost thirty years, Voûte identified and described 11,000 binary star systems.

Voûte was born at Madioen (Java, Indonesia) in 1879, the eldest child of Dutch colonists Christoffel Voûte, who was descended from Huguenot exiles, and Maria Antoinnetta de Dieu Stierling. Joan Voûte and his brothers were educated in the Netherlands. Voûte attended a *gymnasium* (a classical secondary school with a curriculum centered on Greek and Latin) in Amsterdam, where he lived with his Welsh grandmother. Upon graduation, he enrolled in the Delft Institute of Technology, one of the finest engineering schools in Europe. He received a civil-engineering diploma from the school in 1908, at the rather late age of twenty-eight. By this time both his parents had died, leaving him a modest inheritance.

Fascinated by astronomy, Voûte worked at the Leiden Observatory for two years without salary, from 1908 to 1910, when he was named to the post of "third observer." It was normal for professional astronomers to work their way up from the bottom, and this lowest post in the observatory hierarchy could indeed lead into something more prestigious: the third observership had been created in 1896 for the talented astronomer and socialist Antonie Pannekoek, who eventually received an associate professorship at the University of Amsterdam; previously, in 1878, Jacobus Cornelius Kapteyn jumped from the post of "second observer" to a full professorship at the University of Groningen. Voûte remained third observer for five years. Financially independent, he was in no hurry to begin publishing or even take a doctorate at the university.

Voûte married Anna Lorch around 1908. With money from his in-laws, he purchased some astronomical equipment and set off for South Africa. There he carried out observations at the Royal Observatory of the Cape of Good Hope, a British institution that had long cooperated with Dutch astronomers—notably Kapteyn and **Willem Sitter**. While in South Africa, Voûte's personal life underwent major changes. He divorced, remarried, and divorced a second time. By 1918 he began a campaign to find a permanent astronomical position, either in Leiden or at the new Afrikaans-language University of Stellenbosch. In 1919, at the age of forty and with few accomplishments in the world of science, Voûte returned to his native land, accepting the position of temporary scientist at the Royal Magnetical and Meteorological Observatory in Batavia (now Jakarta)—the finest geophysical institution in Asia.

Directs Bosscha Observatory

He arrived at the moment when Indonesia's principal scientific philanthropist, Karel Albert Rudolf Bosscha, had endowed a magnificent institute of technology at Bandung on central Java. Bosscha and his first cousin Rudolf Albert Kerkhoven had long been interested in astronomy, and they then decided to erect the finest observatory in the Southern Hemisphere, creating a private association to finance the project. Voûte, with his heritage and family ties in the Dutch colony, became Bosscha's choice as the observatory's first director; his lack of a doctorate was no drawback for Bosscha, who himself had been forced to withdraw from the Delft Institute of Technology without taking a diploma.

By the middle 1920s, the new Bosscha observatory at Lembang, near Bandung on Java, had become the finest one in Dutch hands. The observatory's jewel was a 60-centimeter double photographical refractor, constructed by Zeiss in Jena, Germany, complemented by a 37-centimeter Schmidt telescope, constructed in Mittweida. Voûte, as director of the new observatory at Lembang, energetically resisted the attempts of physicists in the Netherlands to control his operation.

Voûte remarried in 1923 (to Frieda Johanna Gertrud Elsbeth Adloff), and he and his wife lived in a villa on the observatory grounds. They hosted a string of temporary observers, including Dutch astronomers P. G. Meesters, Pannekoek, and Egbertus A. Kreiken, German astronomer Paul Bruggencate, Russian astronomer Gleb Victor Simonow, and Swedish astronomer A angstrom ke Anders Edvard Wallenquist. Voûte's own observing program focused on binary star systems, which are systems of two stars that orbit around a common center of gravity. The binary stars play an important role in astronomy because their orbits reveal the nature of the gravitational field of each star. Knowledge of a star's gravitational field, in turn, makes it possible to deduce its mass. Eventually, astronomers were able to construct a theory of stellar evolution in part on the basis of stellar mass. Voûte found partners in his endeavors to identify double stars in the Jesuit astronomers at Riverview Observatory, located in a suburb of Sydney, Australia, and provided them with a telescope.

Voûte retired as director in 1939. In his place came Aernout de Sitter (son of astronomer **Willem Sitter**). With a war footing, however, research at the observatory slowed. De Sitter, his assistant Willem Christiaan Martin, and the observatory's mechanic A. J. Witlox, became prisoners of the Japanese in 1942; all three died in a labor camp. Voûte was permitted to return to the observatory under the Japanese administrator Misasi Miyadi. After Indonesian independence, Voûte retired to Amsterdam, where he died in 1963.

SELECTED WRITINGS BY VOÛTE:

Periodicals

Annalen, Description of the Observatory, Volume 1, part 1, 1933.

Journal des observateurs, Measures of Double Stars, War Series, Made at the Bosscha Observatory Lembang (Java), Volume 78, number 6, 1955, pp. 109–163.

FURTHER READING:

Books

Pannekoek, Antonie, *Herinneringen,* edited by B. A. Sijes, [Amsterdam], 1982, pp. 229–274.

Pyenson, Lewis, *Empire of Reason: Exact Sciences in Indonesia, 1840–1940,* E. J. Brill, 1989, pp. 45–82.

Periodicals

O'Connell, D. J. K., *Quarterly Journal of the Royal Astronomical Society,* Joan George Erardus Gijsbertus Voûte, Volume 5, 1964, pp. 296–297.

van der Bilt, J., *Hemel en Dampkring,* Het eerste decennium der Bosscha-Sterrenwacht, Volume 29, 1931, pp. 1–8.

van der Hucht, Karel, and C. L. M. Kerkhoven, *Zenit,* De Bosscha-Sterrenwacht: Van thee tot sterrenkunde, Volume 9, 1982, pp. 292–300.

Wallenquist, A. A. E., *Moesson,* Over het leven en werken op de Bosscha Sterrewacht bij Lembang: Een halve eeuw geleden, December 15, 1982, pp. 6–9.

Sketch by Lewis Pyenson

Hugo de Vries
1848–1935
Dutch botanist and geneticist

Hugo de Vries was a Dutch plant physiologist who developed a great interest in the infant disciplines of evolution and genetics around the turn of the twentieth century. He is best known for his rediscovery of the work of Gregor Mendel in plant genetics and for his own work on the theory of mutation, the changes in the genetic makeup of plants and animals that provide a mechanism for evolution. His research also laid the foundation to the discovery that the genes on chromosomes form the "blueprint" of a cell.

Hugo de Vries was born in Haarlem, the Netherlands, on February 16, 1848. His father, Gerrit de Vries, a lawyer and legislator, was also an expert on water management, and later the minister of justice in the cabinet of William III. De Vries' paternal grandfather was a minister and the librarian for the city of Haarlem as well as an expert on the history of printing. Hugo de Vries' mother, Maria Everardina Reuvens, also came from a scholarly family. Her father was the first professor of archaeology at the University of Leiden.

At a young age, de Vries began collecting varieties of plants to add to his herbarium. After the family moved to The Hague in 1862, de Vries went to Leiden on weekends for religion classes. There he met Willem Suringar, a professor of botany, who asked de Vries to classify plants for the Netherlands Botanical Society. By the time he entered the University of Leiden in 1866, de Vries was already quite an expert on the flora of the Netherlands.

Conducts Independent Research in Plant Physiology

During his university days, two new disciplines in the forefront of science held great interest for de Vries: plant physiology and evolution, the latter stemming from his reading of Charles Darwin's *Origin of Species.* Because of these interests, de Vries grew increasingly dissatisfied with his education at the university. Plant physiology was not taught at Leiden and his work on his dissertation was conducted in his own attic laboratory. His former mentor from Leiden, Suringar, was not open to the idea of evolution, and this caused a permanent rift between the two.

In 1870 de Vries left the Netherlands for Heidelberg and then Wurzburg in Germany, where he studied plant physiology under Julius von Sachs, a noted botanist and author. His work was primarily on the growth patterns in plants, including zones of growth in climbing plants, geotropism (the movement of plant roots toward the earth) and heliotropism (stem growth toward the sun). When de Vries returned to Amsterdam the next year to teach natural history, he continued to spend summers at Sachs's laboratory in Wurzburg. Upon a recommendation from Sachs, de Vries began work for the Prussian Ministry of Agriculture in 1875, writing monographs on important crops such as potatoes and sugar beets. During this time, he also became interested in osmosis in plant cells, which concerns the flow of fluid through the cell wall in order to balance the pressure inside and outside of the cell. By investigating this, he sought to find out how much of the growth of a cell was due to stretching of its cell wall. This involved calculating the amount of pressure caused by the fluid within the cell, or turgor pressure.

De Vries did further work on the stretching of cells in 1877 after which he received an appointment at the University of Hall. His teaching there was short-lived and after returning to Amsterdam in 1877, de Vries became the first instructor in plant physiology in the Netherlands. That summer he and another great mind of science, Charles Darwin, met when de Vries visited England.

For the next decade, de Vries taught while conducting experiments on plant plasmolysis, or the shrinking of the cytoplasm—the substance between the cell wall and the nuclear membrane—away from the cell wall due to the outward flow of water by osmosis. He did this by analyzing the pressure due to osmosis caused by different cell components and their concentrations. He came up with coefficients to determine the proportional contribution to the total pressure for each component in the fluid of a cell's protoplasm (the organic and inorganic substances within a cell and its nucleus), and also conjectured about the compounds that contribute to cell turgor and theorized about the function of minerals.

Reaches Breakthrough in Genetic Study with Mutation Theory

In the latter part of the 1880s de Vries abandoned his work on plant physiology and began devoting his study to heredity, a work that he would carry on until his death. He studied the experiments and writings of Darwin and others and came up with his own theory that "pangenes" were the structures that carried inherited traits. Later, Johannsen would derive the term "gene" from de Vries' term "pangene."

De Vries studied the distribution of variations of traits in about twenty species, showing how traits segregate, or become inherited by separate independent units that can be studied. His theoretical model of a pangene was made of molecules which divided when the cells divided into daughter cells, separating before blending in the next generation. After checking the literature for any earlier research along these lines, in 1900 de Vries happened upon a reprint of Gregor Mendel's paper in which Mendel had proposed these same ideas after conducting his experiments with pea plants. Although in 1866 Mendel's ideas had made little impact, now, at the turn of the twentieth century, de Vries gave credit to Mendel's work. Because de Vries did make note of Mendel's work, two other scientists also working on heredity, Karl Erich Correns and Eric Tschermak von Seysenegg, were obligated to follow suit. Thus, at the turn of the century, Mendel's work was "rediscovered" by all three men.

De Vries's ideas, however, went beyond Mendel's theory of the segregation of traits. He proposed that most characters are inherited unchanged from one generation to the next, but that sometimes pangenes start to multiply in extraordinary ways and change somehow during cell division. This change creates a new characteristic, known as a mutant. Such new varieties provide changes that can be acted upon by natural selection and thus hasten the evolution of a species.

While crossing flowers with a genus of plants, *Oenotheras*, the evening primrose, de Vries' work would prove most fascinating. De Vries came up with many mutants which he considered to be new species. Some other scientists of the time disputed de Vries' idea, hypothesizing that these plants were merely varieties of the same species.

But de Vries had the notion that mutations were changes in the pangenes that provided the mechanisms by which variations were introduced into a population and thus caused evolution. Along the way he also made the discovery that some mutants are lethal. His major work on mutations, *Die Mutationstheorie,* gained him fame in Europe and in the United States. De Vries was invited to lecture at the University of California at Berkeley in 1904 and 1906. Several years later in 1912, de Vries again came to the United States and lectured at the Rice Institute in Houston, Texas.

Despite the imperfections, de Vries' theory of mutations provided much of the groundbreaking work in genetics, having great impact on geneticists working on both continents. At Columbia University, **Thomas Hunt Morgan** and his students **A. H. Sturtevant**, **Hermann Joseph Muller**, and Calvin Bridges were experimenting on *Drosophila* (fruit flies) and attempting to describe mutations of that species. They never discovered the great number of mutants that de Vries had with the evening primrose, but found enough mutants to provide data for the first map of chromosomes.

Later studies conducted by followers of de Vries showed that inheritance in the evening primrose was indeed very complicated. Some of the varieties were not different species, but rather plants in which the chromosomes were tetraploid, that is, they had double the normal number of chromosomes. Although mutations were not as abundant as de Vries predicted, his work still was seminal to the discovery that the cell's genetic makeup was found on the genes located in the chromosomes and to the theory of evolution, which depends on research into mutant species.

For his work, de Vries was bestowed with eleven honorary doctorates and awarded seven gold medals and memberships into major academic societies. After retiring to a country house in Lunteren, Holland, de Vries continued experimenting, using plants from his own garden. Many of his friends and pupils visited his remote laboratory, breaking up his rather solitary life of experimenting which continued to yield scientific papers. He died there on May 21, 1935.

SELECTED WRITINGS BY VRIES:

Books

De invloed der temperatuur op de levensverschijnselen der planten, The Hague, 1870.
Opera e periodicis collata, seven volumes, Utrecht, 1918–1927.

Periodicals

Archives néerlandaises des sciences exactes et naturelles, Sur la perméabilité du protoplasme des betteraves rouges, Volume 6, 1871, pp. 117–126.

Archives néerlandaises des sciences exactes et naturelles, Sur la mort des cellules végétales par l'effet d'une températuré éleveé, Volume 6, 1871, pp. 245–295.

Die Mutationstheorie, Versuche und Beobachtungen über die Entstehung von Arten im Pflanzenreich, two volumes, [Leipzig], 1901–1903, edited version translated as The Mutation Theory, Experiments and Observations on the Origin of Species in the Vegetable Kingdom, two volumes, [Chicago], 1909–1910.

FURTHER READING:

Books

Gillispie, Charles Coulston, editor, *Dictionary of Scientific Biography,* Volume 14, Scribner, pp. 95–104.

Periodicals

Allen, G. E, *Journal of the History of Biology,* Hugo de Vries and the Reception of the Mutation Theory, number 2, 1969, pp. 55–87.

Sketch by Barbara A. Branca

Salome Waelsch
1907–
American geneticist

Salome Waelsch was born and educated in Germany, but came to the United States in 1933 after the rise of Nazi dictator Adolf Hitler. She trained as a geneticist under 1935 Nobel Prize-winner **Hans Spemann** in Germany, and Leslie Dunn at Columbia University. For more than half a century Waelsch has studied the role of genes in the early stages of development and cellular differentiation, research that has important implications for the treatment of congenital diseases. In addition, she taught the first course on medical genetics in the United States.

Salome Gluecksohn Waelsch was born in Danzig, Germany, on October 6, 1907, to Ilyia and Nadia Glueck-sohn. Waelsch's early life was made difficult by a number of factors. First, her father died during the flu epidemic of 1918, when she was only eleven years old. Next, her mother lost all the family's money in the inflation following World War I. Finally, as a young girl Waelsch had to deal with both antifemale and anti-Jewish taunts of her schoolmates and neighbors.

Waelsch persevered in her goal of obtaining a college education. She attended the universities of Königsberg, Berlin, and Freiburg, intending at first to major in classical languages. Her interest in biology arose as the result of a friend's offhand suggestion that she take a course in that subject. "That was the beginning," she later told Jamie Talan, an interviewer for *Newsday.* "I found my love." Eventually Waelsch entered a doctoral program in genetics at Freiburg. Her advisor there was the eminent geneticist Hans Spemann; Waelsch completed the work required of her and was awarded her Ph.D. from Freiburg in 1932.

Waelsch's job prospects did not seem particularly bright at the time. In an interview with Harriet Zuckerman and Jonathan R. Cole for *The Outer Circle: Women in the Scientific Community,* she reported that in 1932 one prospective employer said to her: "You—a woman and a Jew—forget it." Despite such prejudice, she obtained an appointment as a research assistant in cell biology at the University of Berlin after leaving Freiburg. Perhaps the most important event that occurred during her one year at Berlin was her marriage to Rudolf Schoenheimer, a young biochemist at the university.

Immigrates to the United States

Given the rabid anti-Semitic policies and pronouncements of Hitler's government, it rapidly became clear to Salome and Rudolf that they had no future in Germany. Thus they moved to the United States, where Schoenheimer was offered a position at Columbia University's College of Physicians and Surgeons. His equally qualified wife received no similar offer, however, although she was allowed, three years later, to work in the laboratories of the famous geneticist Leslie Dunn, without pay. Waelsch became a naturalized citizen of the United States in 1938.

Initiates Studies on Differentiation

It was in Dunn's laboratories that Waelsch began the studies that were to occupy her for the next fifty years. The studies were designed to find out how specific genes in an organism affect the development and differentiation of various body parts within the embryo. Waelsch's studies have been particularly helpful in understanding how errors occur during embryonic development and may ultimately lead to the discovery of methods for curing genetic disorders that begin before birth.

Rudolf Schoenheimer died in 1941, and a little more than a year later, on January 8, 1943, Salome was married a second time, again to a biochemist, Heinrich B. Waelsch. The couple had two children, Naomi Barbara and Peter Benedict. Waelsch was widowed a second time in 1966. In 1953, after seventeen years in Dunn's laboratories, Waelsch was appointed a research associate in the department of obstetrics at the College of Physicians and Surgeons.

Two years later, Waelsch's major professional break came with the founding of the Albert Einstein College of Medicine in New York City. She was offered the post of associate professor of anatomy, a position she held until 1958, when she was promoted to full professor. During this period Waelsch offered what are believed to be the first courses in medical genetics taught at any U.S. university. In 1963 her title was changed to professor of genetics and she was made chair of the Department of Genetics at Einstein. Although she retired officially in 1978 and was named professor emerita, she has continued her research.

During her career Waelsch has authored or coauthored more than one hundred papers on developmental genetics. She was elected to the National Academy of Sciences in 1979 and awarded the National Medal of Science by President Bill Clinton in 1993. In 1982 she was awarded a gold doctoral diploma by her alma mater, the University of Freiburg, in recognition of her life's work. She declined the award, however, because of her terrible memories of the Holocaust and her forced departure from her homeland.

FURTHER READING:

Books

Zuckerman, Harriet, Jonathan R. Cole, and John T. Bruer, editors, *The Outer Circle: Women in the Scientific Community,* Norton, 1991, pp. 71–93.

Periodicals

Talan, Jamie, *Newsday,* The Mouse Lady: 60 Years of Genes, September 30, 1993.

Sketch by David E. Newton

Julius Wagner-Jauregg
1857–1940
Austrian physician

Julius Wagner-Jauregg was an Austrian psychiatrist whose experimental work in the first part of the twentieth century led to a new appreciation of the beneficial effects of bodily stress in the treatment of mental illness. In 1927 he became the first psychiatrist to win the Nobel Prize for his discovery that syphilis, a chronic, usually venereal disease caused by spirochete bacteria, could be cured by clinically induced malaria, which is characterized by symptoms of fever and chills.

Wagner-Jauregg was born Julius Wagner on March 7, 1857, in the village of Wels, Austria. He was the oldest son of Ludovika Ranzoni and Adolf Johann Wagner, a government official. The family name became "Wagner von Jauregg" when Adolf Johann was raised to the nobility, but following the collapse of the Austro-Hungarian empire in 1918, the "von" was dropped. After the early death of his mother, Julius Wagner-Jauregg was raised at home. In his youth he successfully fought off typhoid and tuberculosis to graduate from Vienna's prestigious Schottengymnasium.

While attending medical school at the University of Vienna, Wagner-Jauregg received thorough training in experimental biology and met the father of psychoanalysis, Sigmund Freud, who was studying at the Institute of General and Experimental Pathology. Despite Wagner-Jauregg's lack of interest in psychoanalysis, the two remained lifelong friends. In 1880 Wagner-Jauregg was awarded a medical degree for his thesis on the heart under conditions of acceleration.

Originally, Wagner-Jauregg hoped to practice general medicine, but when Vienna's two teaching hospitals turned him down, he reluctantly accepted a position as an assistant in the university's psychiatric clinic. Although he had little training in mental illness, he quickly became a qualified instructor in psychiatry and neurology. Wagner-Jauregg was a clinician, skilled in detailed observation and careful case analysis. Using the latest techniques of animal experimentation, he spent his life working to advance the biological understanding of mental illness. His first research entailed the investigation of how certain chemicals stimulate breathing after strangulation.

In 1889 Wagner-Jauregg was appointed professor of psychiatry at the University of Graz and for the next four years studied the effect of the thyroid gland on behavior. An ardent vivisectionist, he discovered that, when the thyroid was removed from a cat, the animal's behavior became convulsive and violent. Cretinism in humans, Wagner-Jauregg put forth in an early paper, was due to a malfunction of the thyroid. During his years in Graz, he travelled frequently in central and southeastern Austria studying peasants with goiter and found that small amounts of iodine reduced their hugely swollen necks. He urged the sale of iodized salt in alpine regions, a measure the Austrian government undertook belatedly in 1923.

In 1893 Wagner-Jauregg was made a full professor at the University of Vienna and appointed director of the Hospital for Nervous and Mental Diseases and the State Mental Asylum. As a member of the Austrian Board of Health, he helped draft important legislation protecting the rights of the mentally ill and regulating the certification of the insane. At his urging, psychiatry became a compulsory subject in the undergraduate curriculum.

Discovers That Fever Can Cure the Mentally Ill

While still only a medical assistant, Wagner-Jauregg had studied the beneficial effect of high fever on psychotic patients. For a monograph that he published in 1888, he surveyed instances where epidemics of typhoid, malaria, small pox, and scarlet fever had swept through mental asylums. In 30 cases reaching back to antiquity, he described how bouts of high fever had brought dramatic relief in cases of melancholy, mania, and paresis. At the end of his monograph, Wagner-Jauregg suggested that malaria might be used experimentally to induce a "fever cure" in psychotic patients, although at the time he lacked the authority to undertake so radical a treatment.

The monograph received little notice when it was published. In it, Wagner-Jauregg had formulated two bold hypotheses: first, that some psychoses were organic in nature, and second, that one disease might be employed to eradicate another disease. In Graz, he had produced fever with injections of tuberculin, a protein used to treat tuberculosis, until it was learned that tuberculin was unsafe. In Vienna, he injected paralytic patents with typhus vaccine and staphylococci but was disappointed by the results. Most of the cures proved to be temporary, and patients soon relapsed.

It was not until World War I that conditions were ripe for a radical trial. By then a series of important discoveries had confirmed the link between paresis and syphilis. In 1905 researchers had identified the syphilis bacillus, *Spirochaete pallida*. A year later, the Wasserman test for syphilis revealed that paresis was a progressive disease of the brain caused by untreated syphilis. In Wagner-Jauregg's time, paresis accounted for fifteen percent of the patients confined to mental hospitals. The disease was thought to be incurable and invariably ended in insanity, paralysis, and death within three to four years.

In the final years of World War I, Wagner-Jauregg was treating victims of shell shock when he encountered a soldier suffering from malaria. On June 14, 1917, Wagner-Jauregg used blood drawn from the malarial soldier to infect nine patients suffering from paresis. Quinine, the medicine used to treat malaria, was withheld until each patient had endured seven to eleven attacks of fever. The results were astonishing. Six patients experienced a dramatic remission of symptoms, and three were able to return to normal life. In 1919 Wagner-Jauregg began full-scale clinical trials.

At first, Wagner-Jauregg's reports were greeted with considerable skepticism by the medical community. Some physicians considered it unethical to deliberately induce a disease as serious as malaria. Others feared the outbreak of malaria epidemics in major metropolitan centers. But trials elsewhere produced similar results. Employing only a mild strain of malaria easily cured by quinine, mortality remained low while complete recovery was experienced by thirty to forty percent of all patients. Patients who had only recently contracted syphilis could be cured completely when the "malaria cure" was used in conjunction with injections of Salvarsan and Neosalvarsan, two drugs used to treat early syphilis. In 1927 Wagner-Jauregg became the first psychiatrist to be awarded the Nobel Prize in physiology or medicine.

Safer methods of inducing fever were tried—preparations of colloidal sulfur, hot-water baths, and "fever cabinets"—but none had the high rates of success typical of malaria. Until the discovery of penicillin during World War II, malaria remained the preferred treatment for advanced syphilis. Medical opinion differed on just how the fever cure worked since it seemed unlikely that the fever killed all of the spirochete bacteria, which cause syphilis. Instead, it was believed that the stress produced by the malaria attack in some way strengthened the body's defenses against the syphilitic infection. Stress treatments such as electroshock continue to play a role in the treatment of psychiatric disorders.

In 1928, one year after receiving the Nobel Prize, Wagner-Jauregg retired at the age of seventy-one. In his youth he had been an avid mountaineer, and he was an accomplished chess player. During his long career he published some eighty papers and received several distinguished honors. In 1935 the University of Edinburgh awarded Wagner-Jauregg the Cameron Prize, and in 1937 he received the Gold Medal of the American Committee for Research on Syphilis. Julius Wagner-Jauregg died on September 27, 1940, in Vienna at age eighty-four, shortly before the discovery of penicillin made his fever cure obsolete. He was survived by his wife, Anna Koch, a daughter, Julia, and a son, Theodor, who became a distinguished professor of chemistry at the University of Vienna.

SELECTED WRITINGS BY WAGNER-JAUREGG:

Books

Fieber und Infektionstherapie. Ausgewählten Beitrage 1887–1935, Verglag für Medizin, Weidmann, 1936.
Lebenserinnerungen, edited by L. Schönbauer and M. Jantsch, Springer, 1950.

Periodicals

Jahrbuch für Psychiatrie und Neurologie, Über die Einwirkung Fieberhafter Erkrankungen auf Psychosen, Volume 7, 1887, pp. 94–131.
Psychiatrisch-neurologische Wochenshrift, Über den Einwirkung der Malaria auf die progressive Paralyse, Volume 20, 1918–1919, pp. 132–134.

FURTHER READING:

Books

De Kruif, Paul, *Men Against Death,* Harcourt, 1932, pp. 249–279.
Fox, Daniel M. et al, editors, *Nobel Laureates in Medicine or Psychology: A Biographical Dictionary,* Garland Publishing, 1990, pp. 545–548.
Magill, Frank N., editor, *The Nobel Prize Winners: Physiology or Medicine,* Volume 1, 1901–1944, Salem Press, 1991, pp. 277–284.
Valenstin, E. S., *Great and Desperate Cures: The Rise and Decline of Psychosurgery and Other Radical Treatments for Mental Illness,* Baru Book, 1986, pp. 29–31.

Periodicals

Breutsch, W. L., *Archives of Neurology and Psychiatry,* Julius Wagner von Jauregg—Eminent Psychiatrist and Originator of the Malaria Treatment of Dementia Paralytica (1857–1940), Volume 44, 1940, pp. 1319–1322.
Riebl, L., and P. Sharp, *Australian and New Zealand Journal of Psychiatry,* Julius Wagner von Jauregg: A Reappraisal, June 1, 1992, pp. 302–306.

Sketch by Philip Metcalfe

Arnold C. Wahl
1937–1982
American chemical physicist

Arnold Wahl was a chemical physicist who pioneered the use of computers to study the structure and properties of atoms and molecules as well as the changes these particles undergo in different physical and chemical conditions. He worked for most of his professional life at the Argonne National Laboratory in Argonne, Illinois. In the later years of his life, he was in generally poor health and left Argonne in 1977 to take a job with Science Applications, Inc. He died in 1982.

Wahl was born on February 18, 1937, in Chicago in a house only a block from Lake Michigan. His father was a brewmaster and for many years was in charge of the production of beer at a local company. After he retired, he operated a correspondence school for brewmasters. Friends say that Wahl had a natural curiosity about the world around him as a child, and his parents often allowed him to decorate portions of their house with his latest scientific "finds."

Wahl attended the Latin High School in Chicago and then enrolled at the Rensselaer Polytechnic Institute for his undergraduate studies. He worked briefly as a student aide at the Union Carbide Company in 1957. In 1959, Wahl received his bachelor of chemical engineering degree from Rensselaer, and then returned to Chicago for his doctoral studies. While at the University of Chicago, he was a university fellow (1961), a National Science Foundation fellow (1962–1963), and an Argonne fellow (1963–1964). He was awarded his Ph.D. in chemical physics in 1964.

Upon his graduation from Chicago, Wahl accepted a position as research associate and fellow at the Argonne National Laboratory. A year later, he left Argonne to take a post as assistant professor at the University of Wisconsin. However, he only remained at Wisconsin for a year before returning to Argonne as senior scientist and group leader. In addition to his work at Argonne, Wahl worked as a consultant at the Illinois Institute of Technology (1965–1966), the Center for Applied Quantum Mechanics in Paris (1966–1967), and the Lawrence Livermore Laboratory (1969–1977).

The Use of Computers for Chemical Research

Wahl's research involved the combination of two crucial fields, quantum mechanics and computer technology. In a review paper written for *Scientific American* in 1970, he outlined his view of the way these two fields could be integrated to produce a better understanding of chemical phenomena. "Assuming that one starts with a fundamentally sound theoretical model of the structure of the individual atoms or molecules, and of the nature of the forces between them, the laws of basic electrostatics, classical physics, quantum mechanics, and statistical mechanics in principle provide a means for computing the macroscopic outcome of a chemical experiment—without ever performing the experiment!"

That is, atoms and molecules are nothing other than collections of electrically charged particles. The way in which these particles interact with each other can all be described by well-known laws from classical and quantum physics. The only problem is that these interactions are incredibly complex for any but the very simplest of systems. It would take a human years to solve the relevant mathematical equations involved in the description of most atomic and molecular systems.

What Wahl realized was that the computer made it possible to perform these calculations at a speed that made the solution of complex mathematical equations a realistic possibility. Thus, it should be possible to predict the results of various interactions without ever having to try those reactions out in the laboratory. Wahl pointed out that this approach involved using the computer as a source of information, not a device for collecting and collating information from other sources. In this respect, Wahl's vision of the role of the computer in studying chemical reactions has been more than justified by the kinds of computer programs now used by chemists to draw and study chemical structures of all kinds.

One of the techniques developed by Wahl for the study of two- and three-atom systems was called MultiConfiguration Self-Consistent Field (MCSF) theory. This theory has been, and remains, a powerful tool in the field of theoretical chemistry.

Wahl applied his knowledge of and interest in computer-based chemistry to a number of different situations. For example, he organized a theoretical chemistry group at Argonne and supervised studies on the application of his work to atmospheric and molecular beam chemistry. He also served as a member of the Committee on Electronic Structure of Atoms and Molecules of the U.S. Air Force Office of Scientific Research. In addition, he created a number of films and wall charts representing the results of his computer studies on the properties of atoms and molecules.

SELECTED WRITINGS BY WAHL:

Periodicals

(With P. Bertoncini, K. Kaiser, and P. Land) "BISON: A New Instrument for the Experimentalist," *International Journal of Quantum Chemistry*, Symposium No. 3, Part 2 (1970): pp. 499-512.

"Chemistry by Computer," *Scientific American* (April 1970): 12, pp. 54-70.

"Chemistry from Computers," *Argonne National Laboratory Reviews* 5, Vol. 1 (April 1969): pp. 43-69.

FURTHER READING:

Periodicals

Wahl, Arnold C., "Chemistry by Computer," *Scientific American* (April 1970): 12, pp. 54-70.

Sketch by David Newton

Selman Waksman

Selman Waksman
1888–1973
American microbiologist

Selman Waksman revolutionized medicine, thanks to his discoveries of life-saving antibacterial compounds. His investigations have also spawned further studies for other disease-curing drugs. Waksman isolated streptomycin, the first chemical agent that was effective against tuberculosis. Prior to his discovery, tuberculosis was a lifelong debilitating disease, and was fatal in some forms. Streptomycin effected a cure, and for this discovery, Waksman received the 1952 Nobel Prize in physiology or medicine. In pioneering the field of antibiotic research, Waksman had an inestimable impact on human health and well-being, creating both a new field of medicine and a new industry.

The only son of a Jewish furniture textile weaver, Selman Abraham Waksman was born in the tiny Russian village of Novaya Priluka on July 22, 1888. Life was hard in late-nineteenth-century Russia. Waksman's only sister died from diphtheria when he was nine. There were particular tribulations for members of a persecuted ethnic minority. As a teen during the Russian revolution, Waksman helped organize an armed Jewish youth defense group to counteract oppression. He also set up a school for underprivileged children and formed a group to care for the sick. These activities prefaced his later role as a standard-bearer for social responsibility.

Several factors led to Waksman's immigration to the United States. He had received his diploma from the *Gymnasium* in Odessa and was poised to attend university, but he doubtless recognized the very limited options he held as a Jew in Russia. At the same time, in 1910, his mother died, and cousins who had immigrated to New Jersey urged him to follow their lead. Waksman did so, and his move to a farm there, where he learned the basics of scientific farming from his cousin, likely had a pivotal influence on Waksman's later choice of field of study.

Begins Research on Soil Microbes

In 1911 Waksman enrolled in nearby Rutgers College (later University) of Agriculture, following the advice of fellow Russian immigrant Jacob Lipman, who led the college's bacteriology department. He worked with Lipman, developing a fascination with the bacteria of soil, and graduated with a B.Sc. in 1915. The next year he earned his M.S. degree. Around this time he also became a naturalized United States citizen and changed the spelling of his first name from Zolman to Selman. Waksman married Bertha Deborah Mitnik, a childhood sweetheart and the sister of one of his childhood friends, in 1916. Deborah Mitnik had come to the United States in 1913, and in 1919 she bore their only child, Byron Halsted Waksman, who eventually went on to a distinguished career at Yale University as a pathology professor.

Waksman's intellect and industry enabled him to earn his Ph.D. in less than two years at the University of California, Berkeley. His 1918 dissertation focused on proteolytic enzymes (special proteins that break down proteins) in fungi. Throughout his schooling, Waksman supported himself through various scholarships and jobs. Among the latter were ranch work, caretaker and night watchman, and tutor of English and science.

Waksman's former advisor invited him to join Rutgers as a lecturer in soil bacteriology in 1918. He was to stay at Rutgers for his entire professional career. When Waksman took up the post, however, he found his pay too low to support his family. Thus, in his early years at Rutgers he also worked at the nearby Takamine Laboratory, where he produced enzymes and ran toxicity tests.

In the 1920s Waksman began to gain recognition in scientific circles. Others sought out his keen mind, and his prolific output earned him a well-deserved reputation. He wrote two major books during this decade. *Enzymes: Properties, Distribution, Methods, and Applications,* coauthored with Wilburt C. Davison, was published in 1926, and in 1927 his thousand-page *Principles of Soil Microbiology* appeared. This latter volume became a classic among soil bacteriologists. His laboratory produced more than just books. One of Waksman's students during this period was **René Dubos**, who would later discover the antibiotic gramicidin, the first chemotherapeutic agent effective against gram-positive bacteria (bacteria that hold dye in a stain test named for Danish bacteriologist Hans Gram). Waksman became an associate professor at Rutgers in the mid–1920s and advanced to the rank of full professor in 1930.

During the 1930s Waksman systematically investigated the complex web of microbial life in soil, humus, and peat. He was recognized as a leader in the field of soil microbiology, and his work stimulated an ever-growing group of graduate students and postdoctoral assistants. He continued to publish widely, and he also established many professional relationships with industrial firms that utilized products of microbes. These companies that produced enzymes, pharmaceuticals, vitamins, and other products were later to prove valuable in Waksman's researches, mass producing and distributing the products he developed. Among his other accomplishments during this period was the founding of the division of Marine Bacteriology at Woods Hole Oceanographic Institution in 1931. For the next decade he spent summers there and eventually became a trustee, a post he filled until his death.

Research Finds Practical Applications in Wartime

In 1939 Waksman was appointed chair of the U.S. War Committee on Bacteriology. He derived practical applications from his earlier studies on soil microorganisms, developing antifungal agents to protect soldiers and their equipment. He also worked with the navy on the problem of bacteria that attacked ship hulls. Early that same year Dubos announced his finding of two antibacterial substances, tyrocidine and gramicidin, derived from a soil bacterium (*Bacillus brevis*). The latter compound, effective against gram-positive bacteria, proved too toxic for human use but did find widespread employment against various bacterial infections in veterinary medicine. The discovery of gramicidin also evidently inspired Waksman to dedicate himself to focus on the medicinal uses of antibacterial soil microbes. It was in this period that he began rigorously investigating the antibiotic properties of a wide range of soil fungi.

Waksman set up a team of about fifty graduate students and assistants to undertake a systematic study of thousands of different soil fungi and other microorganisms. The rediscovery at this time of the power of penicillin against gram-positive bacteria likely provided further incentive to Waksman to find an antibiotic effective against gram-negative bacteria, which include the kind that causes tuberculosis.

In 1940 Waksman became head of Rutgers' Department of Microbiology. In that year too, with the help of Boyd Woodruff, he isolated the antibiotic actinomycin. Named for the actinomycetes (rod- or filament-shaped bacteria) from which it was isolated, this compound also proved too toxic for human use, but its discovery led to the subsequent finding of variant forms (actinomycin A, B, C, and D), several of which were found to have potent anti-cancer effects. Over the next decade Waksman isolated ten distinct antibiotics. It is Waksman who first applied the term antibiotic, which literally means against life, to such drugs.

Breakthrough with Isolation of Streptomycin

Among these discoveries, Waksman's finding of streptomycin had the largest and most immediate impact. Not only did streptomycin appear nontoxic to humans, but it was highly effective against gram-negative bacteria. (Prior to this time the antibiotics available for human use had been active only against the gram-positive strains.) The importance of streptomycin was soon realized. Clinical trials showed it to be effective against a wide range of diseases, most notably tuberculosis.

At the time of streptomycin's discovery, tuberculosis was the most resistant and irreversible of all the major infectious diseases. It could only be treated with a regime of rest and nutritious diet. The tuberculosis bacillus consigned its victims to a lifetime of invalidism and, when it invaded organs other than the lungs, often killed. Sanatoriums around the country were filled with persons suffering the ravages of tuberculosis, and little could be done for them.

Streptomycin changed all of that. From the time of its first clinical trials in 1944, it proved to be remarkably effective against tuberculosis, literally snatching sufferers back from the jaws of death. By 1950 streptomycin was used against seventy different germs that were not treatable with penicillin. Among the diseases treated by streptomycin were bacterial meningitis (an inflammation of membranes enveloping the brain and spinal cord), endocarditis (an inflammation of the lining of the heart and its valves), pulmonary and urinary tract infections, leprosy, typhoid fever, bacillary dysentery, cholera, and bubonic plague.

Waksman arranged to have streptomycin produced by a number of pharmaceutical companies, since demand for it soon skyrocketed beyond the capacity of any single company. Manufacture of the drug became a $50-million-per-year industry. Thanks to Waksman and streptomycin, Rutgers received millions of dollars of income from the royalties. Waksman donated much of his own share to the establishment of an Institute of Microbiology there. He summarized his early researches on the drug in *Streptomycin: Nature and Practical Applications* (1949). Streptomycin ultimately proved to have some human toxicity and was supplanted by other antibiotics, but its discovery changed the course of modern medicine. Not only did it directly save countless lives, but its development stimulated scientists around the globe to search the microbial world for other antibiotics and medicines.

Research Yields Other Antibiotics

In 1949 Waksman isolated neomycin, which proved effective against bacteria that had become resistant to streptomycin. Neomycin also found a broad niche as a topical antibiotic. Other antibiotics soon came forth from his Institute of Microbiology. These included streptocin, framicidin, erlichin, candidin, and others. Waksman himself discovered eighteen antibiotics during the course of his career.

Waksman served as director of the Institute for Microbiology until his retirement in 1958. Even after that time, he continued to supervise research there. He also lectured widely and continued to write at the frenetic pace established early in his career. He eventually published more than twenty-five books, among them the autobiography *My Life with the Microbes,* and hundreds of articles. He was author of popular pamphlets on the use of thermophilic (heat-loving) microorganisms in composting and on the enzymes involved in jelly-making. He wrote biographies of several noted microbiologists, including his own mentor, Jacob Lipman. These works are in addition to his numerous publications in the research literature.

On August 16, 1973, Waksman died suddenly in Hyannis, Massachusetts, of a cerebral hemorrhage. He was buried near the institute to which he had contributed so much over the years. Waksman's honors over his professional career were many and varied. A complete listing of his awards would fill many pages. Besides receiving the Nobel Prize in 1952, he was recognized by the French Legion of Honor, won the Lasker award for basic medical science, was elected a fellow of the American Association for the Advancement of Science, and received commendations from academies and scholarly societies in Brazil, Britain, Denmark, Italy, Japan, the Netherlands, Spain, and other countries. It can safely be said that Selman Waksman changed the face of modern medicine around the world.

SELECTED WRITINGS BY WAKSMAN:

Books

Enzymes: Properties, Distribution, Methods, and Applications, Williams & Wilkins, 1926.
Principles of Soil Microbiology, Williams & Wilkins, 1927, revised edition, 1932.
Streptomycin: Nature and Practical Applications, Williams & Wilkins, 1949.
My Life with the Microbes, Simon & Schuster, 1954.

FURTHER READING:

Books

Magill, F. N., editor, *The Nobel Prize Winners: Physiology or Medicine, Volume 2, 1944–1969,* Salem Press, 1991, pp. 647–657.

Periodicals

Magill, F. N., editor, *Nature,* December 7, 1973, p. 367.
Magill, F. N., editor, *New York Times,* August 17, 1973, pp. 1, 34.
Sakula, Alex, *British Journal of Diseases of the Chest,* Selman Waksman (1888–1973), Discoverer of Streptomycin: A Centenary Review, Volume 82, number 1, 1988, pp. 23–31.

Sketch by Ethan E. Allen

George Wald
1906–1997
American biochemist

George Wald first won a place in the spotlight as the recipient of a Nobel Prize for his discovery of the way in which hidden biochemical processes in the retinal pigments of the eye turn light energy into sight. Among Wald's important experiments were the effects of vitamin A on sight and the roles played by rod and cone cells in black and white and color vision. Outside the laboratory, his splendid lectures at Harvard to packed audiences of students generated great intellectual excitement. It was as a political activist during the turbulent 1960s, however, that Wald garnered further public recognition. Wald's personal belief in the unity of nature and the kinship among all living things was evidenced by the substantial roles he played in the scientific world as well as the political and cultural arena of the 1960s.

Wald's father, Isaac Wald, a tailor and later a foreman in a clothing factory, immigrated from Austrian Poland, while his mother, Ernestine Rosenmann Wald, immigrated from Bavaria. Most of Wald's youth was spent in Brooklyn, New York, where his parents moved after his birth on the Lower East Side of Manhattan on November 18, 1906. He attended high school at Brooklyn Tech, where he intended to study to become an electrical engineer. College changed his mind, however, as he explained for the *New York Times Magazine* in 1969, "I learned I could talk, and I thought I'd become a lawyer. But the law was man-made; I soon discovered I wanted something more real."

George Wald

Wald's bachelor of science degree in zoology, which he received from New York University in 1927, was his ticket into the reality of biological research. He began his research career at Columbia University, where he was awarded a master's degree in 1928, working under Selig Hecht, one of the founders of the field of biophysics and an authority on the physiology of vision. Hecht exerted an enormous influence on Wald, both as an educator and a humanist. The elder scientist's belief in the social obligation of science, coupled with the conviction that science should be explained so the general public could understand it, made a great impression on the young Wald. Following Hecht's sudden death in 1947 at the age of 55, Wald wrote a memorial as a tribute to his colleague.

In 1932 Wald earned his doctorate at Columbia, after which he was awarded a National Research Council Fellowship in Biology. The two-year fellowship helped to support his research career, which first took him to the laboratory of **Otto Warburg** in Berlin. It was there, in 1932, that he discovered that vitamin A is one of the major constituents of retinal pigments, the light sensitive chemicals that set off the cascade of biological events that turns light into sight.

Warburg sent the young Wald to Switzerland, where he studied vitamins with chemist **Paul Karrer** at the University of Zurich. From there Wald went to **Otto Meyerhof**'s laboratory of cell metabolism at the Kaiser Wilhelm Institute in Heidelberg, Germany, finishing his fellowship in the Department of Physiology at the Universi-

ty of Chicago in 1934. His fellowship completed, Wald went to Harvard University, first as a tutor in biochemistry and subsequently as an instructor, faculty instructor, and associate professor, finally becoming a full professor in 1948. In 1968, he became Higgins Professor of Biology, a post he retained until he became an emeritus professor in 1977.

Wald did most of his work in eye physiology at Harvard, where he discovered in the late 1930s that the light-sensitive chemical in the rods—those cells in the retina responsible for night vision—is a single pigment called rhodopsin (visual purple), a substance derived from opsin, a protein, and retinene, a chemically modified form of vitamin A. In the ensuing years, Wald discovered that the vitamin A in rhodopsin is "bent" relative to its natural state, and light causes it to "straighten out," dislodging it from opsin. This simple reaction initiates all the subsequent activity that eventually generates the sense of vision.

Wald's research moved from rods to cones, the retinal cells responsible for color vision, discovering with his co-worker Paul K. Brown, that the pigments sensitive to red and yellow-green are two different forms of vitamin A that coexist in the same cone, while the blue-sensitive pigments are located in separate cones. They also showed that color blindness is caused by the absence of one of these pigments.

For much of his early professional life, Wald concentrated his energy on work, both research and teaching. His assistant, Brown, stayed with him for over 20 years and became a full-fledged collaborator. A former student, Ruth Hubbard, became his second wife in 1958, and they had two children, Elijah and Deborah. (His previous marriage to Frances Kingsley in 1931 ended in divorce; he has two sons by that marriage, Michael and David.) Wald, his wife, and Brown together became an extremely productive research team.

Research Efforts Receive Recognition with Nobel Prize

By the late 1950s Wald began to be showered with honors, and during his career he received numerous honorary degrees and awards. After Wald was awarded (with **Haldan K. Hartline** of the United States and **Ragnar Granit** of Sweden) the Nobel Prize in physiology or medicine in 1967 for his work with vision, John E. Dowling wrote in *Science* that Wald and his team formed "the nucleus of a laboratory that has been extraordinarily fruitful as the world's foremost center of visual-pigment biochemistry."

As Wald's reputation flourished, his fame as an inspiring professor grew as well. He lectured to packed classrooms, inspiring an intense curiosity in his students. The energetic professor was portrayed in a 1966 *Time* article that summarized the enthusiasm he brought to teaching his natural science course: "With crystal clarity and obvious joy at a neat explanation, Wald carries his students from protons in the fall to living organisms in the spring, [and] ends most lectures with some philosophical peroration on the wonder of it all." That same year, the *New York Post* said of his lectures, "His beginnings are slow, sometimes witty. . . . The talk gathers momentum and suddenly an idea *pings* into the atmosphere—fresh, crisp, thought-provoking."

Six days after he received the Nobel Prize, Wald wielded the status of his new prestige in support of a widely popular resolution before the city council of Cambridge, Massachusetts—placing a referendum on the Vietnam War on the city's ballot of November 7, 1967. Echoing the sentiments of his mentor Hecht, he asserted that scientists should be involved in public issues.

The Cambridge appearance introduced him to the sometimes stormy arena of public politics, a forum from which he never retired. The escalating war in Vietnam aroused Wald to speak out against America's military policy. In 1965, during the escalation of that war, Wald's impromptu denunciation of the Vietnam war stunned an audience at New York University, where he was receiving an honorary degree. Shortly afterward, he threw his support and prestige behind the presidential campaign of Eugene McCarthy. His offer to speak publicly on behalf of McCarthy was ignored, however, and he became a disillusioned supporter, remaining on the fringe of political activism.

Political Activism Punctuated with "The Speech"

Then on March 4, 1969, he gave an address at the Massachusetts Institute of Technology (MIT) that, "upended his life and pitched him abruptly into the political world," according to the *New York Times Magazine*. Wald gave "The Speech," as the talk came to be known in his family, before an audience of radical students at MIT. The students had helped to organize a scientists' day-long "strike" to protest the influence of the military on their work, a topic of much heated debate at the time.

Although much of the MIT audience was already bored and restless by the time Wald began, even many of those students who were about to leave the room stopped to listen as the Nobel laureate began to deliver his oration, entitled, "A Generation in Search of a Future." "I think this whole generation of students is beset with a profound sense of uneasiness, and I don't think they have quite defined its source," Wald asserted as quoted in the *New York Times Magazine.* "I think I understand the reasons for their uneasiness even better than they do. What is more, I *share* their uneasiness."

Wald's discourse evoked applause from the audience as he offered his opinion that student unease arose from a variety of troublesome matters. He pointed to the Vietnam War, the military establishment, and finally, the threat of nuclear warfare. "We must get rid of those atomic weapons," he declared. "We cannot live with them." Speaking to the students as fellow scientists, he sympathized with the their unease at the influence of the military establishment on

the work of scientists, intoning, "Our business is with life, not death. . . .."

The speech was reprinted and distributed around the country by the media. Through these reprints, Wald told readers that some of their elected leaders were "insane," and he referred to the American "war crimes" enacted in Vietnam. In the furor that followed, Wald was castigated by critics, many of whom were fellow academics, and celebrated by sympathizers. A letter writer from Piney Flats, Tennessee was quoted in the *New York Times Magazine* as saying, "So good to know there are still some intellects around who can talk downright horsesense." Wald summed up his role as scientist-political activist in that same article by saying, "I'm a scientist, and my concerns are eternal. But even eternal things are acted out in the present." He described his role as gadfly as putting certain controversial positions into words in order to make it, "easier for others to inch toward it."

His role as a Vietnam war gadfly expanded into activism in other arenas of foreign affairs. He served for a time as president of international tribunals on El Salvador, the Philippines, Afghanistan, Zaire, and Guatemala. In 1984, he joined four other Nobel Prize laureates who went with the "peace ship" sent by the Norwegian government to Nicaragua during that country's turmoil.

In addition to his interests in science and politics, Wald's passions included collecting Rembrandt etchings and primitive art, especially pre-Columbian pottery. This complex mixture of science, art, and political philosophy was reflected in his musings about religion and nature in the *New York Times Magazine.* "There's nothing supernatural in my mind. Nature is my religion, and it's enough for me. I stack it up against any man's. For its awesomeness, and for the sense of the sanctity of man that it provides."

In addition to the Nobel Prize, Wald received numerous awards and honors, including the Albert Lasker Award of the American Public Health Association in 1953, the Proctor Award in 1955 from the Association for Research in Ophthalmology, the Rumford Premium of the American Academy of Arts and Sciences in 1959, the 1969 Max Berg Award, and the Joseph Priestley Award the following year. In addition, he was elected to the National Academy of Science in 1950 and the American Philosophical Society in 1958. He is also a member of the Optical Society of America, which awarded him the Ives Medal in 1966. In the mid–1960s Wald spent a year as a Guggenheim fellow at England's Cambridge University, where he was elected an Overseas fellow of Churchill College for 1963–64. Wald also held honorary degrees from the University of Berne, Yale University, Wesleyan University, New York University, and McGill University.

Wald died on April 12, 1997, at his home in Cambridge, Massachusetts, at the age of 90.

SELECTED WRITINGS BY WALD:

Books

General Education in a Free Society. Cambridge: Harvard University Press, 1945.

Visual Pigments and Photoreceptors: Review and Out-look, Academic Press, 1974.

Periodicals

"The Molecular Basis of Visual Excitation," *American Scientist* (January 1954).

FURTHER READING:

Periodicals

Dowling, John E., "News And Comment; Nobel Prize: Three Named for Medicine, Physiology Award," *Science* (27 October 1967).

Dudar, Helen, "Profile . . ." *New York Post* (1 May 1966): p. 32.

Dudar, Helen, "George Wald: The Man, the Speech," *New York Times Magazine* (17 August 1969): pp. 28-29.

Dudar, Helen, "Profile . . ." *Time* (6 May 1966).

Pace, Eric, "George Wald, Nobel Biologist, Dies at 90" (obituary), *New York Times* (14 April 1997): p. B9.

Sketch by Marc Kusinitz

John E. Walker

John E. Walker
1941–
English biochemist

John E. Walker was awarded a share of the 1997 Nobel Prize in chemistry for his research on the enzyme ATP synthase. That enzyme is responsible for the biologically critical molecule known as adenosine triphosphate (ATP) that provides the energy needed to drive a host of biochemical reactions in cells. Walker's research dovetailed with similar work carried out by the second 1997 Nobel Laureate, **Paul Boyer**, who devised a theory that explained the process by which the ATP synthase enzyme operates. Walker has been employed at the Laboratory of Molecular Biology of the Medical Research Council in Cambridge for more than two decades.

Walker was born on January 7, 1941, in Halifax, England. He attended the Rastrick Grammar School in Brighouse, Yorkshire, and then enrolled at St. Catherine's College, Oxford, in 1960. He was awarded his B.A. degree in chemistry by St. Catherine's in 1964. Walker then spent four years as a research student at the Sir William Dunn School of Pathology at Oxford before earning his M.A. and D. Phil. degrees from Oxford in 1969.

Upon completion of his doctoral studies, Walker spent two years as a postdoctoral fellow at the School of Pharmacy at the University of Wisconsin. He then spent three additional years as a NATO fellow at CNRS, in Gif-sur-Yvette, France, and as an EMBO fellow at the Institut Pasteur in Paris. In 1974, Walker accepted an appointment as a member of the scientific staff at the Cambridge Laboratory of Molecular Biology of the Medical Research Council. He was assigned to the Division of Protein and Nucleic Acid Chemistry of the laboratory. In 1982, Walker was promoted to senior scientist at the laboratory, and in 1987, he was given a special appointment (professorial grade) at the laboratory.

Structure and Function of ATP

Adenosine triphosphate (ATP) is one of the most important molecules in the cells of living organisms. It has been described as an "energy-carrying" molecule because it provides the energy needed to drive many essential biochemical reactions.

The energy carried by an ATP molecule is stored in its phosphate bonds. A molecule of ATP is produced through a series of steps in which a phosphate group is first attached to a molecule of adenosine monophosphate (AMP) to form adenosine diphosphate (ADP). ADP then adds a second phosphate group to form adenosine triphosphate (ATP). As each phosphate group is added to the growing molecule, it brings with it energy stored in the form of the chemical bonds by which the phosphate is attached to the core molecule.

ATP acts as an energy-provider because it tends to break down to form first ADP plus a phosphate group, and then AMP and a second phosphate group. Each time one of these steps occurs, energy is released. That energy is transferred to some other set of chemical reactants in a cell, making it possible for those reactants to form new compounds.

Mechanism of ATP Synthesis

Scientists have long been very interested in learning precisely how ATP is formed and how it carries out its biochemical functions. Discovered in 1929 by the German chemist Karl Lohmann, ATP was first synthesized two decades later by the Scottish chemist **Alexander Todd**. The role of ATP in providing energy to cell reactions was first elucidated by the German-American biochemist **Fritz Lipmann** in the period 1939–1941.

One important line of ATP research has focused on the mechanism by which the molecule is formed. In 1960, the American biochemist Efraim Racker found a substance in the mitochondria of cells that appeared to be responsible for the synthesis of ATP. They called the enzyme $F_0 F_1$ ATPase, although it is now better known as ATP synthase. The original name for the enzyme comes from the fact that it consists of two parts, an F_0 domain that is attached to a cell membrane, and an F_1 domain that protrudes from the membrane.

During the 1950s, the American biochemist Paul D. Boyer developed a theory to explain how ATP synthase is able to produce ATP. Essentially, he argued that a flow of hydrogen ions within the cell membrane causes the F_0 domain of the enzyme to rotate in much the same way that the wind causes the blades on a windmill to turn. Boyer hypothesized that the turning of the F_0 membrane sequentially exposed structurally different regions of the F_1 domain in such as way as to make possible the ADP + phosphate reaction to occur. Walker's research completely identified the amino acid sequence of ATP synthase and proteins attached to it and determined much of the three-dimensional structure of the molecule. It was for this research that he was awarded the 1997 Nobel Prize in chemistry.

Honors and Awards

Walker has received a host of honors and awards in addition to the Nobel Prize. Among these have been the A. T. Clay Gold Medal for academic distinction in 1959, the Johnson Foundation Prize of the University of Pennsylvania Medical School in 1994, the CIBA Medal and Prize of the Biochemical Society in 1995, the Peter Mitchell Medal of the European Bioenergetics Congress in 1996, and the Gaetana Quagliariello Prize for Mitochondrial Research from the University of Bari, Italy, in 1997. Walker has also been elected a fellow of the Royal Society (1995), a fellow of Sidney Sussex College at Cambridge (1997) and an honorary fellow of St. Catherine's College at Oxford (1997). He has also been asked to give named lectures at the University of California at San Diego (the Nathan Kaplan Memorial Lecture), Copenhagen (the Novo-Nordic Lecture), Sheffield University (the Krebs Lecture), the Biochemical Society (the CIBA Lecture), the EBEC Conference at Louvain, Belgium (the Peter Mitchell Lecture), and the Netherlands Biochemical Society (Lecture of the Year).

For two decades, Walker has also been active in a variety of professional responsibilities. He has served on the editorial board of *The Biochemical Journal*, *Biochemistry International*, *Molecular Biology*, *Journal of Bioenergetics*, and *Structure*. He is the author or coauthor of more than 175 papers and book chapters. Walker is married and has two children.

SELECTED WRITINGS BY WALKER:

Periodicals

"The Mechanism of ATP Synthesis," *The Biochemist*, 16 (1994): pp. 31-35.
"The Mitochondrial Transporter Family," *Current Opinion in Structural Biology*, 2 (1992): pp. 519-526.
"The Regulation of Catalysis in ATP Synthase," *Current Opinion in Structural Biology*, 4 (1994): pp. 912-918.
"Structure at 2.8? Resolution of F121-ATPase from Bovine Heart Mitochondria," *Nature*, 370 (1994): pp. 621-628.

FURTHER READING:

Other

"Information," at http://www.nobel.se/announcement-97/chemistry97.html.

Sketch by David Newton

Otto Wallach
1847–1931
German chemist

Otto Wallach was a highly regarded professor of chemistry whose curiosity about essential oils led to research that benefited both organic chemistry and an important industry. For his meticulous procedures and initiative in the study of terpenes, a class of compounds he identified and named as essential oils, Wallach received the

Nobel Prize in chemistry in 1910. Essential oils, called ethereal oils in Wallach's time, are fragrant extracts from plant materials that are used in perfumes, flavorings, and medicines. Terpenes are responsible for much of the pleasant odor associated with essential oils. Wallach's work provided a scientific foundation for the fragrance industry.

Otto Wallach was born on March 27, 1847, in Königsberg, in East Prussia (Königsberg is now called Kaliningrad and is part of the reorganized former Soviet Union). Wallach's mother was Otillia Thoma Wallach; his father, Gerhard Wallach, was an official in the Prussian government whose post necessitated moves from Königsberg to Stettin (now in Poland and called Szczecin) and then to Potsdam, near Berlin, Germany. Wallach graduated from the Potsdam *Gymnasium* (high school). In school he became fascinated with chemistry and the history of art, and pursued both interests throughout his life. Early in 1867 he entered the University of Göttingen and received his doctorate in chemistry in 1869. Wallach never married.

Doctoral Dissertation and Chance Lead to Important Discoveries

Wallach's doctoral dissertation was on isomers of toluene. Isomers (*iso* means same; *mer* means parts) are substances with identical composition but different arrangements of the parts, giving the substances different physical and chemical properties. Toluene is one of the products of distillation of coal, and among its many uses is as a solvent in the preparation of fragrances. Wallach's doctoral studies were to provide the background for his most important research.

After graduation Wallach worked briefly in Berlin, then went to the University of Bonn to assist August Kekulé (1829–1896), a renowned German professor of chemistry whose most noted contribution was the discovery of the structural formula of benzene, another important coal product and a substance similar to toluene. Kekulé was interested in turning much of his laboratory work over to a young assistant. Wallach remained at the University of Bonn until 1889, except for a period of two years, from 1871 to 1873, when he tried research at Aktiengesellschaft für Anilinfabrikation (Agfa).

In 1879, as a professor at the University of Bonn, Wallach was assigned to teach pharmacy. He had little background in the chemistry of essential (ethereal) oils, used in medicines. In Kekulé's laboratory he found abandoned samples of essential oils that Kekulé thought were too complex even to attempt to analyze. A very patient researcher, Wallach distilled and redistilled each oil sample until he could identify a pure substance. By 1881 he had repeated his procedure with different oils and identified eight pure, very similar, fragrant substances that he named terpenes, from the Greek *terebinthos*—turpentine.

Work Rewarded with Nobel Prize

Wallach did not work alone. While some colleagues worked on synthesizing new and similar compounds, he devoted most of his effort to studying how the terpenes he separated from essential oils were related. By 1887 Wallach discovered that all the terpenes he identified in essential oils are derived from a multiple of a particular arrangement of five carbon atoms, now called isoprene units. Some examples of terpenes found naturally are bayberry, rose oil, peppermint, menthol, camphor, and turpentine.

In 1889 Wallach was appointed director of the Chemical Institute at the University of Göttingen, where he continued his work on terpenes. In 1910 he received the Nobel Prize in chemistry "for his initiative work in the field of alicyclic substances," the terpenes, discovered to have carbon atoms arranged in rings, or cycles. Kekulé was the first person to identify a compound (benzene) as shaped like a ring.

One of the most important outcomes of Wallach's work was the research it spawned, which, combined with his own work, forever changed the fragrance industry. Before Wallach, there was little scientific background for production of fragrances. Processes used were much like the ones brought to Europe by the Crusaders. Wallach described the change his work inspired in his Nobel address. "The fragrant components of plants were merely distilled and the distillate brought to market. In this process, the products obtained were not always handled rationally, in the absence of all knowledge of their chemical nature, and the doors were wide open for every kind of falsification. When this was carried out with only some skill, the consumer was helpless against it.

"This has now been changed thoroughly. Thanks to the possibility of distinctly characterizing single components of the ethereal oils, we now possess a significant analytical system to detect falsifications and to guard against them." Wallach's work, combined with the work of others he inspired, was credited with putting science into the production of perfumes, flavorings, and medicines that use terpenes.

Many universities and scientific societies honored Wallach. In 1912 he received the Davy Medal, awarded to outstanding scientists in memory of the British chemist, Sir Humphrey Davy (1778–1829), who identified a number of chemical elements through his pioneering work with electrochemistry. Wallach retired from Göttingen in 1915, but continued with research until he was eighty years old. In his lifetime Wallach published 126 papers on his research of essential oils. He died in Göttingen, Germany, on February 26, 1931, a month short of his eighty-fourth birthday.

SELECTED WRITINGS BY WALLACH:

Books

Die Terpene und Campher, ("Terpenes and Camphor"), Leipzig, 1909.

Nobel Prize Winners in Chemistry, (contains translation of portions of his Nobel Prize address), Henry Schuman, 1953, pp. 43–44.

FURTHER READING:

Books

Dictionary of Scientific Biography, Scribner, 1980, Volume 14, pp. 141–142.

Periodicals

Partridge, William S., and Ernest R. Schierz, *Journal of Chemical Education,* Otto Wallach: The First Organizer of the Terpenes, Volume 24, 1947, pp. 106–108.

Sketch by M. C. Nagel

Ernest Walton

Ernest Walton
1903–1995
Irish experimental physicist

Ernest Thomas Sinton Walton was an Irish experimental physicist who gained renown for achieving, with physicist **John D. Cockcroft,** the first artificial disintegration of an atomic nucleus, without the use of radioactive elements. Their breakthrough was accomplished by artificially accelerating a beam of protons (basic particles of the nuclei of atoms which carry a positive charge of electricity) and aiming it at a target of lithium, one of the lightest known metals. The resultant emission of alpha particles, that is, positively charged particles given off by certain radioactive substances, indicated not only that some protons had succeeded in penetrating the nuclei of the lithium atoms but also that they had somehow combined with the lithium atoms and had been transformed into something new. Although the process was not an efficient energy producer, the work of Walton and Cockcroft stimulated many theoretical and practical developments and influenced the whole course of nuclear physics. For their pioneering work, Walton and Cockcroft shared the 1951 Nobel Prize in physics.

Ernest Thomas Sinton Walton was born October 6, 1903, in Dungarven, County Waterford, in the Irish Republic. His father, John Arthur Walton, was a Methodist minister, while his mother, Anna Elizabeth (Sinton) Walton, was from a very old Ulster family, who had lived in the same house in Armagh for over two hundred years. The young Walton was sent to school at Belfast's Methodist

College, where he demonstrated an aptitude for science and math. It was no surprise, then, when in 1922 he decided to enroll in math and experimental science at Dublin's Trinity College. He graduated in 1926 with a B.A. degree, in 1928 with a M.Sc., and in 1934 with a M.A.

Joins the Cavendish During its Heyday

The following year he headed to Cambridge University, England, on a Clerk Maxwell research scholarship. There, he joined the world-famous Cavendish Laboratory, headed by the great New Zealand-born physicist, **Ernest Rutherford.** Walton was assigned cramped laboratory space in a basement room. While his quarters were less than luxurious, he was at least blessed by having roommates with whom he struck up an immediate friendship, physicists T. E. Allibone and John D. Cockcroft. Walton went on to make scientific history, in collaboration with the latter, for a project that would pave the way for the development of the atom bomb. Walton had first to learn to crawl before he could take such giant steps. At the suggestion of Rutherford, he began attempting to increase the velocity of electrons (the negatively charged particles of the atom) by spinning them in the electric field produced by a changing circular magnetic field as a method of nuclear disintegration. Although the method was not successful, he was able to figure out the stability of the orbits of the revolving electrons, and the design and engineering problems of creating an accelerating machine with minimal tools and materials. This early work of Walton's later led to the development of the betatron, that is, a particle accelerator in which electrons are propelled by the inductive action of a rapidly varying magnetic field.

Next, Walton tried to build a high frequency linear accelerator. His goal was to produce a stream of alpha particles traveling at high speed which could be used to shed light on various aspects of the atomic nucleus. Rutherford had long been keen to get his hands on such as source of alpha particles but despaired of any short-term breakthrough. As it transpired, Rutherford's wish was granted sooner than he expected.

What was needed was a fundamentally different way of viewing the problem. Walton and his colleagues at the Cavendish were trying to accelerate electrons to a speed sufficient to enable them to penetrate an atomic nucleus. Such high velocities were necessary, they believed, in order to counteract the repulsive charge of the nuclei. The speeding electrons, they figured, would literally bully their way through. However, achieving such high speeds was easier said than done. It required the application of enormous amounts of electricity, about four million volts, which at that time was impossible to generate in a discharge tube (a tube that contains a gas or metal vapor which conducts an electric discharge in the form of light). A crucial breakthrough came in 1929, when the Russian physicist **George Gamow** visited the Cavendish laboratory. With physicist **Niels Bohr** in Copenhagen, he had worked out a wave-mechanical theory of the penetration of particles, in which they believed particles tunneled through rather than over potential barriers. This meant that particles propelled by about five hundred thousand volts, as opposed to millions, could possibly permeate the barrier and enter the nucleus, if present in sufficiently large numbers. That is, one would need a beam of many thousands of millions of moving particles to produce atomic disintegrations that would be capable of being observed.

Rutherford gave Walton and Cockcroft the go-ahead to test the supposition. It was a measure of his confidence in them—the high voltage apparatus they constructed to enable them to accelerate atomic particles cost almost one thousand British pounds to build. It was an enormous sum in those days, and represented almost the entire annual budget for the laboratory.

The machine, the first of its kind ever built, and today on view at the London Science Museum in South Kensington, was built out of an ordinary transformer enhanced by two stacks of large condensers (or what would today be called capacitors), which could be turned on and off by means of an electronic switch. This arrangement generated up to half a million volts, which were directed at an electrical discharge tube. At the top of the tube protons were produced. The velocity of the protons was increased into a beam which could be used to hit any mark at the bottom of the tubes. Although it would be considered primitive by today's standards, their apparatus was, in fact, an ingenious construction, cobbled together from glass cylinders taken from old fashioned petrol pumps, flat metal sheets, plasti-

cene, and vacuum pumps. The current generated by the discharge tube was almost one hundred-thousandth of an ampere, which meant that about 50 million protons per second were being produced. The availability of such a large and tightly controlled source of particles—compared with that produced by, say, a radioactive source—greatly increased the odds of a nucleus being penetrated by the speeding atomic particles.

Halfway through 1931, while their experiment was still in its early stages, Walton and Cockcroft were forced to vacate their subterranean basement when it was taken over by physical chemists. They were obliged to deconstruct their installation and build it again. As it happened, it turned out to be a lucky break. Their new laboratory was an old lecture theater, whose high ceiling was much more suitable for their purposes. When Walton and Cockcroft went to reassemble their massive apparatus, they used the opportunity to introduce a few modifications. This time around, they incorporated a new voltage multiplying circuit, which Cockcroft had just developed, into their apparatus. It took them until the end of 1931 just to produce a steady stream of five or six hundred volts.

When the accelerator was finally completed, they restarted the laborious process of trying to penetrate an atomic nucleus using a stream of speeded up protons. They positioned a thin lithium target obliquely across from the beam of protons, in order to observe the alpha particles on either side of it. In order to detect the alpha particles that they hoped would be produced, they set up a tiny screen made of zinc sulfide, which they observed with a low-power microscope; a technique borrowed from Rutherford.

Walton's Scintillating Discovery

The first few months of 1932 were spent in rendering the installation more reliable and measuring the range and speed of the accelerated protons. It was not until April 13, 1932, that they achieved a breakthrough. On that fateful date, Walton first realized that their experiment had been successful. On the tiny screen, he detected flashes, called scintillations. These indicated that not only had the stream of protons succeeded in boring through the atomic nuclei but also that, in the process, a transformation had occurred. The speeding protons had combined with the lithium target to produce a new substance, the alpha particles, which appeared on the screen as scintillations.

Walton and Cockcroft confirmed Walton's observations using a paper recorder with two pens, each operated by a key. Walton worked one key, Cockcroft the other. When either noticed a flash, he pressed his key. As both keys were consistently pressed at the same time, it was clear that the alphas were being emitted in pairs. The implication was that the lithium nucleus, with a mass of seven and a charge of three had, on contact with an accelerated proton, split into two alpha particles, each of mass four and charge two. In the transformation, a small amount of energy was lost, equivalent to about a quarter of a percent of the mass of lithium.

Walton and Cockcroft's achievement was ground-breaking and historic in many ways. It represented the first time that anyone had produced a change in an atomic nucleus by means totally under human control. They had also discovered a new energy source. Furthermore, they had confirmed Gamow's theory that particles could tunnel or burrow their way into a nucleus, despite the repulsion of the electrical charges. And finally, they furnished a valuable confirmation of physicist **Albert Einstein's** theory that energy and mass are interchangeable. The extra energy of the alpha particles, when allowance was made for the energy of the proton, exactly corresponded to the loss of mass.

Walton and Cockcroft's achievement was announced in a letter in *Nature* and later at a meeting of the Royal Society of London, on June 15, 1932. By that time, they had succeeded in splitting the nuclei of fifteen elements, including beryllium, the lightest, to uranium, the heaviest. All produced alpha particles, although the most spectacular results were obtained from fluorine, lithium, and boron. The news caused a sensation throughout the world. As a result of their discovery, Walton and Cockcroft were the star attractions at the Solvay Conference, an important gathering of international physicists, held in 1933, and at the International Physics Conference, held in London in 1934.

Walton and Cockcroft's particle accelerator spawned many more sophisticated models, including one built by their colleague physicist Marcus Oliphant at the Cavendish. It was capable of producing a more abundant supply of particles; not only protons, but also deuterons (nuclei of heavy hydrogen). With this, many groundbreaking nuclear transformations were carried out. Their invention also inspired the American nuclear physicist, **Ernest Orlando Lawrence,** to build a cyclotron, a cyclical accelerator, capable of reaching tremendous speeds. Although scientists in the close of the twentieth century may regard the equipment Walton and Cockcroft used as primitive, the basic idea behind the particle accelerator has stayed the same.

In 1932, Walton received his Ph.D. from Cambridge and two years later returned to Dublin as a fellow of Trinity College, his reputation preceding him. He remained there for the rest of his career. The year 1934 was memorable not only for Walton's shifting bases but also because it was the year he married Freda Wilson, a former pupil of the Methodist College, Belfast. They had two sons and two daughters, Alan, Marian, Philip, and Jean.

The next few years passed rather uneventfully for Walton. While his erstwhile partner, Cockcroft, went from one high profile position to another, Walton preferred to remain slightly aloof from the mainstream of physics. He concentrated instead on establishing his department's reputation for excellence. His efforts were rewarded in 1946 when he was appointed Erasmus Smith Professor of Natural and Experimental Philosophy.

Shares 1951 Nobel Prize with Cockcroft

In 1951, almost twenty years after achieving the breakthrough that changed the face of nuclear physics, Walton and Cockcroft finally achieved the recognition that many believed was long overdue them. The Nobel Prize for physics was awarded to them jointly for their pioneering work on the transmutation of atomic nuclei by artificially accelerated atomic particles. The following year, Walton became chairman of the School of Cosmic Physics of the Dublin Institute for Advanced Studies. He was elected a senior fellow of Trinity College in 1960.

Outside of his scientific work, Walton was active in committees concerned with the government, the church, research and standards, scientific academies, and the Royal City of Dublin Hospital. He has been described as "quiet, undemonstrative, and little given to talk," according to Robert L. Weber in *Pioneers or Science: Nobel Prize Winners in Physics.* Walton died on June 25, 1995, at a hospital in Belfast, Northern Ireland.

SELECTED WRITINGS BY WALTON:

Other

The First Penetration of Nuclei by Accelerated Particles (sound recording). Educational Materials and Equipment Co., Spring Green Multimedia, 1974.

FURTHER READING:

Books

Andrade, E. N. da C., *Rutherford and the Nature of the Atom,* Doubleday Anchor, 1964.

Andrade, E. N. da C., *Biographical Dictionary of Scientists,* Volume 2, Facts-on-File, 1981, p. 823.

Crowther, J. G., *The Cavendish Laboratory, 1874–1974,* Science History Publications, 1974.

Crowther, J. G., *Modern Men of Science,* McGraw-Hill, 1966, p. 509.

Oliphant, Mark, *Rutherford: Recollections of the Cambridge Days,* Elsevier Publishing Co., 1972.

Weber, Robert L., *Pioneers of Science: Nobel Prize Winners in Physics,* Bristol and London, The Institute of Physics, 1980, p. 141.

Wilson, David, *Rutherford: Simple Genius,* MIT Press, 1983.

Sketch by Avril McDonald

An Wang
1920–1990
American computer scientist

An Wang

An Wang, a computer scientist and commercial computing executive, is best remembered for founding Wang Laboratories, a prominent manufacturer of office wordprocessing and dataprocessing computers in the 1970s and 1980s. His early work as a computer scientist focused on the development of magnetic core memories for computers in the late 1940s and early 1950s.

Wang, whose name means "Peaceful King" in Chinese, was born in Shanghai, China, on February 7, 1920. Because of its strategic location at the mouth of the Yangtze River, Shanghai was often a war zone during Wang's youth. Other areas of China were also at war: Japan captured the Chinese province of Manchuria in 1931. Wang's father, Yin Lu Wang, taught English in a private school and practiced traditional Chinese herbal medicine. Wang's mother was Zen Wan Chien. In elementary school, Wang excelled in math and science, but his grades in other subjects were so bad that he almost did not graduate. In high school some of his textbooks were written in English, which was to help him later when he moved to the United States.

Wang entered the prestigious Chiao-Tung University after high school and was elected class president. He studied electrical engineering, but spent more time competing at table tennis than studying. During this time, the Japanese began to conquer more and more of China. Wang managed to stay safe because the fighting was usually far away from him. He received his bachelor of science degree from Chiao-Tung University in 1940, remaining at the university as a teaching assistant from 1940 to 1941. As his part in the Chinese war effort against Japan, he designed and built radio transmitters at the Central Radio Works in China from 1941 to 1945.

In April of 1945, Wang left China for America with some fellow engineers on a two-year apprenticeship. They were to learn about Western technology so they could rebuild China after the war. Wang, however, did more to build Western technology than to rebuild China. After arriving in the United States, Wang decided to apply to Harvard, where some of his teachers at Chiao-Tung University had studied. Many American men were still at war (Japan would not surrender until August, 1945), and Harvard needed students, so they admitted Wang. He performed well in Harvard's electrical engineering courses because he already had years of experience designing radios for the Chinese government. He received his master of science in electrical engineering in 1946.

Wang intended to return to China after he got his degree, but he had no money for the transportation. Through a school friend, he obtained a job with the Chinese Government Supply Agency in Ottawa, Ontario, Canada, where he worked from 1946 to 1947. The job was clerical, and he found it very boring. He decided to return to Harvard for a Ph.D., and he was accepted into the applied physics department. He completed his program quickly and wrote his doctoral dissertation on nonlinear mechanics. Late in 1948, he finished his doctorate in applied physics.

Developing Magnetic Core Computer Memories at Harvard

Wang got his start in applied computer electronics when he went to work as a research fellow for **Howard Aiken** at the Harvard computation laboratory in May of 1948. Aiken, a computer pioneer, had developed the Mark I, the first automatic binary computer, in 1944. Wang did his most important work at Harvard in computer memories. Computer memories are essential to the development of computers as we know them today. Without computer memories, stored programs cannot exist, nor can programming languages or computer applications. When Wang went to work in the Harvard computation lab, there were already several kinds of memories: magnetic drums, punched cards, vacuum tubes, electromechanical relays, mercury delay lines, and cathode ray tubes. Each kind of memory had its disadvantages. Magnetic drums and punched cards were too slow, vacuum tubes burned out too often, and electromechanical relays were too noisy. Mercury delay lines made it hard for users to retrieve specific bits of data in a larger data set, and cathode ray tubes required a constant source of power or the data were lost.

Aiken wanted Wang to invent a memory that would let a computer read and record data magnetically without the mechanical movement involved in a relay or rotating drum. Wang was perplexed for a while, because he found that, when magnetic data were read, the process of reading the data destroyed them. But Wang soon discovered that he could use the data to rewrite the information in magnetic cores immediately after he destroyed it in the process of reading. Wang's ideas were used extensively in computers until magnetic core memories were replaced in the late 1960s by silicon chips. In 1955 Wang patented his ideas about reading and rewriting the information in magnetic memory cores.

In 1948, Wang met Lorraine Chiu, who was also from Shanghai, though her parents had been born in Hawaii. She was in the United States studying English at Wellesley College. They married in 1949. In September, 1950, their first child, Frederick, was born. A second son, Courtney, and a daughter, Juliette, were to follow. In April of 1955, both Wang and his wife became naturalized American citizens.

Building Wang Laboratories

Harvard preferred to sponsor basic research and decreased its work in computers when they started to be developed commercially. Aware of this, Wang began thinking about starting his own company. On June 22, 1951, he founded Wang Laboratories in Cambridge, Massachusetts, to manufacture magnetic core memories. He had six hundred dollars, and, as he said in his autobiography, "I had no orders, no contracts, and no office furniture." He subsisted for a while on contracts for manufacturing memories, on teaching, and on consulting. In November 1953, Wang began a consulting contract with IBM for a thousand dollars a month that was to bring him some financial stability. In March of 1956 Wang sold his patent on magnetic core memories to IBM for $500,000.

In the early 1960s, Wang Laboratories developed a popular typesetting system that would justify and hyphenate text on a page. By 1964 the company had sales of more than $1,000,000 for the first time. Then Wang began to develop desktop calculators. One of these, the Model 300, was very successful because it was user friendly, small, and relatively cheap at $1,695. By 1967, Wang's sales were up to $6.9 million per year. To raise money and eliminate some of its debt, Wang Labs publicly offered its stock for sale in August of 1967. The stock was so popular that the value of the company soared. Before the sale of stock, on August 22, Wang Labs was worth about one million dollars. One day later, after its stock went on sale, it had a market capitalization of $70,000,000.

Wang began to realize that the future of the company was not in desktop calculators but in computers. He feared that desktop calculators would become lower-valued commodities because of increasing competition. In 1971 the first pocket calculator was manufactured by Bowmar Instruments, and in the following decades, the appliances became even smaller and less expensive. Wang Laboratories began producing its first word processors, the Wang 1200, in 1972. The Wang 1200 was very primitive by today's standards. It stored data on a tape cassette and had no means of displaying text. Wang decided on some major improvements, and Wang Labs caused a sensation when it demonstrated its first CRT (cathode ray tube)-based word processor in June of 1976. In two years it was the largest distributor of such systems in the world. By 1982, Wang Laboratories had over a billion dollars in sales a year. By 1989, sales were $3 billion a year.

Wang received over a dozen honorary doctorates for his accomplishments, and, among other honors, was a fellow of the American Academy of Arts and Sciences. He underwent surgery to remove a cancerous tumor of the esophagus in 1989. He was readmitted to Massachusetts General Hospital in March of 1990 and died of cancer at the age of 70 on March 24, 1990.

SELECTED WRITINGS BY WANG:

Books

Lessons: An Autobiography, Addison-Wesley, 1986.

FURTHER READING:

Books

Cortada, James W., *Historical Dictionary of Data Processing: Biographies,* Greenwood Press, 1987.

Periodicals

Bulkeley, William M. and John R. Wilke, *Wall Street Journal,* Steep Slide: Filing in Chapter 11, Wang Sends Warning to High-Tech Circles, August 1992, pp. Al, A6.
Wilke, John R, *Wall Street Journal,* Wang Labs Reorganization Is Cleared, Allowing Emergence from Chapter 11, September 21, 1993, p. B6.

Sketch by Patrick Moore

James C. Wang
1936–
American biochemist

James C. Wang is a biochemist who trained as a chemical engineer before turning to biophysical chemistry and molecular biology. Wang discovered deoxyribonucleic acid (DNA) topoisomerases (or local enzymes) and proposed a mechanism for their operation in the 1970s. He also studied the configuration (or topology) of DNA, an approach that proved fruitful in helping to explain how the structure of the double helix coils and relaxes.

Wang was born in mainland China on November 18, 1936. Less than a year later the Sino-Japanese War began. Wang lost his mother during the conflict, and shortly after it ended, his older sister also died. His father remarried, moving the family to Taiwan in 1949. Because of the war, Wang received only about two years of elementary education before starting junior high school in Taiwan. As a child, he wanted to study medicine, but his father encouraged him to become an engineer. A high school teacher inspired him to follow his interest in chemistry. Chemical engineering became Wang's course of study, and he earned a B.S. in 1959 from National Taiwan University. Continuing his studies in the field of chemistry, he earned a masters from the University of South Dakota in 1961, and a doctorate from the University of Missouri in 1964.

In the same year that Wang received his doctorate, he became a research fellow at the California Institute of Technology, remaining there until 1966. He then taught at the University of California in Berkeley from 1966 until 1977, when he joined the faculty at Harvard University. He was named the Mallinckrodt Professor of Biochemistry and Molecular Biology at Harvard in 1988.

Study of DNA Topology Leads to Revelations

Wang once noted that his interest in DNA topology came about by chance. His training in engineering and chemistry had led him to study the physical basis of chemical processes. He began to think about the questions raised by the double helix structure of DNA soon after its discovery by molecular biologists **James Watson** and **Francis Crick**. His own study of DNA confirmed the unique structure. But it was not clear how the two tightly intertwined strands could unravel at the speed at which the biochemical processes were thought to occur. Topologically, it did not seem possible for the strands to unravel at all. Wang studied supercoiling in *E. coli* bacteria and found that the rotation speed of an unraveling DNA strand is 10,000 revolutions per minute. He also found that the same enzyme, a DNA topoisomerase, is responsible for both breaking and rejoining the DNA strands.

Wang believed that the topological characteristics of the double helix affected all its chemical transformations, including transcription, replication, and recombination. In a 1991 interview in *Cell Science,* Wang remarked that he relied on intuition to further his scientific understanding, particularly when trying to make sense of "bits and pieces of information" that didn't obviously fit together. "There are times," he told the interviewer, "when results that seem to make no sense are key to new advances."

Wang has served on the editorial boards of several scholarly journals, including *Journal of Molecular Biology, Annual Review of Biochemistry,* and *Quarterly Review of*

Biophysics. He was a Guggenheim fellow in 1986, and was elected to the U.S. National Academy of Sciences in 1984. In 1961 Wang married a former classmate; they have two daughters.

SELECTED WRITINGS BY WANG:

Periodicals

Scientific American, DNA Topoisomerases, Volume 247, 1982, pp. 94–109.
Nature, DNA Gyrations in Reverse, Volume 309, 1984, pp. 682–87.
Journal of Biological Chemistry, DNA Topoisomerases: Why So Many?, Volume 266, 1991, pp. 6659–62.

Sketch by Valerie Brown

Felix Wankel
1902–1988
German inventor

The distinction for designing the first practical rotary engine belongs to Felix Wankel, who experimented for years to properly integrate the necessary systems. Although concepts for an engine with pistons that spin rather than move back and forth had existed for centuries, Wankel was the first to develop the technologies required for its use in internal combustion engines. He became the leading developer of engine improvements based upon rotation and engine sealing systems, and Wankel engines are still used in thousands of automobiles manufactured each year. Wankel continued to perform experiments and develop new projects until his death in Lindau, Germany, on October 9, 1988.

Felix Heinrich Wankel was born to Rudolf Wankel and Gerty Heidlauff Wankel on August 13, 1902, in the town of Lahr, located in the Black Forest region of Germany. Wankel's father, a forest commissioner, was killed at the beginning of World War I when Wankel was twelve years old. As a result, Wankel worked to support himself and his mother after he finished high school. This prevented him from pursuing an apprentice position in foreign industry, the route often followed by men of his day who were talented in mechanics. Instead, Wankel moved to Heidelberg and worked in the print shop of a university book store until illness forced him to move from the print shop to the stock room. While there, however, he devised an improved method of stacking books for storage.

After work, Wankel attended night school and took correspondence courses. At the age of twenty-two he opened a machine shop in Heidelberg, quickly learning the important aspects of machining, production, and precision shaping and finishing of parts. Wankel began to experiment with improvements to automobile engines, specifically with reciprocating internal combustion engines, which use pistons and valves that move in a back-and-forth motion.

Wankel was aware of the shortcomings of reciprocating engines. Many parts were required to achieve the back-and-forth motion, which in turn caused a high degree of vibration and noise. In addition, as the speed of the engine increased, power losses occurred more frequently. Wankel believed that a rotary engine, one based on pistons which move in a circular motion, could perform much better than engines based upon reciprocating motion, and he began sketching designs of internal combustion engines with rotary pistons as early as 1924. He knew that ideas for rotary engines had been proposed since the sixteenth century, but a model that could withstand the heat, pressure, and wear created by internal combustion engines had not yet been developed. Wankel's own evaluations of his earliest designs led him to the conclusion that they did not justify further pursuit.

Designs Innovative Leak-Proof Valves

Wankel initially experimented with adapting rotary valves for motorcycle engines. His work in 1926 included improvements to the valve seals to prevent leakage of gas from the cylinders that house the pistons. He recognized that the lack of such seals in previous rotary valve designs was a primary cause of their failure. He began experimenting with a disc valve, rotating valves which turned on top of the engine cylinders, and by 1933 Wankel had successfully operated a disk valve engine on a motorcycle. His innovations in sealing became one of the most important steps in Wankel's development of a rotary engine.

In 1928 Wankel met Wilhelm Keppler, who later became the business consultant to Adolf Hitler. At their meeting Wankel expressed his desire to help Germany maintain her position as a great nation by building his technologically superior rotary engine. Keppler played a central role in Wankel's work on the engine during World War II and for several years after the war.

In 1933 Wankel contracted with Daimler-Benz A.G., an auto manufacturer, to research sealing, rotary valves, and engines. After a year he began conducting similar research for another automobile maker, Bayerische Motoren Werke (BMW). As a result of this work, Wankel obtained a patent for "packing bodies" in 1936. Packing bodies were specially designed materials that were attached to primary components to achieve the seal. This customized approach provided much tighter seals than previous sealing attempts by precisely finishing primary components and pressing them tightly together in direct contact. Wankel also used the pressure of the gases in the engine to help tighten the seals. Wankel received many patents for his work on sealing systems, and by 1936 all possible rotary valve applications to internal combustion engines and compressors were

covered by his patents. Wankel developed his first rotary piston internal combustion engine, one with rotating instead of reciprocating pistons, during this period. This first engine was impractical, but Wankel's unique solution to sealing the cylinders proved critical to future development.

War Research Provides Avenue for Improved Rotary Technology

As Germany became involved in the Second World War, Wankel's work toward the development of a practical rotary engine slowed. He was branded a traitor and imprisoned by then-State Chancellor Hitler for his assistance in uncovering an embezzlement operation run by members of Hitler's party. Hans Nibel, the chief engineer at Daimler-Benz, learned of Wankel's circumstances and convinced Wilhelm Keppler to have Wankel released. Keppler acted as Wankel's protector throughout World War II.

Upon his release from prison in 1935, Wankel moved his workshop closer to his home in Lahr. The following year Hermann Goering, the head of Germany's air force, heard of Wankel's work and invited him to conduct his research in Berlin. Wankel declined to move to Berlin, but convinced Goering to establish a separate research facility for him on Lake Constance near his home. Goering's air ministry invested millions of dollars in Wankel's facility and the development of a rotary valve airplane engine. By 1939 Wankel's rotary disk valve was part of the new Daimler-Benz DB601 aircraft engine. The outbreak of World War II prevented a scheduled speed flight that was expected to break records, but by 1942 the DB601 engine was in production for use in many German fighter planes and light bombers.

During the war, another company, Junkers, began using Wankel's rotary valves in the designs for their torpedo engines. The valves were critical to the development of Junkers's product because they greatly reduced the amount of space required by the engine. Junkers designed and tested several engines using Wankel's valves. The final design was for an engine that fit inside a twenty-one inch diameter torpedo.

Wankel was in Berlin performing research for Goering's air ministry from 1940 through 1944. He was able to use the successful DB601 engine as a springboard for further development of rotary valves. In 1944 Wankel built a rotary compressor, and by 1945 he had contracts with several government agencies and automobile and railroad corporations to develop rotary parts.

At the conclusion of World War II, the politics of war again interrupted Wankel's work. French occupation forces jailed the inventor from 1945 to 1946 as a war criminal for his work on German airplane engines. His research facility on Lake Constance was dismantled, and he was forbidden to conduct research or experiments. Wankel used this time to review his work, write papers, and work on designs for engines that included his rotary valves and pistons and sealing system.

Develops Practical Rotary Engine in Partnership with NSU

In 1951 Wilhelm Keppler helped Wankel open a new research and development facility on Lake Constance, not far from the site of his wartime laboratories. Keppler had influence in German industry and guided Wankel into a working relationship with NSU Werke, the motorcycle manufacturer. Some of Wankel's early work at NSU included the development of sealing systems for air compressors and conventional pistons. Wankel carefully developed his relationship with NSU, never becoming a company employee. Instead he contracted with NSU for the company's use of his motorcycle engines and future research. In addition, Wankel negotiated his contracts so that he was free to work with other clients and run his own shop.

NSU funded the development of Wankel's compressor into a supercharger for their racing motorcycles. The supercharger, completed in 1954, pushed the mixture of gas and air into the cylinder of a small NSU moped engine, increasing the power by more than 800 percent. For three and a half years Wankel and NSU experimented with ways to develop a rotary engine from the supercharger's fundamental design. The shape of the chamber in which a rotary piston spins is particularly critical to a practical rotary engine. Wankel identified the shapes for his early engines empirically. Only later would Professor Othmar Baier of the Technical College in Stuttgart employ geometric principles. Professor Baier's work greatly facilitated the analysis of Wankel's engine and simplified manufacturing by allowing the application of analytic mathematics to the shape of the Wankel engine.

During this time Wankel was assisted by a team of NSU engineers led by Dr. Walter Froede. On February 1, 1957, the group successfully tested their first rotary engine. A second, larger test engine was built and tested that same year. It produced no mechanical vibration, proving the ability of the Wankel engine to overcome a primary disadvantage of reciprocating engines. However, the engine required additional modifications before it could be used for such practical applications as the power plant in an automobile. In this early design, while the triangular shaped piston spun inside the chamber, the chamber itself rotated as well. A stationary housing would be required to protect the engine for use in practical applications, but instead of adding the cost and weight of an additional housing to the engine, Dr. Froede redesigned it so that the chamber remained stationary instead of turning. This allowed the chamber to act as the engine's protective housing. Froede's design resulted in the KKM engine, which made the Wankel engine truly practical. Wankel initially opposed the KKM on technical grounds, but after testing the improved engine design, his research and experimentation with NSU progressed.

Wankel was forced to divert some of his attention away from the development of his engine during its long technological progression. Financial difficulties at NSU forced him to find additional funding in order to continue his research. Wankel joined forces with Ernst Hutzenlaub, an architect turned inventor who provided $250,000 to market licenses for Wankel's engine. In order to use the Wankel engine in their airplanes, in 1958 Curtiss-Wright became one of the first companies to purchase a license. NSU continued to have a volatile financial status, but Wankel was able to conduct further research.

Wankel and the NSU engineers improved and modified the design of the KKM engine over the course of several years until a production model of the Wankel engine was ready. The KKM became the basis for numerous applications, including a water cooled version for boats. Wankel and NSU were very interested in using the engine for automobiles. In 1963 Toyo Kogyo (Mazda) produced the Cosmo Sports, the first prototype car using a Wankel engine. Several other corporations with licenses for Wankel engines, including Mercedes-Benz and General Motors, developed improvements to Wankel's basic design. In 1970 the first publicly available automobile powered by a Wankel engine arrived in the United States from Japan. Wankel's dream of a rotary piston engine for automobiles had finally become reality. After the development of a practical version of the engine, Wankel continued to experiment with new seals and geometric applications. He also performed extensive research into adapting the engine for diesel power and large rotary compressors.

Wankel showed unusual innovation and persistence in the pursuit of his dream of a practical rotary engine, and in 1969 the Technical Institute of Munich awarded him an honorary doctorate. Based upon an idea that is centuries old, Wankel's efforts have resulted in the development of valuable innovations in power systems.

SELECTED WRITINGS BY WANKEL:

Books

Rotary Piston Machines, Illiffe Books Ltd., 1965.

Periodicals

Automotive Engineer, Rotary Piston Engine Performance Criteria, September 1964.

FURTHER READING:

Books

Corbett, Scott, *What About the Wankel Engine?* Four Winds Press, 1974.
Dark, Harris Edward, *The Wankel Rotary Engine, Introduction and Guide,* Indiana University Press, 1974.

Faith, Nicholas, *Wankel, the Curious Story Behind the Revolutionary Rotary Engine,* Stein and Day, 1975.

Norbye, Jan P., *The Wankel Engine,* Chilton Book Co., 1971.

Yamamoto, Kenichi, *Rotary Engine,* Sankaido Co. Ltd., 1981.

Periodicals

Yamamoto, Kenichi, *Changing Times,* Is the Wankel the Auto Engine of the Future? July 1972.

Yamamoto, Kenichi, *Forbes,* Wangle Yourself a Wankel, December 15, 1972.

Sketch by David N. Ford

Otto Warburg

Otto Warburg
1883–1970
German biochemist

Otto Warburg is considered one of the world's foremost biochemists. His achievements include discovering the mechanism of cell oxidation and identifying the iron-enzyme complex, which catalyzes this process. He also made great strides in developing new experimental techniques, such as a method for studying the respiration of intact cells using a device he invented. His work was recognized with a Nobel Prize for medicine and physiology in 1931.

Otto Heinrich Warburg was born on October 8, 1883, in Freiburg, Germany, to Emil Gabriel Warburg and Elizabeth Gaertner. Warburg was one of four children and the only boy. His father was a physicist of note and held the prestigious chair in physics at University of Berlin. The Warburg household often hosted prominent guests from the German scientific community, such as physicists **Albert Einstein**, **Max Planck**, **Emil Fischer**—the leading organic chemist of the late-nineteenth century—and **Walther Nernst**—the period's leading physical chemist.

Warburg studied chemistry at the University of Freiburg beginning in 1901. After two years, he left for the University of Berlin to study under Emil Fischer, and in 1906 received a doctorate in chemistry. His interest turned to medicine, particularly to cancer, so he continued his studies at the University of Heidelberg where he earned an M.D. degree in 1911. He remained at Heidelberg, conducting research for several more years and also making several research trips to the Naples Zoological Station.

Warburg's career goal was to make great scientific discoveries, particularly in the field of cancer research, according to the biography written by **Hans Adolf Krebs**, one of Warburg's students and winner of the 1953 Nobel Prize in medicine and physiology. Although he did not take up problems specifically related to cancer until the 1920s, his early projects provided a foundation for future cancer studies. For example, his first major research project, published in 1908, examined oxygen consumption during growth. In a study using sea urchin eggs, Warburg showed that, after fertilization, oxygen consumption in the specimens increased 600 percent. This finding helped clarify earlier work that had been inconclusive on associating growth with increased consumption of oxygen and energy. A number of years later, Warburg did some similar tests of oxygen consumption by cancer cells.

World War I Interrupts Research

Warburg was elected in 1913 to the Kaiser Wilhelm Gesellschaft, a prestigious scientific institute whose members had the freedom to pursue whatever studies they wished. He had just begun his work at the institute when World War I started. He volunteered for the army and joined the Prussian Horse Guards, a cavalry unit that fought on the Russian front. Warburg survived the war and returned to the Kaiser Wilhelm Institute for Biology in Berlin in 1918. Now 35 years old, he would devote the rest of his life to biological research, concentrating on studies of energy transfer in cells (cancerous or otherwise) and photosynthesis.

One of Warburg's significant contributions to biology was the development of a manometer for monitoring cell respiration. He adapted a device originally designed to measure gases dissolved in blood so it would make measurements of the rate of oxygen production in living cells. In related work, Warburg devised a technique for preparing thin slices of intact, living tissue and keeping the samples alive in a nutrient medium. As the tissue slices consumed oxygen for respiration, Warburg's manometer monitored the changes.

During Warburg's youth, he had become familiar with Einstein's work on photochemical reactions as well as the experimental work done by his own father, Emil Warburg, to verify parts of Einstein's theory. With this background, Warburg was especially interested in the method by which plants converted light energy to chemical energy. Warburg used his manometric techniques for the studies of photosynthesis he conducted on algae. His measurements showed that photosynthetic plants used light energy at a highly efficient sixty-five percent. Some of Warburg's other theories about photosynthesis were not upheld by later research, but he was nevertheless considered a pioneer for the many experimental methods he developed in this field. In the late 1920s, Warburg began to develop techniques that used light to measure reaction rates and detect the presence of chemical compounds in cells. His "spectrophotometric" techniques formed the basis for some of the first commercial spectrophotometers built in the 1940s.

Discovers Details of Cell Respiration

His work on cell respiration was another example of his interest in how living things generated and used energy. Prior to World War I, Warburg discovered that small amounts of cyanide can inhibit cell oxidation. Since cyanide forms stable complexes with heavy metals such as iron, he inferred from his experiment that one or more catalysts important to oxidation must contain a heavy metal. He conducted other experiments with carbon monoxide, showing that this compound inhibits respiration in a fashion similar to cyanide. Next he found that light of specific frequencies could counteract the inhibitory effects of carbon monoxide, at the same time demonstrating that the "oxygen transferring enzyme," as Warburg called it, was different from other enzymes containing iron. He went on to discover the mechanism by which iron was involved in the cell's use of oxygen. It was Warburg's work in characterizing the cellular catalysts and their role in respiration that earned him a Nobel Prize in 1931.

Nobel Foundation records indicate that Warburg was considered for Nobel Prizes on two additional occasions: in 1927 for his work on metabolism of cancer cells, then in 1944 for his identification of the role of flavins and nicotinamide in biological oxidation. Warburg did not receive the 1944 award, however, because a decree from Hitler forbade German citizens from accepting Nobel Prizes. Two of Warburg's students also won Nobel Prizes in medicine and physiology: Hans Krebs (1953) and **Axel Theorell** (1955).

In 1931 Warburg established the Kaiser Wilhelm Institute for Cell Physiology with funding from the Rockefeller Foundation in the United States. During the 1930s, Warburg spent much of his time studying dehydrogenases, enzymes that remove hydrogen from substrates. He also identified some of the cofactors, such as nicotinamide derived from vitamin B_3 (niacin), that play a role in a number of cell biochemical reactions.

Warburg conducted research at the Kaiser Wilhelm Institute for Cell Physiology until 1943 when the Second World War interrupted his investigations. Air attacks targeted at Berlin forced him to move his laboratory about 30 miles away to an estate in the countryside. For the next two years, he and his staff continued their work outside the city and out of the reach of the war. Then, in 1945, Russian soldiers advancing to Berlin occupied the estate and confiscated Warburg's equipment. Although the Russian commander admitted that the soldiers acted in error, Warburg never recovered his equipment. Without a laboratory, he spent the next several years writing, publishing two books that provided an overview of much of his research. He also traveled to the United States during 1948 and 1949 to visit fellow scientists.

Survives Nazi Germany

Even though Warburg was of Jewish ancestry, he was able to remain in Germany and pursue his studies unhampered by the Nazis. One explanation is that Warburg's mother was not Jewish and high German officials "reviewed" Warburg's ancestry, declaring him only one-quarter Jewish. As such he was forbidden from holding a university post, but allowed to continue his research. There is speculation that the Nazis believed Warburg might find a cure for cancer and so did not disturb his laboratory. Scientists in other countries were unhappy that Warburg was willing to remain in Nazi Germany. His biographer Hans Krebs noted, however, that Warburg was not afraid to criticize the Nazis. At one point during the war when Warburg was planning to travel to Zurich for a scientific meeting, the Nazis told him to cancel the trip and to not say why. "With some measure of courage," wrote Krebs, "he sent a telegram [to a conference participant from England]: 'Instructed to cancel participation without giving reasons.'" Although the message was not made public officially, the text was leaked and spread through the scientific community. Krebs believed Warburg did not leave Germany because he did not want to have to rebuild the research team he had assembled. The scientist feared that starting over would destroy his research potential, Krebs speculated.

In 1950 Warburg moved into a remodeled building in Berlin which had been occupied by U.S. armed forces following World War II. This new site was given the name of Warburg's previous scientific home—the Kaiser Wilhelm Institute for Cell Physiology—and three years later renamed the Max Planck Institute for Cell Physiology. Warburg continued to conduct research and write there, publishing 178 scientific papers from 1950 until his death in 1970.

For all of his interest in cancer, Warburg's studies did not reveal any deep insights into the disease. When he wrote about the "primary" causes of cancer later in his life, Warburg's proposals failed to address the mechanisms by which cancer cells undergo unchecked growth. Instead, he focused on metabolism, suggesting that in cancer cells "fermentation" replaces normal oxygen respiration. Warburg's cancer studies led him to fear that exposure to food additives increased one's chances of contracting the disease. In 1966 he delivered a lecture in which he stated that cancer prevention and treatment should focus on the administration of respiratory enzymes and cofactors, such as iron and the B vitamins. The recommendation elicited much controversy in Germany and elsewhere in the Western world.

Warburg's devotion to science led him to forego marriage, since he thought it was incompatible with his work. According to Karlfried Gawehn, Warburg's colleague from 1950 to 1964, "For him [Warburg] there were no reasonable grounds, apart from death, for not working." Warburg's productivity and stature as a researcher earned him an exemption from the institute's mandatory retirement rules, allowing him to continue working until very near to the end of his life. He died at the Berlin home he shared with Jakob Heiss on August 1, 1970.

SELECTED WRITINGS BY WARBURG:

Books

The Metabolism of Tumors, Constable and Co., 1930.
Heavy Metal Prosthetic Groups and Enzyme Action, translated by Alexander Lawson, Clarendon Press, 1949.
New Methods of Cell Physiology, Interscience Publishers, 1962.

Periodicals

Science, On the Origin of Cancer Cells, Volume 123, 1956, p. 312.

FURTHER READING:

Books

Krebs, Hans, *Otto Warburg: Cell Physiologist, Biochemist and Eccentric,* Clarendon Press, 1981.

Sketch by Lee Katterman

Warren M. Washington
1936–
American meteorologist

Warren M. Washington is an atmospheric scientist whose research focuses on the development of computer models that describe and predict the earth's climate. He is the director of the Climate and Global Dynamics Division of the National Center for Atmospheric Research (NCAR), in Boulder, Colorado. He has advised the U.S. Congress and several U.S. presidents on climate-system modeling, serving on the President's National Advisory Committee on Oceans and Atmosphere from 1978 to 1984.

Washington was born on August 28, 1936, in Portland, Oregon. His father, Edwin Washington, Jr., had hoped to be a school teacher, but in the 1920s Portland wouldn't hire a black man to teach in the public schools. Instead, the elder Washington supported Warren and his four brothers by waiting tables in Pullman cars. His wife, Dorothy Grace (Morton) Washington, became a practical nurse after the Washington children were grown.

Washington's interest in scientific research developed early and was nurtured by high school teachers who encouraged him to experiment. Refusing once to directly answer his question about why egg yolks were yellow, a chemistry teacher inspired Washington to study chicken diets and eventually to learn about the chemistry of sulfur compounds. Despite the boy's aptitude for science, Washington's high school counselor advised him to attend a business school rather than college, but Washington's dream was to be a scientist. He earned his bachelor's degree in physics in 1958 from Oregon State University. As an undergraduate, Washington become interested in meteorology while working on a project at a weather station near the campus. As part of the project, the station used radar equipment to track storms as they came in off the coast. In 1960 he earned his master's degree in meteorology from Oregon State. When he completed his graduate work in 1964 at Pennsylvania State University, he became one of only four African Americans to receive a doctorate in meteorology.

Washington began working for the NCAR in 1963 and has remained affiliated with that institution throughout his career. His research there has attempted to quantify patterns of oceanic and atmospheric circulation. He has helped to create complex mathematical models that take into account the effects of surface and air temperature, soil and atmospheric moisture, sea ice volume, various geographical features, and other parameters on past and current climates. His research has contributed to our modern-day understanding of the greenhouse effect, in which excess carbon dioxide in Earth's atmosphere causes the retention of heat, giving rise to what is known as global warming. Washington's research also provided understanding for other mechanisms of global climate change.

Washington was appointed the director of the Climate and Global Dynamics Division at NCAR in 1987. In 1994 he was elected president of the American Meteorological Society. He is a fellow of the American Association for the Advancement of Science and a member of its board of directors, a fellow of the African Scientific Institute, a distinguished alumnus of Pennsylvania State University, a fellow of Oregon State University, and founder and president of the Black Environmental Science Trust, a nonprofit foundation that encourages African American participation in environmental research and policymaking.

Washington has published over 100 professional articles about atmospheric science. He coauthored, with Claire Parkinson, *An Introduction to Three-Dimensional Climate Modeling* in 1986, and the book has since become a standard reference text for climate modeling. Washington, a widower, has six children and ten grandchildren.

SELECTED WRITINGS BY WASHINGTON:

Books

An Introduction to Three-Dimensional Climate Modeling, Oxford University Press, 1986.

Periodicals

Natural History, Where's the Heat? March 1990, pp. 66–70.

FURTHER READING:

Periodicals

Clemmitt, Marcia, *Scientist,* Minority Scientists Broaden Efforts to Fight Environmental Woes of Poor, April 29, 1991, p.1.

Hill, Richard, *Oregonian,* Acclaimed Scientist Rejected Advice to Go to Business School, November 18, 1993, p. A–21.

Jackson, Robert, *Rocky Mountain News,* Coloradan to Head Meteorologists, (Colorado), February 9, 1993.

Roberts, Chris, *Daily Camera,* Mr. Washington Goes to Washington, February 11, 1993, pp. 1–2C.

Saunders, Ellen, *Oregon Stater,* Global Warming Expert Hopes to Encourage Others, December 1990, p. 21.

Sketch by Leslie Reinherz

Levi Watkins, Jr.
1945–
American cardiac surgeon

Levi Watkins, Jr., the first black graduate of Vanderbilt University School of Medicine, has conducted research on congestive heart failure and also performed the first implantation of the automatic defibrillator in February 1980 at Johns Hopkins Hospital in Baltimore. The Automatic Implantation Defibrillator (AID) is designed to restore the heart's normal rhythm during an attack of ventricular fibrillation or arrhythmia, an irregularity of the heartbeat caused by coronary scar tissue or hardening of the coronary artery. When arrhythmia occurs, the heart is unable to pump blood and, unless corrected by devices such as the AID, the sufferer can die.

Watkins was born on June 13, 1945, in Parsons, Kansas, to Levi Watkins, Sr., an educator who became the president of Alabama State University, and Lillian Bernice Varnado. He graduated from Tennessee State University with honors in 1966. Watkins received his medical degree from the Vanderbilt University School of Medicine in Nashville in 1970 and completed his residency at the Johns Hopkins University Hospital, where he was the first black chief resident of cardiac surgery.

After his residency, Watkins was appointed assistant professor and then professor of surgery at Johns Hopkins. Watkins also spent two years conducting research at Harvard Medical School's Department of Physiology, investigating the relationship between congestive heart failure and the renin angiotensin system. Within the renin angiotensin system, a kidney enzyme is associated with the production of a hormone that causes dilation of blood vessels and contraction of muscles. Watkins's research led to the use of angiotensin blockers to treat congestive heart failure.

In 1982, discussing the ground-breaking AID device in *Ebony,* Watkins observed that "Now we can give patients the ultimate protection from this sudden death." At that time, it was estimated that 500,000 people died from arrhythmia annually, making the disorder one of the leading causes of death in the United States. Invented by Michel Mirowski, the director of the coronary care unit at Sinai Hospital in Baltimore, the AID is a small, battery-operated generator that is implanted in the patient's abdomen. One electrode leading from the AID is inserted into the right chamber of the heart; a second electrode is affixed to the tip of the heart. When the AID senses an abnormal heart rhythm, it administers mild shocks to restore the normal rhythm. The success of the device means a positive prognosis for patients who do not respond to medication for the disorder (about twenty-five percent). Watkins's initial AID surgical procedure was soon followed by dozens of successful implantations, and representatives of medical centers throughout the country applied to be trained for the procedure.

In addition to his work with cardiac arrhythmia at Johns Hopkins, Watkins has been a pioneer in the application of lasers to heart surgery, and has directed research on heart disease, particularly as it affects minorities, through Maryland's Minority Health Commission and Panel for Coronary Artery Bypass Surgery. An aggressive recruiter of black students for Johns Hopkins Medical School, he was appointed in 1979 to the university's admissions committee. In 1983, Watkins joined the national board of the Robert Wood Johnson Minority Faculty Development Program. His other professional affiliations include the American Board of Surgery and the American Board of Thoracic Surgery.

SELECTED WRITINGS BY WATKINS, JR.:

Periodicals

The New England Journal of Medicine, Termination of Malignant Ventricular Arrhythmias with an Implanted Automatic Defibrillator in Human Beings, August 7, 1980, pp. 322–324.
Journal of Cardiac Surgery, Implantation of the Automatic Implantable Cardioverter Defibrillator, March 3, 1988, pp. 1–7.
Annals of Thoracic Surgery, Treatment of Impending Sudden Cardiac Death, March 1989, pp. 484–485.

FURTHER READING:

Periodicals

Science Digest, Device Averts Heart Attacks, March 1981, p. 103.
Black Enterprise, Finding New Breakthroughs in Heart Care, October, 1988, p. 58.
Ebony, Young Surgeon Brings New Hope to Heart Patients, January, 1982, pp. 96–98; 100.

Sketch by Jane Stewart Cook

James D. Watson
1928–
American molecular biologist

James D. Watson won the 1962 Nobel Prize in physiology and medicine along with **Francis Crick** and **Maurice Wilkins** for discovering the structure of DNA, or deoxyribonucleic acid, which is the carrier of genetic

James D. Watson

information at the molecular level. Watson and Crick had worked as a team since meeting in the early 1950s, and their research ranks as a fundamental advance in molecular biology. More than thirty years later, Watson became the director of the Human Genome Project, an enterprise devoted to a difficult goal: the description of every human gene, the total of which may number up to one hundred thousand. This is a project that would not be possible without Watson's groundbreaking work on DNA.

James Dewey Watson was born in Chicago, Illinois, on April 6, 1928, to James Dewey and Jean (Mitchell) Watson. He was educated in the Chicago public schools, and during his adolescence became one of the original Quiz Kids on the radio show of the same name. Shortly after this experience in 1943, Watson entered the University of Chicago at the age of fifteen.

Watson graduated in 1946, but stayed on at Chicago for a bachelor's degree in zoology, which he attained in 1947. During his undergraduate years Watson studied neither genetics nor biochemistry—his primary interest was in the field of ornithology; in 1946 he spent a summer working on advanced ornithology at the University of Michigan's summer research station at Douglas Lake. During his undergraduate career at Chicago, Watson had been instructed by the well-known population geneticist **Sewall Wright**, but he did not become interested in the field of genetics until he read **Erwin Schrödinger**'s influential book *What is Life?* It was then, Horace Judson reports in *The Eighth Day of Creation: Makers of the Revolution in*

Biology, that Watson became interested in "finding out the secret of the gene."

Work with the "Phage Group"

Watson enrolled at Indiana University to perform graduate work in 1947. Indiana had several remarkable geneticists who could have been important to Watson's intellectual development, but he was drawn to the university by the presence of the Nobel laureate **Hermann Joseph Muller**, who had demonstrated twenty years earlier that X rays cause mutation. Nonetheless, Watson chose to work under the direction of the Italian biologist **Salvador Edward Luria**, and it was under Luria that he began his doctoral research in 1948.

Watson's thesis was on the effect of X rays on the rate of phage lysis (a phage, or bacteriophage, is a bacterial virus). The biologist **Max Delbrück** and Luria—as well as a number of others who formed what was to be known as "the phage group"—had demonstrated that phages could exist in a number of mutant forms. A year earlier Luria and Delbrück had published one of the landmark papers in phage genetics, in which they established that one of the characteristics of phages is that they can exist in different genetic states so that the lysis (or bursting) of bacterial host cells can take place at different rates. Watson's Ph.D. degree was received in 1950, shortly after his twenty-second birthday.

Watson was next awarded a National Research Council fellowship grant to investigate the molecular structure of proteins in Copenhagen, Denmark. While Watson was studying enzyme structure in Europe, where techniques crucial to the study of macromolecules were being developed, he was also attending conferences and meeting colleagues.

From 1951 to 1953, Watson held a research fellowship under the support of the National Foundation for Infantile Paralysis at the Cavendish Laboratory in Cambridge, England. Those two years are described in detail in Watson's 1965 book, *The Double Helix: A Personal Account of the Discovery of the Structure of DNA.* (An autobiographical work, *The Double Helix* describes the events—both personal and professional—that led to the discovery of DNA.) Watson was to work at the Cavendish under the direction of **Max Perutz**, who was engaged in the X-ray crystallography of proteins. However, he soon found himself engaged in discussions with Crick on the structure of DNA. Crick was twelve years older than Watson and, at the time, a graduate student studying protein structure.

Intermittently over the next two years, Watson and Crick theorized about DNA and worked on their model of DNA structure, eventually arriving at the correct structure by recognizing the importance of X-ray diffraction photographs produced by **Rosalind Franklin** at King's College, London. Both were certain that the answer lay in model-building, and Watson was particularly impressed by Nobel laureate **Linus Pauling**'s use of model-building in determining the alpha-helix structure of protein. Using data published by Austrian-born American biochemist **Erwin Chargaff** on the symmetry between the four constituent nucleotides (or "bases") of DNA molecules, they concluded that the building blocks had to be arranged in pairs. After a great deal of experimentation with their models, they found that the double helix structure corresponded to the empirical data produced by Wilkins, Franklin, and their colleagues. Watson and Crick published their theoretical paper in the journal *Nature* in 1953 (with Watson's name appearing first due to a coin toss), and their conclusions were supported by the experimental evidence simultaneously published by Wilkins, Franklin, and Raymond Goss. Wilkins shared the Nobel Prize with Watson and Crick in 1962.

Career Since the Discovery of DNA

After the completion of his research fellowship at Cambridge, Watson spent the summer of 1953 at Cold Spring Harbor, New York, where Delbrück had gathered an active group of investigators working in the new area of molecular biology. Watson then became a research fellow in biology at the California Institute of Technology, working with Delbrück and his colleagues on problems in phage genetics. In 1955, he joined the biology department at Harvard and remained on the faculty until 1976. While at Harvard, Watson wrote *The Molecular Biology of the Gene* (1965), the first widely used university textbook on molecular biology. This text has gone through seven editions, and now exists in two large volumes as a comprehensive treatise of the field. In 1968, Watson became director of Cold Spring Harbor, carrying out his duties there while maintaining his position at Harvard. He gave up his faculty appointment at the university in 1976, however, and assumed full-time leadership of Cold Spring Harbor. With John Tooze and David Kurtz, Watson wrote *The Molecular Biology of the Cell,* originally published in 1983 and now in its third edition.

In 1989, Watson was appointed the director of the Human Genome Project of the National Institutes of Health, but after less than two years he resigned in protest over policy differences in the operation of this massive project. He continues to speak out on various issues concerning scientific research and is a strong presence concerning federal policies in supporting research. In addition to sharing the Nobel Prize, Watson has received numerous honorary degrees from institutions, including one from the University of Chicago, which was awarded in 1961, when Watson was still in his early thirties. In 1968, Watson married Elizabeth Lewis. They have two children, Rufus Robert and Duncan James.

Watson, as his book *The Double Helix* confirms, has never avoided controversy. His candor about his colleagues and his combativeness in public forums have been noted by critics. On the other hand, his scientific brilliance is attested to by Crick, Delbrück, Luria, and others. The importance of his role in the DNA discovery has been well supported by Gunther Stent—a member of the Delbrück phage group—in an essay that discounts many of Watson's critics through well-reasoned arguments.

Most of Watson's professional life has been spent as a professor, research administrator, and public policy spokesman for research. More than any other location in Watson's professional life, Cold Spring Harbor (where he is still director) has been the most congenial in developing his abilities as a scientific catalyst for others. His work there has primarily been to facilitate and encourage the research of other scientists.

In addition to Watson's 22 honorary degrees from academic institutions, he has also been the recipient of the following awards:

• John Collins Warren Prize of Massachusetts General Hospital (1959)

• Eli Lilly Award in Biochemistry (1960)

• Albert Lasker Prize, awarded by the American Public Health Association (1960)

• Research Corporation Prize (1962)

• John J. Carty Gold Medal of the National Academy of Sciences (1971)

• Presidential Medal of Freedom (1977)

• Copley Medal of the British Royal Society (1993)

• Charles A. Dana Distinguished Achievement Award in Health (1994)

• Lomonosov Medal, Russian Academy of Sciences (1995)

• National Medal of Science for his "five decades of scientific and intellectual leadership in molecular biology" (1997).

He has been honored by the American Academy of Arts and Sciences (1958), the National Academy of Sciences (1962), the Danish Academy of Arts and Sciences (1963), Clare College, Cambridge University (1968), the American Philosophical Society (1977), Athenaeum, London (1980), the Royal Society, London (1981), the Academy of Sciences, Russia (1989), Oxford University (1994), National Academy of Sciences, Ukraine (1995), University College Galway, The Society of Saints & Scholars (1995), Institute of Biology, London (1995), and the Tata Institute of Fundamental Research (1996). Watson's professional affiliations include the American Society of Biological Chemists and the American Association for Cancer Research.

SELECTED WRITINGS BY WATSON:

Books

The Molecular Biology of the Gene, Benjamin, 1965.
The Double Helix: A Personal Account of the Discovery of the Structure of DNA, Norton, 1968.

The DNA Story, 1981.
The Molecular Biology of the Cell, Benjamin, 1983.

Periodicals

Nature, A Structure for Deoxyribose Nucleic Acid, April 25, 1953, pp. 738–740.
Nature, Genetical Implications of the Structure of DNA, May 30, 1953, pp. 964–967.

FURTHER READING:

Books

Crick, Francis, *What Mad Pursuit: A Personal View of Scientific Discovery*, Basic Books, 1988.
Judson, Horace Freeland, *The Eighth Day of Creation: Makers of the Revolution in Biology*, Simon and Schuster, 1979.
Olby, Robert, *The Path to the Double Helix*, Macmillan, 1974.
Stent, Gunther, *Paradoxes of Progress*, Chicago, 1985.

Sketch by Russell Aiuto

Robert Watson-Watt
1892–1973
Scottish physicist

Robert Watson-Watt's major contribution to science was the development of radar, the process of using radio waves to detect objects. First used successfully as a defense mechanism during World War II, many authorities have described it as one of the two most significant scientific achievements (along with nuclear weapons) resulting from research conducted during the war. The discovery stemmed from Watson-Watt's research on tracking thunderstorms by means of radio waves during World War I, when he served as a member of the British Meteorological Office. Following the war, Watson-Watt ended his long affiliation with the British government and established his own business, Sir Robert Watson-Watt and Partners.

Robert Alexander Watson-Watt was born on April 13, 1892, in Brechin, Scotland. His father, Patrick Watson Watt, a master carpenter, took his last name from his father (Watt) and his mother (Watson) and passed them both along to his son. Watson-Watt's mother was the former Mary Small Matthew. The hyphenation of Watson-Watt's name occurred in 1942, when he was knighted.

Develops Early Interest in Radio Sciences

Watson-Watt attended the Damacre Road School and then the local high school in Brechin. After graduation, he won a scholarship to University College, Dundee, where he pursued a degree in electrical engineering and was introduced to the field of wireless telegraphy. His fascination with the subject would eventually guide and motivate nearly all of the research he was to conduct throughout his life. In 1912, Watson-Watt was granted a bachelor of science degree in electrical engineering and offered a post as assistant professor of physics at his alma mater, a position he would hold only briefly. At the outbreak of World War I in 1914, his application for a job with the British War Office was denied, but he succeeded in obtaining a position with the government's Meteorological Office, where he proposed a method for tracking severe weather patterns by triangulation with radio waves. Progress in the development of this technique was slow, however, because the technology required to perform related experiments had not yet been perfected.

At the conclusion of the war, Watson-Watt in 1919 received a bachelor of science in physics from the University of London and was transferred to a field observing station at Ditton Park, Slough. In 1927, that station was combined with a nearby facility of the National Physical Laboratory to form a single unit called the Radio Research Station under the authority of the Department of Scientific and Industrial Research. Watson-Watt was appointed director of the new station. Over the next decade, Watson-Watt directed research on the radio location of thunderstorms, the detection of naval signals, and studies of the atmosphere. In connection with the latter work, he proposed the name "ionosphere" for the reflecting layer of the atmosphere discovered in 1924 by Sir **Edward Appleton**.

Invents Radar

Watson-Watt's most notable accomplishment, the invention of radar, came about as the result of an inquiry made by an official of the Air Ministry in 1935. He asked if it would be possible to concentrate radio waves in such a way that they could be used to destroy enemy aircraft. Though Watson-Watt's assistant, A. F. Wilkins, pointed out the impossibility of creating such a device, they explained how radio waves could at least be used for detecting aircraft. This can be accomplished by sending out a beam of radio waves in the direction of a given object. The time required for the beam to reflect off of the object and return to its source provides a means of accurately calculating the object's distance.

Watson-Watt outlined this method in a memo to the Air Ministry dated February 12, 1935. In his autobiography, Watson-Watt identifies that date clearly as being "the birth of radar and as being in fact the invention of radar." The term radar, coined in the United States, is an acronym for "radio detection and ranging." The British government quickly initiated a program for the development of Watson-Watt's idea. Radar stations in Britain were fully operational by the opening months of World War II and, most military authorities agree, served as the deciding factor in repulsing Germany's air invasions during the Battle of Britain in 1940.

Throughout his life, Watson-Watt displayed an interest in important social issues outside the field of science. From 1929 to 1936, for example, he was an active member of the Institute of Professional Civil Servants, serving as vice chairman of the organization in 1932, and as chairman in 1934. He was also a fellow and treasurer of the Institute of Physics, a fellow of the Royal Society, and the recipient of numerous honorary degrees and other recognitions. In 1946, Watson-Watt formed the private consulting company, Sir Robert Watson-Watt and Partners, and consulted with a number of agencies within the British government.

Watson-Watt was married three times between 1916 and 1966. His last wife, Air Chief Commandant Dame Katherine Jane Trefusis-Forbes, formerly head of the Women's Royal Air Force, died in 1971. Details surrounding the last two decades of his life are somewhat clouded. In his obituary of Watson-Watt in the *Biographical Memoirs of the Fellows of the Royal Society*, J. A. Ratcliffe writes: "From about 1952 onwards, Watson-Watt lived chiefly in Canada and the U.S.A., and it is difficult to find anyone who can give much account of his activities. From what evidence there is it seems that he acted from time to time as a freelance scientific advisor, occasionally with a small staff of one or two people." Watson-Watt died in Inverness, Scotland, on December 5, 1973.

SELECTED WRITINGS BY WATSON-WATT:

Books

Applications of Cathode-Ray Oscillograph in Radio Research, H. M. Stationery Office, 1933.
Three Steps to Victory: A Personal Account by Radar's Greatest Pioneer, (autobiography), Odhams, 1957, abbreviated version published in the U.S. as The Pulse of Radar, Dial, 1959.
Man's Means to His End, Heinemann, 1962.

Periodicals

Nature, Radar in War and Peace, Volume 156, 1945, p. 319.
Journal of the Institute of Electrical Engineering, The Evolution of Radiolocation, Volume 93, III A, 1946, p. 11.

FURTHER READING:

Books

Biographical Memoirs of Fellows of the Royal Society, Volume 21, Royal Society (London), 1975, pp. 549–568.

Contemporary Authors, Permanent Series, Volume 1, Gale, 1975.

Holmes, Frederic L., *Dictionary of Scientific Biography,* Volume 18, Scribner, 1982, pp. 977–978.

Sketch by David E. Newton

Anne Antoinette Weber-van Bosse
1852–1943
Dutch botanist

Anne Antoinette Weber-van Bosse, one of the world's leading experts on algae and marine botany, was born in Amsterdam to Jacob van Bosse, a successful merchant, and Jaquéline Jeanne Beynvaan. She had three brothers and a sister, ten years her senior, who ran the Van Bosse household after their mother died. She received her education at home from a Swiss governess, and from an early age she was fascinated by botany and by exotic animals at the Amsterdam zoo. In 1870 Van Bosse married the painter Wilhelm Ferdinand Willink van Collen; when van Collen died in 1877, van Bosse returned to live with her father.

In 1880 she enrolled at the University of Amsterdam, where she was one of three women botanical students. There she was captivated by the courses in plant physiology taught by **Hugo de Vries**. After three years of study she specialized in algae, the subject which would become her life's work. In 1883 she married Max Weber, a university lecturer in anatomy, who in 1884 became professor of zoology and director of the zoological museum at Amsterdam.

Begins Research on Algae

Weber-van Bosse's first research on algae concerned those varieties that lived on the body of the South American sloth. She later accompanied her husband on research trips to Norway and, in 1889, to Indonesia. While in the tropics she studied the symbiosis between algae and sponges, as well as the algae that lives on the leaves of the plant *Pilea.* In 1898 her husband undertook an ambitious deep-sea oceanographical expedition on board the ship *Siboga;* the analysis of the material collected during this expedition occupied the Webers for the rest of their lives.

Weber-van Bosse often assisted her husband in his research, but she also published independent papers and monographs. On her own account she analyzed algae collected on the *Siboga,* and she published a popular account of the expedition. In 1934 she gave her algae herbarium of 50,000 specimens to the Royal Herbarium at Leiden. Among her other interests, she was active in the Montessori educational movement. Her scientific work resulted in an honorary doctorate, awarded by the University of Utrecht in 1910; in 1935 she was made a knight of the Order of Orange-Nassau, one of the highest honors in the Netherlands.

SELECTED WRITINGS BY WEBER-VAN BOSSE:

Books

Monographie des Caulerpes, E. J. Brill, 1898.
Een jaar an boord H. M. Siboga, E. J. Brill, 1904.
Liste des algues du Siboga, E. J. Brill, 1928.

FURTHER READING:

Books

Koster, Joséphine Th. and Tera S. S. van Benthem Jutting, *Blumea: Tijdschrift voor de systamatiek en de geografie der planten,* supplement II, [Leiden], 1942.
Querner, Hans, *Dictionary of Scientific Biography,* Max Wilhelm Carl Weber (1852–1937), Scribner, 1976, p. 203.

Sketch by Lewis Pyenson

Ernst Weber
1901–1996
Austrian-born American electrical engineer

Ernst Weber is noted for his significant contributions to the development of microwave technology used in radar and communications systems. He is also noted for decades of work as an educator whose enthusiasm and method of teaching inspired several generations of students and colleagues in the field of electrical engineering.

Weber was born on September 6, 1901, in Vienna, Austria. He grew up in Vienna and graduated from the Vienna Technical University with a degree in electrical engineering in 1924. He continued his education at the University of Vienna, where he received a Ph.D. in physics in 1926. He then returned to the Vienna Technical University to earn an Sc.D. degree in electrical machinery in 1927. During this time he also worked as a research engineer, first at Osterreichische Siemens-Schuckert-Werke in Austria from 1924 to 1929, and later at Siemens-Schuckert-Werke in Germany from 1929 to 1930.

Ernst Weber

Emigrates to America and Begins a Long Career as an Educator

In 1930, Weber came to America to take a temporary position as a visiting professor of electrical engineering at the Polytechnic Institute of Brooklyn in New York. He was appointed to a permanent research professor position at the institute in 1931, where he taught electromagnetic theory, high-frequency phenomena, and other advanced subjects in electrical engineering. Many engineers working in industry were attracted to Polytechnic because of Weber's courses, and in 1936 the institute began offering the first evening doctoral program for electrical engineers in the United States. This program became so popular that by 1947 it accounted for almost half of the part-time Ph.D. candidates in the country.

In the mid-1930s, war clouds began to form over Europe. Weber decided to remain in the United States permanently, and he became a naturalized citizen in 1936. That same year he married. He and his wife had two children during their marriage. Weber continued his role at Polytechnic as a researcher and teaching professor until 1941.

Contributes to the Development of Radar During World War II

With the onset of World War II, Weber organized a research team at Polytechnic in 1941 under contract with the Office of Scientific Research and Development. Working with the Radiation Laboratory at the Massachusetts Institute of Technology, Weber and his team worked on several problems facing the development of early radar systems. One of the problems involved measurements of the very high frequency microwaves used in radar. In order to do this they had to coat glass tubes with a very thin layer of conducting metal. Weber recalled the art of decorating chinaware with gold and silver, and drew on this ancient skill to produce some of the first successful components for testing. Later the Polytechnic team substituted a mixture of platinum and palladium to replace the gold and silver. Their designs and production techniques contributed to the overall development of radar during the war, and Weber was awarded the Presidential Certificate of Merit for his work.

In 1943, while working on the radar development project, Weber helped establish the Microwave Research Institute at Polytechnic to develop microwave components and devices. In 1945, Weber was named director of the Microwave Research Institute and head of the electrical engineering department at Polytechnic. He held both positions until 1957. The success of the Microwave Research Institute led to the development of several commercially saleable products, and the Polytechnic Research and Development Company was formed in 1944 to market those products. Weber served as company secretary from 1944 to 1952, and as president from 1952 to 1959, in addition to his teaching, research, and other duties. The company was sold to Harris-Intertype Corporation in late 1959.

Receives Honors for His Work

Weber was named president of Polytechnic Institute of Brooklyn in 1957. He held that position for 12 years until 1969, when he retired to become president emeritus. In 1970, Polytechnic awarded him an honorary doctorate in engineering—one of six honorary doctorates he received during his lifetime. As a result of Weber's commitment to the highest quality education during his years as a professor and as president, the graduate electrical engineering program at Polytechnic was ranked sixth in the nation by the American Council of Education in 1966. Weber himself was named one of the top ten all-time educators by the Institute of Electrical and Electronic Engineers and was awarded the IEEE Education Medal by that group.

Outside of the academic world, Weber was also active. He was president of the Institute of Radio Engineers in 1959 and helped merge that group with the American Institute of Electrical Engineering to become the first president of the Institute of Electrical and Electronic Engineers in 1963. He became a founding member of the National Academy of Engineering in 1964 and was elected to the National Academy of Science in 1965.

After his retirement from Polytechnic, Weber moved to North Carolina. He joined the National Research Council in 1969 and served in various capacities until 1978, when he became a consultant to that group. In 1986 the Microwave Research Institute at Polytechnic was renamed the Weber

Research Institute in honor of his work in the development of microwave technology. One year later, in 1987, Weber was awarded the prestigious National Medal of Science for his lifetime contributions to electrical engineering. In addition to his many awards, Weber also held numerous patents in microwave technology and was the author of many scientific papers and several books. Ernst Weber died on February 15, 1996, at the age of 94.

SELECTED WRITINGS BY WEBER:

Books

Linear Transient Analysis. 2 volumes. [publisher unknown], 1954–1956.
Electromagnetic Theory, Static Fields and Their Mapping. [publisher unknown], 1965.
The Evolution of Electrical Engineering–A Personal Perspective. [publisher unknown], [date unknown].

FURTHER READING:

Other

http://catt.poly.edu/polytech/alumni/cable/spring96/weber.html This website includes a notice of Weber's death, a summary of his life and work, and a photo of his receiving the National Medal of Science in 1987 from then-Vice President George Bush.

Sketch by Chris Cavette

Julia Weertman
1926–
American physicist

J ulia Weertman is a physicist who significantly furthered knowledge of high temperature metal failure and the nanocrystalline structures of metals. Her study of small angle neutron scattering also aided in understanding the basic characteristics of different materials.

Weertman was born Julia Randall on February 10, 1926, in Muskegon, Michigan. Her parents, Louise Neumeister Randall and Winslow Randall, had one other daughter, Louise. Weertman grew up in Pittsburgh, graduating from Mount Lebanon High School in 1943. As a youngster, Weertman loved airplanes and flying. She announced to her parents that she wanted to fly. Weertman's parents replied that she would have to become an aeronauti-

cal engineer before they would consent to letting her learn to fly. Pursuing this goal, Weertman studied science vigorously, eventually deciding that she liked physics best.

After high school, Weertman received her bachelor of science degree in physics in 1946, her master's in 1947, followed by a doctorate in 1951, all from the Carnegie Institute of Technology. While at graduate school, Weertman met Johannes Weertman, and they married on her birthday, February 10, 1950.

Under the auspices of a Rotary International fellowship, Weertman followed graduate school with postdoctorate work at the Ecole Normale Superieure in Paris during 1951 and 1952. In 1952, Weertman returned to Washington, D.C. to work at the Naval Research Laboratory. Most of her work centered around ferro-magnetic spin resonance and study of the basic concepts of magnetism. Weertman's work at the Naval Research Laboratory lasted until 1958, when her husband accepted a position in London, working for the Office of Naval Research. By this time, Weertman had a daughter, Julia. She put her career on hold to raise her daughter.

In early 1960, Johannes Weertman accepted a position at Northwestern University in Evanston, Illinois. A year later, son Bruce was born. During this interval, Weertman occupied herself with raising her children, community work, and being a Girl Scout troop leader. During this time, she also collaborated with her husband to write a textbook entitled *Elementary Dislocation Theory,* published in 1964.

Much of the work Weertman did early in her career centered not only on dislocation, a condition which allows metals to be manipulated more easily, but on studying the effects of very high temperatures on pure metals and alloys with respect to their fatigue and failure. Weertman studied the mechanical effects of high heat as it related to such properties as tensile strength and brittleness. Weertman also studied small angle neutron scattering. Her work helped characterize materials so that boundary interactions and mechanical properties were more easily understood.

In 1972, Weertman became a visiting assistant professor at Northwestern University. After her third year at Northwestern, Weertman was teaching full time, eventually receiving tenure. By 1982, she was a full professor, working in the Material Science and Engineering Department. In 1986, she briefly taught at a technical college in Switzerland. She returned to Northwestern University and assumed leadership of the Material Science and Engineering Department in 1987, serving until 1992.

Weertman has been active in a number of professional organizations, receiving awards from many of them. She was a member of the American Institute of Physics, the American Crystalline Association, the Mining, Metals and Materials Society, and was also an ASM International fellow. Weertman served on one of the National Academy of Sciences' standing committees as chairman of the Solid States Science Committee. She was also an advisor to the National Science Foundation, the United States Department of Energy, the National Bureau of Standard and Technology, and Argonne and Oak Ridge National Laboratories.

From the National Science Foundation, Weertman twice received the Creativity Award, in 1981 and 1986. The City of Evanston presented her with its Environmental Award in 1979. In 1988, Weertman received the National Academy of Engineering Award. The Society of Women Engineers awarded Weertman its highest honor in 1991.

SELECTED WRITINGS BY WEERTMAN:

Books

Elementary Dislocation Theory, Macmillan, 1964.

Periodicals

Scripta Metallurgica et Materialia, Growth Rates of Grain Boundary Cavities During High Temperature Fatigue of Copper, February 1, 1990, p. 227.
Acta Metallurgica et Materiallia, Orientation Effects on the Elevated Temperature Fatigue of Copper Single Crystals, March 1, 1990, p. 509.
Acta Metallurgica et Materialia, Microstructural Evolution and Mechanical Properties of Rapidly Solidified Al-Zr-V Alloys at High Temperatures, May 1, 1990, p. 771.
Journal of Applied Crystallography, High-Resolution, Small-Angle X-Ray Scattering Camera for Anomalous Scattering, February 1, 1991, p. 30.
Journal of Materials Research, Mechanical Behavior of Nanocrystalline Cu and Pd, May 1, 1991, p. 1012.
Material Science and Engineering, Hall-Petch Strengthening in Nanocrystalline Metals, July 15, 1993, p. 161.
Journal of Materials Research, Chemical Reaction Strengthening of Al/TiC Metal Matrix Composites by Isothermal Heat Treatment at 913K, September 1, 1993, p. 2370.

FURTHER READING:

Periodicals

Weertman, Julia R., *Interview with Susan Kolmer,* conducted February 18, 1994.

Sketch by Susan E. Kolmer

Alfred Wegener
1880–1930
German meteorologist and geophysicist

Alfred Wegener was primarily a meteorologist who became much more famous for proposing the idea of continental drift. Decades after his death, the theory of continental drift that he had proposed in 1912 became the well-established foundation for the plate tectonics revolution in the earth sciences. Wegener heard mostly ridicule of his continental drift idea during his lifetime, but in the 1960s oceanic data convinced scientists that continents do indeed move. Wegener was an eminent meteorologist in his time, but he was appointed professor late in his professional career and died during one of his scientific trips to Greenland.

Wegener was born in Berlin on November 1, 1880, to Richard, a minister and director of an orphanage, and Anna Wegener. From an early age he hoped to explore Greenland, and he walked, hiked, and skated in order to build up his endurance for such a trip. He studied at the universities in Heidelberg, Innsbruck, and Berlin, receiving a doctorate in astronomy from the latter in 1905. Wegener's thesis involved conversion of a thirteenth-century set of astronomical tables into decimal notation; thereafter he abandoned astronomy in favor of meteorology. He carried out experiments with kites and balloons, fascinated with the new science of weather. In 1906, he and his brother Kurt set a world record in an international balloon contest by flying for 52 hours straight.

That year Wegener also fulfilled his dream of going to Greenland. Wegener was chosen as official meteorologist for a Danish expedition to northeastern Greenland from 1906 to 1908. It was the first of four trips to Greenland he would take. In 1912 he returned to Greenland with an expedition to study glaciology and climatology; this trip was the longest crossing of the ice cap ever made on foot.

In 1908, Wegener accepted a job teaching meteorology at the University of Marburg. His lectures were very popular with students for their clarity and frankness. He admitted disliking mathematical details, yet in 1911 he published a textbook on the thermodynamics of the atmosphere, which included in embryonic form the modern theory on the origins of precipitation. The following year Wegener married Else Köppen, the daughter of the "Grand Old Man of Meteorology" in Germany, Wladimir Köppen. During World War I Wegener served as a junior military officer and was wounded twice. After the war he succeeded his father-in-law as director of the meteorological research department of the Marine Observatory near Hamburg. There he conducted experiments to reproduce lunar craters by hurling projectiles at various ground substances, demonstrating that the craters were probably of impact, rather than volcanic, origin. He also continued to analyze the data from Green-

Alfred Wegener

land, observe meteorological phenomena, and develop his earlier ideas on the origin of the continents and the oceans.

Continental Drift Is Born

Wegener had first thought of the idea of continental drift in late 1910 while looking at a world map in an atlas. He noticed that the east coast of South America matched like a puzzle piece with the west coast of Africa, but dismissed the idea of drifting continents as improbable. The next year, however, he came across a list of sources arguing that a land bridge must have connected the two continents at one time, since similar fossils from the same time period appeared in both Africa and Brazil. Wegener immediately began to search out fossil evidence to support the idea of drifting continents. Within a few months he presented his hypothesis in two public forums.

Wegener spoke on "The Geophysical Basis of the Evolution of the Large-Scale Features of the Earth's Crust (Continents and Oceans)" at a meeting of geologists in Frankfurt on January 6, 1912. Four days later he addressed a scientific society in Marburg on the same topic. For the first time, he proposed that the continents had actually moved thousands of miles away from each other instead of being connected by a stationary land bridge. Wegener wrote up his theory in two brief papers that year before leaving for his second expedition to Greenland.

Wegener published an extended account of his idea as *Die Entstehung der Kontinente und Ozeane (The Origin of*

Continents and Oceans) in 1915. The first edition was only 94 pages long with no index. The second edition, much expanded and revised, attracted attention in Europe. The third edition was translated into English, French, Spanish, Swedish, and Russian in 1924 and was then widely read for the first time. The first English translation correctly referred to the idea of "continental displacement," as Wegener had termed it. The name "continental drift" was coined later.

Wegener was not the first to come up with the idea of continental drift. In 1620, English philosopher and author Francis Bacon noted the physical similarities between the American and African coasts. In 1858 Antonio Snider-Pellegrini published a book that described the breaking up of a giant continent, accompanied by deluges and other biblical catastrophes; his work sunk into relative oblivion. In 1910 German physicist Frank Bursey Taylor published a carefully worked-out hypothesis that anticipated Wegener's theory by two years. But Taylor's paper did not address the mechanism of continental movement and thus had little impact on the geological community.

Wegener's was the first coherent and logical argument for continental drift that was also supported by concrete evidence. He proposed that a huge supercontinent had once existed, which he named Pangaea, meaning "all land." He suggested that Pangaea was surrounded by a supersea, Panthalassa, and that two hundred million years ago, in the Mesozoic period, Pangaea began to rift into separate continents that moved away from each other. The Americas drifted westward from Europe and Africa, forming the Atlantic Ocean. India moved east from Africa, and Australia severed its ties with Antarctica and moved towards the equator.

Wegener's hypothesis departed radically from the accepted view of the earth in his day. Other geologists believed that the earth was still cooling and contracting from a molten mass, and that lighter rocks such as granite (termed "sial"), moved towards the surface, underlain by denser rocks such as basalt ("sima"). Mountain ranges, they believed, were produced by the cooling contraction, like wrinkles appearing on a drying fruit. To these scientists, the continents and the ocean basins were initial and set features. It seemed impossible for continents to move through the ocean rocks.

Wegener instead proposed that the lighter sial that made up continents could move horizontally through the oceanic sima; if the continents can rise up vertically, he argued, they must be able to move horizontally as well, as long as sufficient force is provided. Thus the Rocky Mountains and the Andes, on the western edges of the Americas, were formed by the resistance of the sima layer to the continents plowing through them. Island arcs like Japan and the West Indies were fragments left behind in the wake of these giant drifting continents.

Wegener's strongest argument was the similarities of rocks, animals, and plants on both sides of the Atlantic. He pointed to the fossils of several reptiles and flora that were known only in Africa and South America, and to the fact that the distribution of some living animals was hard to explain unless the continents had once been connected. Scientists had previously explained these in terms of a land bridge that had once connected the continents and then sunk into the ocean. Wegener argued that this was impossible; if a bridge was made of sial, it could not simply sink and disappear.

However, Wegener couldn't find an adequate mechanism to explain continental drift. He suggested two mechanisms, which were later disproved. One was *Pohlflucht*, or "flight from the poles," to explain why continents seemed to drift towards the equator. *Pohlflucht,* also known as the Eötvös force, came from the fact that the earth is an oblate spheroid, slightly flattened at the poles and bulging at the equator. Second, Wegener had to explain the westward movement of the Americas; he suggested that some kind of tidal force must be doing the work.

Reactions to Wegener's Hypothesis: Then and Now

Wegener's hypothesis was received with ridicule. For decades, other geologists scoffed at the idea of drifting continents. Some scientists supported him, but there was not enough geological evidence to prove beyond a doubt that he was essentially right. Wegener's first critic was his father-in-law, Köppen, who apparently wanted Wegener to stay in meteorology and not wander into unknown areas like geophysics. At the first lecture in Frankfurt in 1912, some geologists were apparently indignant at the very notion of continental drift. The initial reaction was mixed at best and hostile at worst. In 1922, when *The Origin of Continents and Oceans* first appeared in English, it was blasted in a critical review and at a scientific meeting. Subsequently continental drift provoked a huge international debate, with scientists ranging themselves on both sides.

Detractors had plenty of ammunition. It was soon shown that *Pohlflucht* and tidal forces were about one millionth as powerful as they needed to be to move continents. The paleontological evidence was thought to be inconclusive. In 1928, at a meeting of fourteen eminent geologists, seven opposed it, five supported it without reservation, and two supported it with reservations. From then until after World War II, the subject was put on the back burner of scientific debate. In the only major variant on the theory, South African geologist Alex du Toit, a vigorous defender of continental drift, proposed in 1937 that instead of Pangaea there were two supercontinents, Laurasia in the Northern Hemisphere and Gondwanaland in the south.

Many eminent geologists, such as **Sir Harold Jeffreys** in England and, later, American paleontologist George Gaylord Simpson, were vehement critics of Wegener and his continental drift theory. Science historians consider it likely that the prestige of the critics often carried too much weight in the argument over the theory itself. Wegener himself often complained about the narrow-mindedness of geophysicists who could not accept new ideas. In 1926 Wegener was finally given a professorship in meteorology and geophysics at the University of Graz. Four years later he

sailed from Copenhagen to Greenland as leader of a major expedition. On November 1 of that year, he and others in the party celebrated his fiftieth birthday at a camp in the center of the Greenland ice cap. Wegener headed for the west coast that day, and apparently died of heart failure. His body was later found about halfway between the two camps.

After World War II, and several decades after Wegener's disappearance, other geologists began to uncover clues that eventually led to the plate tectonics revolution. The development of paleomagnetism in the early 1950s demonstrated that rocks in different continents appeared to have different directions of magnetization, as if continents had drifted apart from each other. In addition, oceanographers began to map the ocean floor to learn about its origin. They learned that the ocean floor was not a fixed glob of sima at all. In 1960, American geologist **Harry Hammond Hess** proposed the theory of seafloor spreading: that the ocean floor is constantly being created at underwater ridges in the middle of the oceans, spreading outward, and being consumed in trenches underneath the continents. By the mid-1960s, new data on magnetic anomalies in the Pacific Ocean revealed that seafloor spreading did indeed occur. Here was the mechanism by which Wegener's continents could drift: The ocean floor was constantly regenerating itself. By the end of the 1960s, continental drift had begun to be accepted by the entire earth science community. It had taken half a century, but Wegener's hypothesis became the foundation for a revolution among geologists and a cornerstone for modern views of the earth's history.

SELECTED WRITINGS BY WEGENER:

Books

Thermodynamik der Atmosphäre, Leipzig, 1911.
Die Entstehung der Kontinente und Ozeane, Brunswick, 1915, fourth revised edition translated by John Biram as The Origin of Continents and Oceans, Dover Publications, 1966.

FURTHER READING:

Books

Hallam, *A Revolution in the Earth Sciences: From Continental Drift to Plate Tectonics,* Clarendon Press, 1973.
Hallam, Anthony, *Great Geological Controversies,* Oxford University Press, 1983.
LeGrand, H. E., *Drifting Continents and Shifting Theories,* Cambridge University Press, 1988.
Marvin, Ursula B., *Continental Drift: The Evolution of a Concept,* Smithsonian Institution Press, 1973.

Sketch by Alexandra Witze

Franz Weidenreich
1873–1948
German anatomist and physical anthropologist

Most closely associated with the study of Peking man (the name given to early human remains found in Asia), Franz Weidenreich earned a reputation as an exceptionally thorough and meticulous cataloger of human fossils, as well as one of the most prolific writers on the subject. He studied the source of human evolution from what he believed to be a single common ancestor through various racial developments, influenced by environment and other factors, to modern human beings. Weidenreich's work helped establish current knowledge of human evolution.

Born on June 7, 1873, in Edenkoben, Palatinate, Germany, Weidenreich was the youngest of the four children of Carl Weidenreich and Frederike Esesheimer. He received his early education at the Landau Humanist Gymnasium and later attended the universities of Munich, Kiel, and Berlin. He received his M.D. from the University of Strassburg in 1899, where he taught anatomy from 1899 until 1918; he became a professor there in 1904. At Strassburg he studied under Gustav Schwalbe, a prominent specialist in the study of Neanderthal humans. He also served as president of the democratic party of Alsace-Lorraine during World War I but was expelled from France in 1918 because he was a German national.

In the field of anatomy, Weidenreich specialized in the study of blood cells, the hemopoietic and lymphatic systems, and the central nervous system. It was his studies of skeletal anatomy, however, that led him to anthropology through his investigation of locomotion, posture, and bone structure as they related to human evolution. He became professor of anthropology at the University of Heidelberg from 1921 until 1924 and held the same post at the University of Frankfurt from 1928 until 1933, at which time he was removed from his position by the Nazis because he was Jewish. Leaving Germany, he had a brief tenure at the University of Chicago; this was followed by a position at the Peking Union Medical College, replacing **Davidson Black**, who had died suddenly. There he began his studies of the early human remains found in China, concentrating on the dentition, jawbones, and skull. During this period he also published a study of three *Homo sapiens* skulls from sites at Choukoutien, China.

Examines Link between Early Human Forms and Modern Humans

Weidenreich believed that the development of modern human types resulted from the evolution of a number of major lineages from a single ancestral group. He proposed that isolated populations evolved from groups that had already become differentiated into "racial" types. Although he acknowledged the effects of genetic mixing resulting from migration, he felt that remnants of the original genetic material could be found in modern populations.

In addition to its concern with the origin of racial types in modern humans, much of the research on human evolution during this period was devoted to the discovery of the links between the earliest human forms and modern man. Part of the theoretical investigation of the link between the earliest remains then known and modern humans was concerned with the position of the Neanderthals. Although most paleontologists now see the Neanderthals as an evolutionary dead end, some scientists early in the twentieth century—including Weidenreich's teacher, Schwalbe—held to the so-called Neanderthal-phase theory, which posited that Neanderthals were a distinct species that was transitional between *Homo erectus* forms and modern *Homo sapiens*. This belief formed the basis for Weidenreich's own view. Such a linear view of human evolution came under increasing attack during the 1930s as more fossil evidence became available and seemed to indicate otherwise. Others adopted the view that the Neanderthals were not ancestral to modern humans but rather had been displaced by a more advanced population with more sophisticated tools. This scheme, known as the presapiens theory, dominated paleontology in the years between the world wars; it postulated an earlier development of modern humans than the Neanderthal-phase theory and was based in part on the belief that there had not been enough evolutionary time for the Neanderthals to develop into modern humans.

Weidenreich's initial study of human fossil remains, in 1926, focused on the Neanderthal skull found at Ehringsdorf in 1925. Weidenreich's theory, first presented in 1928, held that early Neanderthal types migrated out of Africa after they had already developed "racial" distinctions. The groups in various parts of the world continued to undergo development, producing the various racial varieties existing today. He based his theory in part on the perception that there were morphological similarities between specific fossil remains and certain modern populations—what he called local regional continuity.

Partakes in Study of Peking Man

When Weidenreich began his investigation into human evolution, remains found in Java, designated *Pithecanthropus erectus* and popularly known as Java man, comprised the bulk of human fossil remains discovered up to that time. In the late 1920s Davidson Black had discovered a fossilized human tooth in Zhoukoudien (then called Choukoutien), southwest of Beijing, that was from approximately the same era as the *Pithecanthropus* remains and assigned it the designation *Sinanthropus pekinensis* (Peking man). (Both *Pithecanthropus* and *Sinanthropus* are now considered examples of *Homo erectus*.) Further finds in 1928 and many more between 1929 and 1932, including a complete skull, along with signs that the remains were indeed human (stone tools and evidence of fire), contributed to the creation of a new prehistoric figure in the scientific and popular communities: Peking man. These *Sinanthropus* remains became the focus of Weidenreich's detailed study, an endeavor that produced an extensive series of monographs, including *The Mandibles of Sinanthropus pekinensis* (1936), *The Dentition of Sinanthropus pekinensis* (1937), *The Extremity Bonds of Sinanthropus pekinensis* (1941), and *The Skull of Sinanthropus pekinensis* (1943). Publication of these works was fortunate, as the specimens themselves, packed for shipment to the United States, were apparently destroyed during the Japanese invasion of China in the 1940s.

Discovery of the *Sinanthropus* specimens in China rekindled interest in the *Pithecanthropus* remains found in Java, and additional discoveries by Ralph von Koenigswald during the 1930s of *Pithecanthropus* led Weidenreich to comparative studies of the two. He theorized that they were not separate species but rather variants of a form ancestral to the Neanderthals and therefore to modern humans. He held that there was at no time more than one species of human living concurrently. Significantly, he stated that these variants represented racial distinctions maintained throughout the subsequent stages of evolution. In Weidenreich's model, there was a single path of hominid descent consisting of parallel lines representing racial variants; these developed from the early hominids to modern humans independently, each going through the same evolutionary phases, all with increasing cranial capacity and increasingly erect posture, and maintaining their racial distinctions to the present day. He defined three phases of human development: the Archanthropine of approximately one million years ago, representing the period of *Pithecanthropus erectus* and *Sinanthropus pekinensis;* the Paleoanthropine (the period of the Neanderthals); and the Neoanthropine, which includes subsequent evolutions up to modern man. He divided modern humans into four major groups: Australian, Mongolian, African, and Eurasian, and theorized that modern Europeans were descended from a western subgroup of the Asian Neanderthals.

In Weidenreich's best-known book, *Apes, Giants, and Man* (1946), he theorized that, before the separation of humans into various "racial" types, the common ancestor of modern humans was a massive creature—especially in regard to its skull and jaw. This conclusion was corroborated by evidence derived from the so-called Solo skulls, the subject of Weidenreich's last phase of research.

From 1941 until his death on July 11, 1948, Weidenreich was associated with the American Museum of Natural History in New York. In 1947 he was awarded the Viking Fund Medal for his work in physical anthropology. At the time of his death, he was married, with three daughters, to the former Matilda Neuberger.

SELECTED WRITINGS BY WEIDENREICH:

Books

Apes, Giants, and Man, University of Chicago Press, 1946.

Periodicals

American Anthropologist, Facts and Speculations Concerning the Origin of Homo Sapiens, Volume 49, 1947, pp. 187–203.
Evolution, The Trend of Human Evolution, Volume 1, 1947, pp. 221–36.

FURTHER READING:

Books

Bowler, Peter J, *Theories of Human Evolution: A Century of Debate 1844–1944,* Johns Hopkins University Press, 1986.
Gregory, W. K., *Anthropological Papers of Franz Weidenreich 1939–1948,* Franz Weidenreich, 1873–1948, edited by S. L. Washburn and Davida Wolffson, Viking Fund, 1949, pp. 251–56.
Smith, Fred H., and Frank Spencer, *The Origins of Modern Humans: A World Survey of the Fossil Evidence,* Alan R. Liss, 1984.

Periodicals

Howells, W. W., *American Journal of Physical Anthropology,* Franz Weidenreich, 1873–1948, Volume 56, 1981, pp. 407–10.

Sketch by Michael Sims

André Weil
1906–1998
French mathematician

André Weil was responsible for important advances in algebraic geometry, group theory, and number theory and belonged to the group of French mathematicians who published many important works under the collective pseudonym of Nicolas Bourbaki. Many of his peers in the 1950s considered him the finest living mathematician in the world. In 1980, he was presented with the Barnard Medal by Columbia University; prior recipients of the medal, which is awarded every five years, include **Albert Einstein**, **Ernest Rutherford**, and **Neils Bohr**. The prize recognizes outstanding accomplishment in physical or astronomical science or a scientific application of great benefit to humanity.

Weil was born May 6, 1906, in Paris, France, to free-thinking Jewish parents. His father, Bernard, was a physician, and his mother, Selma Reinherz Weil, came from a cultured Russian family. His sister was the famous writer, social critic, and World War II French Resistance activist,

Simone Weil. When he was eight years old, Weil happened upon a geometry book and began to read it for recreation. By the time he was nine, he was absorbed in mathematics and was solving difficult problems. In her biography of Weil's sister, Simone Pétrement quotes Weil's mother as saying that at nine years of age André "is so happy that he has given up all play and spends hours immersed in his calculations." Weil's father was drafted into the military in 1914, and the family accompanied him to various medical assignments around France during World War I. At age sixteen, Weil was accepted at the elite Ecole Normale Supérieure in Paris, where he received his doctorate in 1928. He also studied at the Sorbonne, the University of Göttingen, and the University of Rome. From 1930 to 1932, he taught at the Aligarh Muslim University in India. From 1933 to 1940, he was a professor of mathematics at the University of Strasbourg in France. In 1937, he married.

Weil was in Finland with his wife when France entered World War II. He believed that he could do France more good as a mathematician and refused to return to his home country and join the army. He was walking near an anti-aircraft gun emplacement when the Russians invaded Finland, and the Finns arrested him, thinking that he was a spy. The letters to Russian mathematicians in his room did not help his case, and for a while it appeared that he would be executed. The Finns, however, released Weil to the Swedes, who sent him to England, from where he returned to France to be imprisoned and tried for not reporting for military service. He was tried on May 3, 1940 and convicted, and he asked to be sent to the front. The court obliged, and he was to be sent to an infantry unit along the English Channel at Cherbourg. Weil's boat, however, wound up in a British port, and he made his way back to France later in 1940. He soon rejoined his wife, Eveline, and they escaped the war to the United States. Their daughter, Sylvie, was born on September 12, 1942. Weil taught at Haverford and Swarthmore colleges in the United States in 1941 and 1942, and at the University of São Paulo in Brazil from 1945 to 1947.

In 1947, Weil was recruited to the mathematics department at the University of Chicago, where he taught until 1958. One of his colleagues at Chicago was Irving Kaplansky, who gives a sense of Weil's personality in *More Mathematical People:* "There we were at Chicago, lucky enough to have André Weil, one of the greatest mathematicians in the world. There were several times in my life that I've, one way or another, got that feeling, my gosh, here is a tremendous mathematician. . . . He was very impatient with what he regarded as incompetence." Kaplansky added, "Then there is his extraordinary quickness. . . . You can take an area of mathematics that he presumably never heard of before and just like that he'll have something to say about it." From 1958 until his retirement, Weil taught at the Institute for Advanced Study at Princeton.

Reveals Discovery of "Uniform Space"

Weil's mathematical innovations were highly technical and involved complex formulas. One of his discoveries was the concept of "uniform space," a kind of mathematical space that cannot be readily visualized like the three-dimensional space that we occupy in our daily lives. The *Science News Letter* pronounced Weil's discovery of uniform space one of the most important mathematical discoveries of 1939. In 1947, Weil developed some formulas in the field of algebraic geometry, which are known as the "Weil conjectures." Weil's conjectures, as Ian Stewart explains in *Scientific American,* "give formulas for the number of solutions to an algebraic equation in a finite field. In particular they allow one to deduce that a given equation does or does not have solutions; this information can be transferred to analogous equations involving integers or algebraic numbers. . . . [T]hey are of fundamental importance in algebraic geometry."

Weil's algebraic and geometrical innovations of the first half of the twentieth century were especially important for the technological innovations of the second half of the twentieth century. Complex computer software that models black holes for astronomers, scientific graphics for research physicists, and special effects visualizations for Hollywood filmmakers all rely in part on mathematical innovations in algebra and geometry. As the *Science News Letter* said in 1939, in the decades to come, mathematical innovations like Weil's may lead to "some concept that will illumine the universe as glimpsed by the 200-inch telescope or the atom as created or smashed by the powerful cyclotron."

Becomes Involved with Influential Group

In the mid–1930s, Weil and other important young French mathematicians—among them Jean Dieudonné, Claude Chevallier, and Henri Cartan—began to write a series of mathematical works under the pseudonym of Nicolas Bourbaki. As Paul Halmos said in *Scientific American,* one writer called Bourbaki a "polycephalic mathematician." The group has varied in number from ten to twenty and has been composed, predominantly, of those of French nationality. Their purpose was quite serious: to write a series of books about such fundamental mathematical areas as set theory, algebra, and topology. The resulting series of books, which number over thirty, was called the *Elements of Mathematics.* As Halmos said, "The main features of the Bourbaki approach are a radical attitude about the right order for doing things, a dogmatic insistence on a privately invented terminology, a clean and economical organization of ideas, and a style of presentation which is so bent on saying everything that it leaves nothing to the imagination." Their work has been very thorough (for example, it took them two hundred pages to define the number "1") and influential. Among other things, they inspired the "new math" that was introduced into American schools in the 1960s.

While their purpose was serious, the Bourbakians cultivated an atmosphere of mystery about their identities: they attempted to keep their names secret, they liked to make up stories about themselves, and they loved pranks. One story about their origin, which could well be a hoax, is that they got the idea for their name from the annual visit of a character named Nicolas Bourbaki to the Ecole Normale Supérieure, where many of them were educated. This character was an actor who gave a mock-serious lecture on mathematics in double-talk. Some of their own double-talk consisted of saying that the home institution of Nicolas Bourbaki was the "University of Nancago," a fusion of the Universities of Nancy and Chicago, where several members of the group taught. Another story reported is that the name was inspired by General Charles Denis Sauter Bourbaki, a colorful figure in the Franco-Prussian war. One of the group's pranks was to apply for a membership to the American Mathematical Society under the name of N. Bourbaki. They played another prank on Ralph P. Boas, the executive editor of *Mathematical Reviews*. Boas had said in one of the *Encyclopedia Britannica*'s annual *Book of the Year* volumes that Nicolas Bourbaki did not exist. The Bourbakians sent a letter to the editors of the *Britannica* complaining about Boas's charge. Later, as Paul Halmos said in *Scientific American,* the Bourbakians "circulated a rumor that Boas did not exist. Boas, said Bourbaki, is the collective pseudonym of a group of young American mathematicians who act jointly as the editors of *Mathematical Reviews.*"

Weil died August 6, 1998 at his home in Princeton, New Jersey at the age of 92. Among his most notable accomplishments was winning Japan's Kyoto Prize, an award that some mathematicians consider equivalent to the Nobel Prize, in 1994. He was the author of *Foundations of Algebraic Geometry* (1946), as well as of an autobiography, *The Apprenticeship of a Mathematician* (1992).

SELECTED WRITINGS BY WEIL:

Books

Foundations of Algebraic Geometry, American Mathematical Society, 1946.
Basic Number Theory, 3rd edition, Springer-Verlag, 1974.
Number Theory, Birkhäuser, 1984.

FURTHER READING:

Books

Albers, Donald J., Gerald Alexanderson, and Constance Reid, *More Mathematical People,* Harcourt, 1990.
Pétrement, Simone, *Simone Weil: A Life,* translated by Raymond Rosenthal, Pantheon, 1976.

Periodicals

Halmos, Paul R., *Scientific American,* Nicolas Bourbaki, May, 1957, pp. 88–99.
Halmos, Paul R., *Science News Letter,* New Kind of Space, Year's Discovery in Mathematics, January 21, 1939, pp. 45–46.

Stewart, Ian, *Scientific American,* Gauss, July, 1977, pp. 122–131.

Sketch by Patrick Moore

Robert A. Weinberg
1942–
American molecular biologist and biochemist

Massachusetts Institute of Technology's (MIT's) Daniel K. Ludwig Professor for Cancer Research and an American Cancer Society Research Professor, Robert A. Weinberg, has made important discoveries in the field of cancer research. Along with colleagues, he produced tumors in healthy mice by transferring individual, cancer-causing genes, called oncogenes, to normal cells. These oncogenes were almost indistinguishable from normal genes—in some cases, the difference between a normal gene and an oncogene was a single amino acid along the chain. Weinberg used new forms of genetic engineering to isolate genes in the cells of human tumors. He demonstrated that these oncogenes, when introduced into normal mouse cells grown in a laboratory environment, modified the normal cells and made them cancerous. This work was of great importance to cancer research, as it shifted the focus of biomedical research to investigations at the molecular level. Medical researchers had previously thought cancer was caused in several different ways: by chemical carcinogens, tumor viruses, and radiation. Weinberg's work with oncogenes made it apparent that normal cells have genes with malignant potential, and that those previously mentioned causes of cancer must be viewed in terms of their effect in activating genes that exist in a dormant state in normal cells.

Robert Allan Weinberg was born in Pittsburgh, Pennsylvania, on November 11, 1942. He was the son of dentist Fritz E. Weinberg and Lore (Reichhardt) Weinberg, who both had escaped Nazi Germany and emigrated to the United States in 1938. Weinberg studied at MIT, receiving a B.S. in 1964, an M.A. in 1965, and a Ph.D. in 1969, all in biology. He also worked as an instructor in biology at Stillman College in Tuscaloosa, Alabama, from 1965 to 1966. Upon graduation, Weinberg went to Israel where he spent two years as a research fellow at the Weizmann Institute in Rehovoth, working with Dr. Ernest Winocour. He received a fellowship from the Helen Hay Whitney Foundation in 1970, and worked with Dr. **Renato Dulbecco** as a fellow of the Salk Institute in La Jolla, California, from 1970 to 1972. Returning to MIT as a research associate in 1972, he began work with Dr. **David Baltimore**.

Before the 1970s, scientists had spent much time searching for viruses as the cause of cancer. But in spite of all efforts, researchers could not establish a connection between viruses and the great majority of human cancers. Then cancer research began to take another direction—this was the beginning of the scientific search for oncogenes.

From 1972 to 1973, Weinberg also worked as an assistant professor in the Department of Biology and at the Center for Cancer Research at MIT. He received the resident scholar award from the American Cancer Society from 1974 to 1977. In 1976, he was promoted to associate professor at MIT; he was also designated as Rita Allen Foundation scholar from 1976 to 1980.

DNA Transfer Yields Results

Weinberg tackled the problem of oncogenes in his own way. By the late 1970s, although about a dozen oncogenes had been identified, no one had managed to prove that these oncogenes could cause cancer without the presence of a virus to activate them. Weinberg finally demonstrated this in 1980. Taking DNA from active cancer cells in humans, he transferred it into normal mouse cells. The altered cells became cancerous.

Weinberg's next step was to attempt to identify particular genes as the oncogenes associated with specific cancers in humans. In 1981 he and his colleagues were able to identify genes for human leukemia, as well as colon and bladder cancers. Once the molecular basis of carcinogenesis had been established, and once it was possible to isolate and characterize specific oncogenes, it still remained to analyze those genes in exact structural detail, to find out precisely what changes in the DNA had induced the normal cell to behave differently.

Weinberg, through cloning bladder and lung cancer oncogenes in 1981, proved that the transforming genes are actually present in normal cells, but are either dormant or active at much lower levels, until they are activated or stimulated by some change. This activation might come about as a response to a seemingly insignificant change—in theory, a carcinogen might affect the gene, causing a slightly different amino acid protein to be manufactured along the chain, and somehow disrupting the cell's normal regulatory mechanism. This implied that there might be a two-step system for developing cancer: first, the creation of an oncogene, and second, an exposure to a carcinogen of some sort, perhaps even years later. And this two-step system, if accurate, might offer some explanation for the fact that the incidence of cancer increases with advancing age.

In 1982, Weinberg was promoted to professor of biology at MIT. During that same year, he was made Millard Schult lecturer at Massachusetts General Hospital, became a member of the Whitehead Institute for Biomedical Research, and was named 1982 Scientist of the Year by *Discover* Magazine. In 1983, while teaching at MIT, he was awarded the Warren Triennial Prize and the Robert Koch Foundation Medal (Bonn, Germany). In 1984, Weinberg was the recipient of the National Academy of Science's

Armand Hammer Cancer Foundation Award and U.S. Steel Foundation Award, as well as the Howard Taylor Ricketts Award from the University of Chicago Medical Center, the Brown-Hazen Award from the New York State Department of Health, and the Antonio Feltrinelli Prize from Academia Lincei in Rome. He also received the Bristol-Meyer Award for Distinguished Achievement in Cancer Research, and was awarded an honorary doctorate by Northwestern University.

In 1985 Weinberg was made honorary professor of biology by the American Cancer Society. He received the Katherine Berkann Judd Award from the Memorial Sloan-Kettering Cancer Center in 1986, the Sloan Prize from General Motors Cancer Research Foundation in 1987, and was made a member of the MIT Medical Consumers Advisory Committee in 1988, at which time he was also the recipient of an honorary doctorate from State University of New York at Stonybrook.

The next year, 1989, brought Weinberg yet another honorary doctorate, this time from City University, New York. He became a member of the Committee on Biological Warfare, Federation of American Scientists, and received the Lucy Wortham James Award from the Society of Surgical Oncologists. In 1990, Weinberg was given the Research Recognition Award by the Samuel Roberts Noble Foundation, the distinguished basic scientist award by the Milken Family Medical Foundation, and the Lila Gruber cancer research award by the American Academy of Dermatology. In 1997, he was awarded the National Medal of Science in recognition of his discoveries in the field of cancer research in 20 years of work on retroviruses, oncogenes, and tumor suppressor genes. He received MIT's Killian Faculty Achievement Award for 1999. Other awards include the Harvey Prize from the Technion-Israel Institute of Technology, the Gairdner Foundation International Award, and the Elizabeth A. Wood Science Writing Award from the American Crystallographic Association.

Weinberg has been either the author or editor of six books, and has published more than 250 articles.

Weinberg married Amy Shulman, a teacher, in 1976, and they had two children: Aron and Leah Rosa. Weinberg has many other interests in addition to science. He built his own vacation house in New Hampshire, literally from the ground up. He cleared the land himself, then framed the house and created a garden. He is also interested in genealogy.

SELECTED WRITINGS BY WEINBERG:

Books

Selected Abstracts on DNA Viral Transforming Proteins, [Bethesda, MD], 1983.
Selected Abstracts on Protein Kinases Associated with Growth, Differentiation, and Transformation, [Bethesda, MD], 1983.

Periodicals

Technology Review, The Dark Side of the Genome, April, 1991, pp. 44–48.
Science, Tumor Supressor Genes, November 22, 1991, pp. 1138–1139.

FURTHER READING:

Periodicals

NY Times Magazine, October 24, 1982, p. 39.
Science News, November 13, 1982, p. 316.

Sketch by Jessica Jahiel

Steven Weinberg
1933–
American physicist

Steven Weinberg shared the 1979 Nobel Prize in physics with **Sheldon Glashow** and **Abdus Salam** for his contributions to the development of a theory unifying the electromagnetic and weak forces, two of the four forces governing nature. He predicted that one of the three particles inherent in the weak force could be found in "neutral currents." Its subsequent discovery in 1983 may have brought scientists one step closer to a unified theory of the universe.

Weinberg was born in New York City on May 3, 1933, to Frederick Weinberg, a court stenographer, and the former Eva Israel. Weinberg's early interests in science were nurtured both at home and at the world-famous Bronx High School of Science, from which he graduated in 1950. Like Glashow, his classmate at the Bronx High School, Weinberg decided to major in physics at Cornell University, graduating with a B.A. in 1954. He then spent a year at the Niels Bohr Institute (formerly the Institute for Theoretical Physics) in Copenhagen, studying under the noted theoretical physicist Gunner Källén. In 1955, Weinberg returned to the United States and Princeton University, where he began his doctoral research under Samuel Treiman; he was awarded a Ph.D. for his thesis on weak interactions in 1957.

Weinberg took teaching positions at Columbia University from 1957 to 1959, the Lawrence Berkeley Laboratories of the University of California from 1959 to 1969, the Massachusetts Institute of Technology (MIT) from 1969 to 1973, and Harvard University in 1973, where he replaced **Julian Schwinger** as Eugene Higgins Professor of Physics. He took a concurrent position beginning in 1973 at the Smithsonian Astrophysical Observatory, where he served as senior scientist. During much of this period, Weinberg was engaged in a relatively wide variety of research, including studies on muon physics, scattering theory, broken symmetries, and Feynman graphs.

Weinberg Focuses on Problems of the Electroweak Force

For nearly half a century, physicists had recognized the existence of four fundamental forces: gravity, the strong nuclear force, the weak nuclear force, and electromagnetism. At no time, however, were physicists entirely convinced that these forces acted as separate entities. In fact, there had been a continuing effort to find a theory allying the four forces into a single fundamental force. A model of that nature had already been conceived during the mid-nineteenth century by James Clerk Maxwell, who showed that two apparently different kinds of forces, the electrical and magnetic forces, were actually two manifestations of a single, more basic electromagnetic force.

By the early 1960s, efforts toward unification were directed specifically at finding ways of relating the electromagnetic and weak forces. Electromagnetism causes such phenomena as sunlight and radio waves, and the weak force operates over very short distances within the nucleus and is responsible for some forms of radioactive decay. The theories put forth all assumed that, while the electromagnetic and weak forces are clearly distinct at energy levels we encounter in everyday life, they are indistinguishable at much greater energies, such as those encountered in cosmic rays and the most powerful particle accelerators.

Between 1960 and 1968 a theory unifying the electromagnetic and weak forces was developed independently by Weinberg, Pakistani physicist Salam, and, to an extent, by Glashow. There were a number of ways in which the premises and conclusions of these theories could be tested, including the detection of "neutral currents." Weinberg in 1971 had indicated that, in the collisions of neutrinos and matter, a neutral current was produced which contained one of the three weak force carrying particles. In 1973, experiments at the European Center for Nuclear Research (CERN) confirmed the existence of these currents, and, a decade later, the three types of particles were detected in further experiments carried out at CERN by a group headed by the Italian and Dutch physicists **Carlo Rubbia** and **Simon Meer**. For their contributions to the development of the electroweak theory, Weinberg, Glashow, and Salam were jointly awarded the 1979 Nobel Prize in physics.

Weinberg has continued to work on a wide variety of topics in physics and cosmology. In 1974, with Howard Georgi and Helen Quinn, he made the first estimate of the energy at which the strong, weak, and electromagnetic forces would all be unified. In 1982, Weinberg joined the physics and astronomy departments of the University of Texas at Austin as Josey Regental Professor of Science.

Weinberg was married on July 6, 1954, to Louise Goldwasser, a professor of law. The couple has one daughter, Elizabeth. Weinberg's numerous honors include the 1977 Dannie Heineman Prize of the American Physical Society, the 1979 Elliott Cresson Medal of the Franklin Institute, election to the Royal Society of London in 1981, the 1992 National Medal of Science, and many honorary doctoral degrees. Weinberg, who left Harvard in 1983 to become Josey Professor of Science at the University of Texas at Austin, lists his primary leisure time interest as reading history and walking in the Austin Hills.

SELECTED WRITINGS BY WEINBERG:

Books

Gravitation and Cosmology: Principles and Applications of the General Theory of Relativity, Wiley, 1972.
The First Three Minutes: A Modern View of the Origin of the Universe, Basic Books, 1977.
The Discovery of Subatomic Particles, W. H. Freeman, 1983.
Dreams of a Final Theory, Pantheon, 1993.

Periodicals

Physical Review Letters, A Model of Leptons, Volume 19, 1967, p. 1264.
Reviews of Modern Physics, Recent Progress in Gauge Theories of the Weak, Electromagnetic and Strong Interactions, Volume 46, 1974, pp. 255–77.

FURTHER READING:

Books

McGraw-Hill Modern Scientists and Engineers, Volume 10, McGraw-Hill, 1980, pp. 286–287.
Pioneers of Science: Nobel Prize Winners in Physics, American Institute of Physics, 1980, pp. 261–262.

Periodicals

Coleman, Sidney, *Science,* The 1979 Nobel Prize in Physics, December 14, 1979, pp. 1290–1291.
Coleman, Sidney, *Physics Today,* Nobel Prizes: To Glashow, Salam and Weinberg for Physics . . . , December, 1979, pp. 17–19.
Coleman, Sidney, *New Scientist,* Nobels for Getting It Together in Physics, October 18, 1979, pp. 163–164.

Sketch by David E. Newton

Wilhelm Weinberg
1862–1937
German geneticist

Wilhelm Weinberg was an obstetrician in private practice who used his experience delivering babies for gathering data and wrote a number of pioneering papers on genetics and medical statistics. At the beginning of the twentieth century, he was one of the first to apply Gregor Mendel's laws of heredity to observable human characteristics. Working independently for most of his life, Weinberg collected data on multiple births, genetic diseases, and mortality, and he used these statistics to derive generalized mathematical laws and statistical relationships. The most notable of these, the Hardy-Weinberg law, is now widely used to predict gene frequencies within a population, and it has become one of the fundamental laws of genetics.

Weinberg was born December 25, 1862 in Stuttgart, Germany. His father, Julius Weinberg, was a cloth merchant and a member of Stuttgart's Jewish middle class; Wilhelm Weinberg and his mother, the former Maria Magdelena Humbert, were Protestant. Weinberg attended secondary school at the Stuttgart Realgymnasium, then enrolled as a medical student at the University of Tübingen. He finished his academic career at the University of Munich, where he received his medical degree in 1886, and he began his clinical work as a medical assistant in Berlin, Frankfurt, and Vienna. In 1889, Weinberg returned home to Stuttgart, where he established a practice in general medicine and obstetrics.

Medical Practice Stimulates Interest in Genetics

Over the course of his career, Weinberg supervised a large number of twin births. This experience not only established him as an authority on obstetrics but also stimulated his interest in heredity, especially concerning families which had experienced multiple births. He was initially interested in the differences between twins who were identical and twins who were fraternal, as well as the question of whether a woman could inherit a tendency to give birth to twins. In 1901, Weinberg wrote his first important paper on heredity, in which he developed the "difference method"—a mathematical rule that geneticists could use to determine the proportion of identical versus fraternal twin births within a population, simply by knowing the number of same-sex twin pairs. Weinberg did not invent the difference method and he acknowledged that it had been used previously, but he was the first to use the method without unnecessary alteration of data. Weinberg also discovered a number of differences between fraternal and identical twins, and he concluded that women could inherit a tendency to bear fraternal twins but not identical twins.

In the early twentieth century, new attention paid to the work of Gregor Mendel was transforming the field of genetics. In 1866, Mendel had determined that observable biological traits are passed down from generation to generation according to certain proportional laws. Weinberg became interested in Mendelism through Valentin Haecker, a Stuttgart zoologist and associate of renowned geneticist August Weismann, and he began looking for ways to apply it to his work. Since his medical practice brought him into contact with hundreds of families, and he witnessed the creation of new generations on a daily basis, Weinberg decided to explore the ways in which Mendelian laws influenced the genetic relationships between family members, thus testing Mendel's equations on observable human characteristics.

Weinberg would publish over 220 papers in his career, but between 1908 and 1910 he wrote four of the most important. These publications represented his attempts to apply the mathematical laws of Mendelian genetics to his statistical observations. Mendel had determined that genetic characteristics, whether rare or common, appear in the population according to predictable laws and occur in particular proportions. Weinberg expanded this notion to demonstrate that over several generations of a randomly mating population, one may consistently predict the frequency of an inherited trait according to a mathematical law, called the law of equilibrium. In 1904, British geneticist **Karl Pearson** had published an equilibrium law for special cases of Mendelian genetics, but in January 1908 Weinberg generalized Pearson's rule for all populations, and in doing so laid the foundation for modern genetics. A few months later, **Godfrey Harold Hardy**, an English mathematics professor at Cambridge University, independently published a similar finding, and the equilibrium law eventually became known as the Hardy-Weinberg formula.

Weinberg also applied his new knowledge of Mendelian genetics to older studies he had done on multiple births. In several of his earlier experiments on multiple births, Weinberg had pointed to his data as proof of "blending inheritance," which is incompatible with Mendelism. Now he was able to demonstrate that the tendency to bear twins, for example, could be inherited as a recessive trait (a weaker genetic characteristic, often masked). He was also one of the first geneticists to apply equilibrium laws and Mendelian proportions to common human traits, rather than unusual ones such as albinism or rare birth defects. In addition, he was the first to distinguish between genetic and environmental factors in the variance of observed characteristics between close relatives—work which anticipated the research of well-known population biologists **Ronald A. Fisher** and **Sewall Wright** by several years. For his work in medicine and genetics, Weinberg was awarded the title of Sanitätsrat by the King of Württemberg in 1911.

Weinberg changed the face of genetics over the span of only three years, and he continued to produce original ideas even after his most prolific period. In 1912, he made a significant contribution not only to the analysis of statistical data but also to the methodology which determined how that data should be collected. Weinberg published useful new techniques for ascertainment, the process of ensuring that statistical data truly represent a random selection of individuals. For Weinberg's research on the frequency of twin births, for example, he realized that if he only counted births within families of women who had already given birth to twins, he must subtract that original twin birth from his statistics to have a truly random sample. In other words, to determine the correct proportion of a certain observable trait, a researcher must use the ratio of affected to nonaffected persons only among the siblings of someone who is already affected—otherwise the researcher is guilty of unintentional selection of data. This simple trick was called the sibling method, and was adapted by Munich psychiatrist Ernst Rüdin to become a fundamental procedure in German psychiatry.

In addition to his landmark discoveries in population genetics, Weinberg was also instrumental in the gradual refinement of the methods of medical statistics. He was an expert at analysis as well as collection of data, and he was responsible for correcting several long-standing but mistaken assumptions in the interpretation of data. He also supervised many thorough, specialized studies of mortality statistics, as well as studies of the genetics of specific diseases such as cancer, tuberculosis, and mental illness. Many of Weinberg's contemporaries used his numerous methods of correction, ascertainment, and statistical analysis to refine their own data.

Weinberg was not unaware of the broader, societal implications of his work, particularly in the area of eugenics. Eugenics is the science of improving genetic fitness by imposing artificial selection. Weinberg agreed with Karl Pearson that certain restrictions on fertility should be imposed by the government to improve the human gene pool, including legal sterilization and marriage prohibition in families with heritable genetic diseases. Weinberg did not, however, approve of eugenic abortions.

Recognition of Weinberg's Work Delayed

Weinberg's professional life was an unusual one: He continued to practice medicine even as he performed his most important research in genetics. In a medical career of forty-two years, he worked on a private basis for fees but also served the poor. He had relatively little interest in making money and occasionally forgot to collect the fees owed him. He never had a single student or collaborator, and it was this independence, along with a relatively inaccessible writing style, which isolated Weinberg from his contemporaries, both in the scope of his ideas and the recognition of his work.

Even though Weinberg had developed his equilibrium principle several months before Hardy's work was published, the formula was known as Hardy's Law for decades, even in Germany. His resentment regarding this oversight was evident as early as 1909, when he argued for his own priority in a review of Hardy's paper. Weinberg insisted that his work had been more inclusive and yet more simple than that of his British counterpart, and in 1927 he publicly defended his priority once again at the Berlin International Congress of Genetics. Weinberg was neglected, at least in part, because he was not member of the academic establishment, but his 1908 paper had been published in a relatively obscure German journal, while Hardy's article had appeared in *Science*. It was only in 1943, after diligent lobbying by his friend Curt Stern, that Hardy's Law became known as the Hardy-Weinberg Law. Also, whether an effect or an additional cause of his isolation, Weinberg was known for his unpleasantness in professional correspondence. He did not hesitate to turn professional debates into personal ones, and he frequently engaged in public feuds with Pearson and Lenz, among others, arguments which often concerned their ignorance or oversight of his work.

In an obituary in *Genetics*, Curt Stern compared Weinberg's career to Mendel's, claiming that "both men made their discoveries at a time when their contemporaries were unable to appreciate them." Weinberg's work on ascertainment was given proper credit and his statistical methodology borrowed by geneticists worldwide. However, his most important work in population genetics, perhaps because he was not a professional population geneticist, was overlooked for decades, just as Mendel's had been, and it was left to be rediscovered by others in a later generation.

Weinberg retired from his medical practice in 1931 and moved to Tübingen, Germany, with his wife, the former Bertha Wachenbrönner, whom he had married in 1896. Weinberg and his wife had one daughter and four sons, the oldest of whom died in World War I. In Tübingen, he lived in poverty and poor health for six years until his death on November 27, 1937. Despite his professional reputation as caustic, he was remembered by friends as an essentially gentle man whose impatience was the result of his bitterness over his scientific career. As quoted in *Genetic Counseling*, H. Luxenburger wrote of Weinberg: "It was to his own harm that he carefully hid his goodness, his kindness, and his sense of justice. Therefore, it is largely his own fault that his achievement was not noticed in the way it should have deserved."

SELECTED WRITINGS BY WEINBERG:

Periodicals

Jahreshefte des Vereins für Vaterländische Naturkunde in Württemburg, Uber den Nachweis der Vererbung beim Menschen, Volume 64, 1908, pp. 368–382.

FURTHER READING:

Books

Dunn, L. C., *A Short History of Genetics,* McGraw-Hill, 1965, pp. 121–123.
Gillispie, C. C., editor, *Dictionary of Scientific Biography,* Scribners, Volume 14, 1976, pp. 230–231
Provine, William B, *The Origins of Theoretical Population Genetics,* University of Chicago Press, 1971, pp. 134–136.
Tiley, N. A., *Discovering DNA,* Van Nostrand, 1983, p. 29.

Periodicals

Kallman, F. J., *Journal of Nervous and Mental Diseases,* Wilhelm Weinberg, M.D., Volume 87, 1938, pp. 263–264.
Luxenburger, H., *Allgemeine Zeitschrift für Psychiatrie,* Wilhelm Weinberg, Volume 107, 1938, pp. 378–381.
Stern, Curt, *Genetics,* Wilhelm Weinberg, Volume 47, 1962, pp. 1–5.
Süss, Jochen and Dorothee Früh, *Genetic Counseling,* Wilhelm Weinberg, M.D. (1862–1937): The Man Behind the 'Hardy-Weinberg-Equilibrium,' Volume 1, pp. 279–285.

Sketch by G. Scott Crawford

Mary Catherine Bishop Weiss
1930–1966
American trigonometrist

Mary Weiss helped to create methods of harmonic analysis that apply to higher–dimensional geometry and one problem in lacunary series that defied solution for 20 years. Her work was recognized and supported by the National Science Foundation.

Weiss was born on December 11, 1930, to Albert Bishop, a mathematics professor, and his wife, Helen, in Wichita, Kansas. Both Weiss and her brother, Errett, would follow in their father's footsteps. Mr. Bishop had become an army officer after graduating from the United States Military Academy at West Point, but began teaching at the university level following his retirement from the military. He died while Weiss and her brother were still very young, and the family moved to another region in Kansas to be closer to relatives. Weiss and her mother moved to the Chicago area when Errett entered the University of Chicago, where she also enrolled in the institution's experimental Laboratory School. During her undergraduate years she met and married a fellow student, Guido Weiss. They both earned their doctorates at the University of Chicago, both working in the same general area of inquiry under Antoni Zygmund. Zygmund would later become Weiss's colleague, cowriter, and editor, a collaboration which lasted until her death.

Weiss's Ph.D. thesis, completed in 1957, laid the foundation for three years of work on lacunary series, the subject of her first five published papers. During this time she provided a proof for a theorem of Raymond Paley's and solved a problem first posed by one of the founders of the Hardy–Littlewood series, John E. Littlewood. Her investigations held a lot in common with some tenets of probability theory involving random variables.

Weiss had a mathematician's temperament, in the sense that she could summon great concentration for days at a time when absorbed by some mathematical enigma. Yet she was highly sociable. During her career as a lecturer, she worked individually with students at De Paul, Washington, and Stanford universities as well as her alma mater. She read widely and held an appreciation for the fine arts, and she often participated in campus protests against the Vietnam War.

Overseas Experiences

Between 1960 and 1961, Weiss and her husband took a sabbatical to Buenos Aires and Paris, yet it was a working vacation for both of them. Guido had been wrestling with Hardy spaces in the framework of classical mathematics. Once both of them attacked the topic they extended its domain onto the complex or Gaussian plane, and also into higher dimensions. Later during this period they invited J. P. Kahane to aid their continued efforts with general lacunary power series. Upon returning from sabbatical Weiss contacted Zygmund and **Alberto P. Calderón** about their discoveries in harmonic analysis, and the three wrote a paper on Calderón–Zygmund singular integral operators in higher dimensions. Weiss's central contribution was in proving the early assumptions of Zygmund and Calderón. She also continued work with her husband on the theory of Hardy spaces in higher dimensions with E. M. Stein. Here, she applied mainly geometric methods of analysis which have yet to be fully exploited by her successors.

During the academic year of 1965–66, the National Science Foundation funded Weiss's senior postdoctoral fellowship at Cambridge University, after which she returned to America. She began work that fall at the University of Illinois, but died on October 8, a few weeks after the semester had begun. In 1967, a symposium on harmonic analysis was held at the Edwardsville campus of Southern Illinois University in Weiss's honor. At this gathering, her mentor Zygmund presented a technical summary of her published work.

SELECTED WRITINGS BY WEISS:

Periodicals

"The Law of the Iterated Logarithm for Lacunary Trigonometric Series," *Transactions of the American Mathematical Society* 91 (1959): pp. 444–469.

(With Guido Weiss), "A Derivation of the Main Results of the Theory of Hp Spaces," *Revista de la Union Matematica Argentina* 22 (1960): pp. 63–71.

(With Alberto P. Calderón and Antoni Zygmund) "On the Existence of Singular Integrals," in *Singular Intervals: Proceedings of Symposia in Pure Mathematics. Volume 10*, edited by Alberto P. Calderón, 1967.

"A Theorem on Lacunary Trigonometric Series," in *Orthogonal Expansions and Their Continuous Analogues*, edited by D. T. Haimo, 1968, pp. 227–230.

FURTHER READING:

Books

Pless, V., and B. Srinivansan, "Mary Catherine Bishop Weiss (1930–1966)," *Historical Encyclopedia of Chicago Women* (in production).

Weiss, Guido, "Mary Catherine Bishop Weiss," in *Women of Mathematics*, edited by Louise S. Grinstein and Paul J. Campbell, Westport, CT: Greenwood Press, 1987, pp. 236–40.

Zygmund, A., "Mary Weiss: December 11, 1930–October 8, 1966," in *Orthogonal Expansions and Their Continuous Analogues*, edited by D. T. Haimo, Carbondale, IL: Southern Illinois University Press, 1968, pp. xi–xviii.

Other

"Mary Catherine Bishop Weiss," *Biographies of Women Mathematicians*.

http://www.scottlan.edu/lriddle/women/chronol.htm (July 1997).

Sketch by Jennifer Kramer

Carl F. Von Weizsäcker
1912–
German physicist

Carl F. Von Weizsäcker's achievements encompass both the scientific and philosophical examination of the creation of the universe. In a career that spanned several decades, Von Weizsäcker taught at several institutions, published over thirty books, and founded the renowned Max Planck Institute for Social Sciences in Starnberg, Germany. His best-known scientific theory is known as the "Carbon Cycle," which he, along with fellow German physicist **Hans Bethe**, proposed as a nuclear reactive process by which energy is generated in stars.

Carl Friedrich Freiherr von Weizsäcker was born on June 28, 1912, in Kiel, Germany. The term *Freiherr,* which means "free man," is more loosely translated as *baron,* a name by which von Weizsäcker is often addressed. His parents were Ernest Freiherr von Weizsäcker and the former Marianne von Graevenitz. Von Weizsäcker's lineage included distinguished scholars and civil servants, including a famous Protestant theologian (von Weizsäcker's great-grandfather), the last prime minister of the Kingdom of Württemburg (his grandfather), and one of the founders of psychosomatic medicine (an uncle). His own father was a high official in Adolf Hitler's Nazi government in Germany. As a child, von Weizsäcker was fascinated by both science and religion. Even very early in his life, he did not view them as two distinct subjects, but as two facets of a single topic. In this respect, von Weizsäcker was following a tradition from the early days of modern science when boundaries between science and religion were often difficult to distinguish. By the twentieth century, however, this tradition had become a minor theme for most scientists who, with a few exceptions, saw clear distinctions between their own work and religious or philosophical speculations.

Von Weizsäcker completed undergraduate and graduate work at the Universities of Berlin, Göttingen, and Copenhagen, receiving his Ph.D. in physics from the University of Leipzig in 1933. He then began working as a researcher at Leipzig's Institute of Theoretical Physics, going on to become a lecturer in theoretical physics at the University of Berlin. His work during this period focused largely on nuclear physics, and his most notable accomplishment was the derivation of a method for calculating the total energy of an atomic nucleus.

Works on Problems of Astrophysics

In the early years of World War II, von Weizsäcker was appointed to the post of associate professor of theoretical physics at the University of Strasbourg, located in a German-occupied region of France. He was also assigned to work on the development of Germany's atomic bomb. However, the project received little attention from Hitler's government and never made significant progress. It was during these years that von Weizsäcker also worked on the two scientific problems for which he is best known, the origin of stellar energy and the creation of the planets.

Scientists had long been puzzled about the mechanism by which stars produce energy. Well-known and obvious processes, such as combustion, could not explain the conversion since stars would rapidly exhaust the raw materials needed for such a procedure. In the late 1930s, at approximately the same time, von Weizsäcker and a German physicist, Hans Bethe, proposed that a series of nuclear reactions generated energy in stars. The net result of these reactions, said the scientists, was the conversion of four protons (hydrogen nuclei) to one helium atom. Since carbon was a catalyst in this process, the series of reactions became known as the carbon cycle.

During the 1940s, von Weizsäcker turned his attention to the study of planetary formation. In particular, he applied his knowledge of nuclear physics to a theory originally proposed by the French mathematician and philosopher, René Descartes, in the seventeenth century. The theory had subsequently been developed by German philosopher, Immanuel Kant, in the eighteenth century and, especially, by the French mathematician and physicist, Pierre-Simon Laplace, around the late 1700s. According to the Descartes-Kant-Laplace theory, the planets were originally formed when large clumps of matter condensed from a disk of gases rotating around the sun. Although von Weizsäcker's own elucidation of this problem did not resolve all the questions about planetary formation, his update of this "nebular" theory was a significant step forward in the evolution towards understanding planetary formation.

Shifts Attention to Problems of Philosophy, Religion and Social Activism

After World War II, von Weizsäcker took the post of professor of theoretical physics at the University of Göttingen and also became department head at the university's Max Planck Institute for Physics. While working here, he continued his research on nuclear and astrophysics. Then, in 1957, he accepted an appointment as professor of philosophy at the University of Hamburg, a move that startled many of his colleagues. This decision was indicative of his intention to spend more time in thinking, writing, and talking about the need for integrating the sciences with each other, and with other aspects of human life, especially religion and philosophy. Von Weizsäcker, who has more than thirty books to his credit, outlined some of these ideas in his work titled *The Relevance of Science: Creation and Cosmogony.* Explaining the historical process by which the various sciences became compartmentalized, von Weizsäcker went on to expound on the harmful effects of this change on science and on society, showing how and why this process should be reversed in modern society. During the 1960s, von Weizsäcker became very active in the peace movement and became a strong spokesman for nuclear disarmament.

In 1970 von Weizsäcker founded the Max Planck Institute on the Preconditions of Human Life in the Modern World (later renamed the Max Planck Institute for Social Sciences) in Starnberg, Germany. He served as director of the institute until his retirement in 1980. Also in 1970, he became honorary professor of philosophy at the University of Munich. Von Weizsäcker was married to Gundalena Wille on March 30, 1937. Their children are Carl Christian, Ernest Ulrich, Elizabeth, and Heinrich. Among his awards are the Max Planck Medal in 1957 and 1966, the Goethe Prize from the city of Frankfurt in 1958, the Order of Merit for Sciences and Arts in 1961, the Arnold Reymond Prize for Physics in 1965, the Wilhelm Boelsche Gold Medal in 1965, and the Erasmus Prize in 1969.

SELECTED WRITINGS BY WEIZSÄCKER:

Books

The History of Nature, translated by F. D. Wieck, University of Chicago Press, 1949.
The Rise of Modern Physics, translated by A. J. Pomerans, Braziller, 1957.
The Relevance of Science: Creation and Cosmogony, Harper, 1964.
The Biological Basis of Religion and Genius, NC Press, 1971.
The Politics of Peril: Economics, Society and the Prevention of War, translated by M. Shaw, Seabury Press, 1978.

FURTHER READING:

Books

Tango, Gerardo G., *Great Events from History II,* Von Weizsäcker Finalizes His Quantitative Theory of Planetary Formation, edited by Frank N. Magill, Science and Technology Series, Volume 3, 1931–1952, pp. 1208–11.

Sketch by David E. Newton

Thomas Weller
1915–

American pediatrician, parasitologist, and virologist

Thomas Weller was corecipient, with **John F. Enders** and **Frederick Robbins**, of the Nobel Prize in physiology or medicine in 1954. This award was given for the trio's successful growth of the poliomyelitis (polio) virus in a non-neural tissue culture. This development was significant in the fight against the crippling disease polio, and eventually led to the development, by **Jonas Salk** in 1953, of a successful vaccination against the virus. It also revolutionized viral work in the laboratory and aided the recognition of many new types of viruses. Weller also distinguished himself with his studies of human parasites and the viruses that cause rubella and chicken pox.

Thomas Huckle Weller was born June 15, 1915, in Ann Arbor, Michigan. His parents were Elsie A. (Huckle) and Dr. Carl V. Weller. He received his B.S. in 1936 and M.S. in 1937, both from the University of Michigan, where his father was chair of the pathology department. He continued his studies at Harvard Medical School, where he met and roomed with his future Nobel corecipient Robbins. In 1938 Weller received a fellowship from the international health division of the Rockefeller Foundation, which allowed him to study public health in Tennessee and malaria in Florida, topics which first interested him during his undergraduate years.

Weller graduated from Harvard with magna cum laude honors in parasitology, receiving his M.D. in 1940. He also received a fellowship in tropical medicine and a teaching fellowship in bacteriology. He completed an internship in pathology and bacteriology (1941) at Children's Hospital in Boston. He then began a residency at Children's, with the intention of specializing in pediatrics, before enlisting in the U.S. Army during World War II.

Weller served in the Army Medical Corps from 1942 to 1945. He was initially given teaching assignments in tropical medicine, but he was soon made officer in charge of bacteriology and virology work in San Juan, Puerto Rico. His major research there related to pneumonia and the parasitic disease schistosomiasis, an infection that is centered in the intestine and damages tissue and the circulatory system. Before his military service ended, he moved to the Army Medical School in Washington D.C. Upon his discharge in 1945, Weller was married to Kathleen Fahey, with whom he had two sons and two daughters. Returning to Boston's Children's Hospital, he finished his residency and began a postdoctoral year working with Enders.

Helps Solve the Polio Puzzle

During 1948, Weller was working with the mumps virus, which Enders had been researching since the war. After one experiment, Weller had a few tubes of human embryonic tissue left over, so he and Enders decided to see what the virus poliomyelitis might do in them. A small amount of success prompted the duo, who had been joined in their research by Robbins, to try growing the virus in other biological mediums, including human foreskin and the intestinal cells of a mouse. The mouse intestine did not produce anything, but the trio finally had significant viral growth with human intestinal cells. This was the first time poliomyelitis had been grown in human or simian tissue other than nerve or brain. Using antibiotics to ward off unwanted bacterial invasion, the scientists were able to isolate the virus for study.

Once poliomyelitis was grown and isolated in tissue cultures it was possible to closely study the nature of the virus, which in turn made it possible for Salk to create a vaccine in 1953. Besides leading to an inhibitor against a debilitating disease, a major result of the trio's development was a decrease in the need for laboratory animals. As Weller was quoted saying in the *Journal of Infectious Diseases,* "In the instance of poliomyelitis, one culture tube of human or monkey cells became the equivalent of one monkey." In times prior, viruses had to be injected into living animals to monitor their potency. Now, with tissue culture growth, cell changes were apparent under the microscope, showing the action of the virus and eliminating the need for the animals.

The techniques for growing cells in tissue cultures developed by Weller and his associates were not only applicable to the poliomyelitis virus, however. They were soon copied by many other labs and scientists and quickly led to the identification, control, and study of several previously unrecognized virus types. For their work, and the improvements in scientific research it made possible, Weller, Enders, and Robbins shared the 1954 Nobel Prize in physiology or medicine.

Concurrent with his work with Enders and Robbins, Weller was named assistant director of the research division of infectious diseases at Children's Hospital in 1949. He held this position until 1954. At the same time, he began teaching at Harvard in tropical medicine and tropical public health, moving from instructor to associate professor. In 1953, Weller and Robbins shared the Mead Johnson Prize for their contributions to pediatric research. Then, in 1954, Weller was named Richard Pearson Strong Professor of Tropical Public Health and chair of the public health department at Harvard. As a consequence, he moved his research facilities to the Harvard Medical School. Later, he was appointed director of the Center for Prevention of Infectious Diseases at the Harvard School of Public Health.

Advances Knowledge of Parasites and Viruses

From the end of World War II until 1982 Weller also continued his research on two types of helminths, *trichinella spiralis* and *schistosoma mansoni*. Helminths are intestinal parasites, and these two cause, respectively, trichinosis, which can also severely affect the human musculature, and schistosomiasis. Weller was concerned with the parasites' basic biology and performed various diagnostic studies on them. His contributions to current understanding of these parasites are significant, advancing an understanding of the ailments they cause.

Weller spent a portion of the same period (1957 to 1973) establishing the basic available knowledge concerning cytomegalovirus (commonly known as CMV), which causes cell enlargement in various organs. Weller's most important finding in this area regarded congenital transmission of both CMV and rubella, a virus also known as German measles. A pregnant woman infected with either of these viruses may pass the infection on to her fetus. Weller showed that infected newborns excreted viral strains in their feces, providing another source for the spread of the diseases. His findings became significant when it was also learned that children born to infected mothers often risked birth defects.

In 1962 Weller, along with Franklin Neva, was able to grow and study German measles in tissue cultures. These two also went on to grow and isolate the chicken pox virus. Subsequently, Weller was the first to show the common origin of the varicella virus, which causes chicken pox, and the herpes zoster virus, which causes shingles. In 1971, Weller was the first to prove the airborne transmission of *pneumocystis carinii*, a form of pneumonia that later appeared as a frequent side effect of the human immunodeficiency virus commonly known as HIV.

Weller was elected to the National Academy of Sciences in 1964. In addition, he served on advisory committees of the World Health Organization, the Pan American Health Organization, the Agency for Internation Development, and the National Institute of Allergy and Infectious Disease. He continued his position at Harvard until 1985, when he became professor emeritus. While at Harvard, he helped establish the Public Health Department's international reputation. In 1988, Weller gave the first John F. Enders Memorial Lecture to the Infectious Disease Society of America. In addition to his Nobel Prize, Weller was the recipient of many awards and honorary degrees during his career.

SELECTED WRITINGS BY WELLER:

Periodicals

Science, Cultivation of the Lansing Strain of Poliomyelitis Virus in Cultures of Various Human Embryonic Tissues, January 28, 1949, pp. 85–87.

Post Graduate Medicine, The Importance of Tropical Public Health to World Peace, Volume 13, 1953, pp. 339–43.

Journal of Infectious Diseases, As It Was and As It Is: A Half-Century of Progress, March 1989, pp. 378–83.

FURTHER READING:

Books

Chernin, Eli, *Tropical Medicine at Harvard: The Weller Years, 1954–1981. A Personal Memoir,* Harvard University Press, 1985.

Chernin, Eli, *Current Biography Yearbook 1955,* H. W. Wilson, 1955, pp. 183–84.

Chernin, Eli, *Nobel Laureates in Medicine or Physiology,* Garland, 1990, pp. 563–66.

Chernin, Eli, *McGraw-Hill Modern Scientists and Engineers,* Volume 3, Mcgraw-Hill, 1980, pp. 292–94.

Periodicals

Chernin, Eli, *Time,* November 1, 1954, p. 49.

Sketch by Kimberlyn McGrail

Frits Went
1903–1990
American botanist

Lush, weed-free lawns owe their beauty in large part to American botanist Frits Went's discovery of the role of the plant growth hormone auxin. Went's 1927 discovery paved the way for the development of modern fertilizers and weed killers and the genetic engineering of plants. Went also developed a greenhouse that has enhanced botanical research by enabling scientists to control the plants' climate. Later in his career, the versatile scientist turned his attention toward environmental problems, including smog and the degradation of the Amazon rain forest.

A career in botany seemed virtually destined for Went, who was born in a garden and raised in a botany lab. He was born May 18, 1903, in Utrecht, the Netherlands, the son of Catharina Jacomina (Tonckens) and Friedrich August Ferdinand Christian Went. The Wents lived in a 300-year-old house in the botany garden of the State University of Utrecht, where the senior Went worked as a professor and director of the garden and botany lab. Just across from the house was the newly rebuilt laboratory, which was considered one of the finest in the world.

The young Went was fascinated by the Venus fly traps, cacti, palms, and other exotic plants in the garden's greenhouse. Many hours of his boyhood years were spent there and in the laboratory. Went considered himself lucky to have been surrounded by such a variety of plants and some of the best minds in the field of botany. He credited his career choice to his boyhood at the university, although his father carefully avoided pushing him into science. Went earned his bachelor's, master's and doctoral degrees at the State University of Utrecht between 1920 and 1927.

Discovers Role of Plant Hormone

For the subject of his doctoral thesis, Went chose the plant growth hormone auxin. He was intrigued by phototropism, the tendency of plants to bend toward light. He knew they bent by growing faster on the dark side of the stem and slower on the side facing the light. He suspected the growth hormone auxin was responsible, but he was not sure how. Went conducted his research on oat seedlings. His most important finding was that auxin, which is produced at the tip of the stem, is unevenly distributed under unidirectional light. More auxin flows down the dark side, making it grow faster. His theory also explained why the phototropic curve in plants moves farther down the stem over time. Went made his discovery in 1927, at the same time as Russian botanist N. Cholodny. Since then, their theory of phototropism has been called the Cholodny-Went theory.

Knowledge of growth hormones in plants later gave rise to the field of agricultural chemistry. Many herbicides, fungicides, and fertilizers use auxins. These hormones are also used in genetic engineering to develop better plant species. Back in the 1920s and 1930s, however, Went's theory was rejected by many of his peers. The controversy disturbed the gentle, amiable scientist. Yet dispute seemed to follow him throughout his career. After earning his Ph.D. in 1927, Went accepted his first job as a botanist at the botanical garden in Bogor, Java. That same year he married Catharina Helena van de Koppel. They would have two children, Hans Went and Anneke (Went) Simmons.

Two years after arriving in Bogor, Went was appointed director of the Foreigners Laboratory there. He left in 1933 to become an assistant professor of plant physiology at California Institute of Technology in Pasadena. He was named a full professor in 1935, a position he held until he left the institute in 1958. While there, Went continued his research on auxins, which culminated in the 1937 publication of the book *Phytohormones,* which he wrote with K. V. Thimann.

The book's publication ended Went's research into the internal control of plant growth. By that time he had grown discouraged by the naysayers. "If a field becomes too controversial or too theoretical, I prefer to leave it, as I did the growth factor field in the early 1940s," he wrote in an introductory chapter for the *Annual Review of Plant Physiology.* "After Thimann and I had written *Phytohormones,* I felt that I degenerated to a policeman, overseeing the auxin field, checking doubtful statements or questionable results." Went shifted his studies from the internal factors affecting plant development to the external ones.

The laboratory for his new field was the first air-conditioned research greenhouse, which California Institute of Technology opened in 1939. By varying the temperature, Went learned that plants grew best when the daytime temperature was several degrees higher than at night. Since his discovery, commercial greenhouses have routinely varied the day and night temperatures for optimal growth. Went also learned that greenhouse plants cultivated under temperatures similar to those occurring in the wild would grow just like those in nature. The best way to research the effects of climate on plant growth, he reasoned, was to duplicate the natural climate. So he persuaded his friend H. Earhart from Michigan to finance a phytotron—a greenhouse that could duplicate the full range of naturally occurring temperature, lighting, wind, and humidity conditions—at the institute. In June of 1949, the institute opened the Earhart Plant Research Laboratory as the first phytotron. Soon, phytotrons became a fixture of the best botany departments at universities throughout the world.

In 1947, Went was elected to the prestigious National Academy of Sciences. He would be elected to the French Academy of Sciences in 1956, the Dutch Academy of Sciences in 1958, and the German Academy for Natural Sciences in 1977.

Theorizes Smog Comes From Plants

In the 1950s, Went again shifted his focus, this time toward the effects of plants on the environment. He began by analyzing the smog that hovers over Los Angeles. Until that time, it had been assumed that the smoky haze was sulfur dioxide. But Went rejected that assumption based on the reaction of plants to the smog. He organized a joint venture of the California Institute of Technology, the University of California, and the Los Angeles County Air Pollution Control District to identify the components of the haze. Went theorized that most of the smog in the atmosphere comes not from cars and factories, but from plants. During the process of photosynthesis, he claimed, the hydrocarbons in plants—known as terpene—decompose to produce a blue haze. This natural haze inspired the names of the Blue Ridge and the Smoky Mountains in Virginia and North Carolina. Went lacked the scientific data to prove his theory and had no desire to obtain it. He had grown away from the detailed analysis used in his early research on auxins. Yet his reluctance to research his hypothesis once again subjected his theory to widespread rejection.

"He was so far in front that mainstream scientists could shoot his theories full of holes," said Thomas Sharkey, Went's former colleague and chair of the Department of Botany at the University of Wisconsin in Madison, in an interview for *NTCS.* "The idea that most of hydrocarbon comes from plants turns out to be correct. Now the atmospheric scientists agree with him." Not all of Went's far-flung theories turned out to be correct. He theorized that the greenhouse effect leading to global warming was caused by the smoky vapors coming from vegetation, rather than carbon dioxide. In that case, Went was proven wrong. Carbon dioxide from fossil fuels contributes greatly to the greenhouse effect.

While spending his days with textbooks and microscopes, Went never lost his appreciation of the beauty of gardens. He was elected president of the California Arboretum Foundation and was the sponsor of the Los Angeles State and County Arboretum. In his *Annual Review* article, Went wrote that those positions "gave me the advantage of coming close to the living plant, to acquaint myself not only with its appearance and occurrence, but also with its workings. And it has prevented me from becoming a narrow specialist, spending my life on the response of a single plant or organ."

Went's second book, *The Experimental Control of Plant Growth,* was published in 1957. The following year, he left California to become a professor at Washington University in St. Louis and the director of the Missouri Botanical Gardens. Also in 1958, Went received the Stephen Hales Award from the American Society of Plant Physiologists for his outstanding career contributions. In 1959, he was awarded an honorary Ph.D. from McGill University.

Went used his knowledge of the phytotron in 1960 to build a large display greenhouse at the botanical gardens, where different climates could be replicated in different areas of the greenhouse. He ran the botanical gardens until 1963 and taught at the university until 1965. In 1964, his third book, *The Plants,* was published. Went returned to research in 1965 as a distinguished professor of botany at the University of Nevada's Desert Research Institute in Reno. That same year, the American Society of Plant Physiologists gave him the Charles Reid Barnes Life Membership Award.

Finds Key to Sustaining Amazon Rain Forest

In the late 1960s, Went made one of his most important discoveries on the floor of the Amazonian rain forest. He was travelling aboard the research vessel *Alpha Helix* and planned to conduct research on the Amazon basin. When Brazilian customs agents impounded his laboratory equipment, Went turned his attention toward the ground. There he found a garden of fungi among the dead leaves, branches, and other debris, making up a litter layer. Running throughout this layer was a network of tree roots. Went concluded that the fungi digest the litter and pass the extracted nutrients to the tree roots in a continuous nutrient cycle.

Converting this rich land to temperate-zone agriculture irreparably harms the rain forest, Went warned. He urged rain forest developers to avoid annual crops and instead plant Brazil nuts, oil palms, or cacao trees, which would perpetuate the rich forest. Although clear-cutting of the rain forest continues, by the late 1980s, Went's warning had become gospel for the growing movement to save the Amazonian rain forest.

In 1967, Went received the Hodgkins Award from the Smithsonian Institute for his contribution to the understanding of the environment. He retired from the Desert Research Institute as a research professor emeritus in 1975, but his devotion to studying the living world never ceased. Went spent his last years researching the effects of smog on weather. He concluded that most of the soot collects on the surface of cumulus clouds, then returns to the earth as dirty rain or snow. In 1989, months before his death, he received the Henry Shaw Medal from the Missouri Botanical Gardens.

The 86-year-old scientist died of a heart attack on May 2, 1990, during a visit from his retirement home in Portland, Oregon, to the Desert Institute in Reno. A manuscript he had written for a book about hydrocarbons and their relationship to thunderstorms was found in his suitcase. His children published the book posthumously to distribute to Went's friends and peers. It is titled *Black Carbon, Blue Sky.* Had he lived longer, Went most likely would have continued his research. In his 1974 article for the *Annual Review of Plant Physiology,* he wrote of his dream to delve into such uncharted fields as the sociology and physiology of ants; and galls, or tumors, that insects develop on leaves. Went's son Hans, a retired zoology professor, told *NTCS* in an interview that even in his leisure time, his father's sole interest was science. "He was always out looking at plants, analyzing, comparing," Hans said of his father. "Science was his life."

SELECTED WRITINGS BY WENT:

Books

Phytohormones, Macmillan, 1937.

The Experimental Control of Plant Growth, With Special Reference to the Earhart Plant Research Laboratory at the California Institute of Technology, Chronica Botanica Co., 1957.

Life, magazine) The Plants, Time, Inc., 1964.

Annual Review of Plant Physiology, Reflections and Speculations, Annual Reviews, 1974, pp. 1–26.

Periodicals

Nature, Blue Hazes in the Atmosphere, Volume 187, 1960, pp. 641–643.

FURTHER READING:

Other

Sharkey, Thomas, *Interview with Cynthia Washam,* conducted August 11, 1993.

Went, Hans, *Interview with Cynthia Washam,* conducted August 15, 1993.

Sketch by Cynthia Washam

Alfred Werner
1866–1919
Swiss chemist

Alfred Werner was a chemist and educator whose accomplishments included the development of the coordination theory of chemistry. This theory, in which Werner proposed revolutionary ideas about how atoms and molecules are linked together, was formulated in a span of only three years, from 1890 to 1893. The remainder of his career was spent gathering the experimental support required to validate his new ideas. For his work on the linkage of atoms and his coordination theory, Werner became the first Swiss chemist to win the Nobel Prize.

Werner was born December 12, 1866, in Mulhouse, a small community in the French province of Alsace. He was the last of four children born to Jean-Adam Werner, a factory foreman and farmer, and Salome Jeanette Tesche, daughter of a wealthy German family. Alsace was French when Werner was born but was annexed into Germany during the Franco-Prussian war. Although the Werner family maintained strong patriotic ties with France and continued to speak French in their home, young Werner began his education in German schools.

At age six he was enrolled at the Ecole Libre des Freres, partly because of his mother's recent conversion to Catholicism. In 1878 he entered the Ecole Professionelle, a technical school, and began studying chemistry. The family had moved from the city to take up residence on a nearby farm, where Werner's father was engaged in dairying. The farm provided an ideal place for young Werner to begin his experiments. During this time, an unpleasant explosion in his home lab almost ended his career in chemistry and forced him to move his vials and chemicals into the barn. Werner's earliest known work was a paper on urea that he submitted in 1885 to the director of the Mulhouse Chemie Schule. He was 18. Although the paper was scientifically unsound and showed youthful inexperience, it did reveal a talent for classification and systematization that would prove invaluable in later years.

In late 1885 Werner began serving a one-year term of compulsory military duty. Stationed in the town of Karlsruhe, Werner enrolled in two organic chemistry courses taught at the Technical University there. After his tour of duty, he relocated to Zurich, Switzerland, to continue his education in chemistry at the Federal Institute of Technology. Werner excelled in chemistry but performed poorly in mathematical courses, especially descriptive geometry. After six semesters of work and completion of a paper describing the successful preparation of five compounds, he received a diploma in technical chemistry. A year later, in 1890, he was awarded a Ph.D.

Werner's doctoral thesis in 1890 was his first publication and his most important work in organic chemistry. Along with his graduate advisor, Werner showed that the shape of nitrogen compounds are similar to carbon compounds. His second paper, "Contribution to the Theory of Affinity and Valence," concerned the forces of attraction that hold carbon atoms together. Werner attacked the traditional theory that pictured atoms of carbon held together in rigid formations. He suggested that attractive forces emanate in all directions from the center of a central atom. Using this novel idea, Werner was able to derive kekulé formulas—notations for chemical structures in which valence bonds are illustrated with short lines—for organic carbon compounds.

Dream Inspires Coordination Theory

His most important paper, "Contribution to the Construction of Inorganic Compounds," was written in 1893. Werner awoke at 2 A.M. one morning with the solution to the riddle of molecular structure. He began writing furiously and by 5 P.M. his monumental paper on coordination theory was finished. In his paper Werner proposed that single atoms or molecules could be grouped around a central atom according to simple geometrical principles. These coordination bonds were immensely successful in explaining the properties of observed compounds and in predicting the existence of unknown compounds.

During this time, Werner had been developing other dimensions of his career as well. In 1891 he went to Paris as a postdoctoral student and worked with the French chemist Pierre Berthelot on thermochemical problems. Werner began his teaching career during the summer semester of 1892, as a lecturer in atomic theory at the Federal Institute of Technology. In the fall of 1893, as a result of his almost overnight success with the publication of his theory, he was appointed professor of organic chemistry at the University of Zurich. In his first course, the chemistry of aromatic compounds, Werner proved to be a demanding professor whose exuberance and contagious enthusiasm for atoms and molecules inspired and enthralled students. Although Werner's theoretical and experimental work was primarily in the field of inorganic chemistry, it was not until 1902 that he was allowed to teach inorganic chemistry.

After writing his ground-breaking papers, Werner had set about immediately to prove his theory. In a span of some 25 years he painstakingly prepared over 8000 compounds and published his findings in more than 150 publications. In 1907 he succeeded in preparing a beautiful ammonia-violeo salt, a compound predicted by his theory. With this preparation his opponents finally conceded defeat. Werner's greatest experimental success came in 1911 with the successful resolution of optically active coordination compounds—substances able to deflect polarized light. A few years later he resolved carbon-free coordination compounds and ended forever carbon's dominance in stereochemistry. For his theoretical and experimental work on coordination theory, Werner was awarded the Nobel Prize in chemistry in 1913.

Werner married Emma Wilhelmine Giesker in 1894, the same year he became a Swiss citizen. They had two children, a boy and a girl. Werner was a robust man with a jovial sense of humor. He was a connoisseur of good foods and wine and enjoyed billiards and chess with friends and family. Werner's hobbies included photography, stamp collecting, mountain climbing, and ice skating.

Werner published prolifically in both organic and inorganic chemistry. He wrote two textbooks on inorganic and stereochemical topics. In addition to the Nobel Prize, he was the recipient of many awards and honorary degrees, including the prestigious Leblanc Medal of the French Chemical Society. Werner died on November 15, 1919, at a Zurich psychiatric institution, from arteriosclerosis of the brain. At his funeral he was remembered for his numerous contributions to science and teaching.

SELECTED WRITINGS BY WERNER:

Books

Lehrbuch der Stereochemie, Verlab von Gustav Fischer, Jena, 1904.

FURTHER READING:

Books

Kauffman, George B., *Alfred Werner, Founder of Coordination Chemistry,* Springer-Verlag, 1966.
Kauffman, George B., *Nobel Prize Winners,* H. W. Wilson, 1987, pp. 1110–12.

Sketch by Mike McClure

Harold Dadford West
1904–1974
American biochemist

For forty-seven years Harold Dadford West was involved in biochemical research and education at Meharry Medical College. For thirteen of those years, he was president of the institution. He was selected to be the first honorary member of the National Medical Association, and the Science Center at Meharry was named for him.

Born in Flemington, New Jersey, on July 16, 1904, West was the son of George H. West and the former Mary Ann Toney. He attended the University of Illinois, where he received a bachelor of arts degree in 1925. He was an associate professor and head of the science department at Morris Brown College in Atlanta from 1925 to 1927. On December 27, 1927, West married Jessie Juanita Penn. They eventually had one daughter and one son.

In 1927 West joined the faculty of Meharry Medical College in Nashville, Tennessee, as an associate professor of physiological chemistry. Meharry Medical College had become an independent institution in 1915. Prior to that it was part of Central Tennessee College, established by the Freedmen's Aid Society of the Methodist Episcopal Church after the American Civil War in 1866. During his early years on the faculty of Meharry Medical College, West completed a master of arts degree and a doctorate. He was a recipient of a fellowship from the Julius Rosenwald Fund at the University of Illinois while he earned a master of arts degree in 1930. Following that he was a Rockefeller Foundation fellow, receiving a doctorate degree from the same university in 1937. The title of his dissertation was "The Chemistry and Nutritive Value of Essential Amino Acids." In 1938 West became professor of biochemistry and chairperson of the department.

West's work in biochemical research was vast, including studies of tuberculosis and other bacilli, the antibiotic biocerin, and aromatic hydrocarbons. He worked with amino acids, becoming the first to synthesize threonine. As noted in the *Journal of the National Medical Association,* among his other investigations were "the role of sulfur in biological detoxification mechanisms; blood serum calcium levels in the Negro in relation to possible significance in tuberculosis; relation of B vitamins, especially pantothenic acid, to detoxification of sulfa drugs and susceptibility to bacillary disease."

West's studies were supported by the John and Mary R. Markle Foundation, the Nutrition Foundation, the National Institutes of Health, and the American Medical Association. His research papers were published in a number of professional journals, including the *American Journal of Physiology, Southern Medical Journal,* and *Journal of Biological Chemistry.*

In 1952 West was named the fifth president of Meharry Medical College, its first African American president. In 1963 he was the first black American to serve on the State Board of Education. West retired as president in 1965, returning to the position of professor of biochemistry. When he retired from Meharry in 1973 he became a trustee of the college. In his final years he worked on a complete history of the college. West died on March 5, 1974.

During his career, West was awarded two honorary degrees. In 1955 he received a doctor of laws from Morris Brown College, and in 1970 a doctor of science from Meharry Medical College. He was a member of many honorary and professional societies, including the American Chemical Society, the Society of Experimental Biology and Medicine, and the American Society of Biological Chemists. He was also elected to Sigma Xi, the scientific research society, which describes itself "as an honor society for scientists and engineers. . . . Its goals are to foster interaction among science, technology and society."

FURTHER READING:

Books

Sammons, Vivian Ovelton, *Blacks in Science and Medicine,* Hemisphere, 1990, p. 246.

Periodicals

Sammons, Vivian Ovelton, *Journal of the National Medical Association,* September 1974, pp. 448–449.

Sketch by M. C. Nagel

George West Wetherill
1925–
American geophysicist

George West Wetherill is a geophysicist and planetary scientist who is involved in many fields of research. He has done work on geochronology—the study of the earth from its origin to the present—and lunar history, but he is probably best known for his work on the origins of our solar system. He has concentrated much of his research on the asteroid belt, and he has been extensively involved in debates about what the belt, and the asteroids that fall to Earth as meteorites, can tell us about how the planets were formed. He has designed computer simulations to model how bodies orbit in a solar system and what happens when they collide.

Wetherill was born to George and Leah Victoria Wetherill on August 12, 1925 in Philadelphia, Pennsylvania. He attended the University of Chicago, where he received a succession of degrees, including an M.S. in 1951 and a Ph.D. in physics in 1953. At the conclusion of his schooling, Wetherill joined the Department of Terrestrial Magnetism of the Carnegie Institution of Washington; he remained there until 1960, when he moved to the University of California at Los Angeles. While at UCLA, he served as a professor of geophysics and geology and then as chair of the Department of Planetary and Space Science from 1968 to 1972. Wetherill returned to the Carnegie Institution in 1975, where he assumed the title of director of the Department of Terrestrial Magnetism. He remained as director until 1991, when he moved to a consultative position with the institution.

In astronomy, it is generally accepted that the solar system formed from an initial cloud of dust and gas with the Sun at the center. In this cloud there were innumerable tiny bodies, also referred to as planetesimals, which were in revolution around the Sun. The conventional scientific wisdom is that these bodies eventually combined to form planetary "embryos," about the size of our moon. Over time, the embryos pulled in more and more matter until they reached their present form. This theory, however, fails to explain the existence of the asteroid belt. Located between Mars and Jupiter, the belt measures 400 million kilometers in width and is in orbit around the Sun. There are over 4000 asteroids within the belt, and one of the problems facing astronomers is explaining why they would not have combined to form a planet of their own.

In 1991, Wetherill completed work on a project dealing with this problem and other aspects of the origin of the solar system. His project made use of complex three-dimensional computer models. By randomly selecting distributions of matter, energy, and angular momentum, Wetherill was able to create solar systems by chance. Surprisingly, the simulations yielded systems similar to our present solar system nearly every time. Through these experiments Wetherill observed the evolution of asteroid regions, and they underwent a process of "self clearing." During the evolution of the solar system, the collision of planet embryos have a different result in the areas where asteroid belts are formed, such as the area between Mars and Jupiter. The collision of these embryos causes varying degrees of fragmentation, but instead of being drawn into a planet like Jupiter, they are flung away from it. The gravitational field of the planet acts like a slingshot, which propels the fragments out of orbit.

Wetherill ran twenty-seven simulations with his computer models and found, on average, that 4.2 planets formed in the area occupied in our solar system by Mercury, Venus, Mars, and Earth. He also discovered that a large body like Jupiter did not always form, but a planet similar to Earth in size always formed at approximately the same distance from the Sun. Wetherill believes that the asteroid fragments which fall to earth may also provide some answers. He considers meteorite collections to be fossil evidence of the origin of the solar system.

Wetherill is often consulted for his opinion on the controversies of the day. There is an ongoing debate between meteoriticists and the revisionist astronomers over the origin of asteroids. The meteoriticists hold that the asteroids have remained unchanged in the 4.5 billion years since their origin. The revisionists contest this theory, claiming that asteroids underwent severe heating to the point of melting, thus experiencing radical alterations. An expert in the orbital and collisional behavior of solar systems bodies, Wetherill sides with neither group. He does, however, reject the revisionists' theory that smaller bodies exist in the belt which are of a radically different constitution than other asteroids in the belt. Wetherill made use of the revisionists' own belief in fragmentation of asteroids through collisions, and he pointed to the lack of larger bodies of a radical nature in the belt from which the smaller bodies would have to have been chipped.

Wetherill is a regular contributor to many periodicals and professional journals. He is an editor with the *Annual Review of Earth and Planetary Science*. He is also affiliated with both *Icarus* and *Meteoritics* as an associate editor. He has been retained as a consultant by the National Science Foundation, the National Academy of Science, and NASA. He is a member of the American Astronomical Society and the National Academy of Science and a fellow of the American Academy of Arts and Sciences and the American Geophysical Society. Wetherill served as vice president of the Meteoritical Society from 1972 to 1974, and again from 1980 to 1982. He was elected president in 1982 and served in this capacity until 1984. He served as vice president and president of the Geochemical Union from 1973 to 1975. Wetherill's work has brought him recognition from many quarters. He received the Leonard Medal from the Meteoritical Society in 1981, and the G. K. Gilbert Award from the Geological Society of America in 1984. He was awarded the G. P. Kuiper prize from the American Astronomical Society in 1986, and the American Geophysical Society made him

the recipient of their 1991 H. H. Hess Medal. In 1997, Wetherill was awarded the National Medal of Science in recognition of his work on radiometric clocks, which have provided reliable dates for the origin and early history of the earth, the chronology of planetary evolution, the history of plate tectonics, and the origin of humans on earth; and also for showing how earth-like planets may be created in evolving solar systems.

Wetherill married Phyllis May Steiss on June 17, 1950. They have three children. Wetherill is currently a member of the staff at the Department of Terrestrial Magnetism and is active in the International Society for the Study of the Origin of Life.

SELECTED WRITINGS BY WETHERILL:

Books

Asteroids II, Origin of the Asteroid Belt, edited by Richard P. Binzel, Tom Gehrels, and Mildred S. Matthews, University of Arizona Press, 1989.

Periodicals

Science, Occurrence of Giant Impacts During the Growth of Terrestrial Planets, May 17, 1985, pp. 877–879.
Science, Occurrence of Earth-like Bodies in Planetary Systems, August 2, 1991, pp. 535–538.

FURTHER READING:

Periodicals

Kerr, Richard, *Science,* The Great Asteroid Roast: Was It Rare or Well-done? February 2, 1990, pp. 527–528.
Suplee, Curt, *The Washington Post,* Astronomy: Solar System Pattern May Be Typical, August 5, 1991.

Sketch by Chris McGrail

Nancy Wexler
1945–
American neuropsychologist

Nancy Wexler's research on Huntington's disease has led to the development of a presymptomatic test for the condition as well as the identification of the genes responsible for the disease. The symptoms of this fatal, genetically based disorder (for which Wexler herself is at risk) usually appear around middle age, and the disease leads to the degeneration of mental, psychological, and physical functioning. For her pivotal role in these achievements, Wexler was granted the Albert Lasker Public Service Award in 1993.

Nancy Sabin Wexler was born on July 19, 1945, to Milton Wexler, a Los Angeles psychoanalyst, and Leonore Sabin Wexler. She studied social relations and English at Radcliffe and graduated in 1967. Wexler subsequently traveled to Jamaica on a Fulbright scholarship and studied at the Hampstead Clinic Child Psychoanalytic Training Center in London.

In 1968 Wexler learned that her mother had developed the symptoms of Huntington's disease, a condition to which Wexler's maternal grandfather and three uncles had already succumbed. Efforts to fight the disease became a primary mission for Wexler and her family: Her father founded the Hereditary Disease Foundation in 1968, and Wexler herself, who was then entering the doctoral program in clinical psychology at the University of Michigan, eventually wrote her doctoral thesis on the "Perceptual-motor, Cognitive, and Emotional Characteristics of Persons-at-Risk for Huntington's Disease," and received her Ph.D. in 1974.

After graduating from University of Michigan, Wexler taught psychology at the New School for Social Research in New York City and worked as a researcher on Huntington's disease for the National Institutes of Health (NIH). In 1976 she was appointed by congress to head the NIH's Commission for the Control of Huntington's Disease and its Consequences. In 1985 she joined the College of Physicians and Surgeons at Columbia University.

In 1979 Wexler's research led her to Lake Maracaibo in Venezuela, where she studied a community which had a high incidence of Huntington's disease. Wexler kept medical records, took blood and skin samples, and charted the transmission of the disease within families. Wexler sent the samples she collected to geneticist James Gusella at Massachusetts General Hospital, who used the blood samples to conduct a study to locate the gene—the first such genetic mapping of a disease. Gusella eventually discovered a deoxyribonucleic acid (DNA) marker close to the Huntington's gene. Based on this study, Gusella introduced a test that was ninety-six percent accurate in detecting whether an individual bears the Huntington's gene. Because there was still no cure for the Huntington's disease, the test proved to be controversial, raising many issues involving patient rights, childbearing decisions, and discrimination by employers and insurance companies. In her interviews and writings Wexler has stressed the importance of keeping such genetic information confidential.

In 1993 the Huntington's gene was identified through research based on the Venezuelan blood samples and the work of the Huntington's Disease Collaborative Research Group. In October, 1993, Wexler received an Albert Lasker Public Service Award for her role in this effort. In addition, she has served as an advisor on social and medical ethics issues to the Human Genome Project—a massive interna-

tional effort to map and identify the approximately 100,000 genes in the human body. Wexler also has assumed directorship of the Hereditary Disease Foundation founded by her father, to which she donated the honorarium that accompanied the Lasker Award.

SELECTED WRITINGS BY WEXLER:

Books

Advances in Neurology, Volume 23: Huntington's Disease, Raven, 1979.
Mama Can't Remember Anymore: Care Management of Elders and Their Families, Wein & Wein, 1991.

FURTHER READING:

Books

Newsmakers, Gale, 1992, pp. 530–33.

Periodicals

U.S. News & World Report, An Array of New Tools Against Inherited Diseases, April 22, 1985, pp. 75–76.
Bluestone, Mimi, *Ms.,* Science and Ethics: The Double Life of Nancy Wexler, November/December 1991, pp. 90–91.
Grady, Denise, *Discover,* The Ticking of a Time Bomb in the Genes, June 1987.
Jaroff, Leon, *Time,* Making the Best of a Bad Gene, February 10, 1992, pp. 78–79.
Konner, Melvin, *New York Times Magazine,* New Keys to the Mind, July 17, 1988, pp. 49–50.
Konner, Melvin, *New York Times,* October 1, 1993, p. A24.

Sketch by David Sprinkle

Hermann Weyl
1885–1955
American mathematician

Hermann Weyl was one of the most wide-ranging mathematicians of his generation, following in the footsteps of his teacher **David Hilbert**. Weyl's interests in mathematics ran the gamut from foundations to physics, two areas in which he made profound contributions. He combined great technical virtuosity with imagination, and devoted attention to the explanation of mathematics to the

Hermann Weyl

general public. He managed to take a segment of mathematics developed in an abstract setting and apply it to certain branches of physics, such as relativity theory—a theory that holds that the velocity of light is the same for all observers, no matter how they are moving, that the laws of physics are the same in all inertial frames, and that all such frames are equivalent; and quantum mechanics—a theory that allows mathematical interpretation of elementary particles through wave properties. His distinctive ability was integrating nature and theory.

Claus Hugo Hermann Weyl was born on November 9, 1885, at Elmshorn, near Hamburg, Germany. The financial standing of his parents (his father, Ludwig, was a clerk in a bank and his mother, Anna Dieck, came from a wealthy family) enabled him to receive a quality education. From 1895 to 1904 he attended the Gymnasium at Altona, where his performance attracted the attention of his headmaster, a relative of an eminent mathematician of that time, David Hilbert. Weyl soon found himself at the University of Göttingen where Hilbert was an instructor. He remained there for the rest of his student days, with the exception of a semester at the University of Munich. He received his degree under Hilbert in 1908 and advanced to the ranks of privatdocent (unpaid but licensed instructor) in 1910.

Weyl married Helene Joseph (known as Hella to the family) in 1913 and in the same year took a position as professor at the National Technical University (ETH) in Zurich, Switzerland. He declined the offer to be Felix Klein's successor at Göttingen, despite the university's central role in the mathematical world. It has been suggested

that he wanted to free himself, somewhat, of the influence of Hilbert, especially in light of the fact that he had accepted an invitation to take a chair at Göttingen when Hilbert retired. In any case, he brought a great deal of mathematical distinction to the ETH in Zurich, where his sons Fritz Joachim and Michael grew up.

It is not surprising that Weyl's early work dealt with topics that which Hilbert held an interest. His *Habilitationsschrift* was devoted to boundary conditions of second-order linear differential equations. (The way the German educational system worked, it was necessary to do a substantial piece of original research beyond the doctoral dissertation in order to qualify to teach in the university. This "entitling document" was frequently the launching point of the mathematical career of its author.) In other words, he was looking into the way functions behaved on a given region when the behavior at the boundary was specified. His results were sufficient for the purpose of enabling him to earn a living, but he rapidly moved on to areas where his contributions were more innovative and have had a more lasting effect.

One of the principal areas of Weyl's research was the topic of Hilbert spaces. The problem was to understand something about the functions that operated on the points of Hilbert space in a way useful for analyzing the result of applying the functions. In particular, Weyl wanted to know where the functions behaved more simply than on the space as a whole, since the behavior of the function on the rest of the space could be represented in terms of its behavior on the simpler regions. Different kinds of functions behaved in radically different ways on a Hilbert space, so Weyl had to restrict his attention to a subclass of functions small enough to be tractable (for example, the functions could not "blow up") but large enough to be useful. His choice of self-adjoint, compact operators was justified by their subsequent importance in the field of functional analysis.

Among the areas he brought together were geometry and analysis from the nineteenth century and topology, which was largely a creation of the twentieth century. Topology sought to understand the behavior of space in ways that require a less-detailed understanding of how the elements of a structure fit together than geometry demanded. One of the basic ideas of topology is that of a "manifold," first introduced by G. F. B. Riemann in his *Habilitationsschrift* as a student of Gauss. Riemann had little material with which to work, while Weyl was able to take advantage of the work of Hilbert and the Dutch mathematician **Luitzen Egbertus Jan Brouwer**. This effort culminated in his 1913 book on Riemann surfaces, an excellent exposition on how complex analysis and topology could be used together to analyze the behavior of complex functions.

Weyl served briefly in the German army at the outbreak of World War I, but before this military interlude, he did research that led to one of his most important papers. He looked at the way irrational numbers (those that cannot be expressed as a ratio of two whole numbers) were distributed. What he noticed was that the *fractional* parts of an irrational number and its integral multiples seemed to be evenly distributed in the interval between O and 1. He succeeded in proving this result, and it is known as the Kronecker-Weyl theorem, owing half of its name to an influential number theorist who had had an effect on Hilbert. Although the result may seem rather narrow, Weyl was able to generalize it to sequences of much broader application.

During his time in Zurich, Weyl spent a year in collaboration with **Albert Einstein** and picked up a dose of enthusiasm for the relativity theory. Among the other results of this collaboration was Weyl's popular account of relativity theory, *Space, Time, Matter* (the original German edition appeared in 1918). In those early days of general relativity, which describes gravity in terms of how mass distorts space-time, the correct mathematical formulation of some of Einstein's ideas was not clear. He had been able to use ideas developed by differential geometers at the end of the nineteenth century that involved the notion of a tensor. A tensor can be thought of as a function on a number of vectors that takes a number as its value. Weyl used the tensor calculus that had been developed by the geometers to come up with neater formulations of general relativity than the original version proposed by Einstein. In later years, he took the evolution of tensors one step further while maintaining a strict mathematical level of rigor.

Constructs New Foundations

One of the most visible areas in which Weyl worked after World War I was in the foundations of mathematics. He had used some of the topological results of the Dutch mathematician Brouwer in working on Riemann surfaces. In addition, he had looked at some of Brouwer's ideas about the philosophy of mathematics and was convinced that they had to be taken seriously. Although it was not always easy to understand what Brouwer was trying to say, it was clear that he was criticizing "classical" mathematics, that is, the mathematics that had prevailed at least since Euclid. One of the standard methods of proof in classical mathematics was the reductio ad absurdum, or proof by contradiction. If one wished to prove that P was true, one could assume that not-P was true and see if that led to a contradiction. If it did, then not-P must not be true, and P must be true instead. This method of proof depended on the principle that either P was true or not-P was true, which had seemed convincing to generations of mathematicians.

Brouwer, however, found this style of argument unacceptable. For reasons having to do with his understanding of mathematics as the creation of the human mind, he wanted to introduce a third category besides truth and falsity, a category we could call "unproven." In other words, there was more to truth than just the negation of falsity—to claim P or not-P, something had to be proven. This argument of Brouwer was especially directed against so-called nonconstructive existence proofs. These were proofs in which something was shown to exist, not by being constructed, but by arguing that, if it didn't exist, a contradiction arose. For ordinary, finite mathematics it was usually easy to come up with a constructive proof, but for claims about infinite sets nonconstructive arguments were popular. If Brouwer's objections were to be sustained, a good part of mathematics even at the level of elementary calculus would have to be rewritten and some perhaps have to be abandoned.

This attitude aroused the ire of David Hilbert. He valued the progress that had been made in mathematics too highly to sacrifice it lightly for philosophical reasons. Although Hilbert had earlier expressed admiration for Brouwer's work, he felt obliged to negate Brouwer's philosophy of mathematics known as intuitionism. What especially disturbed Hilbert was Weyl's support of Brouwer's concepts, since Hilbert knew the mathematical strength of his former student. In the 1920s, while the argument was being considered, Hilbert was discouraged about the future of mathematics in the hands of the intuitionists.

Although Weyl never entirely abandoned his allegiance to Brouwer, he also recognized that Hilbert's program in the philosophy of mathematics was bound to appeal to the practicing mathematician, more than Brouwer's speculations. In 1927, responding to one of Hilbert's lectures concerned with the foundations of mathematics, Weyl commented on the extent to which Hilbert had been led to a reinterpretation of mathematics by the need to fight off Brouwer's criticisms. The tone of Weyl's remarks suggested that he would not have been unhappy if Hilbert's point of view was to prevail. This flexibility with regard to the foundations of mathematics indicates that Weyl was sensitive to the changes in attitude that others ignored, but also may explain why Weyl never founded a philosophical school: he was too ready to recognize the justice of others' points of view.

In general, Weyl took questions of literature and style seriously, which goes far to explain the success of his expository writings. His son recalls that when Weyl would read poetry aloud to the family, the intensity and volume of his voice would make the walls shake. He kept in touch with modern literature as well as the classics of his childhood. While he continued to enjoy the poetry of Friedrich Hölderlin and Johann Wolfgang von Goethe, he also read Friedrich Nietzsche's *Also Sprach Zarathustra* and Thomas Mann's *The Magic Mountain*. He could cite quotations from German poetry whenever he needed them. For those of a psychologizing bent, it has even been argued that his fondness for poetry may be in line with his preference for intuitionism as a philosophy of mathematics. The kind of poetry he preferred spoke to the heart, and he used quotations to add a human dimension to otherwise cold mathematical writing.

Leaves Germany for the United States

After he accepted a chair at Göttingen in 1930, Weyl did not have long to enjoy his return to familiar surroundings. In 1933 he decided that he could no longer remain in Nazi Germany, and he took up a permanent position at the Institute for Advanced Study, newly founded in Princeton, New Jersey. Although Weyl himself was of irreproachably Aryan ancestry, his wife was partly Jewish, and that would have been enough to attract the attention of the authorities. There may have been the additional attraction of the wealth of intellectual company available at the institute, between its visitors from all over the globe and permanent residents such as Einstein. Weyl took his official duties as a faculty member seriously, although his reputation could be terrifying to younger mathematicians unaware of the poet within.

Weyl's work continued to bridge the gap between physics and mathematics. As long ago as 1929, he developed a mathematical theory for the subatomic particle the neutrino. The theory was internally consistent but failed to preserve left-right symmetry and so was abandoned. Subsequent experimentation revealed that symmetry need not be conserved, with the result that Weyl's theory reentered the mathematical physics mainstream all the more forcefully. Another area for the interaction of mathematics and physics was the study of spinors, a kind of tensor that has proven to be of immense use in quantum mechanics. Although spinors had been known before Weyl, he was the first to give a full treatment of them. Perhaps it was this work that led **Roger Penrose**, one of the most insightful mathematical physicists of the second half of the twentieth century, to label Weyl "the greatest mathematician of this century."

One of the challenges of physical theories is to find quantities that do not change (are conserved) during other changes. Felix Klein in the nineteenth century had stressed the importance of group theory, then a new branch of mathematics, in describing what changed and what remained the same during processes. Weyl adapted Klein's ideas to the physics of the twentieth century by characterizing invariant quantities for relativity theory and for quantum mechanics. In a 1923 paper Weyl had come up with a suitable definition for congruence in relativistic space-time. Even more influential was his 1928 book on group theory and quantum mechanics, which imposed a model that would have been welcome to Klein due to the previously rather disjointed results assembled by quantum physicists. Weyl was an artist in the use of group theory and could accomplish wonders with modest mathematical structure.

After the end of World War II, Weyl divided his time between Zurich and Princeton. His first wife died in 1948, and two years later he married Ellen Bär. He took a serious view of the history of mathematics and arranged with Princeton to give a course on the subject. One of his magisterial works was a survey of the previous half-century of mathematics that appeared in the *American Mathematical Monthly* in 1951. Although he never became as fluent in English as he had in German, he retained a strong commitment to the public's right to be informed about scientific developments.

John Archibald Wheeler, an American physicist, called attention to Weyl's anticipation of the anthropic principle in cosmology. In a 1919 paper Weyl had speculated on the coincidence of the agreement of two enormous numbers of very different origin. In the 1930s this speculation had been given with the title "Weyl's hypothesis," although later authors referred more to its presence elsewhere. What cannot be denied is that the recent discussion of the anthropic principle concerning features necessary for human existence in the universe has, as Wheeler noted, taken up Weyl's point once again.

Weyl was unaware of the rules governing the length of time that a naturalized citizen could spend abroad at one time without losing citizenship. By inadvertence he exceeded the time limit and lost his American citizenship in the mid 1950s. To remedy the situation required an act of Congress, but there was no lack of help in securing it. In the meantime, Weyl celebrated his seventieth birthday in Zurich amid a flurry of congratulations. On December 8, 1955, as he was mailing some letters of thanks to well-wishers, he died of a heart attack. With his death passed one of the links with the great era of Göttingen as a mathematical center and one of the founders of contemporary mathematical physics, but even more, a mathematician who could convey the poetry in his discipline.

SELECTED WRITINGS BY WEYL:

Books

Die Idee der Riemannschen Fläche, Teubner, 1913.
Raum, Zeit, Materie, Springer, 1918.
Philosophie der Mathematik und Naturwissenschaft, R. Oldenbourg, 1926.
Grüppentheorie und Quantenmechanik, Hirzel, 1928.
Symmetry, Princeton University Press, 1952.
Selecta Hermann Weyl, Birkhäuser, 1956.
Gesammelte Abhandlungen, four volumes, Springer, 1968.

FURTHER READING:

Books

Chandrasekharan, K., editor, *Hermann Weyl: Centenary Lectures,* Springer, 1986.
Deppert, Wolfgang, and others, editors, *Exact Sciences and Their Philosophical Foundations,* Peter Lang, 1988.
Deppert, Wolfgang, and others, editors, *Dictionary of Scientific Biography,* Volume 14, Scribner's, pp. 281–285.

Sketch by Thomas Drucker

Anna Johnson Pell Wheeler
1883–1966
American algebraist

A distinguished mathematics researcher and educator, Anna Johnson Pell Wheeler is best remembered for her interest and research in biorthogonal systems of functions and integral equations. Much of her work was in the area of linear algebra of infinitely many variables—an area which she studied her entire career. Wheeler struggled to gain equality with men in the field of mathematics. In 1910, she was only the second woman at the University of Chicago to receive a doctorate in mathematics. Finding a full–time teaching position was difficult, even though she was often more qualified than the male applicants. Her break came when she substituted for her incapacitated first husband, Alexander Pell, at the Armour Institute in Chicago. There, although she did not obtain a permanent position, she convinced her superiors of her competency. She was then hired as an instructor in mathematics at Mount Holyoke College in Hadley, Massachusetts, in 1911, leaving there in 1918 to take a position as associate professor at Bryn Mawr College in Pennsylvania. She remained at Bryn Mawr until her retirement in 1948, becoming head of the mathematics department in 1924. A champion of women in the field of mathematics, she urged her students to persevere toward terminal degrees despite the gender prejudices exhibited by authorities at colleges and universities at that time. It is significant, in her tenure at Bryn Mawr College, that seven of her graduate students received doctorates in mathematics.

During her career, Wheeler was active in many professional associations. She served on the council and the board of the American Mathematical Society, and was also a member of the Mathematical Association of America and the American Association for the Advancement of Science. (In 1927, Wheeler was invited by the American Mathematical Society to deliver their annual Colloquium Lectures—the only woman so honored until 1970.) In 1940, she received recognition from the Women's Centennial Congress as one of the 100 women honored who had succeeded in non–traditional careers. Continuing her support of women mathematicians, Wheeler helped **Emmy Noether**, the eminent German algebraist, to relocate to Bryn Mawr when she sought political asylum from Nazi Germany in 1933.

Wheeler, of Swedish heritage, was born in Hawarden, Iowa, on May 5, 1883. Her parents were Amelia (Frieberg) and Andrew Johnson. Her father was an undertaker and furniture dealer in the small town of Akron, Iowa. Anna attended the local high school there and received her undergraduate degree from the University of South Dakota in 1903. There, her exceptional ability in mathematics was observed by her professor, Alexander Pell (later to become her first husband). She furthered her education at the University of Iowa and at Radcliffe College, earning master's degrees from both institutions.

Fellowship Allows Study in Europe

In 1906, Wheeler received an Alice Freeman Palmer Fellowship, allowing her to continue her studies at Göttingen University in Germany. There, she was guided in her work in integral equations by such eminent mathematicians as **Hermann Minkowski**, Felix Klein, and **David Hilbert**. Her thesis was completed under Hilbert's instruction, but for some reason—speculated to have been a dispute with Hilbert—she did not receive a degree from Göttingen.

Although Wheeler accepted the fellowship with the understanding she could not marry during its term, Pell joined her in Germany at the end of the year, and they were married there in 1907. Her new husband had an interesting past. He was actually a Russian revolutionist named Sergei Degaev, who had fled his country after being implicated in the murder of an officer of the Russian secret police. After emigrating to the United States, Dagaev changed his name to Alexander Pell, and began his new life as a mathematics professor.

The Pells left Germany and returned to the University of South Dakota. Shortly after their return, Pell accepted a position to teach at the Armour Institute of Technology in Chicago. Wheeler completed the work for her Ph. D. at the University of Chicago, and when Pell suffered a stroke in 1911, she assumed his teaching duties. She had hoped for a permanent position with a Midwestern university, but was unsuccessful. Other than taking over her husband's classes, the closest Wheeler came to being employed while in Chicago was when she taught a course at the University the fall semester of 1910. When she did find permanent work, it was out east at Mount Holyoke, and later, at Bryn Mawr. Pell, who was a semi–invalid after his stroke, died in 1921. In 1925, she married Arthur Leslie Wheeler, a classics scholar who had just become professor of Latin at Princeton University in New Jersey. Wheeler continued to teach at Bryn Mawr, even though they lived in Princeton where her husband was teaching. They also enjoyed a summer home in the Adirondack Mountains, to which she often invited her students. When Arthur died suddenly in 1932, she moved back to Bryn Mawr, where she lived and taught for the rest of her life.

Strengthens School's Reputation in Mathematics

Wheeler's work at Bryn Mawr took her beyond the classroom. She was well aware of the need to strengthen the reputation of the school's mathematics department, and set about doing so. She advised reducing teaching loads so that more research could be carried out by the faculty and encouraged professional collaboration and theoretical exchanges with other schools in the Philadelphia area. During this time of increasing administrative responsibilities,

Wheeler remained active in publishing the results of her research intointegral equations andfunctional analysis. Her Colloquium Lectures, however, were never published.

Although suffering from arthritis, Wheeler continued to participate in mathematics association meetings after her retirement. She died at Bryn Mawr on March 26, 1996, after suffering a stroke. She was eighty–two.

SELECTED WRITINGS BY WHEELER:

Books

Biorthogonal Systems of Functions, 1911.

FURTHER READING:

Books

Bailey, Martha J. *American Women in Science: A Biographical Dictionary.* Santa Barbara, CA: ABC–CLIO, Inc., 1994, pp. 414–415.
Ogilvie, Marilyn Bailey. *Women in Science: Antiquity through the Nineteenth Century.* Cambridge, MA: MIT Press, 1986, pp. 173–174.
Sicherman, Barbara and Carol Hurd Green, editors. *Notable American Women: The Modern Period, A Biographical Dictionary.* Cambridge, MA: The Belknap Press, 1980, pp. 725–726.

Periodicals

"Dr. Anna Pell Wheeler" (obituary). *The New York Times* (April 1, 1966): 35: 1.

Other

"Anna Johnson Pell Wheeler." *Biographies of Women Mathematicians.* June 1977. http://www.scottlan.edu/lriddle/women/chronol.htm (July 22, 1997).

Sketch by Jane Stewart Cook

John Archibald Wheeler
1911–

American physicist

John Archibald Wheeler's work with **Niels Bohr** and Edward Teller helped advance the processes of nuclear fission and fusion. Wheeler conducted a variety of military research in association with the Manhattan Project, the effort which developed the atomic bomb during World War II, and also was instrumental in the creation of the hydrogen bomb. A professor of physics and director of the Center for Theoretical Physics at the University of Texas at Austin, Wheeler added the term "black hole" to astronomy dictionaries. Throughout his career, Wheeler has made fundamental contributions to the studies of nuclear structure, nuclear fission, scattering theory, relativity, geometrodynamics, and other subjects. A long-time professor at Princeton University, his students include the Nobel-honored physicist **Richard P. Feynman**. Wheeler was born in Jacksonville, Florida, on July 9, 1911. His parents, Dr. Joseph Lewis Wheeler and Mabel Archibald Wheeler, were both librarians. Dr. Wheeler was later head of the Enoch Pratt Free Library in Baltimore, Maryland, when his son entered Johns Hopkins University as an undergraduate. Wheeler's plans to major in electrical engineering changed after his first year, according to Dennis Overbye's essay on Wheeler in *A Passion To Know,* because of "a frustrating summer spent rewinding electrical motors in a silver mine in New Mexico." Wheeler then changed his major to theoretical physics, a field in which he earned his Ph.D. in 1933.

Studies at Copenhagen Lead to Nuclear Model

A postdoctoral fellowship from the National Research Council in 1933 allowed Wheeler to continue his studies first at New York University with **Gregory Breit** and then at the Institute for Theoretical Physics in Copenhagen. There, he worked closely with Bohr; Wheeler would later tell Overbye that "you can talk about people like Buddha, Jesus, Moses, Confucius, but the thing that really convinced me that such people existed were the conversations with Bohr."

While studying with Bohr, Wheeler began to think about one of the questions that was to occupy his attention for many years: the structure of the atomic nucleus. At the time, two models of the nucleus were popular, one which emphasized the properties of the nucleus as a whole and one that emphasized the properties of the nucleons (protons and neutrons) that make up the nucleus. More than a decade later, in 1953, Wheeler and a colleague, D. L. Hill, made one of the first and most successful attempts to combine these two models into a single theory, the "collective model" of the atomic nucleus. Wheeler, in collaboration with Bohr, also devised a theory explaining the process of nuclear fission, predicting the fissility of plutonium produced from the uranium isotope ^{238}U. The Wheeler-Bohr discovery was later to become critical in the development of the first atomic weapons.

Works on Theoretical Problems and Military Research

Throughout his career, Wheeler has pursued some of the most difficult and most fundamental questions in all of physics. Some of his earlier research dealt with the search for a unified field theory, which would show how the fundamental forces of nature (the strong, weak, electromagnetic, and gravitational forces) are related to each other. His 1962 book, *Geometrodynamics,* is a collection of his papers on this subject. He also worked during the 1940s with Feynman on the problem of action at a distance, a line of research for which Feynman shared the 1965 Nobel Prize in physics.

During World War II, Wheeler took a leave of absence from Princeton to consult on various aspects of the Manhattan Project, working at the University of Chicago's Metallurgical Laboratory, where the first atomic pile was constructed; at Washington States' Hanford Engineering Works, where plutonium was manufactured; and at the Los Alamos Scientific Laboratory, where the first atomic bombs were assembled and tested. Wheeler maintained scientific affiliations with the government, serving as a member of the U.S. General Advisory Committee on Arms Control and Disarmament from 1969 to 1976, science advisor to the U.S. Senate Delegation to the 1957 NATO Conference of Parliamentarians, project chairman of the Department of Defense Advance Research Project Agency in 1958, and consultant to the U.S. Atomic Energy Commission in 1958. Wheeler received the Albert Einstein Award of the Strauss Foundation in 1965 for his contributions in the field of nuclear energy.

One of Wheeler's best known and most controversial activities was his participation in the design and construction of the first thermonuclear fusion (hydrogen) bomb. Invited by Teller in 1949 to assist in this project, Wheeler was at first hesitant to become involved, but eventually became convinced that such a weapon was necessary to preserve worldwide peace. Wheeler's part in the project took place primarily between 1951 and 1953 at his Princeton offices under the code name Project Matterhorn.

Expands on Black Holes and Collapsing Universes

In 1939, **J. Robert Oppenheimer** described the theoretical effects of the curvature of space, when thermo-nuclear reactions cease to function in stars and gravitational forces cause their collapse. Wheeler carried out his own investigations into this phenomenon and, in 1967, coined the term "black hole." Expanding upon this concept even further, he rationalized that the whole universe might be subject to what he called the Big Crunch. As the universe contracts upon itself to super-dense dimensions, it would cause an explosion similar to that of the big bang, creating a totally new universe. As part of this research, Wheeler has developed the concept of "superspace," a highly complex mathematical construct that may be all that remains of the universe after the Big Crunch. His ideas on the Big Crunch and superspace have continued to evolve over time, resulting in the better understanding of black holes and imaginative theoretical constructs such as "wormholes," which deal with holes in space containing electrical forces.

Wheeler was married to Janette Latourette Zabriskie Hegner in 1935, "three days after [his] return from Copenhagen," according to Overbye. The couple has three children, one son and two daughters. Upon his return,

Wheeler accepted a job as assistant professor of physics at the University of North Carolina. He remained there three years before taking a similar post at Princeton University, an affiliation that lasted until 1976. Wheeler took early retirement in order to accept an appointment at the University of Texas at Austin, as professor of physics and director of the Center for Theoretical Physics and then, in 1979, as Ashbell Smith Professor of Physics. He has also retained his Princeton rank of Joseph Henry Professor Emeritus.

Wheeler has received a host of honors and awards, including the Cressey-Morrison Prize of the New York Academy of Sciences, 1946, the Enrico Fermi Award of the U.S. Energy Research and Development Agency, 1968, the Franklin Medal of the Franklin Institute, 1969, the National Medal of Science, 1971, the Niels Bohr International Gold Medal, 1982, the Oersted Medal, 1983, and the J. Robert Oppenheimer Memorial Prize, 1984.

SELECTED WRITINGS BY WHEELER:

Books

Geometrodynamics, Academic Press, 1962.
Gravitation Theory and Gravitational Collapse, University of Chicago Press, 1965.
Spacetime Physics, W. H. Freeman, 1966.
Black Holes, Gravitational Waves and Cosmology, Gordon & Breach, 1974.

FURTHER READING:

Books

Contemporary Authors, Volumes 57–60, Gale, 1976.
McGraw-Hill Modern Scientists and Engineers, Volume 3, McGraw-Hill, 1980, pp. 299–302.
Overbye, Dennis, *A Passion To Know,* John Wheeler: Messenger at the Gates of Time, edited by Allen L. Hammond, Scribner, 1984.

Sketch by David E. Newton

John R. Whinfield
1901–1966
English textile chemist

John Rex Whinfield invented terylene, a synthetic polyester fiber that is equal to or surpasses nylon in toughness and resilience, and has become used universally as a textile fiber. The invention of terylene, also known as

Dacron, was the culmination of many years of study and reasoning about the molecular structure and physical and chemical properties of polymers. Whinfield's major inventive work on terylene was carried out aside from his primary research in the small laboratory of a company that had little or no interest in research on fibers. He spent his life working as an industrial research chemist and eventually became director of the fibers division of Imperial Chemical Industries. Recognition for his work came in the later years of his life.

Whinfield was born February 16, 1901, in Sutton, Surrey, England, to John Henry Richard Whinfield, a mechanical engineer, and Edith Matthews Whinfield. As a boy, Whinfield showed an early interest in science and chemistry. He was educated at Merchants Taylors' School and Caius College of Cambridge, reading in natural sciences (1921) and chemistry (1922). In 1922 he married Mayo Walker, the daughter of the Rev. Frederick William Walker. She died in 1946, and in 1947 he married Nora Hodder of Worthing.

Discovers a Process to Make Terylene

Whinfield was interested in the molecular makeup and properties of synthetic fibers, and to gain experience in fibers after graduating, he worked for a year without pay in the London laboratory of C. F. Cross and E. J. Bevan, who in 1892 had invented the "viscose reaction" for the production of rayon. In 1924, Whinfield was employed by the Calico Printers' Association as a research chemist, where he worked primarily on the chemistry of fabric dyeing and finishing. He continued his studies of the physical and chemical properties of synthetic fibers, however, and followed with interest the work of **Wallace Hume Carothers** in the United States, who in 1928 published the first of a long series of papers on condensation polymerization reactions. Carothers' work led to the invention of nylon, a polyamide; he had worked on but rejected the polyester group as a source of synthetic textile fibers because he thought the melting points were too low.

Whinfield's studies and rough analogies led him to believe that a polyester might work, specifically a polyester made from terephthalic acid and ethylene glycol. The latter chemical was available commercially, but terephthalic acid had been produced only in small quantities. Whinfield pressed his company to try some fiber work; in 1940 he was finally able to devote some time to the fiber research he had been thinking about, and in March 1941 he and his assistant, James T. Dickson, discovered a method of condensing terephthalic acid and ethylene glycol to produce a compound that could be drawn into fibers. Empirical work demonstrated—happily, because this had not been predictable from theoretical word—that the fibers had a high melting point and were resistant to hydrolytic breakdown. Whinfield and Dickson filed their patent on terylene in July 1941. Britain was engaged in World War II at the time, and terylene's potential utility for the war industry was examined briefly by the Ministry of Supply, for whom Whinfield

had come to work during the war. It was known to be an important invention, but production was not thought to be practicable for the war effort, and registration of the patent was delayed until 1946, after the war.

The Calico Printers' Association decided not to develop terylene, and consequently sold their rights to the product to Imperial Chemical Industries (ICI), who obtained world manufacturing rights. Whinfield went to work for ICI in 1947. Du Pont in the United States independently prepared terylene and purchased the U.S. patent application filed by the British in 1946. Although Du Pont had been working on terylene, there was no question of the priority of its invention. Du Pont first called it "Fiber V," then "Dacron," and began full-scale production in the United States in 1953. ICI, after operating two pilot plants for several years, began commercial production of terylene fibers in 1955.

In the production of terylene, dimethyl terephthalate and ethylene glycol, derived from coal, air, water, and petroleum, are polymerized. Then the substance is "melt spun" into filaments. The filaments are stable, but springy; Whinfield found that the fibers would stretch to 10-25% of their original length before rupturing. Terylene was shown to be equal to nylon in its potential usefulness, and it contributed greatly to the popularity of "wash and wear" clothing.

Works as Chemist at ICI

At ICI, Whinfield worked first in the Fibers Development Department of the plastics division with W. F. Osborne, then in the Fibers Division, where he eventually became director. In 1954, he received a Commander of the Order of the British Empire (C.B.E.) for his work on terylene. The same year, he was engaged to advise on *Point of Departure*, an educational film on manmade fibers made by the Film Producers Guild. He was a clear explicator, but somewhat unexpectedly, he also proved to be an accomplished actor, and as a result played a leading role in the film. In 1955, he was elected an honorary fellow of the Textile Institute, and in 1956 he received the Perkin medal of the Society of Dyers and Colourists. During his tenure at ICI, Whinfield traveled widely, including to the former Union of Soviet Socialist Republics as a guest of the Russian government. He retired in 1963. In 1965, the University of York named its chemical library and a number of traveling fellowships after Whinfield.

Whinfield died on July 6, 1966, at Dorking, at age 65. In an obituary published in *Chemistry in Britain* (1967), P. C. Allen wrote, "[He] remained until the end of his life an essentially modest and simple man. He had a host of friends and no wonder for no one could be a more charming companion, or when he was in the mood, a better talker. He wrote very clearly also; his publications are a model of clarity."

SELECTED WRITINGS BY WHINFIELD:

Periodicals

"Fibres From Aromatic Polyesters." *Endeavour* XI, no. 41 (January 1952): 29-32.

FURTHER READING:

Books

Biographical Dictionary of Scientists, 2nd ed. Bristol: Institute of Physics Publishing, 1994, p. 521.
The Dictionary of National Biography: Missing Persons. Oxford: Oxford University Press, 1993, p. 709.
Jewkes, John, David Sawers, and Richard Stillerman. *The Sources of Invention*. New York: St. Martin's Press, 1959, pp. 18, 165, 388-392.

Periodicals

Allen, P. C. "John Rex Whinfield, 1901-1966." *Chemistry in Britain* 3, (1967): 26.

Sketch by Jill Carpenter

John R. Whinnery
1916–
American electrical engineer

John R. Whinnery has made significant contributions to the field of electrical engineering, both as a researcher and as an educator. His research includes work on microwave electron devices, wave guiding systems, optical guiding systems, and laser communications. As an educator at the University of California, Berkeley, Whinnery progressed from lecturer in 1946 to Dean of the College of Engineering in 1959. He has received numerous honors and awards, including the National Medal of Science in 1992, the 1976 Institute of Electrical and Electronics Engineers (IEEE) Microwave Career Award, and the 1974 Lamme Medal of the American Society for Engineering Education. In 1993 he was named to the Hall of Fame of the American Society for Engineering Education.

John Roy Whinnery was born in Read, Colorado, on July 26, 1916, to Ralph V. and Edith Mable (Bent) Whinnery. His father was a farmer whose hobbies included mechanics and electricity, and Whinnery became interested in electrical engineering at an early age. After attending high school and junior college in Modesto, California, Whinnery enrolled at the University of California, Berkeley, and graduated with a B.S. in electrical engineering in 1937. Following graduation he joined the research staff of the General Electric Company in Schenectady, New York. He spent one year as an assistant engineer before becoming supervisor of the High Frequency Section. There he was one of the leading members of a team working on the disk seal triode, a device significant in the field of high-frequency (microwave) electronics. This device, and others which he helped develop at GE, remain important elements of electronic technology in the fields of communication and radar. While at GE, Whinnery also worked on problems in waveguide discontinuities. Waveguides, like transmission lines, are devices which transmit electromagnetic energy. Discontinuities dissipate the transmitted energy, preventing it from reaching the intended destination.

Whinnery did not spend all his time conducting research, however. With Simon Ramo, a colleague at GE, he coauthored the textbook *Fields and Waves in Modern Radio*. This publication, and later editions under a slightly different name, became the definitive text on electromagnetic theory, both in the U.S. and abroad. Additionally, Whinnery was active during the Second World War, teaching training classes and lecturing at Union College in Schenectady. On September 17, 1944, Whinnery married his childhood sweetheart, Patricia Barry.

A Return to Berkeley: From Lecturer to Dean

Returning to the University of California in 1946 as an electrical engineering lecturer, Whinnery began work toward his doctorate. He was awarded a Ph.D. in 1948 and was promoted to associate professor. From 1951 to 1952 he was on leave from the university as head of Microwave Tube Research at the Hughes Aircraft Company. He then returned to Berkeley, attained full professorship, and became director of the Electronics Research Laboratory. Whinnery held this position until 1956, when he was named chairperson of the engineering department.

Throughout this time, Whinnery taught courses in electromagnetic theory and microwave networks and continued his research in microwave electronics with the aid of his graduate students. This research centered on problems with antennae, electron tube noise, and crossed-field amplifiers, and led to significant developments, including the backward wave amplifier. In 1959, after being honored with a Guggenheim Fellowship, Whinnery was made dean of the College of Engineering at Berkeley. He remained in that position until 1963, when he took another leave of absence, this time going to Bell Laboratories in Murray Hill, New Jersey. At Bell, he began research in quantum electronics, specifically lasers and optical communication problems. A year later, Whinnery again returned to Berkeley, where he continued the research begun at Bell.

A Leader in Education

After 1964 Whinnery remained primarily at Berkeley, where he continued to act as a lecturer and a researcher in optics, lasers, and optical communications. Additionally, he has served both the engineering community at large, and the nation, by assuming a leadership role in educating students and in formulating engineering education programs. This leadership has included chairing the Commission on Engineering Education from 1966 to 1968, serving as a visiting professor at Stanford University and the University of California, Santa Cruz, and serving on advisory committees for engineering departments at Massachusetts Institute of Technology, California Institute of Technology, Harvard, Yale, and Worcester Polytechnic Institute. Whinnery also achieved international acclaim as a visiting professor at the National Defense Academy in Yokosuka, Japan, and when he was made an Honorary Professor at Chengdu Institute of Radio Engineering in the People's Republic of China.

In addition to his efforts regarding engineering education, Whinnery has also served on various government committees, including the Science and Technical Advisory Committee for Manned Space Flight at NASA from 1963 to 1969, the President's Committee for the National Medal of Science from 1970 to 1972 and 1979 to 1981, and the Atomic Energy Commission's standing committee on controlled thermonuclear research from 1970 to 1973. He has won numerous engineering awards, including the 1992 National Medal of Science, the 1985 Institute of Electrical and Electronics Engineers Medal of Honor, and the 1967 IEEE Education Medal, and was named Outstanding Educator of America in 1974. He was also elected to both the National Academy of Engineering and the National Academy of Sciences. Whinnery has also served on the board of directors of the IEEE and on a number of IEEE award committees. In addition to his many honors, in a letter to G. A. Ferrance, Whinnery wrote that he is "most proud of the outstanding students I have had the privilege to work with."

SELECTED WRITINGS BY WHINNERY:

Books

Fields and Waves in Modern Radio, John Wiley & Sons, 1944.
Introduction to Electronic Systems, Circuits and Devices, McGraw-Hill, 1964.
The World of Engineering, McGraw-Hill, 1965.

Periodicals

Proceedings of the Institute of Radio Engineers, Power Amplifiers with Disk-Seal Tubes, with H. W. Jamieson34, July, 1946.
Journal of Applied Physics, The Effect of Input Configuration Antenna Impedance, 21, October, 1950.
IEEE Student Journal, Thermal Lens Effect in Laser Beams, Volume 6, No. 2, March, 1968, pp. 7–10.
Accounts of Chemical Research, Laser Measurement of Optical Absorption in Liquids, 7, June, 1974, pp. 225–31.

IEEE Transactions on Education, The Teaching of Electromagnetics, Volume 33, No. 1, February, 1990, pp. 3–7.

FURTHER READING:

Books

McGraw-Hill Modern Scientists and Engineers, McGraw-Hill, 1980, pp. 302–303.

Other

McGraw-Hill Modern Scientists and Engineers, Whinnery, John R., personal correspondence with G. A. Ferrance, January 19, 1994.

Sketch by George A. Ferrance

Fred Lawrence Whipple
1906–
American astronomer

The discoverer of six comets, Fred Lawrence Whipple is best known for his work on advancing the understanding of the nature of comets and meteors. His other interests include planetary nebulae (gases and dust), spectrophotometry (the measurement of intensities of light in different parts of a spectrum), the evolution of stars and the solar system, and the earth's upper atmosphere. Whipple also was at the forefront of tracking artificial satellites following the 1957 launch of *Sputnik.*

Fred Lawrence Whipple was born on November 5, 1906, in Red Oak, Iowa, the son of Henry Lawrence and Celestia (MacFarland) Whipple. The Whipples were farmers, and the youngster spent his first fifteen years on the farm. When Fred Whipple was a teenager, his family moved to California. After completing high school, Whipple enrolled at Occidental College, which he attended from 1923 to 1924, then entered the University of California at Los Angeles (UCLA), where he majored in mathematics. Following his graduation from UCLA in 1927, he married his first wife, Dorothy Woods. The couple had one son, Earle Raymond, before they divorced in 1935. Eleven years later, on August 20, 1946, Whipple married his second wife, Babette Frances Samuelson, and the couple had two daughters: Dorothy Sandra and Laura. In the meantime Whipple had attended the University of California at Berkeley and received his Ph.D. in astronomy in 1931. He had also accepted an invitation to join the staff of the

Harvard College Observatory. His main areas of interest were comets, meteors, and interplanetary dust.

Although astronomers had long observed comets, scientists had virtually no clue as to the origin of the phenomena. Some observers of the 1600s believed comets had been flung out into space by rapidly rotating planets. Various astronomers of the nineteenth century theorized that comets were caused by the eruption of volcanoes on Jupiter and Saturn, or on their moons; the explosive eruptions had ejected the comets into highly elliptical orbits. Other scientific theories suggested that comets were densely packed hailstorms that orbited around the sun. In 1932 Estonian astronomer Ernst Julius Öpik proposed that an invisible cloud, lying far out in deep space, surrounded the solar system, and this was where comets and meteors originated.

Enters the Fray

Whipple began his investigation into meteors by developing a "two-station" photographic method of observing. Using cameras with rotating shutters, he was able to measure a meteor's trajectory, atmospheric drag, velocity, and orbit around the sun. His observing program, which lasted approximately fifteen years, led him to theorize that all visual meteors were related to comets—meteors were made up of the debris that followed comet-type orbits around the sun. Analyses of the spectra of meteors, as they burned in the atmosphere, indicated they contained silicon, iron, and other materials. It seemed reasonable to conclude that comets were comprised of much the same material.

The fact that comets did not precisely obey the laws of English physicist and mathematician Isaac Newton caused considerable consternation; Newton's First Law of Motion essentially states that the velocity of an object does not change unless a force acts on it. Some comets, like Halley's Comet, gain energy, causing their orbits (and consequently the amount of time it takes to complete their orbits) to increase. Meanwhile, other comets, like Comet Encke, lose energy, causing their orbits to decrease. Among the questions confronting scientists was: What is the force that changes the orbits of comets? Whipple devised a theory that not only explained the mysterious force, but also resolved the question of the composition of comets and revealed how they could survive close encounters with the sun.

The Demystification of Comets

To account for the mysterious force, Whipple suggested in 1949 that comets contain a solid nucleus several kilometers in diameter, composed chiefly of frozen water, ammonia, methane, and dust (silicates and primitive hydrocarbons)—in essence, Whipple proposed that comets were massive, dirty snowballs. When far from the influence of the sun, and in the cold darkness of space, the comet was a solid, frozen ice-ball. As the comet drew closer to the sun it would begin to heat up. The nucleus of the comet would undoubtedly be rotating, Whipple presumed, and as the ice

layer began to melt, a thin layer of "dirt" would be left behind. This layer would absorb energy from the sun and prevent it from penetrating deeper into the nucleus. However, the heat would eventually radiate through the dirt layer, penetrate the nucleus, reach the highly volatile gases within the nucleus, and cause a "jet" of gas to erupt. This would have the same effect as a rocket engine on a spacecraft: If the jet was aimed behind the comet, it would cause the velocity to increase; if the jet was aimed in front of the comet, it would cause the velocity to decrease. (If the jet occurred on either side of the comet, an appropriate deviation would be introduced to the orbit.)

By studying the orbits of approximately sixty comets, Whipple and his colleague S. Hamid found that their results were consistent with the "dirty snowball" model. While comets lose material with each passage around the sun, an extremely large nucleus would permit repeated visits; hence, a short period comet, such as Comet Encke, could last a very long time. On the other hand, a comet with a small nucleus might last only a few orbits before disintegrating, and this would explain why some periodic comets fail to return when predicted. The dirty snowball model also explained how a comet could survive a passage through the sun's outer atmosphere. Undoubtedly, there would be a considerable loss of cometary material by such an event, but the solid nucleus would resist disintegration by holding the comet together. Whipple also considered the fact that great amounts of gas are emitted by comets with each visit; in previous studies of comets, scientists had wondered if the gases constituted an atmosphere surrounding the comet, and, if so, how the gases were replenished. Scientists had supposed that if comets had solid surfaces, they wouldn't be able to absorb enough gas to replenish themselves, and, in addition, there simply isn't enough gas in space to replenish their reserves. With Whipple's model, however, there is no need for replenishment: frozen gas is distributed throughout the nucleus, and it is released as the snowball evaporates.

The Emergence of Additional Theories

At about the same time that Whipple published his dirty snowball theory (in 1950), Dutch astronomer **Jan Hendrik Oort** revised Öpik's theory—that comets and meteors originated in an invisible cloud that surrounded the solar system—and suggested a manner in which comets could be "replenished." He conceived of passing stars whose gravitational attraction disturbed the distant Öpik cloud, continually sending cometary debris hurtling into the inner solar system. According to Oort, the comets would all arrive at different times and establish individual orbits as they plummeted toward the sun. Some of the orbits would become periodic, and these comets would return regularly; others would skim the solar system, and still others would fall into the sun and never again be seen.

The Whipple dirty snowball and the Oort cloud theories are presently the accepted models of comets and their origin, although they are not the only ones. In 1978 Thomas Van Flandern suggested that approximately five million years ago a gigantic planet orbiting the sun between Mars and Jupiter broke apart. The debris of that planet is the source of the comets.

Halley's Comet Provides Whipple with His Proof

In 1986, Halley's Comet returned, an event that had been long awaited and which became one of the most vigorously observed astronomical phenomena in history. In addition to a battery of telescopes and cameras of professionals and amateurs on the earth, as well as in high-flying aircraft, there were six spacecraft on a flyby trajectory to observe Halley. The United States sent the International Comet Explorer, and other countries, including Japan and the former Soviet Union, also sent space probes. The measurements and photographs attained from these launches confirmed Whipple's predictions: the "jets" he had forecasted were observed directly on Comet Halley's surface. It was learned that most of the comet's dust was composed of carbon and hydrocarbon compounds, rather than silicates, but Whipple's theory was more than substantiated, for Comet Halley had provided direct proof. In 1986 Mauritania, a West African republic, issued a postage stamp to commemorate the return of Halley, and an engraving of Whipple was included on it to honor his contribution to the understanding of the previously misunderstood celestial spectacles.

Prior to the excitement surrounding the return of Comet Halley, Whipple had been occupied with other endeavors. In 1942 he published his book *Earth, Moon, and Planets,* which is regarded as an authoritative volume on its subject; the work has been revised several times and went into a third edition in 1968. In the years 1943 to 1945, Whipple conducted war-related work at the Harvard Radio Research Laboratories, where he was in charge of researching, developing, and producing "confusion reflectors." These were small pieces of aluminum foil that were dropped from Allied planes. Tuned to interact with German radar, the foil simulated a multitude of aircraft on German radar scopes. In 1948 Whipple received the Presidential Certificate of Merit for his work, and two years later he assumed the position of professor of astronomy at Harvard, a post he retained for more than twenty-five years. In 1955 he became the director of the Smithsonian Institution's Astrophysical Observatory in Cambridge, and remained in that capacity until 1973, when he became Senior Scientist. He also served as a participant in the International Geophysical Year of 1957–58, during which time he organized multitudes of professional and amateur observers to keep track of artificial satellites, following the surprising launch of the Soviet Union's *Sputnik* in October of 1957. He also worked to formulate reliable ways of tracking the increasing number of satellites, for which he received the American Astronautical Society's Space Flight Award in 1960.

Throughout his career, Whipple has received several other honors: He was awarded the Donahue Medal six times (for independently discovering six new comets), and he received the J. Lawrence Smith Medal of the National

Academy of Sciences in 1949. In 1960 he was the recipient of a medal from the University of Liège for his astronomical research, and in 1971 the American Association for the Advancement of Science presented him with their Kepler Medal. In addition to his ongoing interest in astronomy, Whipple is a science fiction enthusiast and cultivates roses for relaxation.

SELECTED WRITINGS BY WHIPPLE:

Books

Earth, Moon, and Planets, Blakiston Co., 1942, revised 3rd edition, Harvard University Press, 1968.
History of the Solar System, Astrophysical Observatory, Smithsonian Institution, 1964.
Studies in Interplanetary Particles, Astrophysical Observatory, Smithsonian Institution, 1967.
Smithsonian Astrophysical Observatory Star Atlas of Reference Stars and Nonstellar Objects, MIT Press, 1969.
Orbiting the Sun: Planets and Satellites of the Solar System, Harvard University Press, 1981.
The Mystery of Comets, Smithsonian Institution Press, 1985.

FURTHER READING:

Books

Abell, George, David Morrison, and Sidney Wolff, *Exploration of the Universe,* 6th edition, Holt, 1991.
Berry, Arthur, *A Short History of Astronomy,* Dover, 1961.
Calder, Nigel, *The Comet Is Coming!,* Viking, 1981.
Sagan, Carl, *Cosmos,* Random House, 1980.

Sketch by Raymond E. Bullock

George Hoyt Whipple
1878–1976
American pathologist

George Hoyt Whipple knew he would be a physician from the time he was in elementary school at the turn of the century. The son and grandson of doctors, Whipple followed the family tradition by choosing a career in medicine, researching the creation and breakdown of oxygen-carrying hemoglobin in the blood; this research resulted in not only a treatment for pernicious anemia, but also in a share of the 1934 Nobel Prize. An industrious,

George Hoyt Whipple

Sets His Course for Research

During his years as a student at Johns Hopkins, Whipple earned his way with a paying instructorship. Initially Whipple had considered going into pediatrics, but upon receiving his M.D. in 1905 instead joined the Johns Hopkins staff as an assistant in pathology, working under the renowned pathologist William Henry Welch. It was as a 29-year-old assistant performing an autopsy on a missionary doctor that Whipple made his first notable medical contribution, describing a rare condition in the intestinal tissues, which has since come to be called Whipple's disease. A year spent at a hospital in the Panama Canal Zone led to further notable advances in malaria and tuberculosis research.

When he returned to Johns Hopkins in 1908, Whipple turned his attention to studies in liver damage and the way in which liver cells repair themselves. Studies with dogs led Whipple to realize the importance of bile, a substance manufactured in the liver by the breakdown of hemoglobin, a complex pigment in red corpuscles. In normal concentrations, bile helps to break down fats during digestion, but can produce jaundice when present in excessive amounts. Beginning his assistant professorship at Johns Hopkins in 1911, Whipple came to focus on the interrelationship of bile, hemoglobin, and the liver. In 1913, along with a talented medical student, Charles W. Hooper, Whipple was able to show that bile pigments could be produced outside of the liver, solely from the breakdown of hemoglobin in the blood. Using this experiment as a starting point, Whipple set a new course for his studies. Since bile pigments are formed from hemoglobin, Whipple reasoned that he should tackle the question of hemoglobin itself, beginning with how it is manufactured. It was a fateful decision.

In 1914 Whipple accepted a position as director of the Hooper Foundation for Medical Research at the University of California in San Francisco. In that same year he also married his long-time sweetheart, Katharine Ball Waring, and the couple moved to California. Though burdened with administrative duties, Whipple continued his researches into hemoglobin production. His assistant, Hooper, came with him to California and together with a new assistant, Frieda Robscheit-Robbins, they began experiments which would lead to a major breakthrough. By systematically bleeding laboratory dogs, Whipple and his team were able to induce a controlled anemic condition. They then tested various foods and their effects upon hemoglobin regeneration, finding that a diet of liver produced a pronounced increase in hemoglobin regeneration. While such short term effects were encouraging, they were still far from conclusive.

Research Proved Conclusive at Rochester

Though in 1920 Whipple was named dean of the University of California Medical School, he remained in California for just a year before accepting (somewhat reluctantly) a similar position at a new medical complex at the University of Rochester in New York—a facility heavily

hard-working Yankee from New Hampshire, Whipple authored more than 200 publications on anemia, pigment metabolism, liver injury and repair, and other related subjects. Yet in his last days, it was as an educator that he hoped to be remembered.

Whipple was born on August 28, 1878, in Ashland, New Hampshire, the son of Frances Anna Hoyt Whipple and Ashley Cooper Whipple, a general practitioner held in high esteem by his patients and colleagues. Whipple's father died of typhoid fever just two years after the birth of his son, and Whipple and his sister Ashley were brought up by their mother and grandmothers. His was an outdoor life in rural New Hampshire, and he took a love of hunting, fishing, and camping with him into adulthood. At the age of fourteen Whipple entered Phillips Academy in Andover, Massachusetts, enrolling at Yale College (now Yale University) as a premedical student four years later. At Yale, he was a star baseball player and was on the gymnastics and rowing teams, as well as an outstanding student. Though versed in the humanities in these years of public and private schools, he had always been attracted by science and mathematics. After graduating with high standing in 1900, Whipple spent a year teaching and coaching at Holbrook Military Academy in New York to earn money for medical studies, and in 1901 he entered Johns Hopkins University's School of Medicine.

endowed by Kodak founder George Eastman and the Rockefeller Foundation. Courted enthusiastically by Eastman and university president Rush Rhees, Whipple moved home and laboratory to New York, bringing Robscheit-Robbins and the group of anemic dogs with him.

The next decade proved busy for Whipple: he directed the building and staffing of the University of Rochester School of Medicine and Dentistry, all the while directing further hemoglobin research. Perfecting their technique of bleeding the dogs, Whipple and Robscheit-Robbins induced long-term anemia and were able to prove conclusively that a liver diet was successful in counteracting its effects by increasing the production of hemoglobin. His results were published in 1925, and the pharmaceutical firm of Eli Lilly, with Whipple's cooperation, began producing a commercially available liver extract within a year. Whipple refused to patent his findings, and directed all royalties from the sales of the extract to fund additional research. Whipple's experiments paved the way for further studies by two Boston researchers, **George Richards Minot** and **William P. Murphy**, who used liver therapy to successfully treat pernicious anemia in 1926.

Whipple's work soon won international repute and in 1934 he received word that he, along with Minot and Murphy, was going to receive the Nobel Prize for physiology or medicine for their separate work in liver therapy. Whipple did not let fame slow him down. He continued his hemoglobin experiments, turning now to the study of iron in the body and utilizing the new technology of radioisotope elements to follow the distribution of iron in the body. He also made important contributions to the study of an anemic disorder peculiar to people of Mediterranean extraction, a disorder for which Whipple suggested the name *thalassemia*. Other studies involved the use of plasma or tissue proteins to rebuild hemoglobin in cases of anemia. A spin-off of this latter research was the development of intravenous feeding.

Despite the administrative and research duties that pressed upon him, Whipple did not forget his students, and took real pleasure in teaching. When in later years he was offered the position of Director of the Rockefeller Institute, he politely but adamantly declined, preferring his classes and his research. Whipple finally relinquished his chair as dean in 1953 at the age of 75, after a long and distinguished career that had seen the once-small university grow to more than 12,000 graduates in medicine and other related fields. He remained on the faculty of the University of Rochester teaching pathology until 1955. In 1963 he established a medical and dental library for the university valued at $750,000. In addition to the Nobel Prize, Whipple was also a trustee of the Rockefeller Foundation from 1927-43, a Kober Medal winner in 1939, and a recipient of the Kovalenko Medal of the National Academy of Sciences in 1962, among others.

Whipple's life was long and productive. He was an active outdoorsman well into his ninth decade. With his wife Katharine, he had two children: a son, Hoyt, who followed in the Whipple tradition of medicine, and a daughter, Barbara. He died in Rochester on February 1, 1976, in the hospital he had helped to build.

SELECTED WRITINGS BY WHIPPLE:

Books

Hemoglobin, Plasma and Cell Protein, Charles C. Thomas, 1948.
The Dynamic Equilibrium of Body Proteins, Charles C. Thomas, 1956.

Periodicals

Johns Hopkins Hospital Bulletin, A Hitherto Undescribed Disease Characterized Anatomically by Deposits of Fat and Fatty Acids in the Intestines and Mesenteric Lymphatic Tissues, Volume 18, 1907, pp. 382ff.
Journal of Biological Chemistry, The Metabolism of Bile Acids, with Marjorie G. Foster and C. W. Hooper, Volume 38, 1919, pp. 367–433.
American Journal of Physiology, Blood Regeneration in Severe Anemia, parts 1–3, with Frieda Robscheit-Robbins, Volume 72, 1925, pp. 395–430.
Journal of the American Medical Association, Hemoglobin Generation as Influenced by Diet and Other Factors, Nobel Prize Lecture, Volume 104, 1935, p. 791ff.
Journal of Pediatrics, Mediterranean Disease—Thalassemia (Erythroblastic Anemia of Cooley). Associated Pigment Abnormalities Simulating Hemochromatosis, Volume 9, 1936, pp. 279ff.
Perspectives in Biology and Medicine, Autobiographical Sketch, Volume 2, 1959, pp. 253–87.

FURTHER READING:

Books

Corner, George W., *George Hoyt Whipple and His Friends,* Lippincott, 1963. Nobel Laureates in Medicine or Physiology, Garland Publishing, 1990.
Corner, George W., *Nobel Prize Winners,* H. W. Wilson, 1987.

Periodicals

Diggs, Lemuel W., *The Johns Hopkins Medical Journal,* Dr. George Hoyt Whipple, November, 1976, pp. 196–200.
Diggs, Lemuel W., *New York Times,* February 2, 1976, p. 26.
Young, Lawrence E., *Transactions of the Association of American Physicians,* George Hoyt Whipple 1878–1976, Volume 89, 1976, pp. 34–37.

Sketch by J. Sydney Jones

Augustus White
1936–
American orthopedic surgeon

A surgeon and biomedical engineer, Augustus White is an expert on back pain whose mechanical studies of the human spine have helped to develop technologies with direct clinical value. His surgical and engineering systems have aided patients in recovering more rapidly from spinal injuries. Throughout a career as a professor at both Yale and Harvard Medical Schools, and as a surgeon at Beth Israel Hospital in Boston, White has educated the public on preventative measures to head off chronic back pain.

Augustus Aaron White III, son of Augustus, Jr., and Vivian Dandridge White, was born on June 4, 1936, in Memphis, Tennessee. Attending Brown University, White initially intended to go into psychiatry. This career goal was altered, however, when he played football for Brown and became interested in sports injuries and their treatment. As a result, White decided on a career as an orthopedic surgeon, and after graduating cum laude from Brown in 1957, he went on to Stanford University where he earned his M.D. in 1961.

After serving an internship at University Hospital in Ann Arbor, Michigan, White worked as a resident orthopedic surgeon in both San Francisco and New Haven, Connecticut. He then served in Vietnam from 1966 to 1968, rising to the rank of captain in the medical corps and being awarded the Bronze Star. In 1969 White joined the faculty of Yale Medical School as assistant professor and remained at the university for the next decade, becoming a full professor and then director of its biomechanical research department for orthopedics.

In 1969 White was awarded a doctorate from the Karolinska Institute in Sweden for his research in the biomechanics of the spine, work which focused on all aspects of spine mechanics and on fracture healing. He then went on to coauthor a basic and first-of-its kind text on the subject, *Clinical Biomechanics of the Spine*. Leaving Yale in 1978 to accept a position as professor of orthopedic surgery at Harvard Medical School, he also assumed a concurrent position as orthopedic surgeon-in-chief at Beth Israel Hospital in Boston. Not limiting his studies to orthopedics, White graduated in 1984 from the advanced management program at the Harvard Business School.

Married to Anita Ottemo, White is the father of three children, Alissa Alexandra, Atina Andrea, and Annica Akila. His work has been recognized by numerous awards and honors, including the Martin Luther King, Jr., Medical Achievement Award in 1972, the National Award for Outstanding Orthopedic Research from Kappa Delta in 1975, the *Ebony* Magazine Black Achievement Award in 1980, and the William Rogers Award from the Associated Alumni of Brown University in 1984.

White's work has helped to draw attention to back pain, a malady that effects eighty per cent of Americans between the ages of thirty and fifty. Almost anyone who has to sit for long periods at either a desk or behind the wheel of a vehicle is susceptible to back pain, according to White. The results of his research on the mechanics of the human spine have had practical applications; White advises that one should use the proper chair to provide lower back support, should know the correct way to lift heavy weights, and should practice sufficient exercise in between long periods of sitting. Involving the patient in the cure for back pain through education—spelling out the do's and don'ts of lifting and sitting, for example—was highly encouraged by White.

SELECTED WRITINGS BY WHITE:

Books

Clinical Biomechanics of the Spine, Lippincott, 1978.
Symposium on Idiopathic Low Back Pain, Mosby, 1982.
Your Aching Back: A Doctor's Guide to Relief, Bantam, 1983.

Periodicals

Acta Orthopaedica Scandanavica, An Experimental Study of the Immediate Load Bearing Capacity of Some Commonly Used Iliac Bone Grafts, Volume 42, 1971, pp. 482–490.
Journal of Biomechanics, Kinematics of the Normal Spine As Related to Scoliosis, October, 1971, pp. 405–411.
Archives of Surgery, Cervical Spine Fusions—Psychological and Social Considerations, February, 1973, pp. 150–152.
Clinical Orthopaedics and Related Research, Chronic Ankle Pain Associated with the Peroneus Accessorius, Volume 103, 1974, pp. 53–55.
Journal of Bone and Joint Surgery, The Use of Psychological Tests in the Evaluation of Low-Back Pain, April, 1983, pp. 560–565.
Journal of Biomechanics, Variations of Stiffness and Strength Along the Human Cervical Spine, Volume 24, 1991, pp. 95–107.

FURTHER READING:

Books

Hawkins, Walter L., *African American Biographies*, McFarland, 1992, pp. 440–442.

Periodicals

Hawkins, Walter L., *Ebony*, June, 1964, p. 215; February, 1980, p. 84.

Howell, Ronald, *Ebony*, My Aching Back, June, 1979, pp. 44–52.

Sketch by J. Sydney Jones

Gilbert Fowler White
1911–
American geographer

Gilbert Fowler White is admired for his many contributions to the fields of geography and natural resource management. His research has covered a number of subjects that affect people on a personal, regional, and global basis, including water-systems in developing countries; global environmental change; nuclear winter; geography education; and strategies for coping with natural hazards. Many scientists particularly hold in high esteem White's ideas about a broad range of alternatives needed to cope with the risks of floods, calling him "the father of flood-plain management." For his work on the environment, White has won a number of awards, including the United Nations Sasakawa International Environment Prize in 1985 and the Tyler Prize for Environmental Achievement in 1987.

White was born on November 26, 1911, in Chicago, Illinois, where his father, Arthur Edward White, worked for the Burlington Railroad. The White family lived near the University of Chicago because Arthur wanted his children to have a good education and his wife, Mary Louise (Guthrie) White, was impressed by the president of the new university. Their son Gilbert attended the University of Chicago High School and eventually received an S.B., S.M., and Ph.D. from the university. Later in life he would join the University of Chicago faculty, teaching there from 1956 to 1969.

White's family influenced his education and career in other ways. In addition to his job with the railroad, White's father was a partner in a ranch in Tongue River Valley, Wyoming. Young White worked at the ranch during the summer months and saw first-hand the impact of decisions about water and land use, an interest he never lost. While an undergraduate, White discovered a group in the University of Chicago geography department that studied water, land, and natural resources. He had found his intellectual niche.

As a graduate student in 1934, White obtained a six-month appointment in Washington, D.C., as a geographer. In this capacity he conducted community-oriented research, a characteristic of much of his work since. The job was stretched to eight years, beginning with work on the Mississippi Valley Committee and ending with the President's Bureau of the Budget. Studying the Mississippi River

Basin for the federal government in the 1930s, White opposed prevailing views about flood management, which called for the construction of levees and dams. He instead advocated the prevention of disastrous consequence from floods by keeping people out of the path of floodwaters. The wisdom of White's assessment reported in his 1942 landmark doctoral dissertation, *Human Adjustment to Floods,* was evident a half century later, when severe flooding of the Mississippi River devastated people and commerce in the American midwest for several weeks during the summer of 1993.

White has often expressed the opinion that solutions to complex problems are likely to be found in local activities. He told a *New York Herald Tribune* Forum audience in October 1952, "The tide of poverty will be turned only by the concurrent development of a vast number of small-scale projects centering on the patient, simple action of workers in rural communities of Asia, the Middle East, and Latin America."

White's belief in the importance of local activities is evident in the work he considers his most important. With his wife, the economist Anne Elizabeth (Underwood) White, and David Bradley of the London School of Tropical Hygiene and Medicine, he studied 30 sites in East Africa where women drew and carried all the water consumed for domestic use. The resulting 1972 report, *Drawers of Water,* put forth for the first time information about the collection and transport by women of domestic water, activities critical to 60 percent of the world's population. From their data, the scientists calculated the participants' costs in time and energy and the impact of those expenditures on resources, discovering in the process that the amounts of water used and the behaviors associated with the task varied enormously. The research results of White and his collaborators changed the attitudes of many governments toward the quality and quantity of water provisions. In a 1992 interview for *Summit,* White noted that this project "certainly was the most influential research work I've done in terms of affecting the lives of people."

Warns of Environmental Dangers in International Forums

Throughout his career, White has taken this concern for people on an individual and community level and applied it to efforts with a more global perspective. In 1953, White served in the Arid Zone Program of the United Nations Education and Cultural Organization (UNESCO). The arid lands research conducted by the organization paved the way for the concerns discussed at the 1972 Stockholm conference on the world's environment, which in turn led to the massive 1992 United Nations Conference on Environment and Development held in Rio de Janeiro.

In 1979 White spoke to the world community about the environment when he issued a declaration with Mostafa Tolba, head of the United Nations Environment Programme, suggesting that human activities might lead to climate change. His concerns with human activity and the earth have extended to issues of nuclear danger as well. As president of the Scientific Committee on Problems of the Environment (SCOPE), White launched a study of the environmental effects of nuclear war and helped draft *The Environmental Effects of Nuclear War*, a 1984 document providing a unified statement on nuclear disaster from a community of 300 scientists in 30 countries.

The leadership and organizational abilities demonstrated by White's ability to bring such a wide range of people together in the SCOPE project has been seen in White's other efforts as a scholar and administrator. At the age of 35, he became the president of Haverford College, a small liberal arts college near Philadelphia, Pennsylvania, founded by Quakers. He remained president there for ten years. His years at the University of Colorado have been equally productive. There he founded the school's Natural Hazards Research and Applications Information Center and served as director of the university's Institute for Behavioral Science. He is currently Gustavson Distinguished Professor Emeritus at the university.

White has been honored for his work on numerous occasions. In 1973, he was elected to the National Academy of Sciences. His many other recognitions and awards have included the Association of American Geographers' Distinguished Service Award in 1955 and 1974; the National Council for Geographic Education's Master Teacher award in 1985; the United Nations Sasakawa International Environment Prize in 1985; the Tyler Prize for Environmental Achievement in 1987; and the Vautrin Lud International Prize in Geography in 1992.

White's Quaker heritage underlies his activist approach to the problems he has studied. The great-grandson of Quakers, White was drawn to the religion's beliefs while in college. His adaption of the Quakers' philosophy of non-violence compelled him to serve as a conscientious objector during World War II, during which time he worked for the American Friends Service Committee (AFSC) as an administrator of Quaker relief efforts. White's active participation with AFSC has continued throughout his life, an influence which is evident in his strong views on the sanctity of life and on the responsibility humans have to care for the natural world. White's late wife Anne, whom he married in 1944 and with whom he had two sons and a daughter, was quoted in *Summit* as once attributing his ability to get things done to these very beliefs. She observed that White was driven by his "Quaker faith in the ability of humans to marshal their inner resources to deal competently and lovingly with the outer world and with their fellow human beings. . . . And not least there is his innate and humble desire to leave the world a bit better place than he found it."

SELECTED WRITINGS BY WHITE:

Books

Human Adjustment to Floods, University of Chicago Department of Geography, 1942.

Strategies of American Water Management, University of Michigan Press, 1969.
Drawers of Water: Domestic Water Use in East Africa, University of Chicago Press, 1972.
Natural Hazards: Local, National, and Global, Oxford University Press, 1974.
The Environmental Effects of Nuclear War, Westview Press (Boulder, CO), 1984.
Geography, Resources, and Environment, Volume I: The Selected Writings of Gilbert White, edited by Robert W. Kates and Ian Burton, University of Chicago Press, 1986.

Periodicals

Great Plains Quarterly, The Future of the Great Plains Revisited, Volume 6, 1986, pp. 84–93.
Environment, SCOPE: The First Sixteen Years, Volume 14, number 1, 1987, pp. 7–13.

FURTHER READING:

Books

Reuss, Martin, *Water Resources People Issues: An Interview with Gilbert F. White*, Office of History, U.S. Army Corps of Engineers (Fort Belvoir, VA), 1993.

Periodicals

Caughey, Peter, *Summit*, A Quiet Leader, (University of Colorado-Boulder publication), winter, 1992–93, pp. 16–19.
Caughey, Peter, *New York Herald-Tribune*, October 26, 1952, p. 8.

Sketch by Margaret DiCanio

Raymond L. White
1943–
American molecular biologist

Raymond L. White has contributed greatly to the understanding of how human genes are arranged on chromosomes and how they contribute to the occurrence of hereditary diseases. He is best known for developing a technique for mapping and locating genetic deoxyribonucleic acid (DNA) markers. Markers are genetic sequences that are located near defective genes and can be used to indicate the presence or absence of such genes, because they are often passed along with the defective gene. White's work, and that of others who are involved with the Human Genome Project, will help scientists in their quest to understand the genetic causes of such diseases as hemophilia, Duchenne muscular dystrophy, and breast cancer, and to discover ways to conquer or control them.

White was born on October 23, 1943, in Orlando, Florida, the son of a dentist. Although he at first intended to enter the field of medicine, he became interested in molecular biology and genetics while a student at the University of Oregon. After he received his bachelor of science degree in microbiology in 1965, White attended the Massachusetts Institute of Technology (MIT), where in 1971 he earned his Ph.D. in microbiology. From 1971 to 1972, he was a research associate and instructor at MIT. After postdoctoral work at Stanford from 1972 to 1975, White returned to Massachusetts and became an assistant professor in the microbiology department at the University of Massachusetts School of Medicine in Worcester. He held that position from 1975-1978, when he became an associate professor in the department.

In 1980, White joined the staff of the University of Utah Medical School as an associate professor in the department of cellular, viral, and molecular biology, and as an investigator at the university's Howard Hughes Medical Institute (he was an investigator there until 1994). In 1984, he was named co-chair of the medical school's human genetics department. Since 1985, White has served as a professor in the departments of oncological sciences and human genetics. In addition, he is currently chairman of the department of oncological sciences at the University of Utah School of Medicine and is the executive director of the Huntsman Cancer Institute at the University of Utah. He has held both positions since 1994.

Begins Tracking Defective Genes

While at the University of Massachusetts, White began investigating a question that intrigued many scientists, namely, whether or not it was possible to discover where on certain chromosomes the genes responsible for many hereditary illnesses were located. Much of the genetic material is identical from person to person, but some parts were different, and these different parts (called polymorphisms) accounted for the variety in human hair color, eye color, and many other inherited features—including the presence or absence of such disorders as hemophilia, a genetic disease in which the blood lacks the factors that allow it to clot normally. It was possible that people who showed the effects of these defective genes would share certain polymorphisms. If so, perhaps the polymorphisms could be used to flag the defective genes.

The polymorphisms White was interested in were called restriction fragment length polymorphisms, or RFLPs. But RFLPs were scattered across 23 chromosomes that comprised about 100,000 genes, and finding them at all would be a tremendous task. Working with Arlene Wyman in 1979, he began looking for RFLPs by first eliminating all the parts of the human genome that were identical. In the

end, they narrowed down their search to five sequences of DNA that contained between 15,000 and 20,000 "bases." By combining radioactively labeled copies of these sequences with the DNA from 56 donors, White and Wyman were able to find eight RFLPs.

Throughout the 1980s, White worked on proving his theory that RFLPs could be used as genetic markers. The first genetic marker was discovered by British researchers in 1981; it was an RFLP on the X chromosome that was linked to the gene that can cause Duchenne muscular dystrophy. Combined with the efforts of other researchers, White's work has allowed for the creation of a map of the human genome, and for the discovery of many genes. This genetic mapping allows scientists to predict what will happen when certain genes are present, and to take steps to develop therapies that will lessen the effects of the genes.

White's laboratory has been working with two important genes, both of which normally work in the body to suppress tumor formation. One gene, NF1, normally takes part in signal pathways for cell growth; when it is mutated, however, it causes peripheral neurofibromatosis. NF1 has also been found in tumors that are not usually associated with it, which makes researchers believe that the gene is a growth regulator. The other gene, APC, can cause adenomatous polyposis when mutated, and further mutation can lead to colon cancer. Interestingly, mutations in the different parts of the APC gene lead to different physical manifestations (phenotypes) of the illness.

Another gene White is studying is BRCA1, another tumor-suppressor gene found on chromosome 17q. This gene makes certain women predisposed to early-onset breast and ovarian cancer. By studying these genes, White and his staff may gain more information about what mechanisms in the body cause the formation of cancer, and may lead to ways in which medical professionals can help detect who is at risk for breast cancer and help prevent this disease.

The author of nearly 300 scientific papers, White is a member of the National Academy of Sciences, the American Association for Cancer Research, the Human Genome Organization, and the American Society for Human Genetics. He has served on a variety of advisory boards and committees. Among the many honors he has received in recognition of his work are the American Cancer Society's Sword of Hope Award (Utah chapter, 1995), the Utah Governor's Medal for Science and Technology (1993), the National Health Council National Medical Research Award (1991), the National Neurofibromatosis Foundation's Friedrich von Recklinghausen Award, and the Allan Award for Cancer Research.

SELECTED WRITINGS BY WHITE:

Periodicals

"DNA in Medicine: Human Genetics." *The Lancet* 1, (December 1984):1257-62.

"Polymorphic DNA Markers on the Genomic Map: Signposts for Localization of Unknown Genes." *Somatic Cell and Molecular Genetics* 13, (1987): 361-63.

(With others) "Tightly Linked Markers for the Neurofibromatosis Type 1 Gene." *Genomics* 1, (1987): 364-67.

"Molecular Biology of the APC Protein." *Pathologie Biologie* 45 (1997):240-44.

Sketch by Fran Hodgkins

Alfred North Whitehead

Alfred North Whitehead
1861–1947
American mathematician

Albert North Whitehead began his career as a mathematician, but eventually became at least as famous as a philosopher. His first three books, *A Treatise on Universal Algebra, The Axioms of Projective Geometry,* and *The Axioms of Descriptive Geometry,* all dealt with traditional mathematical topics. In 1900, Whitehead first heard about the new system for expressing logical concepts in discrete symbols developed by the Italian mathematician **Giuseppe Peano**. Along with **Bertrand Russell**, his colleague and former student, Whitehead saw in Peano's symbolism a method for developing a rigorous, nonnumerical approach to logic. The work of these two men culminated in the publication of the three-volume *Principia Mathematica,* widely regarded as one of the most important books in mathematics ever written. In 1924 Whitehead became professor of philosophy at Harvard University, where he devoted his time to the development of a comprehensive and complex system of philosophy.

Whitehead was born on February 15, 1861, at Ramsgate in the Isle of Thanet, Kent, England. Both his grandfather, Thomas Whitehead, and his father, Alfred Whitehead, had been headmasters of a private school in Ramsgate. Alfred Whitehead had later joined the clergy and become vicar of St. Peter's Parish, about two miles from Ramsgate. In his autobiography, Whitehead said of his father that he "was not intellectual, but he possessed personality." Whitehead's mother was the former Maria Sarah Buckmaster, daughter of a successful London businessman. As a young man, Whitehead often traveled to London to visit his maternal grandmother.

Educated at Sherborne and Trinity College

For the first fourteen years of his life, Whitehead was educated at home primarily by his father. Then, in 1875, he was sent to the public school at Sherborne in Dorsetshire.

Whitehead described his education as traditional, with a strong emphasis on Latin and Greek. But, he continued, "we were not overworked," so that he had plenty of time for sports such as cricket and football, private reading, and a study of history. At Sherborne he also had his introduction to science and mathematics, at which he excelled. In fact, he was apparently excused from some Latin requirements in order to have more time for his mathematical studies.

In 1880 Whitehead received a scholarship to continue his studies at Trinity College, Cambridge. While at Trinity, all of Whitehead's formal education was in the field of mathematics, the British system not having yet accepted the concept of a broad liberal education for all students. Still, he later wrote, his mathematics courses "were only one side of the education" he experienced at Trinity. Another side consisted of regular evening meetings with other undergraduates at which virtually all subjects were discussed. Whitehead later referred to these meetings as "a daily Platonic dialogue." Through these dialogues, Whitehead rapidly expanded his knowledge of history, literature, philosophy, and politics.

Whitehead was awarded his bachelor of arts degree in 1884 for a thesis on James Clerk Maxwell's theory of electromagnetism. A few months later he was elected a fellow of Trinity College and appointed assistant lecturer in mathematics. Whitehead was awarded his M.A. in 1887, and in 1903, was named senior lecturer. Two years later he was granted his doctor of science degree.

Meets and Marries Evelyn Wade

While still at Trinity, Whitehead met Evelyn Willoughby Wade, described in the *Dictionary of American Biography* as the "daughter of impoverished Irish landed gentry" who was "witty, with passionate likes and dislikes, a great sense of drama, and . . . a keen aesthetic sense." Whitehead himself credits his wife with teaching him "that beauty, moral and aesthetic, is the aim of existence; and that kindness, and love, and artistic satisfaction are among its modes of attainment." The two were married on December 16, 1890. They later had four children, Thomas North in 1891, Jesse Marie in 1893, Eric Alfred in 1898, and an unnamed boy who died at birth in 1892. Eric later became a pilot with the Royal Flying Corps and was killed in March, 1918, during World War I.

Whitehead's first book, *A Treatise on Universal Algebra,* was begun in January, 1891, and published seven years later. The book was an attempt to expand on the works of three predecessors, Hermann Grassmann, William Rowan Hamilton, and George Boole, the founder of symbolic logic. Whitehead later wrote that Grassmann, in particular, had been "an original genius, never sufficiently recognized." All of Whitehead's future work on mathematical logic, he said, was derived from the contributions of these three men. Whitehead's book was a tour de force that earned him election to the Royal Society five years after its publication. In the book, Whitehead argues that algebraic concepts have an existence of their own, independent of any connection with real objects.

Begins a Long Working Relationship with Russell

The year of Whitehead's marriage, 1890, also marked the beginning of another long and fruitful relationship, with Russell. The two had met when Russell was still a freshman at Cambridge; Whitehead was one of his teachers. In later years their student-and-teacher relationship blossomed into a full-blown working relationship as professional colleagues. They were eventually to collaborate on a number of important mathematical works.

An important event in their association occurred in July, 1900, when they attended together the First International Congress of Philosophy in Paris. It was there that Whitehead and Russell were introduced to the techniques of symbolic logic developed by the Italian mathematician Giuseppe Peano. They immediately saw that Peano's symbolism could be used to clarify fundamental concepts of mathematics. When Russell returned to England, he began to incorporate Peano's approach into the book on which he was then working, *Principles of Mathematics.*

Before long, however, it occurred to Russell that he and his former teacher were both working on very similar topics, he on his *Principles of Mathematics* and Whitehead on a second volume of his *Universal Algebra.* The two agreed to start working together, with the result that the second volume of neither work ever appeared. Instead, they developed the three-volume masterpiece, *Principia Mathe-*

matica. Principia Mathematica The fundamental concept behind the book was that the basic principles of mathematics can be derived in a strict way through the precise rules of symbolic logic. The *Principia Mathematica* has since been described by one of Whitehead's biographers, Victor Lowe, in the *Dictionary of American Biography* as "one of the great intellectual monuments of all time."

Moves from Cambridge to London

In 1910, the year in which the first volume of *Principia Mathematica* appeared, Whitehead ended a twenty-five-year teaching career at Trinity College and moved to London. He remained without an academic appointment for one year, during which time he wrote his *Introduction to Mathematics,* which James R. Newman has called "a classic of popularization" of mathematics. Whitehead then accepted an appointment as lecturer in applied mathematics and mechanics at University College, London, and two years later, was made reader in geometry there. In 1914 he was named professor of applied mathematics at the Imperial College of Science and Technology in Kensington.

The London period was for Whitehead a particularly busy time in the political and administrative arenas. He served on a number of faculty and governmental committees and was outspoken in his concern about educational reform. Perhaps his best-known remarks on this subject came in a 1916 address to the Mathematical Association, "The Aims of Education: A Plan for Reform." In this address, Whitehead pointed out that the narrow view of education in which the classics are taught to a select number of upper-class men had become outmoded in a world of a "seething mass of artisans seeking intellectual enlightenment, of young people from every social grade craving for adequate knowledge."

During the latter years of his London period, Whitehead's interests shifted from mathematics to the philosophy of science. The fourth volume of *Principia Mathematica,* dealing with the foundations of geometry, was never completed. Instead, Whitehead began to write on the philosophical foundations of science in books such as *An Enquiry Concerning the Principles of Natural Knowledge* in 1919, *The Concept of Nature* in 1920, and *The Principle of Relativity, with Applications to Physical Science* in 1922.

The main theme of these books was that there exists a reality in the physical world that is distinct from the descriptions that scientists have invented for that reality. Scientific explanations certainly have their functions, according to Whitehead, but they should not be construed as being the reality of nature itself.

Invited to Join Harvard's Philosophy Department

As early as 1920, Harvard University had been interested in offering Whitehead a position in its philosophy department. For financial reasons, a firm offer was not made until 1924, when Whitehead was sixty-three years old. He accepted the offer partly because he was nearing mandatory retirement age at Imperial College and partly because he looked forward to the opportunity of expanding his intellectual horizons. On September 1, 1924, Whitehead's appointment at Harvard became official.

Until the Harvard post became available, Whitehead had remained rather strictly within the areas of mathematics and natural science. After 1924, however, he extended the range of his writings to include far broader topics. His first work published in the United States, *Science and the Modern World*, discussed the significance of the scientific enterprise for other aspects of human culture. The book was an instant professional and commercial success and earned Whitehead an immediate reputation as a profound thinker and a writer of great clarity and persuasiveness.

His next book, *Religion in the Making*, was the first of a number that carried Whitehead far beyond the fields of mathematics and science. Its publication in 1926 was followed by *Symbolism, Its Meaning and Effect* in 1927, *The Aims of Education and Other Essays* in 1929, *The Function of Reason*, also in 1929, and a half dozen more books over the next two decades. In recognition of his work, Whitehead was elected a fellow of the British Academy in 1931, and he was awarded the Order of Merit, the highest honor that Great Britain can bestow on a man of letters, in 1945. Whitehead retired from active teaching at Harvard in 1937, at which time he was named emeritus professor of philosophy. He died at his home in Cambridge, Massachusetts, on December 30, 1947.

SELECTED WRITINGS BY WHITEHEAD:

Books

A Treatise on Universal Algebra, Cambridge University Press, 1898.

The Axioms of Projective Geometry, Cambridge University Press, 1906.

The Axioms of Descriptive Geometry, Cambridge University Press, 1907.

Principia Mathematica, three volumes, Cambridge University Press, 1910–13.

An Introduction to Mathematics, Williams & Norgate, 1911.

An Enquiry Concerning the Principles of Natural Knowledge, Cambridge University Press, 1919.

The Concept of Nature, Cambridge University Press, 1920.

The Principle of Relativity, with Applications to Physical Science, Cambridge University Press, 1922.

Science and the Modern World, Macmillan, 1925.

Religion in the Making, Macmillan, 1926.

Symbolism, Its Meaning and Effect, Macmillan, 1927.

The Aims of Education and Other Essays, Macmillan, 1929.

The Function of Reason, Princeton University Press, 1929.

Process and Reality: An Essay in Cosmology, Macmillan, 1929.

Adventures of Ideas, Macmillan, 1933.

Nature and Life, University of Chicago Press, 1934.

Modes of Thought, Macmillan, 1938.

Essays in Science and Philosophy, Philosophical Library, 1947.

Dialogues of Alfred North Whitehead, edited by L. Price, Little, Brown, 1954.

The Interpretation of Science: Selected Essays, edited by A. H. Johnson, Bobbs Merrill, 1961.

FURTHER READING:

Books

Johnson, R. C., *Dictionary of Literary Biography*, Alfred North Whitehead, Volume 100, edited by Robert Baum, 1990, pp. 306–315.

Newman, James R., *The World of Mathematics*, Volume 1, Simon & Schuster, pp. 395–401.

Price, Lucien, *Dialogues of Alfred North Whitehead*, Little, Brown, 1954, pp. 3–20.

Schilpp, Paul Arthur, *The Philosophy of Alfred North Whitehead*, Tudor, 1941.

Sketch by David E. Newton

Robert Harding Whittaker
1920–1980
American ecologist

Robert Harding Whittaker was a central figure in twentieth-century ecology, developing a variety of innovative research methods and advancing novel theories on plant community ecology. He was an influential teacher, directing the research of a number of graduate students. He also conducted numerous field studies of his own, both in the United States and abroad. According to R. K. Peet, who edited a collection of essays in Whittaker's honor, his meticulous field research helped to advance his sometimes unorthodox and controversial hypotheses.

Born December 27, 1920 in Wichita, Kansas, Whittaker was raised in the small farming community of Eureka. His parents, Clive and Adeline Whittaker, were teachers at Fairmount College (now the University of Wichita). Though Clive Whittaker left his zoology teaching post when Robert was born and took up oil-drilling, he passed on to his son a love of natural history and an interest in academic studies. As a child, Whittaker collected butterflies and enjoyed summer holidays climbing mountains in Colorado, where his family often vacationed.

Challenges Orthodoxies as a Young Researcher

Like many of his generation, Whittaker saw his university education interrupted by World War II. He attended Washburn Municipal University in Topeka, was awarded a B.A. in Biology in 1942, and promptly joined the Air Force, where he served as a weather observer in England. After the war, he returned to the United States and entered the graduate school of the University of Illinois. Though his original application to the botany program was rejected, he later applied and was accepted to the university's zoology program.

During the 1930s and 1940s, the field of natural history was highly charged with divergent theories on how species interacted in communities. Whittaker began his graduate career with ties to two alternative opinions of species distribution. His official advisor, Charles Kendeigh, held to the traditional Clementsian theory of plant association; this theory argued for a holistic view of plant community, focusing on interdependence and cooperation. Whittaker, however, was drawn to the alternative theory put forth by Henry Gleason, who argued for individualism rather than cooperation as a basis for species interaction.

Whittaker's graduate research ultimately provided vital evidence to support Gleason's view. In order to complete his doctorate, Whittaker undertook field research in the Great Smoky Mountains. Originally intended to focus on insects, the project eventually became an examination of vegetation patterns and densities. Whittaker found ample evidence to demonstrate that plant species exist independently along different gradients—in other words, at different elevations and topographies, the distribution of vegetation species tends to vary rather than form discrete communities. Later, Whittaker would describe the distribution pattern as a continuum.

Whittaker's research on species distribution became the basis for his dissertation, which he defended in 1948. Although the research impressed leading ecologists and was generally considered to represent revolutionary methodology, according to Peet, it was not published until 1956, when it appeared in *Ecological Monographs* as "Vegetation of the Great Smoky Mountains."

After receiving his Ph.D., Whittaker taught for several years at Washington State College, continuing field work in and around southern Oregon. However, his teaching contract was not renewed, and in 1951 he left academia for a brief stint in industry. He joined the Aquatic Biology Unit of General Electric in Richland, Washington, where he studied the movement of microcosmic aquatic nutrients. At General Electric he met Clara Buehl, whom he married on January 1, 1953. They raised three sons.

In 1954, Whittaker landed a position in the Biology Department of Brooklyn College, City University of New York. During his years at Brooklyn, he spent summers in the Great Smoky Mountains conducting field research on plant productivity. In subsequent years, working first at Brookhaven National Laboratory (from 1964 to 1966) and then at the University of California at Irvine (from 1967 to 1968), he developed a reputation as a skilled field-based ecologist and ecological theorist.

Whittaker continued to produce studies on gradient analysis and plant productivity, developing important data that challenged traditional theories of plant communities. One field-research project, undertaken with William Niering of Connecticut College, eventually resulted in Whittaker and Niering sharing the 1966 Mercer Award of the Ecological Society of America.

With his growing reputation came recognition and an appointment as Professor of Biology at Cornell University in 1968, where he would remain for the rest of his life. There he advised graduate students and became involved in a number of important research projects. One, concerning the use of ordination techniques to compare and analyze vegetation in Mendocino County, led Whittaker into potential conflict with European ecologists, who were wedded to an approach that favored traditional classification of species. In a successful attempt to negotiate a middle ground, Whittaker delivered a paper entitled "Convergences of Ordination and Classification" at the Rinteln symposium in Germany.

International Recognition Grows

Whittaker's Rinteln paper marked his growing importance as an international figure in the field of ecology. In 1973 he became the editor of the influential journal *Vegetatio*. To this international journal he brought a new perspective, soliciting articles by American ecologists advancing the ordination and gradient analysis approach, which he published alongside articles by Europeans representing the more traditional classification approach.

During his career, Whittaker translated his research into scores of articles and textbooks. He was the senior author for many of these articles, and he authored, edited, co-authored, or co-edited numerous books and texts. His works were often cited in the works of other ecologists. Among his most influential books are *Communities and Ecosystems*, 1970; *Handbook of Vegetation Science, Part V: Ordination and Classification of Vegetation*, 1973; *Niche: Theory and Application*, 1975; *Classification of Plant Communities*, 1978.

Whittaker received numerous honors during his years at Cornell, including election to the Academy of Sciences, election to the American Academy of Arts and Sciences, and honorary membership in the British Ecological Society and the Swedish Phytogeographical Society. He served as Vice-President of the Ecological Society of America in 1971, and at the time of his death was serving as the President of the American Society of Naturalists. Shortly before his death Whittaker was awarded the Ecological Society of America's highest honor, Eminent Ecologist.

After the death of his wife in 1977, Whittaker continued field research both in the United States and abroad. In 1979 he married one of his doctoral students, Linda Olsvig; the two traveled to Israel and South Africa, where Whittaker continued a study comparing the diversity of species in similar climates—a project he was still working on when he died of cancer in 1980.

SELECTED WRITINGS BY WHITTAKER:

Books

Communities and Ecosystems, Macmillan, 1970.
Handbook of Vegetation Science, Part V: Ordination and Classification of Vegetation, W. Junk, 1973.
Primary Productivity of the Biosphere, Springer-Verlag, 1975.
Niche: Theory and Application, Dowden, Hutchinson & Ross, 1975.
Classification of Plant Communities, W. Junk, 1978.

FURTHER READING:

Books

Peet, R. K., editor, *Plant Community Ecology: Papers in Honor of Robert H. Whittaker,* Kluwer Academic Publishers, 1985.

Sketch by Katherine Williams

Frank Whittle
1907–1996
English aviation engineer

Frank Whittle, along with German engineer Hans von Ohain, invented the jet engine. Neither Whittle nor von Ohain was aware of the other's work, however, until after World War II. Whittle first began working on the concept of a jet engine in the 1920s, but he was repeatedly rebuffed by those who insisted that the idea was unworkable or impractical. With persistence during the 1930s and into World War II, Whittle developed his concept into the first flyable jet airplane outside of Germany. His creation, the Gloster-Whittle E28/39, first flew on May 15, 1941.

Whittle was born to working-class parents in Coventry, England, on June 1, 1907. His father had talents as a machinist and inventor, and in 1916 he bought a small business that he called the Leamington Valve and Piston Ring Company. The young Whittle acquired some experi-

Frank Whittle

ence here in manufacturing, helping with odd jobs such as drilling valve stems or working on the lathe. Whittle later wrote in his autobiography that he inherited his inventiveness and love for things mechanical from his father.

When Whittle turned eleven he received a small scholarship to attend secondary school. His school work was spotty. Most of the subjects he liked best, such as astronomy, engineering, and natural science, were not taught at the school. He read whatever he could find on popular science and became interested in chemistry. Still, he hated homework, and excelling at school seems to have been undermined by what Whittle himself called, in *Jet: The Story of a Pioneer,* "a natural laziness."

It was in secondary school that Whittle developed an interest in aeronautics and flying, an interest that would carry him through a brilliant and sometimes frustrating career as an aviation engineer. After graduating from secondary school, Whittle joined the Royal Air Force as an aircraft apprentice, although he had difficulty getting accepted because he stood only five feet tall. After he spent three years rigging aircraft, the RAF College at Cranwell accepted Whittle as a cadet. While at Cranwell he joined the Model Aircraft Society, which, Whittle later wrote, played a critical role in his early education as an engineer.

After graduating from the cadet college, Whittle was assigned to 111 Fighter Squadron, where he reported in August 1928. Here, along with his regular duties, Whittle continued pilot training, this time at Central Flying School at Wittering. Lectures at Wittering added to his fund of knowledge and helped nurture to maturity Whittle's ideas about jet propulsion. The problem under much discussion then was that propellers and piston engines limited an airplane's altitude and speed. The air was too thin at higher altitudes to properly engage a propeller, and the content of oxygen in the air was too lean to keep a piston-driven engine from stalling. Whittle thought that the problem could be solved by using a turbine instead of a piston engine. This way a lean mixture of oxygen could be compressed, combined with fuel, and ignited. The expanding gases caused by igniting the mixture of compressed oxygen and fuel would result in a jet blast that would propel the aircraft forward.

Overcomes Resistance

Convincing officials in the Air Ministry, however, was perhaps as great a challenge as developing the engine itself. One of the main objections was that materials did not yet exist that could withstand the heat and stress present in a jet engine. Whittle persisted. Eventually he found supporters who were willing to give him financial backing for his project. In return for their support, Whittle promised his backers each a quarter share of the commercial rights. The result of their agreement was the formation in March 1936 of a small corporation called Power Jets.

Development and testing of prototype jet engines continued into the war years after the German invasion of Poland in September 1939. The British surmised that Germany was also working on a jet engine, but could only speculate on the nature of that work. As for Whittle, he eventually prevailed over what at times seemed like insurmountable odds posed by technical difficulties and bureaucratic infighting.

By April 1941 Whittle and the Power Jet corporation began testing their W.1 jet engine in the Gloster-Whittle E28/39 airplane (after Gloster Aircraft Company, which constructed the airplane) by making taxi runs to see how the engine handled on the ground. With this testing and confidence-building measure, the engineers were able to make further adjustments, so that by the evening of May 15, 1941, a test pilot could take the aircraft aloft. The flight lasted seventeen minutes during which the aircraft reached a speed of 370 miles (592 km) per hour at an elevation of twenty-five thousand feet (7,500 m). This easily exceeded the speed of the next fastest airplane in the Royal Air Force, the redoubtable Spitfire, which in many minds had defeated Germany's best aircraft in the Battle of Britain.

Despite the successful flight of the E28/39 with its W.1 engine (other models of this engine were also undergoing tests), more refinement was needed before they could be mass produced. With this in mind, engineers and other decision makers decided to start production of aircraft and engines in June 1942. As it was, production models of Britain's first jet did not appear in the skies until mid–1944. The production model, dubbed the Meteor I, was used against the German V–1 rockets that pummeled London late in the war.

In 1944, Great Britain nationalized the Power Jets company, which had been taken over by Rolls-Royce in 1943. The company was now called Power Jets R & D, and was limited to research and development. Whittle became chief technical advisor to the board, but because of poor health he played an increasingly marginal role, the more so since by the end of 1944 it had become clear that further development of a jet fighter would contribute little to what then seemed like the inevitable defeat of Germany. Morale sank and Whittle left the company in January, 1946.

Awarded Knighthood

By this time, Whittle's fame had become well established, and he was in demand as a lecturer in the United Kingdom. During the latter part of 1946 Whittle undertook a lecture tour in the United States, but again fell ill and required two months' hospitalization. In the United Kingdom, Whittle had received the Clayton Prize (£1,000) from the Institution of Mechanical Engineers for his work on jet engines. The Royal Commission on Awards to Inventors honored Whittle in 1945 with an interim award of £10,000, which it increased in 1948 to £100,000. That same year, King George VI granted him knighthood. Whittle's personal life was subsumed by his career, and *Jet*, his book about his work on jet propulsion, gives scant attention to life at home. Nonetheless, Whittle married Dorothy Mary Lee, whom he had known in Coventry, in 1930. Their first son, Francis David, was born in May of the following year. A second son was born, but the marriage ended in 1976.

After the war, Whittle worked for a while as a mechanical engineering specialist for the Dutch oil company, Bataafsche Petroleum Maatschappij, where he designed an oil-drilling motor called the Whittle turbo-drill. Thereafter he became a technical consultant to a number of aerospace firms, emigrated to the United States in 1976, and married his second wife, Hazel, after having accepted a lectureship with the U.S. Naval Academy. Whittle also worked on jet propulsion at Wright-Paterson Air Force Base in Dayton, Ohio, and became chief scientist at Wright-Paterson's Aero Propulsion Laboratory. Thereafter, Whittle worked as a senior research engineer at the University of Dayton Research Institute.

Whittle's research in jet propulsion revolutionized air travel and provided the technical groundwork for America's first jet airplane, the Bell XP–59A, which had its maiden flight in 1942. In recognition of Whittle's achievements, in 1991 the National Academy of Engineering in Washington, D.C., awarded him and Hans von Ohain its prestigious Charles Draper Prize, which included a grant of $375,000 to be divided between the two engineers. Whittle died at his home in Columbia, Maryland, on August 8, 1996, at the age of 89.

SELECTED WRITINGS BY WHITTLE:

Books

Jet: The Story of a Pioneer. Frederick Muller, 1953.

Gas Turbine Aero-Thermodynamics. Tarrytown, NY: Pergamon, 1981.

Whittle: The True Story. Washington, DC: Smithsonian Institution Press, 1987.

FURTHER READING:

Periodicals

"Air Commodore Sir Frank Whittle." *Times (London)* (10 August 1996: 21).

Fink, Donald E. "Jet Engine Milestone." *Aviation Week & Space Technology* (13 April 1987): 15.

Joyce, Christopher. "Jet Pioneers Win Engineering's 'Nobel Prize,'" *New Scientist* (5 October 1991): 31.

Stix, Gary. "Smaller World: The Draper Prize Recognizes the Fathers of the Jet Age." *Scientific American* (December 1991): 15.

Stix, Gary. "Turbojet's Inventors Earn Draper Prize." *Science News* (19 October 1991): 252.

Vietmeyer, Noel. "They Created the Jet Age." *Reader's Digest* (May 1987): 162-66.

Sketch by Karl Preuss

William E. Wickenden
1882–1947
American engineer

William E. Wickenden was a noted engineer and educator who, as president of Cleveland's Case School of Applied Science—as the institution was then known—brought the worlds of science and industry together. During his tenure from 1930 to 1947, Wickenden became a national spokesman for the engineering profession, enhancing not only the reputation and teaching standards of Case, but also attracting young scholars to the sciences. As a president of the American Institute of Electrical Engineering, Wickenden also promoted engineering as an educational option, while at the same time stressing the importance of a well-rounded education as the starting point for "turning a life experience into an education." A humanistic scientist, Wickenden served as the model for an entire generation of new scientists who blended the ideas of culture and technology.

William Elgin Wickenden was born on December 24, 1882, one of eight children of Thomas Rogers and Ida Consaul Wickenden. The elder Wickenden was a self-trained civil engineer who had immigrated to Toledo, Ohio, from England. He worked as an engineer for the city of Toledo, married the daughter of a local farmer, and raised his large family with a respect not only for God, but also for the humanizing effects of education. Seven of the eight Wickenden children graduated from college, a high ratio indeed for the late nineteenth century. William Wickenden graduated valedictorian of his high school class, working year-round delivering papers and in the summer for a construction firm, and saving enough money to enter Denison University in Granville, Ohio, in 1900.

A small liberal arts college, Denison was also supported by the Baptist Church. While at college, Wickenden worked setting type for the *Granville Times,* and in 1904 earned his B.S., was Phi Beta Kappa, and valedictorian of his class. After a brief stint as an instructor at Mechanics Institute in Rochester, New York, Wickenden won a physics scholarship to the University of Wisconsin and became an instructor of electrical engineering at that university from 1905 to 1909. On September 2, 1908, he married Marion Susan Lamb of Toledo, Ohio, a fellow graduate of Denison University.

In 1910, Wickenden's first book, *Illumination and Photometry,* was published. Thereafter, he accepted a post as assistant professor of electrical engineering at the Massachusetts Institute of Technology (MIT), and was made associate professor in 1914. He was a popular teacher and a most approachable scholar. The years he spent at MIT were fruitful ones, and indicative of the direction that the mature Wickenden would take: teaching and encouraging interest in engineering.

From 1918 to 1923, Wickenden left academia, first to become a personnel manager for Western Electric Company in New York, and then from 1921 to 1923 as the assistant vice-president for American Telephone and Telegraph. But the pull of engineering scholarship soon brought him back to education. As director of investigations for the Society for the Promotion of Engineering Education, Wickenden worked from 1923 to 1929 studying engineering schools worldwide, using a Carnegie endowment to help fund his researches. He researched schools in the U.S. and Canada and spent a full 18 months in Europe and Great Britain. His final report, known popularly as the "Wickenden report," was published in 1929 and greatly influenced universities and technical schools. As the pre-eminent specialist in engineering education, Wickenden found himself a man in demand.

Tenure at Case an Inspiration

In 1929, just finishing up on his study of engineering schools, Wickenden was offered and accepted the position of president of the Case School of Applied Science in Cleveland, Ohio. Case, established in 1881, had been intended as a strong magnet school for science in the American heartland. By 1929 several attempts had failed at establishing real national prominence for the school, though it did enjoy a strong regional reputation. Sister college to Western Reserve University, with which it shared a vast building site, Case had a long and contentious rivalry with the older institution. To Wickenden it made sense that the two schools cooperate instead of compete—a dream only fully realized in the 1960s when the two institutions merged into Case Western Reserve University. To that end, he proposed the sharing of teaching responsibilities between the two: Case being responsible for undergraduate science courses, and Western Reserve's Adelbert College tackling the humanities for both schools. It was only a cooperative effort, but it met with much opposition from those who feared Reserve would swallow up the smaller institution. In any event, Case's reputation grew because of the association, and Wickenden's model of the all-round scientist—both researcher and humanist—became more of a reality because of the shared teaching.

Other obstacles stood in the way of Wickenden's high hopes for creating a national institution out of Case: the Great Depression dried up funds not only from benefactors, but also from new students. By 1934 the student body had dwindled by a third, necessitating a corresponding reduction in faculty. It was this last action which hurt the most, for Wickenden had made a concerted effort since coming to Case to recruit well qualified faculty, making Ph.D. status a requirement. Thereafter, however, the situation improved, and with the coming of the World War II, Case became a training center for much needed civil engineers as well as for U.S. Navy officers. Wickenden—a critic of Roosevelt's conduct of defense preparation and production—instituted year-round schooling to enable students to graduate in three years. During the war years another barrier was broken: undergraduate women were admitted for the first time in 1943. The postwar years were again ones of growth for Case: the advent of the G.I. Bill enabled thousands of young men to pursue academic careers who might otherwise have not been able to afford such an investment. The years of the Cold War also made technology increasingly valued, and engineers were more in demand than ever before in the country's history.

Wickenden was a tireless proselytizer for engineering. In the early 1940s he served as president of the American Institute of Electrical Engineers and travelled more than 40,000 miles through North America and Mexico speaking on over 100 occasions annually at regional meetings of the association. Known for his eloquence as well as his great erudition, Wickenden was a personal example of the well-rounded scientist for which he campaigned. He was widely honored for his work both in education and civic activities: the recipient of 11 honorary degrees, he was awarded the Lamme Medal from the Society for the Promotion of Engineering Education in 1933, and served on the boards of both academic institutions and private industries. In 1947, citing declining energy and a wish to spend more time with his wife and two children, Elizabeth and William C., Wickenden decided to retire from Case. He presided over the 68th commencement exercises, but suffered a massive heart attack on August 23 at his summer home in New Hampshire. He died on September 1, 1947, in Peterboro, New Hampshire, one day after his retirement had become effective. As reported in *Case Western Reserve: A History of the University 1826–1976,* Wickenden's friend and pastor, Dr. Frank Ferris, summed up the man in a funeral tribute: "He was one of the most completely civilized men it has been my good fortune to know."

SELECTED WRITINGS BY WICKENDEN:

Books

Illumination and Photometry, McGraw-Hill, 1910.
A Comparative Study of Engineering Education in the United States and Europe, Lancaster Press, 1929.
A Professional Guide for Junior Engineers, Engineers' Council for Professional Development, 1949.

FURTHER READING:

Books

Cramer, C. H., *Case Western Reserve: a History of the University,* Little, Brown, 1976, pp. 245–260.

Periodicals

Cramer, C. H., *New York Times,* Dr. W. E. Wickenden of Case Institute, September 2, 1947, p. 21.

Other

Cramer, C. H., *curriculum vitae,* William Elgin Wickenden, 1882–1947, courtesy of Case Western Reserve University Archives.

Sketch by J. Sydney Jones

Sheila E. Widnall
1938–
American aeronautical engineer

Sheila E. Widnall is an accomplished researcher, educator, and writer in the field of aerospace engineering. A specialist in fluid dynamics at the Massachusettes Institute of Technology (MIT) for nearly three decades, she has also served in numerous administrative and advisory posts in industry, government, and academia. In August, 1993, Widnall was appointed Secretary of the United States Air Force, the first woman to head one of the country's military branches.

Sheila Evans Widnall was born to Rolland John and Genievieve Alice Evans in Tacoma, Washington, on July 13, 1938. Her father worked as a rodeo cowboy before

Sheila E. Widnall

becoming a production planner for Boeing Aircraft Company and, later, a teacher. Her mother was a juvenile probation officer. Interested in airplanes and aircraft design from her childhood, Widnall decided to pursue a career in science after she won the first prize at her high school science fair. She entered MIT in September, 1956, one of twenty-one women in a class of nine hundred, and received her Bachelor of Science degree in aeronautics and astronautics in 1960. She continued on at MIT to earn a Master of Science degree in 1961 and the Doctor of Science degree in 1964, both in aeronautics and astronautics. Upon graduation, MIT awarded Widnall a faculty post as assistant professor in mathematics and aeronautics. She was the first alumna to serve on the faculty in the school of engineering. In 1970 MIT promoted her to associate professor, and in 1974 to full professor. During her tenure at MIT, Widnall served as head of the Division of Fluid Mechanics from 1975 to 1979, and as director of the Fluid Dynamics Laboratory from 1979 to 1990.

Establishes the Anechoic Wind Tunnel

Widnall specialized in the theories and applications of fluid dynamics, particularly in problems associated with air turbulence created by rotating helicopter blades. Her research focused on the vortices or eddies of air created at the ends and at the trailing edge of helicopter blades as they swirl through the air. These vortices are the source of noise, instability, and vibrations that affect the integrity of the blades and the stability of the aircraft. Widnall pursued

similar interests in relation to aircraft that make vertical, short take-offs and landings (that is, V/STOL aircraft) and the noise associated with them. To this end, her studies led her to establish the anechoic wind tunnel at MIT, where researchers study the phenomenon of noise and V/STOL aircraft. During her tenure at MIT, Widnall established a reputation as an expert in her field and lectured widely on her research in vortices and their relation to aerodynamics. Widnall is the author of seventy papers on fluid dynamics as well as other areas of science and engineering; she has also served as associate editor for the scientific publications *Journal of Aircraft, Physics of Fluids,* and the *Journal of Applied Mechanics.*

In addition to writing about aerodynamics, Widnall has also published articles and delivered talks about the changing attitudes and trends in education for prospective engineers and scientists. In 1988, as newly elected president of the American Association for the Advancement of Science (AAAS), Widnall addressed the association on her longstanding interest in seeing more women become scientists and engineers and the problems they face in attaining higher degrees and achieving professional goals. In recognition of Widnall's efforts on behalf of women in science and engineering, in 1986 MIT awarded her the Abby Rockefeller Mauze chair, an endowed professorship awarded to those who promote the advancement of women in industry and in the arts and professions.

Begins a Distinguished Public Career

Along with her technical and scientific interests, Widnall has been active in administration, public policy, and industry consulting. In 1974 she became the first director of university research of the U.S. Department of Transportation. In 1979 MIT nominated Widnall to be the first woman to chair its 936-member faculty; she chaired MIT's Committee on Academic Responsibility for a year beginning in 1991; and she was named associate provost at the university in 1992. In addition to her term as president of the AAAS, Widnall has served on the board of directors for the American Institute of Aeronautics and Astronautics, as a member of the Carnegie Commission on Science, Technology, and Government, and as a consultant to businesses and colleges, including American Can Corporation, Kimberly-Clark, McDonnell Douglas Aircraft, and Princeton University. Her career has been recognized with numerous awards, including the Lawrence Sperry Award from the American Institute of Aeronautics and Astronautics in 1972, the Outstanding Achievement Award from the Society of Women Engineers in 1975, and the Washburn Award from the Boston Museum of Science in 1987. She was elected to the National Academy of Engineering in 1985.

Widnall's association with the Air Force developed through her appointment by President Carter to two three-year terms on the Air Force Academy's board of visitors, which she chaired from 1980–1982. She also served on advisory committees to the Military Airlift Command and to

Wright-Patterson Air Force Base in Dayton, Ohio. As Secretary of the Air Force, Widnall is responsible for all administrative, training, recruiting, logistical support, and personnel matters, as well as research and development operations.

She married William Soule Widnall, also an aeronautical engineer, in June, 1960. The couple has two grown children, William and Ann Marie. In her spare time, Widnall enjoys bicycling, wind surfing, and hiking in the Cascade Mountains with her husband in her native Washington.

SELECTED WRITINGS BY WIDNALL:

Periodicals

Science, Science and the Atari Generation, August 12, 1983, p. 607.
Science, AAAS Presidential Lecture: Voices from the Pipeline, September 30, 1988, pp. 1740–1745.

FURTHER READING:

Periodicals

Ewing, Lee, *Air Force Times,* Panelists Laud Widnall, Approve Her Nomination, August 2, 1993, p. 4.
Jehl, Douglas, *New York Times,* M.I.T. Professor Is First Woman Chosen as Secretary of Air Force, July 4, 1993, sec. 1, p. 20.
Sears, William R., *Association Affairs,* Sheila E. Widnall: President-Elect of AAAS, June 6, 1986, pp. 1119–1200.
Stone, Steve, *Norfolk Virginian-Pilot,* Air Force Secretary Salutes Female Aviators, October 10, 1993, p. B3.
Stone, Steve, *Aviation Week & Space Technology,* USAF Head Approved, August 9, 1993, p. 26.
Stone, Steve, *Physics Today,* Widnall of MIT Is New President-elect Of AAAS, February 1986, p. 69.

Other

Biography, *Dr. Sheila E. Widnall,* Office of the Secretary of the Air Force/Public Affairs, November 1993.

Sketch by Karl Preuss

Emil Wiechert
1861–1928
German geophysicist

Emil Wiechert's contributions to the fields of geophysics and seismology laid the foundations of the modern understanding of the internal movement and constitution of the earth. He also invented the most accurate seismographs of his day. Wiechert's other research topics included atmospheric structure and electricity. He was the founder of the University of Göttingen Institute of Geophysics and one of the founders of the International Association of Seismology.

Wiechert was born on December 26, 1861, in Tilsit, Germany, to Johann Christian Wiechert, a merchant who died when his son was a child. Wiechert's mother encouraged her son in his studies and accompanied him to Königsberg when he enrolled as a physics student at the university there. After receiving his bachelor's degree in 1889, Wiechert became a lecturer and began his graduate studies with a research project on atomic structure in relation to basic properties of matter and electrical particle theory.

In 1890 Wiechert began the first of several scientific collaborations with graduate and post-graduate students which involved geophysical problems that resulted in his designs for instruments to be used in applied physics. The Physics and Economics Society at the University of Königsberg awarded a prize for the interpretation of the data on the earth's temperature collected at the school's meteorological observatory. Wiechert and **Arnold Sommerfeld**, a theoretical physicist whose specialty was boundary value mathematics, constructed a harmonic analyzer to facilitate interpretation of the data. The analyzer reduced the data, plotted as a temperature curve, to a series of trigonometric figures. The harmonic analyzer's results allowed for an interpretation of the earth's temperature variations as a function of thermodynamic heat conduction.

In 1897 Wiechert moved to the University of Göttingen, and his career as a geophysicist began in earnest. Shortly after his arrival he founded the Göttingen Institute of Geophysics, where he studied seismology, the study of earthquakes and other vibrations of the earth. The seismograph, an instrument that records earth oscillations, dates back to the second century A.D., but it was not until 1892 that a seismograph was developed that was capable of worldwide monitoring rather than local recording. Wiechert's entrance into the field of seismology occurred shortly after this data became available for study. However, his experience with a variety of seismographs convinced him that he could invent a more accurate instrument than those in use at that time. He turned to the idea of an inverted pendulum design to obtain the accuracy he desired.

Develops an Improved Seismograph

Wiechert applied his acumen for instrumental design when he invented the inverted pendulum seismograph in 1900. The design used a heavy inertial mass equilibrium positioned to overcome friction and balanced on a knife-edge pen indicator. Support for oscillation was afforded by sets of small springs anchored at the top of the seismograph frame, a design much different than other seismographs of the day. Wiechert's first model only recorded the two horizontal component directions of earth movement. Further modifications enabled recording in the vertical component as well, so that all three required directions of seismic oscillation were eventually covered.

Wiechert's seismographs were the largest of the time, some with masses of more than two tons. Whereas earlier seismographs had used an optical method (light reflected through the oscillating horizontal pendulum arm onto light-sensitive paper) to register seismic activity, Wiechert used a mechanical method employing a sheet of smoked paper wrapped on a rotating drum, which shifted with each rotation to avoid superimposition of the recording. This was a simpler recording method, and the resulting chart, or seismogram, was more detailed and closer to a true reflection of earth activity. By 1920 there were eighty Wiechert seismographs in operation, more than any other type in use worldwide. Prior to World War I, Wiechert himself was able to establish several geophysical observatories in the German colonies, which provided an important link to the early world network of seismic stations.

Using his seismograph, Wiechert and a group of dedicated students and collaborators, most notably Karl Zöppritz and **Beno Gutenberg**, provided a landmark perspective on the earth's internal structure from their data, which helped establish the fundamentals of modern seismological theory. One of their most important results was determining seismic wave travel time through the layered structure of the earth, which Zöppritz compiled into comprehensive tables. Another addition to the theory came from Gutenberg, who later emigrated to the United States and became director of the seismology lab at the California Institute of Technology. Wiechert and his colleagues formed a basic theoretical model of the earth, concluding that there were three basic layers in the earth: a dense core, a liquid mantle, and a solid crust. Using the seismic wave data and the mathematical theory of the wave time-depth relation, Gutenberg calculated the depth of the earth's core to be 2,900 kilometers or 1,780 miles.

Contributions to the Inter-Geophysical Community

Wiechert remained active in his research endeavors even though a progressive deafness overtook him in later years. He finalized the work on the mathematics of seismic waves with Gustav Herglotz, which culminated in their equations determining deep-earth seismic wave velocities derived from the travel-time tables (Wiechert-Herglotz method). He eventually returned to seismograph design to create smaller-sized, portable instruments for use with controlled explosions to study shock wave propagation in the earth's crust. Wiechert's artificial detonation method was used in exploratory geophysics and solid earth structural research and prospecting.

Relatively late in his career Wiechert returned to elementary electrical theory but applied it to the study of the atmosphere. His research contributed to the development of planetary electrodynamics as a discipline. Wiechert also supervised the development of galvanometric instruments—those used to measure small electric currents in the atmosphere—and experiments to determine potential gradients of atmospheric layers and their electrical conductivity. Further research involved applying his knowledge of seismic waves to studies regarding the atmosphere. By transmitting sound waves through the atmosphere, he was able to better understand how it was stratified.

Wiechert helped found the International Association of Seismology in 1905. Wiechert married the daughter of a Göttingen lawyer in 1908. The couple, who had no children, lived with Wiechert's mother until her death in 1927. Wiechert died on March 19, 1928, in Göttingen.

SELECTED WRITINGS BY WIECHERT:

Periodicals

Abhandlungen der K. Gesellschaft der Wissenschaften zu Göttingen, Theorie der automatischen Seismographen, number 1, 1903.

Report of the Board of Regents of the Smithsonian Institution, Our Present Knowledge of the Earth, 1908, pp. 431–449.

Physikalische Zeitschrift, Bestimmung des Weges der Erdbebenwellen im Erdinneren, Volume 11, 1910, pp. 294–311.

Sketch by William J. McPeak

Heinrich Wieland
1877–1957
German chemist

Heinrich Wieland was one of the greatest organic chemists of the century, admired for the breadth of his knowledge and his devotion to arduous, painstaking research. Wieland is known for his studies on the structures of important complex natural products, from toad poisons to butterfly pigments. He also made major contributions to biochemistry, especially in the study of the mechanism of biological oxidation. His most famous work, for which he was awarded the Nobel Prize in chemistry in 1927, was the determination of the molecular structure of the bile acids. This research combined superb experimental skill with precise deductive reasoning and remains a model of organic chemical investigation.

Heinrich Otto Wieland was born on June 4, 1877, in Pforzheim, Germany, to Theodor and Elise Blom Wieland. Theodor Wieland was a pharmaceutical chemist, and Heinrich studied the subject in school in Pforzheim. At that time, instead of studying at a single university to obtain a degree, a student enrolled at several universities, listening to the lectures of the best professors. Wieland spent 1896 at the University of Munich, 1897 at the University of Berlin, and 1898 at the Technische Hochschule at Stuttgart. In 1899 he returned to Munich to work toward his Ph.D. under the direction of Johannes Thiele, in the laboratory of Adolf von Baeyer. After he received his Ph.D. in 1901, Wieland remained at Munich to do research, eventually becoming a lecturer in 1904 and a senior lecturer in 1913. In 1917 he was appointed professor at the Technische Hochschule in Munich, but was granted leave to work for **Fritz Haber**'s chemical warfare research organization at the Kaiser Wilhelm Institute in Berlin. At the end of World War I he returned to Munich, but left in 1921 to accept a professorship at the University of Freiburg. In 1925, Wieland returned to the University of Munich as professor and director of the Baeyer Laboratory, succeeding **Richard Willstätter**, who personally recommended Wieland for the position. By this time, Wieland was recognized as a world leader in organic chemistry, and he remained at Munich until his retirement in 1950.

Wieland's early research was concerned with the chemistry of organic nitrogen compounds. He explored the addition of dinitrogen trioxide and nitrogen dioxide to carbon-carbon double bonds. A large series of papers described the reactions of aromatic amines (a type of organic compound derived from ammonia), especially their oxidations. One line of experiments led to the discovery of nitrogen free radicals, unusually reactive short-lived species in which nitrogen is bonded to two atoms, instead of the usual three atoms. Wieland published almost one hundred papers on organic nitrogen chemistry, which in itself was a notable achievement.

Another series of experiments led to Wieland's 1912 theory of biological oxidation, a process by which biologic substances are changed by combining with oxygen or losing electrons. For years, the accepted theory involved some kind of change to molecular oxygen inside the cell in which the oxygen becomes "activated" and reacts with the oxidizable substance. Wieland proposed that the oxidizable substance itself becomes "activated" and loses hydrogen atoms in the oxidation process. Wieland published more than fifty papers from 1912 to 1943 on biological oxidation and was able to demonstrate that many reactions proceed through dehydrogenation and could proceed in the absence of oxygen. He was challenged, however, by the German physiologist **Otto Warburg**, who showed that respiratory enzymes which contain iron (sometimes copper) do activate oxygen, and

both types of oxidation mechanism are found in nature. Warburg received the Nobel Prize in 1931 for his contribution to understanding oxidation, but Wieland's work has been recognized as equally significant by biochemists.

Determining Structure of Bile Acids Leads to Nobel Prize

In 1912, the year Wieland proposed his theory of biological oxidation, he published his first paper on the structure of the bile acids. This topic would occupy his interest for twenty years and earn him the Nobel Prize. Bile is a golden yellow liquid which is produced in the liver, stored in the gall bladder, and secreted in small amounts into the intestines. The sodium salts of bile acids, the principal constituent of bile, are essential to the digestion of fats. Although bile acids had been isolated early in the nineteenth century, their structural formulas were unknown when Wieland began his work. As the work progressed, it was shown by **Adolf Windaus**, a chemist at the University of Göttingen, that cholesterol and the bile acids share a common basic structure, allowing Windaus's research results on the structure of cholesterol (for which he won the Nobel Prize in 1928) to be used by Wieland, and vice versa. Later it was shown that the common basic structure, the steroid nucleus, is found in many naturally occurring sources, such as the sex hormones, adrenal hormones (cortisone), digitalis (a plant cardiac poison, used medicinally as a stimulant), and toad poison. Steroid chemistry became essential to the development of many powerful medicines, as well as oral contraceptives. The pioneering work of Wieland and his students on the bile acids became a foundation of modern pharmaceutical chemical research.

The work on bile acids was an enormous challenge for organic chemistry in the first quarter of the century. First, a procedure for isolation and purification of the various acids, obtained from ox bile, was required. Then, each acid had to be characterized and chemically related to the others. The acids each contain 24 carbon atoms and differ in the number of hydroxyl (alcohol) groups. Wieland used the method of selective degradation to break the acids into simpler compounds, thus allowing him to identify the smaller molecules. Although his work was somewhat simplified because he could use the results of Windaus, Wieland admitted in his Nobel Lecture that "the task would appear to be a long and unspeakably wearisome trek through an arid desert of structure." In this lecture he outlined the course of his research, showing the failures as well as successes. Although the structures of the bile acids and cholesterol appeared to be solved when Wieland and Windaus received their Nobel prizes, in fact a conclusion which they had made based on analogous reactions was not correct, and the final, unequivocal structures were proposed by Wieland and others in 1932.

In addition to the bile acids, Wieland also investigated other natural products. He contributed to the determination of the structures of morphine, lobeline, and strychnine alkaloids, as well as butterfly wing pigments and mushroom and toad poisons. He had a wide range of interests, encompassing all areas of organic chemistry, and for twenty years he was editor of the major chemical journal *Justus Liebigs Annalen der Chemie*. His work was recognized throughout his career, and he was honored by scientific societies and universities in many countries. In 1955 he was named the first recipient of the German Chemical Society's Otto Hahn Prize for Physics and Chemistry.

Wieland remained at the University of Munich during World War II. He had little regard for the Nazi government in Germany and made no secret of it. He protected Jews in his laboratory and in 1944 testified on behalf of students who had been accused of treason.

Wieland married Josephine Bartmann in 1908. All three of their sons became scientists: Wolfgang, a pharmaceutical chemist; Theodor, a professor of chemistry; and Otto, a professor of medicine. Their daughter, Eva, married **Feodor Lynen**, a professor of biochemistry who won the Nobel Prize in physiology or medicine in 1964. In addition to his love of family and his work, Wieland also enjoyed painting and music. He died in Starnberg, Germany, on August 5, 1957, two months after his eightieth birthday.

SELECTED WRITINGS BY WIELAND:

Books

On the Mechanism of Oxidation, Yale, 1932.
Nobel Lectures: Chemistry, 1922–1941, The Chemistry of the Bile Acids, Elsevier, 1966, pp. 94–104.

FURTHER READING:

Books

Farber, Eduard, *Great Chemists,* Heinrich Wieland, edited by E. Farber, Interscience, 1961, pp. 1442–51.
Fieser, Louis F. and Mary Fieser, *Steroids,* Structure of the Bile Acids and of Cholesterol, Reinhold, 1959, pp. 53–89.
Follweiler, Joanne M., *Nobel Laureates in Chemistry, 1901–1992,* Heinrich Wieland edited by L. K. James, American Chemical Society, 1993, pp. 164–68.
Shuman, R. Baird, *The Nobel Prize Winners: Chemistry,* Heinrich Otto Wieland, Volume 2, edited by F. N. Magill, Salem, 1990, pp. 291–98.

Sketch by Martin R. Feldman

Wilhelm Wien
1864–1928
German physicist

Wilhelm Wien is best known for his studies of radiation. Of the two laws he developed dealing with this topic, one was later confirmed, and is now known as Wien's displacement law. The second law was later shown to be inadequate and was replaced by **Max Planck**'s brilliant theoretical analysis of the quantum nature of energy emission. Although Wien never made discoveries later in life of the quality of those from his early career, he eventually became a highly respected leader of German science in the early part of the twentieth century.

Wilhelm Carl Werner Otto Fritz Franz Wien was born on January 13, 1864, on his family's farm at Gaffken, near Fischhausen, in East Prussia. He was the only child of Carl Wien and the former Caroline Gertz, both descended from land-owning Prussian aristocracy. When Wien was two years old, the family moved to a smaller farm at Drachenstein, in the district of Rastenburg. As a young child, Wien received private tutoring and learned to speak French before he could write his native German. He was quite introverted, however, and spent a great deal of time by himself riding and swimming. Wien's mother was a particularly strong influence in her son's life. She was responsible for operating the Drachenstein farm after her husband had become ill, and according to Wien's entry in the *Dictionary of Scientific Biography,* "her excellent knowledge of history and literature stimulated [Wien's] interest in those subjects." Wien was sent to the local Gymnasium at Rastenburg in 1875, but he showed little interest in his classes and was brought home five years later without graduating. For a period of time, he stayed at home learning agriculture and studying with another private tutor. He then returned to formal classes at the Königsberg Altstädtisches Gymnasium, graduating in 1882.

Undecided about Becoming a Farmer

At his mother's urging, Wien then enrolled at the University of Göttingen to study mathematics and natural science. After only one semester, he became bored and left the university, setting off for an extended vacation through the Rhineland and Thüringen. He returned home once again, convinced that as the only child in the family he should take over the farm from his parents. That commitment lasted only a few months, however, and he headed back to school again in the fall of 1883, this time to the University of Berlin.

His academic experience this time was very different. He came under the tutelage of the great German physicist, mathematician, and physiologist Hermann von Helmholtz and, according to his own reports, "really came into contact with physics for the first time." He now applied himself vigorously to his studies and in the spring of 1886 received his doctorate. His dissertation dealt with the behavior of light diffracted by the sharp edge of a piece of metal.

After receiving his doctorate, Wien returned yet another time to the Drachenstein farm. The occasion for this trip was a disastrous fire that had destroyed some of the farm buildings. For four years Wien remained in a mood of indecision, feeling that he should continue to operate the farm, but still maintaining an interest in physics and continuing to do research on his own.

Joins Helmholtz at Charlottenberg

In 1890 a decision was made for Wien. An extended period of drought forced the Wien family to sell the farm, and Wien decided to take a job as Helmholtz's assistant at the newly established Physikalisch-Technische Reichsanstalt in Charlottenberg, outside Berlin. His parents also moved to Berlin, where his father died less than a year later. In 1892 Wien was promoted to lecturer at Berlin and then, four years later, he was offered a position as professor of physics at the Technical University in Aachen. He remained at Aachen for three years before moving on to the University of Giessen in 1899 and then to the University of Würzburg in 1900.

Wien's most productive period was the decade of the 1890s, when his main area of interest was the nature of blackbody radiation. The term *blackbody* refers to a theoretical substance that absorbs all of the radiation that falls on it; the fact that it reflects none of the radiation makes it black. In the 1860s, Gustav Kirchhoff had thoroughly studied the thermal properties of blackbodies. He pointed out that they are a perfect tool for studying radiation since when heated they emit radiation of all wavelengths. This fact makes it possible to study in great detail the nature of radiation emitted at different temperatures.

In about 1893 Wien began a theoretical analysis of the characteristics of blackbody radiation beginning with the fundamental laws of thermodynamics. He eventually developed two important conclusions. The first of these, now known as Wien's displacement law, says that the wavelength of radiation emitted by a blackbody is inversely proportional to the temperature of the body. That is, at low temperatures a blackbody will radiate energy with a long wavelength (red light). As the temperature rises, the most abundant wavelength radiated becomes smaller, and the color of the emitted light changes to orange, yellow, and then white.

Wien next attempted to find a mathematical formula that would fit the empirical graphical representation of the relationship between the amount of energy radiated at each wavelength for various temperatures. He obtained a complex equation that works fairly well at short wavelengths, but not very well at long wavelengths. He published this result in June 1896. In the meantime **J. W. Strutt** (Lord

Rayleigh) in England had derived a formula that worked well at long wavelengths, but not at short wavelengths. It was not until Max Planck introduced the concept of a quantum of energy in 1900 that the problem of blackbody radiation was finally solved.

By 1897 Wien had moved on to a new field of interest, cathode rays. Although he completed some excellent studies in this field, he did not produce any major breakthroughs. His two most notable accomplishments were probably his confirmation of the nature of cathode rays as rapidly moving negatively charged particles (1897–98) and of canal rays as rapidly moving positively charged particles (1905). He also carried out some of the earliest studies on the diffraction of x rays by crystals, anticipating the discoveries of **Max Laue** in this area by at least five years.

Wien's tenure at Würzburg lasted for two decades, during which time he was awarded the 1911 Nobel Prize in physics for his work on radiation. He also traveled extensively, including trips to Norway, Spain, Italy, and England (in 1904), to Greece (in 1912), to the United States (where he visited Columbia, Yale, and Harvard in 1913), and to the Baltic states (in 1918). Wien's last academic position was at the University of Munich, where he became professor of physics in 1920. There he supervised construction of a new physics institute and served as rector from 1925 to 1926. He died in Munich on August 30, 1928.

Wien was married to Luise Mehler in 1898. They had two sons, Waltraut and Karl, and two daughters, Gerda and Hildegard. In addition to the Nobel Prize, Wien was honored with membership in the scientific societies of Berlin, Göttingen, Vienna, and Stockholm. He was also a member of the U.S. National Academy of Sciences. From 1906 until his death, he was joint editor with Planck of the prestigious *Annalen der Physik* and later, with F. Harms, of the *Handbuch der Experimental Physik*.

SELECTED WRITINGS BY WIEN:

Books

Lehrbuch der Hydrodynamik, S. Hirzel, 1900.
Kanalstrahlen, Akademische Verlagsgesellschaft, 1917.
Aus dem Leben und Wirken eines Physikers, J. A. Barth, 1930.

Periodicals

Annalen der Physik, Über die Energievertheilung im Emissionsspectrum eines schwarzen Körpers, Volume 294, 1896, pp. 662–669.
Annalen der Physik, Zur Theorie der Strahlung schwarzer Körper: Kritisches, Volume 308, 1900, pp. 530–539.

FURTHER READING:

Books

Dictionary of Scientific Biography, Volume 14, Scribner, 1975, pp. 337–342.

Magill, Frank N., editor, *The Nobel Prize Winners: Physics,* Volume 1, 1901-1937, Salem Press, 1989, pp. 159–165.

Wasson, Tyler, editor, *Nobel Prize Winners,* Wilson, 1987, pp. 1118–1121.

Weber, Robert L., *Pioneers of Science: Nobel Prize Winners in Physics,* American Institute of Physics, 1980, pp. 42–44.

Sketch by David E. Newton

Alexander Wiener
1907–1976
American physician and immunohematologist

Alexander Wiener was a physician who, along with fellow scientist **Karl Landsteiner**, discovered the Rh factor in blood. He also discovered a number of other antigens (substances in the blood that cause the development of antibodies). The Rh factor is an antigen named after the rhesus monkey, the animal in which it was first discovered. Blood that contains the factor is called Rh-positive, whereas blood that lacks it is labeled Rh-negative. The discovery of the Rh factor led to an understanding of adverse reactions to blood transfusions that occurred inexplicably in some patients even though compatibility of blood type (A, B, AB, and O) in donor and recipient had been observed. The discovery of the Rh factor also brought about an understanding of the possible adverse reactions when an Rh-negative mother carried an Rh-positive fetus. Wiener developed a life-saving method of replacing the damaged blood of new-born infants who had erythroblastosis fetalis, the infant blood disease that sometimes results from Rh incompatibility. He was also instrumental in getting the results of his research applied to legal issues such as disputed paternity, and to cases involving crimes such as homicide and assault. Author or co-author of more than five hundred scientific articles, he also wrote several books, including what for years was the standard textbook on the subject, *Blood Groups and Transfusion.* His many awards include the Lasker Award of the American Public Health Association, which he received in 1946, and the Passano Foundation Award, received in 1951.

Alexander Solomon Wiener was born March 16, 1907, in Brooklyn, New York, the son of George Wiener, an attorney who had emigrated from Russia in 1903, and Mollie (Zuckerman) Wiener. He attended Brooklyn public schools, graduating from Brooklyn Boys' High School at the age of 15. He was awarded scholarships to attend Cornell University, where he was elected to Phi Beta Kappa in his senior year. Both in high school and in college he pursued an interest in mathematics. In high school he took courses in analytic geometry and calculus and was a member of the mathematics team and president of the mathematics club. He continued his study of mathematics at Cornell University, and contributed mathematical problems to the *American Mathematical Monthly.* He majored in biology, however, receiving his A.B. in 1926. He then entered the Long Island College of Medicine (now the SUNY College of Medicine) and was awarded an M.D. in 1930.

While he was in medical school, Wiener began his first research on blood groups at the Jewish Hospital of Brooklyn, where he would also intern from 1930 to 1932 and with which he would be affiliated for his entire professional career. From 1933 to 1935 he served as the head of the Division of Genetics and Biometrics, from 1932 to 1952 as head of the blood transfusion division, and thereafter as attending immunohematologist. From 1949 he was also affiliated with Adelphi Hospital, including three years (1949–1952) as the head of the blood transfusion division. In addition, he began a private medical practice in 1932, but three years later he founded Wiener Laboratories, where he limited his practice to clinical pathology and blood grouping. In 1938 he joined the faculty of the Department of Forensic Medicine of New York University School of Medicine, moving up the academic ranks to professor by 1968. In 1938 he also began his long-time association with the Office of the Chief Medical Examiner of New York City. He married Gertrude Rodman in 1932. They had two daughters, Jane Helen and Barbara Rae. Wiener died of leukemia in New York on November 6, 1976.

Searches for Blood Antigens

The background to the discovery of the Rh factor lay in earlier discoveries concerning the nature of blood. In 1901 Karl Landsteiner had distinguished four main human blood groups: A, B, AB, and O. These classifications refer to antigens (substances that produce antibodies) on the surface of the red blood cells. Blood type A contains the A antigen, B contains the B antigen, AB contains both, and O contains neither. However, in the 1920s other blood factors or antigens were discovered—M, N, and P.

In the 1930s Wiener began collaborating with Landsteiner, who was affiliated with the Rockefeller Institute for Medical Research in New York. In 1937 Landsteiner and Wiener were studying the M factor in apes and monkeys, focussing on its action as an agglutinogen (its ability to clump red blood cells together). They showed that different anti-M sera (blood sera samples with antibodies opposing the M antigen) produced differing reactions, and concluded that there were at least five distinct M blood factors. This led to further experimentation in which they tested the sera of rabbits immunized with rhesus monkey blood cells. The antibodies produced by rabbit blood in response to rhesus monkey antigens led them to believe that unknown blood factors might be discovered in human blood by the same method. They began experiments using human blood and the anti-sera from rhesus blood, and thereby discovered a new antigen that they called the Rh factor. The importance of this discovery in transfusions was recognized in 1939 when it was understood that although the first transfusion of Rh-positive blood into an Rh-negative person may be harmless, the sensitization that resulted meant that a second transfusion could cause a dangerous hemolytic reaction involving the damage or destruction of red blood cells.

Wiener then studied the sera from Rh negative patients who had hemolytic transfusion reactions, and the sera from Rh-negative mothers of erythroblastotic babies. These babies have Rh positive blood, some of which enters the mother's blood, usually shortly before or during birth. The mother's blood forms an antibody to the Rh factor and crosses back to the fetal blood supply. The result is the damage or destruction of the fetal red blood cells containing the Rh antigen. He discovered that the expected Rh antibodies often could not be found. He hypothesized that there must be two different forms of Rh antibodies, one that caused the agglutination of cells (which he called bivalent antibodies), the other capable of coating the red blood cells without clumping them (which he called univalent or blocking antibodies). In 1944 and 1945 he developed tests for both types of antibodies.

Wiener noted the fallacy of assuming a one-to-one correspondence between antigens and antibodies. One antigen could produce multiple blood specificities. He soon discovered additional Rh factors that were related to the original one. In the human Rh system (now known as the Rh-Hr system), Wiener and others established as many as 25 different blood factors that form the basis of a large number of blood types.

Practical Implications of Wiener's Discoveries

Wiener's research had many practical implications. It led to an understanding of erythroblastosis fetalis, for which Wiener himself devised (1944–1946) a treatment by means of a complete exchange transfusion replacing the damaged Rh-positive blood of the infant with Rh-negative blood. This treatment led to a significant decline in the rate of infant mortality. Knowledge of Rh factors also made blood transfusions far safer. Other implications of Wiener's research derived from the fact that all blood factors are inherited in predictable fashion, and that they combine in a highly specific way in individuals, allowing a sophisticated method of "fingerprinting." Blood factor analysis became important in legal matters (such as establishing paternity), as well as criminal matters, such as the use of blood for identification in homicide and assault. It also facilitated advances in physical anthropology—different groups of people have different proportions of various blood factors, so that tribal movements can sometimes be traced by analysis of blood factor percentages in populations.

Wiener's research had significant legal implications. He was a member of the American Medical Association legal committee that sponsored blood test laws in all states, and he was the co-author of its 1935 report. He was instrumental in the passage of the New York State law allowing blood tests in disputed paternity cases. He and his father, attorney George Wiener, assisted in drafting a number of laws concerning blood testing that became part of the New York State domestic relations, civil, and criminal codes.

Wiener liked playing the piano, going to the movies, and playing cards. He also enjoyed tennis and gulf. In addition, he continued his life-long interest in mathematics and physics by avidly reading in these areas. A member of many professional organizations, he was also an honorary member of the Mystery Writers of America.

SELECTED WRITINGS BY WIENER:

Books

Blood Groups and Transfusion, 3rd ed., Hafner, 1943.
Rh-Hr Blood Types: Applications in Clinical and Legal Medicine and Anthropology, Grune, 1954.
Heredity of the Blood Groups, Grune, 1958.
Advances in Blood Grouping, Grune, 1961.
An Rh-Hr Syllabus: The Types and Their Applications, 2nd ed., Grune, 1963.
A-B-O Blood Groups and Lewis Types: Questions and Answers; Problems and Solutions: A Teaching Manual, Stratton Intercontinental Medical Book Corp., 1976.

FURTHER READING:

Books

McGraw-Hill Modern Scientists and Engineers, Volume 3, McGraw, 1980, pp. 314–315.
National Cyclopaedia of American Biography, Volume G, 1943–1946, James T. White, 1946, pp. 469–470.
New York Times, November 7, 1976.

Sketch by Pamela Long

Norbert Wiener
1894–1964
American mathematician

Norbert Wiener was one of the most original mathematicians of his time. The field concerning the study of automatic control systems, called cybernetics, owes a great deal not only to his researches, but to his continuing efforts at publicity. He wrote for a variety of popular journals as well as for technical publications and was not

Norbert Wiener

reluctant to express political views even when they might be unpopular. Perhaps the most distinctive feature of Wiener's life as a student and a mathematician is how well documented it is, thanks to two volumes of autobiography published during his lifetime. They reveal some of the complexity of a man whose aspirations went well beyond the domain of mathematics.

Wiener was born in Columbia, Missouri, on November 26, 1894. His father, Leo Wiener, had been born in Bialystok, Poland (then Russia), and was an accomplished linguist. He arrived in New Orleans in 1880 with very little money but a great deal of determination, some of it visible in his relations with his son. He met his wife, Bertha Kahn, at a meeting of a Browning Club. As a result, when his son was born, he was given the name Norbert, from one of Browning's verse dramas. In light of the absence of Judaism from the Wiener home (Norbert was fifteen before he learned that he was Jewish), it is surprising that one of Leo Wiener's best-known works was a history of Yiddish literature.

As the title of the first volume of his autobiography *Ex-Prodigy* suggests, Wiener was a child prodigy. Whatever his natural talents, this was partly due to the efforts of his father. Leo Wiener was proud of his educational theories and pointed to the academic success of his son as evidence. Norbert was less enthusiastic and in his memoirs describes his recollections of his father's harsh disciplinary methods. He entered high school at the age of nine and graduated two years later. In 1906 he entered Tufts University, as the

family had moved to the Boston area, and he graduated four years later.

Up until that point Wiener's education had clearly outrun that of most of his contemporaries, but he was now faced with the challenge of deciding what to do with his education. He enrolled at Harvard to study zoology, but the subject did not suit him. He tried studying philosophy at Cornell, but that was equally unavailing. Finally, Wiener came back to Harvard to work on philosophy and mathematics. The subject of his dissertation was a comparison of the system of logic developed by **Bertrand Russell** and **Alfred North Whitehead** in their *Principia Mathematica* with the earlier algebraic system created by Ernst Schröder. The relatively recent advances in mathematical research in the United States had partly occurred in the area of algebraic logic, so the topic was a reasonable one for a student hoping to bridge the still-existent gap between the European and American mathematical communities.

Although Wiener earned a Harvard travelling fellowship to enable him to study in Europe after taking his degree, his father still supervised his career by writing to Bertrand Russell on Norbert's behalf. Wiener was in England from June 1913 to April 1914 and attended two courses given by Russell, including a reading course on *Principia Mathematica*. Perhaps more influential in the long run for Wiener's mathematical development was a course he took from the British analyst **G. H. Hardy**, whose lectures he greatly admired. In the same way, Wiener studied with some of the most eminent names in Göttingen, Germany, then the center of the international mathematical community.

Wiener returned to the United States in 1915, still unsure, despite his foreign travels, of the mathematical direction he wanted to pursue. He wrote articles for the *Encyclopedia Americana* and took a variety of teaching jobs until the entry of the United States into World War I. Wiener was a fervent patriot, and his enthusiasm led him to join the group of scientists and engineers at the Aberdeen Proving Ground in Maryland, where he encountered Oswald Veblen, already one of the leading mathematicians in the country. Although Wiener did not pursue Veblen's lines of research, Veblen's success in producing results useful to the military impressed Wiener more than mere academic success.

Takes the Mathematical Turn

After the war two events decisively shaped Wiener's mathematical future. He obtained a position as instructor at the Massachusetts Institute of Technology (MIT) in mathematics, where he was to remain until his retirement. At that time mathematics was not particularly strong at MIT, but his position there assured him of continued contact with engineers and physicists. As a result, he displayed an ongoing concern for the applications of mathematics to problems that could be stated in physical terms. The question of which tools he would bring to bear on those problems was answered by the death of his sister's fiancé.

That promising young mathematician left his collection of books to Wiener, who began to read avidly the standard texts in a way that he had not in his earlier studies.

The first problem Wiener addressed had to do with Brownian motion, the apparently random motion of particles in substances at rest. The phenomenon had earlier excited **Albert Einstein**'s interest, and he had dealt with it in one of his 1905 papers. Wiener took the existence of Brownian motion as a sign of randomness at the heart of nature. By idealizing the physical phenomenon, Wiener was able to produce a mathematical theory of Brownian motion that had wide influence among students of probability. It is possible to see in his work on Brownian motion, steps in the direction of the study of fractals (shapes whose detail repeats itself on any scale), although Wiener did not go far along that path.

The next subject Wiener addressed was the Dirichlet problem, which had been reintroduced into the mathematical mainstream by German **David Hilbert**. Much of the earliest work on the Dirichlet problem had been discredited as not being sufficiently rigorous for the standards of the late nineteenth century. Wiener's work on the Dirichlet problem produced interesting results, some of which he delayed publishing for the sake of a couple of students finishing their theses at Harvard. Wiener felt subsequently that his forbearance was not recognized adequately. In particular, although Wiener progressed through the academic ranks at MIT from assistant professor in 1924 to associate professor in 1929 to full professor in 1932, he believed that more support from Harvard would have enabled him to advance more quickly.

Wiener had a high opinion of his own abilities, something of a change from colleagues whose public expressions of modesty were at odds with a deep-seated conviction of their own merits. Whatever his talents as a mathematician, Wiener's expository standards were at odds with those of most mathematicians of his time. While he was always exuberant, this was often at the cost of accuracy of detail. One of his main theorems depended on a series of lemmas, or auxiliary propositions, one of which was proven by assuming the truth of the main theorem. Students trying to learn from Wiener's papers and finding their efforts unrewarding discovered that this reaction was almost universal. As Hans Freudenthal remarked in the *Dictionary of Scientific Biography,* "After proving at length a fact that would be too easy if set as an exercise for an intelligent sophomore, he would assume without proof a profound theorem that was seemingly unrelated to the preceding text, then continue with a proof containing puzzling but irrelevant terms, next interrupt it with a totally unrelated historical exposition, meanwhile quote something from the 'last chapter' of the book that had actually been in the first, and so on."

In 1926 Wiener was married to Margaret Engemann, an assistant professor of modern languages at Juniata College. They had two daughters, Barbara (born 1928) and Peggy (born 1929). Wiener enjoyed his family's company and found there a relaxation from a mathematical community that did not always share his opinion of the merits of his work.

During the decade after his marriage, Wiener worked in a number of fields and wrote some of the papers with which he is most associated. In the field of harmonic analysis, he did a great deal with the decomposition of functions into series. Just as a polynomial is made up of terms like x, x^2, x^3, and so forth, so functions in general could be broken up in various ways, depending on the questions to be answered. Somewhat surprisingly, Wiener also undertook putting the operational calculus, earlier developed by Oliver Heaviside, on a rigorous basis. There is even a hint in Wiener's work of the notion of a distribution, a kind of generalized function. It is not surprising that Wiener might start to move away from the kind of functions that had been most studied in mathematics toward those that could be useful in physics and engineering.

In 1926 Wiener returned to Europe, this time on a Guggenheim fellowship. He spent little time at Göttingen, due to disagreements with **Richard Courant**, perhaps the most active student of David Hilbert in mathematical organization. Courant's disparaging comments about Wiener cannot have helped the latter's standing in the mathematical community, but Wiener's brief visit introduced him to Tauberian theory, a fashionable area of analysis. Wiener came up with an imaginative new approach to Tauberian theorems and, perhaps more fortunately, with a coauthor for his longest paper on the subject. The quality of the exposition in the paper, combined with the originality of the results, make it Wiener's best exercise in communicating technical mathematics, although he did not pursue the subject as energetically as he did some of his other works.

In 1931 and 1932 Wiener gave lectures on analysis in Cambridge as a deputy for G. H. Hardy. While there, he made the acquaintance of a young British mathematician, R. E. A. C. Paley, with whom a collaboration soon flourished. He brought Paley to MIT the next academic year and their work progressed rapidly. Paley's death at the age of twenty-six in a skiing accident early in 1933 was a blow to Wiener, who received the Bôcher prize of the American Mathematical Society the same year and was named a fellow of the National Academy of Sciences the next. Among the other areas in which Wiener worked at MIT or Harvard were quantum mechanics, differential geometry, and statistical physics. His investigations in the last of these were wide ranging, but amounted more to the creation of a research program than a body of results.

Creates Cybernetics

The arrival of World War II occupied Wiener's attention in a number of ways. He was active on the Emergency Committee in Aid of Displaced German Scholars, which began operations well before the outbreak of fighting. He made proposals concerning the development of computers, although these were largely ignored. One of the problems to which he devoted time was antiaircraft fire, and his results were of great importance for engineering applications regarding filtering. Unfortunately, they were not of much use in the field because of the amount of time required for the calculations.

Weiner devoted the last decades of his life to the study of statistics, engineering, and biology. He had already worked on the general idea of information theory, which arose out of statistical mechanics. The idea of entropy had been around since the nineteenth century and enters into the second law of thermodynamics. It could be defined as an integral, but it was less clear what sort of quantity it was. Work of Ludwig Boltzmann suggested that entropy could be understood as a measure of the disorder of a system. Wiener pursued this notion and used it to get a physical definition of information related to entropy. Although information theory has not always followed the path laid down by Wiener, his work gave the subject a mathematical legitimacy.

An interdisciplinary seminar at the Harvard Medical School provided a push for Wiener in the direction of the interplay between biology and physics. He learned about the complexity of feedback in animals and studied current ideas about neurophysiology from a mathematical point of view. (Wiener left out the names of those who had most influenced him in this area in his autobiography as a result of an argument.) One area of particular interest was prosthetic limbs, perhaps as a result of breaking his arm in a fall. Wiener soon had the picture of a computer as a prosthesis for the brain. In 1947 he agreed to write a book on communication and control and was looking for a term for the theory of messages. The Greek word for messenger, *angelos,* had too many connections with angels to be useful, so he took the word for helmsman, *kubernes,* instead and came up with *cybernetics.* It turned out that the word had been used in the previous century, but Wiener gave it a new range of meaning and currency.

Cybernetics was treated by Wiener as a branch of mathematics with its own terms, like signal, noise, and information. One of his collaborators in this area was **John Neumann**, whose work on computers had been followed up much more enthusiastically than Wiener's. The difference in reception could be explained by the difference in mathematical styles: von Neumann was meticulous, while Wiener tended to be less so. The new field of cybernetics prospered with two such distinct talents working in it. Von Neumann's major contribution to the field was only realized after his death. Wiener devoted most of his later years to the area. Among his more popular books were *The Human Use of Human Beings* in 1950 and *God and Golem, Inc.* in 1964.

In general, Wiener was happy writing for a wide variety of journals and audiences. He contributed to the *Atlantic, Nation,* the *New Republic,* and *Collier's,* among others. His two volumes of autobiography, *Ex-Prodigy* and *I Am a Mathematician,* came out in 1953 and 1956, respectively. Reviews pointed out the extent to which Wiener's memory operated selectively, but also admitted that he did bring the mathematical community to life in a way seldom seen. Although Wiener remarked that mathematics was a young man's game, he also indicated that he felt himself lucky in having selected subjects for investigation that he could pursue later in life. He received an honorary degree from Tufts in 1946 and in 1949 was Gibbs lecturer to the American Mathematical Society.

In 1964 Wiener received the National Medal of Science. On March 18, while travelling through Stockholm, he collapsed and died. A memorial service was held at MIT on the June 2, led by Swami Sarvagatananda of the Vedanta Society of Boston, along with Christian and Jewish clergy. This mixture of faiths was expressive of Wiener's lifelong unwillingness to be fit into a stereotype. He was a mathematician who talked about the theology of the Fall. He did not discover that he was Jewish until he was in graduate school but found great support in the poems of Heinrich Heine. Nevertheless, his intellectual originality led him down paths subsequent generations have come to follow.

SELECTED WRITINGS BY WIENER:

Books

Cybernetics, MIT Press, 1948.
The Human Use of Human Beings, Houghton, 1950.
Ex-Prodigy, Simon & Schuster, 1953.
I Am a Mathematician, Doubleday, 1956.
God and Golem, Inc., MIT Press, 1964.
Selected Papers, MIT Press, 1964.

FURTHER READING:

Books

Dictionary of Scientific Biography, Scribner, Volume 14, 1970–1978, pp. 344–347.
Heims, Steve J., *John von Neumann and Norbert Wiener,* MIT Press, 1980.
Masani, P. R., *Norbert Wiener,* Birkhäuser, 1990.

Sketch by Thomas Drucker

Eric F. Wieschaus
1947–
American biologist

Eric F. Wieschaus won the 1995 Nobel Prize in Physiology or Medicine, along with **Edward B. Lewis** and **Christaine Nüsslein-Volhard**, for his work on identifying key genes that make a fertilized fruit fly egg develop into a segmented embryo. His research could help improve knowledge of how genes control embryonic development in higher organisms, including identifying genes that cause human birth defects.

Wieschaus was born in South Bend, Indiana, in 1947 but grew up in Alabama. He received his bachelor's degree in biology from the University of Notre Dame in 1969 and his doctorate from Yale in 1974. His doctoral dissertation involved using genetic methods to label the progeny (offspring) of single cells in fly embryos. He showed that even at the earliest cellular stages, cells were already determined to form specific regions of the body called segments.

Wieschaus married Gertrud Schupbach, who is a professor of molecular biology at Princeton. They have three children, Ingrid, Eleanor, and Laura. Over the years, Wieschaus has been described by colleagues as a dedicated, hard worker. He spends time in the lab, doing experiments himself, unlike some professors who delegate lab work to their graduate students.

Early in his career, Wieschaus was recognized with a John Spangler Niclaus Prize in 1974 for his dissertation on experimental embryology. At the University of Zurich, Switzerland, Wieschaus held a post-doctoral fellowship from 1975-78. There he studied sex determination in flies and developed techniques to create flies with mosaic ovaries composed of mutant and normal cells.

Wieschaus joined the Princeton faculty in 1981 as an assistant professor and became Squib Professor of molecular biology in 1987. In 1989 he was bestowed the National Institutes of Health Merit Award, and in 1995 he became the first professor in Princeton's Life Science Department to receive the Nobel Prize.

Experiments With Fruit Fly DNA

Wieschaus began his Nobel-winning work in the latter part of the 1970s. The Alabama native spent three years with Christiane Nüsslein-Volhard in the European Molecular Biology Lab at the University of Heidelberg, Germany, tackling the question of why individual cells in a fertilized egg develop into various specific tissues. They elected to study *Drosophila*, or fruit flies, because of their extremely fast embryonic development. New generations of fruit flies can be bred in a week. In addition, fruit flies have only one set of genes controlling development compared to the four sets humans possess. This means that testing each fruit fly gene individually takes one-fourth the time it would involve to test human genes.

To begin their experiment, Nüsslein-Volhard and Wieschaus damaged male fruit fly deoxyribonucleic acid (DNA) by applying ultraviolet light to the genes or by feeding the flies sugar water laced with chemicals. Then the team "knocked out" one gene from the fly, breeding generations of fruit flies without that particular piece of code. In this way, Nüsslein-Volhard and Wieschaus were able to isolate all the genes crucial to the early stages of embryonic development. When the male flies were bred

with female fruit flies, the females produced dead embryos. These lifeless embryos resulted from only 150 different mutations of the 40,000 mutations applied. These 150 genes proved to be essential to the proper development of the fly embryo because, when damaged, the genes caused extraordinary deformities that killed the embryo. For example, a fly with skin comprised only of nerve cells resulted from one of the mutations. By viewing the fly embryos with a two-person microscope, Wieschaus and Nüsslein-Volhard were able to simultaneously view and classify a large quantity of malformations caused by gene mutations. Next, they identified 15 different genes, that, when mutated, eliminate specific body segments in the fly embryos. Wieschaus also established that systematic categorizing of genes that control the various stages of development could be accomplished. For example, he was able to isolate the genes that form specific organs and body segments.

While working together in the 1970s, Nüsslein-Volhard and Wieschaus had their research results first published in *Nature*, an English scientific journal, in 1980. They reported that the number of genes controlling early development was not only limited, but could also be classified into specific functional groups. They also identified genes that cause severe congenital defects in flies. After additional experimentation, the principles involved with the fruit fly genes were found to apply to higher animals and humans. This led to the realization that many similar genes control human development, and this finding could have a tremendous impact on the medical world. The applications of their research extend to in vitro fertilization, identifying congenital birth defects, and increased knowledge of substances that can endanger early stages of pregnancy.

Wieschaus's research was not without its share of setbacks. One major accident involved Wieschaus bumping into a table with 40,000 test tubes full of fruit flies and watching his experiment crash to the floor. However, he did not become discouraged by this catastrophe, nor did he give up. He knew that he would have to pick up all the test tubes and start over because " . . . the only thing that really matters is to get the experiment to work," he stated. "Someday you will know something that no one has ever known before."

SELECTED WRITINGS BY WIESCHAUS:

Periodicals

"Mutations Affecting Segment Number and Polarity in Drosophila." *Nature,* Volume 287, 1980, pp. 795-801.

"Kruppel, a Gene Whose Activity is Required Early in the Zygotic Genome for Normal Segmentation." *Developmental Biology,* Volume 104, 1984, pp. 172-186.

"Mutations Affecting the Pattern of the Larval Cuticle in Drosophila melangaster." *Developmental Biology,* Volume 193, 1984, pp. 296-307.

"Embryonic Transcription and the Control of Developmental Pathways." *Genetics,* 1996 (in press)

Sketch by Nicole Beatty

Torsten Wiesel
1924–
American neurophysiologist

Torsten Wiesel, in collaboration with **David H. Hubel**, has been instrumental in describing the physiology of vision. His work on charting the visual or striate cortex, the posterior section of the cerebral cortex, has not only provided new insights into the complexity of the visual process, but has also had direct clinical applications. His discovery of critical periods in childhood development for "learning" to see has led to earlier clinical intervention in visual problems in children. In 1981 Wiesel, along with Hubel and another brain researcher, **Roger W. Sperry**, shared the Nobel Prize for physiology or medicine.

Torsten Nils Wiesel was born on June 3, 1924, in Uppsala, Sweden, the son of Anna-Lisa Bentzer Wiesel and Fritz S. Wiesel, the chief psychiatrist at the Beckomberga Mental Hospital in Stockholm. Wiesel lived at his father's hospital as a youth, attending a private school where he was more interested in sports than academics. But this attitude changed in 1941 when Wiesel entered medical school at the Karolinska Institute in Stockholm and studied neurophysiology under **Carl Gustaf Bernhard**. He also studied psychiatry during this time, and in 1954 he received his medical degree, becoming an instructor at the institute as well as an assistant in the Department of Child Psychiatry at Karolinska Hospital. Wiesel then came to the United States in 1955 to do postdoctoral work at the Wilmer Institute of Johns Hopkins School of Medicine in Baltimore, Maryland.

Focuses on the Neurophysiology of Vision

At Johns Hopkins, Wiesel worked under Stephen Kuffler, a researcher in visual physiology who had studied the nerve activity in the retina of the cat as well as in animals of other classes. Kuffler's exhaustive work had proved that the vision of mammals is distinctly different from that of non-mammals. Research with frogs had shown that their vision occurred in the optical nerve: that they had neurons, or nerve cells, sensitive not only to light and dark, but also to shapes, movements, and the boundaries between light and dark. Cats have no such specification in their ganglia, no ability to give the detailed boundary information that is found in frogs. Yet mammalian vision is stereoscopic, whereas non-mammalian appears to be in most cases binocular but lacking three dimensions. Wiesel became interested in the direction in which such investigations must logically lead: namely that the critical level of visual perception must take place in the brain of mammals. In 1958 David Hubel, a graduate of McGill University, returned to the institute from military service, and together Wiesel and Hubel set off on researches that would result in a new theory of visual perception.

The striate or visual cortex is located at the back of the brain, an area of about 15 square centimeters in some of the monkeys Wiesel and Hubel would study. It had long been known, from accident victims, that this region of the cortex was involved with vision, and it is here that Wiesel and Hubel began their studies. They painstakingly measured electrical discharge of cells in the visual cortex with the aid of a microelectrode, a microscopic needle with an electrode built in to measure electrical impulses. Initially using anesthetized cats whose sight was trained on various patterns of light and dark, lines and circles, and probing the animal's visual cortex with their microelectrode at various angles, they discovered which cells in the cortex responded to which pattern or level of light. They also conducted experiments in which they injected the eyes of experimental animals with radioactively labeled amino acid. These amino acids would be taken up by the cell bodies of the retina and transported to cells in the visual cortex, giving a map of the pathway of vision. In some cases the laboratory animals were sacrificed and their visual cortexes dissected in order to see, by the use of autoradiographs or X-ray like photos, where the labeled amino acids actually ended up. Such experiments, begun in 1959, used both cats and macaque monkeys. That same year Kuffler was appointed a professor at the Harvard University Medical School, and Wiesel and Hubel joined him there. Wiesel was appointed assistant professor of physiology, and became a full professor in 1964.

Complexity of Visual Process Revealed

The Wiesel-Hubel team soon began publishing the results of their experimental method, and it was clear that they had uncovered new complexities to the visual process. Mapping the path of vision with radioactive amino acid, they showed that vision passed in coded signals from neuron to neuron through the optic nerve and split at the optic chiasm so that a representation of each half of the visual scene is projected deep in the brain on a nest of cells called the lateral geniculate nucleus, a way station to the cells in the cortex. From here the path of vision continues to the back of the brain to various parts of the visual cortex, depending on the specialization of each cell. But the pathway does not end there; indeed, the visual cortex was shown to be an early step in the processing of visual information. Information is sent back to parts of the brain from the cortex as well as back to the geniculate nuclei.

Within the visual cortex itself, Wiesel and Hubel made two important discoveries. First they showed that there is a hierarchy of types of cells in the cortex, ranking from simple to complex to hypercomplex, depending on the information each is able to process. They termed the process of putting the millions of building blocks of visual information back together into a picture convergence. Various cells have preferences for the bits of visual information they process: size, shape, light, and sharpness of boundary differentiation, as well as which eye is sending the information. Such a complexity of visual processing destroys the old notion of sight being simply a film played in the mind. Instead, the accretion of bits of visual information into visual representation appears more similar to language processing than to an analogy of a film. Cells in the visual cortex "read" neuron messages. Their second major discovery was a further organization of the cortical cells into roughly vertical divisions of two types: orientation columns and ocular dominance columns. The orientation columns transform what is essentially circular information from the retina and geniculate nerve cells into linear information, while the ocular combine the neural information from both eyes to provide three-dimensional vision. Within these columns are simple, complex, and hypercomplex cells working toward a progressive convergence of visualization. Until the time of Wiesel's and Hubel's work, it was assumed that all cells of the cerebral cortex were more or less uniform. Wiesel and Hubel showed that the visual cortex is constituted of a cell pattern, which appears to be designed specifically for vision. As a result of their discovery, current theory now posits that the rest of the cerebral cortex may follow this form-follows-function rule.

Later Work Yields Clinical Results

Wiesel and Hubel researched another experimental model in which they used kittens to study the effect of various visual impairments on development. They discovered that if one eye were deprived of certain or all visual stimuli during the third to fifth postnatal weeks, the central functioning of that eye would always be suppressed from cortical processing. Kittens, and by extension mammals in general, though born with a complete visual cortex, must still "learn" to see. Even if an early impairment is later corrected, the repaired eye will still remain functionally impaired as far as the visual cortex is concerned. The realization that there is a critical stage for visual development revolutionized the field of pediatric ophthalmology, calling for the earliest possible intervention in cases of strabismus, or crossed eyes, and congenital cataracts.

By 1973 Wiesel succeeded Kuffler as chair of the Department of Neurobiology at Harvard, and was named the Robert Winthrop Professor of Neurobiology in 1974. His first marriage, to Teiri Stenhammer, ended in divorce after 14 years in 1970. Wiesel was married again in 1973, to Grace Yee. The couple had one child, Sara Elisabet. His second marriage also ended in divorce in 1981. Wiesel became a naturalized U.S. citizen in 1990. Wiesel has been the recipient of many awards over the years, including the Lewis S. Rosentiel Award in 1972, the Jonas S. Friedenwald Memorial Award in 1975, the Karl Spencer Lashley Prize in 1977, the Louisa Gross Horowitz Prize in 1978, and the

George Ledlie Prize in 1980. But none were as prestigious as the Nobel Prize, which he and Hubel won in 1981, sharing it with Sperry from Caltech. The Karolinska Institute in Stockholm, which administers the prize and where Wiesel began his professional career, praised Hubel and Wiesel for their discoveries concerning information processing in the visual system. Wiesel and Hubel continued their close working relationship until Wiesel left Harvard in 1984 to head the neurobiology lab at Rockefeller University where he continued his researches on vision. In 1992 he was named president of Rockefeller University.

SELECTED WRITINGS BY WIESEL:

Periodicals

Journal of Physiology, Receptive Fields of Single Neurons in the Cat's Striate Cortex, Volume 148, 1959, pp. 574–91.

Journal of Physiology, Integrative Action in the Cat's Lateral Geniculate Body, February, 1961, pp. 385–98.

Journal of Physiology, Receptive Fields, Binocular Interaction and Functional Architecture in the Cat's Cortex, January, 1962, pp. 106–54.

Journal of Neurophysiology, Single-cell Responses in Striate Cortex of Kittens Deprived of Vision in One Eye, November, 1963, pp. 1003–17.

Journal of Neurophysiology, Extent of Recovery from the Effects of Visual Deprivation in Kittens, November, 1965, pp. 1060–72.

Journal of Neurophysiology, Receptive Fields and Functional Architecture in Two Non Striate Visual Areas (18 and 19) of the Cat, November, 1965, pp. 229–89.

Journal of Physiology, Receptive Fields and Functional Architecture of Monkey Striate Cortex, Volume 195, 1968, pp. 215–43.

Journal of Comparative Neurology, Anatomical Demonstration of Orientation Columns in Macaque Monkey, Volume 177, 1978, pp. 361–80.

Scientific American, Brain Mechanisms of Vision, September, 1979, pp. 150–62.

FURTHER READING:

Books

Hubel, David H, *Eye, Brain, and Vision,* Scientific American Library, 1988.

Periodicals

Altman, Lawrence K., *New York Times,* Studies Advance Work on Brain, October 10, 1981, p. 50.

Barinaga, Marcia, *Science,* At Rockefeller, Wiesel Is the Calm after the Storm, June 4, 1993, pp. 1426–8.

Lettvin, Jerome Y, *Science,* Filling out the Forms: An Appreciation of Hubel and Wiesel, October 30, 1981, pp. 518–20.

Lettvin, Jerome Y, *Los Angeles Times,* Nobel Prize Goes to Two Americans, Swedish Scientist, October 10, 1981, p. 1.

Russell, Christine, *Washington Post,* Three in U.S. Win Nobel Prize for Brain Research, October 10, 1981, p. 1.

Schmeck, Harold M., Jr., *New York Times,* Three Scientists Share Nobel Prize for Studies of the Brain, October 10, 1981, p. 1.

Schmeck, Harold M., Jr., *New York Times,* Torsten Nils Wiesel, October 10, 1981, p. 50.

Sketch by J. Sydney Jones

Vincent Wigglesworth
1899–1994
English entomologist

Vincent Wigglesworth was a British entomologist who took the study of entomology from the mere collection and classification of insects to a field of knowledge with significant scientific applications. He specialized in insect physiology, conducting studies to determine how brain hormones trigger molting, metamorphosis, and reproduction in insects. As Anthony Tucker writes in an obituary in the *Guardian,* Wigglesworth's most important contribution may have been his recognition "that insects could be used—instead of mice or other laboratory animals—for the fundamental investigation of animal physiology and function."

Vincent Brian Wigglesworth was born on April 17, 1899 in Kirkham, Lancashire, England. His father, Sidney Wigglesworth, was a medical doctor in general practice. Wigglesworth attended Repton School and then Gonville and Caius College at Cambridge. He entered the army during World War I, and he served in the field artillery in France from 1917 to 1918. Upon his return, he completed his graduate work in physiology and biochemistry at Cambridge, including two years as a researcher under **John Burdon Sanderson Haldane** and **Frederick Gowland Hopkins**. Wigglesworth demonstrated an aptitude for and a deep interest in basic research. He decided to take up the challenge, issued by Patrick Buxton, to improve the practical application of entomology by increasing the scientific knowledge of insect physiology. Most of Wigglesworth's research at the time was on the role of insects in the transmission of human diseases; diseases such as malaria and Chagas' disease made this issue of immediate importance but it was poorly understood.

In order to further his understanding of human diseases, Wigglesworth completed a medical degree at St. Thomas's Hospital in London. In 1926, he became a lecturer at the London School of Hygiene and Tropical Medicine, where he began his famous studies with *Rhodnius prolixus,* a South American blood-sucking insect known to be a carrier of Chagas' disease. The insect was thereafter known among entomologists as "Wigglesworth's bug." Wigglesworth was appointed Reader in Entomology at London University in 1936. He returned to Cambridge in 1945 and in 1952 was named Quick Professor of Biology at Cambridge. He served as director of the Agricultural Research Council's entomological unit from 1943 to 1967.

Wigglesworth's research concentrated on insect hormones and how they affected physiological processes. It was known that brain secretions initiated certain physiological processes; for example, a decapitated insect would live but it would not molt. Wigglesworth implanted different sections of the brain into the bodies of decapitated insects, and he was thus able to identify the particular areas of the brain where neurosecretory cells were located. He also proved that the brain was the only place in the body of these insects that produced the triggering hormones. This was the first time the role of neurosecretory brain cells in animal development was established experimentally.

Wigglesworth's further studies of insect hormones showed that brain secretions controlled not only molting but also how and when insect larvae would metamorphose into adult forms. He established that it was a hormone, identified as the juvenile hormone, which prevented larvae from developing adult characteristics until they were fully grown. He conducted an experiment in which larvae were continually exposed to the juvenile hormone; as a result of this exposure, larvae maintained their immature form but continued to grow in size. The study of this and other phenomena associated with insect hormones led Wigglesworth to develop a theory of metamorphosis which proposes that the genetic factors necessary for larval development are regulated by the juvenile hormone.

Wigglesworth's research did not concentrate solely on neurological issues but ranged over a wide array of physiological phenomena. He determined how insects are able to make their feet adhere to walking surfaces, how insect eggs breathe, and how symbiotic microorganisms provide vitamins to insects which live solely on blood. The comprehensive nature of his curiosity and understanding enabled him to write books integrating the complete scope of knowledge about insect physiology. His book, *Principles of Insect Physiology,* first published in 1939, became a standard international text. His work has become so basic to entomology that most of it has been incorporated into the standard body of educational material.

Tucker writes of Wigglesworth: "His manner always remained that of a very senior medical consultant; the careful form of question, the cautious, almost shy, analytical progression of thought, and the decisive separation of important and trivial evidence." Wigglesworth continued to work full time until shortly before his death. Known for his strong scientific judgment, care in formulating hypotheses, and precision in discussing scientific ideas, Wigglesworth also advocated caution in using sweeping measures to control insects. He warned against heavy use of pesticides and supported the study of species-specific pheromones to affect insect populations.

Wigglesworth was a member of scientific societies around the world, and he lectured at many universities in the United States and Europe. He was a member of the Royal Entomological Society and the U.S. National Academy of Sciences, and he received several honorary degrees. He was awarded the Gregor Mendel Gold Medal in 1967 from the Czechoslovak Academy of Science. He was knighted in 1964, and the British Royal Entomological Society awards a Wigglesworth Medal in his name.

Wigglesworth married Mabel Katherine Semple in 1928. They had three sons and a daughter. His wife died in 1986. One of their sons, William R. B. Wigglesworth, became England's Deputy Director General of Telecommunications. Wigglesworth died on February 12, 1994.

SELECTED WRITINGS BY WIGGLESWORTH:

Books

Insect Physiology, Methuen & Co., 1934, 2nd edition, 1938.
The Principles of Insect Physiology, E. P. Dutton, 1939.
Physiology of Insect Metamorphosis, Cambridge University Press, 1954.
Control of Growth and Form, Cornell University Press, 1959.
The Life of Insects, New American Library, 1964.
Insect Hormones, W. H. Freeman, 1970.
Insects and the Life of Man, Wiley, 1976.

FURTHER READING:

Books

McGraw-Hill Modern Scientists and Engineers, Volume 3, McGraw-Hill, 1980, pp. 316–17.

Periodicals

Tucker, Anthony, *Guardian,* Unearthing Insects' Mysteries (Obituary)February 14, 1994, p. 12.

Sketch by Valerie Brown

Eugene Paul Wigner
1902–1995
American mathematical physicist

Eugene Paul Wigner's enormous contribution to various branches of physics, notably quantum and nuclear, was confirmed by his receipt of the 1963 Nobel Prize for Physics (he shared the award with **Maria Goeppert-Mayer** and **J. Hans D. Jensen**). Recognizing the role of symmetry principles in predicting certain physical processes, Wigner formulated many of the laws governing this theory. Wigner is remembered as being one of the first physicists to call attention to the problems of nuclear energy, and also as one of the first scientists to forge links between science and industry around nuclear energy.

Wigner was born in Budapest, Austria-Hungary (now Hungary) on November 17, 1902, the son of a businessman. At school, Wigner discovered an interest in physics, but he realized that job opportunities as a physicist in Hungary would be very limited. He therefore decided to study chemical engineering. After receiving a doctorate in chemical engineering from the Technische Hochschule in Berlin in 1925, Wigner returned to Budapest for a year to take up a post in a leather-tanning plant. He left Hungary for the last time in 1926 upon receiving an invitation to return to Berlin to work as an assistant to the well-known physical chemist R. Becker. "The whole of quantum physics was being created within my own eyesight," he said of physics in Germany during the 1920s, as quoted in *Pioneers of Science: Nobel Prize Winners in Physics.* Inspired by such inventiveness, Wigner began writing papers of his own; specifically, he was interested in exploring how the mathematical concept known as group theory could be used as a tool in the new quantum mechanics. On the strength of this work, Wigner was invited in 1927 to join the physics department of the University of Göttingen, as assistant to the mathematician **David Hilbert**.

At Gottingen Wigner developed his law of the conservation of parity, which states that no fundamental distinction can be made between left and right in physics. The laws of physics are the same in a right-handed system of coordinates as they are in a left-handed system. Based on Wigner's law of parity conservation, particles emitted during a physical interaction should emanate from the nucleus to the right and the left in equal numbers. In practical terms, the law meant that a nuclear process should be indistinguishable from its mirror image, that is, an electron emitted from a nucleus will be indifferent as to whether it is ejected to the left or right and will shoot off in equal numbers in both directions along the spin axes of the aligned nucleus. This theory remained steadfast until 1956 when two Chinese-American physicists, **Tsung-Dao Lee** and **Chen Ning Yang**, disproved it by showing experimentally that parity is not conserved in weak interactions.

Eugene Paul Wigner

82, or 126. The longer binding periods are thought to be caused by the existence in the nucleus of shells or orbits, similar to those that surround the nucleus and contain the electrons, the negatively charged particles. Armed with this data, Wigner forecasted an optical spectra based on the long periodicity model. His findings were published in one of the first papers on the subject. Wigner also contributed significantly to the understanding of short periodicity in his application of mathematical group theory to the energy levels of nuclei up to atomic weight 50. His book on group theory has become a classic in the physics canon.

In 1933, the year after **James Chadwick** discovered the neutron, Wigner composed a paper which postulated the existence of an energy state of the deuteron which differed from the ground state that had been observed. A deuteron is the nucleus of an atom of deuterium, the hydrogen isotope that has twice the mass of regular hydrogen, and which occurs in water. A deuteron contains one proton and one neutron. Wigner's theory provided an explanation for a hitherto unaccounted-for phenomenon: the large deflections of slow neutrons when they pass close to protons. Although Wigner discounted the idea's importance and did not deem it worthy of publication, it proved to be the foundation for numerous other papers.

In 1936, while working with **Gregory Breit,** Wigner examined the phenomenon of neutron absorption by a compound nucleus. Their Breit-Wigner formula did much to throw light on this subject. Continuing his work around atomic nuclei, Wigner postulated in 1937 that protons and neutrons were analogous to isotopes in the periodic table of the elements. The manifestation of a particle as a proton or as a neutron could be accounted for by different degrees of spin on the particle, known as isotopic spin or isospin for short.

Turning his attention to nuclear fission in 1938, Wigner developed a number of theoretical techniques of reactor calculations, some of which formed the basis of the first controlled chain reaction carried out by the Italian physicist **Enrico Fermi**. Together with his fellow Hungarians, **Leo Szilard** and **Edward Teller,** Wigner persuaded **Albert Einstein** to send a letter to President Franklin Roosevelt urging him to beat Hitler in the race to develop an atom bomb. The letter was crucial in convincing the American government to build nuclear reactors and was also directly responsible for the establishment of the Manhattan Project, on which Wigner played a key role.

In 1941, Wigner married Mary Annette Wheeler, with whom he had two children, David and Martha. His second marriage, to Eileen Hamilton, produced a daughter, Erika. Despite his many scientific commitments, Wigner tried to find time to devote to his family and to pursue his hobbies of bowling and figure skating.

The outbreak of war in Europe caused Wigner to turn his full attention to nuclear physics. At the Metallurgical Laboratory at the University of Chicago, he began work on the Manhattan Project as the chief engineer of the water-cooled Hanford plutonium reactors. Wigner's colleagues

Instead, their experiments revealed that far more electrons were emitted from the south end of the nucleus than from the north. For invalidating the widely held concept of the conservation of parity, they shared the 1957 Nobel Prize for Physics.

Wigner returned in 1928 to the Technische Hochschule and continued his work on group theory until 1930, when he moved to the United States to accept a position as lecturer in mathematical physics at Princeton University. For eight years he served as a part-time professor at Princeton, until he was elevated to the position of Thomas D. Jones Professor of Mathematical Physics in 1938. The year before, Wigner had become an American citizen.

Develops Short Periodicity of Binding Energies

Wigner's tenure at Princeton afforded him the time and space to do his most important work. As a young physicist, he had become interested in symmetry principles, especially with the patterns found in atomic and molecular spectra. Important discoveries in the 1930s of the binding forces within a nucleus paved the way for Wigner's research. It was found that nuclei containing even numbers of protons (the positively charged particles in the nucleus) and neutrons (the neutral particles) are bound together more strongly than those with an uneven number of protons and neutrons. This is referred to as the short periodicity of binding energies. Longer periods of binding energy are also possible, and show especially strong binding when the number of protons or neutrons or both is 2, 8, 20, 28, 40, 50,

observed that, for a theorist, he had a remarkably precise knowledge of the engineering design of reactors. Also remarkable was the tremendous speed at which the latest scientific findings in the laboratory were converted into engineered chain reactors. After the war, Wigner accepted a position as director of research and development at the Clinton Laboratories at Oak Ridge from 1946 to 1947.

Career Honored with Copious Awards

Wigner's many contributions to physics have been recognized in a variety of prizes and honorary degrees. He was elected to the National Academy of Sciences in 1945. He was awarded the U.S. Atomic Energy Commission's Enrico Fermi Prize in 1958 and the Atoms for Peace Award in 1960. Most significantly, in 1936, Wigner won the Nobel physics prize for "systemically improving and extending the methods of quantum mechanics and applying them widely." Specifically, he was commended for his contribution to the theory of atomic nuclei elementary particles, especially for his discovery and application of fundamental principles of symmetry. This marked an unusual departure for the Nobel Committee, which normally awards the prize for a single discovery or invention.

Wigner, who retired from Princeton in 1971, was also active on behalf of other scientists. He was one of thirty-three Nobel Prize winners who sent a telegram to President Podgorny of the former Soviet Union asking that **Andrei Sakharov** be permitted to receive the Nobel Peace Prize in Stockholm. Wigner died in Princeton, New Jersey, on January 1, 1995, of pneumonia. He was 92.

SELECTED WRITINGS BY WIGNER:

Books

Nuclear Structure. Princeton: Princeton University Press, 1961.

Symmetries and Reflections. Bloomington: Indiana University Press, 1967.

Who Speaks for Civil Defense? New York: Scribner, 1968.

Survival and the Bomb. Bloominton: Indiana University Press, 1969.

Aspects of Quantum Theory, Cambridge: Cambridge University Press, 1972.

Reminiscences about a Great Physicist: Paul Adrian Maurice Dirac. Cambridge: Cambridge University Press, 1987.

FURTHER READING:

Books

Asimov, Isaac. *Atom: Journey Across the Subatomic Cosmos.* New York: Truman Talley Books, 1991.

Asimov, Isaac. *Great American Scientists: America's Rise to the Forefront of World Science.* Prentice Hall, 1967, pp. 21–22, 119.

Weber, Robert L. *Pioneers of Science: Nobel Prize Winners in Physics.* Philadelphia: Institute of Physics, 1980, p. 188.

Periodicals

"Physicist Eugene Wigner Dies; Won Nobel, Pioneered A-bomb" (obituary). *Washington Post* (5 January 1995): B7.

Sketch by Avril McDonald

Andrew J. Wiles
1953–
American mathematician

A professor of mathematics at Princeton University, Andrew J. Wiles has formulated a proof which may solve a puzzle which has frustrated mathematicians for centuries. In his seven-year quest to solve the famous Fermat's Last Theorem, Wiles brought together separate schools of mathematical thought; his work has been submitted to a review process by other mathematicians and if it passes, the ancient problem will be considered solved.

Wiles was born in Cambridge, England, in April 1953. His father was a professor of theology. Wiles attended Clare College at Cambridge University, where he studied elliptical curves, earning his master's degree in 1977 and his Ph.D. in 1980. Elliptical curves would play a central role in his proof of Fermat's Last Theorem, but it was years before Wiles recognized this. He came to the United States in 1980 to accept a position as professor of mathematics at Princeton University. In 1988, Wiles received the Whitehead Prize from the London Mathematics Society, and he returned to England for two years as Research Professor in Maths and Professorial Fellow at Merton College, Oxford. He returned to Princeton in 1990.

Fermat's Last Theorem is the most famous problem in mathematics, and Wiles became intrigued with it when he was ten years old. He even worked on it as a teenager, but as he began his professional life he realized it was more complicated than he had initially thought. In 1637, French lawyer and number theorist Pierre Fermat scrawled a general math equation in the margin of his copy of Diophantus's *Arithmetic,* along with a very bold statement declaring that the equation $a^n + b^n = c^n$ can never be true when the exponent n is greater than two. Fermat provided no proof of his theorem because, he wrote, "the margin is too small to hold it." The theorem concerns an equation similar to the well-known Pythagorean theorem. Pythagorus said that the square of the longest side of a right triangle equals the sum of the squares of the other two sides ($a^2 + b^2 = c^2$). For example three squared (nine) plus four squared (sixteen) equals five squared (twenty five). Many other values also make this equation true, as long as the exponent is two. According to Fermat's theorem, however, an equation of the same form will never be true with any other whole number.

Like Wiles, many mathematicians had tested and tried to prove or disprove Fermat's Last Theorem in the 300 hundred years since it was published. Fermat himself had shown that when the exponents are four, the equation cannot be true. In 1780, Leonhard Euler proved the same for the exponent three. Others proved that exponents of five, seven, and thirteen cannot produce correct equations. Eventually computers were used to search for an equation which was true and would thereby disprove Fermat's Last Theorem. Exponents up to 4,000,000 were tested without finding an equation which showed that Fermat's Last Theorem was wrong. But an infinite number of possibilities remained to be tested. A different approach was needed to provide a definitive proof of Fermat's Last Theorem. In 1954, a Japanese mathematician named Yutaka Taniyama proposed a modular form to a set of mathematical equations called elliptical curves. His proposal was called the Taniyama conjecture. A conjecture in mathematics is a fascinating but unproved theory. The next advance came out of Germany in the 1980s from Gerhard Frey, who suggested that proving the Taniyama conjecture might indirectly prove Fermat's Last Theorem; an elliptical curve could be used to represent all the solutions to Fermat's equation. Kenneth Ribet in the United States proved Frey's idea in 1986, and this changed Wiles's perception of the theorem. He dedicated himself to solving Fermat's Last Theorem on the same day he heard of Ribet's proof.

Begins Seven-Year Journey to Prove the Theorem

Wiles believed he could prove that the elliptical curve representing the solutions to Fermat's equation could not exist and thereby prove Fermat's Last Theorem to be true. He virtually withdrew from professional life, except to teach classes at Princeton, and pursued his quest. Wiles spent seven years in seclusion in the attic of his home, without computer or telephone, working exhaustively to prove the theorem. He wanted to develop the proof completely on his own, and he was extremely secretive about his attic work, consulting only with one trusted colleague. He made steady progress in the first few years; progress eventually slowed, but in 1991 he made a discovery that reduced the problem to a calculation that had been used unsuccessfully by others. Wiles worked without interruption on this calculation, and by May of 1993 he felt he had a proof that was complete except for one single but critical special case. While reading a paper by Harvard mathematician Barry Mazur, Wiles realized that a mathematical construction described in the paper was the approach that would help him over this last hurdle.

Wiles announced his proof in an unusual manner. His withdrawal from most professional activities within the mathematics community had made his presentations at conferences rare. He asked to give three lectures at a small mathematics meeting in Cambridge, England, and rumors of an exciting announcement abounded, though the title of his lectures had no relationship to Fermat's theorem. In his first lecture, Wiles remained secretive about the final outcome of his series of talks, but twice as many people attended his second lecture. On the third day, June 23, 1993, Wiles announced that he had proven the Taniyama conjecture. Almost as an afterthought, he added that this meant that Fermat's Last Theorem was also proven to be true. Word of Wiles's proof spread throughout the mathematics world at the speed of electronic mail, and both mathematics journals and the general press hounded him for interviews. He sought refuge from the media coverage at his parents' home near the conference but was discovered there. He soon returned to Princeton, and he has continued his secretive approach to his proof of Fermat's Last Theorem even after his announcement. He withheld the document from almost everyone but the reviewers, unwilling to release it until he considers it to be absolutely correct and ready for publication.

When asked how he felt about his proof, Wiles told *People Weekly,* "There is a sense of loss, actually." But his work on Fermat's Last Theorem was not finished. Acceptance of a proof as important and complex as this is neither automatic nor immediate; there is an exhaustive review process used to verify that mathematical proofs are complete and clearly stated. Only a handful of mathematicians are fully able to understand the work Wiles has done, making the process one that may last as long as a year. Some refinement of the 200-page document was considered inevitable; Wiles resolved many of the reviewer's concerns quickly, though one particular flaw found in December of 1993 requires more work. But neither Wiles nor others believe that the integrity of his proof is threatened. In the meantime, Wiles continues to live in Princeton with his wife and two daughters.

SELECTED WRITINGS BY WILES:

Periodicals

Annals of Mathematics, An Ordinary Lambda-adic Representation Associated to Modular Forms, Volume 94, 1988, pp. 529–573.

Annals of Mathematics, The Iwasawa Conjecture for Totally Real Fields, Volume 131, 1990, pp. 493–540.

Annals of Mathematics, On a Conjecture by Brumer, Volume 131, 1990, pp. 555–565.

FURTHER READING:

Periodicals

Cipra, Barry, *Science,* Fermat's Last Theorem Finally Yields, Volume 261, July 2, 1993, pp. 32–33.

Davidson, K., *San Francisco Chronicle,* Amazement to the Nth, June 27, 1993, p. A4

Folger, Tim, *Discover,* Sure, Pierre. Sure You Knew, January 1994, p. 61.

Gleick, James, *New York Times Magazine,* Fermat's Theorem, October 3, 1993, pp. 52–53.

Grossman, Ron, *Chicago Tribune,* He's Numero Uno, July 14, 1993, p. D1.

Kolata, Gina, *New York Times,* At Last, Shout of 'Eureka!' In Age-Old Math Mystery, June 24, 1993, p. A1.

Kolata, Gina, *New York Times,* Math Whiz Who Battled 350-Year-Old Problem, June 29, 1993, p. C1.

Kolata, Gina, *New York Times,* Flaw Is Found in Math Proof, but Repairs Are Under Way, December 11, 1993, p. A9.

Schwartz, John, *The Washington Post,* This Equation Figures to Answer a 17th Century Puzzle, August 2, 1993, p. A3.

Schwartz, John, *People Weekly,* The 25 Most Intriguing People of 1993—Andrew Wiles, December 27, 1993, p. 104.

Sketch by David N. Ford

Maurice Wilkes
1913–
English computer engineer

Maurice Wilkes developed an interest in radio as a child and specialized in radar research during World War II. After the war, Wilkes became involved in pioneering research on the development of computers and is best known for his development of EDSAC, the Electronic Delay Storage Automatic Calculator, the first computing machine to make use of the concept of a stored program. Over the last five decades, Wilkes has been actively involved in the formation of a number of computer organizations and associations.

Maurice Vincent Wilkes was born on June 26, 1913, in Dudley, England. His father, Vincent J. Wilkes, was employed at the time on the South Staffordshire estate of the Earl of Dudley. His mother's name is not mentioned in the usual biographical records nor in Wilkes's own autobiography *Memoirs of a Computer Pioneer.* She is described in the latter reference, however, as "one of a pioneering band of women who went into offices in their hobble skirts and worked the new-fangled type-writing machines."

Develops an Early Interest in Science and Mathematics

Wilkes's early education in Dudley was interrupted by severe bouts of asthma, which he apparently inherited from his mother's side of the family. While he was still young, Wilkes's father moved the family to nearby Stourbridge in order to find a more congenial environment for his mother's health. Wilkes entered the King Edward VI Grammar School in Stourbridge at the age of eight and quickly developed an interest in science and mathematics. He was later to report in his *Memoirs,* "I think it was already clear to me [in the Sixth Form] that my life would be in physics or in physics-based engineering. I had seen enough to realize that there was a magic power in mathematics and I burned to be initiated fully into that mystery."

The other field that attracted Wilkes's interest at an early age was radio. The early 1920s were an era when "the wireless" was just becoming popular, with small amateur stations and crystal sets beginning to proliferate. Wilkes subscribed to *Wireless World* while he was still a teenager and a short time later was asked to build some equipment for station G6OJ, operated by the chemistry master at King Edward VI. In 1931 Wilkes applied for and received his own amateur radio operator's license.

Continues His Education at St. John's College and Cambridge University

Also in 1931 Wilkes graduated from King Edward VI and was accepted as a student at St. John's College, Cambridge. He concentrated in mathematics there and in June 1934 graduated with honors. He then applied for and received a research grant from the department of scientific and industrial research. He chose to use that grant to continue his studies at the Cavendish Laboratories at Cambridge, where he began work with the radio group in July 1934.

The first topic on which Wilkes was asked to work at the Cavendish involved a study of long radio waves. As he completed this project, the future direction of his career became more clear to him. He found that he was not particularly interested in pure or theoretical mathematics itself, but math "as application to any sort of physics was concerned. I did not have," he later wrote, "and indeed have never had, that interest in mathematical puzzles and fine points that characterize the natural theoretician. I looked forward to being able to apply the math I had learnt to physical problems."

Introduced to the Differential Analyzer

An important turning point in Wilkes's life came in March 1936 when he attended a lecture given by D. R. Hartree of Manchester University. Hartree's lecture involved the demonstration of a differential analyzer, a mechanical device for solving differential equations. Wilkes says that he found the machine "irresistible," and, more than that, exactly the tool he needed to solve some of the mathematical problems involved in his study of long waves. His future in the computing sciences appears to have been set.

Before long, Wilkes was involved in the operation of Cambridge's own differential analyzer and, in later 1937 he was asked to join the university's newly established "Mathematical Laboratory," which was, in fact, a "computing laboratory." (The facility's name was actually corrected thirty-three years later.) Wilkes's official appointment at the time was as university demonstrator. In early 1938 he was awarded his M.A. degree and in October of the same year, his Ph.D.

Begins Wartime Research on Radar

The year of Wilkes's graduation was one of profound unrest in Great Britain and across Europe. Some observers expected the outbreak of war momentarily and were encouraging preparation for that event. Others held to the hope that peace could still be salvaged. Within a year of receiving his degree, Wilkes had been drafted into the program for the development of radarlike devices for the detection of, at first, submarines, and, later, surface ships and aircraft. His first assignment was at the radar station at Dunkirk, where he reported on August 28, 1939. Within a short time he was back in Cambridge, working on antisubmarine devices before returning to Dunkirk and, later, to other stations along the coast.

By 1941 Wilkes had been assigned to the Operations Research Group (ORG) headquartered in Petersham. Most of his work with the ORG involved the development of ten-centimeter radar instruments and, in particular, of the GL Mark I, II, and III detection systems. In 1943 Wilkes moved on to a new assignment in Malvern, where he worked on the development of the Oboe system. In his autobiography, Wilkes describes Oboe as a "blind-bombing system that depended on measurement of range from two land-based stations to the bombing aircraft."

At the war's conclusion, Wilkes volunteered for an assignment in Germany interviewing captured German scientists. His account of the two months he spent in Germany is an equal mix of new information gained from his interviewees, sparkling travelogue about the German countryside, and ongoing complaints about endless bureaucratic confusion. Wilkes returned to Cambridge from his Germany assignment on August 1, 1945, to an offer of a university lectureship and the post of acting director of the mathematical laboratory. In May 1946 Wilkes was given a copy of **John Neumann**'s "Draft Report on EDVAC." The report contained, Wilkes later wrote, "the principles on which the development of the modern digital computer was to be based." "I recognized this at once as the real thing," he went on, "and from that time on never had any doubt as to

the way computer development would go." In October 1946 Wilkes was given the title of director of the laboratory.

Wilkes's interest in computers had not precluded his continued research on atmospheric physics begun before the war. Indeed, this topic was one to which he kept returning for many years, even after he had earned his reputation in computer science. One of his accomplishments in the immediate postwar period was to confirm, using the differential analyzer, a prediction by C. L. Pekeris regarding factors affecting resonance in the atmosphere.

Makes Important Contacts at a Moore School Course

In early 1946 Wilkes was invited to attend a course on Electronic Computing to be held at the Moore School of Electrical Engineering in Philadelphia on August 8–31. Travel was still difficult in the postwar year of 1946, and Wilkes actually arrived two weeks late for the class. However, he had an opportunity to see the world's first electronic computer, the ENIAC, which, although it had already become something of a dinosaur in the computer world, still provided the standard for the future of computer development.

During this visit to the United States—the first of many over the next forty years—Wilkes spoke with most of the pioneers of computer science in the United States, including **Howard Aiken** at Harvard, S. H. Caldwell at the Massachusetts Institute of Technology (MIT), and **John William Mauchly** and H. H. Goldstine at the Moore School. It was during this visit that Wilkes "first began to sketch out the design of the machine that finally became the EDSAC," he states in his autobiography. Actual work on the machine then began about two months after his return to England.

The key innovation in Wilkes's EDSAC was that the programs needed to operate the machine were actually built into the machine itself rather than having to be fed into it, as in earlier machines. The key part of the machine was a 1.5 meter-long, mercury-filled tank, called a "tube," that held sixteen words of thirty-five bits each. The final design of the EDSAC was to consist of thirty-two such tubes.

Actual construction of the EDSAC was a long and complex process, filled with the problems and frustrations to be expected of such an undertaking. At a key point, officials of J. Lyons and Company offered an infusion of cash that made completion of the computer possible and at the same time led to the development of the first commercial versions of EDSAC, LEO 1, LEO 2, and LEO 3.

The first successful run of EDSAC took place on May 6, 1949. The machine read a program tape for computing a table of squares and correctly printed out the results. In a short period of time, researchers were making use of the powerful new computing tool. In early 1949, for example, the eminent statistician **Ronald A. Fisher** inquired about the use of EDSAC in the solution of a second-order nonlinear differential equation. A year later, Wilkes provided him with the results, results about which Wilkes later wrote, "I do not think that he had for one moment expected that we would produce." In 1950 Wilkes wrote a report describing the development and uses of EDSAC, a report that was published in 1951 by Addison-Wesley as *Preparation of Programs for an Electronic Digital Computer, with Special Reference to the EDSAC and the Use of a Library of Subroutines.* The book was reissued in 1982 as volume 1 of the Charles Babbage Institute reprint series on the history of computing. In July 1950 Wilkes left for his second visit to the United States, one that was to last for two months and was to include stops at every major computing center in the country. He visited the Institute for Advanced Studies in Princeton, New Jersey; the Eckert-Mauchly Corporation in Philadelphia; the National Bureau of Standards in Washington, D.C.; the U.S. Army proving ground in Aberdeen, Maryland; Harvard and MIT in Cambridge, Massachusetts; IBM World Headquarters in New York City; the navy proving ground in Dahlgren, Virginia; the University of Illinois; and the University of California at Berkeley.

Begins Work on EDSAC 2

Less than six months after his return from the United States, Wilkes had become deeply involved in the planning for the next stage in computing machinery, EDSAC 2. He recognized that the time had come to move from the experimental level represented by EDSAC 1 to a fully operational working machine that could begin to take on many of the research projects already envisioned by university researchers in many departments. By June 1951 funding had been obtained from the Nuffield Foundation, and construction was under way by the summer of 1953. An intermediary model, EDSAC 1.5, passed initial tests, and early in 1958 EDSAC 2 was formally put into operation. A few months later, on July 11, 1958, EDSAC 1 was formally closed down and dismantled, its parts sold for scrap.

In very little time, EDSAC 2 proved its worth to the scientific community. Its first notable success was in connection with the work of **John Kendrew**, who was working on the molecular structure of myoglobin. Kendrew had used EDSAC 1 to help analyze four hundred x-ray diffraction patterns in the early part of his research and had then turned to EDSAC 2 to examine ten thousand more photographs when that machine became available. In his 1962 Nobel lecture, Kendrew acknowledged the role of the EDSAC machines in facilitating the research for which he had received that coveted prize.

At nearly the same time, astronomer **Martin Ryle** found another use for EDSAC 2. Ryle was working on the problem of creating a radio telescope with a very large aperture capable of obtaining resolutions far better than any existing instruments. Ryle's approach was to construct the telescope of movable sections whose individual photographs could then be analyzed and combined by means of complex computer programs. The EDSAC 2 provided the technology that made that approach workable and that brought to Ryle the 1974 Nobel Prize in physics.

By the time EDSAC 2 was powered down on November 1, 1964, Wilkes had become a senior statesman in the field of computer hardware. Although he continued to be active in research, he also began to assume more responsibility in professional organizations. For example, in 1957 he was elected the first president of the British Computer Society, a post he held for three years. In 1965 he was appointed chairman of the Computer Advisory Committee of the Agricultural Research Council, a post he held for ten years. After 1950 Wilkes made many trips to the United States; when he reached mandatory retirement age at Cambridge in 1980, he moved to Maynard, Massachusetts, and took a job as staff consultant at the Digital Equipment Corporation. A year later he was also appointed adjunct professor at MIT. In 1986 Wilkes returned to Cambridge, where he became a consultant for the Olivetti Research Board.

Wilkes was married to Nina Twyman in 1947. They have three children, Margaret, Helen, and Anthony. Among his many awards have been the Harry Goode Memorial Award (1968) and the Eckert-Mauchly Award (1980) of the American Federation of Information Processing Societies, the McDowell Award of the Institute of Electrical and Electronics Engineers (1981), the Pender Award of the University of Pennsylvania (1982), the C and C Prize (Tokyo, 1988), and the Italgas Prize (Turin, 1991). He has also received honorary doctorates from eight universities.

SELECTED WRITINGS BY WILKES:

Books

Oscillations of the Earth's Atmosphere, Cambridge University Press, 1949.

Preparation of Programs for an Electronic Digital Computer, with Special Reference to the EDSAC and the Use of a Library of Subroutines, Addison-Wesley, 1951.

Automatic Digital Computers, Methuen, 1958.

A Short Introduction to Numerical Analysis, Cambridge University Press, 1966.

Time-Sharing Computer Systems, Elsevier, 1968.

The Cambridge CAP Computer and Its Operating System, North Holland, 1979.

Memoirs of a Computer Pioneer, MIT Press, 1985.

FURTHER READING:

Books

Cortada, James W., *Historical Dictionary of Data Processing: Technology,* Association for Computing Machinery, 1987, pp. 149–151.

Sketch by David E. Newton

J. Ernest Wilkins, Jr.
1923–
American mathematician and physicist

A distinguished applied mathematician and nuclear engineer, J. Ernest Wilkins, Jr., has enjoyed a diverse career spanning governmental, industrial, and academic positions. He was involved in the Manhattan Project—the top-secret quest to construct a nuclear bomb during the 1940s—and was a pioneer in nuclear reactor design. He served as President of the American Nuclear Society, and contributed to the mathematical theory of Bessel functions, differential and integral equations, the calculus of variations, and to optical instruments for space.

Jesse Ernest Wilkins, Jr. was born in Chicago on November 27, 1923, the son of J. Ernest Wilkins, Sr., and Lucile Beatrice Robinson Wilkins. The senior Wilkins was a prominent lawyer who was president of the Cook County Bar Association in 1941–42, and an Assistant Secretary of Labor in the Eisenhower administration. Wilkins's mother was a schoolteacher with a master's degree. Both parents remained active in the Methodist church. Wilkins's two brothers became lawyers, but Wilkins preferred mathematics, entering the University of Chicago at the age of thirteen, and becoming the youngest student ever admitted to that institution. He completed his baccalaureate in 1940, his master's in 1941, and, by the age of nineteen, had earned his doctoral degree.

Wilkins went to the Institute for Advanced Study on a Rosenwald scholarship in 1942, then taught at Tuskegee Institute in 1943–44. He returned to the University of Chicago, where he worked on the Manhattan Project at the Metallurgical Laboratory from 1944 to 1946. Wilkins spent the bulk of his career in industry, however, starting with a position as Mathematician at the American Optical Company in Buffalo, New York, in 1946. He left to become a Senior Mathematician at the Nuclear Development Corporation of America (NDA), later United Nuclear Corporation, in White Plains, New York, in 1950. There he became Manager of the Physics and Mathematics Department in 1955 and later Manager of Research and Development. While he was at NDA, Wilkins earned a B.M.E. degree in 1957, and an M.M.E. in 1960, from New York University.

Beginning in the sixties, Wilkins held various offices in the American Nuclear Society, becoming President of the organization during 1974–75. In the early sixties, Wilkins moved to the General Atomic Division of General Dynamics Corporation in San Diego, where he remained until 1970. Wilkins next took an academic position as Distinguished Professor of Applied Mathematical Physics at Howard University in Washington, DC., remaining in that position for the next seven years.

In 1977 Wilkins went to EG&G Idaho in Idaho Falls, where he was Associate General Manager and then Deputy General Manager. Leaving in 1984, Wilkins was an Argonne Fellow at Argonne National Laboratory in 1984 and 1985, and although retired beginning in 1985, he remained active as a consultant. In 1990, Wilkins joined Clark Atlanta University as Distinguished Professor of Applied Mathematics and Mathematical Physics.

Completes Gamma Ray Research

During his career Wilkins published roughly a hundred papers and reports on pure and applied mathematics, nuclear engineering, and optics. He is best-known for studies with Herbert Goldstein on gamma-ray penetration, the results of which are used for the design of nuclear reactor and radiation shielding, and of neutron absorption, which produced the Wigner-Wilkins approach to estimating the distribution of neutron energies in nuclear reactors. Wilkins also wrote papers on reactor operation and design and heat transfer. In addition, Wilkins continued to write on optical optimization problems and did interesting work on the estimation of the number of real roots of polynomials with random coefficients.

Wilkins served on advisory committees on scientific and engineering education for the National Academy of Engineering, the National Research Council, and other organizations and universities. Wilkins married Gloria Stewart in 1947. They had two children, Sharon and J. Ernest III. Wilkins remarried in 1984.

SELECTED WRITINGS BY WILKINS, JR.:

Books

Proceedings of the International Conference on the Peaceful Uses of Atomic Energy, Status of Experimental and Theoretical Information on Neutron Slowing-Down Distributions in Hydrogenous Media, United Nations, 1956, Volume 5, pp. 62–76.
Progress in Approximation Theory, The Landau Constants, Academic Press, 1991, pp. 829–842.
Topics in Polynomials and Their Applications, Mean Number of Real Zeroes of a Random Trigonometric Polynomial, II, World, 1993, pp. 581–594.

Periodicals

Physical Review, Systematic Calculations of Gamma-Ray Penetration, Volume 89, 1953, p. 1150.
Nuclear Engineering and Design, Steady-state Heat Conduction in Slabs, Cylindrical and Spherical Shell with Non-uniform Heat Generation, Volume 24, 1973, pp. 62–77.
Nuclear Science and Engineering, Minimum Critical Mass Nuclear Reactors, Part I and Part II, Volume 82, 1982, pp. 307–315, 316–324.

Journal of the Optical Society of America. A, Optics and Image Science, Apodization for Maximum Central Irradiance and Specified Large Rayleigh Limit of Resolution, II, Volume 1, 1984, pp. 337–343.

FURTHER READING:

Books

Glasstone, Samuel and Alexander Sesonske, *Nuclear Engineering,* Van Nostrand, 1955.

Glasstone, Samuel and Alexander Sesonske, *In Black and White, A Guide to Magazine Articles, Newspaper Articles and Books Concerning more than 15,000 Black Individuals and Groups,* Volume 2, third edition, Gale, 1980, p. 1040.

Periodicals

Glasstone, Samuel and Alexander Sesonske, *Ebony,* February, 1958, pp. 60–67.

Sketch by Sally M. Moite

Maurice Hugh Frederick Wilkins

Maurice Hugh Frederick Wilkins
1916–
English biophysicist

Maurice Hugh Frederick Wilkins is best known for the assistance he provided to molecular biologists **James D. Watson** and **Francis Crick** in their quest to uncover the structure of deoxyribonucleic acid (DNA), the genetic blueprint of heredity in humans and many other organisms. Specifically, Wilkins' contribution to their discovery involved discerning the structure of DNA through the use of x ray diffraction techniques. For his efforts, Wilkins shared the 1962 Nobel Prize in physiology or medicine with Watson and Crick.

Wilkins was born in Pongaroa, New Zealand on December 15, 1916, to Irish immigrants Edgar Henry, a physician, and Eveline Constance Jane (Whittaker) Wilkins. Superior education began at an early age for Wilkins, who began attending King Edward's School in Birmingham, England, at age six. He later received his B.A. in physics from Cambridge University in 1938. After graduation, he joined the Ministry of Home Security and Aircraft Production and was assigned to conduct graduate research on radar at the University of Birmingham. Wilkins' research centered on improving the accuracy of radar screens.

Soon after earning his Ph.D. in 1940, Wilkins, still with the Ministry of Home Security, was relocated to a new team of British scientists researching the application of uranium isotopes to atomic bombs. A short time later Wilkins became part of another team sent to the United States to work on the Manhattan Project—the military effort to develop the atomic bomb—with other scientists at the University of California at Berkeley. He spent two years there researching the separation of uranium isotopes.

Switches Research Focus to Biophysics

Wilkins's interest in the intersection of physics and biology emerged soon after his arrival to the United States. He was significantly influenced by a book by **Erwin Schrödinger**, a fellow physicist, entitled *What is Life? The Physical Aspects of the Living Cell.* The book centers on the possibility that the science of quantum physics could lead to the understanding of the essence of life itself, including the process of biological growth. In addition to Schrödinger's book, the undeniable and undesirable ramifications of his work on the atomic bomb also played a role in Wilkins' declining interest in the field of nuclear physics and emerging interest in biology.

After the war, the opportunity arose for Wilkins to begin a career in biophysics. In 1945, Wilkins' former graduate school professor, Scottish physicist John T. Randall, invited him to become a physics lecturer at St. Andrews University, Scotland, in that school's new biophysics research unit. Later, in 1946, Wilkins and Randall moved on to a new research pursuit combining the sciences of physics, chemistry and biology to the study of living cells. Together they established the Medical Research Council Biophysics Unit at King's College in London. Wilkins was, for a time, informally the second in command. He officially became deputy director of the unit in 1955 and was promoted to director in 1970, a position he held until 1972.

Delves into Research on DNA Structure

It was at this biophysics unit, in 1946, that Wilkins soon concentrated his research on DNA, shortly after scientists at the Rockefeller Institute (now Rockefeller University) in New York announced that DNA is the constituent of genes. Realizing the enormous importance of the DNA molecule, Wilkins became excited about uncovering its precise structure. He was prepared to attack this project by a number of different methods. However, he fortuitously discovered that the particular makeup of DNA, specifically the uniformity of its fibers, made it an excellent specimen for x ray diffraction studies. x ray diffraction is an extremely useful method for photographing atom arrangements in molecules. The regularly-spaced atoms of the molecule actually diffract the x rays, creating a picture from which the sizing and spacing of the atoms within the molecule can be deduced. This was the tool used by Wilkins to help unravel the structure of DNA.

Physical chemist **Rosalind Franklin** joined Wilkins in 1951. Franklin, who had been conducting research in Paris, was very adept in x ray diffraction. Although their personal relationship was not ideal, (Franklin was more outgoing whereas Wilkins was a quiet, non-confrontational person), together they were able to retrieve some very high quality DNA patterns. One initial and important outcome of their research was that phosphate groups were located outside of the structure, which overturned **Linus Pauling**'s theory that they were on the inside. In another important finding, Wilkins thought the photographs suggested a helical structure, although Franklin hesitated to draw that conclusion. Subsequently, Wilkins, some say unbeknownst to Franklin, passed on to Watson one of the best x ray pictures Franklin had taken of DNA. These DNA images provided clues to Watson and Crick, who used the pictures to solve the last piece of the DNA structure puzzle.

X Ray Images Lead to Discovery of DNA Structure

Consequently, in 1953, Watson and Crick were able to reconstruct the famous double-helix structure of DNA. Their model shows that DNA is composed of two strands of alternating units of sugar and phosphate on the outside, with pairs of bases—including the molecular compounds adenine, thymine, guanine, and cytosine—inside, bonded by hydrogen. It is important to note that while Wilkins' contribution to the discernments of DNA's structure is undeniable, controversy surrounds the fact that Franklin was not recognized for this scientific breakthrough, particularly in terms of the Nobel Prize. Some feel that Franklin, who died of cancer in 1958, did not receive due recognition, whereas others maintain that it was solely Watson's ability to discern the structure in Franklin's photograph that made possible the discovery of the DNA structure.

The knowledge of the DNA structure, which has been described as resembling a spiral staircase, has provided the impetus for advanced research in the field of genetics. For example, scientists can now determine predispositions for certain diseases based on the presence of certain genes. Also, the exciting but sometimes controversial area of genetic engineering has developed.

Studies Composition of RNA

Wilkins, Watson, and Crick were awarded the 1962 Nobel Prize for physiology or medicine for their work which uncovered the structure of hereditary material DNA. After winning the Nobel Prize, Wilkins focused next on elucidating the structure of ribonucleic acids (RNA)—a compound like DNA associated with the control of cellular chemical activities—and, later, nerve cell membranes. In 1962 he was able to show that RNA also had a helical structure somewhat similar to that of DNA. Besides his directorship appointments at the Medical Research Council's Biophysics Unit, Wilkins was also appointed director of the Council's Neurobiology Unit, a post he held from 1974 to 1980. Additionally, he was a professor at King's College, teaching molecular biology from 1963 to 1970 and then biophysics as the department head from 1970 to 1982. In 1981, he was named professor emeritus at King's College. Utilizing some of his professional expertise for social causes, Wilkins has maintained membership in the British Society for Social Responsibility in Science (of which he is president), the Russell Committee against Chemical Weapons, and Food and Disarmament International.

Wilkins is an honorary member of the American Society of Biological Chemists and the American Academy of Arts and Sciences. He was also honored with the 1960 Albert Lasker Award of the American Public Health Association (given jointly to Wilkins, Watson, and Crick), and was named Fellow of the Royal Society of King's College in 1959.

Wilkins, known to be a quiet and polite man, married Patricia Ann Chidgey in 1959. The couple have four children, two sons and two daughters.

FURTHER READING:

Books

Current Biography, H. W. Wilson, 1963, pp. 465–466.
McGraw-Hill Modern Scientists and Engineers,
    McGraw-Hill, 1980, pp. 320–321.
Wasson, Tyler, editor, *Nobel Prize Winners,* H. W.
    Wilson, 1987, pp. 1127–1129.

Periodicals

Judson, Horace Freeland, *Science Digest,* The Legend of Rosalind Franklin, January, 1986, pp. 78–81.

Judson, Horace Freeland, *New York Times,* October 19, 1962, p. 1.

Sketch by Carla Mecoli-Kamp

Geoffrey Wilkinson
1921–
English chemist

Geoffrey Wilkinson is best known for establishing the structure of a "sandwich molecule" he called ferrocene. In sandwich compounds a metal atom is the "filling" between two "slices" which are flat, typically carbon-based, rings. Since Wilkinson's original discovery of an iron filling between two cyclopentadienyl (five carbon atoms linked in a circle) slices, many different sandwiches have been built. Various metal fillings have been used, as have numerous other slices. Sandwich compounds have found widespread use as catalysts in industrial processes, and their previously unknown chemical bonding structure has proven to be of great theoretical interest to various branches of chemistry. Wilkinson's discovery revolutionized how chemists thought about chemical structure and opened up new avenues of chemical exploration.

Wilkinson was born on July 14, 1921, in Yorkshire, England, to Henry and Ruth Crowther Wilkinson. It was an uncle, the owner of a small chemical company in the town of Todmorden, who encouraged Wilkinson's interest in chemistry and had the most influence on his career choice. Wilkinson attended the Todmorden Secondary School and then the Imperial College of Science and Technology at the University of London. Supported by a scholarship, he obtained his B.S. degree in 1941 and his doctorate in 1946.

In 1942, while still a doctoral student, Wilkinson worked with the National Research Council on a joint atomic energy project. His work involved separating the various products of atomic fission reactions from one another so they could be studied and the fission process better understood. In the course of this work Wilkinson developed a new technique, ion-exchange chromatography, which has since proven useful in many chemical analyses. Using this technique, Wilkinson identified a number of new isotopes, atomic species which vary only in the number of neutrons within their nuclei. After the Second World War, Wilkinson continued his research on nuclear chemistry at the University of California at Berkeley. His work there focused on identifying neutron-deficient isotopes, products of atomic fission that are unstable because they have too few neutrons in their nuclei.

In 1950, Wilkinson moved to the Massachusetts Institute of Technology as a research associate. He had come to the end of what he considered to be his effectiveness in nuclear synthesis research, and began to study the chemical nature of the transition elements. These are the elements found in the center of the periodic table; they often have more than a single stable electrical charge state and unusual magnetic properties. One of Wilkinson's first major breakthroughs was to synthesize a compound in which the transition element nickel was chemically bound to phosphorus within a larger molecule.

Despite his decision to change the focus of his research, it was Wilkinson's expertise as a nuclear chemist that earned him a position as an assistant professor at Harvard University in 1951. He would only remain at Harvard for four years, but it was a very productive time in his life. It was here that he first deduced the sandwich-type molecular structure.

Discovers Structure of Ferrocene

Early in 1952, while preparing to teach an inorganic chemistry course, Wilkinson read about a newly synthesized compound, bicyclopentadienyl iron (a chemical made from an iron atom bonded to two five-carbon rings). The structure proposed seemed unlikely to Wilkinson. Based on theories developed by **Linus Pauling**, he thought that the key to the structure must lie in the distribution of the so-called pi electrons in the cyclopentadienyl ring. Pauling's work indicated that this ion would have its pi electrons very evenly distributed in rings parallel to the plane of the carbon atoms. Wilkinson realized that a stable structure would result if the iron atom bonded through the pi electrons and was thus held equidistant from all of the carbon atoms in the cyclopentadienyl ring. In bicyclopentadienyl iron this would be possible only by having the iron atom "sandwiched" between the two flat cyclopentadienyl groups.

Along with a colleague, **Robert B. Woodward**, Wilkinson experimentally proved this novel structure in a few days. Woodward coined the term ferrocene, due to the similarity of the structure to the well-known compound benzene. Wilkinson rapidly adapted the synthesis methods to create a number of other sandwich compounds. For discovering this previously unknown class of chemical structure, Wilkinson shared the 1973 Nobel Prize in chemistry with **Ernst Otto Fischer**. Fischer had also worked on these compounds, and in presenting the award the committee congratulated both men for creating a new field of chemistry.

While at Harvard in the 1950s, Wilkinson also pioneered the use of the nuclear magnetic resonance (NMR) technique in chemical analysis. In NMR spectroscopy, chemists study the movement of atoms (most often hydrogen) within a magnetic field; each atom emits a distinct spectral line according to its bond. This technique helped to explain the concept of fluctionality, a theory which states that some chemical species may fluctuate back and forth from one bonding structure to another. This technique has since also found considerable use in medicine, where it is called magnetic resonance imaging or MRI. But despite the widespread recognition of the importance of his work, Harvard University did not offer Wilkinson tenure.

In 1955 Wilkinson returned to the Imperial College of Science and Technology to assume the chair of the inorganic chemistry department. Here he continued his work on transition elements and how they form complexes with organic species through pi electrons. In particular, Wilkinson concentrated on several ways in which transition metal complexes serve as catalysts. (A catalyst speeds up a chemical reaction and is then converted back into its original form, enabling it to serve for multiple cycles of the reaction.)

Wilkinson wrote widely, publishing more than four hundred articles on the transition metals and their complexes with organic compounds. He also coauthored *Advanced Inorganic Chemistry* (1962), which has remained a classic text in the field, and *Basic Inorganic Chemistry* (1976). Wilkinson received numerous honors in addition to the Nobel Prize. The French Chemical Society honored him in 1968 with its Lavoisier Medal, the Royal Society presented him with the Transition Metal Chemistry Award in 1972, and he won the Gallileo Medal from the University of Pisa, Italy, in 1973.

Wilkinson married Lise Solver Schau in 1951, soon after arriving at Harvard. They have two daughters.

SELECTED WRITINGS BY WILKINSON:

Books

Advanced Inorganic Chemistry, Interscience, 1962.
Basic Inorganic Chemistry, Wiley, 1976.

Periodicals

Nucleonics, Chemical Separation of Fission Products by Oxidation-Reaction, Volume 9, 1951.
Journal of the American Chemical Society, The Structure of Bicyclopentadienyl Iron, Volume 74, 1952.
Journal of Organometallic Chemistry, The Iron Sandwich: A Recollection of the First Four Months, Volume 100, 1975, pp. 273–278.

Sketch by Ethan E. Allen

Anna W. Williams
1863–1954
American bacteriologist

Anna W. Williams's work as one of America's pioneering bacteriologists was accomplished during her long tenure at the research laboratory of the New York City Department of Health. Her discovery of the *Corynebacterium diphtheriae* bacillus led to the development of a diphtheria antitoxin and the conquering of this dreaded childhood disease. Williams's wide-ranging research also led to the development of a rabies vaccine and an improved method for diagnosing rabies.

Anna Wessels Williams was born in Hackensack, New Jersey, on March 17, 1863, to William and Jane (Van Saun) Williams. Although her English-born father was a private school teacher, the family, which included her five siblings and several half-siblings, could not afford private school tuition. Williams was schooled at home until she was twelve; she then entered the State Street Public School, where her father was a trustee. Williams attended the New Jersey State Normal School in Trenton, New Jersey, in 1883; she subsequently taught school until 1885. Williams decided on a medical career in 1887, the year one of her sisters suffered a severe illness. She obtained her medical degree in 1891 from the Women's Medical College of the New York Infirmary, and remained there as a pathology and hygiene instructor until 1893 and as department assistant until 1895. Williams also served as consulting pathologist at the Women's Medical College from 1902 to 1905.

Discovery of Diphtheria Antitoxin and Rabies Vaccine

In 1894, Williams volunteered to serve in the bacteriology laboratory at the New York City Department of Health, the nation's first city-operated diagnostic laboratory, whose director was William H. Park. Her work at the Department of Health began with a search for a antitoxin for diphtheria—at that time a leading cause of death among children. Williams' discovery in 1894 of the *Corynebacterium diphtheria* bacillus (a disease-producing bacterium) led to the development of a diphtheria antitoxin soon in use for immunization throughout North America and Great Britain. The isolation of this bacillus strain, known as Park-Williams #8, was generally credited to Park, even though he was not involved in the initial discovery. In 1895, Williams joined the laboratory staff as assistant bacteriologist.

Williams also researched streptococcal and pneumococcal infections (caused by the bacterium responsible for "strep throat" and pneumonia, respectively), and conducted diagnostic studies related to trachoma and the chronic eye infections commonly found among the city's underprivileged children. In 1896, she traveled to the Pasteur Institute in Paris in the hopes of developing an antitoxin for scarlet fever. Although she was not successful in this effort, her experiments with a rabies virus culture she obtained at the Pasteur Institute resulted in the mass production of a rabies vaccine by 1898. In 1905, Williams was named assistant director of the laboratory at the Department of Health.

In this same year, Williams published an improved method of rabies diagnosis based on a technique of analyzing brain tissue samples. This method stemmed from her own research and the parallel studies of Adelchi Negri, an Italian physician, on the presence of distinctive cells in rabies-infected brain tissue. Until Williams's publication of her method, a diagnosis of rabies took ten days; her technique took minutes, and was not improved upon for over thirty years. In recognition of this advance, the American Public Health Association in 1907 appointed Williams as chair of its newly-formed committee on the diagnosis of rabies.

In 1915, Williams became president of the Women's Medical Association. During World War I, she served on the influenza commission, trained medical laboratory workers, and contributed to a military program to detect meningococcal carriers. In 1931, she was elected vice-chair of the laboratory section of the American Public Health Association. Williams also published extensively over the course of her career. She was co-author, with Park, of the widely-used *Pathogenic Microörganisms Including Bacteria and Protozoa: A Practical Manual for Students, Physicians and Health Officers;* their edition first came out in 1905. She published her authoritative treatise, *Streptococci in Relation to Man in Health and Disease,* in 1932. Williams's controversial forced retirement in 1934 came about because of Mayor Fiorello La Guardia's decree of mandatory retirement for all city employees over seventy years old. Despite the urging of Williams's colleagues and other scientists that she be allowed to continue her important research, La Guardia refused to make an exception. She left New York City for retirement in Woodcliff Lake, New Jersey, and subsequently moved to Westwood, New Jersey, where she lived with her sister, Amelia Wilson. Williams died from heart failure on November 20, 1954, at the age of ninety-one.

SELECTED WRITINGS BY WILLIAMS:

Books

Pathogenic Microörganisms Including Bacteria and Protozoa: A Practical Manual for Students, Physicians and Health Officers, Lea Brothers, 1905.
Who's Who among the Microbes, Century, 1929.
Streptococci in Relation to Man in Health and Disease, Williams & Williams, 1932.

Periodicals

Journal of Medical Research, Persistence of Varieties of the Bacillus Diphtheriae and of Diphtheria-like Bacilli, June, 1902.

Journal of Infectious Diseases, A Study of Trachoma and Allied Conditions in the Public School Children of New York City, March, 1914.

FURTHER READING:

Books

Notable American Women: The Modern Period, Belknap, 1980, pp. 737–739.

Periodicals

New York Times, November 21, 1954, p. 86.

Sketch by Jane Stewart Cook

Cicely Delphin Williams
1893–1992
Jamaican-English physician

Cicely Delphin Williams devoted her life to improving the health of women and children all over the world. She is known for discovering the causes of the malnutrition illness kwashiorkor, as well as Jamaican vomiting disease. She was the first female physician to be appointed by the British Colonial Medical Service to Ghana and to hold the post of head of Maternity and Child Welfare. She was also noted for her personal heroism as a prisoner of war during World War II.

Williams was born on Dec. 2, 1893, the daughter of a long-established plantation family in Jamaica, originally from Wales. Her father, James Towland Williams, was the director of education in Jamaica. Williams wanted to attend Oxford, where her father had studied, but when it came time to enter college, the family had no money to send her. She was discouraged from becoming a nurse, so Williams resigned herself to an unchallenging existence at home with her family.

William's break came during World War I, when women were admitted to Oxford because of a shortage of doctors. She decided to study tropical medicine and hygiene and was tutored by one of the famed physicians of the time, Sir William Osler. In 1929, she received her B.A. degree from Oxford.

Williams then went on to study for her M.D. degree. However, after she had taken her finals and it came time for her residency, World War I had ended and along with it the doctor shortage. Williams applied to 70 hospitals before being accepted for a gynecological surgery residency at South London Hospital for Women and Children. It was here that Williams discovered that she loved working with children. Although she found the work at South London Hospital challenging, she really wanted to work overseas. Positions for women were still scarce, so Williams decided the best course of action was to work for the overseas British Colonial Office. After two years of petitioning the office, officials finally relented and posted her in the Gold Coast (now Ghana).

In one year, Williams learned the Ghanaian language and started to develop real fondness for her patients. She was struck by how devoted they were to their children and amused at how often they brought them in to see her. Williams began to notice a common illness among toddlers in Ghanaian families. These children had swollen legs and bellies, rashes, and a red tinge to their hair. Williams thought this might be a nutritional disease, but the other doctors told her she was misdiagnosing the illness pellagra, an already identified malnutrition disease that had similar symptoms.

To test her theory, Williams wanted to do autopsies on the children who had died from the disease but was told that local burial customs would not permit it. But in truth, the families were rushing their children home after death because they could not pay the high cost of moving the body. So Williams offered to pay this fee and began to perform postmortems. She found that the Ghanaians called the disease kwashiorkor, or weaning disease, because children developed it when a new baby was born. Williams surmised correctly that the toddlers were not getting enough protein because they were no longer breast-fed and were not yet eating adult food. Convinced she had found a new type of malnutrition, she identified the disease in *Archives of Disease in Children* in 1933. She also wrote an article in the medical journal *Lancet,* which described the differences between kwashiorkor and pellagra.

While performing an autopsy in her investigations of kwashiorkor, Williams contracted blood poisoning. When she recovered she was transferred to the city of Kumasi. She was disappointed, but decided to make the best of it by writing her delayed doctoral thesis "Child Health in the Gold Coast." The thesis was accepted and she received her M.D. degree in 1936.

Williams wanted to return to Africa but was sent to Trengganu, Malaya (now Malaysia) instead. She never achieved the same fondness for Malaya as she did for the Gold Coast, and found health conditions were horrible. The local religious beliefs regarded illness as fate. Infant mortality was high, partly because Western companies were persuading new mothers to buy canned milk that had little nutrition. Williams tried to take on these companies, but was unable to stop them from sending "nurses" to visit new mothers with their products.

When the Japanese invaded Malaya in 1941, Williams escaped to Singapore. Her safety was short-lived when the Allied forces left Singapore in 1942 and the Japanese strafed the city with bombs. Williams moved children in the city's hospitals from makeshift shelter to makeshift shelter until the Japanese troops entered Singapore. Then, to save her young charges, she offered them to any family that would take them. All were placed.

During the Japanese occupation, Williams was held in the Changi prison camp in Singapore. Her life there was filled with hardship and disease. The Japanese Secret Police, the Kempaitai, began to suspect her after she became head of the women's side of the camp and arrested her. She spent her fiftieth birthday in a tiny prison cell with seven men.

In March 1944, suffering from dysentery and the psychological and physical cruelty she had endured, Williams was returned to Changi prison camp. Seven months later the prisoners saw Allied planes. Weak from dysentery and malaria, Williams survived to see the Japanese surrender.

When Williams recovered, she returned to Malaya as head of the Maternity and Child Welfare Services. It was the first powerful post to be held by a woman in the Colonial Service. In 1948, the new World Health Organization named her to be the first director of the Child and Maternal Health section. But Williams was asked to return to Jamaica to direct an investigative team studying Jamaican vomiting sickness. In a year, her team discovered the culprit was a substance in spoiled ackee fruit, and designed the life-saving treatment of glucose therapy.

In 1955, Williams entered the more sedate life of academia when she became a senior lecturer in nutrition in London University. In 1960, she was hired as professor of maternal and child health with the American University in Beirut. After four years, she went back to London to work with the Family Planning Association as an advisor. In 1965 she was awarded the James Spence Memorial Gold Medal by the British Paedeatric Association.

In 1968, she became professor of international family health at Tulane University's School of Public Health. In 1971 the American Public Health Association gave her the Martha May Eliot Award, and a year later she was awarded the Dawson Williams Prize in Paediatrics by the British Medical Association. At her retirement, she remained active and was an honorary Fellow at Somerville and Green Colleges of Oxford. At age 90, she was still making appearances and speeches. In her speeches she often encouraged young doctors to become general practitioners, citing a need for doctors who would look after people and not just diseases. She died on July 13, 1992 at age 98.

SELECTED WRITINGS BY WILLIAMS:

Periodicals

"Kwashiorkor: A Nutritional Disease of Children Associated with a Maize Diet." *Lancet* 16 (November 1935): 1151-52.
"A Nutritional Disease of Childhood Associated with a Maize Diet." *Archives of Disease in Childhood* 8 (1933): 423-33.

FURTHER READING:

Books

Craddock, Sally. *Retired Except on Demand: The Life of Cicely Williams*. Oxford: Green College, 1983.
Dally, Ann. *Cicely: The Life of a Doctor*. London: Gollancz, 1968.

Sketch by Barbara Boughton

Daniel Hale Williams
1858–1931
American surgeon

Arguably the most prominent black physician of his time, Daniel Hale Williams performed the first recorded successful heart surgery; founded Provident Hospital in Chicago; reorganized Freedmen's Hospital in Washington, D.C.; instituted policies and programs that made Meharry Medical College in Nashville a first-class institution for the training of black medical practitioners; and helped found the National Medical Association, the black counterpart to the segregated American Medical Association. Williams's distinguished career was recognized in 1913 when he was asked to become a charter member of the American College of Surgeons, the only black doctor so honored.

Williams was born January 18, 1858, in Hollidaysburg, Pennsylvania. He was the fifth child of Daniel Williams, a barber, and Sara (Price) Williams. After his father's death, his mother moved the family to Rockford, Illinois, and later to Janesville, Wisconsin, where Williams completed his secondary education. In 1878, he began an apprenticeship under Henry Palmer, a physician who had served as Wisconsin's surgeon general. His training under Palmer enabled him to enter Chicago Medical College, an affiliate of Northwestern University, where he received his medical degree in 1883. After serving an internship at Mercy Hospital in Chicago, Williams opened his practice in an integrated neighborhood on the south side of Chicago.

These early years saw Williams successful in his new practice, where he was meticulous in observing the sterilization and antiseptic procedures (newly advanced by the English surgeon Joseph Lister, based on the germ theory of French microbiologist Louis Pasteur) in the domestic locales of his surgeries. In 1884, he became a surgeon for the South Side Dispensary and an attending physician at the Protestant Orphan Asylum. He began instructing in anatomy at Chicago Medical College in 1885 and also served during this time as surgeon to the City Railway Company. In 1889, he was appointed to a four-year term on the Illinois State Board of Health, where he played a role in drafting important public health regulations.

Founding of Provident Hospital

In spite of his many medical commitments, "Doctor Dan," as he was affectionately called, was determined to establish a progressive interracial hospital that would focus on offering internships to black doctors and training for black nurses. Williams realized this dream in 1891 with the opening of Provident Hospital. It was here that he performed the first recorded heart surgery by suturing a tear in a stabbing victim's pericardium (the membrane that encloses the heart); the patient completely recovered from the risky operation. Williams was subsequently to perfect a suture for spleen hemorrhage.

In 1894, President Cleveland appointed Williams as surgeon-in-chief of Freedmen's Hospital in Washington, D.C. At Freedmen's, Williams used his administrative skills to reorganize and upgrade what was essentially a collection of decrepit Army buildings that had been converted to civilian medical use. Under his guidance, Freedmen's hospital was divided into seven departments: dermatological, genito-urinary, gynecological, medical, obstetrical, surgical, and throat and chest. The number of internships was increased, the nurses training program was strengthened, and a horse-drawn ambulance was put into service. During his tenure, the hospital saw a significant decrease from its former ten percent mortality rate. Williams's administrative achievement at Freedmen's was substantial, although he did not realize all of his far-reaching plans for the institution. In 1895, Williams helped found the Medico-Chirurgical Society of Washington. Ultimately discouraged by political infighting, he resigned from Freedmen's in 1897 and returned to Chicago.

In Chicago, Williams resumed his affiliation with Provident, and also began practicing at other hospitals. In 1899, in addition, Williams accepted a professorship of clinical surgery at Meharry Medical College in Nashville, Tennessee, where he began holding annual surgery clinics. In 1900, Williams presented research to the Chicago Medical Society refuting the myth that black women were not at risk for ovarian cysts. His association with the white-clientele St. Luke's Hospital, beginning in 1913, was instrumental in building one of the largest gynecological practices in Chicago. Over this period, Williams also helped establish forty hospitals in twenty states to serve black communities.

Although Williams retained his affiliation with Provident for many years, his return to Chicago and the hospital came at a time of dissension: it was said that jealous and powerful associates, among them Dr. George C. Hall, looked unfavorably on Williams's advancements within the white medical establishment. The rivalry between Williams and George C. Hall eventually forced Williams to cut his ties to the hospital he had founded. In 1925, Williams invited Leon Tancil to assist him in his practice. Tancil remained for a few years, but then left to establish his own office. Shortly thereafter, Williams's failing health forced him to end his long and distinguished practice.

Williams married Alice Johnson, a school teacher, in 1898; their only child died during birth a year later. Williams' favorite hobby was music; he often played his bass viol for charitable affairs. In 1926, two years after the death of his wife, Williams suffered a stroke and remained in ill health. He died at his summer home in Idlewild, Michigan, on August 4, 1931, and was buried in Chicago's Graceland Cemetery.

SELECTED WRITINGS BY WILLIAMS:

Periodicals

New York Medical Record, Stab Wound of the Heart and Pericardium, Suture of the Pericardium. Recovery. Patient Alive Three Years Afterward, March 27, 1897, pp. 437–439.

National Hospital Record, The Need of Hospitals and Training Schools for the Colored People of the South, Detroit (Reprint of paper read before the Phillis Wheatley Club, Nashville, Tennessee, January 23, 1900).

FURTHER READING:

Books

The African American Encyclopedia, Marshall Cavendish, 1993, pp. 1705–1707.
Blacks in Medicine and Science, Hemisphere, 1990, pp. 251–252.
Buckler, Helen, *Daniel Hale Williams, Negro Surgeon,* Pitman, 1968.
Buckler, Helen, *Doctor Dan, Pioneer in American Surgery,* Little, Brown, 1954.
Fenderson, Lewis R., *Daniel Hale Williams: Open-Heart Doctor,* McGraw-Hill, 1971.
Patterson, Lillie, *Sure Hands, Strong Heart: The Life of Daniel Hale Williams,* Abingdon, 1981.
Patterson, Lillie, *Scientists in the Black Perspective,* The Lincoln Foundation, 1974, pp. 101–103.

Sketch by Jane Stewart Cook

Evan James Williams
1903–1945
English physicist

Evan Williams is known both for his experiments involving atomic particles and for his work as an operational researcher for the British forces during World War II. Just as Williams gained stature among his fellow physicists for his ability to choose the correct experiment and carry it out, he soon became known to the Royal Air Force as someone who rejected traditional ideas of bombing effectiveness and proposed new approaches of much greater efficiency. His untimely death a month after the end of World War II probably contributed to the lack of recognition of his important role in planning the aerial campaigns.

Evan James Williams, the son of a stonemason, was born on June 8, 1903, at Cwmsychpant, Wales. He was fortunate in his early schooling, since the headmaster of his country school had been an outstanding mathematics student at Cambridge University and was able to recognize Williams's ability and to encourage his interest in physics and mathematics. Williams graduated from the Swansea (Wales) Technical College—now part of the University of Wales—and continued his studies at the University of Manchester in England and at Cambridge University. He obtained a Ph.D. in physics from Manchester in 1926 and another degree at Cambridge in 1929, where he worked with **Ernest Rutherford** and **C. T. R. Wilson** at the Cavendish Laboratory. In 1930 Williams returned to Manchester, where, with the exception of a year at the Copenhagen Institute of Niels Bohr, he taught physics and conducted experiments until 1937. He then moved to the University of Liverpool to work with **James Chadwick**, who had won the Nobel Prize two years earlier for the discovery of the neutron.

Williams in the 1920s and '30s specialized in exacting measurements of particle paths using the Wilson cloud chamber. C. T. R. Wilson near the end of the nineteenth century had been studying cloud formation and had invented a way to create miniature clouds by suddenly expanding moist air in a small chamber. When x rays were discovered, Wilson discovered that x rays had a profound effect on his cloud chambers. By 1911 he had developed at the Cavendish Laboratory a version of the cloud chamber with which he could photograph the tracks of individual charged particles. The tracks become visible by a process similar to the one that causes jet airplanes to leave contrails. The Wilson cloud chamber became the observational device of choice for atomic scientists before World War II.

Williams's work with the cloud chamber generally consisted of making very precise measurements that could be used to confirm or deny particular theories. In 1927, for example, he calculated the stopping power of alpha and beta particles by various different gases. (The three common forms of radiation produced by a radioactive element were labeled alpha, beta, and gamma. Beta particles were found to be energetic electrons, while gamma rays are very high energy x rays. Alpha particles are the nuclei of helium atoms propelled from the radioactive atoms.) For these experiments, Wilson replaced the air in the cloud chamber with the gases hydrogen, helium, nitrogen, oxygen, and neon, then photographed and measured the tracks. The reason for such experiments was to determine whether or not the Bohr model of the atom as a nucleus with electrons in orbit was sufficient. Wilson's work showed that the Bohr model was successful in predicting how hydrogen would stop alpha and beta particles, but that the situation was more complicated for heavier atoms and that a different theory would be needed.

In 1930 Wilson turned to another problem, which was the nature of the various decay products that were being discovered. He used the cloud chamber to observe the particle tracks produced by the substance then known as "radium E," a radioactive substance near the end of the chain of decay products of uranium. Today radium E is called bismuth-210. It decays either by emitting a beta particle to become radium F (polonium-210) or by an alpha particle and a beta particle into lead-206, the stable end of uranium decay.

In the late 1930s one of the great problems of particle physics was understanding the nature of particles found in cosmic rays. Williams and a coworker used the Wilson cloud chamber to analyze the decay pattern of the cosmic ray particles in 1940. This was exacting experimental science. They shielded the cloud chamber with a lead plate to keep out all particles but the energetic cosmic rays. The cloud chamber was kept in a strong magnetic field so that the charge of the particles and their masses could be determined. A magnet bends positively charged particles in one direction and negatively charged particles in the other. The degree of bending tells how heavy the particle is. Williams photographed the tracks made by the cosmic rays. In two photographs he obtained a clear picture of decay, from which he was able to show that the decay product was an electron.

During World War II Williams was associated with **Patrick Maynard Stuart Blackett**, later Baron Blackett, a colleague from Cavendish Laboratory days who had worked on many problems similar to those Williams had studied, including transmutation of elements and cosmic rays. They were among the chief founders of operations research. The classic example of operations research from this period concerned the use of depth bombs released by aircraft pursuing submarines. Conventional military assumed that submarines would immediately dive when a plane was spotted, so bombs should be set to explode at a depth of about 100 yds (91 m) beneath the sea. However, most submarines escaped such bomb attacks. The analysis from operations research demonstrated that if a submarine spotted an enemy airplane, it saw it far enough away to dive below 100 yds (91 m) in a direction unknown to the bomber on the plane. Yet, if the submarine had failed to notice the approaching aircraft until the bomb was about to be released, the submarine could not dive as deep as 100 yds (91 m). Thus, the best strategy for an air attack would be to use bombs that explode on the surface and only bomb submarines on the surface or just as a dive was beginning. The number of submarines sank by aerial bombardment doubled when the new strategy was adopted. After the war, the mathematical techniques of operations research became popular in analyzing business enterprises.

SELECTED WRITINGS BY WILLIAMS:

Periodicals

Correlation of Certain Collision Problems with Radiation Theory. 1927.

FURTHER READING:

Books

Ernest Rutherford, James Chadwick, and C. D. Ellis. *Radiation from Radioactive Substances.* Cambridge: University Press, 1930 (reprinted 1951).

Sketch by Bryan Bunch

Frederic C. Williams
1911–1977
English electrical engineer

Sir Frederic C. Williams, an electrical engineer, is best known for his development of the Williams tube, an early data storage system for electronic digital computers. Although his invention was soon superseded by the magnetic-core system developed by **Jay Forrester**, it was a significant development at the time and allowed electronic computers to access data in memory randomly instead of serially, which made for much faster data retrieval. Williams was such a prolific inventor and developer of electronic and mechanical devices that his name ultimately appeared in over one hundred patent applications. His work extended from airplane radar and storage devices for electronic computers to early automatic transmissions for automobiles.

Frederic Calland Williams was born on June 26, 1911 in Romiley, Cheshire, England, the only son of Frederic Williams, a locomotive draftsman, and Ethel Alice Williams (whose maiden name was Smith). He entered the school of engineering at the University of Manchester on a scholarship in 1929, graduating with honors in 1932 and winning the Fairbairn prize. A year later he received his Master of Science degree. After a brief apprenticeship at the Metropolitan-Vickers Electrical Company, he entered Magdalen College of Oxford University in 1934 on a scholarship awarded by the Institution of Electrical Engineers. His research in the engineering laboratories at Oxford focused on the study of circuit and valve noise. For recreation, he was a coxswain (steersman) in the eight-man boating races on the Thames River.

After receiving his Doctor of Philosophy degree from Oxford in 1936, Williams returned to the University of Manchester and became an assistant lecturer in the school of engineering. In 1939, the University of Manchester awarded him a Doctorate in Science for his research. Williams married Gladys Ward in 1938, and they had two children, a daughter and a son. Their son eventually became a professor of civil engineering.

Major Contributions to the War Effort

During World War II, Williams worked on several important projects, including the development of radar and of automatic target acquisition equipment for aircraft. Although airplanes had played only a minor role in World War I, developments in aeronautical engineering made the war in the air vastly more important during World War II. Now far larger and having much greater ranges, aircraft could traverse great distances with many men and large stores of supplies. Aircraft had also become much more varied, comprising bombers, cargo planes, long-range reconnaissance aircraft, and fighter planes. Some kinds of planes were crewed by one person; others needed a large crew to carry out their complicated missions. All these aircraft had to be able to fly in all kinds of weather.

As part of his contribution to the war effort, Williams developed many of the instruments that enabled different aircraft to carry out their missions. In 1939, Williams went to the Bawdsey Research Station, where he worked on the equipment that enabled radar operators to distinguish between friendly and enemy aircraft. His work on aircraft identification systems also included developing intricate coding procedures that allowed aircraft to disguise themselves electronically so that they could not be detected by enemy radar. For single-seat airplanes, Williams developed a fully automatic radar system that took up little of the pilot's attention. Williams's system could automatically locate a target, filter out distracting ground echoes and echoes from other airplanes with electronic identification signals, and indicate the direction of the target and its range. This equipment enabled accurate bombing through heavy cloud cover and permitted planes to navigate by radio at night or during bad weather when the crew could not see the stars or geographical landmarks.

Developed the First Random Access Memory

After the war, Williams made his most important discovery, a way of storing data on a cathode-ray tube similar to those used in television receivers. For electronic computers to process data, they need some way to store instructions in memory and to access them in performing operations on data in a systematic way. In early electronic digital computers, the memory storage consisted of mercury delay lines. These lines, however, were highly sensitive and difficult to manufacture. Also, they could only store data serially. That is, to read a single instruction in the middle of the instruction set, the computer had to start at the beginning and read all the way through to the middle for the one instruction that it needed to use. It was like reading all of a dictionary's entries from A through M in order to access the word "Neolithic." Obviously, this serial method of accessing memory took a long time.

Working at the University of Manchester in 1946, Williams discovered a way to store instructions in spots on a cathode-ray tube that would serve as a computer memory. A key problem with storing spots on a cathode-ray tube was that the spots would fade away rapidly. One of Williams's innovations was to develop electronic circuits for refreshing the spots on the tube, so that a spot could be stored indefinitely. An important benefit of using cathode-ray tubes for storing instructions in memory was that the instructions could be accessed randomly. That is, if the instruction that the computer needed was at the middle of the instruction set, then the computer could find that instruction immediately, without having to start from the beginning. As Andrew Hodges has said, another benefit of the Williams tube was that "one could actually see the numbers and instructions held in the machine, as bright spots on the three monitor tubes. Indeed, at this stage it was essential to see them, for there was no other output mechanism. Nor was there any form of input but that of hand switches, used to insert digits one at a time into the storage tube."

Using this innovation, Williams and other electronics experts working with him at the University of Manchester built one of the first working stored-program digital computers in the world. The Manchester Mark I or MADM computer was produced commercially by Ferranti, Ltd., and approximately twenty of the computers were installed in Britain and other countries.

Williams went on to develop a second computer before turning his attention to work with motors. Late in his career he built an automatic transmission for automobiles, which he used in his own car. Williams was named an Officer of the British Empire in 1945 and Commander of the British Empire in 1961; he was knighted in 1976. He received several honorary doctorates and many awards in Britain and the United States, including the Benjamin Franklin medal from the Royal Society of Arts in 1957 and the John Scott award from the city of Philadelphia in 1960. He was elected a Fellow of the Royal Society in 1950. Williams died in Manchester, England, on August 11, 1977.

FURTHER READING:

Books

Biographical Memoirs of Fellows of the Royal Society, Volume 24, Royal Society (London), 1978.

Cortada, James W., *Historical Dictionary of Data Processing: Biographies,* Greenwood Press, 1987.

Hodges, Andrew, *Alan Turing: The Enigma,* Simon & Schuster, 1983.

Shurkin, Joel, *Engines of the Mind,* Pocket Books, 1984.

Sketch by Patrick Moore

Heather Williams
1955–
American ornithologist

Heather Williams is a truth seeker. Whether it is as a world class orienteer (long distance running using a map and compass to find specific points and traverse a course) or as an ornithologist/neuroethologist, she challenges herself both mentally and physically in order to give greater meaning and understanding to the world in which she lives. Her tenacious approach to research and discovery has brought Williams substantial success, most notably the MacArthur Foundation award and grant in 1993 as well as recognition as one of the top female orienteers during the 1980s.

Heather Williams was born on July 27, 1955, in Spokane, Washington, to James Edward Williams and Maria Greig Williams. She has three siblings, Greig, Reid, and Alexandra. Because her father was employed by the U.S. foreign service, Williams moved frequently during her childhood. With each move, she was exposed not only to different cultures but also to vastly different flora and fauna. While living in such places as Laos, Turkey, and Bolivia, Williams explored her surroundings and was attracted to the indigenous animal species. The fact that she was exposed to many different animals and enjoyed collecting the smaller of those species further developed her interest in biology.

Williams cultivated her interests through formal study, receiving an A.B. in biology from Bowdoin College in Maine in 1977. Always an achiever, she graduated *summa cum laude* from that institution, and her interests blossomed into a career of scientific inquiry. Williams spent 1977-78 as a Thomas J. Watson Fellow at Hebrew University in Eilat, Israel, before continuing with her masters and then doctoral degrees. While in Israel, she conducted research in marine biology. While she was pursuing her higher degrees, she found her life's work.

Williams chose to continue her studies at Rockefeller University in New York. Her mentor at Rockefeller was Fernando Nottebohm, whose own research pertained to the canary and its behavior. Expanding Nottebohm's research, Williams was award her doctorate in 1985 for her studies of the zebra finch. Her dissertation was entitled "A Motor Theory for Bird Song Perception," and it has been the basis for her scientific endeavors ever since.

Concerned with how a bird hears the sounds or songs of other birds, Williams's research pinpoints both the nerves and parts of the brain that are involved in song recognition, organization, and reconstruction. She has discovered that zebra finches learn songs in three syllable "chunks," which they reorganize to create new songs. The way in which the zebra finch executes the song is also highly stylized and fits into specific behavioral patterns. As with speech, a bird's song is a lateralized function, primarily executed by one half of the brain. The other brain hemisphere does, however, contribute to the song production. This is an interesting fact in that birds do not have a connection (corpus callosum) to coordinate the activity of each of the brain hemispheres. Williams is investigating how brain activity occurring between hemispheres is regulated. She is also interested in sexual dimorphism and its role in song perception, as well as how distinct dialects are maintained within delineated finch groups. Her work not only has insight into zebra finch behavior and biology, but it also implies parallels with other animal species and their communication. Her findings will cross the boundaries of biology to broaden our understanding of neuroscience and psychology.

During the same time period as Williams was pursuing her doctoral degree and conducting postdoctoral research, she also found the time to become the third ranking orienteer in the United States (1980-89) and marry Patrick D. Dunlavey (1986). In 1988, Williams joined the faculty at Williams College in Williamstown, Massachusetts. Still close enough to Rockefeller University in New York, Williams was drawn to the small town atmosphere, knowing she could still confer closely with her Rockefeller colleagues. In 1993, Williams was a member of the course-mapping team for the world championships in orienteering. She and her husband have two children, Maria Greig and Alan Peter Dunlavey.

SELECTED WRITINGS BY WILLIAMS:

Periodicals

(With Jessica McKibben) "Changes in Stereotyped Central Vocal Motor Patterns are Induced by Peripheral Nerve Injury." *Behavioral and Neural Biology* 57 (1992): 67-78.

(With Kirsten Staples) "Syllable Chunking in Zebra Finch (*Taeniopygia guttata*) Song." *Journal of Comparative Psychology* 106 (1992): 278-286.

(With Linda Crane, Timothy Hale, et. al.) "Right-side Dominance for Song Control in the Zebra Finch." *Journal of Neurobiology* 23 (1992): 1006-1020.

Other

(With Franklin Mullins and Jennifer Danforth) "A Comparison of the Effects of Deafening and Vocal Disruption on the Stability of Crystallized Song." *Society for Neuroscience Abstracts* 23. 1997. http://www.williams.edu:803/Biology/ZFinch/nsci97.html (30 October 1997).

FURTHER READING:

Books

King, Kathleen Palombo. "Heather Williams." *Notable Women in the Life Sciences: A Biographical Dictionary.* Benjamin F. Shearer and Barbara S. Shearer, eds. Westport, Connecticut: Greenwood Press, 1996.

Other

Williams College faculty information directory. http://www.williams.edu:803/Biology/hwilliams.html (October 30, 1997).

Sketch by Jacqueline L. Longe

O. S. Williams
1921–

American aeronautical engineer

The second African American to receive a degree in aeronautical engineering, O. S. Williams headed the team that originated the first experimental airborne radio beacon for tracking crashed aircraft. Williams also managed the development of the control rocket systems that successfully guided the Apollo lunar landers.

Oswald S. "Ozzie" Williams was born on September 2, 1921 in Washington, D.C., to Oswald S. Williams, a postal worker, and Marie (Madden) Williams, a housewife. He grew up in New York, graduating from Boys High School in Brooklyn in 1938. Williams became interested in engineering as a teenager. He loved to make model airplanes and decided to become an engineer after a family friend described an engineer as a person who designs things.

When Williams went to New York University, he was discouraged by a dean. As he recounted in an interview with Terrie M. Romano, the dean told him that "people of your race are not ready for engineering, and engineering is not ready for you. I warn you not to waste your ambition and training where you cannot get a job." Despite such advice, Williams completed his bachelor's degree in aeronautical engineering at New York University in 1943; he received his master's degree in aeronautical engineering from the same institution in 1947.

Aids in Design of War Planes

During World War II, Williams was a senior aerodynamicist with the Republic Aviation Corporation. He helped to design the P47 Thunderbolt, which was pivotal in the war effort. The P47 was the escort plane that protected the American high-altitude bombers. As an aerodynamicist, he was responsible for estimating and calculating from wind tunnel testing, the lift of the plane's wings, its propelling forces and its drag in order to determine how well the airplane would fly and its overall stability.

In 1947 Williams moved to the Babcock and Wilcox company, where he was a design draftsman. He then spent two years as a technical writer with the United States Navy Material Catalog Office, leaving in 1950 to take an engineering position at Greer Hydraulics, Inc. At Greer, as a group project leader, he was responsible for the development of the first experimental airborne radio beacon, which was used to locate crashed airplanes. The project was very challenging since the beacon had to operate equally well wherever it landed and whatever the weather conditions. The beacon would be fired by catapult and parachute to the ground as the airplane disintegrated, potentially landing anywhere: in water, in a tree, on level ground, or on a mountainside. Williams's team developed a beacon that could recognize where it had landed and transmit its position, but unfortunately, it was never produced commercially.

In 1956, Williams moved to the Reaction Motors Division of Thiokol Chemical Corporation, where he was responsible for pioneering work on small rocket engines. Williams was hired as a propulsion engineer by Grumman International in 1961 because of his expertise on liquid-fuel rockets. He had published several papers on the subject, one of which, "On the feasibility of liquid bipropellant rockets for spacecraft attitude control," was translated into Russian by Dr. Leonid Sedov, the president of the Soviet Space Academy.

Helps Develop Apollo Lunar Module

At Grumman, Williams managed the development of the Apollo Lunar Module reaction control subsystem. Williams was fully responsible for the $42 million effort for eight years. He managed the three engineering groups that developed the small rocket motors—which used one hundred pounds of thrust in comparison to the 10,500 pounds of thrust of the lunar module's main engine—that guided the lunar module, the part of the Apollo spacecraft that actually landed on the moon.

Williams went on to a career in marketing at Grumman, culminating in his election as a company vice president in 1974. After leaving Grumman he became a marketing professor at St. John's University in Queens, New York, where he had completed an M.B.A. in 1981. Williams was a member of the American Institute of Aeronautics and Astronautics, as well as an associate fellow and past chair of its Liquid Rockets Technical Committee. His varied career was profiled on Queens Public Television in the one-hour program, *O.S. Williams, A Man of Three Careers.*

In 1993, O. S. and Doris Reid Williams celebrated their fiftieth wedding anniversary. They had three children: Gregory (who died in 1982), Bruce, and Meredith.

FURTHER READING:

Books

Biography provided by Grumman International Inc., dated August, 1985.

O. S. Williams, interviews with Terrie M. Romano, conducted March 18 and 21, 1994.

Sketch by Terrie M. Romano

James S. Williamson
1949–
American mathematician

James S. Williamson, a Chippewa scientist, has gained recognition in many fields including mathematics, solar energy, and education. He was instrumental in developing the nation's first solar central receiver electric generating plant and later improving the receiver's design. Throughout his career, Williamson has taught and has also helped formulate new methods for educating students in mathematics. He has also been active in government; in 1978, he was appointed by President Jimmy Carter to the Domestic Policy Review Panel for Solar Energy Research.

Williamson was born November 30, 1949, the eighth of twelve children, in Williston, North Dakota. His mother, Cecelia (Falcon) was a homemaker and his father, Fritz Williamson, was a civil servant. His oldest brother, F. Dale Williamson, is also a scientist, with a doctorate in chemistry. Academically, Williamson's background is in mathematics, a discipline which he has applied to several career fields. He graduated with a bachelor of science degree from Montana State University in 1971 and then completed his master's degree at the University of California, Berkeley, in 1974. His research centered on the hyperbolic and elliptical functions of imaginary numbers, which, at that point, only had application in space travel. While at Berkeley, he taught undergraduate courses in mathematics, as well as being part of a curriculum development team deriving new teaching methods for mathematics.

His career in solar energy research began as Project Manager for the Atomic Energy Commission in 1971, first in Idaho Falls, Idaho, then in Oakland, California. For six years he provided project management for solar systems for satellite power, managed subcontractor projects for the development of a nuclear reactor system and radio-isotope thermonuclear power systems for satellites, and directed the design of the solar thermal test facility. Williamson told contributor Marianne Fedunkiw in an interview that he was originally hired as a mathematician/statistician to evaluate, using mathematical models, how to clean up fuels coming out of a spent reactor. When an opportunity arose to work on applications in space, he took it, a move which brought him into the field of solar energy. "Solar energy was used in space long before it was on the ground," he said. Williamson was the program manager for the design of the central receiver test facility in Albuquerque, New Mexico, and for the design of the nation's first solar central receiver electric generating plant at Barstow, California. The Barstow plant has more than 1,800 large mirrors, each of which reflect onto a steam boiler mounted on a tower several hundred feet in the air to make steam; this steam, in turn, drives a turbine to generate electricity for the Los Angeles area.

In 1977 Williamson moved to the Martin Marietta Corporation in Denver, Colorado, as Deputy Program Manager for Advanced Solar Technologies, followed by eight years (1978–86) as Program Director for International Solar Energy Programs at Midwest Research Institute. He spent the first four years in Golden, Colorado, and then the next four years in Kansas City, Missouri. His research concentrated on water desalination, independent utility power systems, and solar systems. Although he was active in government and the private sector, he never abandoned teaching. During his last two years at Midwest, he taught evening courses in mathematics at the University of Missouri in Kansas City.

Williamson left Midwest in 1986 to become Associate Partner and Director of the Technology Management Group, Meridian Corporation in Washington, where he had a staff of sixty who provided management support to the Department of Energy as well as conducted biomass resource surveys and developed a technology assessment guide for public utilities. He also spent seven months of 1989 as the President of Engineering and Product Services, a small engineering consulting firm. One project of this firm was the development of a recruiting strategy for Native American health centers.

The late 1980s marked another shift in Williamson's career, applying solar energy programs and activities to increase young students' interests in science and mathematics. Since 1989, he has been Assistant to the Director for Education & Special Projects at the National Renewable Energy Laboratory, originally in Washington, D.C. Later, in 1992, he returned to Golden, Colorado. He has also served as Adjunct Lecturer at Regis University in Denver, Colorado, lecturing on the business and economics of alternative energy technologies, and at the Air Force Academy, Colorado Springs, Colorado, lecturing on thermodynamic applications in solar energy. His most recent work has been in developing science, mathematics, and technology education for students from kindergarten to the university level. "This includes curriculum modules, organizing and managing student competitions," he explained to Fedunkiw, "basically things to get kids interested in science." One example was the development of a mini solar-powered car competition, complete with ramp tests, speed tests, and a design contest.

Evaluating his contributions to science to Fedunkiw, Williamson divided it into two periods: he considers his early mathematics work at Berkeley to have been significant as well as his later work in solar energy—specifically the development of advanced solar central receiver technology while at Martin Marietta. He was a codesigner, with Tom Tracy, of advanced concepts for heat transfer and solar receiver designs using a molten salt transfer fluid.

Williamson's achievements also include joint solar energy research projects between Saudi Arabia and the United States; researching air conditioning systems to generate electricity from sunlight; nuclear material safeguards systems for nuclear power plants; and the design of nuclear and solar power systems for space travel to Saturn, Mars, and Jupiter.

Williamson is a charter member of the American Indian Science and Engineering Society, as well as a member of the American Solar Energy Society and International Solar Energy Society. He also holds memberships to the Institute of Electrical and Electronic Engineers and the American Management Association. Among his awards are the 1991 Organization Committee Award, Conference for Economics of Ethanol Fuels, Montana State University and the Management Award, given by the Saudi Arabian National Center for Science and Technology in 1983 for contributions made as U.S. Program Director for the Joint U.S./Saudi Arabia Solar Research Program.

Williamson married Virginia Hansen in 1968. They have two children, James and Kerry. When he is not working, Williamson raises and breeds paint horses on a small farm. "My father used to raise horses," he told Fedunkiw. "I started about ten years ago."

SELECTED WRITINGS BY WILLIAMSON:

Periodicals

Energy Policies of Ethanol Fuels, Ethanol Producers and Consumers Conference, November, 1990.
College Chemistry, Chemistry of Solar Energy Technologies, November, 1990.
Economics of Alternative Fuels, Women Involved in Farm Economics, Arkansas Conference, June, 1991.
Education Programs at the National Renewable Energy Laboratory, American Solar Energy Society Annual Conference, June, 1992.

Books

Unsolicited Proposal Evaluation, Solar Energy Research Institute, 1979.
Solar Energy Water Desalination, Conference Proceedings of U.S./Saudi Arabian Joint Research Program for Solar Energy, 1982.

Solar for Remote Applications, Conference Proceedings of U.S./Saudi Arabian Joint Research Program for Solar Energy, 1986.

FURTHER READING:

Books

Directory of the National Society of the Sons of the American Revolution, 1993.

Other

American Indian Science and Engineering Society Biography Booklet, 1984–85, p. 29.
Williamson, James S., *Interview with Marianne Fedunkiw,* conducted March, 1994.

Sketch by Marianne Fedunkiw

Richard Willstätter
1872–1942
German chemist

A gifted experimentalist, Richard Willstätter's pioneering work on natural products, especially chlorophylls and anthocyanins (plant pigments), was honored with the 1915 Nobel Prize in chemistry. In 1924 Willstätter, who was Jewish, resigned from his position at the University of Munich in protest against the anti-Semitism of some of the faculty. This act of conscience seriously hampered his research activity. In 1939 the anti-Semitic policies of the Third Reich forced him to emigrate to Switzerland, where he spent the remaining few years of his life.

Education and Early Career

Richard Martin Willstätter was born in Karlsruhe, Germany on August 13, 1872, the second of two sons of Max and Sophie Ulmann Willstätter. Willstätter's father was a textile merchant and his mother's family was in the textile business. Willstätter's education began in the classical Gymnasium in Karlsruhe. When he was eleven years old, his father moved to New York in search of better economic opportunities and to escape the circumscribed life in Karlsruhe; although this separation was meant to be short, it lasted seventeen years. Willstätter's mother took him and his brother to live near her family home in Nürnberg, a change to which Willstätter had difficulty adjusting, in part because of the more overt anti-Semitism he experienced there.

Richard Willstätter

One effect of the move to a new school was that, although receiving good grades in his other subjects, he did poorly in Latin, the most important subject in the gymnasia of the time. A family council decided he should switch to the Realgymnasium and be educated for business instead of a profession. Ironically, it was at this time, stimulated by some home experiments and good teachers, that he decided to become a chemist. In his autobiography, Willstätter observed that excellence in academic subjects caused one to be disliked, while athletic excellence resulted in popularity. He was also attracted to medicine and might have become a physician instead of a chemist, but because of the longer schooling required his mother would not permit him to change. An interest in biological processes remained with him, though, and is evident in the kinds of chemical problems he attacked. Much later, while teaching at Zurich, he still thought of studying physiology and internal medicine, but the death of his wife ended the idea.

In 1890 the eighteen-year-old Willstätter entered the University of Munich and also attended lectures at the Technische Hochschule. In 1893 he began his doctoral studies and was assigned to do his research under Alfred Einhorn on some aspects of the chemistry of cocaine. It was at this time that **Adolf Baeyer**, the leading organic chemist in Germany, began to take Willstätter under his wing. Although Willstätter never worked directly for Baeyer, he thought of himself as Baeyer's disciple. Willstätter completed his doctoral work in a year and stayed on doing independent research, becoming a privatdocent, or unsalaried lecturer, in 1896.

In his work with Einhorn, Willstätter had come to suspect that the structure assigned to cocaine by Einhorn and others was incorrect. When he started his independent research, Einhorn forbade him to work on the cocaine problem. Willstätter, with Baeyer's approval, decided to work instead on the closely related chemical tropine, whose structure was suspected to be similar to that of cocaine; once the structure of tropine was known, the structure of cocaine could be easily derived. Willstätter showed that, indeed, the cocaine structure was not what it had been thought to be; for the remainder of his stay at Munich, Einhorn refused to speak to him. In 1902 Willstätter was appointed professor extraordinarius (roughly equivalent to associate professor), although Baeyer thought he should have accepted an industrial position. Baeyer, himself partly Jewish, also recommended that Willstätter be baptized, an act that would have removed the legal barriers he faced as a Jew. This Willstätter refused to consider. During Easter vacation in 1903 Willstätter met the Leser family from Heidelberg, and that summer he and Sophie Leser were married. Their son Ludwig was born in 1904 and their daughter, Margarete, in 1906.

Switzerland and Nobel Prize Work

In 1905 Willstätter accepted a call to the Eidgenössische Technische Hochscuhle in Zurich as professor of chemistry, beginning the most productive phase of his career. While at Munich he had begun an investigation into the chemical nature of chlorophyll, the green pigment in plants that converts light into energy through photosynthesis; at Zurich, he and his students made great strides in understanding this important material. They developed methods for isolating chlorophyll from plant materials without changing it or introducing impurities. Willstätter was then able to prove that the chlorophyll from different plants (he examined over two hundred different kinds) was substantially the same—a mixture of two slightly different compounds, blue-green chlorophyll a and yellow-green chlorophyll b, in a 3 to 1 ratio.

He also showed that magnesium, which had been found in chlorophyll by earlier workers, was not an accidental impurity but an essential component of these chlorophyll molecules, bonded in a way very similar to that in which iron is bonded in hemoglobin, the oxygen-carrying constituent of blood. The later work of others, especially **Hans Fischer**, in elucidating the detailed structures of the chlorophylls and hemoglobin would not have been possible without the pioneering work of Willstätter and his students. In 1913, Willstätter, in collaboration with his former student and good friend, Arthur Stoll, reviewed the work on chlorophyll in a book, *Untersuchungen über Chlorophyll*. In all, between 1913 and 1919, Willstätter published twenty-five papers in a series on chlorophyll. A preliminary step in the isolation of chlorophyll from plant materials yielded a yellow solution that on further study proved to contain carotenoid pigments. These had been described before, but Willstätter's work marked the beginning of our understanding of these materials that produce the color of tomatoes, carrots, and egg yolk.

In 1908, Willstätter suffered a devastating blow in the death of his wife after an operation for appendicitis had been delayed for thirty-six hours after the appendix had ruptured. He consoled himself with the care of his two children and with his work; in his autobiography he wrote that he took no vacations for the next ten years. During his stay at Zurich, Willstätter also did work on quinones and the mechanism of the oxidation of aniline to aniline black—a process of importance to the dye industry. He also completed a project begun eight years earlier, by synthesizing the chemical cyclooctatetraene and showing that it did not behave as an aromatic compound despite its structural similarities to benzene.

Berlin and the War

The Kaiser Wilhelm Institutes were founded in 1910 to afford outstanding scientists the chance to do research on problems of their own choosing, free of any teaching obligations. In 1911 Willstätter accepted the position of director of the Kaiser Wilhelm Institute of Chemistry and in 1912 moved into the new building at Berlin-Dahlem. The institute was situated next to the Institute for Physical Chemistry and Electrochemistry, headed by **Fritz Haber**, and a deep and lasting friendship developed between the two directors.

At Zurich, Willstätter had initiated a study of the pigments of various red and blue flowers, a class of compounds now known as anthocyanins. He began with dried cornflowers, or bachelor's button, because it was winter and they were commercially available. This choice, as it turned out, was not a good one; cornflowers only contained a percent or less of the pigment. In Berlin, Willstätter planted fields of double cornflowers, asters, chrysanthemums, pansies, and dahlias around the Institute and his residence. In these fresh flowers he found a much higher pigment content, up to 33 percent in blue-black pansies. Before World War I brought an end to this line of research, Willstätter published eighteen papers in an anthocyanin series between 1913 and 1916. He showed that the various shades of red and blue in these flowers as well as in cherries, cranberries, roses, plums, elderberries, and poppies all arose mainly from three closely related compounds, cyanidin, pelargonidin, and delphinidin chlorides, and were very dependent on the acidity or alkalinity of the flower. During the first year of the war, most of Willstätter's co-workers went into military service, and the flowers were taken to military hospitals instead of to the laboratory. Willstätter was bitterly disappointed by this interruption and could not bring himself to return to the problem after the war.

In 1915 Haber, who was in charge of Germany's chemical warfare work, asked Willstätter's assistance in developing the chemical absorption unit for a gas mask that would protect against chlorine and phosgene (a severe respiratory irritant). In five weeks, Willstätter came up with a canister containing activated charcoal and hexamethylene-tetramine (also called urotropin). The use of charcoal was not new, but the use of hexamethylenetetramine was. When asked after the war how he had come to try so unusual a compound, he said that the idea had just popped into his head. For this work he received an Iron Cross, Second Class. He was also involved in an industrial research project with **Friedrich Bergius** on the hydrolysis of cellulose with hydrochloric acid to give dextrose, which could then be fermented to produce alcohol. The process, which was only perfected later, is now known as the Bergius-Willstätter process.

In the spring of 1915 Willstätter's ten-year-old son, Ludwig, died suddenly, apparently from diabetes. Willstätter wrote that his memory of the months following was blurred. Ironically, in November, while engaged in the work on gas masks, Willstätter learned that he had been awarded the 1915 Nobel Prize in chemistry in recognition of his work on chlorophylls and anthocyanins. Because of wartime conditions he did not travel to Stockholm to receive the prize until 1920, when a ceremony was held for a group of those who had been honored during the war. Willstätter made the trip in the company of fellow German awardees **Max Planck**, Fritz Haber, **Max Laue**, and **Johannes Stark**.

The Return to Munich and the Final Years

An offer of a full professorship to succeed Baeyer at Munich also came in 1915. This offer, recommended by Baeyer, was precipitated by an offer to succeed **Otto Wallach**, a pioneer in natural product chemistry, at Göttingen. Willstätter maintained that left to his own inclinations, he would have preferred Göttingen, because a medium-sized university would provide more contact with colleagues and greater interaction with different disciplines than was possible at large institutions. However, he accepted the appointment as professor and director of the state chemical laboratory in Munich and moved there in the spring of 1916.

He made two major demands before accepting the offer: that the old institute building be remodeled and a large addition to the chemical institute be built housing laboratories and a large lecture hall, and that a full professorship in physical chemistry be established. The first of these was contrary to the advice that the physical chemist **Walther Nernst** gave him before he left Berlin, "Don't ever build!" In fact, the construction, delayed by the war and post-armistice turmoil in Munich, was not completed until the spring of 1920.

At Munich, as before, Willstätter experienced the anti-Semitism that had troubled him during his earlier residence, and that finally brought about his resignation in 1924. The final straw was the refusal of the faculty to appoint the noted geochemist **Victor Goldschmidt** of Oslo, Norway, to succeed the mineralogist Paul von Groth, who had himself named Goldschmidt as the only one who could take his place. The sole reason for the refusal was that Goldschmidt was Jewish. When Willstätter's resignation became known, students and faculty joined in expressions of respect and confidence, urging him to reconsider. Nonetheless, he remained only for the time needed to see his students finish their research and to install **Heinrich Wieland** in his place. He received offers of positions at universities and in industry in Germany and abroad, but he declined all of them, finally leaving the university in September 1925 never to return.

Some of Willstätter's assistants continued work at the University, and in 1928 Wieland made room in what had been Willstätter's private laboratory for Willstätter's private assistant, Margarete Rohdewald, one of his former students. From 1929 until 1938 she collaborated with Willstätter in a series of eighteen papers on various aspects of enzyme research. It was an odd collaboration, conducted almost entirely over the telephone; Willstätter never saw her at work in the laboratory.

During the few years at Munich before his resignation, Willstätter began to concentrate his research on the study of enzymes. He had first encountered these biological catalysts in his early work on chlorophyll. Now he worked to develop methods for their separation and purification. His method for separation was to adsorb the materials on alumina or silica gel and then to wash them off using solutions of varying acidity, among other solvents. In this connection, Willstätter carried out a systematic study (comprised of nine papers) of hydrates and hydrogels during which he, with his assistants Heinrich Kraut and K. Lobinger, was able to show that aluminum hydroxide, silicic acid, ferric hydroxide, and stannic hydroxide do actually exist in solution and are not colloidal sols (dispersions of small solid particles in solution) of the corresponding oxides. Willstätter reported that this foray of an organic chemist into inorganic chemistry was not well received by inorganic chemists.

The enzyme studies were not as successful, in part because Willstätter thought that enzymes were relatively small molecules adsorbed on a protein or some other giant (polymer) molecule. The modern view, of course, is that enzymes are themselves proteins. Though Willstätter's chemical intuition failed him, there were positive results—for example, the enzymatic reduction of chloral and bromal resulted in the formation of trichloroethanol, a sedative (Voluntal), and tribromoethanol, an anesthetic (Avertin).

In 1938 the situation for Jews in Germany was becoming impossible. On a visit to Switzerland, Stoll tried to persuade Willstätter to stay, but he insisted on returning to Munich. There, after some trouble with the Gestapo, he was ordered to leave the country. After much red tape, which entailed the confiscation of much of his property, papers, and art collection, and an abortive attempt to leave unofficially, he entered Switzerland in March 1939 to stay for a while with Stoll and then to settle in the Villa Eremitaggio in Muralto. There he wrote his autobiography to pass the time. On August 3, 1942, Willstätter died of cardiac failure in his sleep. Among the honors received by Willstätter in addition to the Nobel prize were honorary membership in the American Chemical Society (1927),

honorary fellowship in the Chemical Society (1927), the Willard Gibbs Medal for distinguished achievement in science from the Chicago Section of the American Chemical Society (1933), and election as foreign member of the Royal Society (1933). Willstätter's obituary by Sir **Robert Robinson** in *Obituary Notices of Fellows of the Royal Society,* has an eleven page bibliography, probably incomplete, listing over three hundred papers between 1893 and 1940.

SELECTED WRITINGS BY WILLSTÄTTER:

Books

Investigations on Chlorophyll; Methods and Results, translated by F. M. Schertz and A. R. Merz, Science Press, 1928.
From My Life, (autobiography), foreword by Stoll, translated by Lilli S. Hornig, Benjamin, 1965.

Periodicals

Science, A Chemist's Retrospects and Perspectives, Volume 78, 1933, pp. 271–274.

FURTHER READING:

Books

Dictionary of Scientific Biography, Volume 14, Scribner, 1976, pp. 411–412.
Nobel Lectures Including Presentation Speeches and Laureates' Biographies, Volume 3, Chemistry: 1901–1921, Elsevier, 1966, pp. 297–314.
Obituary Notices of Fellows of the Royal Society, Volume 8, Morrison & Gibb, 1954, pp. 609–634.
Partington, J. R., *A History of Chemistry,* Macmillan, 1964, pp. 860–866.

Periodicals

Huisgen, Rolf, *Journal of Chemical Education,* Richard Willstätter, Volume 38, number 1, 1961, pp. 10–15.
Robinson, Robert, *Journal of the Chemical Society,* Willstätter Memorial Lecture, 1953, pp. 1012–1026.

Sketch by R. F. Trimble

Ian Wilmut
1944–
English embryologist

Ian Wilmut, an embryologist working at the Roslin Institute in Scotland, made headline news around the world when he announced that he had cloned the first mammal—a sheep named Dolly—from an adult animal.

Ian Wilmut

Conducted in February 1997, his experiment was a giant step forward for animal science, genetics, and medicine. It meant animals could be cloned in order to further human medical advancements. Cloned animals could produce large quantities of proteins useful in the manufacture of certain pharmaceuticals. They might also provide a source for organs that could be transplanted to human beings.

Wilmut's work caused a sensation because it carried startling implications. If a sheep could be cloned, so could a human being. Many scientists believe that humans can be cloned. Wilmut, a quiet, intense scientist, believes it would be a mistake—and an inhumane choice—to do so. He intended for his work to benefit animal science, not to create new Frankensteins, he told a *New York Times* reporter in a 1997 interview. "I am not a fool," he said. "I know what is bothering people about this. I understand why the world is suddenly at my door. But this is my work. It has always been my work, and it doesn't have anything to do with creating copies of human beings."

Ian Wilmut was born on July 7, 1944, in Hampton Lucey, England in Warwick. He attended the University of Nottingham, where he became fascinated with embryology after meeting G. Eric Lamming, a world-renowned expert in reproduction. The meeting became a turning point for Wilmut, who set out on a singular quest—to understand the genetic engineering of animals. He graduated from Nottingham in 1967, with a degree in agricultural science.

Wilmut continued his studies at Darwin College at Cambridge University in England. There he received his

doctoral degree in 1973, awarded after he completed his thesis on the techniques for freezing boar semen. A workaholic by nature, he immediately took a position at the Animal Breeding Research Station, an animal research institute supported by government and private funds. The research station eventually became the Roslin Institute. It is headquartered in Roslin, near Edinburgh, Scotland.

In 1973, after receiving his doctorate, Wilmut produced the first calf ("Frosty") born from a frozen embryo that had been implanted into a surrogate mother. The motivation for such an experiment was to harvest cows that provide the best meat and milk by implanting their embryos into other females. The average cow can birth five to 10 calves during their lifespan. With the ability to transfer embryos, cattle breeders could increase the quality of their animal stock.

Wilmut continued his research during the 1980s, despite other scientists' growing discouragement in the possibility of cloning. In 1996, Wilmut overheard a story in an Irish bar, while attending a scientific meeting, that solidified his belief in cloning. The rumor that Wilmut heard was that Dr. Steen M. Willadsen of Grenada Genetics in Texas had cloned a lamb using a differentiated cell from an already developing embryo.

Like a fertilized egg that contains enough deoxyribonucleic acid (DNA) to build an entire organism, a differentiated cell carries a full complement of the genetic material for DNA, which forms a blueprint for an animal's characteristics. To clone an animal, an adult animal cell would have to be harvested, and the nucleus placed in an embryo cell, thereby replacing the nucleus of the embryo cell. Yet the problem was how to get the new nucleus to spawn growth in the embryo cell.

Keith Campbell, a biologist at the Roslin Institute, had an insight that proved to be crucial. He deduced that an egg probably will not use genetic material from a transplanted adult cell because the cycles of each cell are not synchronized. Cells go through specific cycles, growing and dividing and making an entirely new package of chromosomes each time. In order to synchronize the cells, Campbell slowed down adult mammal cells—in fact, nearly stopping them—so they would actually exist in synchrony with the embryos. Then each embryo could be joined with an adult cell, and in turn, they could join together and grow. To slow an already developing or adult cell down, Campbell forced it into a hibernating state by depriving it of nutrients. With this method, he and Wilmut were able to clone two sheep from developing embryo cells. They named the sheep Megan and Morag.

To clone an adult sheep, Wilmut and Campbell harvested udder, or mammary, cells from a six-year-old ewe. The cells were preserved in test tubes and starved by reducing their serum concentration for five days. Out of 277 attempts, Dolly's embryo was the only one to survive. They implanted Dolly's embryo when it was six days old into a surrogate mother, and on July 5, 1996, Dolly was born. She was named for the country singer Dolly Parton. They kept the lamb's birth secret until they had received a patent for the process that had created her. As a government employee working at Roslin, Wilmut does not own the patent on his cloning procedure. The company which runs Roslin, called PPL P.L.C. Therapeutics, will benefit from the patent proceeds, and will produce new drugs through the procedure.

Wilmut continues to work nine-hour days at the Roslin Institute, often bringing work home. He lives in a small village near Edinburgh with his wife, Vivian. They have three children, Helen, Naomi, and Dean. Wilmut is an honorary fellow at the Institute of Ecology and Resource Management at the University of Edinburgh. He enjoys walks in the Scotish highlands and an occasional single-malt scotch whisky.

Those working with Wilmut describe him as careful, diligent, honest, and thoughtful. Perhaps that is why Wilmut was puzzled and a bit angry about all the attention his work received from news reporters around the world. "People have sensationalized this in every way," he told the *New York Times*. Many public figures expressed dismay over the negative implications of cloning animals—and perhaps humans. The British government was even considering cutting the highly respected Roslin Institute's finances as a result of the cloning experiment. "People say that cloning means that if a child dies you can get that child back," he commented to the Times. "You could never get that child back. It would be something different. You need to understand the biology. People are not genes. They are so much more than that."

Wilmut remains passionate about his work. His goal is to push the work of cloning animals forward, so that it can help solve some of the world's worst medical problems. He continues his cloning projects so he and other scientists can study genetic diseases for which there are presently no cures. He sees a day when genetic engineering and cloning can produce proteins like the clotting factor that hemophiliacs lack. Other diseases, resulting from the lack of a genetic material, might also be cured.

SELECTED WRITINGS BY WILMUT:

Periodicals

"Sheep Cloned by Nuclear Transfer from a Cultured Cell Line." *Nature* 380 (1996): 64-66.

FURTHER READING:

Periodicals

Ibrahim, Youssef M. "Ian Wilmut: Secrecy Gives Way to Spotlight for Scientist." *The New York Times* (February 24, 1997): B8.

Kolata, Gina. "With Cloning of Sheep, the Ethical Ground Shifts." *The New York Times* (February 24, 1997): A1.

Specter, Michael and Gina Kolata. "After Decades of Missteps, How Cloning Succeeded." *The New York Times* (March 3, 1997): A1.

Sketch by Barbara Boughton

C. T. R. Wilson
1869–1959
Scottish physicist

A Scottish physicist, C. T. R. Wilson invented the cloud or expansion chamber, which enabled physicists to track the paths of individual atoms and electrons. It was described by the physicist W. B. Lewis as being "to the atomic physicist what the telescope is to the astronomer." Lord Ernest Rutherford described the cloud chamber as "the most original and wonderful [invention] in scientific history." For his invention, Wilson shared the 1927 Nobel Prize for physics with **Arthur Holly Compton**. Wilson is also credited with the discovery of cosmic rays, that is, speeding atomic nuclei from outer space that enter the earth's atmosphere.

Charles Thomson Rees Wilson was born on the 14th of February, 1869, in Glencorse, near Edinburgh, Scotland, to John Wilson, a sheep farmer, and his second wife, Annie Clark Harper Wilson. When Wilson senior died in 1873, the family moved to Manchester. There Wilson attended first a private school then, when he was fifteen, Owens College, later renamed the Victoria College of Manchester. Although he had registered as a medical student, he switched to science and graduated with a First Class degree in zoology when he was only eighteen years of age. At the urging of his tutors, he decided to sit for the scholarship exams for Cambridge in practical physics and chemistry. Although he had received no instruction in either subject, he performed so well in the exam that he was awarded a scholarship to Sidney Sussex College.

Begins Career at Cambridge

In 1888, when he was nineteen years old, Wilson entered Cambridge to study physics and chemistry. He found it a thoroughly stimulating environment. He attended physics lectures at its world-renowned Cavendish Laboratory—he was, in fact, the only student in his year taking physics as a main subject—and began to develop what would be a lifelong interest in meteorological physics. After graduating from Cambridge in 1892, Wilson found work as a demonstrator and a private coach. Although it helped him

C. T. R. Wilson

to keep body and soul together, it left him with precious little time or energy for his own research. At the time, his work was devoted to a comparison of the behavior of different substances in solution. In a bid to secure his future, Wilson somewhat reluctantly accepted the post of science teacher at Bradford Grammar School, but he quickly realized that his career was on the wrong track. In 1894 he decided, therefore, to return to Cambridge, where the University's decision to extend the teaching of physics to medical students had opened up a post as supervisor of the students' practical work.

Returning to Cambridge afforded him more time and space to continue his own work. With the encouragement of the eminent physicist, **J. J. Thomson**, who at the time headed the Cavendish, he began constructing an expansion chamber which would enable him to track the paths of atoms and electrons. In 1895, the first cloud chamber was finished. Wilson intended to use the apparatus to create artificial clouds in the laboratory. His work was inspired by the meteorological phenomena he had witnessed during a visit to Ben Nevis, Britain's highest mountain, in the Scottish Highlands the year before. During a two-week stint as temporary observer to the observatory atop Ben Nevis, he had been captivated by the extraordinary sight of the sun shining on the clouds and the magical optical effects it produced. He was so awestruck that he vowed to create similar clouds to the ones he had witnessed. His theory was that if he expanded moist air in an enclosed chamber, a cloud would thereby be created.

Wilson's hunch was based on results that had been obtained in 1888 by another Scottish physicist, John Aitken. Aitken had discovered that when compressed air is permitted to suddenly expand, a cloud is formed if the air contains dust particles. The latter act as nuclei on which the water vapor can condense—in their absence, the air becomes supersaturated and no clouds are formed. At the beginning of 1895, Wilson began trying to manufacture clouds in the Cavendish laboratory. Within a short space of time, he succeeded in producing them and in recreating the optical effects he had witnessed on the mountain. In the process, he obtained some interesting results. Using his cloud chamber, Wilson discovered that, contrary to Aitken's theory, a cloud could indeed form even if the air was dust free, so long as the moist air was expanded beyond a certain precise limit. No drops were formed unless the expansion exceeded this limit, in which case a shower of drops was produced.

Encouraged by his preliminary results, Wilson embarked on a series of experiments using more sophisticated equipment. He now discovered that if the air was expanded beyond a second precise limit, equivalent to an approximately eight-fold supersaturation of the vapor, dense clouds were formed in dust-free air. In the process, extraordinary optical effects were also created. Wilson published his results in early 1895. They indicated that two different kinds of clouds could be produced in dust-free air by different degrees of expansion, corresponding to two different types of nuclei. The first kind were less common than the second, which were very numerous, but required more expansion to come into effect.

In 1895, Wilson was appointed one of Cambridge's Clerk Maxwell Students. That same year, he also began investigating electrical fields and thunderstorms inspired, once again, by the weather; during another visit to the Scottish Highlands he had witnessed a mighty thunderstorm, which started him thinking about electrical fields in the atmosphere. Over the next five years he developed his basic knowledge of atmospheric electricity and put forward the proposition that atmospheric ions, which produce electricity, might in fact be produced by sources of radiation outside the earth's atmosphere.

In 1895, x rays were discovered. Wilson quickly took advantage of the new technology and used x rays to investigate the behavior of ions as condensation nuclei. He found that x rays produced large numbers of the nuclei in gases that Wilson had been creating in much smaller amounts in his cloud chamber. He found that not only x rays, but also other ionizing agents such as uranium rays and ultraviolet rays, produce condensation nuclei in gases, which are identical with respect to the supersaturation needed to enable water to condense on them and form clouds. These ionizing agents allowed Wilson to successfully test his idea that the two kinds of nuclei he had discovered when he expanded moist air in his dust free cloud chamber were in fact positive and negative ions, of the kind that had been discovered in ionized gases. This work preoccupied him from 1896 to 1898. Between 1898 and 1899, he was engaged full-time in studying condensation on negative and positive ions. Eventually, he was able to render individual ions visible to the eye, and to distinguish between positive and negative ions.

In 1899, Wilson joined the Meteorological Council as a researcher on atmospheric electricity. The following year, he was elected fellow of Sidney Sussex College, Cambridge, and appointed a lecturer in physics. For the next eighteen years, he remained in this position, building a solid advanced physics research team around him and teaching at the Cavendish. Wilson preferred a practical method of instruction. He liked to set his students minor research problems to carry out in the laboratory themselves rather than having them rely on textbook experiments. His was a close and small coterie, however. He felt comfortable working at a measured pace with just a few, well-chosen pupils to whom he could devote his full attention. He was a dedicated mentor, who took his responsibilities as a teacher extremely seriously. Although he was known as a shy and somewhat plodding lecturer, his insights were considered second to none and inspired subsequent generations of experimental physicists.

Since Wilson had invented his first cloud chamber in 1895, much more had been learned about the phenomena of electricity in ions. But a mystery remained as to where the ions originated. Wilson himself provided the answer in 1900. Using his cloud-expansion chamber, he demonstrated that ions are constantly present in the air, incessantly regenerating. He was able to prove this because, given the right degree of expansion of moist air in the cloud chamber, he was always able to obtain nuclei. Their presence meant that the air should always be conducting. He tested his hypothesis using a gold-leaf electroscope, and discovered that positive and negative ions are constantly being produced in air in equal numbers, at the rate of about 14 per cubic meters of air per second. This discovery provided an explanation as to how an electrical discharge could pass through air, in the laboratory or in the atmosphere, in the form of lightning. Moreover, it represented the first step in the discovery of cosmic rays. These are the streams of atomic nuclei of heterogeneous, extremely penetrating character, that enter the earth's atmosphere from outer space at speeds approaching that of light; when they enter the earth's atmosphere, they bombard atmospheric atoms to produce mesons as well as secondary particles possessing some of the original energy. However, it was not until 1912 that Wilson had obtained enough information about the phenomena that he felt confident enough to postulate their existence. His cloud chamber, particularly the more sophisticated versions of it devised by the English physicist, Sir **Patrick Blackett**, was an essential tool in the study of cosmic radiation.

In 1908, at the age of thirty-nine, Wilson married Jessie Fraser Dick. The marriage produced two children. In 1910, he started work on designing a new, much improved cloud chamber. His first two prototypes had been used, respectively, to create clouds and to help in research on ions. The third model was to be used to measure an atom's electrical charge. He proposed to do this by condensing

drops of nuclei on atoms and thus rendering them visible. By measuring the total charge and counting the number of drops, the charge per atom could be figured. Before Wilson could finish his research, however, another scientist discovered the charge per atom before him.

Wilson's attention turned to the possibility of rendering visible the vapor trail or tracks of positively charged alpha rays. By 1911, he had built an apparatus to carry out the experiment. Although he did not have high hopes of success, he was pleasantly surprised when the tracks were actually revealed. When the cloud chamber was subjected to a magnetic field, the nature of the curved path showed if the charge was positive or negative and what size the particle was.

In 1911, Wilson was appointed observer in meteorological physics at the Solar Physics Observatory. He was promoted reader in electrical meteorology in 1918. In 1925, he was made Jacksonian Professor of Natural Philosophy at the University of Cambridge. He retired from Cambridge in 1934. Wilson remained highly active after his retirement. He moved back to Scotland where he was able to indulge his love of mountain climbing until he was well into his eighties. Until the age of eighty-six, he took weather flights over the Outer Scottish Isles as an honorary member of the University of Edinburgh's meteorology department.

Honored with Many Awards

During his long career, Wilson received many honors. He was elected a Fellow of the Royal Society of London in 1900 and awarded its Hughes Medal in 1911. He received the Hopkins Prize of the Cambridge Philosophical Society in 1920, the Royal Society of Edinburgh's Gunning Prize in 1921, and the Franklin Institute's Howard Potts Medal in 1925. He was given the highest honor in 1927 when he was awarded the Nobel Prize for physics, "for his discovery of the vapor condensation method of rendering visible the paths of electrically charged particles." He shared the award with the American theoretical physicist, Arthur Holly Compton, whose theory of the scattering of x rays upon contact with matter was confirmed using Wilson's cloud chamber.

Wilson kept working right up to the end of his long life. In 1956, at the age of eighty-seven, he presented his paper, *A Theory of Thundercloud Electricity,* to the Royal Society. It was the last presentation given by the Society's oldest fellow. Wilson died in 1959 at Carlops, Peebleshire, Scotland.

SELECTED WRITINGS BY WILSON:

Books

Condensation Nuclei, Smithsonian Institution, 1905.
A Theory of Thundercloud Electricity, Royal Society, 1957.

FURTHER READING:

Books

Crowther, J. G., *The Cavendish Laboratory, 1874–1974,* Science History Publications, 1974.

Heathcote, Niels H. deV, *Nobel Prize Winners in Physics, 1901–1950,* Books for Libraries Press, 1953, p. 269.

Johnston, Marjorie, editor, *The Cosmos of Arthur Holly Compton,* Knopf, 1967.

Weber, Robert L., *Pioneers of Science: Nobel Prize Winners in Physics,* Institute of Physics (London), 1980, pp. 85–87.

Wilson, David, *Rutherford: Simple Genius,* MIT Press, 1983, p. 556.

Sketch by Avril McDonald

Edmund Beecher Wilson
1856–1939
American biologist

Edmund Beecher Wilson emphasized careful experimentation and analysis in biology at a time when the field was rife with theories based on little more than speculation. Indeed, Wilson's work was instrumental in transforming biology into a rigorous, scientific discipline. Although known for his meticulous approach to the study of the structure and function of the cell, he never lost sight of biology as a unified field that included embryology, evolution, and genetics. His influence in biology was felt through his position as a professor first at Bryn Mawr College and then at Columbia University, and through his highly influential textbook, *The Cell in Development and Inheritance.* His study of chromosomes, and especially his discovery of the sex chromosomes, helped lay the foundation for the study of genetics and evolution in the early-twentieth century. Many of the problems that Wilson tackled, including the details of cell development, remain unsolved today.

Edmund Wilson was born on October 19, 1856, in Geneva, Illinois. He was the second of four surviving children of Isaac Grant Wilson, a lawyer and eventually judge, and Caroline Louisa Clark, both of whom were originally from New England. When Edmund was two years old, his father was appointed a circuit court judge in Chicago. Rather than separate him from her childless sister and brother-in-law in Geneva, Edmund's mother left him to live with them while the rest of the family moved to Chicago. In this manner, he was "adopted" by Mr. and Mrs.

Charles Patten and grew up counting himself very lucky to have two homes and four parents.

Shortly before he turned 16, Wilson taught school for one year from 1872 to 1873. As his older brother, Charles, had done the previous year, Wilson taught everything, including reading and arithmetic, to twenty-five pupils aged six to eighteen in a one-room schoolhouse. The following year he attended Antioch College (Yellow Springs, Ohio), following in the footsteps of an older cousin, Samuel Clarke. At Antioch, Wilson decided to devote himself to the study of biology, which, at that time, largely meant natural history.

In the fall of 1874, Wilson did not return to Antioch because he wished to prepare for studying at the Sheffield Scientific School of Yale University, which had been highly recommended to him by his cousin. To ready himself for Yale, Wilson moved to Chicago where he lived with his parents and took courses at the old University of Chicago from 1874 to 1875. He entered Yale in 1875 and received his bachelor's degree in 1878.

Lifelong Research Interest in Cell Development

Although Wilson's particular focus of research changed many times in his long career, his work was always concerned with gaining a better understanding of how the single fertilized egg gave rise to a complete individual, whether that individual be an earthworm, jellyfish, or human. This interest in the development of the organism led Wilson to study cell structure and function, heredity, and evolution.

During his years of graduate and postgraduate work, Wilson studied the embryology and morphology of earthworms, sea spiders, the colonial jellyfish (*Renilla*), and other invertebrates. After Yale, he again followed Sam Clarke's educational path, this time to Johns Hopkins University. A close friend, William T. Sedgwick, entered Johns Hopkins along with him. From 1878 to 1881, Wilson worked closely with William Keith Brooks, obtained his Ph.D. in 1881, and remained at Johns Hopkins for an additional year of postdoctoral work. In 1882 Wilson studied in Europe with the help of a loan from his older brother, Charles. He studied in Cambridge, and, with Thomas H. Huxley's recommendation, gave a paper on *Renilla* before the Royal Society in London. From England, he went to Leipzig, Germany, and then to the Zoological Station at Naples. Wilson worked for almost a year there and formed strong friendships with director Anton Dohrn and zoologist Theodor Boveri. (For Wilson, the embryos of marine invertebrates were more easily studied than those of terrestrial animals, and for almost 50 years, Wilson spent his summers working at the Marine Biological Laboratory in Woods Hole, Massachusetts.)

To visit Naples, Wilson had worked out an arrangement with Clarke, who was then teaching at Williams College (Massachusetts). The college would pay for a laboratory bench at Naples for two years as part of a professorship at Williams. Wilson would work at Naples the first year while Clarke taught at Williams, then the two would switch places. Wilson's stint at Williams College lasted between 1883 and 1884.

From Williams, Wilson moved to the Massachusetts Institute of Technology as an instructor from 1884 to 1885. There, he collaborated with his friend, William T. Sedgwick, in the creation of a textbook titled *General Biology* (1886). Wilson's next teaching appointment, unlike his previous two, offered him the time and opportunity to continue his research. M. Carey Thomas, the first dean of Bryn Mawr College (Bryn Mawr, PA), invited Wilson to become the first professor of biology at the new women's college. he taught there between 1885 and 1891. While at Bryn Mawr, the scientist tackled the problem of cell differentiation—the way in which the fertilized egg gives rise to many kinds of specialized cells. To do this, he studied the cell-by-cell development of the earthworm and *Nereis,* a marine worm. This work, known as "cell lineage," established Wilson's reputation as a biologist of considerable skill. His 1890 and 1892 papers on *Nereis* demonstrated the value of cell lineage and inspired other scientists to pursue this fruitful avenue of research.

In 1891 Wilson accepted an appointment to become an adjunct professor of zoology in the new zoology department at Columbia University being organized by Henry Fairfield Osborn. He spent the rest of his career at Columbia, eventually becoming chair of the department, and retiring as DaCosta Professor in 1928. Before settling on campus, however, Wilson spent another fruitful year in Munich and Naples from 1891 to 1892. A series of lectures on the study of the cell that he gave during his first teaching year at Columbia formed the basis of his textbook *The Cell in Development and Inheritance,* published in 1896. Written before the fundamentals of heredity were understood, the book added a balanced, careful voice to the fierce debates over modes of inheritance and cell development that were occurring in biology at that time. The book, which illuminated Wilson's penchant for observation and experimentation, was hugely influential and further cemented his already substantial reputation. The book was dedicated to Boveri, the Italian zoologist.

On September 27, 1904, Wilson married Anne Maynard Kidder. Kidder and her family lived in Washington, D.C., but spent their summers at their cottage in Woods Hole, and it was there that the two met. Their only child, Nancy, became a professional cellist. Wilson himself was an avid amateur musician, and his trips to Europe were warmly remembered as much for the music he heard as for the science he learned. A flutist as a young man, he began taking cello lessons while he was living in Baltimore. For the rest of his life, in Bryn Mawr and then New York, he always found himself a quartet of amateur musicians with which to play.

Helps Usher in Modern Era of Genetics

In 1900 the modern era of genetics was born. Three scientists, working independently from each other, stated that inherited characteristics were determined by the combination of two hereditary units, one from each parent. (Today, those two hereditary units are known as genes.) This theory had actually been published 36 years earlier by Gregor Johann Mendel, but had lain dormant until it was "revived" at the turn of the 19th century by **Hugo De Vries**, Karl Erich Correns, and Erich Tschermak von Seysenegg.

Wilson quickly saw the connection between the rediscovery of the laws of heredity and his own work with cells and cell structures. The laws of heredity stated that the fertilized egg received half of the blueprint for its own expression from each parent. Chromosomes, he theorized, were the cell structures responsible for transmitting the units of inheritance. By following instructions from the chromosomes, the fertilized egg gave rise to a complete individual.

In 1905 Wilson and **Nettie Maria Stevens** of Bryn Mawr College independently showed that the X and Y chromosomes carried by the sperm were responsible for determining gender: in many species, including humans, females had an XX pair of chromosomes while males had an XY pair. In eight papers published from 1905 to 1912 entitled "Studies on Chromosomes," Wilson brilliantly extended his study of the chromosomal theory of sex determination, and it is for this work with chromosomes that he is best remembered. He is also recognized for setting the stage for the zoology department's future excellence in genetics, as personified by **Thomas Hunt Morgan** and **Hermann Joseph Muller**.

In the last years of his career, Wilson continued his study of cell structures. Despite failing health, he also wrote the third edition of *The Cell in Development and Inheritance,* over 1200 pages, which was published in 1925. In most respects, this was actually a completely new book that included the new discoveries in biology of the twentieth century. Wilson retired from Columbia University in 1928. He died in New York, on March 3, 1939, of bronchial pneumonia, and his ashes were buried in the churchyard of the Church of the Messiah in Woods Hole, Massachusetts.

SELECTED WRITINGS BY WILSON:

Books

General Biology, [New York], 1886.
The Cell in Development and Inheritance, [New York], 1896, second edition, 1900, third edition, revised and enlarged as The Cell in Development and Heredity, 1925.

Periodicals

Science, Science and Liberal Education, Volume 42, 1915, pp. 625–30.

FURTHER READING:

Books

Biographical Memoirs, Volume 21, National Academy of Sciences, 1941, pp. 315–42.

Obituary Notices of the Fellows of the Royal Society,
    Volume 3, Royal Society (London), 1939–41, pp.
    123–38.

Periodicals

Morgan, Thomas Hunt, *The American Naturalist,* Ed-
    mund B. Wilson—An Appreciation, Volume 77,
    1943, pp. 5–37 (January/February issue) and pp.
    142–72 (March/April issue).

Sketch by Liz Marshall

Edward O. Wilson
1929–
American zoologist

Edward O. Wilson

W orld-renowned entomologist Edward O. Wilson is nicknamed "Dr. Ant," but his achievements impact much of the field of biology. He is co-founder of the modern field of sociobiology, believed by some to be one of the great paradigms of science, which has touched off much controversy but also a great deal of research in animal and human social behavior. From his posts as Harvard Univer-isty's Frank B. Baird, Jr. Professor of Science and Mellon Professor of Science, Wilson is the recipient of Sweden's Crafoord Prize (equal in stature to the Nobel Prize), a 1979 Pulitzer Prize for literature, and the 1977 National Medal of Science. He has influenced the field of animal taxonomy through his work in speciation theory, conducted research which led to the discovery of pheromones—chemicals which cause behavior in animals—and has been a harbinger of the threat of mass extinction resulting from man's unchecked use of the environment.

Fateful Fishing Trip Determines Career

Edward Osborne Wilson was born on June 10, 1929 in Birmingham, Alabama. A descendant of farmers and shipowners in subtropical Alabama, Wilson had already decided to become a naturalist explorer by age seven. Fate intervened, however, when on a fishing trip he vigorously pulled his catch out of the water and its fin hit and damaged his right eye. He thus developed the habit of examining animals and objects close-up with his keen left eye, and when he subsequently read a National Geographic article entitled "Stalking Ants, Savage and Civilized" at age 10, the entomologist was born. Wilson later studied biology at the University of Alabama, obtaining a B.S. degree in this discipline in 1949 and an M.S. in 1950. In 1955, at age 26, he received his Ph.D. in biology from Harvard. He gained

full professorship in 1964, and became Frank B. Baird, Jr. Professor of Science in 1976.

The field of new systematics—the attempt to classify species based on the principles of evolutionary theory—occupied Wilson during the early years of his career. With his colleague William L. Brown, Wilson critiqued the utilization of the subspecies category, prompting revised procedures among taxonomists. In 1956, Wilson also co-developed the concept of "character displacement," which occurs when two similar species begin a process of genetic differentiation to avoid competition and cross-breeding.

During the mid- to late–1950s, Wilson traveled to Australia, the South Pacific islands, and Melanesia to further study and classify ants native to those regions. As a result of his field work in the Melanesian archipelagoes, he developed the concept of the taxon cycle, which has since been found among birds and other insects. Wilson described the taxon cycle of Melanesian ants as the process through which a species disperses to a new, harsher habitat and evolves into one or more new "daughter" species, which then adapt to the new habitat.

All the while, Wilson was developing the foundation for what would he would term "sociobiology" two decades later. In 1959, influenced by the rise of molecular biology, he proved his hypothesis that social insects such as ants communicate through chemical releasers. Wilson crushed a venom gland extracted from a fire ant and created a trail of the chemical near a colony of the same species. He had anticipated that a few ants would trace the chemical path.

Instead, dozens of fire ants swarmed out of the colony to follow the trail, and were baffled at its end. "That night I couldn't sleep," Wilson notes. "I envisioned accounting for the entire social repertory of ants with a small number of chemicals." Indeed, the chemicals came to be known as pheromones, and this discovery launched an "explosion of research" on the behavior of social insects—research which continues still. Wilson wrote later that pheromones were "not just a guidepost, but the entire message." These chemicals communicate complex instructions for fellow ants—everything from the location of food and how to obtain it to a call for help when in distress.

First to Identify Species Equilibrium Theory

In the early and middle 1960s, Wilson collaborated with Princeton University mathematician **Robert H. Mac-Arthur** to develop the first quantitative theory of species equilibrium. Prior to their work in this area, it was believed that the regularity of species in a given area was maintained through incomplete colonization. Wilson and his coauthor hypothesized that the number of species on a small island would remain constant, though the variety of species would undergo constant reshuffling.

Two factors affect the number of species in an ecosystem: extinction and immigration. In Wilson and MacArthur's island model, these factors are determined by the size and proximity of the islands—larger, less crowded islands typically have lower extinction rates, for example, and islands that are close together experience greater species immigration from one island to another. The "equilibrium hypothesis of island biogeography" describes the relationship between these factors in a mathematical model. The two determinants in the number of species are the rate of extinction of species (depicted by a positive sloping curve) and the rate of immigration of new species (indicated by a negative sloping curve). The actual number of species is found at the intersection of the two curves.

MacArthur and Wilson's hypothesis was borne out by a 1968 study by Wilson and biologist Daniel Simberloff, who examined the insect life on six islands off the Florida Keys. They first counted the number of insect species, then fumigated the islands and recounted eight months later. As Wilson had predicted, the number of species remained the same, while the composition of species was significantly different and did in fact evolve over time.

For this landmark work, Wilson received the Crafoord Prize in 1990, awarded by the Royal Swedish Academy of Sciences. "This relatively simple idea transformed the study of species richness into a quantitative and experimental branch of biology," the academy noted. "Arguably, hardly a single important work in conservation biology is written today without the author making use of this theory as a launching ramp."

Founds Field of Sociobiology

But Wilson's greatest milestone probably was his 1975 book, *Sociobiology: The New Synthesis*. In it he defines sociobiology as "the systematic study of the biological basis of all social behavior." The term was in use prior to Wilson's landmark book, but he identified the interdisciplinary endeavor as one which was to change the way animal and human behavior is viewed and researched by the scientific community. Arthur Fisher, in *Society* magazine, declares, "Many biologists believe that sociobiology is indeed one of the great scientific paradigms, a powerful new tool for understanding some of the most baffling phenomena in the living world." Fisher compares the new framework to Darwin's theory of natural selection and Einstein's revolution of space/time theory. In fact, many of the tenets Wilson put forth in his book have gained widespread acceptance, and have aroused controversy over the ideological implications for human behavior.

The roots of Wilson's journey into this field lay in the beginning of his career. "In the forties and fifties," he says in *Society,* "we were in the midst of a very exciting development, called the new synthesis, which reinvigorated evolutionary biology by applying modern population genetics to what had previously been scattered and highly descriptive subjects. . . . It was a period of grand synthesis in which it seemed possible to understand some of the most intrinsically interesting phenomena."

Simultaneously, the field of molecular biology was gaining prominence, and Wilson observed that this threatened to relegate the softer study of animal behavior to a tiny corner of Harvard's biology department. Wilson began focusing on the significance of organisms as carriers of genetic information. Viewing the complex behavior of ants and other social insects in this framework prompted Wilson to describe behavior which served survival not of the individual, but of the population.

Thus Wilson was able to explain, in Darwinian terms, such characteristics as altruism, significance of kinship, communication, and specialization of labor—characteristics which had previously confounded scientists. Cooperation among individuals or between species was consistent with early evolutionary theory because it enabled individuals to survive and carry on the gene pool. But altruism (behavior in which one individual helps another at possible or certain cost to itself) and spiteful behavior (when an individual harms another and itself) were largely unexplained by biologists.

Explains Altruism in Ants

The answer lies in the broader view of population survival. In a colony of ants, sterile members will work for their family members who share similar genes and who will reproduce on their behalf. Wilson maintains that selflessness is a characteristic of most ant species. He describes their colonies as "superorganisms," in which the welfare of the colony—not the individual—is paramount. On the other end of the behavioral spectrum, a species of Malaysian ants will rupture glands of poison on their own bodies if invaded by enemies—killing themselves and their intruders, while signaling for help from members of their own colony. Other complex and intricate behavior is explained by Wilson's sociobiology. The European red amazon ant, for example, is an aggressive creature which actually invades the nests of more peaceful ant species, killing some individuals and capturing others for use as slaves in their own nests. The slave ants actually do "housework," digging chambers and feeding and nurturing the young Amazons.

Applies Sociobiology to Humans

It was the twenty-seventh chapter of *Sociobiology* which touched off a controversy that continues today. In "Man—From Sociobiology to Biology," Wilson argued for expanded research on the role of biology in human behavior. "There is a need for a discipline of anthropological genetics," he wrote. "By comparing man with other primate species, it might be possible to identify basic primate traits that lie beneath the surface and help to determine the configuration of man's higher social behavior."

Wilson noted that humans have always been characterized by "aggressive dominance systems, with males generally dominant over females." He also wrote that "a key early step in human social evolution was the use of women in barter." In a separate article, Wilson wrote: "In hunter-gatherer societies, men hunt and women stay at home. This strong bias . . . appears to have a genetic origin. Even with identical education and equal access to all professions, men are likely to continue to play a disproportionate role in political life, business, and science."

The anger with which Wilson's words were received led to noisy protests at a 1978 meeting of the American Association for the Advancement of Science. Intruders on the meeting first yelled a diatribe against him and then poured a pitcher of water over him. A letter of protest signed by, among others, two of Wilson's colleagues at Harvard, asserted that theories such as his in the past had led to the "sterilization laws and restrictive immigration laws by the United States between 1910 and 1930 and also for the eugenics policies which led to the establishment of gas chambers in Nazi Germany."

Wilson's worst detractors believed that the inevitable conclusion of his theories was "biological determinism." Harvard Professor **Stephen Jay Gould** (who had signed the letter of protest) sought a middle ground, since Wilson's theory didn't preclude the possibility that "peacefulness, equality, and kindness are just as biological as violence, sexism and general nastiness." But Gould maintained that there is no direct evidence in existence that specific human behaviors are genetically determined. In 1978, Wilson penned a follow-up to *Sociobiology*, the Pulitzer Prize–winning *On Human Nature*. In this volume he attempted to defend his hypotheses forwarded in chapter twenty-seven of *Sociobiology*, as well as to clear up certain areas that had become targets for controversy and prejudice. In particular, Fisher notes, Wilson "aimed for a fuller explanation of his views of the issues of free will, ethics, and development." Wilson's continuing research led to a collaboration with University of Toronto professor Charles Lumsden, with whom he penned 1981's *Genes, Mind and Culture* and 1983's *Promethean Fire*—the latter of which Wilson describes as his "last word on the subject" of human sociobiology.

Whatever the ramifications of Wilson's attempt to apply his entomological expertise to human behavior, his books and life's research represent great forward strides in the field of biology. His fascination with ants, begun in his childhood, culminated with the publication of 1990's *The Ants,* which he co-authored with German entomologist Bert Holldobler. Wilson, the world's leading authority on the creature with 8,800 species, believes they are essential to the world's ecosystems.

Wilson also is forthright in arguing for increased protection of the environment to minimize the mass species extinction now underway. He has warned that the current extinctions due to rainforest destruction will rival those which marked the end of the dinosaur age. Wilson has argued for surveyance of the earth's flora and fauna (the majority of which remain unclassified), the promotion of sustainable development, the wise use of the earth's plant and animal resources for food and medicine, and the restoration of terrains already damaged.

His many achievements include the Cleveland Prize (1967), the Mercer Award of the Ecological Society of America (1971), the Founders' Memorial Award from the Entomological Society of America (1972), the Leidy Medal (1978), the Carr Medal (1978), the L. O. Howard Award of the Entomological Society of America (1985), and the Tyler Prize for Environmental Achievement (1984). Wilson served on the World Wildlife Fund Board of Directors from 1984 to 1990. He is a member of the National Academy of Sciences, a fellow of the American Academy of Arts and Sciences, a fellow of the American Philosophical Society, the former president of the Society for the Study of Evolution, and an honorary member of the British Ecological Society.

Of his lifelong exploration of the insect world, Wilson says, "God is in the details." His contributions to species classification, biogeography, insect social organization, and his founding of sociobiology, have left a legacy the depth of which is yet to be measured.

SELECTED WRITINGS BY WILSON:

Books

The Theory of Island Biogeography, Princeton University Press, 1967.
The Insect Societies, Belknap Press, 1971.
A Primer of Population Biology, Sinauer Associates, 1971.

Life on Earth, Sinauer Associates, 1973.
Sociobiology: The New Synthesis, Belknap Press, 1975.
Caste and Ecology in Social Insects, Princeton University Press, 1978.
On Human Nature, Harvard University Press, 1978.
Genes, Mind, and Culture: The Coevolutionary Process, Harvard University Press, 1981.
Promethean Fire: Reflections on the Origin of the Mind, Harvard University Press, 1983.
Biophilia: The Human Bond to Other Species, Harvard University Press, 1984.
The Ants, Harvard University Press, 1990.
The Diversity of Life, Harvard University Press, 1992.

FURTHER READING:

Books

McGraw-Hill Modern Scientists and Engineers, McGraw-Hill 1980, pp. 334–35.

Periodicals

Brownlee, Shannon, *U.S. News & World Report,* A Celebration of Pests, May 7, 1990, pp. 63–66.
Fisher, Arthur, *Society,* Sociobiology: Science or Ideology?, July/August 1992, pp. 67–79.
Murphy, Jamie, *Time,* The Quiet Apocalypse, October 13, 1986, p. 80.
Murphy, Jamie, *Scientific American,* March, 1993, pp. 146–50.

Sketch by Karen Withem

J. Tuzo Wilson
1908–1993
Canadian geophysicist

An early proponent of the continental drift theory, J. Tuzo Wilson is chiefly remembered for his proposition that transform faults were present in the ocean floor, an idea that led to conclusive evidence that the sea floor and the earth's crust are constantly moving. Wilson later hypothesized that an ancestral Atlantic Ocean basin had opened and closed during the Paleozoic era, in turn creating the huge land mass known as Pangaea. This theory helps account for the presence of the Appalachian mountains in eastern North America, the striking similarity of many rock features in Western Europe and North America, and parallel cyclical developments on the seven continents.

John Tuzo Wilson was born in Ottawa, Ontario, Canada, on October 24, 1908. His father, John Armitstead Wilson, was an engineer who held a civil service position. His mother, Henrietta Tuzo, was an avid mountain climber who met her husband at the first gathering of Canada's Alpine Club. The Wilsons later shared their love of geology and the outdoors with their children, who were brought up to respect the pursuit of knowledge and were educated under the direction of an English governess.

Chooses Career in Geophysics

In 1924 Wilson's father obtained a position for him at a forestry camp. Wilson grew so fond of outdoor work that he signed on as an assistant to the legendary mountaineer Noel Odel, who persuaded him to pursue a career in geology. Following his freshman year at the University of Toronto, Wilson switched majors from physics to geology. After earning a B.A. in 1930, Wilson received a scholarship to study at Cambridge University under Sir **Harold Jeffreys**. When Wilson returned to Canada in the early 1930s, he had difficulty finding work, so he continued his education, enrolling in Princeton University, where he earned a Ph.D. in 1936. He made the first recorded ascent of Mount Hague in Montana in 1935, and in 1938 married Isabel Jean Dickson, with whom he had two children, Patricia and Susan.

With the outbreak of World War II in 1939, Wilson joined the Canadian Army. During his seven-year stint, he authored more than 500 technical reports and later claimed that these military papers had helped him develop the lucid prose style which he utilized in a number of scientific studies. By 1946 he had reached the rank of colonel. That same year, after resigning from the army, he succeeded his professor at the University of Toronto. Geophysics had finally become a lucrative field of study in Canada, thanks in large part to the discovery of oil in Alberta, which increased demand for geophysical exploration and led to the development of more advanced instruments and measurement techniques. Wilson investigated a number of geological mysteries, including Canadian glaciers, mountain building, and mineral production. He conducted these investigations with a characteristic reverence toward nature: "Everywhere in science modern tools and ideas bring to light the elegant and orderly skeins by which nature builds the glory that we see about us, knit in regular patterns from simple stitches," he wrote in *I.G.Y.: The Year of the New Moons* (1961). "Indeed, we may think of all nature in terms of music, as infinitely ingenious and elaborate variations on a few simple themes."

Geophysical Work Legitimizes Theory of Continental Drift

From 1957 to 1960 Wilson served as president of the International Union of Geodesy and Geophysics. During his tenure he led a series of geologic expeditions to China and Mongolia, the details of which are recorded in his highly praised book, *One Chinese Moon* (1959). In the early 1960s he became a key figure in what was then the most controversial issue in geology—the continental drift theory.

The origins of the continental drift theory date back hundreds of years. Since the time of the first global maps people have reasoned that at one time the continents might have been a single huge land mass. However, the first formal hypothesis of continental drift was made by German geophysicist **Alfred Wegener** in 1912. The idea was generally overlooked for decades but reemerged prominently in 1960, when geologist **Harold Hess** theorized that the ocean floors were being continuously created and changed. Hess attributed this activity to two physical structures: mid-ocean ridges, where the ocean floor is created, and ocean trenches, where the sea floor is destroyed.

Wilson was one of the first scientists to recognize the immense implications of this idea. For the next decade, he was at the very center of this theoretical debate. Using Hess's theory, Wilson postulated the existence of a third category of physical structure on the ocean floor which he called "transform faults," horizontal shears located between ridge sites and trenches. He suggested that transform faults could not exist unless the earth's crust was moving, and that the physical confirmation of these faults might prove the scientific validity of the continental drift theory. In 1967, seismologist Lynn Sykes partially tested Wilson's theory by studying seismic patterns and oceanic focal mechanisms. Wilson brought the idea to the attention of the general public by exhibiting a continental drift model at Montreal's Expo '67. By the late 1960s the theory had gained wide acceptance and was eventually incorporated into the larger concept of plate tectonics, which maintains that the Earth's lithosphere is made up of a number of plates that move independently.

Wilson's hypothesis and the publicity it garnered earned him numerous honors, including a Fellowship in the Royal Society (1968), the Penrose Medal of the Geological Society of America (1968), the Walter H. Bucher Medal of the American Geophysical Union (1968), the John J. Carty Medal of the National Academy of Sciences (1975), the Vetlesen Prize of Columbia University (1978), and the Wollaston Medal of the Geological Society of London (1978).

Wilson retired from his professorship at the University of Toronto in 1974. He then assumed the directorship of the Ontario Science Centre and in that capacity helped transform the center from a traditional science museum into an interactive science lab for public use. Of the center's roughly 1,000 exhibits, 400 were designed to be handled by patrons, and during the late 1970s and 1980s, the exploratory museum attracted approximately 1.5 million visitors annually.

Throughout his life Wilson traveled extensively. He lectured at more than 200 colleges and universities. One of his passions was collecting books on the Arctic and Antarctic, both of which he had visited. A mountain range in Antarctica was named the Wilson range in his honor. He

died in Toronto on April 15, 1993, at the age of 84. In an obituary tribute in *Nature,* colleague Fred Vine wrote, "Tuzo Wilson was a big man; in stature, in his magnanimity, on the Canadian science scene, and internationally in the Earth sciences. His seminal contributions to our new view of the Earth will be long remembered."

SELECTED WRITINGS BY WILSON:

Books

One Chinese Moon, Hill and Wang, 1959.
I.G.Y.: The Year of the New Moons, Knopf, 1961.
Continents Adrift: Readings from "Scientific American,", W. H. Freeman, 1972.
Unglazed China, Saturday Review Press, 1973.
Continents Adrift and Continents Aground: Readings from "Scientific American," W. H. Freeman, 1976.

FURTHER READING:

Books

The Continental Crust and Its Mineral Deposits, (proceedings of a symposium held in honor of Wilson), Geological Association of Canada, 1980.

Periodicals

Vine, Fred, *Nature,* John Tuzo Wilson (1908–1993), 363, June 3, 1993, p. 400.

Sketch by Tom Crawford

Kenneth G. Wilson
1936–
American physicist

K enneth G. Wilson was awarded the 1982 Nobel Prize in physics for his development of a theory to describe phase changes that take place close to critical points. Phase transitions are changes that take place in the physical state of a system (a simple and familiar phase transition is the melting of ice, during which water changes from the solid to the liquid state). The critical point is the temperature or pressure at which the transition takes place. The award was described by colleague P. W. Anderson in *Science* as one of the most clearly justified of all Nobel Prizes in physics "in terms of [its] total influence on the world of theoretical and experimental physics and chemistry."

After earning his Ph.D. under **Murray Gell-Mann** at the California Institute of Technology in 1961, Wilson spent terms as junior fellow at Harvard University from 1959 to 1962 and as a Ford Foundation Fellow at the European Organization for Nuclear Research (CERN) from 1962 to 1963. Working his way up the professorial ranks at Cornell University, he was appointed James A. Weeks Professor of Physical Science in 1974. In 1988, Wilson left Cornell to accept an appointment as Hazel C. Youngberg Trustees Distinguished Professor of Physics at Ohio State University. In recent years, his research has focused on computer simulations and modeling of a variety of physical phenomena.

Born in Waltham, Massachusetts, on June 8, 1936, Kenneth Geddes Wilson was the oldest of six children born to Edgar Bright Wilson, Jr., and the former Emily Fisher Buckingham. Wilson's parents were both involved in the sciences; his father was professor of chemistry at Harvard University and an authority in microwave spectroscopy, while his mother had completed a year of graduate study in physics before her marriage. Kenneth's maternal grandfather had been a professor of mechanical engineering at the Massachusetts Institute of Technology, and his paternal grandfather had been a lawyer and one-time speaker of the Tennessee House of Representatives.

Exhibits a Flair for Science

Wilson showed a talent for mathematics at an early age; according to a writer for the *New York Times,* when Wilson was a boy he spent his time waiting for the school bus by calculating the cube roots of numbers in his head. He attended grade schools in Wellesley and Woods Hole and at the Shady Hill School in Cambridge, all in Massachusetts; and his secondary education was completed at the Magdalen College School in Oxford and at the George School in Bucks County, Pennsylvania (a Quaker school). Wilson also studied a great deal on his own, teaching himself the basic principles of calculus and learning symbolic logic from his father.

At the age of sixteen, Wilson was accepted as a freshman into Harvard University, from which he received a B.A. in math and physics in 1956. He chose to do his graduate work in theoretical physics at the California Institute of Technology, where his advisor was Murray Gell-Mann. Wilson's doctoral thesis dealt with quantum field theory, an area of physics that attempts to integrate relativity theory with quantum mechanics (the object behind combining these two major theories was to develop an overall conceptual picture of the physical world). In particular, Wilson investigated an aspect of quantum electrodynamics (QED) that had been particularly troubling for theoretical physicists. The use of traditional QED theory, which describes the interaction of particles within an electromagnetic field, sometimes resulted in bizarre and nonsensical results, such as the prediction of particles with infinite electrical charges. One way around this dilemma had been the use of a mathematical procedure developed by

Gell-Mann, among others, known as renormalization; this procedure could extract important physical values from a calculation running into infinity. In his own thesis, Wilson used the techniques of renormalization to study the properties of an elementary particle known as the K meson.

After completing his doctorate, Wilson spent three years at Harvard University as a junior fellow in Harvard's Society of Fellows. He then continued his research on elementary particles as a Ford Foundation Fellow at the CERN particle accelerator facility in Geneva. At the completion of that fellowship in 1963, he was appointed assistant professor of physics at Cornell University. Over the next few years, Wilson was promoted to associate, and then full professor in 1970. In 1974, he was appointed to the James A. Weeks Chair of Physical Science at Cornell.

The Investigation of Phase Transitions

It was at Cornell that Wilson became interested in a new aspect of theoretical physics, the study of phase transitions at critical points. Physicists had been studying critical phenomena since the early 1870s; in the process, they discovered a number of examples of phase transitions, such as the sudden loss of magnetism demonstrated by iron, cobalt, and nickel at a distinctive temperature, the "Curie point." But most critical phenomena are complex events, and early theories were able to do no more than to predict that they did occur, not how or under what circumstances.

Wilson's approach was to break a phase transition down into smaller, more easily studied subunits, a technique that had been developed by others. He then applied the principles of renormalization to these subunits. In a pair of articles published in 1971 in *Physical Review B* Wilson outlined the result of his analysis, a theory that correctly predicts known critical data. It was for this work that Wilson received the 1982 Nobel Prize for physics. At the presentation ceremonies, Stig Lundqvist of the Royal Swedish Academy of Sciences stated that Wilson's theory "gave a complete theoretical description of the behavior close to the critical point and gave also methods to calculate numerically the crucial quantities."

Since the mid–1970s, Wilson has returned to the research of his graduate years, the study of elementary particles. Like many others, he has been attempting to use the methods of renormalization to understand the interaction of quarks, one group of fundamental particles of which all matter seems to consist. As a result of this research, he has also developed another interest: the development of faster and more efficient computers. As he has seen how his own research and that of others is limited by existing computer technology, he has become an outspoken advocate for the development of improved hardware to deal with problems of particle physics. In connection with this interest, Wilson accepted an appointment as director of the Center for Theory and Simulation in Science and Engineering at Cornell in 1985.

Wilson was married in 1982 to Alison Brown, a computer specialist at Cornell Computer Services, whom he had met in 1975. He enjoys hiking, folk dancing, and playing the oboe. Outdoor activities in general have long been an important part of Wilson's life. During high school, he ran the mile and cross country for his track team; as a graduate student, he spent one summer hiking the John Muir Trail from Yosemite Park to Mount Whitney. And in 1962, he climbed Mount Blanc with fellow physicists **Henry Kendall** and James Bjorken.

Elected a member of the National Academy of Sciences in 1975, Wilson has been awarded a number of prestigious honors including the Dannie Heineman Prize of the American Physical Society in 1973, Israel's Wolf Prize in 1980 (shared with Michael Fisher and Leo Kadanoff), and the Franklin Medal of the Franklin Institute in 1982. In 1988, he ended his long affiliation with Cornell to become Hazel C. Youngberg Trustees Distinguished Professor at Ohio State University. Since 1990, Wilson has also become active on two important national committees dealing with science policy, the National Academy of Science's Committee on Physical Science, Mathematics and Applications and the Committee on the Federal Role in Educational Research.

SELECTED WRITINGS BY WILSON:

Periodicals

Physical Review B, Renormalization Group and Critical Phenomena, November 1, 1971, pp. 3174–3205.

FURTHER READING:

Books

Nobel Prize Winners, H. W. Wilson, 1987, pp. 1136–1138.
Weber, Robert L., *Pioneers of Science: Nobel Prize Winners in Physics,* American Institute of Physics, 1980, pp. 277–278.

Periodicals

Weber, Robert L., *New York Times,* October 10, 1982, p. C6.
Weber, Robert L., *Science,* November 19, 1982.

Sketch by David E. Newton

Robert R. Wilson
1914–2000
American physicist

Robert R. Wilson was a rare combination of particle physicist, philosopher, and artist. His work on protons in the 1950s significantly advanced knowledge of these elementary particles. He also made contributions to the use of magnetic forces to guide beams of particles. In addition, Wilson had been an active sculptor during his years as a physicist, and his experience in both fields culminated in the design of the Fermi National Accelerator Laboratory at Batavia, just west of Chicago, Illinois. Fermilab, as it is known, is a high-energy particle accelerator, designed to collide electrically charged particles at high speeds. The debris from the collisions gives scientists valuable information regarding the structure and behavior of matter. Wilson was director of Fermilab from its inception in the mid–1960s until 1978.

Wilson brought a philosophical approach to the building of Fermilab, comparing the process of building the lab to the process of building the great cathedrals in Europe. Physicist Leon Lederman, in his book *The God Particle: If the Universe Is the Answer, What Is the Question?,* quotes Wilson as follows: "I even found, emphatically, a strange similarity between the cathedral and the accelerator: The one structure was intended to reach a soaring height in space; the other is intended to reach a comparable height in energy." Wilson's unusual approach to building scientific instruments had roots in his early years. He was born Robert Rathbun Wilson in Frontier, Wyoming, on March 4, 1914. His father was Platt Elvin Wilson, a local politician, and his mother was Edith (Rathbun) Wilson. When he was eight, his parents divorced. His youthful experiences on the cattle ranches of Wyoming—particularly his exposure to the blacksmith shop—familiarized him with tool-making and repair. This experience and an attitude that nothing was impossible would prove useful in the future when Wilson designed Fermilab.

The young Wilson was as much a tinkerer as a physicist. In high school, he designed and constructed scientific devices, including a vacuum and a hand-sized particle accelerator. When it came time to go to college, he enrolled at the University of California at Berkeley, intending to study philosophy. But the year was 1932—the middle of the Great Depression—and philosophy seemed impractical during those years of hardship. He became attracted to physics when he walked by a lab one day and saw machines and generators whirring inside. He felt an immediate affinity with the scientists and students working those machines.

Contributes to Atomic Bomb

Wilson remained at the University of California as a graduate student, working with **Ernest Orlando Lawrence**

Robert R. Wilson

who had invented the cyclotron, a type of particle accelerator. After receiving his Ph.D. in 1940, Wilson took a position as physics instructor at Princeton University. When the United States became involved in World War II, he was asked, along with thousands of other expert scientists and mathematicians, to help with the effort to develop an atomic bomb. From 1943 to 1946 he lived in Los Alamos, New Mexico, serving as leader of a group of scientists working on a cyclotron. In 1944 he became head of the division researching experimental nuclear physics, which eventually became responsible for designing instruments to measure the flash produced by the first test bomb.

Wilson had, at first, been a reluctant participant in the war efforts. He had initially opposed the war, but in the early 1940s, with the fighting in Europe escalating, he had accepted an invitation by Dr. Lawrence to attend a conference at the Massachusetts Institute of Technology to discuss the war. There, he heard testimony from witnesses regarding the devastation in Europe. He agreed that Germany must be stopped.

During his stay in Los Alamos, it became clear that the United States government was not going to let the inventors of the weapon have any input about how the bomb was going to be used. Wilson, along with many other scientists involved, became discouraged about the political uses of the weapon they had designed. The power of the bomb was extraordinary; yet only the scientists seemed aware of its awesome power and the ramifications of misuse.

After World War II, Wilson took a position at Harvard University, designing a 150 MeV cyclotron—a machine that accelerates particles to 150 million electron volts. The early machines sprayed out protons in all directions, so that measurements were difficult. Wilson realized that magnets could be used to focus the emerging protons into a concentrated beam. As Lederman wrote in *The God Particle,* Wilson was "the first to understand the subtle but crucial effect the magnetic forces had in keeping the protons from spraying out." As accelerators became more powerful they also became longer, eventually being designed in circular shapes. Magnetic fields were used to guide the particle beams around the accelerator rings.

In 1946 Wilson became a full professor at Cornell University, where he was also named director of the Laboratory of Nuclear Studies. There, he oversaw the construction of a new type of particle accelerator, a 300 MeV synchrotron. (A synchrotron enabled particles to travel in a circular path at increasing speeds.) In the following years he built ever more powerful accelerators to help explore the nature of the proton. From his experiments, the structure of the proton was established.

Builds Fermilab

In the early 1960s, however, Wilson became discouraged with his research in particle physics. He seemed not to be making headway in his field. By the mid–1960s, he was considering a total change. He thought perhaps he should pursue full-time what had been a lifelong hobby, sculpture. It was at this time, when Wilson was casting about for change, that he was offered the opportunity to construct the 200-billion-electron-volt (200 GeV, or gigaelectron volts) synchrotron—the Fermi National Accelerator Laboratory. Wilson approached his new project with zeal and creativity. Construction at Fermilab was started in 1968 and finished in 1971—far less time than had been estimated by other experts. The new accelerator was contained at the world's best experimental facility in particle physics. Protons traveled near the speed of light, with collisions reaching an energy level of 400 gigaelectron volts. A few initial problems were resolved, and it became clear that the power of Fermilab would be useful in many ways. In 1977, for example, upsilon particles were discovered by Wilson's colleague **Leon Lederman**, who went on to win the 1988 Nobel Prize in physics. Wilson was convinced that the discovery was a direct result of the power of the accelerator. One of Wilson's powerful innovations during his tenure at Fermilab was the use of superconducting magnets to optimize energy efficiency and produce a more powerful magnetic field to guide the beams of particles.

By 1974, it was clear that, in order to remain the world's best, Fermilab's power would have to be increased even more. In 1977, Wilson appealed to Congress for increased funding. During his congressional testimony, Wilson remarked that the value of accelerators "has only to do with the respect with which we regard one another, the dignity of men, our love of culture. . . . It has to do with, are we good painters, good sculptors, great poets? I mean all the things we really venerate and honor in our country and are patriotic about. It has nothing to do directly with defending our country except to make it worth defending." Wilson wanted to build a second ring of magnets to boost the energy level to 1000 gigaelectron volts, but Congress denied the funding. Early in 1978, Wilson resigned as director, convinced that he could do more to advance physics on his own than as a director of a minimally funded lab.

Although Wilson remained involved with the lab as director emeritus and architectural consultant, he has spent most of his time after his resignation teaching. From 1978 to 1980, he was the Peter B. Ritzma Professor at the University of Chicago and from 1980 to 1983, the Michael Pupin Professor at Columbia. He has been a guest lecturer at Harvard, the University of Washington and the Los Alamos Scientific Laboratory. Currently, he is professor of physics emeritus at Cornell University. He lives in Ithaca, New York, with his wife, Jane Inez Scheyer, whom he married in 1940. They have three sons. Several of Wilson's sculptures—metal constructions and stone carvings—are displayed at Fermilab.

Wilson was raised in the Quaker heritage of nonviolence, a philosophy that guided him for the rest of his life. Richard Feynman has written that after witnessing that first atomic test at Los Alamos in 1945, Wilson stated: "It's a terrible thing that we made." Wilson later wrote: "I determined at that moment that having played even a small role in bringing it about, I would go all out in helping to make it become a positive factor for humanity."

Wilson died on January 16, 2000, at the age of 85 at a retirement home in Ithaca, New York. Upon his passing, U.S. Department of Energy Secretary Bill Richardson commented that Wilson had had "an unerring sense of what is important to the science of high-energy physics and its importance to the nation," adding that "He was a fearless optimist, believing that even the most difficult things could be accomplished. The nation has lost one of its best in Bob Wilson."

FURTHER READING:

Books

Hilts, Philip, *Scientific Temperaments: Three Lives in Contemporary Science,* Simon & Schuster, 1982.
Lederman, Leon, and Dick Teresi, *The God Particle: If the Universe Is the Answer, What Is the Question?,* Houghton, 1993.

Sketch by Dorothy Barnhouse

Robert Woodrow Wilson
1936–
American astronomer

Robert Woodrow Wilson is best known for the discovery, with coresearcher **Arno Penzias**, of the cosmic background radiation believed to be the remnant of the "big bang" that started the universe. For their work, Wilson and Penzias were honored with numerous awards, including the 1978 Nobel Prize in physics, which they shared with **Pyotr Kapitsa**.

Wilson was born in Houston, Texas, on January 10, 1936. He attended Rice University where he received a B.A. in physics in 1957. He then moved on to the California Institute of Technology (Caltech) for graduate study and received his Ph.D. in 1962. Wilson's thesis work, and postdoctoral research, involved making radio surveys (the use of radio waves bounced off of stellar bodies to create visual approximations) of the Milky Way Galaxy. When he heard of the existence of specialized radio equipment at Bell Laboratories, he left Caltech and accepted a job at Bell's research facility in Holmdel, New Jersey. This was the very same research facility from which **Karl Jansky**, in the 1930s, almost single-handedly invented the science of radio astronomy. Wilson and Penzias, who had preceded Wilson at Bell Labs by about a year, were about to embark on a research odyssey that would culminate in an extremely important discovery almost by accident.

Just as Jansky had done thirty years earlier, Wilson and Penzias were studying the possible causes of static interference that impaired the quality of radio communications. At least, this was what the management at Bell hoped would transpire as the two radio astronomers conducted their research. Wilson and Penzias's long–range plan was to measure radiation in the galactic "halo," a theorized but not well understood cloud of matter and radiation surrounding the Milky Way and other galaxies. Then, they hoped to look for hydrogen gas in clusters of galaxies. Their research instrumentation included a small, sensitive twenty-foot microwave "horn" originally designed to receive bounced radio reflections from the Echo communications satellite.

Since galactic radio radiation is, by its nature, not very energetic, the central problem in measuring its precise intensity was to eliminate all conceivable sources of heat, or thermal noise, which could obscure an accurate reading of the weak radio signals from space. To this end, Penzias had laboriously constructed a "cold load," using frigid liquid helium, which would cool the radio detector down to within only a few degrees above absolute zero. When the equipment was finally ready in the spring of 1964, the radio horn was turned to the sky.

Discovers Cosmic Background Radiation with Penzias

Very early in the research project, it became apparent that the antenna was measuring more radio radiation than Wilson and Penzias had anticipated. The source of the excess radiation could not be determined. A similar problem had surfaced earlier when the twenty-foot horn was used for Echo satellite communications. At that time, researchers added up all the known sources of accounted radio noise, which totaled a heat measurement of nineteen degrees Kelvin. It was therefore puzzling to them that the radio receiver was measuring twenty-two degrees. Wilson and Penzias's results were similar. They had hoped that their carefully modified apparatus would yield more accurate results, but this apparently was not the case. They were measuring a significant amount of excess microwave radiation. The intensity of the signal did not change regardless of where they pointed the receiver. Nor did the radio static appear to be coming from any discrete object in space. The Milky Way Galaxy was not the source either, since the radio signal seemed to be coming from everywhere in the universe at once, not from just a limited zone across the sky. Based on the known sources of radio radiation, the strength of this radiation was far more powerful than expected.

Wilson and Penzias checked for possible explanations for this phenomenon, concluding that atmospheric effects were not to blame. Since the hill upon which their radio horn was perched overlooked New York City, the possibility of interference from man-made sources was considered. After repeated observations, however, Wilson and Penzias were convinced that New York was not to blame. To insure that the signal was not the result of interference from their own electronic apparatus, Wilson and Penzias tracked down and eliminated every conceivable source of noise—including the effects of bird dung, which coated the inside of the radio horn, courtesy of a pair of nesting pigeons. The interior of the radio horn was cleaned out.

The attempts to improve the performance of the radio horn took time. Finally, in 1965, the antenna was re-activated and careful observations were made of the radio flux from the sky. The results revealed that the telescope was performing better than ever, but the mysterious excess signal remained. The intensity of the excess radio noise was what would be expected from an object, or source, with a very low temperature—only a few degrees above absolute zero. In this case, as with the previous observation, the static was not coming from a discrete source but was emanating uniformly from every direction in the sky.

While Wilson and Penzias were trying to make sense of what seemed to them to be a failed experiment, Robert Dicke and his colleagues at Princeton University, unaware of the project at Bell Labs, were building a radio receiver of their own designed to look for the very radiation that Wilson and Penzias had unintentionally observed. Whereas Wilson and Penzias had rather modest hopes of making simple surveys of galactic radio flux, Dicke was looking for physical evidence of the creation of the universe. Dicke had been researching the theoretical effects of the big bang, the expanding fireball theorized as the birth of the universe.

The line of reasoning Dicke followed was this: as the universe expanded after the big bang, gases cooled and thinned but were still dense enough to block electromagnetic radiation. All thermal energy released by atoms, including light and heat, was reabsorbed by other atoms in the gas almost instantly. One consequence of this condition was that if someone could have viewed the universe from the "outside" at this point, they would have seen only blackness, since no light could escape the opaque, light-absorbing gas. Eventually, there must have come a time, thousands of years after the big bang, when the average density of the expanding universe was finally low enough to allow heat and light to escape from atoms unimpeded, much as the light and heat generated in the sun's interior eventually escapes through the sun's transparent photosphere. According to the theory that Dicke was exploring, the rapid release of newly freed energy in the thinning, early universe would have taken the form of an incredibly sudden blaze of heat and light, almost like an explosion.

Hearing the "Echo" of the Big Bang

How could this "primeval fireball," as it came to be called, be observed today? If the remnant of this energy flash had survived after several billion years, it would be detected as a kind of "whisper" in a radio telescope. It would have a specific color and temperature and would be present in nearly equal intensities in every direction, forming a cosmic background radiation. This radiation would flood every available volume of space. In time, the radiation would appear to cool down to a point near absolute zero, due to the further expansion of the universe, but it would still be detectable even in the present-day universe. It was precisely this radiation that Robert Dicke was preparing to look for with his own radio telescope. It was also this radiation, measuring close to absolute zero (around three degrees Kelvin) in uniformity across the sky, that Wilson and Penzias had already discovered.

Wilson and Penzias were not cosmologists, however. They could not explain their observation of the microwave radiation at the 7.3 cm wavelength, and so they contacted Dicke, who they knew was working on this problem. When Dicke heard the details of their findings, he knew that Wilson and Penzias had discovered exactly what he was looking for; the cold, background radiation left over from the big bang. In 1965, Wilson and Penzias published their results in a paper entitled "A Measurement of Excess Antenna Temperature at 4,080 Mc/s." A companion paper written by Dicke, P. J. E. Peebles, P. G. Roll, and D. T. Wilkinson explained the profound cosmological implications of the finding.

The discovery of the cosmic background radiation was like finding the intact skeleton of a dinosaur. The radiation is a "fossil," an ancient relic from a time when the universe was barely 100,000 years old. The discovery of the radiation was to become the second great pillar upon which the big bang theory would rest, second only to the 1920s discovery of the expansion of the universe. The fact that the background radiation was predicted in advance of its discovery helped to strengthen the big bang theory, so much so that most competing theories about the birth of the universe, such as steady state, almost immediately fell away after 1965.

As scientists around the world began making their own confirming observations of the cosmic background radiation, it became apparent to those searching past research papers that clues to the existence of the radiation had existed for over twenty-five years. The most striking example came from 1938, in which optical telescopic observations revealed that interstellar cyanogen gas was being heated, unaccountably, by a 3 degree source. This source was nothing less than the cosmic background radiation. But at the time, no one imagined that the seemingly innocuous source of heat could be the remnants of the big bang fireball. It would not be until Wilson and Penzias's discovery that the cosmic radiation would be identified for what it was.

Wilson and Penzias's discovery was acclaimed by scientists around the world. Less impressed was the management of Bell labs who, according to Wilson in *Serendipitous Discoveries in Radio Astronomy,* essentially held the point of view, "You guys have been doing radio astronomy full time; the effort is supposed to be sort of half time, let's get on with something for the telephone company." In 1976, Wilson was named head of the Radio-Physics department of Bell Telephone. For his work on the cosmic background radiation he also received the Henry Draper Award, in 1977, from the National Academy of Sciences. In 1978, the importance of their achievement in the history of science was fully recognized when Wilson and Penzias shared the Nobel Prize in physics with Kapitsa.

SELECTED WRITINGS BY WILSON:

Periodicals

Serendipitous Discoveries in Radio Astronomy, Discovery of the Cosmic Microwave Background, edited by K. Kellermann and B. Sheets, National Radio Astronomy Observatory, 1983, pp. 185–95.

FURTHER READING:

Books

Astronomers, Peter Bedrick Books, 1984, pp. 157–58.
Weinberg, Steven, *The First Three Minutes,* Basic Books, 1988.

Sketch by Jeffery Bass

Adolf Windaus
1876–1959
German organic chemist

Adolf Windaus devoted his professional life to the investigation of the chemistry of natural products. He was awarded the Nobel Prize for chemistry in 1928 for his work on sterols, which led to his clarifying the chemical structure of cholesterol, and he is also noted for his discoveries of the structure of vitamin D, some of the B vitamins, and histamine. The impact of his work made it possible for many other scientists to study the structures of other natural products; for example, his work on cholesterol helped to establish the study of sex hormones. Windaus's research on digitalis was used in the treatment of heart disease, and his studies of vitamin D led to the development of irradiation, a process of exposing foods, such as milk and bread, to ultraviolet light in order to prevent nutritional deficiencies that could lead to disease.

Adolf Otto Reinhold Windaus came from a family of artisans and craftspeople on his mother's side and from weavers and clothing manufacturers on his father's side. He was born in Berlin to Adolf and Margarete (Elster) Windaus on December 25, 1876. In his youth, he attended the French Gymnasium in Berlin, where literature, not science, was the primary area of study. Young Windaus decided to become a physician after reading about the work of French chemist and microbiologist Louis Pasteur and German physician and microbiologist **Robert Koch**. His mother, who was a widow at the time of his decision, was disappointed, since she had hoped he would continue the long tradition of the family business.

Windaus's career in science began at the University of Berlin in 1895. The chemistry lectures given by **Emil Fischer** there were to be major influences which would shape his future. The physiological applications of Fischer's approach became the foundation of Windaus's investigations. After receiving a bachelor's degree in 1897 from the University of Berlin and abandoning any ideas of pursuing a career in medicine, he continued his studies at the University of Freiburg, where he was influenced by Heinrich Kiliani. Under Kiliani's direction he researched digitalis, which later was found to be a powerful stimulant to the heart and became widely used in the treatment of heart failure. Windaus wrote his dissertation on the chemistry of this substance and received his doctorate in 1899 from Freiburg.

Embarks on the Study of Cholesterol

After a year in military service, Windaus returned to Freiburg to work with Kiliani, turning now to the study of cholesterol. A seroid alcohol present in animal cells and body fluids, cholesterol regulates membrane fluidity and is involved in the process of metabolism. Because it was so widely found in animal cells, Windaus speculated that it must be closely connected with other important compounds. By 1906, he was appointed assistant professor at Freiburg. In 1913, Windaus moved to the University of Innsbruck in Austria to become a professor of applied medical chemistry. Two years later, he was at the University of Göttingen, where he was appointed director of the Laboratory for General Chemistry, succeeding chemist **Otto Wallach**. He remained at Göttingen for twenty-nine years, retiring in 1944.

While Windaus pursued his studies of natural products, a number of other chemists were working in related areas. During his investigation of cholesterol (the best known sterol) and associated substances, **Heinrich Wieland**, a colleague in Munich, was researching the structure of bile acids. By 1919, Windaus was able to show an affinity between sterines, a group of sterols he had established earlier, and bile acids. After this, the work between Wieland and Windaus in both of their laboratories proceeded in close collaboration and led to the clarification of the chemical structure of the sterol ring in 1932.

It was known that rickets could be cured with cod liver oil, which contained vitamin D. Some scientists, such as physiologist Alfred Hess in New York, felt that cholesterol was somehow involved with vitamin activity, which led him to ask Windaus to collaborate in efforts to find the chemical nature of vitamin D. Windaus's cooperation with scientists in New York and London resulted in the findings of other D vitamins and made Göttingen a center for vitamin research.

The results of the research taking place during the 1920s and 1930s on vitamins made it possible for Windaus to identify and characterize many other compounds formed in the process of the photochemical reactions under study. In 1927, Wieland was given the Nobel Prize in chemistry for his study of bile acids, and Windaus received the same award in 1928 for his discovery of the structure of sterols and their connection with vitamins. Windaus was granted numerous honorary degrees and other awards as well, including the Louis Pasteur Medal of the French Academy of Sciences in 1938 and the Goethe Medal of the Goethe Institute in 1941.

Collaboration Leads to the Discovery of Histamine

During his early work on cholesterol, Windaus also had collaborated with biochemist Franz Knoop. They studied the reaction of sugar with ammonia, hoping that they could convert sugar into amino acids, and possibly do the same for carbohydrates into proteins. This work led to the discovery of histamine, a compound that is significant in allergies and inflammation. Consequently, Windaus became involved with pharmaceutical companies that began to suggest problems for him to solve, and supplied him with much of the materials he needed for his work.

Windaus's work on a B vitamin, thiamine, helped to establish its correct structure and synthesis, while other work involved clarifying the structure of colchicine, a substance used in cancer therapy. Although Windaus abandoned the idea of becoming a physician early in his academic career, his contributions to organic chemistry paved the way for new medical treatments of disease.

Windaus's studies on cholesterol opened new research areas for many other investigators and led to an important branch of organic chemistry and biochemistry. He was considered a valuable collaborator because of the close work he did with chemists in Germany and other countries on natural products. He was generous with his students, giving them both freedom to pursue their research interests and full credit for contributions they made. His influence on other research was considerable. For instance, one of his students, **Adolf Friedrich Johann Butenandt**, presented the structure of sex hormones shortly after Windaus presented the structure of the sterol ring.

Windaus married Elisabeth Resau in 1915 and they had two sons, Gunter and Gustav, and a daughter, Margarete. While he was not sympathetic to the Nazi government during World War II, his reputation made it possible for him to continue his work without interference. After his retirement in 1944, he did not publish any further research, but a journal on which he had served editorially, the *Justus Liebigs Annalen der Chemie,* dedicated several volumes to him in 1957 in celebration of his eightieth birthday. He died at the age of eighty-two on June 9, 1959, at Göttingen.

SELECTED WRITINGS BY WINDAUS:

Periodicals

Nachrichten Gesellschaft d. Wissenschaften, Die Konstitution des Cholesterins, Göttingen, 1919.

Nachrichten Gesellschaft d. Wissenschaften, Anwendungen der Spannugstheorie, Göttingen, 1921.

Nachrichten Gesellschaft d. Wissenschaften, Ultraviolet Bestrahlung von Ergasterin, Göttingen, 1929, pp. 45–59.

Proceedings of the Royal Society, Chemistry of Irradiated Ergosterol, B, Volume 108, 1931, pp. 131–138.

FURTHER READING:

Books

Gillispie, Charles Coulson, editor, *Dictionary of Scientific Biography,* Scribner, 1970, pp. 443–446.

Sketch by Vita Richman

Niklaus Wirth
1934–
Swiss computer programmer

Computer language pioneer Niklaus Wirth is well-known to anyone who has studied even the basics of computer programming and technology. His contributions to the field of computer language development—in particular, the creation of the programming language PASCAL—have played an important role in shaping the arts of computer design and programming.

Wirth was born on February 15, 1934 in Winterthur, Switzerland to Walter, a geography professor, and Hedwig (Keller) Wirth. He attended the Federal Institute of Technology (known by the initials ETH) in Zurich, Switzerland, receiving his bachelor's degree in 1958. Moving to Canada, he continued his education with a Master of Science degree in 1960 from Laval University in Quebec. Moving once again, this time to California, he received his doctorate from the University of California at Berkeley in 1963. At the time Wirth received his Ph.D. from Berkeley, nearby Stanford University was assembling its Computer Science Department, and Wirth was offered a position as an assistant professor in the department. There, Wirth and his colleagues developed a host of computer languages, including PL360 and AL- GOL-W. Soon, Wirth had established himself as an expert in computer language development.

The Birth of PASCAL and Structured Programming

In 1967 Wirth moved back to his native Switzerland as an assistant professor of computer science at the University of Zurich. One year later, he accepted a position as a professor of computer science at ETH, his alma mater. Between 1968 and 1970 he developed the computer language PASCAL. Initially, Wirth had not intended for PASCAL to have commercial applications; because the language is so well suited for the microprocessors of today's computer systems, however, it has seen widespread use and development. Phillipe Kahn, an ETH graduate, formed his California-based computer software company around Wirth's language, selling more than a million copies of a modified PASCAL.

In 1971 Wirth introduced the concept of "structured programming," the idea that a program should be designed by dividing it into general but distinct steps, then refining each step until the final product is stripped down to its simplest elements. This concept, while creating quite a stir at the time, has become a standard methodology for most computer program development, and is taught in today's university computer science curriculums. Wirth "changed the way people think about programming," Kahn said in *Business Week.*

By design, structured programming leads to simpler programs. Similarly, Wirth's languages are defined so that programs written with them are easier to read and more bug-free than systems coded in other languages. In today's age of growing reliance upon computer systems, it is critical that those systems be both extremely reliable and user-friendly. Wirth himself traces his respect for simplicity back to his childhood hobby of building model airplanes; in an article in *Business Week,* he was quoted as saying, "If you have to pay [for a model airplane repair] out of your own pocket money, you learn not to make the fixes overly complicated." The journal of the Association of Computing Machinery said in a recent article that Wirth "has established a foundation for future research in the areas of computer language, systems, and architecture."

Beginning in 1979, Wirth developed the language Modula–2 and later a high-performance computer workstation called "Lilith," designed to utilize Modula–2. More recently, he has finished a new language called Oberon, which he hopes will lead to computer programs that are even simpler and more powerful than those created using PASCAL.

Honors and Awards

Wirth was the chairman of ETH's computer science division from 1982 until 1984 and again from 1988 through 1990; he was also appointed to lead the Institute of Computer Systems at ETH. He holds honorary doctorates from the University of York (England) and the Institute of Technology in Lausanne, Switzerland. He received the Emanuel Priore award from the Institute of Electrical and Electronics Engineers (IEEE) in 1983 and the coveted A. M. Turing award from the Association of Computing Machinery (ACM) in 1984. In 1987 Wirth received the Outstanding Contributions to Computer Science Education award from the ACM. In 1988 he was named a Computer Pioneer by the IEEE Computer Society and he was nominated as a Distinguished Alumnus of the University of California at Berkeley in 1992. Wirth and his wife, Nani Tucker, have three children, Carolyn, Christian, and Tina.

SELECTED WRITINGS BY WIRTH:

Books

Systematic Programming, Prentice-Hall, 1973.
PASCAL: User Manual and Report, Springer-Verlag, 1974.
Algorithms and Data Structures: Programs, Prentice-Hall, 1975.
Programming in Modula–2, second corrected edition, Springer-Verlag, 1982.

Periodicals

Communications of the ACM, Program Development by Stepwise Refinement, April, 1971.

Communications of the ACM, Toward a Discipline of Real-Time Programming, August, 1974.

Communications of the ACM, What Can We Do about the Unnecessary Diversity of Notation, November, 1974.

Communications of the ACM, Niklaus Wirth: 1984 ACM A. M. Turing Award Recipient, February, 1985, pp. 159–164.

FURTHER READING:

Books

Contemporary Authors New Revision Series, Volume 21, Gale, 1986.

Periodicals

Levine, Jonathan, *Business Week,* An Endless Campaign to Simplify Software, June 15, 1990, p. 136.

Sketch by Roger Jaffe

Evelyn Maisel Witkin
1921–
American geneticist

Evelyn Maisel Witkin is a specialist in bacterial mutation who has published more than forty-five papers in journals such as *Proceedings of the National Academy of Sciences, Bacteriological Reviews,* and *The Cold Spring Harbor Symposia of Quantitative Biology.* Her research focused on the genetic effects of radiation, spontaneous and induced mutation in bacteria and the enzymatic repair of DNA damage.

Witkin was born in New York City on March 9, 1921, the daughter of Joseph Maisel and the former Mary Levin. After completing high school, she attended New York University, from which she received her bachelor of arts degree magna cum laude in 1941. She then did her graduate work at Columbia University and received her master of arts degree in 1943 and her Ph.D. in 1947. Between 1947 and 1949 Witkin did postdoctoral research at the American Cancer Society. On July 9, 1943, she was married to Herman A. Witkin, with whom she had two children, Joseph, born in 1949, and Andrew, born in 1952. Witkin's husband died in July of 1979.

Begins Teaching Career

In 1950 Witkin accepted an appointment as a member of the genetics department at the Carnegie Institute in Washington, D.C., a post she held until 1955. She was then appointed to the faculty at the Downstate Medical Center of the State University of New York (SUNY) in Brooklyn. She remained at SUNY until 1971, rising to the rank of professor of medicine. In 1971 Witkin became professor of biological sciences at Douglass College of Rutgers University. Eight years later she was named Barbara McClintock Professor of Genetics at Douglass. On her retirement in 1991, she was made Barbara McClintock Professor Emerita.

In addition to her role as a teacher, Witkin also served as editor of the journal *Microbial Genetics* from 1950 to 1964 and as a member of the editorial board of *Mutation Research* since 1960. Among the honors accorded Witkin have been the Prix Charles Leopold Mayer of the French Academy of Sciences in 1977 and the Lindback Award in 1979. She was also elected to membership in the National Academy of Sciences.

SELECTED WRITINGS BY WITKIN:

Periodicals

Bacteriological Review, UV Mutagenesis and Inducible DNA Repair in *E. Coli,*, 1976.

Journal of Bacteriology, Overproduction of DnaE Protein (Alpha Subunit of DNA Polymerase III) Restores Viability in a Conditionally Inviable *Escherichia Coli* Strain Deficient in DNA Polymerase I, Volume 174, 1992, pp. 4166–4168.

Sketch by David E. Newton

Edward Witten
1951–
American mathematical physicist

Edward Witten's work combines physics with advanced mathematical techniques, and he has made major contributions to the field of theoretical physics. Many consider him not only the most brilliant physicist of his generation but a rival to greats such as **Albert Einstein** and Isaac Newton. He is best known for his work on a unified theory of physics called superstring theory, which theorizes that the universe is composed of extremely small particles called strings and posits the existence of ten dimensions.

Witten was born on August 26, 1951, in Baltimore, Maryland. He is the son of Louis W. Witten, a gravitational physicist who is currently at the University of Cincinnati in Ohio. Witten went to a Baltimore Hebrew school as a child and then attended Brandeis University near Boston, Massachusetts. He graduated with a degree in history in 1971, although his real interest was linguistics. After graduation he wrote articles for such publications as the *Nation* and the *New Republic*. In 1972 he worked on George McGovern's campaign for president as an aide to a legislative assistant, but he decided against a career in journalism or politics in favor of returning to school. He was still considering whether to study physics or mathematics when he entered the doctoral program at Princeton University; he earned his master's degree in physics in 1974 and his Ph.D. in 1976.

In 1977 Witten was named junior fellow of the Society of Fellows at Harvard University. Despite receiving several offers from other universities, Witten returned to Princeton in 1980, where he was named full professor in the department of physics at the age of twenty-eight. Although highly respected by his students, Witten's behavior occasionally made him seem otherworldly. Habits such as frequent long pauses for thought during his unusually soft-spoken lectures caused some students at Princeton refer to him as "The Martian."

Witten's early research remained relatively close to traditional physics. He studied electromagnetism, as well as the forces that hold the nuclei of atoms together and the forces responsible for nuclear decay. While a professor at Princeton, Witten excelled in developing new approaches to describing the universe with quantum theory. By 1982 he had become very interested in supersymmetry—a theory which describes how matter and energy particles can be interchanged. In that year he was awarded a MacArthur Fellowship, an honor he earned for his many original theoretical proposals. By the mid 1980s, Witten found himself increasingly drawn to the search for a unified theory in physics, one which would explain all the forces in the universe with a single set of rules. Traditional theories of physics lack a single model that explains all the observed forces in this way.

To search for a unified theory, Witten studied the fundamental building blocks of everything from atoms to the cosmos. He used advanced mathematics, which allowed him to describe these fundamental building blocks using more dimensions than the four used in traditional physics, and in doing so he drew on the work of a number of mathematicians and theoretical physicists who had preceded him. In 1918, a German physicist named Theodor Kaluza attempted to use a fifth dimension to explain inconsistencies between gravity and other laws of nature, particularly electromagnetism. The principal difficulty with Kaluza's theory was that it did not explain why the fifth dimension was not observable. In 1926, the Swedish mathematician Oskar Klein elaborated on Kaluza's theory by explaining a possible reason for failures to find the fifth dimension. He suggested the fifth dimension was so compact or "rolled up" that it existed, in effect, between subatomic particles and was thus too small to be seen by any known technology. The combination of these two ideas is called the Kaluza-Klein theory, and Witten used it in his effort to develop an understanding of the characteristics shared by all the forces found in nature.

String theory had been proposed earlier in the 1970s as a possible unified theory. String theory differed from traditional theories in two basic ways: the shape of the fundamental building blocks it proposed and the number of dimensions used to describe those blocks. According to theories of physics before quantum theory, the fundamental building blocks are tiny ball-shaped pieces of matter. These particles move in a world which is described with the four traditional dimensions of length, width, depth, and time. Forces such as gravity and electricity cause the particles to move. This view of the universe was revolutionized by quantum theory, which proposed that the fundamental building blocks are really locations where matter and energy become interchangeable. The existence of matter results from fields of energy, energy which exists in varying amounts with varying patterns of resonances. The problem with quantum theory, however, is that it cannot account for gravity, and string theory began as an effort to solve this problem. String theory proposes that the fundamental building blocks are mathematical curves or strings formed into loops and that these shapes can only be described with more than four dimensions. Different vibrations of the strings create the many types of matter and energy found in the universe; an example these theorists use is the way different vibrations of the strings on a musical instrument create many different sounds.

Witten first learned about string theory in 1975, and studying it allowed him to combine his unusual mathematical abilities with advanced theoretical physics. Little attention was given to string theory for many years after its introduction, and Witten played a major role in popularizing it among physicists. One problem with the theory was that it originally proposed the existence of twenty-six dimensions, a concept many physicists found difficult to accept. In the 1970s, two researchers combined string theory and supersymmetry into superstring theory, which only required ten dimensions. However, a ten-dimensional universe still had six dimensions more than most physicists were prepared to believe existed, so string theory remained relatively unpopular. In 1984, Witten wrote an important paper with **Luis Alvarez** which identified new anomalies in certain kinds of radioactive decay. Anomalies are mathematical inconsistencies or theoretical defects that yield unacceptable results. Witten and Alvarez first established that these anomalies were topological, or related to intrinsic geometric shapes. They then showed that the topology of these anomalies could only be studied using ten dimensions but not using four dimensions. A paper written in response to theirs showed how string theory could explain the elements as well.

By 1985 Witten was completely committed to the study of string theory. He became its foremost proponent, writing nineteen papers about the theory in that year alone. Witten also won both the Einstein Medal and the New York Academy of Science's Award for Physics and Math Science in 1985. The following year the National Science Foundation awarded him its Alan T. Waterman Award for his work in elementary-particle physics and its application to cosmology. In an interview with *Scientific American* Witten remarked: "It was very clear that if I didn't spend my life concentrating on string theory, I would simply be missing my life's calling." A number of traditional physicists remain skeptical about the theory, primarily because the existence of ten dimensions is not substantiated by anything except mathematics. But Witten has observed, as quoted in the *New York Times Magazine,* that mathematical consistency has been "one of the most reliable guides to physicists in the last century."

Witten ended his teaching career in 1987 and joined the Institute for Advanced Study at Princeton, where research is the focus. To delve deeper into string theory Witten created a new technique which combined topology and quantum field theory, naming it topological quantum field theory. He applied his technique to the adjacent mathematical field of knot theory as well as to string theory. According to Witten, his discovery of new symmetries in knot theory using topological quantum field theory was his "single most satisfying piece of work." And for this work, Witten shared the Fields Medal, the most prestigious prize in mathematics, in 1990.

Witten is married to Chiara Nappi, who is also a physicist at Princeton University. They have three children. He is active in the Middle East peace movement through the Tel Aviv based International Centre for Peace in the Middle East, and he traveled to Jerusalem in order to attend their Emergency World Jewish Leadership Peace Conference. He is also a board member of Americans for Peace Now.

SELECTED WRITINGS BY WITTEN:

Books

Superstring Theory, Cambridge University Press, 1987.

Periodicals

Nuclear Physics, Gravitational Anomalies, Volume B234, 1984, p. 269.
Nuclear Physics, Search for a Realistic Kaluza-Klein Theory, Volume B186, 1987, p. 412.
Nuclear Physics, On the Structure of the Topological Phase of Two-Dimensional Gravity, Volume B340, 1990, pp. 281–332.
Physical Review, String Theory and Black Holes, Volume D44, 1991, pp. 314–324.
Jewish Post, Three Months Later, A Mixed Bag of Results, April 8, 1993.

FURTHER READING:

Periodicals

Cole, K. C., *New York Times Biographical Service,* A Theory of Everything, Volume 18, October, 1987, pp. 1062–1067.

Horgan, John, *Scientific American,* The Pied Piper of Superstrings, November, 1991, pp. 42–46.
Horgan, John, *Physics Today,* Muller, Wilczek and Witten Are MacArthur Foundation Fellows, December, 1982, pp. 68–70.
Horgan, John, *Physics Today,* NSF Honors Rabi and Witten, Names Young Investigators, September, 1987, pp. 95–96.
Siegel-Itzokovich, Judy, *Jerusalem Post Magazine,* The Martian, March 23, 1990, pp. 6–8.

Sketch by David N. Ford

Georg Wittig
1897–1987
German chemist

Organic chemist Georg Wittig's investigations led him to discover in 1953 a chemical process for synthesizing complex compounds such as vitamin A, vitamin D derivatives, steroids, and biological pesticides. Because of this process, known as the Wittig reaction, such compounds can now routinely be synthesized. For his work in organic synthesis, and especially for the Wittig reaction, he shared the 1979 Nobel Prize in chemistry with **Herbert C. Brown**.

Georg Friedrich Karl Wittig was born on June 16, 1897, in Berlin, Germany, to Gustav Wittig, a professor of fine arts at the University of Berlin, and Martha (Dombrowski) Wittig. He went to grade school at the Wilhelms-Gymnasium in Kassel. In 1916 he enrolled at the University of Tübingen, but interrupted his college years to serve in World War I. After moving to the University of Marburg in 1920, he began postgraduate studies in chemistry under the guidance of Karl von Auwers. After receiving his doctorate in 1923, Wittig stayed on at Marburg to teach and do research for many years. In 1932, he became associate professor at the technical university in Brunswick. He went to the University of Freiburg five years later in the capacity of associate professor. In 1944 he was appointed full professor and director of the University of Tübingen's Chemical Institute. After twelve years, he transferred to the University of Heidelberg, where he became emeritus professor in 1967. After retirement, he continued to work and publish with various students at the University of Heidelberg.

Among his peers, Wittig won renown as an original thinker and gifted deviser of experiments. During Wittig's tenure at Tübingen, he and his research team started working with a family of organic compounds called ylides. These compounds formed the basis of the Wittig reaction, which easily and predictably joins two carbon atoms from different molecules to form a double bond. The Wittig reaction's reliability enabled other chemists to pursue and publish findings on thousands of applications for linking large carbon molecules.

Prior to the Nobel Prize, Wittig received many accolades, including the Adolf von Baeyer Medal in 1953, the 1967 Otto Hahn Prize of the German Chemical Society, the 1972 Paul Karrer Medal in Chemistry from the University of Zurich and the 1975 Roger Adams Award from the American Chemical Society. He had also been granted honorary degrees from the universities of Hamburg, Tübingen, and Paris. Wittig married Waltraut Ernst in 1930. Together, they had two daughters. Wittig loved the out-of-doors and was an avid mountaineer. While young, he had shown considerable musical ability. Those who knew him often remarked that he could have had a career in music had his early inclinations not led him away from chemistry. Wittig died on August 26, 1987, in Heidelberg at the age of ninety.

SELECTED WRITINGS BY WITTIG:

Books

Stereochemie, Akademische verlag (Leipzig), 1930.

FURTHER READING:

Books

Nobel Prize Winners, H. W. Wilson, 1987.

Sketch by Hovey Brock

Abel Wolman
1892–1989
American engineer

Abel Wolman was one of the world's foremost sanitary engineers. His career spanned three-quarters of a century. He is perhaps best known for establishing, in collaboration with Linn H. Enslow, the standards for application of chlorine to drinking water now used throughout the world. On the occasion of Wolman's death, John B. Mannion wrote in the *Journal of the American Water Works Association,* "No other chemical application undertaken by man has had the public health benefit of the disinfection of water by chlorine." Wolman influenced generations of students in engineering, public health, and environmental

science and was an advisor on water problems to more than fifty foreign governments.

Wolman was born June 10, 1892, in Baltimore, Maryland, to Morris and Rosa Wachsman Wolman. He received a B.A. from Johns Hopkins University in 1913, and a B.S. in engineering there in 1915. In 1937 Johns Hopkins granted him an honorary doctorate in engineering when he accepted the position of professor and chair of the departments of sanitary engineering at both the School of Engineering and the School of Hygiene and Public Health. He continued at Johns Hopkins until 1962. He also taught at Harvard, Princeton, the University of Chicago, and the University of Southern California.

Engineering in the Service of Public Health

Wolman began his career in health services even before completing his engineering degree. In 1913 he conducted pollution studies of the Potomac River in Washington for the U.S. Public Health Service. In 1914 he took a position with the Maryland State Department of Health, serving as chief engineer for the department from 1922 to 1939. He oversaw the formation of the Washington Suburban Sanitary Commission and the consolidation of the Baltimore metropolitan area into a single water supply region, and developed during these years a firm belief in regional solutions to problems of sewerage and water supply.

In 1919 Wolman and former Hopkins classmate Linn H. Enslow published a paper that established standards for the application of chlorine to drinking water. The benefits of using hypochlorite salts to kill bacteria in water had been demonstrated as early as 1896 by George Fuller; however, because no method existed for determining the absorption of chlorine into different kinds of water, it could not be applied to drinking water safely or reliably. Wolman and Enslow devised a formula for calculating the correct amount of chlorine based on particular water conditions and desired qualities. Their methods soon gained universal acceptance.

At the federal level Wolman's advice was sought by the Senate Select Committee on National Water Resources, the House Committee on Science and Astronautics, and the U.S. Geological Survey. At the state level as well, his reputation for careful analysis and his ability always to see the broader impact of policy decisions earned him consultancies to the Tennessee Valley Authority, the Potomac River Commission, and the New Jersey Master Water Plan. Cities around the nation as well as the international community (more than fifty foreign governments, including Brazil, India, and Senegal) benefited from Wolman's knowledge and experience concerning drinking water and waste water systems.

Wolman's expertise guided the National Research Council in its efforts to improve sanitary engineering and environmental health issues in the U.S. military during World War II. When the United Nations was organized after the war, Wolman was chosen to assist the surgeon general of the U.S. Public Health Service in negotiations that established the World Health Organization (WHO). Under his influence the agency broadened its initial mandate to promote health by medical intervention, vaccines, and medicines to include an emphasis on controlling and preventing water-borne disease. Wolman's association with WHO was to last the rest of his life. His work with the National Research Council led to a position as consultant to the Department of Defense, and he later became a consultant to the U.S. Atomic Energy Commission. Wolman formulated sanitary engineering guidelines for the commission, and in the 1940s became a member of its advisory committee on reactor safety.

In the 1950s Wolman became uneasy about the environmental impact of the growing nuclear power industry and made his case eloquently to scientists such as **J. Robert Oppenheimer** and **Edward Teller**. It was Wolman who insisted that the first of the commercial nuclear power plants in West Milton, New York, include a concrete containment structure. Toward the end of his life he was increasingly concerned that overpopulation would neutralize the benefits of improvements to the world's water supply and supporting environmental systems, particularly in developing countries.

Wolman's lifelong contributions were recognized with numerous honors and awards, including the Sedgwick Memorial Medal of the American Public Health Association in 1948 and the Albert Lasker Special Award in 1960. In 1967 he received the William Proctor Prize from the Science Research Society of America. He also received the National Medal of Science in 1974 and the Tyler Ecology Award in 1976. He was a member of the American Association for the Advancement of Science, as well as Britain's Faraday Society and Royal Institute of Public Health. He was elected to the National Academy of Sciences in 1963 and to the National Academy of Engineering in 1965. In 1983 Wolman held his last organizational position as honorary president of the Pan American Health and Education Foundation.

Wolman was editor-in-chief of the *Journal of the American Water Works Association* from 1920 to 1937 and editor of the *Journal of the American Public Health Association, Manual of Water Works Practice,* and *Municipal Sanitation.* He contributed more than 135 papers to professional journals.

Wolman married Anne Gordon on June 10, 1920, and had one son, Markley Gordon. He enjoyed playing the violin, often accompanied by his wife on the piano. Wolman died on February 22, 1989, at the age of ninety-six. Steven Muller, president of Johns Hopkins University, told the *New York Times,* "I can think of no other Johns Hopkins faculty member and alumnus who has touched so many lives around the globe with his life's work."

SELECTED WRITINGS BY WOLMAN:

Books

The Significance of Waterborne Typhoid Fever Outbreaks: 1920–1930, Williams & Wilkins, 1931.

Man's Role in Changing the Face of Earth, University of Chicago Press, 1956, p. 807–816.
Water, Health, and Society: Selected Papers, edited by Gilbert F. White, Indiana University Press, 1959.
Present and Prospective Means for Improved Reuse of Water, U.S. Government Printing Office, 1960.
Cities, Knopf, 1965, pp. 156–174.

Periodicals

State Government, Wanted: A National Water Policy, Volume 19, September, 1946, pp. 215–217, 239.
Journal of the American Water Works Association, Basic Principles of a National Water Resources Policy: Committee Report, Volume 49, July, 1957, pp. 825–833.

FURTHER READING:

Books

Cohen, Harry, and Itzhak J. Carmin, *Jews in the World of Science,* Monde, York, 1956, p. 258.
Cohen, Harry, and Itzhak J. Carmin, *McGraw-Hill Modern Scientists and Engineers,* Volume 3, McGraw, pp. 344–345.

Periodicals

Cohen, Harry, and Itzhak J. Carmin, *Los Angeles Times,* Abel Wolman; Helped Perfect Water Purification Technique, February 24, 1989, part 1, p. 22.
Sullivan, Walter, *New York Times,* Prof. Abel Wolman, 96, Is Dead; Led Efforts to Chlorinate Water, February 24, 1989, p. B4.
Valentine, Paul W., *Washington Post,* Pushing 96, His Creativity Flows; Wolman Still a Water Science Titan, January 9, 1988, p. M1.

Sketch by Kelly Otter Cooper

Harland G. Wood
1907–1991
American biochemist

Harland G. Wood is best known for his work in demonstrating how carbon dioxide is used by heterotrophic as well as autotrophic organisms. An autotroph is any organism that requires only inorganic compounds (carbon dioxide and metals, for example) for nutrition (most plants are autotrophs). Heterotrophs need organic compounds in the form of amino acids, carbohydrates, or vitamins. All animals and some plants are heterotrophs. In collaboration with the scientist C. H. Werkman, Wood proved that carbon dioxide was more than merely a by-product for heterotrophs.

Wood was born in Delavan, Minnesota, on September 2, 1907, the son of William Clark and Inez Goff Wood. He attended Macalester College in St. Paul, Minnesota, from which he received a B.A. in chemistry and mathematics in 1931. He did his graduate work at Iowa State University and received his Ph.D. in 1935. Upon his graduation, Wood began his collaboration with Werkman, and the two demonstrated that carbon dioxide is used by propionic acid bacteria, which are heterotrophic. (Propionic acid is used as a mold inhibitor in bread.) By measuring oxidation levels in controlled experiments, the two scientists were able to determine that some carbon dioxide was in fact used by the organism. This finding was significant because up until then scientists had maintained that the primary distinction between autotrophs and heterotrophs was that only autotrophs could use carbon dioxide.

Wood was named a National Research Council fellow at the University of Wisconsin in 1936, where he and biochemist **Edward Lawrie Tatum** conducted research to prove vitamin B_1 is a requirement for growth of bacteria. He returned to Iowa State University, where he conducted research until 1943. He then joined the faculty of the physiology department at the University of Minnesota. In 1946 he moved on to Case Western Reserve University in Cleveland, Ohio. He remained there for the rest of his career.

Helps Validate Krebs Cycle

During these years Wood was hard at work collaborating with Werkman and several other scientists on a variety of experiments. In the early 1940s, Wood's experimentation with carbon isotopes helped prove the validity of the Krebs cycle and the critical role that carbon dioxide plays in that process. (The Krebs cycle is a series of enzymatic reactions that occur within cells whose ultimate function is to break down glucose to release energy.) Wood and his colleagues attempted to determine how carbon dioxide fit into the equation. The British scientist A. B. Hastings discovered carbon dioxide fixation (the transformation from a volatile to a stable state) while Wood and his colleagues were doing similar research. Sir **Hans Adolf Krebs** noted in his memoirs, *Reminiscences and Reflections,* that Wood "missed the discovery of carbon dioxide fixation . . . by a hair's breadth." But Wood was able to show how various chemicals reacted on the basis of the by-products they created, and his research showed carbon dioxide is an essential element of the cycle.

Up to this point, all of Wood's experiments with labeled carbon had been done in a laboratory setting. He wanted to prove that the same results could be obtained through experimentation not only with lab specimens but also with living, normal animals. Using rats and then cows, he and his colleagues conducted experiments with labeled carbon, acetate, propionate, butyrate, lactate, and other chemicals. The results, when compared with similar experiments done on lab specimens, proved that laboratory culture experiments are an accurate reflection of what occurs in animal metabolism.

Wood's later career focused on enzymology. He worked to isolate enzymes to discover new sources of energy in organisms. He showed that enzymes can have more complex reactions than scientists had previously believed. He also worked to show that adenosine triphosphate (ATP), a key source of energy in the Krebs cycle, is not the only energy source used by cellular organisms.

Acts As Advisor to Several Organizations

Upon his arrival at Case Western, Wood chaired the biochemistry department. He became dean of sciences in 1967. He served as president of the American Society of Biological Chemists in 1959 and general secretary of the International Union of Biochemistry from 1970 to 1973. He also served on the advisory committee of the American Cancer Society from 1965 to 1969 and the President's Scientific Advisory Committee from 1968 to 1971. He received a Fulbright fellowship in 1955 and a Guggenheim fellowship in 1962.

His later years brought him many honors, notably the President's National Medal of Science in 1989 and the William C. Rose Award in 1990. He also received three honorary degrees, the last coming from Case Western Reserve in 1991. He remained active and vigorous, conducting lab research and meeting with other scientists until his death.

Wood married Mildred Lenora Davis in 1929; the couple had three daughters, one of whom predeceased them. Outside the lab, he was an avid sportsman. The family actually developed a forty-acre deer camp in Minnesota, where Wood hunted, fished, and canoed in his spare time. He learned to ski at the age of fifty-five. Wood died of lymphoma in Cleveland on September 12, 1991, and was buried in Mankato, Minnesota.

SELECTED WRITINGS BY WOOD:

Books

Annual Review of Biochemistry, Then and Now, Volume 54, 1985, pp. 1–41.

FURTHER READING:

Books

Krebs, Hans with Anne Martin, *Reminiscences and Reflections,* Clarendon Press, 1981.

Periodicals

Krebs, Hans with Anne Martin, *Cleveland Plain Dealer,* September 13, 1991, p. C4.

Sketch by George A. Milite

Joseph Woodland
1921–
American engineer and inventor

J oseph Woodland is a mechanical engineer who spent 35 years with the IBM corporation. In the late 1940s, he conceived and patented what later became Universal Product Code (UPC) symbols. While with IBM, he was instrumental in the practical development of this system. which has become an integral part of everyday life. Norman Joseph Woodland was born in Atlantic City, New Jersey, on September 6, 1921, to Lewis Woodland and Lena Peiken. His father was a successful businessman who developed a furniture outlet into a chain of discount stores; his mother was involved in the business as well, eventually becoming the chain's buyer for women's sportswear. Lewis Woodland was an inquisitive, inventive man as well as an entrepreneur, and his son developed his own love of invention from helping his father in their workshop at home.

College and the Manhattan Project

The younger Woodland graduated from high school in 1939. He decided not to follow his father into business, but found other employment opportunities scarce in depression-struck Atlantic City. Instead, he moved to Philadelphia where he enrolled at the Drexel Institute of Technology (later called Drexel University). He joined the Army Reserve at the beginning of World War II, and was called into active duty in 1942.

The Army enrolled him in a crash course at the University of Maryland, then sent him to Oak Ridge, Tennessee, where he was involved in the top-secret Manhattan Project. Woodland spent the next three years as Technical Assistant to the Unit Chief of the "Liquid Thermal Diffusion Project," which separated the uranium isotope U–235 to be used as fissionable material in the atomic bomb. Woodland returned to Drexel after his discharge, and graduated in 1947; after graduation, he accepted a short-term teaching position.

The Conception of Bar Codes

While Woodland was teaching at Drexel, an electrical engineer named Bob Silver came to him and repeated a conversation he had just overheard in the Dean of Engineering's office. "The president of a supermarket chain [Sam Friedland, president of Food Fair] was trying to interest the Dean in undertaking a project that would enable them to automatically capture item prices at the front end of the store," recalls Woodland. "The Dean turned it down because, as I recall, it wasn't in Drexel's charter to undertake that kind of research and development work."

Silver thought it was a great opportunity and asked Woodland how they might go about it. Woodland devised a way to use several colors of fluorescent pigment and an ultraviolet light to encode product prices on the packages. Woodland and Silver constructed the device, proved to themselves that it had some limited potential, then put it aside.

That might have been the end of the matter. Woodland, however, was attending some graduate-level courses in business administration, and one of his assignments was to analyze the investment potential of a local company. In the course of his research he learned that Atlantic City Electric Company's stock was badly undervalued, and showed promise of dramatically increasing in value in the next few months. With borrowed money he bought all the stock he could, doubling his investment in less than a year. This windfall gave Woodland the freedom to pursue the opportunity he and Silver had seen. He resigned his faculty position at the end of the term, moved to Florida, and stayed in his grandfather's apartment while he continued his research.

It was already apparent that his original idea of multicolored codes was not feasible. As a youngster he had learned Morse code, in which data is encoded in dots and dashes. He pondered the idea of stretching the dots and dashes into bars, then shining light on the printed code and using an optical scanner to "read" the information. To make the code omni-directional, he shaped the lines into concentric circles, like a bullseye.

Woodland returned to Philadelphia where he carefully documented his findings. He knew, however, that a product code, however practical, was of little value without a decoder. So before applying for a patent on his code, he enlisted Silver's aid in developing the hardware they needed for a complete system. On October 20, 1949, they jointly applied for a patent; that patent, for a "Classifying Apparatus and Method," was awarded on October 7, 1952.

To their mutual shock, Woodland and Silver found that the very supermarket people who had originally expressed the need were not interested in their invention. The system still needed a lot of development, and none of the supermarket chains wanted to take that plunge. But Woodland knew he had a viable approach to supermarket checkout automation. What he needed was a company with the financial resources to make it happen.

Begins Work at IBM

After researching several companies, he joined IBM's facility at Endicott, New York. Though IBM was not involved with product coding and knew nothing of Woodland's work, he hoped for a chance to change that. For a time Woodland worked on an IBM military contract, developing an electromechanical airborne computer. (This was before digital electronic computers were widespread, or small enough to fit in even a large airplane.) When Tom Watson, Jr. became president of IBM, Woodland sent him a letter of congratulations which also contained detailed plans for an automated supermarket checkout system. Watson was intrigued, and put Woodland in touch with W. W. McDowell, who headed IBM's research & development activity.

McDowell was also interested, and asked that Woodland be moved out of the project to which he had been assigned. For several years little development was done on supermarket scanners; during this time, Woodland designed a bar code scanner at home, a project which took several years. Meanwhile, he took night classes at nearby Syracuse University, receiving his Master's degree in mechanical engineering in 1956.

In 1959 Woodland finally got his chance to head a full-scale development project for a supermarket scanner when IBM conducted a pilot study in conjunction with an Atlanta supermarket chain. Using a scanner built into the supermarket counter, the device scanned a bar code symbol attached to the bottom of market items. The scanner worked, but it had severe limitations. For one thing, the light source—a 500 watt incandescent bulb—produced far too much heat, and provided a very shallow field of focus. Also, the electronics needed for decoding and inventory control (which depended upon thousands of individual transistors) were far too costly for large-scale use. Woodland reluctantly concluded that the concept behind his device was too far ahead of the available technology, and he suggested that his idea be shelved until the necessary scanning light and electronics could become available. Ironically, IBM did not agree at first; they hired a California firm called Stanford Research, Inc. to critique the work to date. They eventually endorsed Woodland's recommendation, and the project was shelved.

Scanning Technology Becomes Available

In 1962, after rejecting two IBM offers as too low, Woodland and Silver sold their patent to Philco. It expired in 1969, and the technology came into the public domain. Shortly after that, RCA put on an exhibition of bullseye-shaped bar codes at a major supermarket trade show. An IBM executive who knew of Woodland's work watched in dismay as crowds flocked to the RCA booth. The very next day, IBM management tracked Woodland down and assigned him to the revitalized project.

A number of important factors had changed in the twelve years since IBM had shelved Woodland's invention. Low-cost integrated circuit chips and readily-available helium neon lasers provided the needed technology boost. Also, in 1970 the National Association of Food Chains had formed a committee to study product codes for inventory control, and in 1971 the food industry settled on a bar code

configuration based largely on Woodland's original concentric circles.

When Woodland got involved the first thing he did was cast doubt on their choice of configurations. Having more experience with bar code configurations than anyone in the world, Woodland had learned the fundamental flaws of the bullseye. When asked what was wrong with it, he replied, "It was a very good idea when I invented it back in 1949." They did not believe they were speaking to the original inventor until he produced a copy of his patent. From then on, as he recalled, "I think I really had them in my hand. I really got their attention." Woodland sold the grocery industry on a parallel-line bar code, and the UPC symbol was launched.

In his 35 years with IBM, Woodland held many senior assignments in mechanical and optical design, system development, long-range planning, and most recently artificial intelligence and expert systems—a field he grew interested in during his final years with IBM. Since his retirement in 1987 he has continued his research, and along with a collaborator is working on a development which he says he is quite excited about, and which he hopes to patent shortly. He has lectured at his alma mater, Drexel University, where in 1992 he was elected to the "Drexel 100," being one of the 100 most distinguished Drexel graduates. He has received other honors for his work as well, including IBM's Outstanding Contribution Award (1973) in appreciation for development of the UPC symbol, and the National Medal of Technology (1992) by President George Bush.

FURTHER READING:

Periodicals

Regardie's Magazine, December, 1990, pp. 42–58
Supermarket News, December, 28 1992, p. 81

Sketch by Joel Simon

Robert B. Woodward
1917–1979
American organic chemist

Robert B. Woodward was arguably the greatest organic synthesis chemist of the twentieth century. He accomplished the total synthesis of several important natural products and pharmaceuticals. Total synthesis means that the molecule of interest—no matter how complex—is built directly from the smallest, most common compounds and is not just a derivation of a related larger molecule. In order to accomplish his work, Woodward combined physi-

Robert B. Woodward

cal chemistry principles, including quantum mechanics, with traditional reaction methods to design elaborate synthetic schemes. With Nobel Laureate **Roald Hoffmann**, he designed a set of rules for predicting reaction outcomes based on stereochemistry, the study of the spatial arrangements of molecules.

When Woodward won the Nobel Prize in chemistry in 1965, the committee cited his contributions to the "art" of organic synthesis. Upon Woodward's acceptance of the award, Bartlett, Westheimer, and Buchi wrote in *Science,* "Woodward's style is polished, showing an insight and sense of proportion that afford him strong convictions and a well-developed dramatic sense. In the laboratory, identifications and structural assignments must be complete, spectra exact, compounds not merely pure but beautifully crystallized, or he will not accept them. His lectures, given without notes or slides, are elegantly organized and illustrated with artistic blackboard formulas, with the key atoms shown in color. . . . Most of the polish comes naturally to a man with such intellectual vitality."

Robert Burns Woodward was born in Boston on April 10, 1917, to Arthur and Margaret (Burns) Woodward. His father died when he was very young. Woodward obtained his first chemistry set while still a child and taught himself most of the basic principles of the science by doing experiments at home. By the time he graduated at the age of sixteen from Quincy High School in Quincy, Massachusetts, in 1933, his knowledge of chemistry exceeded that of many of his instructors. He entered the Massachusetts Institute of Technology (MIT) the same year but nearly flunked out a

few months later, apparently impatient with the rules and required courses.

The MIT chemistry faculty, however, recognized Woodward's unusual talent and rescued him. They obtained funding and a laboratory for his work and allowed him complete freedom to design his own curriculum, which he made far more rigorous than the required one. Woodward obtained his doctorate degree from MIT only four years later, at the age of 20, and then joined the faculty of Harvard University after a year of postdoctoral work there.

Woodward spent virtually all of his career at Harvard but also did a significant amount of consulting work with various corporations and institutes around the world. As is true in most modern scientific endeavors, Woodward's working style was characterized by collaboration with many other researchers. He also insisted on utilizing the most up-to-date instrumentation, theories, and other available tools, which were sometimes looked upon with suspicion by more traditional organic chemists. He was known as an intense thinker, personally reserved and imperiously confident of his intellectual skills. His graduate students, however, still found ways to joke with him; one Halloween, noticing that he virtually always had the same color tie, office, and car, they painted his parking space "Woodward blue."

Contributions to the Theories of Synthesis

The design of a synthesis, the crux of Woodward's work, involves much more than a simple list of chemicals or procedures. Biochemical molecules exhibit not only a particular bonding pattern of atoms, but also a certain arrangement of those atoms in space. The study of the spatial arrangements of molecules is called stereochemistry, and the individual configurations of a molecule are called its stereoisomers. Sometimes the same molecule may have many different stereoisomers; only one of those, however, will be biologically relevant. Consequently, a synthesis scheme must consider the basic reaction conditions that will bond two atoms together as well as determine how to ensure that the reaction orients the atoms properly to obtain the correct stereoisomer.

Physical chemists postulate that certain areas around an atom or molecule are more likely to contain electrons than other areas. These areas of probability, called orbitals, are described mathematically but are usually visualized as having specific shapes and orientations relative to the rest of the atom or molecule. Chemists visualize bonding as an overlap of two partially full orbitals to make one completely full molecular orbital with two electrons. Woodward and Roald Hoffmann of Cornell University established the Woodward-Hoffmann rules based on quantum mechanics, which explain whether a particular overlap is likely or even possible for the orbitals of two reacting species. By carefully choosing the shape of the reactant species and reaction conditions, the chemist can make certain that the atoms are oriented to obtain exactly the correct stereochemical configuration. In 1970 Woodward and Hoffmann published their classic work on the subject, *The Conserva-*

tion of Orbital Symmetry; Woodward by that time had demonstrated repeatedly by his own startling successes at synthesis that the rules worked.

Organic Synthesis Work Leads to Nobel Prize

Woodward and his colleagues synthesized a lengthy list of difficult molecules over the years. In 1944 their research, motivated by wartime shortages of the material and funded by the Polaroid Corporation, prompted Woodward—only twenty-seven years old at the time—and William E. Doering to announce the first total synthesis of quinine, important in the treatment of malaria. Chemists had been trying unsuccessfully to synthesize quinine for more than a century.

In 1947 Woodward and C. H. Schramm, another organic chemist, reported that they had created an artificial protein by bonding amino acids into a long chain molecule, knowledge that proved useful to both researchers and workers in the plastics industry. In 1951 Woodward and his colleagues (funded partly by Merck and the Monsanto Corporation) announced the first total synthesis of cholesterol and cortisone, both biochemical steroids. Cortisone had only recently been identified as an effective drug in the treatment of rheumatoid arthritis, so its synthesis was of great importance.

Woodward's other accomplishments in synthesis include strychnine (1954), a poison isolated from *Strychnos* species and often used to kill rats; colchicine (1963), a toxic natural product found in autumn crocus; and lysergic acid (1954) and reserpine (1956), both psychoactive substances. Reserpine, a tranquilizer found naturally in the Indian snake root plant *Rauwolfia,* was widely used to treat mental illness and was one of the first genuinely effective psychiatric medicines. In 1960, after four years of work, Woodward synthesized chlorophyll, the light energy capturing pigment in green plants, and in 1962 he accomplished the total synthesis of a tetracycline antibiotic.

Total synthesis requires the design and then precise implementation of elaborate procedures composed of many steps. Each step in a synthetic procedure either adds or subtracts chemical groups from a starting molecule or rearranges the orientation or order of the atoms in the molecule. Since it is impossible, even with the utmost care, to achieve one hundred percent conversion of starting compound to product at any given step, the greater the number of steps, the less product is obtained.

Woodward and Doering produced approximately a half a gram of quinine from about five pounds of starting materials; they began with benzaldehyde, a simple, cheap chemical obtained from coal tar, and designed a seventeen-step synthetic procedure. The twenty-step synthesis that led to the first steroid nucleus required twenty-two pounds of starting material and yielded less than a twentieth of an ounce of product. The best synthesis schemes thus have the fewest number of steps, although for some very complicated molecules, "few" may mean several dozen. When Wood-

ward successfully synthesized chlorophyll (which has an elaborate interconnected ring structure), for example, he required fifty-five steps for the synthesis.

Woodward's close friend, Nobel Laureate **Vladimir Prelog**, helped establish the CIBA-Geigy Corporation-funded Woodward Institute in Zurich, Switzerland, in the early 1960s. There Woodward could work on whatever project he chose, without the intrusion of teaching or administrative duties. Initially, the Swiss Federal Institute of Technology had tried to hire Woodward away from Harvard; when it failed, the Woodward Institute provided an alternative way of ensuring that Woodward visited and worked frequently in Switzerland. In 1965 Woodward and his Swiss collaborators synthesized Cephalosporin C, an important antibiotic. In 1971 he succeeded in synthesizing vitamin B_{12}, a molecule bearing some chemical similarity to chlorophyll, but with cobalt instead of magnesium as the central metal atom. Until the end of his life, Woodward worked on the synthesis of the antibiotic erythromycin.

Woodward, who received a Nobel Prize in 1965, helped start two organic chemistry journals, *Tetrahedron Letters* and *Tetrahedron,* served on the boards of several science organizations, and received awards and honorary degrees from many countries. Some of his many honors include the Davy Medal (1959) and the Copley Medal (1978), both from the Royal Society of Britain, and the United States' National Medal of Science (1964). He reached full professor status at Harvard in 1950 and in 1960 became the Donner Professor of Science. Woodward supervised more than three hundred graduate students and postdoctoral students throughout his career.

Woodward married Irji Pullman in 1938 and had two daughters, Siiri and Jean. He was married for the second time in 1946 to the former Eudoxia Muller, who had also been a consultant at the Polaroid Corporation. The couple had two children, Crystal and Eric. An inveterate smoker and coffee-drinker, his only exercise was an occasional game of softball. Woodward died at his home of a heart attack on July 8, 1979, at the age of 62.

SELECTED WRITINGS BY WOODWARD:

Books

The Conservation of Orbital Symmetry, VCH Publishers, 1970.

FURTHER READING:

Periodicals

Bartlett, P. D., F. H. Westheimer, and G. Buchi, *Science,* Robert Burns Woodward, Nobel Prize in Chemistry for 1965, October 29, 1965, p. 585.

Bartlett, P. D., F. H. Westheimer, and G. Buchi, *Chemical and Engineering News,* Robert Woodward Is Dead at Age 62, July 16, 1979, p. 6.

Bartlett, P. D., F. H. Westheimer, and G. Buchi, *Chemical and Engineering News,* Synthesis, General Approach Bring Nobel Prize, November 1, 1965, p. 38.

Sketch by Gail B. C. Marsella

George M. Woodwell
1928–

American ecologist

From the uproar in the 1960s over the insecticide dichlorodiphenyltrichloroethane (DDT), through the debate in the 1990s over global warming, American ecologist George M. Woodwell has been involved in nearly every environmental controversy of the late twentieth century. "I'm a citizen," Woodwell explained in a November, 1993, interview with Cynthia Washam, "and citizens have a role in steering the democracy." Woodwell has taken an active role in ecological issues throughout his career, holding such positions as founder of the Environmental Defense Fund, founding member of the Natural Resources Defense Council, president of the Ecological Society of America, founding trustee of the World Resources Institute, and chair of the World Wildlife Fund. Through his frequent articles and speeches, he has taken his plea to conserve the Earth's resources to politicians, fellow scientists, and laypeople.

While known to the general public as an activist, Woodwell also has earned the respect of his scientific colleagues. Walter Orr Roberts, director emeritus of the National Center for Atmospheric Research in Colorado, has stated that Woodwell "is characterized by solid scientific work that goes into tough issues with total objectivity," as cited by Denise Grady and Thomas Levenson in *Discover.* Woodwell has received four honorary doctoral degrees, won several scientific awards, and served on the editorial boards of three scientific journals. His research has focused on ecosystems, or communities of plants and animals and their environment, and he consistently delves into controversial issues that have significant implications for public policy, using the results of his research to support his activism.

Woodwell traces his interest in ecology to his childhood. Born October 23, 1928, in Cambridge, Massachusetts, he developed an appreciation of nature at his family's farm in Maine, where he spent his summers. There, along with his parents, Philip and Virginia (Sellers) Woodwell, both high school teachers, the young Woodwell cultivated potatoes, made maple syrup, and assisted neighbors on their farms. In 1946 Woodwell began his formal education in ecology at Dartmouth College, where he earned a bachelor's degree in botany in 1950. He joined the U.S. Navy as a lieutenant shortly after graduating and served for three years before returning to academia. While studying for his master's degree at Duke University, Woodwell met fellow graduate student Alice Katharine Rondthaler, who later dropped out of the program. In 1955 the couple married, and eventually they had four children: Caroline, John, Marjorie, and Jane. In 1956, Woodwell completed his master's degree in botany at Duke, and received his doctorate two years later. In the late 1950s he returned to New England as an assistant professor of botany at the University of Maine in Orono, and for several years he taught introductory ecology.

DDT Research Prompts Activist Role

During this time, Woodwell became involved in a project that changed the course of his career. He had been asked by the privately funded Conservation Foundation to study the effects of DDT on Maine forests. At first, he supported the use of the popular pesticide. He changed his mind a short time later, however, when he discovered that only about one half of the DDT sprayed on crops and forests actually settled on the soil—the rest was scattered by the wind. This drifting pesticide made its way into the food chain, as eagles, pelicans, ospreys, and other birds ate contaminated fish, then laid eggs with shells that were too fragile to survive. In 1966, Woodwell, along with some of his colleagues, filed the first of a series of lawsuits calling for a ban on the use of DDT. Their efforts eventually led to the Environmental Protection Agency's ban on the insecticide in 1972. The experience made Woodwell realize the value of taking environmental issues to court. To support further litigation, he founded the Environmental Defense Fund in 1967, which has become a thriving conservation law organization with more than two hundred thousand members. He also helped a group of Yale University law students establish the Natural Resources Defense Council.

By the early 1960s, Woodwell had left his post at the University of Maine to become an assistant scientist at Brookhaven National Laboratory in Upton, New York. At Brookhaven, he conducted an experiment that is recognized as a major contribution to ecological research. He planted radioactive cesium–137 in the center of a fourteen-acre oak and pine forest, and for the next eighteen years studied the radiation's effect on the ecosystem. The forest died in systematic stages: First the pine trees died, then the oaks, and then later the shrubs and grasses. Finally, only some mosses, bacteria, and lichens (plants made up of algae and fungi) were left. His experiment proved that the most sensitive species in an ecosystem died first and that only the most resistant ones survived. It also showed that, when under stress, a community could die in a much smaller amount of time than it had taken to develop.

Founding of Ecosystems Center Leads to Research into Deforestation

The ecologist eventually decided his opportunities for ecological research were limited at the physics laboratory, and in 1975 he left to establish the Ecosystems Center at the Marine Biological Laboratory in Woods Hole, Massachusetts. Woodwell's first major project there was studying sources of carbon dioxide in the atmosphere. Carbon dioxide is a greenhouse gas; in other words, it traps the sun's heat and contributes to dangerous global warming. Woodwell learned that atmospheric carbon dioxide is produced not only by industrial and auto emissions, but also when forests are burned or plowed under: When trees are destroyed, he found, they release the carbon dioxide they normally absorb. Woodwell concluded that deforestation increases atmospheric carbon dioxide in two ways—first, by releasing carbon dioxide, and second, by destroying the forests' ability to absorb the gas. These findings prompted Woodwell to publicly condemn the destruction of the Earth's forests and call for drastic cuts in carbon dioxide emissions. "There's no chance that people will continue on an Earth that continues to warm," he told Washam. "It's important to see that the warming does not proceed. We would control it by reducing the use of fossil fuels by sixty percent and by stopping deforestation." Woodwell has taken his plea to the U.S. Congress several times, but has seen no action. The government's apparent reluctance to take strong steps to save the environment has been his greatest frustration. Still, he persists in fighting for conservation. In 1983, he served as chair of an international conference on the biological effects of nuclear war. There, he succeeded in gaining a consensus among more than one hundred scientists, who ultimately agreed that even a small-scale nuclear war would cause temperatures to drop below zero for months, a phenomenon called nuclear winter. In addition, in the early 1990s, Woodwell proposed the creation of an International Commission on the Conservation and Utilization of World Forests to stem the global destruction of forests. He had the support of several countries, including the United States. "I have no doubt the commission will exist," he told Washam. "The question is when."

Establishes Ecology Research Center

In 1985, Woodwell decided to leave the Ecosystems Center in order to develop his own ecology institute: the Woods Hole Research Center. With funding from federal grants and private foundations, the non-profit center focuses on the ecological impact of toxic waste, air pollution, deforestation, and other major environmental threats. Woodwell, as the director, uses the results of the center's studies to support his demand for an end to environmental destruction.

Woodwell's involvement with ecological issues has been recognized several times by his peers as well as by environmental organizations. In 1975, he garnered the Green World Award from the New York Botanical Garden, and in 1982 he received a Distinguished Service Award from the American Institute of Biological Sciences. He was elected to the National Academy of Sciences in 1990, won the Dartmouth College Class of 1950 Award in 1991, and received the Hutchinson Medal from Garden Clubs of America in 1993. He also has been awarded honorary doctorates from Williams College, Miami University, Carleton College, and Muhlenberg College.

While calling for action from industry and government, Woodwell takes care to monitor his own influence on the health of the planet. He walks to work every day and often travels around the village of Woods Hole on his bicycle. Several years ago, he and his son erected a twenty-eight-foot high structure containing more than twenty solar panels in order to heat the water in their home. Though Woodwell rarely takes a break from his work, he enjoys spending any free time on his boat, whose source of power is simply the wind.

SELECTED WRITINGS BY WOODWELL:

Books

Diversity and Stability in Ecological Systems, Brookhaven National Laboratory, 1967.
Carbon and the Biosphere: Proceedings, DOE, 1973.
The Earth in Transition: Patterns and Processes of Biotic Impoverishment, Cambridge University Press, 1991.
Biotic Feedback in the Global Climatic System: Will the Warming Feed the Wakening?, Oxford University Press, 1993.
Forests for the Future: Their Use and Conservation, Yale University Press, 1993.

Periodicals

Science, Global Deforestation: Contribution to Atmospheric Carbon Dioxide, December 9, 1983, pp. 1081–86.
Scientific American, Global Climatic Change, April, 1989, pp. 36–44.
Natural History, Do the Right Thing, May, 1990, pp. 84–85.
New York Times, Forests, Scapegoats and Global Warming, February 11, 1992, p. A25.

FURTHER READING:

Books

Ehrlich, Paul R., *Healing the Planet: Strategies for Solving the Environmental Crisis,* Addison-Wesley, 1992.
Hardin, Garrett, *Living within Limits: Ecology, Economics, and Population,* Oxford University Press, 1993.
Kennedy, Paul M., *Preparing for the Twenty-First Century,* Random House, 1993.

Periodicals

Grady, Denise, and Thomas Levenson, *Discover,* George Woodwell: Crusader for the Earth, May, 1984, p. 44.

Raeburn, Paul, *Sunday Telegram,* George Woodwell: A Practical Man of Great Conviction, January 5, 1986.

Other

Woodwell, George M., *Interview with Cynthia Washam,* conducted November 24, 1993.

Sketch by Cynthia Washam

Stephen Wozniak
1950–

American electronics engineer

Stephen Wozniak, along with **Steven Jobs**, cofounded Apple Computer, Inc., and developed one of the most popular personal computers ever marketed. His contributions to Apple were almost exclusively technical—Jobs pushed the marketing potential of the Apple, while Wozniak provided the engineering know-how.

Wozniak's father, Jerry, was a Lockheed engineer, and his mother, Margaret, was president of a local Republican women's club. Young Wozniak grew up in Sunnyvale, a suburban development located in the Santa Clara Valley, now known as Silicon Valley. He was surrounded by the technological wizardry that grew out of Sputnik and the race for space. His parents provided a stable, close-knit environment.

Wozniak was an early devotee of electronics and in the fifth grade created a voltmeter from a kit. His interest in science and engineering led to a number of homemade devices: a ham radio, a makeshift electronic tic-tac-toe game, a calculator. By the time he entered Homestead High School, Wozniak had learned so much about the theory and practice of electronics that he became a prize student in the school's electronics courses.

When Wozniak met Steven Jobs in 1968, Wozniak was an accomplished student of electronics, although largely self-taught. Having flunked out of the University of Colorado, he was back home constructing a computer with a friend who also knew Jobs. Both Wozniak and Jobs took summer jobs at Hewlett-Packard, and Wozniak later returned to Hewlett-Packard after dropping out of Berkeley.

Early Work in Computer Design Leads to the Apple II

Together with Jobs, Wozniak spent the early years of the 1970s heavily immersed in the burgeoning computer culture of Silicon Valley, particularly among the hobbyists and video game enthusiasts who were to become the first market for the personal computer. Both young men belonged to the Homebrew Computer Club, a Bay Area users' group that sprang up during the personal computer revolution of the mid-seventies.

This revolution would not have been possible without the development of the microprocessor in 1970 and the later discovery by hobbyists that this inexpensive silicon chip not only shrank the size of the computer but also shrank its price tag. The January 1975 issue of *Popular Electronics* announced the first computer kit, the Altair 8800, using an Intel 8080 microprocessor. Orders from hungry computer enthusiasts poured in—despite the fact that there seemed to be little to do with the computer once it was assembled.

In 1976, Wozniak, who was unable to afford the Altair, took the personal computer revolution a step further by constructing a computer out of a cheaper microprocessor and adding several chips for memory. The result was a naked circuit board, without case, keyboard, or screen, which was able to outperform the Altair. The Apple I formed the basis for the future Apple Computer, Inc. Steven Jobs marketed the crude computer through contacts from the Homebrew club.

The next step was the construction of a computer with a keyboard and color video display. Wozniak's engineering emphasized power and meticulous design. He was able to extract both speed and power out of relatively few chips. By fall 1976, Wozniak and Jobs were able to display their newest computer at a national computer fair. Their new machine attracted attention, although it clearly needed refinement. With Jobs's marketing efforts, Apple Computer, Inc., began to grow. In 1977, Wozniak, who had left Hewlett-Packard to work full time at Apple, completed the technical design of the Apple II.

The Apple II was the first personal computer that could be bought ready-made "off the shelf." Its success was due in part to its sleek design and its ability to accept "add-ons," such as music synthesizers, modems, and enhanced graphics. By 1978, Wozniak had incorporated a floppy disk drive into the Apple II, replacing the cassette tapes that had previously stored information. Using a floppy drive, the user could retrieve information in seconds. With this addition, and the availability in 1979 of VisiCalc, a spreadsheet program, the Apple II became a multimillion dollar success. In 1980, when Apple Computer, Inc., went public, sales stood at $117 million; in 1983, they reached $985 million.

Reaffirms Democratic Values in Computing

Although Wozniak's association with Apple Computer left him a multimillionaire (in 1980, his stock in Apple was worth $88 million), his interest never wavered from the electronics and technical side of the business. He shared with Jobs a vision of democratic computing and believed that computers should be accessible to ordinary people. Early in his design career, he recognized the need for user-friendly software; by the late 1970s, the Apple II provided a growing market for software programs, especially in the educational field.

In 1981, Wozniak was piloting a single-engine plane near his home when it crashed on take-off. He was hospitalized and suffered amnesia. His convalescence lasted two years, during which time he became involved in New Age ventures, providing financial backing for two large music festivals near Los Angeles.

He returned to Apple in 1983, working as an engineer in the Apple II division. Despite the company's successes, its position within the personal computer market was being threatened by IBM. In the next tempestuous years at Apple, Wozniak remained aloof from corporate infighting. In January 1985, he (along with Jobs) was presented with the National Technology Award by President Reagan for his work at Apple. During that month, he resigned from the company to found a new operation called "CL–9 Inc." ("Cloud 9"), which produced remote control devices. The operation shut its doors in 1989.

Wozniak's life after Apple included several business ventures. He became involved in the Electronic Frontier Foundation, founded by Mitch Kapor (developer of Lotus), a user group dedicated to preserving First Amendment rights in the computer and communications fields. With his third wife and their six children, he built an elaborate home with mock caverns and prehistoric carvings in Los Gatos, California. After his retirement from Apple, he returned to the University of California at Berkeley and attained his bachelor's degree in computer science and electrical engineering.

FURTHER READING:

Books

Butcher, Lee, *The Accidental Millionaire: The Rise and Fall of Steve Jobs at Apple Computer,* Paragon House, 1988.
Garr, Douglas, *Woz,* Avon, 1984.
Rose, Frank, *West of Eden,* Viking, 1989.

Periodicals

Alexander, Michael, *Computerworld,* Kapor Group Lines Up for Rights Fight, July 16, 1990, p. 6.
Dalglish, Brenda, *Maclean's,* Wonder Boys Hit Middle Age, May 11, 1992, pp. 36–37.

Sketch by Katherine Williams

Almroth Edward Wright
1861–1947
English bacteriologist

Almroth Edward Wright made several significant contributions to science and is perhaps best known for introducing a vaccination against typhoid fever. Developed near the turn of the twentieth century, the vaccine was used on British soldiers during World War I and was responsible for saving many lives. The disease only claimed the lives of 1,191 British soldiers, instead of a projected 125,000 without the vaccination, according to estimates outlined in Leonard Colebrook's biography, *Almroth Wright: Provocative Doctor and Thinker.* Numerous honors were bestowed upon Wright for his scientific work, including a knighthood and election as a Fellow of the Royal Society of London, both of which were awarded in 1906.

Wright was born August 10, 1861, in Middleton Tyas, Yorkshire, England. He was the second son of Reverend Charles Henry Hamilton and Ebba Johanna Dorothea (Almroth) Wright. His father was an Old Testament scholar and a militant protestant. His mother was the daughter of a chemistry professor who was also governor of the Royal Mint in Stockholm. In his early years Wright was educated by tutors and lived in Germany and France where his father worked as a minister. Eventually, the family settled in Ireland, and Wright received his university education at Trinity College in Dublin, earning a degree in modern literature in 1882 and a degree in medicine in 1883. Winning a traveling scholarship to the University of Leipzig in Germany, Wright studied medicine there for a year.

Wright then returned to England, and was a bit unsure as to whether the future direction of his career led to literature or medicine; he soon decided to read law, and after two years took the civil service exam. Eventually Wright's interest in science took precedence over his other pursuits. After securing a fairly non-demanding position at the Admiralty in 1885, he also immediately began working evenings at the Brown Institution (University of London) as a science researcher on a volunteer basis. Wright was next offered a demonstratorship in the department of pathology at Cambridge in 1887, then soon after transferred to the department of physiology. Upon working in Germany for several months, Wright accepted a demonstratorship at the University of Sydney, in Australia, in 1889. That same year Wright married Jane Georgina Wilson, with whom he had two sons and a daughter.

In 1892 Wright was offered the chair of the pathology department at the Army Medical School in Netley, England. This was the first time Wright worked close to patients, and he claimed the atmosphere was productive since it never allowed the scientist to become too far removed from the ultimate goal of his work, which was to cure the sick. It was at this time Wright began his research on the phenomenon of blood coagulation, eventually linking clotting time to the presence of calcium in the blood. Laboratory instruments during this period were generally crude and home-made, so Wright—a pioneer in laboratory testing—made his own, developing and producing capillary tubes large enough to hold only a few drops of blood. These instruments could test blood without the necessity of drawing a great deal of it from a patient; all that would be required was a finger prick. Wright also recognized the importance of uniformity in laboratory testing, so he made sure each tube was identical.

Wright discovered that if blood was clotting too slowly, giving the patient a dose of calcium by mouth would speed up the process. Conversely, if clotting occurred too quickly, he found administering citric acid to the patient slowed it down. These same principles were also applied to a situation Wright was experiencing at home. Wright's young child seemed to experience distress when fed cow's milk; upon testing, Wright found cow's milk to have a greater concentration of calcium with harder, thicker clots than breast milk. Adding citrate of soda to the milk made the clots softer and thinner, rendering the milk easier for his child to digest, and thus decreasing digestive pains. Wright then tried feeding lemons to the family cow to see if it would change the concentration of calcium in the milk produced. The cow did not respond, but the housekeeper by this point had had enough and turned in her resignation.

Begins Work on Typhus

Near the turn of the century typhoid fever had a death rate of ten to thirty percent. Although the disease had been partially eradicated with better sewage handling, Wright did not think this would eliminate the problem and believed these methods would break down during a war. Wright wanted to test the effects of injection with a heat-killed typhoid culture, to see if it would produce antibodies. He found it did, but there was what he termed a "negative phase"—a period of one to two days where antibodies seemed to decrease. Nonetheless, he believed his vaccine would be beneficial and set out trying to convince medical authorities of its merits. Wright convinced the War Office committee to set up an experimental situation, using military units over a three year period. Frequencies of inoculation and instances of typhoid records were measured, and in 1909 very positive results were published: Colebrook relates in *Almroth Wright* that deaths per 1,000 inoculated soldiers were 0.38, while for uninoculated were 3.93.

In 1906, prior to the publication of the typhoid inoculation results, Wright had been knighted and elected to Fellow of the Royal Society. After this success, he turned his lab over to serum production, so the vaccination would be available. Wright also wrote a long letter to the editor of the *New York Times* urging mandatory inoculation of troops. In 1914, only British troops entered World War I fully inoculated.

In the midst of his typhoid work, Wright had changed positions in 1902, from his professorship at the Army Medical School at Netley to pathologist and professor of pathology at St. Mary's Hospital in London. In 1911, Wright traveled to South Africa to help produce a pneumonia inoculation for the men who were working in the mines. The system Wright developed to inoculate the miners resembled the one he instituted earlier to fight typhus.

During World War I Wright served in France as head of a research lab which worked primarily on wound infections. Wright developed at this time a method using a hypertonic salt solution to draw lymph into open wounds (lymph is a fluid derived from blood and which contains lymphocytes, a type of white blood cell which repels infection). Wright also developed a scientific basis for early wound closure, or suturing, which was not in practice up until that time. Several citations were presented to Wright after World War I, including a special medal of the Royal Society of Medicine in 1920 which credited him with providing the best medical work during the war.

Engages in Philosophical Debate

Wright's direct influence on scientific research seemed to taper off after World War I. His indirect influence was felt for many years, however, as several of his students went on to great fame, including **Alexander Fleming**, the scientist who discovered penicillin. For Wright this era was more a time for reflection and what Colebrook describes in *Almroth Wright* as the scientist's "search for truth".

Among the reasons contributing to Wright's declining influence may be his rather unpopular views. The treatise *The Unexpurgated Case Against Woman Suffrage*, for example, attempted to demonstrate the intellectual and psychological inferiority of women. Although the playwright George Bernard Shaw disagreed with this claim, he was, nevertheless, an admirer of Wright; the lead character in Shaw's play *The Doctor's Dilemma* is modeled after Wright, and the idea for the play came from the many discussions the writer shared with Wright as well as other members of the medical profession.

Wright published over 150 papers during his career. He advanced the truly scientific component of research to a great degree due to his insistence on the use of the scientific method, which involves several steps, including the formation of a hypothesis and the testing and confirmation of that hypothesis. Commonly accepted now, the scientific method was a revolutionary idea during Wright's time.

Wright continued his work at St. Mary's Hospital until 1946 and died shortly after in Buckinghamshire, England, on April 30, 1947. Wright was working—literally to the end—on a philosophical work *Alethetropic Logic* (in Wright's words, "a system of Logic which searches for the Truth"), which was published posthumously through the efforts of his grandson.

SELECTED WRITINGS BY WRIGHT:

Books

Principles of Microscopy, Constable, 1906.

Studies in Immunization, Constable, 1909.

The Unexpurgated Case Against Woman Suffrage, Constable, 1913.

Technique of the Teat and Capillary Glass Tube, Constable, 1921.

Alethetropic Logic, Heinemann, 1953.

FURTHER READING:

Books

Colebrook, Leonard, *Almroth Wright: Provocative Doctor and Thinker,* Heinemann, 1954.

Colebrook, Leonard, *Bibliography of the Published Writings of Sir Almroth E. Wright,* Heinemann, 1952.

Cope, Zachary, *Almroth Wright: Founder of Modern Vaccine-Therapy,* Thomas Nelson, 1966.

Periodicals

Mummest, R. T., *Nature,* Sir Almroth Wright, K.B.E., C.B., F.R.S. (obituary)May 31, 1947, pp. 731–732.

Sketch by Kimberlyn McGrail

Jane Cooke Wright
1919–
American physician

Jane Cooke Wright has carried on the medical legacy of her prominent family through a career in internal medicine, cancer research, and medical education. She has served as director of the Cancer Research Foundation of Harlem Hospital in New York City, faculty member and director of cancer chemotherapy at the New York University Medical Center, and professor of surgery and associate dean at New York Medical College and its affiliate hospitals. Wright has also devoted her efforts to educating fellow practitioners about advances in chemotherapy, a service she performed in her 1983 convention lecture to the National Medical Association entitled "Cancer Chemotherapy: Past, Present, and Future".

Wright was born in New York City on November 20, 1919, to Louis Tompkins and Corinne (Cooke) Wright. Her paternal grandfather was one of the first graduates of Tennessee's Meharry Medical College, an institution founded to give former slaves professional training. Another relative, **Harold D. West**, was Meharry's first black president. Her step-grandfather, William Penn, was the first black person to earn a medical degree from Yale. Her father,

Louis Tompkins Wright —one of the first black graduates of Harvard medical college—was the first black physician to be appointed to the staff of a New York City hospital; he was also a pioneer in cancer chemotherapy, and New York City's first black police surgeon. Jane Cooke Wright was the first of two daughters; her sister, Barbara, also became a physician.

Wright was educated in private elementary and secondary schools and won a four-year scholarship to Smith College in Massachusetts, where she set records as a varsity swimmer. Graduating in 1942, Wright entered New York Medical College, again on a four-year scholarship, and received her medical degree with honors in 1945. An internship and assistant residency followed at Bellevue Hospital in New York City. After leaving Bellevue Hospital, she completed her training with a two-year residency in internal medicine at Harlem Hospital.

Wright's first position after residency was as a school and visiting physician at Harlem Hospital in 1949. She became a clinician later that year at the hospital's Cancer Foundation, which was then headed by her father. There she studied the response of tumors and growths to drugs and the application of chemotherapy in the treatment of cancer. She explored the complex relationships and variations between test animal and patient, tissue sample and patient, and individual patient responses to various chemotherapeutic agents. Upon her father's death in 1952, she became the Cancer Foundation's director.

In 1955, Wright joined the New York University Medical Center to direct the cancer chemotherapy research department and teach research surgery. Her continuing research explored animal and human responses to chemotherapeutic agents (such as triethylene thiophosphoromide, CB 1348 and Dihydro E. 73) and isolation perfusion and regional perfusion chemotherapy techniques. In 1961, Wright became adjunct professor of research surgery at the medical center and also served as vice-president of the African Research Foundation, a position which took her on a medical mission to East Africa. In 1964, she was appointed to the President's Commission on Heart Disease, Cancer, and Stroke; the commission's work resulted in a nationwide network of treatment centers for these diseases. The Albert Einstein College of Medicine presented Wright with its Spirit of Achievement Award in 1965.

Wright became associate dean and professor of surgery at New York Medical College in 1967, where she was also responsible for administrating the medical school and developing a program for the study of cancer, heart disease, and stroke. She was awarded the Hadassah Myrtle Wreath in 1967, and the Smith College medal in 1968. In December, 1975, Wright was one of eight scientists saluted by *Cancer Research* in its observation of International Women's Year, and in 1980 was featured on an Exceptional Black Scientists poster by Ciba Geigy. Since 1987, she has been emerita professor of surgery at New York Medical College.

Wright has served on the editorial board of the *Journal of the National Medical Association* and as a trustee of Smith College and of the New York City division of the American Cancer Association. She married David D. Jones, Jr., a graduate of Harvard Law School, on July 27, 1947; the couple have two daughters, Jane and Alison. Her hobbies include sailing, painting, and reading mystery novels.

SELECTED WRITINGS BY WRIGHT:

Periodicals

Journal of the National Medical Association, Cancer Chemotherapy: Past, Present, and Future, August, 1984, pp. 773–784; September, 1984, pp. 865–876.

FURTHER READING:

Books

Blacks in Medicine and Science, Hemisphere, 1990, p. 258.
Notable Black American Women, Gale, 1992, pp. 1283–1285.

Sketch by Jane Stewart Cook

Louis Tompkins Wright
1891–1952
American surgeon and hospital administrator

Louis Tompkins Wright, one of the first black graduates of the Harvard Medical School, was a distinguished surgeon, hospital administrator, and civil rights activist. His talents and determination as a black leader improved access to quality health care for black people and the professional prospects of his fellow African American medical practitioners. During Wright's prolonged affiliation with Harlem Hospital in New York City, he became the hospital's surgical director and founded its Cancer Research Center. An active member of the New York City chapter of the National Association for the Advancement of Colored People (NAACP), Wright ultimately chaired its national board of directors, holding that position from 1934 until his death.

Wright was born on July 23, 1891, in La Grange, Georgia. He was the younger son of Ceah Ketcham and Lula Tompkins Wright. His father, a doctor who practiced for only a short period before becoming a clergyman, died in 1895; in 1899, his mother married William Fletcher Penn,

also a physician. Wright enrolled in Clark University in Atlanta, where he was valedictorian of the class of 1911. After being subjected to a special examination, Wright was accepted by the Harvard Medical School, where he was to graduate *cum laude* and fourth in his class in 1915. After a two-year internship at Freedmen's Hospital in Washington, D.C., he briefly joined his stepfather's practice in Atlanta.

In 1917, in the midst of World War I, Wright entered the U.S. Army Medical Corps, and was eventually appointed director of surgical wards for an Army field hospital in France. While in France, he was exposed to phosgene gas, which caused him permanent lung damage. For his military service, Wright was awarded the Purple Heart and discharged at the rank of captain, later achieving the rank of lieutenant-colonel in the U.S. Medical Reserve Corps through examination. When Wright returned from France in the spring of 1919, he settled into private practice in New York City.

Association with Harlem Hospital

Shortly thereafter, the Medical Board of Harlem Hospital was persuaded by Civil Service Commissioner Ferdinand Q. Morton to admit Wright and some other black physicians as provisional adjunct surgeons. A few white doctors on the staff of the hospital (whose clientele was then a prosperous white community) resigned in protest, but Wright quickly established himself professionally. In 1926, he was granted a permanent appointment at the hospital. A few years later, in addition to his hospital commitments, he began his service as surgeon for the New York City Police Department, a post he held for more than twenty years. In 1943, he was named director of Harlem Hospital's Department of Surgery. In 1948, he became president of the medical staff board and director of the hospital's Cancer Research Foundation, and founded the *Harlem Hospital Bulletin.*

Wright's contributions to medicine were various. Early in his career, while an intern at Freedmen's Hospital, he was critical of the medical establishment's belief that the Schick test for diphtheria (which, for diphtheria susceptible individuals, reddens the skin where injected) was not useful on black patients; his research proved this supposition to be without basis. He originated an intradermal smallpox vaccination method that minimized undesirable side effects. Wright directed the research team that first tested the antibiotic aureomycin for the treatment of venereal disease, and also conducted research with the antibiotic terramycin; he was to publish over thirty papers on aureomycin and eight papers on terramycin. Wright invented several surgical devices, including a brace for cervical fractures and a plate used in repairing fractures of the knee. His research into skull and brain injuries led to the first authoritative publication in this area by a black doctor. His cancer research, which led to fifteen publications, focussed on the use of teropterin, triethylene melamine, folic acid, and hormones in chemotherapy. Throughout his career, moreover, Wright opposed various forms of medical discrimination, such as efforts to establish segregated medical facilities (including a segregated Veterans Hospital) in New York. Another achievement was fostering solidarity and harmony among Harlem Hospital's ethnically diverse medical staff.

In 1934, Wright became the second black doctor to be admitted to the American College of Surgeons. He received an honorary doctorate from Clark University in 1938, and was awarded the NAACP's Spingarn Medal in 1940. In 1952, he was honored by the John A. Andrews Memorial Hospital of the Tuskegee Institute in Alabama. Wright held membership in numerous professional associations in addition to the American College of Surgeons, including the American Medical Association, the National Medical Association, and the American Board of Surgery; he was also a founding member of the American Academy of Compensation Medicine. In connection with his civil rights activism, he served as president of the Crisis Publishing Company, printers of the *Crisis,* which was to become the official organ of the NAACP.

Wright married Corinne Cooke in 1918. They had two daughters: **Jane Cooke Wright**, a physician who became director of the Cancer Research Foundation on her father's death; and Barbara Penn Wright, also a physician. Wright died of a heart attack on October 8, 1952. The Louis T. Wright Medical Library at Harlem Hospital had been established in his honor that same year; in 1969, the Louis T. Wright Surgical Building at Harlem Hospital was dedicated in his memory.

SELECTED WRITINGS BY WRIGHT:

Books

The Treatment of Fractures, Head Injuries, Chapter 22 of (11th edition), edited by Charles L. Scudder, W. B. Saunders, 1938.

FURTHER READING:

Books

Blacks in Medicine and Science, Hemisphere, 1990, p. 259.
Dictionary of American Negro Biography, W. W. Norton, 1982, pp. 670–671.
Scientists in the Black Perspective, The Lincoln Foundation, 1974, pp. 105–107.

Periodicals

New York Times, October 9, 1952, p. 31.

Sketch by Jane Stewart Cook

Sewall Wright
1889–1988
American geneticist

D uring his long and productive life, Sewall Wright achieved international standing in the disciplines of experimental physiological genetics, which is the study of heredity, as well as quantitative evolutionary biology. He made significant contributions to the fields of genetics, zoology, biometrics (the use of statistics to analyze biological data) and animal breeding but is best known for his comprehensive theory of evolution, the so-called "shifting-balance" theory (which accounts for the spread of certain gene combinations within a population). This theory changed the way scientists think about evolution and took a more mathematical and analytical approach to population genetics. Wright's work brought serious statistical analysis to the forefront of biological science and touched off a long-running debate about the nature of animal species development.

Wright, the oldest of three children, was born on December 21, 1889, to Philip Green Wright, a college professor, and Elizabeth Quincy (Sewall) Wright. When he was seven years old, he wrote a small booklet he called "The Wonders of Nature," a hand-sewn volume printed in capital letters. The precocious Wright spent only five years in grade school as his learning was supplemented at home by his intellectual parents. In 1902, he entered Galesburg High School in Illinois, where he excelled at languages, especially Latin and German. The courses that intrigued him most, however, were algebra, geometry, and physics, all of which he would put to good use in later years. He graduated fifth in his class in 1906, having achieved a grade-point-average of 98.35. Wright then attended Lombard College in Galesburg, where his father was employed. His original intention was to continue the study of languages, but the language professors were not up to Wright's high standards. He enrolled in several classes taught by his father, including general mathematics and economics and a course on the fiscal history of the United States. In his senior year, Wright took two biology classes from Wilhemine Key, who introduced him to the relatively new discipline of theoretical biology and to **R. C. Punnett**'s groundbreaking article, "Mendelism," which had just appeared in the eleventh edition of *Encyclopaedia Britannica*. Key steered Wright toward graduate study in biology and set up an internship in zoology for him at Columbia University's Cold Spring Harbor laboratory on Long Island, New York. After graduating from Lombard College in 1911, Wright spent the summer at Cold Spring Harbor, where he studied marine invertebrates. While there, he also met a number of influential geneticists and began to take an interest in the field.

With the help of a modest state scholarship, Wright moved on to the University of Illinois and received his M.S. in zoology in 1912. The same year, he attended a lecture by the prominent Harvard zoologist, W. E. Castle, who spoke of his selection and mammalian genetics experiments in hooded rats. Castle's work centered on the notion that Mendelian factors, such as recessive and dominant traits, were sometimes variable. He later altered this view, but his experiments seemed to indicate that certain genetic combinations could yield unexpected results. Intrigued by these ideas, Wright signed on as Castle's personal assistant and graduate student.

Introduction to Guinea Pigs Sparks Evolutionary Investigations

In addition to his doctoral classwork, Wright also worked at Harvard's Bussey Institution, a biological research facility, helping Castle maintain a colony of hooded rats and working with other researchers to develop a guinea pig colony. Wright had learned about the genetics of guinea pigs while at Cold Spring Harbor, and Castle assumed that Wright would eventually use the colony for his own research. Wright thought the guinea pig was a valuable research animal, despite the fact that they are disease prone, relatively large and cumbersome, and have long reproductive cycles. At that time, no one knew exactly how many chromosomes the guinea pig had and a number of questions remained about their inheritance patterns; Wright's work with the guinea pig would continue until 1961 and answer many of these questions. His first major finding occurred in 1914, when he discovered a series of four alleles (a series of two or more genes that can occupy the same position on a chromosome) that produced various effects on coat and eye color. Over the next forty years, he would study the inheritance factors of color patterns, hair direction, digit size, and abnormalities in guinea pigs. When Wright received his Sc.D. in zoology from Harvard in 1915, his dissertation was entitled *An Intensive Study of the Inheritance of Color and of Other Coat Characters in Guinea Pigs, with Especial Reference to Graded Variations*.

In 1915, Wright accepted a position as senior animal husbandman at the U.S. Department of Agriculture (USDA) in Washington, D.C. Inheriting an extensive inbreeding study of guinea pigs (which the USDA had begun in 1906), Wright was charged with analyzing the mountains of data generated by this on-going experiment. To make his task easier, he developed a mathematical theory of inbreeding in 1920, the methods of which were published in 1921 under the title *Correlation and Causation*. Wright's early work with Castle had led him to the notion that interaction systems between genes had important implications for evolution and that inbreeding in small populations led to variation within a given species. His mathematical theory enabled him to quantify the effects of inbreeding, and he used this theory extensively during the next ten years.

Wright spent the summer of 1920 at Cold Spring Harbor, where he met Louisa Williams, then an instructor at Smith College in Massachusetts. She had earned her master's degree from Denison University while working under Harold Fish, who had been Wright's colleague at the Bussey Institution. Despite a congenital hip problem, she, like Wright, enjoyed long walks and equally long conversations. She had come to Cold Spring Harbor to help Fish set up a rabbit colony for genetic research and, because of similar interests, became one of Wright's close friends. The two began dating that summer, Wright's first romantic relationship of any kind. The couple married on September 10, 1921, and moved to Washington. They had two sons over the next four years, Richard and Robert.

Wright left the USDA in 1925 and accepted a position in the department of zoology at the University of Chicago, where he would remain until 1954. During the late 1920s, Wright refined his ideas on evolution and developed a more comprehensive theory. He believed that the "random drift" of genes due to inbreeding and the isolation of small groups within a species were important factors in the evolution of any species. These ideas led to his often spirited, life-long scientific debate with geneticist **Ronald A. Fisher**, who proposed that natural selection worked best in large populations in which more mutant genes—genes in which the hereditary material has changed—were available. Fisher believed that each population had a complex gene structure and that many genes affected each characteristic. He postulated the idea of the population as a "gene pool" in which gene frequency was determined by natural selection.

Debate with Fisher Leads to "Shifting-Balance" Theory

When Fisher's *Genetical Theory of Natural Selection* appeared in 1930, Wright reviewed the book, pointing out several errors and stating his overall objections to the theory. The two corresponded and agreed on some common points, but never reached a consensus. In 1931, Wright published a long paper describing in detail his own evolutionary theory, which he called the "three-phase shifting-balance" theory. The three phases were (1) random gene-frequency drift within subpopulations, (2) increase of the preferred combination of genes or what has become known as mass selection, and (3) the dispersal of the preferred gene combination throughout the population.

During the early 1930s, as Wright's reputation grew, his theory attracted worldwide attention. As a result, he was elected to membership in the American Philosophical Society (1932), the National Academy of Sciences (1934), and the Genetics Society of America (1934). He was asked to serve on a number of scientific boards and was sought out as a guest lecturer and reviewer. He received numerous requests from researchers to perform quantitative data analysis on their experimental data. His work with Russian-born geneticist **Theodosius Dobzhansky**, then at the California Institute of Technology, helped further the cause of quantitative genetics. Dobzhansky used Wright's mathematical methods and conclusions to develop an extension of Wright's own evolutionary theory. In 1937, Dobzhansky published *Genetics and the Origin of the Species,* which set the research agenda in population genetics for decades to come.

During the 1940s Wright divided his research between physiological genetics and theoretical population genetics, becoming one of the most respected scientists in the nation as more and more researchers began to grasp the importance of his theories. He was awarded nine honorary doctorates over the next thirty years and also received the National Academy of Sciences Daniel Giruad Elliot Award and Oxford University's Weldon Memorial Medal. During this period, Wright authored a series of papers which argued that genes were responsible for replicating and coding the enzymes (complex proteins which facilitate bio-chemical reactions) that determine an organism's physiology. He continued his genetic experiments with guinea pigs, but the 1947 discovery of DNA—the molecular components of heredity—moved the field more toward the realm of molecular biology; when Wright retired from the University of Chicago in 1954 and moved on to the University of Wisconsin in Madison, he left his guinea pigs behind. It took him years to analyze the cumulative data from these experiments and his final papers on inbreeding in guinea pigs did not appear until 1961.

For the next twenty-five years Wright worked on his massive *Evolution and the Genetics of Populations,* a four-volume text that explained the history of genetics in minute scientific and mathematical detail. These volumes contributed to Wright's growing status. In recognition of his remarkable achievements in genetics and quantitative evolution, he received the National Medal of Science in 1967, the Darwin Medal of the Royal Society of London in 1980, and the Balzan Prize in 1984. His wife, Louisa, died of pneumonia in 1975. During the 1980s, he continued his habit of taking long, vigorous walks and retained his interest in the sciences. Although he began to lose his vision in 1980, he continued to read vociferously with the aid of a magnifying closed-circuit television device. Wright's last paper appeared in 1988 in *American Naturalist,* one of his favorite outlets, when he was ninety-nine years old.

Wright's work had a profound effect on evolutionary biology. In 1991, geneticists M. J. Wade and C. J. Goodnight published an account of an experiment that simulated Wright's shifting-balance theory. They separated a common base population of flour beetles into a series of small subpopulations, produced a migrant pool, and introduced migrants into various groups. The results of this experiment, which were published in *Science,* indicated that Wright's shifting-balance theory was credible and could work under certain favorable conditions. But, like most theories, the shifting-balance idea probably cannot be proven one hundred percent correct. It remains, however, one of the most intriguing evolutionary theories and a lasting testament to Wright's genius.

SELECTED WRITINGS BY WRIGHT:

Books

Evolution and the Genetics of Populations, four volumes, University of Chicago Press, 1968–1978.

Periodicals

American Naturalist, Duplicate Genes, Volume 48, 1914, pp. 638–639.
Genetics, The Effects in Combination of the Major Color Factors of the Guinea Pig, Volume 12, 1927, pp. 530–569.
Genetics, Evolution in Mendelian Populations, Volume 16, 1931, pp. 97–156.

FURTHER READING:

Books

Provine, William B., *Sewall Wright and Evolutionary Biology,* University of Chicago Press, 1986.

Periodicals

Crow, James F., *Science,* Was Wright Right? 1991, Volume 253, p. 973.

Sketch by Tom Crawford

Wilbur Wright
1867–1912
Orville Wright
1871–1948
American inventors and aviators

Wilbur and Orville Wright were inventors with little formal training who are best remembered for inventing the first heavier-than-air, engine-powered passenger flying craft. They not only invented the airplane, but some of the systems we use for flight control today. Had it not been for a bit of over-control of his craft, Wilbur Wright might have been the one who actually flew first, instead of Orville. The brothers were insatiably curious and tenacious tinkerers, two qualities which were vital in overcoming the obstacles to flight posed at the time of their endeavors. They also had a unique partnership as evidenced by this assessment of their relationship by Wilbur Wright, as cited in their *Papers:* "From the time we were little children my brother Orville and myself lived together, played together, worked together and, in fact thought together."

Born the third of five children, Wilbur was born on April 16, 1867, near Millvale, Indiana, with Orville following on August 19, 1871, in Dayton, Ohio. Their parents, Milton and Susan Catharine Koerner Wright, married in 1859 while she was a student and he an instructor at Hartsville College in Indiana. Milton was also pastor of a local church and later rose to become Bishop of the United Brethren Church. It was in 1878 that Bishop Wright brought home a novel toy for his children—a miniature toy helicopter. Wilbur and Orville were fascinated by the toy and how it flew. This sparked the love for aviation that would eventually be their life's undertaking.

From Recluse and High School Dropout to Bicycle Businessmen

Among other things, Wilbur was a keen athlete who loved to compete, excelling at gymnastics. At the age of eighteen, however, his face was smashed with a hockey stick. Wilbur suffered the loss of most of his upper teeth and several lower ones. Even though a lot of medical and dental reconstruction work was done, Wilbur's health suffered significantly. For a long time thereafter, he endured stomach trouble and claimed to suffer heart ailments as well. After his injury, Wilbur became rather reclusive, tending to his mother, who had tuberculosis, and rarely going far from home.

Nonetheless, Wilbur did finish high school, although he opted not to attend graduation ceremonies. Orville didn't even finish his education, having become bored with school in his senior year. Afterward, Wilbur studied Greek and trigonometry and read voraciously. Orville also loved reading and tinkering with printing presses, building bigger ones whenever he felt the need. In the late 1880s, Wilbur assisted Orville in several journalistic ventures, acting as both editor and humor essayist for the *West Side News* and *The Evening News,* which Orville launched from their home using the printing presses he had built.

Then in 1892, the brothers bought two new "safety bicycles." The bicycles were considered new because of their chain-driven gearing and wheels which were the same size. The bikes were quite different from the unwieldy two-wheelers of this period. The Wrights became enamored not only of the sport aspect of bicycling, but of the business aspect, too. Within one year, they opened their own bicycle outlet and repair shop. Business was good, and by 1896, the Wrights were making their own bikes, including the eighteen-dollar Wright Special. Within the first year, Orville ended his journalism career to devote full time to the bicycle shop.

Gears Shift into Aviation Research

August of 1896 brought the tragic crash in which German glider pilot Otto Lilienthal died. Lilienthal was a leading aviation pioneer at the time, having made numerous glider flights and having published tables showing lift on wings of different camber, or curvature. His death caught the Wrights' attention, and rekindled their interest in aviation. The Wright Cycle Company did a brisk business in the spring, summer and early fall, but little during winter. Nonetheless, the business brought in enough money to see the Wrights comfortably through winter, so it was during that season that they started seriously tinkering with the idea of flight.

Being methodical, the Wrights' first steps were to examine all of the current literature on flying. Most of this was done by Wilbur, to the extent that he even wrote to the Smithsonian Institution for information; the Smithsonian at that time was headed by Samuel Pierpoint Langley, another aviation pioneer. They also studied the flights of French-American aviator Octave Chanute, as well as those of Lilienthal. Several things struck Wilbur and Orville as they researched flying: there was very little actual data, and not enough emphasis on flight control. Wilbur also came to the realization that they would have to master the art of flying in an unpowered machine before they attempted anything powered.

Wilbur observed the flight of buzzards and noticed the twisting or warping of their wings as they flew; he then realized that wing warping was a necessary aspect of flight. A customer came in to buy an inner tube one day and stayed to chat. While conversing, Wilbur absent-mindedly twisted the ends of the narrow cardboard box in which the inner tube had come. When the customer left, Wilbur saw how he had twisted the box ends in opposite directions. He instantly envisioned two pairs of wings, one above the other, which would be rigid in the vertical plane but able to move to opposing angles at their tips. Orville quickly caught on to Wilbur's idea. The two fashioned a bi-wing kite with maneuverable wings. Orville was gone on a camping trip when Wilbur tested it. It was such a success that he visited Orville's camp to tell him about it. This led to the development of aglider based on the idea of attaching wings to wires so that they could be warped as needed to provide flight control. It was a significant and innovative development.

On May 13, 1900, Wilbur wrote to aviator Chanute for his advice and opinions. Thus started a long friendship between the brothers and Chanute. Wilbur also wrote to the United States Weather Bureau asking about wind and terrain conditions around the country. The reply indicated that Kitty Hawk, North Carolina, might best suit the Wrights' purposes. So on September 13, 1900, Wilbur arrived there. Being a very remote place at the time, Wilbur stayed with Postmaster William Tate until Orville came with the camping gear on September 28. Together they finished the glider Wilbur had been assembling.

After several glider experiments, it became clear that they weren't getting the lift they expected from the wings. So on October 28, they broke camp and returned to Dayton. However, the flying bug had bitten, and the brothers realized they were closer to flying than anyone else. Thus Wilbur and Orville pursued aviation single-mindedly.

Hiring Charles Taylor to mind the bicycle store for them, the Wrights advanced their plans to return to Kitty Hawk, arriving July 10, 1901. This time they used a much larger and heavier glider with the camber nearly doubled on the wings. Wilbur was the first to try the glider, and it immediately plopped to the ground. As he had to lie prone to fly the glider, Wilbur realized that he was too far forward and inched back until the glider flew on the ninth try. Its center of gravity had shifted back one foot.

By August, the Wrights had a good feel for the glider and decided to try banking turns. Despite brisk winds, Wilbur made the attempt, and encountered many problems, not the least of which was getting into a spin. He and Orville continued experiments until August 20, when they left for Dayton. Much careful analysis led the Wrights to the conclusion that the Lilienthal lift tables were wrong—even though they were considered gospel by the flying world of the time.

Closing in on Powered Flight

By this time, Chanute was so impressed by the brothers' achievements that he invited Wilbur to speak at a meeting for the Western Society of Engineers in Chicago. There, in a ten-thousand-word paper, Wilbur made the startling claim that Lilienthal's lift tables were wrong. Later, to assuage self-doubts about their claim, the Wrights decided to do laboratory work, testing different wing shapes at different wind angles. This eventually led them to build a primitive wind tunnel, only eighteen inches long. Although English inventor Frank Wenham had invented the wind tunnel in 1870, the Wrights were the first to realize its full potential. The result was that they found Lilienthal's tables to be seriously in error, so they researched until they had made a set of their own, using nearly 48 different wings. According to Orville: "I believe we possessed more data on cambered surfaces, a hundred times over, than all of our predecessors put together."

Armed with this new knowledge, the Wrights returned to Kitty Hawk on August 28, 1902. Their new glider had longer, narrower wings and a shallower curvature. For the first time, it also had a tail: two vertical fins for preventing spins. Their first test on September 19 was very good. However, later testing showed that falling into spins was still possible. Eventually, Orville realized that the tail was adding to the problem and that it needed to be controlled just like the wings. Then Wilbur devised the idea of linking the tail fins (today called rudders) to the wing-warping wires. This innovation was a stunning success. When the brothers broke camp that year on October 28, they knew their next step would be a powered craft.

Of all the problems flying a powered craft presented, however, two were especially challenging. One was the need for a propeller, and the other was the need for an engine with sufficient power which was also lightweight. The brothers got their store manager, Charles Taylor, to work on the engine. Meanwhile, they researched propellers. Those used in ships of the time were hit-and-miss devices: shipwrights tried a number of different sizes and shapes until they got a propeller which worked satisfactorily. Wilbur did much library research on the subject, turning up virtually nothing.

The two brothers argued over the propeller problem for weeks. Finally, they realized that a propeller was in reality a wing rotating in the vertical plane. This revelation led to weeks more of calculations and research resulting in tables showing how to design propellers with adequate thrust. The propellers the Wrights used were rear-mounted and rotated in opposite directions. The brothers had already realized that a yaw, or swerving motion, would result if the propellers rotated the same way.

The Wrights returned to Kitty Hawk September 25, 1903. By November 5, the new machine was assembled. They performed pre-flight tests on the engine, with terrible results. It sputtered and backfired. The propellers didn't work well either, rotating jerkily. Finally they came off, damaging their shafts.

It was December, and winter was becoming a problem when the machine was finally ready to try again. On December 14, the brothers flipped a coin, and Wilbur won the toss. Using the new track they had built to launch their flyer, Wilbur took off. However, the take-off was too fast and Wilbur became nose-high. He was unused to how quickly it could all happen and crashed, but not seriously.

The next try was December 17. This time, it was Orville's turn. At 10:35 a.m., Orville took off, rising ten feet, falling, climbing again and landing roughly 100 feet from where he started. In winds as high as 27 miles per hour, Orville became the first man carried by a machine-powered craft which took off under its own power and landed as high as it had started. Thus was born the airplane.

They flew several more times that day, each flight covering a longer distance and time. Then, as they and several helpers were attempting to return the machine to its hangar, the wind caught it and sent it reeling end over end. It was smashed beyond repair. Even after a terse statement issued by the brothers on January 5, 1904, the world took almost no notice of what the Wrights had done.

Uncle Sam Turns a Cold Shoulder, But Europe Is Enthusiastic

The brothers spent 1904 refining the new machine, which the Wrights called Flyer II, since the first Flyer was hopelessly damaged. They built it so they could test it in the more confined flying spaces around Dayton, on what was known as the Huffman Farm. On September 20, Wilbur flew the first complete circle, setting a new distance record of 3/4 mile in one minute and 35.4 seconds. Flyer III debuted in June of 1905. On October 5, it flew 24.2 miles in just over 38 minutes, landing only because it was out of fuel.

Feeling that it was their duty to let the United States Government have the first chance to buy airplanes, the Wrights approached the War Department about their invention. They were brushed off. However, on February 8, 1908, the Army Signal Corps accepted the Wrights' bid to make a plane according to Army specifications for $25,000. The 14th of May brought the first time two men ever flew together. In 1908, Wilbur undertook a tour of Europe to demonstrate the flying machine, and it was wildly successful. Europe was so crazed by the invention that a number of would-be producers launched into the aircraft-making business. Wilbur also returned home with a number of contracts in his pocket.

Meanwhile, on September 17, Orville made the first one-hour flight at Ft. Myer, Virginia, hoping for an Army contract. But the flight ended tragically when a guy wire broke, hurting a propeller and impairing control. In the ensuing crash, Orville's passenger, Lieutenant Thomas Selfridge, was killed—the first man to die in an airplane. Orville suffered a broken leg, four broken ribs and a multi-fractured hip.

It wasn't until 1909 that the brothers were finally recognized for their achievements. Upon Wilbur's return from Europe, Dayton threw a surprise parade and bash on June 17 and 18 in their honor. Both brothers were presented with gold medals from the City of Dayton, the State of Ohio and the United States Congress. In Europe, they had been awarded gold medals from French and British aero clubs, among others. May 21, 1910, turned out to be Wilbur's last flight as the pilot. On May 30, 1912, Wilbur succumbed to typhoid fever. He was forty-five. Orville succeeded him as president of the Wright Company.

In 1914, Orville bought all of the stock in the Wright Company, except for that of Robert Collier. In October of 1915, with Collier's consent, Orville sold the company to an Eastern syndicate. He then founded the Wright Aeronautical Corporation, later becoming Director of the Wright Aeronautical Laboratory in Dayton.

Content to make their refinements gradually, the Wrights relied on their numerous patents to protect them from the innovations of would-be competitors. Both in the United States and in Europe, they became embroiled in patent suits. Particularly acrimonious was the fight between the Herring-Curtiss Company and the Wright Company. Although the courts found for the Wrights in nearly every case, they also allowed ways their competitors could work around them without violating their patents. The net effect was that Europeans made rapid advances in the development of the airplane, while in the United States, the many patent fights and attitude of flying as merely a form of high-flying entertainment stagnated American aviation.

World War I ended the patent bickering. The United States government forced the Wright Company to work with Glenn Curtiss, a partnership that turned out well for all those involved. Then the Navy Bureau of Aeronautics forced Wright Aeronautical Corporation to produce an airplane using the radial air-cooled engine that engineer Charles Lawrance had invented. Although initially reluctant due to their own research into water-cooled, in-line engines, Orville Wright did as ordered. The result, named the Whirlwind, became an international standard almost instantly, proving quite lucrative.

Split flaps were Orville's last major invention. Recognized as a scientific pioneer, Orville received several honorary degrees: from Earlham College in Indiana and Royal Technical College of Munich in 1909, from Yale in 1919 and from Harvard in 1931, as well as a doctorate of Engineering from the University of Dayton in 1943. Wilbur also received honorary degrees from Earlham College in 1909 and Oberlin College of Ohio in 1910. In addition, Orville was also awarded a medal from the French Academy of Sciences in 1909 (with Wilbur), the Langley Medal from the Smithsonian Institution in 1910, the Elliot Cresson Medal from the Franklin Institute in 1914, a Cross of an Officer of the Legion of Honor in 1924, and the Distinguished Flying Cross in February 1929. Orville also became the first recipient of the Daniel Guggenheim Medal in 1930.

Orville was also a member of various aeronautical and technical societies, both in the United States and abroad. In 1940, he was issued Honorary Pilot Certificate #1 by the new Civil Aeronautics Authority. In 1944, Orville took the pilot's controls for the last time, flying Lockheed's new, fast C–69 Constellation, nicknamed "Connie." A few years later, on January 30, 1948, Orville died of a heart attack. Never married, neither he nor Wilbur left any descendants, but together, they left a legacy that reached to the skies and beyond.

SELECTED WRITINGS BY WRIGHT BROTHERS:

Books

The Papers of Wilbur and Orville Wright, edited by Marvin W. McFarland, McGraw-Hill, 1953.

Periodicals

Smithsonian Institute Report, Aeronautical Experiments, 1902, p. 133.

Science, Mechanical Flight, April 6, 1906, p. 557.

Scientific American, Flying as a Sport, February 29, 1908, p. 139.

Scientific American, Our Aeroplane Tests at Kitty Hawk, June 13, 1908, p. 423.

Century, Wright Brothers' Aeroplane, September, 1908, p. 641.

Scientific American, Earliest Wright Flights, July 16, 1910, p. 47.

Scientific American, Stability of Aeroplanes, September 26, 1914, p. 206.

FURTHER READING:

Books

Boyne, Walter J., *The Leading Edge,* Stewart, Tabori & Chang, 1986.

Boyne, Walter J., *The Smithsonian Book of Flight*, Smithsonian Books, 1987.

Hallion, Richard P., *Legacy of Flight*, University of Washington Press, 1977.

Kelly, Fred C., *The Wright Brothers*, Harcourt, 1943.

Moolman, Valerie, *The Road to Kitty Hawk*, Time-Life Books, 1980.

Periodicals

Moolman, Valerie, *Literary Digest*, Mr. Wright Disparages the Glider, January 6, 1923, p. 59.

Moolman, Valerie, *Scientific American*, Portrait of Orville Wright, November 1, 1913, p. 338.

Moolman, Valerie, *Independent*, Portrait of Wilbur Wright, June 6, 1912, p. 194.

Moolman, Valerie, *St. Nicholas*, Visiting the Wright Boys, November, 1910, p. 76.

Sketch by Susan E. Kolmer

Chien-Shiung Wu

Chien-Shiung Wu
1912–1997
American physicist

For more than thirty years, Chien-Shiung Wu was a member of the physicsdepartment at Columbia University, where she earned a reputation as one of the world's foremost nuclear physicists. Wu was best known for a classic experiment on beta decay, completed in 1957, which confirmed a prediction made a year earlier by **Tsung-Dao Lee** and **Chen Ning Yang** regarding the conservation of parity (the basic symmetry of nature) in reactions involving the weak force. A number of observers have commented on the apparent inequity of the Nobel Prize committee's not having included Wu in the 1957 physics prize, which was awarded to Lee and Yang for this work.

Chien-Shiung Wu was born on May 29, 1912, in Liu Ho, near Shanghai, China. Her father, Wu Zhongyi, was a former engineer who had abandoned his profession in 1911 to take part in the revolution that overthrew the Manchu dynasty. After the war, Wu returned to Liu Ho to open a school for girls. Still filled with revolutionary zeal, he saw it as his mission to make sure that girls as well as boys were able to have an education in the "new China." Chien-Shiung's mother, Fan Fuhua, helped her husband in this effort, providing education to their students' families in their own homes.

Wu attended her father's school until she was nine and then continued her education at the Soochow Girls School, about fifty miles (80 km) from her home. During her high school years, Wu was active in a number of political causes; her fellow classmates chose her to represent them in some of the causes because, with her stellar scholastic record, she could not readily be dismissed from school on the basis of her involvement in political issues. In 1930, Wu graduated from Soochow as valedictorian of her class and then entered the National Central University in Nanking. By that time she had decided to pursue physicsas a career, and in 1934 was awarded a bachelor's degree in that field. After teaching and doing research for two years, Wu left China in 1936, intending to obtain the graduate training in physics that was not then available in her native land. Her original plans to enroll in the University of Michigan changed abruptly when she reached San Francisco and was offered an opportunity to attend the University of California at Berkeley.

Among the factors influencing Wu's decision to remain in California was the presence of **Ernest Orlando Lawrence,** inventor of the atom-smashing cyclotron (a device that accelerates the speed of nuclear particles), on the Berkeley campus. The chance to study with Lawrence was, Wu decided, too important to pass up. Another factor in her decision was the presence of "Luke" Chia Liu Yuan—a young man she met soon after arriving in San Francisco. Wu and Yuan were married in 1942 and eventually had one son, Vincent Wei-Chen Yuan.

Teaches at Smith, Princeton, and Columbia

Wu received her Ph.D. in 1940, a time of great turmoil in her homeland and in the world at large. The Japanese army had already invaded China, and U.S. involvement in World War II was only a year away. Wu stayed on as a research assistant at Berkeley for two years after receiving her degree, but spent much of that time on war-related work. In 1942 she was offered her first teaching position, at Smith College in Northampton, Massachusetts. She remained at Smith for only one year before accepting an appointment at Princeton University, where she was assigned to teach introductory physics to naval officers. She held this position for only a few months before she was offered a post at Columbia University, where she would join the Manhattan Project—through which the world's first atomic bombs were designed and built. That job, which began in March 1944, was the beginning of a long relationship with Columbia; she eventually became a research associate in 1945, associate professor in 1952, and finally full professor in 1958. She retired from Columbia in 1981.

Tests the Lee-Yang Theory of Parity Nonconservation

The work for which Wu gained fame took place in 1957. It was based on a revolutionary theory proposed by two colleagues, Tsung-Dao Lee, also of Columbia, and Chen Ning Yang, of the Institute for Advanced Study in Princeton, New Jersey. In 1956 Lee and Yang had raised the possibility that a property known as parity may not be conserved in certain types of nuclear reactions. Conservation laws had long been at the heart of physical theories. These laws said that a number of important physical characteristics—mass, energy, momentum, and electrical charge, for instance—were always conserved during physical or chemical changes. As an example, the law of conservation of electrical charge says that the total electrical charge on all particles involved in a physical change would be the same both before and after the event.

Lee and Yang found theoretical reasons to question the conservation of parity in some instances. Parity refers to the theory that the laws of nature are not biased in any particular direction, a concept long held by physicists. When beta particles are emitted by nuclei during radioactive decay, for example, classical theory predicts that they will be emitted without preference to any particular spin orientation. Lee and Yang developed a mathematical argument showing that this might not be the case and outlined experiments through which their theory could be tested.

Lee and Yang presented their ideas to Wu, already recognized as an authority on beta decay (a radioactive nuclear transformation) and the weak force that causes it. Even before her colleagues had published a paper on their theory, Wu had begun to design experiments to test their ideas. Working with colleagues at the National Bureau of Standards's Low Temperature Physics Group, Wu labored almost without rest for six months. In January of 1957, she announced her results: clear evidence for the violation of parity conservation had been observed. Later that same year, Lee and Yang were awarded the Nobel Prize in physics—an

award that many observers in the field believe might easily have been shared with Wu.

Although she did not receive a Nobel Prize, Wu has won a host of other awards, including the first Wolf Prize awarded by the state of Israel (1978), the first Research Corporation Award (1959) given to a woman, the Comstock Award of the National Academy of Sciences (1964), and the National Science Medal (1975). She was elected to the National Academy of Sciences in 1958. Wu suffered a fatal stroke in Manhattan, New York, on February 16, 1997. She was 84.

SELECTED WRITINGS BY WU:

Books

An Experimental Test of Parity Conservation in Beta Decay. New York, 1957.
Nuclear Physics, Academic Press, 1961.

FURTHER READING:

Books

Kass-Simon, G., and Patricia Farnes, eds. *Women of Science: Righting the Record.* Bloomington: Indiana University Press, 1990, pp. 205-08.
Kass-Simon, G., and Particia Farnes, eds. *McGraw-Hill Modern Men of Science.* Vol. 2. New York: McGraw-Hill, 1984, pp. 541-42.
McGrayne, Sharon Bertsch. *Nobel Prize Women in Science.* Secaucus, NJ: Birchlane Press, 1993, pp. 255-79.
Yost, Edna. *Women of Modern Science.* Dodd, 1959, pp. 80-93.

Periodicals

Dicke, William. "Chien-Shiung Wu, 84, Dies; Top Experimental Physicist" (obituary). *New York TImes* (18 February 1997): B7.

Sketch by David E. Newton

Y. C. L. Susan Wu
1932–
American aerospace engineer

Aerospace engineer Y. C. L. Susan Wu is a researcher who has excelled in both academics and industry. Her work has earned the respect of leading engineers and scientists and has advanced the potential for cleaner and more efficient methods of coal-fired power generation in the United States.

Ying-Chu Lin Wu was born in Beijing, China, on June 23, 1932. Her mother, Kuo-Chun Kung, was a personnel employee for the Taiwanese government; her father, Chi-Yu Lin, was a government accountant. Wu developed an early interest in science, but at that time women were generally discouraged from such pursuits. Her mother's encouragement gave Wu the impetus to continue her studies, and in 1955 she received a bachelor's degree in mechanical engineering from the National Taiwan University.

Engineering jobs were scarce for women in China in the mid–1950s. Because employers viewed jobs as a lifetime commitment for the employee, firms were reluctant to hire women, recognizing the potential pressures of marriage and child-rearing. Wu moved to the United States in 1957 and earned a master's degree from Ohio State University in aeronautical engineering in 1959. After achieving a doctorate from the California Institute of Technology in 1963, Wu found employment at an optics engineering company in Pasadena, California, as a senior engineer. In 1965 Wu accepted a position as an assistant professor at the University of Tennessee Space Institute (UTSI). In 1967 she was promoted to associate professor, and a full professorship in aerospace engineering followed in 1973. She held that position at UTSI for fifteen years.

Focuses on Energy Research

During Wu's tenure at UTSI her research focused on magnetohydrodynamics (MHD) and its application to cleaner coal-fired power generation. Conventional power generators use steam, coal, or oil power to turn an armature on which a continuous wire is wrapped. A magnetic field surrounds the armature and as the wires cut through the magnetic field, a current is induced in the wire, thereby producing electricity. MHD uses conventional power generation theory, but the armature is replaced by plasma, a very hot gas on the order of 5,000°F. When a gas is very hot it becomes an electrical conductor. Sometimes such elements as cesium or potassium ions are introduced into the gas to increase its conductivity. As the electrically conductive plasma cuts through the magnetic field, an electric current is generated. This method of power generation is cleaner and more efficient than traditional coal-fired power plants.

In 1988 Wu left UTSI after twenty-three years to start her own business. She founded ERC, Inc., an aerospace engineering and MHD consulting firm based in Tullahoma, Tennessee. ERC, Inc., works with such agencies as the National Aeronautics and Space Administration (NASA), the Department of Energy, Argonne National Laboratory, Boeing, McDonnell Douglas, and UTSI.

Wu's many honors include the University of Tennessee Chancellor's Research Scholar Award in 1978, Outstanding Educators of America Award in 1973 and 1975, and the Society of Women Engineers Achievement Award

in 1985. She was honored by the National Science Foundation in 1987, and she received the Amelia Earhart Fellowship in 1958, 1959, and 1962, the only three-time recipient of the award. A naturalized U.S. citizen, Wu married Jain-Ming (James) Wu in 1959, and they have three children: Ernest, a biologist; Albert, an aerospace engineering consultant; and Karen, a quality control engineer. In her spare time, Wu enjoys classical music, reading, and civic activities.

SELECTED WRITINGS BY WU:

Periodicals

AIAA Journal, Physical Property Distribution in a Low-Pressure Crossed Field Plasma Accelerator, November, 1965.

AIAA Journal, The Limiting Circles of One-Dimensional MHD Channel Flows, August, 1968.

AIAA Journal, Eddy Currents in an Infinitely Finely Segmented Hall Generator, September, 1970.

AIAA Journal, Study of Pressure Distribution along Supersonic Magnetohydrodynamic Generator Channels, September, 1975.

Mechanical Engineering, MHD Steam Power—Promise, Progress, and Problems, September, 1981.

Journal of Energy, Experimental Results of the UTSI Coal-Fired MHD Generator, May-June, 1982, p. 179.

Journal of Energy, Comparison of Experimental Results from the UTSI Coal-Fired MHD Generator to Theoretical Predictions, May-June, 1982.

Journal of Energy, Power Take-off Analysis and Comparison with Experiments in a Coal-Fired MHD Generator, September-October, 1983.

Journal of Propulsion and Power, Fault Analysis of Mid Channel Power Takeoff in Diagonal Conducting Wall Magnetohydrodynamic Generators, September-October, 1985.

Chemtech, Emission Control by Magnetohydrodynamics, November, 1988.

U.S. Woman Engineer, SWE Personality Profile: Y. C. L. Susan Wu, 1985 SWE Achievement Award Winner, March-April, 1990, pp. 31–32.

FURTHER READING:

Periodicals

Congressional Record, July 15, 1985, p. S–9510.

Other

Wu, Y. C. L. Susan, *Interview with Roger Jaffe,* conducted January 20, 1994.

Sketch by Roger Jaffe

Xie Xide
1921–
Chinese physicist

Xie Xide is a Chinese physicist and the president of Fudan University in Shanghai, China. During the decade of China's Cultural Revolution she was removed from her teaching post and was not allowed to conduct scientific research. Reinstated in 1972, as a university administrator she has been an outspoken advocate for science education in China.

Born in 1921, in South China, she spent her early years in Peking, where her father was a professor of physics at Yenching University, now a part of Beijing University. When the Japanese occupied Peking in July of 1937, she fled with her family. Traveling half-way across China, they eventually reached Guiyang, in Guizhou Province. During the journey Xie became ill with tuberculosis, and was hospitalized in Guiyang for close to four years. After recovering, she began her university studies in physics at Amoy University, where her father had found a new teaching post. To escape the Japanese, Amoy University had been evacuated to the remote hill town of Changding in Fukien Province. In 1946 she received her B.Sc.

Shortly after the war ended Xie took a teaching position in physics at the University of Shanghai. A year later, in 1947, she set sail for the United States, part of a wave of young Chinese intellectuals who were seeking higher education abroad. Leaving behind the civil war and political chaos that preceded the emergence of the Communist government in China, she enrolled in a master's degree program at Smith College, in Amherst, Massachusetts. She received her M.A. in 1949, and then began her doctoral studies in the physics department at the Massachusetts Institute of Technology. Her thesis work there concerned the wave function of electrons in highly compressed gases. She was granted her Ph.D. in 1951.

Unable to return directly home because of U.S. government restrictions on travel to China at the time, Xie instead went to England, where she married Cao Tianquin, a biochemist. Together, in 1952, they made their way back to Shanghai on an arduous route via the Suez Canal and Singapore. Back in China, Xie took a post at Fudan University. Her husband joined the Shanghai branch of the Chinese Academy of Science. Xie soon distinguished herself as one of China's top physicists, publishing many professional articles and two texts, *Semi-conductor Physics* (1958) and *Solid Physics* (1962). In 1962 she was promoted in rank to Professor and was appointed the Deputy Director of the Institute of Technical Physics in Shanghai.

In 1966 when the Cultural Revolution began, Xie and her husband were subjected to the anti-intellectual tyranny of Mao Zedong's government. Despite her allegiance to the Communist Party, she was kept imprisoned in her own laboratory for a period of nine months. Her husband was incarcerated as well, at his own institute, leaving their then ten-year-old boy to look after himself alone in the family's apartment. Xie was forced to clean bathrooms at the university, and was eventually sent to the countryside to work in a silicon wafer factory. In 1972 she was allowed to return to her teaching post, where she taught physics to peasants, workers and soldiers, most of them ill-prepared for university classes. The Cultural Revolution came to a close in 1976 when the "Gang of Four" was arrested (the four were the leaders of the Cultural Revolution; after Mao's death in 1976, the Communist Party rejected the Revolution and the four were sentenced to life in prison). Since then Xie has worked hard to regain her footing. She resumed research in surface physics, and in 1977 founded the educational Modern Physics Institute. One year later Xie was appointed vice-president of Fudan University, and in 1982 she became its president. That same year, she was elected to the Central Committee of the Chinese Communist Party, one of the few women and scientists among this elite body of policy-making leaders. Xie has been awarded numerous honorary degrees and is a member of the Chinese Academy of Sciences and the Praesidium. She continues to work to improve the educational opportunities for students in China.

SELECTED WRITINGS BY XIE XIDE:

Books

Semi-conductor Physics, 1958.
Solid Physics, 1962.

FURTHER READING:

Periodicals

Oka, Takashi, *Christian Science Monitor,* Xie Xide—The Gentle President of China's Fudan University, March 28, 1984, p. 21.

Sketch by Leslie Reinherz

Rosalyn Sussman Yalow
1921–
American medical physicist

Rosalyn Sussman Yalow was co-developer of radioimmunoassay (RIA), a technique that uses radioactive isotopes to measure small amounts of biological substances. In widespread use, the RIA helps scientists and medical professionals measure the concentrations of hormones, vitamins, viruses, enzymes, and drugs, among other substances. Yalow's work concerning RIA earned her a share of the Nobel Prize in physiology or medicine in the late 1970s. At that time, she was only the second woman to receive the Nobel in medicine. During her career, Yalow also received acclaim for being the first woman to attain a number of other scientific achievements.

Yalow was born on July 19, 1921, in The Bronx, New York, to Simon Sussman and Clara Zipper Sussman. Her father, owner of a small business, had been born on the Lower East Side of New York City to Russian immigrant parents. At the age of four, Yalow's mother had journeyed to the United States from Germany. Although neither parent had attended high school, they instilled a great enthusiasm for and respect of education in their daughter. Yalow also credits her father with helping her find the confidence to succeed in school, teaching her that girls could do just as much as boys. Yalow learned to read before she entered kindergarten, although her family did not own any books. Instead, Yalow and her older brother, Alexander, made frequent visits to the public library.

During her youth, Yalow became interested in mathematics. At Walton High School in the Bronx, her interest turned to science, especially chemistry. After graduation, Yalow attended Hunter College, a women's school in New York that eventually became part of the City University of New York. She credits two physics professors, Dr. Herbert Otis and Dr. Duane Roller, for igniting her penchant for physics. This occurred in the latter part of the 1930s, a time when many new discoveries were made in nuclear physics. It was this field that Yalow ultimately chose for her major. In 1939 she was further inspired after hearing American physicist **Enrico Fermi** lecture about the discovery of nuclear fission, which had earned him the Nobel Prize the previous year.

Rosalyn Sussman Yalow

Overcomes Sex Bias

As Yalow prepared for her graduation from Hunter College, she found that some practical considerations intruded on her passion for physics. At the time, most of American society expected young women to become secretaries or teachers. In fact, Yalow's parents urged her to pursue a career as an elementary school teacher. Yalow herself also thought it unrealistic to expect any of the top graduate schools in the country to accept her into a doctoral program or offer her the financial support that men received. "However, my physics professors encouraged me and I persisted," she explained in *Les Prix Nobel 1977.*

Yalow made plans to enter graduate school via other means. One of her earlier college physics professors, who had left Hunter to join the faculty at the Massachusetts Institute of Technology, arranged for Yalow to work as secretary to Dr. Rudolf Schoenheimer, a biochemist at Columbia University in New York. According to the plan, this position would give Yalow an opportunity to take some graduate courses in physics, and eventually provide a way for her to enter a graduate a school and pursue a degree. But

Yalow never needed her plan. The month after graduating from Hunter College in January 1941, she was offered a teaching assistantship in the physics department of the University of Illinois at Champaign-Urbana.

Gaining acceptance to the physics graduate program in the College of Engineering at the University of Illinois was one of many hurdles that Yalow had to cross as a woman in the field of science. For example, when she entered the University in September 1941, she was the only woman in the College of Engineering's faculty, which included four hundred professors and teaching assistants. She was the first woman in more than two decades to attend the engineering college. Yalow realized that she had been given a space at the prestigious graduate school because of the shortage of male candidates, who were being drafted into the armed services in increasing numbers as America prepared to enter World War II.

Yalow's strong work orientation aided her greatly in her first year in graduate school. In addition to her regular course load and teaching duties, she took some extra undergraduate courses to increase her knowledge. Despite a hectic schedule, Yalow earned A's in her classes, except for an A- in an optics laboratory course. While in graduate school she also met Aaron Yalow, a fellow student and the man she would eventually marry. The pair met the first day of school and wed about two years later on June 6, 1943. Yalow received her master's degree in 1942 and her doctorate in 1945. She was the second woman to obtain a Ph.D. in physics at the University.

After graduation the Yalows moved to New York City, where they worked and eventually raised two children, Benjamin and Elanna. Yalow's first job after graduate school was as an assistant electrical engineer at Federal Telecommunications Laboratory, a private research lab. Once again, she found herself the sole woman as there were no other female engineers at the lab. In 1946 she began teaching physics at Hunter College. She remained a physics lecturer from 1946 to 1950, although by 1947 she began her long association with the Veterans Administration by becoming a consultant to Bronx VA Hospital. The VA wanted to establish some research programs to explore medical uses of radioactive substances. By 1950, Yalow had equipped a radioisotope laboratory at the Bronx VA Hospital and decided to leave teaching to devote her attention to full-time research.

That same year Yalow met Solomon A. Berson, a physician who had just finished his residency in internal medicine at the hospital. The two would work together until Berson's death in 1972. According to Yalow, the collaboration was a complementary one. In Olga Opfell's *Lady Laureates* Yalow is quoted as saying, "[Berson] wanted to be a physicist, and I wanted to be a medical doctor." While her partner had accumulated clinical expertise, Yalow maintained strengths in physics, math, and chemistry. Working together, Yalow and Berson discovered new ways to use radioactive isotopes in the measurement of blood volume, the study of iodine metabolism, and the diagnosis of thyroid diseases. Within a few years, the pair began to investigate adult-onset diabetes using radioisotopes. This project eventually led them to develop the groundbreaking radioimmunoassay technique.

Diabetes Mystery Leads to a Discovery

In the 1950s some scientists hypothesized that in adult-onset diabetes, insulin production remained normal, but a liver enzyme rapidly destroyed the peptide hormone, thereby preventing normal glucose metabolism. This contrasted with the situation in juvenile diabetes, where insulin production by the pancreas was too low to allow proper metabolism of glucose. Yalow and Berson wanted to test the hypothesis about adult-onset diabetes. They used insulin "labeled" with iodine–131. (That is, they attached, by a chemical reaction, the radioactive isotope of iodine to otherwise normal insulin molecules.) Yalow and Berson injected labeled insulin into diabetic and non-diabetic individuals and measured the rate at which the insulin disappeared.

To their surprise and in contradiction to the liver enzyme hypothesis, they found that the amount of radioactively labeled insulin in the blood of diabetics was higher than that found in the control subjects who had never received insulin injections before. As Yalow and Berson looked into this finding further, they deduced that diabetics were forming antibodies to the animal insulin used to control their disease. These antibodies were binding to radiolabeled insulin, preventing it from entering cells where it was used in sugar metabolism. Individuals who had never taken insulin before did not have these antibodies and so the radiolabeled insulin was consumed more quickly.

Yalow and Berson's proposal that animal insulin could spur antibody formation was not readily accepted by immunologists in the mid–1950s. At the time, most immunologists did not believe that antibodies would form to molecules as small as the insulin peptide. Also, the amount of insulin antibodies was too low to be detected by conventional immunological techniques. So Yalow and Berson set out to verify these minute levels of insulin antibodies using radiolabeled insulin as their marker. Their original report about insulin antibodies, however, was rejected initially by two journals. Finally, a compromise version was published that omitted "insulin antibody" from the paper's title and included some additional data indicating that an antibody was involved.

The need to detect insulin antibodies at low concentrations led to the development of the radioimmunoassay. The principle behind RIA is that a radiolabeled antigen, such as insulin, will compete with unlabeled antigen for the available binding sites on its specific antibody. As a standard, various mixtures of known amounts of labeled and unlabeled antigen are mixed with antibody. The amounts of radiation detected in each sample correspond to the amount of unlabeled antigen taking up antibody binding sites. In the unknown sample, a known amount of radiolabeled antigen is added and the amount of radioactivity is measured again.

The radiation level in the unknown sample is compared to the standard samples; the amount of unlabeled antigen in the unknown sample will be the same as the amount of unlabeled antigen found in the standard sample that yields the same amount of radioactivity. RIA has turned out to be so useful because it can quickly and precisely detect very low concentrations of hormones and other substances in blood or other biological fluids. The principle can also be applied to binding interactions other than that between antigen and antibody, such as between a binding protein or tissue receptor site and an enzyme. In Yalow's Nobel lecture, recorded in *Les Prix Nobel 1977,* she listed more than one hundred biological substances—hormones, drugs, vitamins, enzymes, viruses, non-hormonal proteins, and more—that were being measured using RIA.

In 1968 she became a research professor at the Mt. Sinai School of Medicine, and in 1970, she was made chief of the Nuclear Medicine Service at the VA hospital. Yalow also began to receive a number of prestigious awards in recognition of her role in the development of RIA. In 1976, she was awarded the Albert Lasker Prize for Basic Medical Research. She was the first woman to be honored this laurel—an award that often leads to a Nobel Prize. In Yalow's case, this was true, for the very next year, she shared the Nobel Prize in physiology or medicine with **Andrew V. Schally** and **Roger Guillemin** for their work on radioimmunoassay. Schally and Guillemin were recognized for their use of RIA to make important discoveries about brain hormones.

Berson had died in 1972, and so did not share in these awards. Ecstatic to receive such prizes, Yalow was also saddened that her longtime partner had been excluded. According to an essay in *The Lady Laureates,* she remarked that the "tragedy" of winning the Nobel Prize "is that Dr. Berson did not live to share it." Earlier Yalow had paid tribute to her collaborator by asking the VA to name the laboratory, in which the two had worked, the Solomon A. Berson Research Laboratory. She made the request, as quoted in *Les Prix Nobel 1977,* "so that his name will continue to be on my papers as long as I publish and so that his contributions to our Service will be memorialized."

Yalow has received many other awards, honorary degrees, and lectureships, including the Georg Charles de Henesy Nuclear Medicine Pioneer Award in 1986 and the Scientific Achievement Award of the American Medical Society. In 1978, she hosted a five-part dramatic series on the life of French physical chemist **Marie Curie**, aired by the Public Broadcasting Service (PBS). In 1980 she became a distinguished professor at the Albert Einstein College of Medicine at Yeshiva University, leaving to become the Solomon A. Berson Distinguished Professor at Large at Mt. Sinai in 1986. She also chaired the Department of Clinical Science at Montefiore Hospital and Medical Center in the early- to mid–1980s.

By all accounts, Yalow was an industrious researcher, rarely taking time off. For example, some reports claim that she only took a few days off of work following the birth of her two children. In *The Lady Laureates,* Opfell reported that when the VA Hospital put on a party in honor of Yalow's selection for the Lasker Prize, Yalow herself "brought roast turkeys from home and stood in the middle of a meeting peeling potatoes and making potato salad while fellows reported to her."

The fact that Yalow was a trailblazer for women scientists was not lost on her, however. At a lecture before the Association of American Medical Colleges, as quoted in *Lady Laureates,* Yalow opined: "We cannot expect that in the foreseeable future women will achieve status in academic medicine in proportion to their numbers. But if we are to start working towards that goal we must believe in ourselves or no one else will believe in us; we must match our aspirations with the guts and determination to succeed; and for those of us who have had the good fortune to move upward, we must feel a personal responsibility to serve as role models and advisors to ease the path for those who come afterwards."

SELECTED WRITINGS BY YALOW:

Books

Radioimmunoassay: Methodology and Applications in Physiology and in Clinical Studies, Publishing Sciences Group, 1974.

Periodicals

Journal of Clinical Investigation, Insulin-I131 Metabolism in Human Subjects: Demonstration of Insulin Binding Globulin in the Circulation of Insulin Treated Subjects, Volume 35, 1956, pp. 170–190.
Nature, Assay of Plasma Insulin in Human Subjects by Immunological Methods, Volume 184, 1959, pp. 1648–1649.

FURTHER READING:

Books

Les Prix Nobel 1977, Almquist & Wiskell International, Stockholm, 1978, pp. 237–264.
Opfell, Olga, *The Lady Laureates: Women Who Have Won the Nobel Prize,* Scarecrow Press, Inc., 1978.

Sketch by Lee Katterman

Chen Ning Yang
1922–
American physicist

In 1945, Chen Ning Yang came to the United States, where he studied physics at the University of Chicago under **Enrico Fermi**. At Chicago, Yang struck up a friendship with another graduate student from China, **Tsung-Dao Lee**, with whom he would have a long and productive professional relationship. In 1956 Yang and Lee developed a hypothesis that one of the fundamental laws of physics, the conservation of parity, might not in fact be valid. As a result of experiments conducted by **Chien-Shiung Wu** along lines suggested by Yang and Lee, that hypothesis was confirmed. The discovery was momentous because it called into question the validity of all conservation laws—laws that support a major part of modern physical theory. For the discovery of the violation of parity conservation, Yang and Lee were jointly awarded the 1957 Nobel Prize for Physics.

Chen Ning Yang was born in the city of Hofei, in Anhwei province, China, on September 22, 1922, to Ke Chuan Yang, a professor of mathematics, and the former Meng Hwa Loh. The Yang family moved in 1929 from Hofei to Peking (now known as Beijing), where Professor Yang took a job with Tsinghua University. In Peking, Yang attended the Chung Te Middle School. The family moved once more eight years later to escape the invading Japanese army. At that time, Tsinghua University was moved to Kunming, where it was consolidated with National Southwest Associated University. When Yang finished high school, he entered the National Southwest Associated University, where he majored in physics and earned his B.S. degree in 1942. He then continued his studies at Tsinghua University, where his father was still professor of mathematics. Yang earned his M.S. at Tsinghua in 1944. He then taught high school for one year before deciding to begin work on a Ph.D. in physics. Because doctoral programs in physics were not then available in China, Yang decided to come to the United States, where he particularly wanted to study with physicist Enrico Fermi. According to an article by Jeremy Bernstein in the *New Yorker,* Yang traveled to New York City (by way of India, the Suez Canal, and Europe) under the impression that Fermi was still at Columbia, where he had come upon his arrival in the United States in 1938. When Yang heard that Fermi had only recently left for a new post at the University of Chicago, he followed Fermi and enrolled in the doctoral program at Chicago.

One of the many benefits of Yang's tenure at Chicago was the association he developed with fellow student Tsung-Dao Lee. Yang and Lee had attended Southwest University in China at the same time, but Yang was a year ahead of Lee, and the two were not particularly close. The

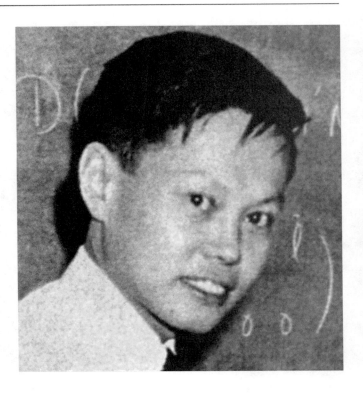

Chen Ning Yang

situation at Chicago was very different. The two compatriots shared housing at the university's International House and soon became close friends. They began to spend time together, talking almost every day about issues in physics. When Yang received his doctorate in 1948, he remained at Chicago as an instructor for one year and then took a job at the Institute for Advanced Study in Princeton, New Jersey. As Lee was not to complete his own degree for two more years, it appeared that their close association was to end; however, in 1951 Lee joined Yang at Princeton for a period of two years. When Lee then took a job at Columbia University in 1953, the two agreed to continue meeting once each week, alternating between New York and Princeton. By the spring of 1956 they had settled on a problem of particular interest to both of them, the decay of the K-meson (a subatomic particle) and the question of parity conservation.

Considering the Possibility of Parity Conservation Violation

Conservation laws lie at the heart of physics, and they are familiar to most students of high school physics. Such laws say that a particular property—mass, energy, momentum, or electrical charge, for instance—is conserved during any change. As an example, when two moving objects strike each other, their total momentum after the collision must be the same as their total momentum before the collision.

The law of parity conservation, first proposed in 1925, defines the basic symmetry of nature, referring to the theory that the laws of nature are not biased in any particular direction. Consequently, nature is unable to distinguish between right- and left-handedness in particles—the smallest building blocks of energy and matter. Any reaction that involves a right-handed particle would be the same for a left-handed particle. By the 1950s, however, one particular kind of nuclear reaction had raised some questions about the validity of that law. That reaction involved the decay of an elementary particle called the K-meson.

Experiments appear to have shown that K-mesons can decay in one of two ways. The explanation that had been postulated for this observation was that two kinds of K-mesons exist; Yang and Lee suggested another possibility. Perhaps only one form of the K-meson exists, they said, and it sometimes decays in such a way that parity is conserved and sometimes in such a way that parity is not conserved. In June of 1956 Yang and Lee formulated their thoughts on the K-meson puzzle in a now-classic paper titled "Question of Parity Conservation in Weak Interactions." They not only explained why they thought that parity conservation might not occur, but they also outlined experimental tests by which their hypothesis could be evaluated.

Within a matter of months, the proposed experiments were under way. They were carried out by a group of researchers under the direction of Chien-Shiung Wu, a compatriot of Yang and Lee at Columbia University. Wu assembled a team of colleagues at Columbia and at the National Bureau of Standards to study K-meson decay along the lines suggested by Yang and Lee. By January of 1957, the preliminary results were in. The evidence confirmed that Yang and Lee were correct: Parity was not conserved in the decay of K-mesons. For their work on this problem, Yang and Lee were awarded the Nobel Prize for Physics only ten months after Wu's experiments had been completed—almost record time for recognition by a Nobel Prize committee.

In 1965, Yang ended his long affiliation with the Institute for Advanced Study to accept an appointment as Albert Einstein Professor of Physics and Director of the Institute of Theoretical Physics at the State University of New York at Stony Brook. In 1950 he had married Chih Li Tu, a former high school student of his in China. They have two sons, Franklin and Gilbert, and a daughter, Eulee. In addition to the Nobel Prize, Yang has been awarded the 1957 Albert Einstein Award and the 1980 Rumford Medal of the American Academy of Arts and Sciences.

SELECTED WRITINGS BY YANG:

Books

Selected Papers, 1945–80, with Commentary, W. H. Freeman, 1983.

Periodicals

Physical Review, Interaction of Mesons with Nucleons and Light Particles, Volume 75, 1949, p. 905.

Physical Review, Mass Degeneracy of the Heavy Mesons, Volume 102, 1956, pp. 290–291.
Physical Review, Question of Parity Conservation in Weak Interactions, Volume 104, 1956, pp. 254–258.
Physical Review, Remarks on Possible Noninvariance under Time Reversal and Charge Conjugation, Volume 106, 1957, pp. 340–345.

FURTHER READING:

Books

Magill, Frank N., editor, *The Nobel Prize Winners—Physics,* Volume 2, Salem Press, 1989, pp. 707–713.
Magill, Frank N., editor, *McGraw-Hill Modern Men of Science,* Volume 1, McGraw-Hill, 1984, pp. 545–546.
Wasson, Tyler, editor, *Nobel Prize Winners,* H. W. Wilson, 1987, pp. 1150–1152.

Periodicals

Bernstein, Jeremy, *New Yorker,* A Question of Parity, May 12, 1962, pp. 49–104.

Sketch by David E. Newton

Shing-Tung Yau
1949–
American mathematician

Shing-Tung Yau has made fundamental contributions to differential geometry which have influenced a wide range of scientific disciplines, including astronomy and theoretical physics. With Richard Schoen, Yau solved a long-standing question in **Albert Einstein**'s theory of relativity by proving that the sum of the energy in the universe is positive; their proof has provided an important tool for understanding how black holes form. Yau was awarded the Fields Medal in 1982, the highest award in mathematics, and he won the 1994 Crafoord Prize from the Royal Swedish Society with **Simon Donaldson** of Oxford University, in recognition of his "development of nonlinear techniques in differential geometry leading to the solution of several outstanding problems." Yau was born April 4, 1949, in Swatow, in southern China, the fifth of the eight children of Chen Ying Chiou and Yeuk-Lam Leung Chiou. Within the year, Communists had overthrown the government and the family fled to Hong Kong, where his father, a respected economist and philosopher, obtained a position at a college which would later be part of Hong Kong University. His mother knit and created other goods by hand to help support the family, for professors were poorly paid. During high school in Hong Kong, Yau told contributor F. C. Nicholson, much emphasis was placed on mathematics, partly because the laboratories for the sciences were ill equipped. He credits his father, who died when Yau was fourteen, with encouraging him to study mathematics and he has retained a passion for it: "It's clean, clear-cut, beautiful, and has a lot of applications," he told the *Harvard Gazette.*

Yau entered the Chinese University of Hong Kong, earning his undergraduate degree in 1968. One of his professors had attended the University of California at Berkeley and suggested he study there. An IBM fellowship made it possible for Yau to attend Berkeley; he studied with Shiing-Shen Chern, the legendary geometer (Yau would later edit a collection of papers honoring his teacher). Yau completed his Ph.D. in mathematics in 1971 at the age of twenty-two. Yau spent a year after receiving his doctorate with the Institute for Advanced Study at Princeton, and then in 1972 he accepted a position as assistant professor of mathematics at the State University of New York at Stony Brook. In 1974, he became a full professor of mathematics at Stanford, where he was to remain until 1979. After leaving Stanford in 1979, Yau returned to the Institute for Advanced Study. He left there in 1984 to become professor of mathematics and chairman of the department at the University of California, San Diego.

Differential geometry, which is Yau's field, was developed during the 1800s, and it uses derivatives and integrals to describe geometric objects such as surfaces and curves. Differential geometry is particularly concerned with geometrical calculations across many dimensions. The simplest kind of geometry would be one and two dimensional, analyzing figures such as squares or circles; the geometry of a three-dimensional figure, such as a cube or a cylinder, is more complicated. Differential geometry is primarily concerned with calculations about geometrical figures in four or more dimensions. An example of a four-dimensional figure would be a three-dimensional one changing over time—the stretching and snapping of a rubber band, for instance, or a drop of water splashing on a surface.

One of the most important applications of differential geometry is Einstein's theory of relativity: Einstein used differential geometry in his original calculations and it was central to his theory of gravity. The general theory of relativity includes a conjecture—that is, an unproven postulate—which proposes that in an isolated physical system the total energy, including gravity and matter, would be positive. Called the positive mass conjecture, this was fundamental to the theory of relativity but no one had been able to prove it.

Yau's first major contribution to differential geometry was his proof of another conjecture, called the Calabi conjecture, which concerns how volume and distance can be measured not in four but in five or more dimensions. But in 1979, Yau and Richard Schoen proved Einstein's positive mass conjecture by applying methods Yau devised. The proof was based on their work with minimal surfaces. A minimal surface is one in which a small deformation creates a surface with a larger area—soap films are often used as an example of minimal surfaces. The mathematical equations that must be used to describe minimal surfaces differ from those used for most problems in differential geometry. The latter use differential equations to describe curves and surfaces, while mathematicians working with minimal surfaces use partial, nonlinear differential equations, which are far more difficult to work with. Schoen and Yau's proof analyzed how such surfaces behave in space and time and showed that Einstein had correctly defined mass. Their methods allowed for the development of a new theory of minimal surfaces in higher dimensions, and they have had an impact on topology, algebraic geometry, and general relativity.

In 1987, Yau joined the faculty of Harvard University as a professor of mathematics. During 1991 and 1992 (concurrent with his position at Harvard), he served as the Wilson T.S. Wang Distinguished Visiting Professor at the Chinese University of Hong Kong and Special Chair of National Tsing Hua University in Hsinchu, Taiwan. In addition to the Fields Medal and the Crafoord Prize, Yau has received the Veblen Prize (1981). He was named an Alfred Sloan Fellow in 1974, and in 1985 he was awarded a MacArthur Fellowship. He received an honorary degree from Harvard University in 1987 and was named an Honorable Doctor of Science by the Chinese University of Hong Kong in 1980.

Yau is a member New York Academy of Science, Academy of Arts and Sciences (Boston), American Physical Society, Society for Industrial and Applied Mathematics, American Academy of Arts and Sciences, National Academy of Sciences; a Fellow of the American Association for the Advancement of Science; and a Foreign Member of the Chinese Academy of Sciences.

In 1997, Yau was awarded the National Medal of Science for his "profound contributions to mathematics with his unparalleled ability for combining the theories of nonlinear partial differential equations and differential geometry." The citation went on to note that his work has "had a great impact on areas of mathematics and physics as diverse as topology, algebraic geometry, representation theory and general relativity as well as differential geometry and partial differential equations."

Yau has published over 150 scientific papers and served as editor-in-chief of the *Journal of Differential Geometry* and the *Asian Journal of Mathematics*, as well as editor of *Communications in Mathematical Physics, Mathematical Research Letters* and *Letters in Mathematical Physics.*

Yau married a fellow Berkeley student, Yu Yun Kuo, in 1976; they have two children.

SELECTED WRITINGS BY YAU:

Books

Chern: A Great Geometer of the Twentieth Century, International Press, 1992.

Periodicals

Communications in Mathematical Physics, On the Proof of the Positive Mass Conjecture in General Relativity, Volume 65, 1979, pp. 45–76.

Communications in Mathematical Physics, The Existence of a Black Hole Due to the Condensation of Matter, Volume 90, 1983, pp. 575–579.

FURTHER READING:

Periodicals

Harvard Gazette, Shing-Tung Yau: Breaking Through Geometric Barriers, November 5, 1987, p. 5.

Other

Yau, Shing-Tung, *Interview with F. C. Nicholson,* February 14, 1994.

Sketch by F. C. Nicholson

Grace Chisholm Young
1868–1944
English mathematician

A distinguished mathematician, Grace Chisholm Young is recognized as being the first woman to receive a Ph.D. in any field from a German university. Working closely with her husband, mathematician William Henry Young, she produced a large body of published work that made contributions to both pure and applied mathematics.

Grace Emily Chisholm Young was born on March 15, 1868, in Haslemere, Surrey, England, to Anna Louisa Bell and Henry William Chisholm. Her father was a British career civil servant who (following his own father) rose through the ranks to become the chief of Britain's weights and measures. Grace Emily Chisholm was the youngest of three surviving children. Her brother, Hugh Chisholm, enjoyed a distinguished career as editor of the eleventh edition of the *Encyclopaedia Britannica.*

As befitted a girl of her social class, Young received an education at home. Forbidden by her mother to study medicine—which the youngster wanted to do—she entered Girton College, Cambridge (one of two women's colleges there) in 1889. She was twenty-one years of age, and the institution's Sir Francis Goldschmid Scholar of mathematics. In 1892 she graduated with first-class honors, then sat informally for the final mathematics examinations at Oxford; there, she placed first. In 1893 she transferred to Göttingen University in Germany, where she attended lectures and produced a dissertation entitled "The Algebraic Groups of Spherical Trigonometry" under noted mathematician Felix Klein. In 1895 she became the first woman to receive a Göttingen doctorate in any subject. The degree bore the distinction magna cum laude.

She returned to London and married her former Girton tutor, **William Henry Young**, who had devoted years to coaching Cambridge students. After the birth of their first child, the Youngs moved to Göttingen. There, William Young began a distinguished research career in mathematics, which would be supported in large part by the work of his wife. Grace Chisholm Young studied anatomy at the university and raised their six children, while collaborating with her husband on mathematics in both co-authored papers and those published under his name alone. In 1905 the pair authored a widely regarded textbook on set theory. Grace Chisholm Young's most important work was achieved between 1914 and 1916, during which time she published several papers on derivates of real functions; in this work she contributed to what is known as the Denjoy-Saks-Young theorem.

The Young family lived modestly, and William Young traveled frequently to earn money by teaching. In 1908, with the birth of their sixth child, the Youngs moved from Göttingen to Geneva. William Young continually sought a well-paying professorship in England, but he failed to obtain such a position; in 1913 he obtained a lucrative professorship in Calcutta, which required his residence for only a few months per year, and after World War I he became professor at the University of Wales in Aberystwyth for several years. Switzerland, however, remained the family's permanent home.

With advancing years, Grace Chisholm Young's mathematical productivity slackened; in 1929 she began an ambitious historical novel, which was never published. Writing fiction was but one of her many varied interests, which included music, languages, and medicine. She also wrote children's books, in which she introduced notions of science. Her children followed the path she had pioneered, becoming accomplished scholars of mathematics, chemistry, and medicine. Her son Frank died as a British aviator during the First World War.

Grace Chisholm Young had lived with her husband's extended absences for her entire married life, and the spring of 1940 found them separated again: she in England, and he in Switzerland. From that time onward, neither spouse was able to see the other again—both were prevented from doing so by the downfall of France during the war. William Young died in 1942, and Grace Chisholm Young died of a heart attack in 1944.

SELECTED WRITINGS BY YOUNG:

Books

The First Book of Geometry, Dent, 1905, reprinted, 1969.

The Theory of Sets of Points, Cambridge University Press, 1906, reprinted, 1972.

Periodicals

Quarterly Journal of Pure and Applied Mathematics, On the Form of a Certain Jordan Curve, Volume 37, 1905, pp. 87–91.

Quarterly Journal of Pure and Applied Mathematics, An Additional Note on Derivates and the Theorem of the Mean, Volume 40, 1909, pp. 144–145.

Acta Mathematica, A Note on Derivatives and Differential Coefficients, Volume 37, 1914, pp. 141–154.

Proceedings of the London Mathematical Society, On the Reduction of Sets of Intervals, Volume 14, 1914, pp. 111-130.

Proceedings of the London Mathematical Society, On the Solution of a Pair of Simultaneous Diophantine Equations Connected with the Nuptial Number of Plato, Volume 23, 1925, pp. 27–44.

FURTHER READING:

Books

Grinstein, Louise S., and Paul J. Campbell, editors, *Women of Mathematics: A Biobibliographic Sourcebook,* Greenwood Press, 1987, pp. 247–254.

Periodicals

Cartwright, M. L., *Journal of the London Mathematical Society,* Grace Chisholm Young, Volume 19, 1944, pp. 185–192.

Grattan-Guinness, Ivor, *Annals of Science,* A Mathematical Union: William Henry and Grace Chisholm Young, Volume 29, 1972, pp. 105–186.

Sketch by Lewis Pyenson

J. Z. Young
1907–1997
English biologist

John Zachary, or "J. Z.," Young was a highly acclaimed biologist whose research on the squid and the octopus has helped greatly in making neurology an exact science. His studies of the regeneration of the nerves of the octopus

qualified him, during World War II, to work with a team of scientists investigating the problems of peripheral nerve injuries and their surgical repair. Young was the first to prove that the giant fibers of the squid are nerves. For his work, which has shed light on the nature of memory, Young was named a fellow of the Royal Society, which also bestowed on him its Royal Medal in 1967. In 1973, he was awarded the Linnean Gold Medal, and two years later he received the London Medal from the Zoological Society.

John Zachary Young, the eldest of five children, was born on March 18, 1907 in Fishponds, Bristol, England, to Philip Young and Constance Maria Lloyd Young. His father's family were yeoman farmers in Gloucestershire and Somerset, becoming prosperous in the eighteenth and nineteenth centuries. His mother's ancestors were Welsh, and they became industrialists and bankers in Birmingham and the West Midlands.

Research on Octopus and Squid Flourishes in Naples

In 1928, Young graduated in zoology at Oxford University. His interest in octopus research led him to the Zoological Station of Naples, which was the first international marine biological observatory in Europe. Young's first paper, on the regeneration of the nerves of octopus, was published in Italian in 1929. It was also at this time that he began research that led to the discovery of the giant nerve fibers of the squid. His studies of squid, which were described in various papers published during the 1930s, provided the basis for the research into the study of nerve impulses in higher animals. "In a squid, the whole jet propulsion system is worked by just *two* nerve cells; but the learning part of the squid's brain has many millions, as has that of an octopus. Multiplicity is a prime clue to the nature of memory," Young wrote in his book, *Philosophy and the Brain.* In 1945, Young was appointed to the Chair of Anatomy at University College London (U.C.L.), a post he held until 1974. Upon his retirement, he chose to work in the Psychology Department at Oxford, where he continued to do experimental work on octopus and squid.

Young's appointment to the chair of anatomy at U.C.L. marked a departure for the college, which previously had sought traditional anatomists for this position. However, by the time of his appointment, Young had acquired a considerable reputation as a researcher on the physiology of lampreys, the nervous system of cephalopods, the autonomic nervous system, as well as the regeneration of mammalian nerves, which assumed much importance during the Second World War. During his tenure as chair, Young continued his research on the octopus. "He must be the first man to have made a really detailed study of the brain of an invertebrate. Perhaps he has reached a greater understanding of the brain of a single type of animal than any other biologist, and it was a stroke of genius on his part to choose such a fascinating and intelligent creature," wrote the editors of *Essays on the Nervous System,* a book dedicated to Young on the occasion of his sixty-seventh birthday.

Young's research touched many people through his books and also through the radio lectures he gave on the British Broadcasting Corporation (BBC). The first of these, the Reith Lectures, were given in 1950 and later published in book form as *Doubt and Certainty in Science.* Young, who had sent a copy of the Reith lectures to the English writer Lewis Mumford, commented in a letter to him dated November 28, 1951, "I cannot help feeling that we are at a point where we could develop a new 'science' lying between fields as wide apart as physics, physiology and history. The more I think of it, the more convinced I become that all scientific study is a study of the behaviour of observers and reactors, which, I suppose, is the same as History."

Young's Work at U.C.L. Inspires Colleagues

At the college itself, Young's octopus research, which shed a great deal of light upon the relationship between brain structure and behavior in higher animals, inspired psychiatrists, neurologists, and engineers. One result was a model electronic brain, devised by an electrical engineer named W. K. Taylor. This model was able to discriminate between various shapes, and even between portraits of people. Young continued his work on the reaction of nerves to injury, gathering around him a group of eager young anatomists who went on to become important researchers in the fields of anatomy and neurology. Several years after Young was chosen to head the anatomy department, he persuaded the college to purchase an electron microscope, which had so impressed him at the American embassy in London. Its use threw much light on the study of cell membranes.

Research on Octopus Brain Illuminates Nature of Memory

The research that Young embarked upon in Naples as a young man continued to absorb him. Focusing on the brain of the octopus, Young also analyzed the structure and functions of the various lobes concerned in memory, differentiating between the short- and long-term memory systems. He demonstrated that there are two separate sets of lobes for recording information about visual and tactile events. Both sets are organized on the same principles, allowing the signals of the results of actions (pleasure and pain) to provide the information for inductive forecasting of the best course of future action. From this work, Young formulated a theory about the units that accumulate in the memory by the release of inhibitory substances, which limit the possible outputs for the classifying cells of the receptors. These researches have illuminated one of the most complex and most challenging of all biological problems—the nature of memory. During his tenure at U.C.L., Young divided his time between research and teaching; one of the first things he did as department chairman was to revise the teaching of gross anatomy. As a result, he substantially reduced the burden it imposed on medical students. In addition, Young played an important role in developing B.Sc. courses in

anatomy at the college, thus offering opportunities to young biologists both within and without the medical field.

Young continued his research on cephalopods through his retirement. He returned to the lab to study the autonomic nervous system of bony fish, and he continued to produce new editions of his textbooks. At the time of his death, he was working with Marion Nixon on a new book to be called *The Brains and Lives of Cephalopods.*

Young married Phyllis Elizabeth Heaney in 1938. They had one son and two daughters before her death in 1987. He subsequently married Raymonde May, with whom he had one daughter. Young wrote numerous scientific papers and books, and delivered several notable lectures. He received many awards and medals and was made an honorary fellow of numerous academies and societies both in the U.K. and abroad. Young died on July 4, 1997, at the age of 90.

SELECTED WRITINGS BY YOUNG:

Books

Doubt and Certainty in Science. Oxford: Oxford University Press, 1960.
From Molecule to Man. New York: Crown, 1969.
Philosophy and the Brain. Oxford: Oxford University Press, 1987.

FURTHER READING:

Books

Bellairs, R. and E. G. Gray, eds. *Essays on the Nervous System.* Oxford: Clarendon Press, 1974.

Periodicals

"Professor J.Z. Young" (obituary). *Times (London)* (9 July 1997).

Other

Letter from J. Z. Young to Lewis Mumford, dated 28 November 1951.

Sketch by Rayma Prince

Lai-Sang Young
1952–
Chinese mathematician

Lai–Sang Young keeps a low profile outside the field of mathematics, but her investigations into the statistical parameters of dynamical systems broke through a mathematical bottleneck that had existed for several years. For this achievement, Young received the 1993 Ruth Lyttle Satter Prize in mathematics. She also won a National Science Foundation Faculty Award for Women Scientists and Engineers, which funds her teaching and research over a number of years.

Lai–Sang Young was born in Hong Kong in 1952. Before emigrating to the United States at an unknown date, her mainly Cantonese education included English classes from a variety of schoolteachers. Her higher education was received in America, however. Young earned a bachelor's degree from the University of Wisconsin at Madison in 1973, and both her M.A. and Ph.D. from the University of California at Berkeley over the ensuing five years.

Young began a teaching career that took her from Northwestern in 1978, to Michigan State in 1980, then on to concurrent posts at the University of Arizona and the University of California at Los Angeles (UCLA). As a recipient of a Sloan Fellowship during 1985–86, she taught at the Universitat Bielefeld in Germany. Young also held visiting positions at institutions at Warwick in England and Berkeley's Mathematical Science Research Institute, and at the Institute for Advanced Study in Princeton, New Jersey, during the 1980s.

Specializes in Ergodic Theory

Young specializes in a field that is fairly new in applied mathematics. In the realm of systems analysis, a rigorous computational method to measure the complexity of non–uniform systems is under current investigation. The subspecialty devoted to the statistical properties of dynamical systems is called "ergodic theory." The probability of the recurrence of any state in a model and the chance that any sample is equally representative of the whole make up the key questions in ergodic theory. The goal is to be able to model deterministic systems in other disciplines, such as anthropology, with a model that is random yet statistically regular.

With this goal in mind, Young has focused on the dynamics of strange attractors. A Henon attractor is a fractal with two variables, an a parameter and a b parameter, that looks something like a fuzzy sketch of a boomerang. It is considered one of the simplest dynamic systems that does not possess a stable periodic cycle. In a joint paper with a colleague, Young showed that a subset of the fractal turns out to have "a common distribution to the limit." This statistical norm is what allows the interdimensional figure to show up on a computer screen as a boomerang shape. Young produced similar work with quadratic maps, another set of simple yet non-uniform systems, that clarified previously contradictory evidence. Finding predictability in chaos was an achievement termed "both unexpected and deep" in Young's Satter Prize citation.

"Embarrassing" Lack of Examples Leads to Breakthrough

Since the 1970s, mathematicians have been able to measure "uniformly hyperbolic" systems, and by the 1980s a number of researchers had come up with an ergodic theory for non–uniform counterparts. This work built a platform for generalizing about both types in terms of being able to predict an outcome for an attractor regardless of any initial condition. That means that no matter where researchers start, they wind up with the same general results. However, a natural invariant measure—the necessary statistical pattern—could not be found for a specific non–uniform case. As Young had stated during her response to the Satter Prize citation, the "lack of examples was starting to get a little embarrassing" for everyone. Investigations into the Henon attractor maps, considered the most likely suspects at that juncture, were already underway when Young was invited to join. She and a teammate constructed invariant measures for the parameters of a Henon, considered the first examples of their kind.

Young has participated in a number of events that bring mathematicians together in formal and informal settings. She delivered the invited address at the 1985 meeting of the American Mathematical Society (AMS). In 1994, she presented at a workshop on lattice dynamics and ergodic theory at the Mathematics Research Centre of Warwick. As the second recipient of the Satter Prize, Young kept the tradition, begun with **Margaret Dusa McDuff**, of helping to select the next winner, **Sun–Yung Alice Chang**, in 1995. Young was most recently part of the AMS Committee on Summer Institutes and Special Symposia, to organize the 1997 Summer Research Institute on differential geometry and control at the University of Colorado.

Gary Froyland, an Australian Ph.D. who shares Young's interest in topological entropy, was at first surprised at how approachable she was. Froyland's supervisor at the University of Western Australia asked Young, considered a world leader in her field, to spare some time at a conference. Young not only met and offered some pertinent explanations to the student, she invited him to UCLA. She also helped him find accommodations there and cover his expenses. During his stay, Froyland was impressed with Young's humor, clarity of mind, and teaching style. In her lectures and consultations Young strives to keep attention to precisely accurate detail without sacrificing the accessibility of everyday examples. Froyland reports that Young is a bit of a mimic, at least when it comes to imitating the accents of all her former English teachers, including a range of British natives and an American priest. The two mathematicians also discovered a shared interest in table tennis. A hint of Young's high personal standards came to light when she admitted she was once ranked among the top 20 female ping–pong players in the United States, but retired at the age of 25 when she felt her reflexes were beginning to slow.

SELECTED WRITINGS BY YOUNG:

Periodicals

(With Huyi Hu) "Nonexistence of SBR Measures for Some Diffeomorphisms that Are 'Almost Anosov'." (31K, TeX) *The Mathematical Physics Preprint Archive.* http://www.ma.utexas.edu/mp_arc/a/97–30

FURTHER READING:

Periodicals

"1993 Ruth Lyttle Satter Prize." *Notices of the American Mathematical Society* 40, no. 3 (March 1993): 229–30.

Other

Froyland, Gary, in an electronic mail interview with Jennifer Kramer conducted July 12, 1997.

Gary Froyland Web Page. http://maths.uwa.edu.au/~gary/mycv.html (August 15, 1997).

"Lai–Sang Young." *Biographies of Women Mathematicians.* http://www.scottlan.edu/lriddle/women/chronol.htm (August 15, 1997).

Sketch by Jennifer Kramer

William Henry Young
1863–1942
English applied mathematician

William Henry Young made advances in several areas of mathematics, but his most significant contribution was the development of a calculus approach that has been adopted by nearly all authors of advanced calculus textbooks since 1910. Together with his wife, **Grace Chisolm Young**, he published widely on a variety of mathematical topics.

The eldest child of Henry Young and Hephzibah Jeal, Young was born in London, England, on October 20, 1863, into a family that had been prominent in banking for several generations. He received his early education at the City of London School. The headmaster of the school, Edwin A. Abbott, author of a mathematical fantasy novel entitled *Flatland*, recognized Young as a skilled mathematician. Young chose to focus on mathematics in his college career at the Peterhouse College of Cambridge University, where he commenced study in 1881. He was expected to place as the senior wrangler, or first place, on the 1884 mathematical tripos, but he only placed fourth. Young later contended that he did not place as expected because he refused to limit his scope to the intensive study of mathematics required to excel on the tripos, and, in addition to mathematics, chose to pursue other intellectual avenues as well as athletics. He studied the works of Molière and competed for a Smith prize in the field of theology rather than mathematics. Young won the prize.

From 1886 to 1892, Young was a fellow of Peterhouse, although he held no official post at the school. Rather than immersing himself in research, Young chose the more lucrative path of private mathematics instruction of undergraduates. During this time, he also laid the foundation for a professional and romantic partnership with one of his students, Grace Chisholm, a student at the Girton College of Cambridge who obtained her first class degree in mathematics in 1892 and obtained senior wrangler status on the mathematical tripos. They were married in 1896.

The Youngs lived primarily in Göttingen, Germany, where Grace earned her doctorate, until 1908, when they moved to Switzerland. They lived first in Geneva and later moved to Lausanne. Young did not seriously pursue research until after his marriage, however, beginning around 1900. Between then and 1924, however, he wrote more than 200 papers with his wife. He devoted significant time to the study ofreal functions, independently discovering what came to be known as Lebesgue integration. Unfortunately, he did not make the discovery until two years after **Henri Lebesgue**, and although Young's definition of integration was different in form from Lebesgue's, it was basically equivalent to it. Young made significant contributions to the further development of this area of study, however, most notably by establishing a method of monotone sequences as used in the Stieltjes integral. Young also made advances in Fourier analysis and measure theory.

Young's career was also noteworthy because of his professional collaboration with his wife, whose doctorial thesis focused on algebraic groups ofspherical trigonometry. The Youngs embarked on projects together prior to their marriage, with Grace conducting most of the research while William provided financial support through his private tutoring. Due to the educational climate at the time, most papers written by the couple were attributed solely to William. This arrangement, with Grace undertaking the bulk of the research, may have hindered William later in life, as his lack of research credits may have been a factor in his inability to obtain positions of the high quality he desired.

One of the most important works to come out of the Youngs' collaboration was their second textbook, *The Theory of Sets of Points*. While set study is now a foundation for studies in all areas of mathematics, it was not yet commonly regarded at the time. On the whole, the mathematical community of the time overlooked this contribution, although **Georg Cantor**, one of the foremost experts in modern set theory, hailed the work.

Young returned to instruction in 1913, when he accepted part–time chair positions at the universities of Calcutta and Liverpool, and a position as professor at Aberystwyth. He was named an honorary doctor of the universities of Calcutta, Geneva, and Strasbourg. Among his many honors was the Sylvester Medal of the Royal Society, bestowed upon him in 1928. He also served as president of the International Union of Mathematicians from 1929 to 1936.

With the travels he undertook to earn a living, Young frequently found himself away from home for extended periods of time. The spring of 1940 found Young in

Switzerland and his wife in England. Although they anticipated no problems reuniting, the escalation of World War II and the downfall of France intervened. For the last two years of his life, Young was separated from his family, which in addition to Grace included two sons and three daughters (a third son was killed in 1917). He died on July 7, 1942, in Lausanne, Switzerland.

In addition to their large body of research, his and Grace's legacy included two children who continued study in the field of mathematics, Professor Laurence Chisholm Young and Dr. Rosalind Cecily Tanner, who both practiced pure mathematics.

SELECTED WRITINGS BY YOUNG:

Books

(With Grace Chisholm Young) *The First Book of Geometry,* reprinted 1969.
(With Grace Chisholm Young) *The Theory of Sets of Points*, 1906; second edition 1972.
The Fundamental Theorems of the Differential Calculus, 1910.

FURTHER READING:

Books

Pycior, Helena M., Nancy G. Slack, and Pnina G. Abir–Am, editors. *Creative Couples in the Sciences*. New Brunswick: Rutgers University Press, 1996, pp. 126–40.

Periodicals

"William Henry Young." *Journal of the London Mathematical Society* 17 (1942): 218–37.
"William Henry Young." *Obituary Notices of Fellows of the Royal Society of London* 3 (1943): 307–23.

Sketch by Kristin Palm

Hideki Yukawa
1907–1981
Japanese physicist

Hideki Yukawa was the first citizen of Japan to receive a Nobel Prize, an award given to him in 1949 for his theory of the meson, the subatomic particle that binds the nucleus' protons and neutrons. In addition to that honor, Yukawa received the Imperial prize of the Japan Academy in 1940, the Lomonosov Gold Medal of the Soviet Academy of Sciences in 1964, the Order of Merit of the Federal Republic of Germany in 1964, and the Order of the Rising Sun (Japan) in 1977.

Hideki Yukawa was born Hideki Ogawa in Tokyo on January 23, 1907. He was the fifth of seven children born to Takuji and Koyuki Ogawa. His father was employed at the Geological Survey Bureau in Tokyo at the time of Hideki's birth and a year later was appointed professor of geology at Kyoto Imperial University. In his autobiography, *Tabibito (The Traveler)*, Yukawa describes the experience of growing up in a large household which included, in addition to his parents and siblings, three grandparents. One of these, his maternal grandmother, had once taught at the samurai school at Tokugawa Castle and was a particularly strong influence in Yukawa's life. She taught him to read and write kanji (Chinese pictographs) before he entered elementary school.

Learns Modern Physics

Yukawa attended the Third High School in Kyoto from 1923 to 1926. There he was a classmate of future Nobel Laureate **Sin-Itiro Tomonaga** who, for his work on quantum electrodynamics, would go on to share the Nobel Prize with **Paul Dirac**. After graduation, Yukawa entered Kyoto Imperial University, where he majored in physics. Yukawa's interest in the subject had been aroused in high school when he discovered a number of books on quantum mechanics and relativity in the school library. One of the most influential of the books he found, **Max Planck**'s *Introduction to Theoretical Physics,* he was able to read only after he had taught himself German.

In 1929, Yukawa received his master's degrees from Kyoto, and then stayed on as a research assistant in the laboratory of Kajuro Tamaki. Then, in 1932, Yukawa accepted an appointment as lecturer in physics at Kyoto. Just prior to accepting his new teaching post, Hideki married Sumi Yukawa, a classical Japanese dancer. He adopted his new wife's family name and went to live with them in Osaka. The Yukawas eventually had two sons, Harumi and Takaai.

In 1933 Yukawa accepted a second position as lecturer in physics, this time at Osaka Imperial University. He continued teaching at Osaka for the next five years, working on his doctorate in physics at the same time. In 1936 he was promoted to associate professor of physics and, two years later, was awarded his Ph.D.

Proposes the Meson Theory

It was during his years at Osaka that Yukawa made the discovery for which he is best known, the meson theory. The early 1930s were a period of some confusion for physicists interested in the atomic nucleus. They had learned from **Werner Karl Heisenberg** that nuclei consist of only two particles, protons and neutrons. Of these two, only protons have electrical charge, a positive charge. It would appear, then, that nuclei should be inherently unstable: the electrostatic force of repulsion among protons should, according to classical theory, tend to blow the nucleus apart.

Yukawa became interested in this problem in about 1930. It occurred to Yukawa that there must be some force far stronger than the electromagnetic force that could hold nucleons (protons and neutrons) together. As he developed his theory, Yukawa came to the conclusion that such a force must take the form of a particle, carrying a force of attraction back and forth between pairs of nucleons.

In his calculations, Yukawa found that this force-carrying particle would have a mass about 200 times greater than the electron, but only one-ninth that of a proton or neutron. Because of the particle's intermediary mass, it was later given the name *meson,* from the Greek for "middle." (Scientists actually considered naming the particle the "yukon," in honor of its discoverer, but discarded it to avoid possible geographical confusion.)

Yukawa first announced his theory of the meson at scientific meetings in Osaka and Tokyo in October and November, 1934, and then in the *Proceedings of the Physico-Mathematical Society of Japan* in February, 1935. For about two years his ideas remained largely ignored; then, in 1937, **Carl D. Anderson** and Seth Neddermeyer discovered a particle that appeared to have many of the properties predicted by Yukawa. The scientific community's initial enthusiasm for this discovery soon died out, however, as additional studies showed that Anderson's meson—later named the mu-meson, or muon—differed in some fundamental ways from Yukawa's prediction. It was not until 1947 that Yukawa's work was fully confirmed. That year, **Cecil Frank Powell** found the Yukawa particle—now called the pi-meson—in a cosmic ray shower. Two years later, Yukawa was awarded the 1949 Nobel Prize in physics for his discovery of the meson—an honor that brought substantial pride to the war-torn Japanese scientific community.

In the mean time, Yukawa had returned to Kyoto University where he had been appointed professor of theoretical physics in 1939. The year he was awarded the Nobel Prize, Yukawa came to the United States on a one-year visiting professorship at the Institute for Advanced Studies in Princeton, New Jersey. At the end of that year he accepted an appointment at Columbia University, where he remained for four more years. In 1946 he founded the scientific journal *Progress of Theoretical Physics,* for which he also served as editor.

In 1953 Columbia awarded Yukawa tenure, but he decided nonetheless to return to Japan. There he assumed his previous post at Kyoto University, as well as the newly-created position as director of the Research Institute for Fundamental Physics, an institute established specifically for him by the Japanese government. Although he retired officially from his academic positions in 1970, Yukawa continued to write, speak, and edit his journal. He was also active in organizations that promoted the peaceful use of science and technology: for example, in 1955 he, along with other scientists, signed the Russell-Einstein paper advocating the settling of political disputes through peaceful means; Yukawa was also in attendance at a number of Pugwash Conferences, in which scientists discussed options for disarmament. He died from pneumonia in Kyoto on September 8, 1981.

SELECTED WRITINGS BY YUKAWA:

Books

Yukawa Hideki Jishenshu, (title means Selected Works of Hideki Yukawa), Asahi Shimbunsha, 1971.
Creativity and Intuition: A Physicist Looks at East and West, Kodansha, International, 1973.
Hideki Yukawa: Scientific Works, Iwanami Shoten, 1979.
Tabibito, (title means The Traveler), translated by L. Brown and R. Yoshida, [Singapore], 1982.

Periodicals

Proceedings of the Physico-Mathematical Society of Japan, On the Interaction of Elementary Particles, Volume 17, 1935, p. 48.

FURTHER READING:

Books

Dictionary of Scientific Biography, Scribner, 1982, pp. 999–1005.
Heathcote, Niels H. de V., *Nobel Prize Winners in Physics, 1901–1950,* Henry Schuman, 1953, pp. 446–447.
Heathcote, Niels H. de V., *McGraw-Hill Modern Men of Science,* McGraw-Hill, 1984, pp. 360–361.
Heathcote, Niels H. de V., *Nobel Prize Winners,* H. W. Wilson, 1987, pp. 1155–1157.
Weber, Robert L., *Pioneers of Science: Nobel Prize Winners in Physics,* American Institute of Physics, 1980, pp. 133–134.

Sketch by David E. Newton

Z

Lotfi Asker Zadeh
1921–
American electrical engineer

Lotfi Asker Zadeh, who described himself in an interview with Jeanne Spriter James as an "American, mathematically oriented, electrical engineer of Iranian descent, born in Russia," is responsible for the development of fuzzy logic and fuzzy set theory. Zadeh is also known for his research in system theory, information processing, artificial intelligence, expert systems, natural language understanding, and the theory of evidence. His first two papers that set forth the fuzzy theories, "Fuzzy Sets" and "Outline of a New Approach to the Analysis of Complex Systems and Decision Processes," have been listed as "Citation Classics" by the *Citation Index,* a publication that counts and lists those papers which have been cited most often in the writings of others. Zadeh received the prestigious Honda Prize—an award that was introduced in 1977 to honor technology that advances a "humane civilization"—from the Honda Foundation in Japan in 1989. That same year Japan's Ministry of Trade and Industry, along with almost fifty corporate sponsors, opened a laboratory for International Fuzzy Engineering Research (LIFE) with a budget of approximately $40 million for a six-year period. Six months after its initiation, Zadeh became an advisor to LIFE. Although fuzzy theory has received less attention in the United States, industrial applications have begun to appear in U.S. organizations as well.

Zadeh was born February 4, 1921, in Baku, a city on the Caspian Sea in the Soviet Republic of Azerbaijan. Originally named Lotfi Aliaskerzadeh, he simplified his name to Lotfi Asker Zadeh when he arrived in the United States. His father, Rahim Aliaskerzadeh (Asker), was a correspondent for Iranian newspapers and also an importer-exporter; his mother, Fannie (Fania) Koriman Aliaskerzadeh (Asker), was a pediatrician. Zadeh and his parents settled in Teheran (Tehrän), the capital city of Iran, in 1931, when he was ten years old. Zadeh explained in an interview that the culture shock he felt as a result of this move was caused by the change from a school which promoted "atheism and the persecution of anyone religiously oriented, to a religious school run by American missionaries where he attended chapel every morning." Zadeh was taught in Persian—a language he had to learn after his arrival in Iran—at American College, the Presbyterian missionary school. He attended this school for eight years and then took the

entrance exams for the University of Teheran, scoring third in the country. As an electrical engineering major he was first in his class his freshman and sophomore years. However, the disruption of World War II was felt at the university and in the electrical engineering department, which graduated only three students, Zadeh among them, in 1942.

During the year after his graduation, Zadeh worked with his father supplying construction materials to the U.S. Army in Iran. His contacts with Americans made him decide to move to the United States in 1943. Arriving in 1944, he enrolled at the Massachusetts Institute of Technology (MIT), which awarded him an M.A. in electrical engineering in 1946. During his years at MIT, the university was abuzz with excitement over developments in cybernetics, information and communication theory, and advances in computer applications. Zadeh caught the excitement as well and enrolled in the doctoral program at Columbia University. At the same time he was appointed an instructor there. He received his Ph.D. in 1949. Rising from instructor to professor of electrical engineering, he was on staff at Columbia from 1946 to 1959, when he moved on to the University of California at Berkeley.

Develops Fuzzy Theory

In 1963 Zadeh was appointed chairman of the electrical engineering department at Berkeley. It was in the following years that he developed the first outlines of fuzzy theory. Fuzzy logic is the logic that underlies inexact or approximate reasoning, and it is most usefully seen as a branch of set theory. While traditional set theory works with sets of clearly defined objects, fuzzy theory deals with objects that belong to sets with what has been called varying degrees of membership. The set of tall trees, for instance, comprises trees that are tall, trees that are very tall, and trees that are not quite so tall. While the human mind can swiftly make qualitative—and therefore to some extent subjective—judgments of what is tall, machines, particularly computers, could traditionally be programmed only to deal with quantitative measures. Fuzzy logic as Zadeh developed it, however, prescribes the rules by which linguistic models containing qualitative judgments are translated into computer algorithms. In effect, machines can then be programmed to process "approximate" data and deal with the gray areas of life.

Although fuzzy theory was enthusiastically received and applied in Japan, China, and several European countries, it was greeted with a great deal of skepticism in the United States. Many scientists claimed that probability theory was already successfully being used to tackle the same problems that fuzzy theory solved. However, probability theory deals with uncertainty arising in a quantitative, mechanistic universe, while fuzzy theory clarifies uncertainty that follows from the subjective aspects of human cognition. Recently, fuzzy theory has gained a foothold in the United States as well. The most important application of the theory to be developed in the United States is AT&T's expert system on a chip. Hiroyuki Watanabe, the computer scientist who built the "first known expert system on a chip" with Masaki Togai, said in an interview with Jeanne Spriter James that manipulation of information is easier with fuzzy logic, which he described as a sophisticated method that allows for a minimum of engineering time to develop applications. Daniel McNeill and Paul Freiberger, in their book *Fuzzy Logic,* sum up Zadeh's contribution to the world of science as follows: "Fuzzy logic is practical in the highest sense: direct, inexpensive, bountiful. It forsakes not precision, but pointless precision. It abandons an either/or hairline that never existed and brightens technology at the cost of a tiny blur. It is neither a dream like AI [artificial intelligence] nor a dead end, a little trick for washers and cameras. It is here today, and no matter what the brand name on the label, it will be here tomorrow."

In 1968 Zadeh took a sabbatical from Berkeley. He spent half a year at IBM and another six months at MIT. When he returned from his leave, he began teaching only computer science courses at Berkeley. Since then he has spent periods as a visiting scientist at the IBM Research Laboratory in San Jose, California, in 1973 and 1978, as a visiting scholar at the Artificial Intelligence Center of SRI International at Menlo Park, California, in 1981, and as a visiting member of the Center for the Study of Language and Information at Stanford University in 1988.

Zadeh's research has earned him many honors and awards, including the Congress Award from the International Congress on Applied Systems, Research and Cybernetics (1980), the Outstanding Paper Award from the International Symposium on Multiple-valued Logic (1984), and the Berkeley Citation, from the University of California at Berkeley (1991). Zadeh is a member of many organizations, including the American Association for Artificial Intelligence, the World Council on Cybernetics, the American Mathematics Society, the National Academy of Engineers, and the Russian Academy of Natural Sciences. He has received honorary doctorates in the United States and Europe, from universities including the State University of New York in Binghamton, Paul Sabatier University in France, Dortmund University in Germany and the University of Granada in Spain. Zadeh still supervises doctoral dissertations at Berkeley and keeps a busy calendar of speaking engagements. He founded the Berkeley Initiative in Soil Computing (called the BISC group) in 1991 and serves as its director, and is a member of the editorial boards of forty journals.

Zadeh married Fay Sand, his childhood sweetheart from Iran, on March 21, 1946, and they have two children, Stella and Norman. He is an accomplished amateur photog-

rapher, specializing particularly in portraiture, and has made portraits of many famous scientists and artists.

SELECTED WRITINGS BY ZADEH:

Books

Linear System Theory, McGraw, 1963.
System Theory, McGraw, 1969.
Fuzzy Sets and Applications: Selected Papers, edited by R. R. Yager, S. Ovchinnikov, R. M. Tong and H. T. Nguyen, Wiley, 1987.

Periodicals

Information and Control, Fuzzy Sets, June, 1965, pp. 338–353.
IEEE Transactions on Systems, Man and Cybernetics, Outline of a New Approach to the Analysis of Complex Systems and Decision Processes, January, 1973, pp. 28–44.
Communications of the ACM (Association of Computer Machinery), Fuzzy Logic, Neural Neutral Networks and Soil Computing, March, 1994.

FURTHER READING:

Books

Klir, George J., and Tina A. Folger, *Fuzzy Sets, Uncertainty and Information,* Prentice-Hall, 1988.
Kosko, Bart, *Neural Networks and Fuzzy Systems,* Prentice-Hall, 1991.
McNeill, Daniel, and Paul Freiberger, *Fuzzy Logic,* Simon & Schuster, 1993.

Periodicals

Dvorak, Wes, *Bell Labs News,* Fuzzy Logic Aids New Expert Chip, January 26, 1986.
Dvorak, Wes, *London Times,* July 17, 1992, p. 26E.
Dvorak, Wes, *New York Times,* April 2, 1989, p. 1.

Other

Watanabe, Hiroyuki, *Interview with Jeanne Spriter James conducted August 23,* 1993.
Zadeh, Lotfi Asker, *Interview with Jeanne Spriter James conducted February 28,* 1994.

Sketch by Jeanne Spriter James

Paul Charles Zamecnik
1912–
American physician and genetic researcher

Paul Zamecnik was one of the first scientists to explore the field of genetics. Beginning his work shortly after the structure of deoxyribonucleic acid (DNA) was discovered in 1953, Zamecnik was the first to describe how the micromachinery of each cell turns the genetic code of DNA into the proteins that build cells and make them work. His groundbreaking research, spanning more than 60 years, opened up vast new areas of inquiry in genetics and pharmaceuticals, especially the hunt for "gene therapy" and drugs that work on the genetic level.

Son of a Musical Family

Zamecnik was born in Cleveland, Ohio, on November 22, 1912. His grandfather was a bandleader and composer who had emigrated from Prague, in what is now the Czech Republic, to Cleveland, where there was a significant population of what were then known as Bohemians. Zamecnik (pronounced ZAM-es-nick) remembers sitting on his father's shoulders as his grandfather's marching band paraded past on Cleveland's Euclid Avenue.

Zamecnik's father was a banker in Cleveland, and Paul decided he wanted to be a doctor. On the advice of a high school teacher whom he admired, he went to Dartmouth College in Hanover, New Hampshire. "I was a city boy, why not try the country? I liked it there," he told contributor Karl Leif Bates in an October 1997 telephone interview. Dartmouth enabled students to complete their premedical curriculum in three years and then go on for two years of medical school there, which Zamecnik did. He then transferred to Harvard University in 1933 to finish his last two years of medical school, earning his M.D. in 1936.

Upon earning this degree, Zamecnik took a departure from the normal course of study, which was to change his career. He took a research-oriented residency at C.P. Huntington Memorial Hospital, a 24-bed cancer facility owned by Harvard. "I thought I would become a surgeon, but I was rather dazzled by the prospect of working in a laboratory and seeing some medical patients," he told Bates. "This idea of pursuing research was rather interesting." But cancer research, at the time, was thought to be a dead-end career.

Just to be sure he wasn't missing anything in medicine, or Cleveland, Zamecnik took a general medicine internship at Western Reserve University Hospital in Cleveland. But from then on, his career has been strongly focused on the lab. Following the internship, he took a fellowship post at the Carlsberg Laboratories in Copenhagen, a biochemistry lab that was "a mecca for Americans at that time." One of his professors at Carlsberg was heard telling a colleague

"that young man is throwing his medical education down the sink," Zamecnik remembers. He had to leave Copenhagen in 1940, as the Nazis began to take over Europe. Americans were neutral in the war at the time, but were having trouble getting their fellowship checks from home cashed.

He returned to the States to work at the Rockefeller Institute under biochemist Max Bergmann, who was trying to figure out how proteins were made in the cell and what their structures and functions were. Zamecnik thought it was a crucial area to study to advance medicine, because surgeons could operate on a disorder after the fact, "but had to leave the rest up to nature." With only one antibiotic on the market at the time, the biochemical approach to medicine was hardly considered.

Bergmann's idea was that the same enzymes involved in breaking proteins apart were also somehow responsible for putting proteins together. He had found a set of enzymes inside cells that were complementary to known break-down enzymes of the digestive system. Bergmann thought that the proteins were so specific that they might synthesize proteins under the proper conditions. Interestingly, Bergmann had initially rejected Zamecnik's query about working in his lab because he was a medical doctor, not an organic chemist. But after his experience in Copenhagen, "I had a little stardust on my shoulders from Carlsberg, so he decided to take me." When the war reached the United States in late 1941 and early 1942, though, plans changed. Zamecnik returned to Harvard to work in the Huntington Labs on war-related research, like separating and typing blood.

Still Puzzled by Source of Proteins

As the war ended, Zamecnik was still puzzling over protein synthesis. "Nothing was known about protein synthesis, there was no map to go by. It took up one paragraph in a biochemical textbook," he said. Why, he wondered, does a tumor cell continue to multiply wildly, when other cells seem to know when to quit? "So, I thought, 'there's something wrong with the regulation, but we've got to get inside the cell to figure out what it is.'"

Two key things had happened during the war. First, a scientist at Massachusetts General Hospital, **Fritz Lippman** proposed that proteins are made by a different set of enzymes, and second, the government's Oak Ridge Labs had developed Carbon-14, a very useful radioactive probe. "So we decided to find out whether Bergmann was right or whether Lippman was right." Using a marker made by attaching C-14 to an amino acid, Zamecnik and colleagues at Harvard found that aminos were the building blocks of proteins, but that assembly would require quite a bit of energy. He then identified where the energy for that assembly came from, adenosine triphosphate, or ATP.

"We felt quite confident that Lippman was right, and that there were a different set of enzymes involved." From 1948 to '52 he worked on finding a cell-free system which produced protein in the presence of an energy donor. This work "created a whole new area of biochemistry. One pearl after another dropped out, as the days went on. It was very exciting."

A Glimpse into the Cell

In 1953, **James Watson** and **Francis Crick** first proposed the double-helix structure of deoxyribonucleic acid (DNA). Now scientists had a better idea about how DNA could convey information and duplicate itself reliably, but still no one knew how that information was turned into action inside the cell. In late 1955, and early '56, Zamecnik proposed the existence of "transfer RNA," a ribonucleic acid like DNA that could form a complement to the genetic strand and carry its information from the nucleus of the cell out into the cytoplasm, where proteins are made. Then he announced the discovery of ribosomes, small globular bodies in the cell's cytoplasm that appear to "read" the stretch of transfer RNA and bring in the amino acid building blocks it specifies to assemble the protein. "It seemed to be a spool on which the reaction took place," Zamecnik said. Then two competing labs were able to put the finishing touches on Zamecnik's idea, decoding the language of transfer RNA and identifying yet another code, messenger RNA, which worked between DNA and transfer RNA.

For the next 20 years Zamecnik turned his attention to research which created a whole new field of inquiry for the pharmaceutical industry, fighting diseases of protein synthesis by jamming the cell's DNA signals. The mechanism for this was something now called "antisense DNA," a complementary short strand of DNA that can be used to bind to a piece of messenger RNA and stop it from working. Zamecnik targeted a virus, Rous Sarcoma Virus, which caused cancer in chickens. As he struggled to sequence the virus's genes and then make thecomplementary DNA sequences which would prevent it from copying itself, the tools of biotechnology took great strides forward.

By 1978, Zamecnik finally had his breakthrough against Rous Sarcoma, a strand of man-made DNA that blocked the virus' ability to copy itself. Other scientists had figured out how to sequence genes, chop them into manageable pieces, and make newsequences to order. Using these new tools, Zamecnik was finally able to make his antisense approach work. "Our results indicated that the small pieces could get in and affect the metabolism of cells. I was astonished that the (man-made sequences) did get into the cell, and blocked the replication of the Rouse's Sarcoma cells." He has been called "the father of antisense," but Zamecnik said he fought the use of the term for years, since it sounds so much like "nonsense."

Drug companies have been striving, since his 1978 breakthrough, to devise man-made antisense strands that will effectively block the genetic signals that cause protein-related diseases. While most drugs in use today treat the disorder after an errant protein has been manufactured by the cell, the antisense approach is believed to have great promise in the treatment of hepatitis, cancers, coronary artery disease and many other disorders, before they occur in the cell.

Zamecnik was a professor of oncologic medicine and director of the Huntington Lab at Harvard from 1956 to 1979. He was also a physician at Massachussets General Hospital for the same period. Upon retiring from Harvard, he joined the Worcester Foundation for Experimental Biology in Shrewsbury, Massachusetts, as principal scientist. In 1989, he founded a company, Hybridon, to pursue antisense drugs. He left the Worcester Foundation in July 1997 when it was acquired by the University of Massachusetts and went to work at Hybridon full time, keeping long hours in the lab well into his 80s. "I'm too old to retire now," he told Bates a month before his 85th birthday. "I've muffed it. I'm not very good at gardening nor at hammering nails and I don't consider this work. It's interesting. Like watching a horse race."

When he received the first ever-awarded Albert Lasker Award for Special Achievement in Medical Science in 1996, Zamecnik was cited for his "brilliant and original science that revolutionized biochemistry and created an entirely new field of scientific inquiry." He was also awarded a National Medal of Science in 1991, The National Cancer Society National Award in 1968, and several honorary degrees.

Zamecnik has been married to Mary Zamecnik since 1936, and she still assists him in the lab. They have three children.

FURTHER READING:

Other

"Welcome to Hybridon, Inc." Oct. 1997. http://www.hybridon.com/ (28 Oct. 1997)

Herald-Sun Newspapers (North Carolina) "Paul C. Zamecnik, M.D." http://www.herald-sun.com/cityomed/com/zamecnik.html. (16 October, 1997)

Sketch by Karl Leif Bates

E. C. Zeeman
1925–
English mathematician

A pure mathematician E. C. Zeeman has devoted most of his career to various aspects of topology—a type of geometry that examines the properties of shapes in many dimensions. He is best known for his work in catastrophe theory and his attempts to apply this method of mathematical modelling to other scientific fields, including biology and psychology. In addition to his contributions to mathematical research, Zeeman has proven to be an effective administrator and a successful educator. He joined the University of Warwick in England in 1964, the year it was founded, and built the mathematics department there into an internationally known research center. He has also spent much time teaching mathematics to children, giving talks on both radio and television, and he was knighted in 1991 by Queen Elizabeth II for his leadership role in the advancement of mathematics education. He has been principal of Hertford College at Oxford University since 1988.

Erik Christopher Zeeman was born in Japan on February 4, 1925, to Christian and Christine Bushnell Zeeman. His mother was an English governess and his father a Danish exporter and importer who died when Zeeman was four years old. After his father's death, his mother took him and his sister back to England, where they grew up. In an interview reprinted as "Private Games," Zeeman recalled his mother showing him how to solve a problem using variables when he was seven years old. This was his first introduction to algebra: "I was absolutely flabbergasted at this technique and I've never forgotten it. And then at school maths was always very easy."

When World War II began in 1939 Zeeman was only fourteen. Four years later with the war still raging, he had joined the Royal Air Force, and he served as a Flying Officer until 1947. He entered Christ's College at Cambridge University the year he left the service; he earned his bachelor's degree and remained there until 1953, when he moved to another Cambridge college, Gonville and Caius, as a lecturer. He did his doctoral work in pure mathematics under Shaun Wylie, receiving his Ph.D. in 1954 for a thesis on knots. "I was particularly intrigued," he recalls in "Private Games," "by all the algebraic machinery you need to actually prove knots exist." Zeeman began his research career in what is known as algebraic topolo- gy, using algebra to address geometric problems, such as the question of whether knots can be tied in many dimensions. In his doctoral dissertation, he was not able to prove that a knot could be tied in more than four dimensions, but he returned to the problem seven years later. He used geometry instead of algebra and discovered he could prove it was possible to untie knots in five dimensions. This proof turned out to have many important ramifications for geometric topology, and he had many research students who subsequently earned their doctorates working on theorems suggested by this proof.

But his best known and most controversial work has been in catastrophe theory. First developed by the French mathematician **René Thom** in the 1960s, catastrophe theory creates models to predict the consequences of a chain of events that has certain discontinuous elements. In the *Times Literary Supplement,* Zeeman describes the applications of this theory: "Throughout nature we observe continuous changes giving rise to discontinuous jumps: for example a continuous rise in temperature will cause water to boil suddenly, which is a sudden jump in density." Catastrophe

theory uses multi-dimensional images to model these sudden changes and Zeeman has argued that it can be used in disciplines as disparate as meteorology and behavioral psychology. He has used catastrophe theory to model anorexia nervosa as well as the concept of punctuated equilibria in evolution. In his paper, "On the Psychology of a Hijacker," Zeeman employs the theory to analyze what could be expected from various types of hijacking cases, arguing that mathematics can help make accurate predictions in hostage situations.

Always concerned about the relevance of mathematics, Zeeman became increasingly interested in the intersection between pure and applied mathematics throughout the course of his career. In a talk on British Broadcasting Corporation radio, he once offered an example of the practical applications of topology: if a ball is entirely covered with hair, it would be impossible to comb the hair down smoothly all around it, without leaving a tuft anywhere. He calls this an example of a topological theorem and observes that one consequence of this theorem is that there can never be a stable weather situation: The wind can never be blowing smoothly all around the globe. Zeeman has also made contributions to brain modelling and he has been involved in the development of chaos theory.

Zeeman joined Warwick University when it was founded in 1964 as Foundation Professor and Director of the Mathematics Research Centre. An articulate man, with an ability to command financial support for research projects in mathematics, he was the driving force behind the development of the department there. In 1982 he was awarded the Whitehead Prize for "his personal work and his leadership," according to a citation published in the *Bulletin of the London Mathematical Society.* In building his department at the University of Warwick into an international center for mathematics, he "displayed talents as a manager and a leader exceptional among pure mathematicians," and the citation continues: "The strong British school of geometrical topologists now consists almost entirely of Zeeman's pupils, his pupil's pupils, and so on to the third or fourth generation."

Zeeman is often conscious of the difference between the way mathematicians see their subject and the way others do, and this awareness is part of what has made him an effective educator, not only of doctoral students and undergraduates but also of children and the public in general. In 1978 he delivered the Royal Institution Christmas Lectures—television broadcasts designed to introduce school children to various scientific disciplines. In the 1980s, he delivered the Mathematics Masterclasses for the Royal Institution. The original television broadcasts of these classes have since been released on videotape, and their purpose, as Zeeman writes in "Christmas Lectures and Mathematics Masterclasses," is "to provide enrichment for the more gifted, because today the gifted can be amongst the educationally most deprived."

In addition to the Whitehead Prize and his knighthood in 1991, Zeeman received the Queen's Jubilee Medal in

1977 and the Faraday Medal in 1988. He was elected to the Royal Society in 1975, and he was president of the London Mathematical Society from 1986 to 1988. He was made an honorary fellow of Christ's College, Cambridge in 1989, and he has received honorary degrees from the University of Strasbourg and the University of York.

Zeeman married for the second time in 1960, to Rosemary Gledhill; they have three sons and two daughters. He also has another daughter from a previous marriage. One of his daughters has followed in his footsteps, pursuing a career in mathematics, and he has collaborated with her on some research projects. Zeeman told contributor Jeanne Spriter James that his primary leisure activity is his family. Dressmaking is another of his hobbies and he has even written an academic paper on the subject, called "The Mathematics of Dressmaking." Of mathematics in general, Zeeman says in "Private Games" that "It's a very noble subject. It's probably one of the oldest and noblest of man's activities. And I would identify, historically, with that very long tradition."

SELECTED WRITINGS BY ZEEMAN:

Books

Catastrophe Theory: Selected Papers, 1972–1977, Addison Wesley, 1977.

Periodicals

Bulletin of the American Mathematical Society, Unknotting Spheres in Five Dimensions, May, 1960, p. 198.
Psychiatric Quarterly, Mathematics and Creative Thinking, Volume 40, 1966, pp. 348–354.
Times Literary Supplement, The Geometry of Catastrophe, December 10, 1971, pp. 1556–1557.
Analysis Conflict and Its Resolution, The Psychology of a Hijacker, edited by P. G. Bennett, Oxford University Press, 1987, pp. 71–91.
A Passion for Science, Private Games, edited by L. Wolpert, Oxford University Press, 1988, pp. 52–65.
The Popularization of Mathematics, Christmas Lectures and Mathematics Masterclasses, edited by A. G. Howson and J. P. Kahane, Cambridge University Press, 1990, pp. 194–206.

FURTHER READING:

Books

Thompson, Michael, *Rubbish Theory,* Oxford University Press, 1979.

Periodicals

Thompson, Michael, *Bulletin of the London Mathematical Society,* Citation for Erik Christopher Zeeman, F.R.S., Volume 14, 1982, p. 569.

Other

Zeeman, Erik Christopher, *Interview with Jeanne Spriter James,* conducted November 6, 1993.

Sketch by Jeanne Spriter James

Pieter Zeeman
1865–1943
Dutch physicist

In 1902 Pieter Zeeman, along with theoretical physicist **Hendrik Lorentz,** received the Nobel Prize for Physics for their research on the effects of magnetism on electromagnetic radiation. That research had been suggested when James Clerk Maxwell demonstrated in the 1860s that light is composed of electrical and magnetic fields oscillating at right angles to each other. That formulation meant that light should be affected by the imposition of external magnetic and electrical fields—phenomena that had already been observed by Michael Faraday in 1845 and John Kerr in 1875. Zeeman's detection of the splitting of the spectral lines of sodium in a strong magnetic field was, however, the most impressive confirmation of Maxwell's theory up to that time.

Pieter Zeeman was born in Zonnemaire, Zeeland, the Netherlands, on May 25, 1865. He was the son of Catharinus Farandinus Zeeman, a Lutheran minister, and the former Wilhelmina Worst. Zeeman's primary education took place in Zonnemaire and his secondary education in the somewhat larger town of Zierikzee, five miles away. From 1883 to 1885 he attended the Delft gymnasium to study the Greek and Latin that were then required for attendance at any Dutch university. At Delft he met physicist **Heike Kamerlingh Onnes,** who was impressed by Zeeman's understanding of Scottish physicist James Clerk Maxwell's famous textbook, *Theory of Heat.*

Begins Research on the Kerr Effect

In 1885 Zeeman was admitted to the University of Leiden, where he was a student of both Kamerlingh Onnes and Lorentz. Five years later he obtained a post as assistant to Lorentz and began his doctoral research on the Kerr effect. First observed by the Scottish physicist John Kerr in 1875, the Kerr effect is produced when plane-polarized light is reflected off a highly polished pole of an electromagnet. During reflection, the light becomes elliptically polarized.

The Kerr effect was an example of the kind of phenomena suggested by Maxwell's theory of electromagnetism, announced in the 1860s. Maxwell demonstrated that a light ray has associated with it an electric field and a magnetic field, both oscillating at right angles to each other and to the direction in which the light ray is moving. It follows from this formulation that one or the other of these two components should be affected by the presence of an external electrical or magnetic field—an effect that would be observed by some change in a light beam forced to pass through an electrical or magnetic field.

The first of these predicted effects had actually been observed by English chemist and physicist Michael Faraday as early as 1845. Faraday had shown that a plane-polarized beam of light experiences a rotation of planes when it passes through a magnetic field. Kerr's 1875 discovery was the first post-Maxwellian confirmation of the same effect. For his doctoral studies, Zeeman repeated and refined Kerr's experiments, obtaining such impressive results that he was awarded a gold medal by the Netherlands Scientific Society of Haarlem in 1892. Zeeman received his Ph.D. from Leiden a year later.

After receiving his doctorate, Zeeman spent a semester at the Kohlrausch Institute in Strasbourg and then returned to Leiden as a privatdocent (an unpaid instructor). In January of 1897, Zeeman moved to the University of Amsterdam as a lecturer in physics. Three years later he was promoted to full professor, and in 1908 he was made director of the university's Physical Institute. In 1923 he also was appointed director of the newly established Laboratorium Physica, which was later renamed the Zeeman Laboratory in his honor. He retired from these posts in 1935.

Observes the Splitting of Spectral Lines

It was during his brief stay at Leiden from 1896 to 1897 that Zeeman made the discovery for which he was to become famous: the splitting of spectral lines. He learned that in 1862 Faraday had attempted—without success—to produce a splitting of spectral lines by placing a sodium flame within a magnetic field. Zeeman decided to repeat the Faraday experiment, but to make use of a more powerful magnetic field and a more accurate detection system. In August of 1896 he was successful. He found that each of the two yellow "D" lines in the sodium spectrum divided into two distinct parts when the sodium flame was situated within the magnetic field. This phenomenon is now universally known as the Zeeman effect.

Although he announced these results on October 31, 1896, Zeeman continued his work using other elements and improved techniques. In the spring of 1897, after he had taken up residence in Amsterdam, he observed the tripling of lines that had been predicted by Zeeman's former advisor Lorentz. Zeeman's last series of confirmatory experiments was conducted at the University of Gröningen, located in a rural part of Holland. This setting was necessary to escape from background noises, such as street traffic, that would have affected the most precise of Zeeman's experiments.

Zeeman also was able in this series of experiments to make very precise measurements of the particle responsible for the sodium radiation. He discovered that the ratio of electrical charge to mass for this particle was identical to that determined by **Joseph John Thomson** for the electron. Zeeman concluded that it was the vibration of electrons in the sodium atom that was responsible for the emission of the D lines in the element's spectrum.

In his later research, Zeeman continued to employ the high precision that had revealed to him the splitting of the sodium spectral lines. In 1915, for example, he carried out a series of experiments on the speed of light in water as a follow-up on the tests of American physicists **Albert Michelson** and **Edward Williams Morley**. Zeeman also became interested in the study of isotopes—groups of chemically identical atoms of the same element and atomic number with differing atomic mass—and he discovered a new argon isotope.

Zeeman married Johanna Elisabeth Lebret in 1895, and they had four children. In addition to the Nobel Prize, Zeeman was awarded the Rumford Medal of the Royal Society, the Wilde Prize of the French Academy of Sciences, the Baumgartner Prize of the Austrian Academy of Sciences, and the Henry Draper Medal of the U.S. National Academy of Sciences. He died in Amsterdam on October 9, 1943.

SELECTED WRITINGS BY ZEEMAN:

Books

Researches in Magneto-Optics, with Special Reference to the Magnetic Resolution of Spectrum Lines, Macmillan, 1913.
Verhandelingen van Dr. P. Zeeman over Magneto-Optische Verschijnselen, E. Ijdo, 1921.

FURTHER READING:

Books

Gillispie, Charles Coulson, editor, *Dictionary of Scientific Biography,* Volume 14, Scribner, 1975, pp. 597–599.
Magill, Frank N., editor, *The Nobel Prize Winners—Physics,* Volume 1, Salem Press, 1990, pp. 45–52.
Wasson, Tyler, editor, *Nobel Prize Winners,* H. W. Wilson, 1987, pp. 1157–1160.
Weber, Robert L., *Pioneers of Science: Nobel Prize Winners in Physics,* American Institute of Physics, 1980, pp. 10–11.

Sketch by David E. Newton

Yakov Borisovich Zel'dovich
1914–1987
Russian physicist and cosmologist

Yakov Borisovich Zel'dovich is perhaps best known for his work in cosmology, the study of the origins and nature of the universe, a field he did not even begin to plumb until he was almost fifty years old. At that age Zel'dovich evolved his famous "pancake model," which described the formation of clusters of galaxies in the early universe. But as a brilliant young scientist who rose through the then-Soviet ranks without a formal education, Zel'dovich made earlier significant contributions as well in the theory of explosions and shock waves, the theoretical foundation of chain reactions, and such basic physics questions as the conservation of baryon and lepton numbers and the theory of electroweak interactions.

Zel'dovich was born March 8, 1914, three years before the Russian Revolution, at his grandfather's house in Minsk. His father, a lawyer, and his mother, a translator of French fiction, moved while Yakov was still an infant to Petrograd (later Leningrad and now St. Petersburg). There, at age 15, Yakov finished high school and began taking courses to become a laboratory technician. But he was nudged off that path by a fortuitous class trip to the Leningrad Physical-Technical Institute in March 1931. During his visit to this center of Soviet physics, young Zel'dovich asked such penetrating questions that he was invited to work at the Institute in his free time. He seized the opportunity and excelled at his work; so impressed was the chemical physics department with his presentation on the ortho-para transformations of hydrogen that he was promptly recruited as a department member. Senior residents at the Institute, which broke off to become the Institute of Chemical Physics, told stories for years afterwards about the youth who stumped the experts and was so well regarded that one laboratory head was said to have traded an expensive oil pump for him.

Zel'dovich's "unusual training strongly influenced the surprising imagery and solidity of his thinking—his ability to see the phenomenon behind every formula, to find physically justified approximations, to simplify the route of problem solving while preserving essential components of the theory," colleague Vitalii Goldanskii recalled in *Physics Today* in December, 1988. In fact, Zel'dovich simply learned on his own, asking questions, observing. Despite his lack of formal university training, in 1936 he earned a Candidate of Science degree with his defense of a thesis that laid the foundations for the theory of adsorption (the adhesion on a surface of a very thin layer of molecules) on heterogenous surfaces. His doctoral thesis, which was awarded in 1939 and gave him the Soviet equivalent of a full professorship in the United States, showed that the oxidation of nitrogen is an unbranched chain reaction with an equilibrium concentration of oxygen atoms serving as active centers—a finding that has major application to today's environmental pollution dilemma. The kinetic scheme of nitrogen oxidation, named after Zel'dovich himself, makes it possible to calculate the amount of pollution from internal combustion engines, chemical industries and coal power stations, and is useful in devising counter-measures.

Zel'dovich Makes Shock Waves

During the 1930s Zel'dovich applied his genius to the theory of explosions and shock waves. In collaboration with David Frank-Kamenetzky, he came up with the first physically grounded theory of flame propagation, based on treating flame as a combustible wave. The Zel'dovich-Neumann-Doring theory of detonation, developed in 1940, made key contributions to the understanding of detonation wave structure. In the early 1940s, while working on theoretical problems related to gunpowder ignition, Zel'dovich discovered a phenomenon of combustion that under certain conditions can cause burning gunpowder in solid-propellant rocket engines to be extinguished. He also made important discoveries about changes in the rate of combustion in rocket engines under the effect of circumfluent gas flow. His work in this area laid the basis for the interior ballistics of solid-propellant rockets.

Zel'dovich's work had obvious military applications, particularly after the discovery of uranium fission. His work with Yuliy B. Khariton on the theoretical bases of explosive and controlled fission reactions—the last such Soviet research to be published openly before the Cold War closed the door on scientific exchange—contributed to the development of the first nuclear reactors. World War II and the Nazi invasion of the Soviet Union brought home the importance of such studies. For his 1940s work on atomic and, later, thermonuclear weapons, Zel'dovich was awarded three Orders of Lenin, three Hero of Socialist Labor awards, the Lenin Prize and four State Prizes (then called Stalin Prizes). In the 1950s Zel'dovich worked on nuclear physics and the physics of elementary particles, proposing the existence and conservation of baryonic and leptonic charges and contributing to the confirmation of the standard model of electroweak interactions, which was not demonstrated until two decades later.

Zel'dovich, who died before the fall of Communism, navigated the treacherous political waters of the Stalinist and post-Stalinist U.S.S.R. by remaining distinctly apolitical. In a 1991 article in *Nature,* John Peacock repeated a famous story of how the famous scientist once protected himself from police harassment by donning his medals before going out drinking. From 1948 to 1968, Zel'dovich worked closely with famous fellow physicist (and later political dissident) **Andrei Sakharov**. But unlike Sakharov, Zel'dovich chose to ignore risky and potentially disturbing political issues. "Zel'dovich strongly disapproved of my social work, which irritated and even frightened him," Sakharov recalled in an obituary published in *Nature* in February 1988. "He once said, 'People like [English astrophysicist **Stephen] Hawking** are devoted to science. Nothing can distract them.' I did not understand why he could not give the help which, given our relationship, I considered myself justified in asking for. I know that all this tormented Zel'dovich."

Turns His Attention to the Stars

In the 1960s Zel'dovich turned his attention to a very different field, cosmology, the study of the nature and evolution of the universe. His work on the dynamics of neutron emission during the formation of black holes led to the acceptance of black holes as observable objects. He is best known for his "pancake model," which suggests that galaxies formed on the surfaces of pancake-like shock fronts created as a result of the "Big Bang," the massive explosion theorized to have generated the universe. Married, with several children, Zel'dovich has been described as a born teacher. "His effect on his pupils was remarkable," Sakharov wrote in his obituary. "He often discovered in them a capacity for scientific creativity which without him would not have been realized or could have been realized only in part and with great difficulty." Zel'dovich died of a heart attack on December 2, 1987.

SELECTED WRITINGS BY ZEL'DOVICH:

Books

Higher Mathematics for Beginners, Nauka, 1960.
Relativistic Astrophysics, 2 volumes, 1971, republished by University of Chicago Press, 1982, 1983.
Basics of Modern Cosmology, 1986, translation published by Editions Frontières, 1991.
Selected Works of Yakov Borisovich Zel'dovich, Volume 1: Chemical Physics and Hydrodynamics, edited by J. P. Ostriker, Princeton University Press, 1992.

FURTHER READING:

Periodicals

Goldanskii, Vitalii I., *Physics Today,* Obituaries: Ya. B. Zel'dovich, December 1988, p. 98.
Maddox, John, *Nature,* Differences of Style in Science, October 29, 1987, p. 786.
Peacock, John, *Nature,* This Strange Universe, May 30, 1991, p. 359.
Priester, Wolfgang, *Sky & Telescope,* The Universe of Yakov Zel'dovich, October 1988, p. 354.
Sakharov, Andrei, *Nature,* A Man of Universal Interests, February 1988, p. 671.
Schwarzschild, Bertram, *Physics Today,* Redshift Surveys of Galaxies Find a Bubbly Universe, May 1986, p. 17.

Sketch by Joan Oleck

E-an Zen
1928–
American geologist and petrologist

E-an Zen's work in the origin and constitution of rocks and minerals has made him an acknowledged expert on New England geology, as well as the geology of the southern Appalachians. His work in applying the principles of thermodynamics and physical chemistry to problems in the structure of granites, sedimentary rocks, and batholiths —masses of igneous rock that have forced themselves into surrounding strata—have earned him awards from both the Geological and Mineralogical Societies of America and the respect of colleagues around the world. Zen's work extends beyond the theoretical, and his field researches have included everything from granites to potholes.

This blending of both intellectual and pragmatic qualities could be foretold from Zen's background. Born in Beijing, China, on May 31, 1928, Zen was the child of versatile academics. His father, Hung-chun Zen, was a chemist, science administrator, and educator, and his mother, Heng-chih Chen Zen, was a historian, essayist, and social reformer. His first decade was spent in Beijing, but then with the coming of World War II, Zen and his family kept one step ahead of the invading Japanese, traveling from Lushan to Kunming to Chungking. What education he had in those years came from his parents, and it was during that difficult time that Zen developed a love for mineralogy. "I was about ten years old," Zen said in an interview, "and my father and I went out for a stroll in the countryside. He picked up a crystal of calcite (Iceland spar) from the roadside gutter and explained to me how the crystal would break repeatedly along fixed directions because of intrinsic arrangement of atoms in the crystal. A casual remark that stuck!" During the war Zen read books on geomorphology and geology, but at this time it was still maps and geography he loved the most.

Pursues Geological Career in the United States

After the war, his mother—who, like her husband had been educated in the United States—sent Zen to America. Despite very little formal education up to that time, he graduated from high school in 1947 and then attended Cornell University, where he initially planned to study geography. Discovering that the university did not offer a major in physical geography, he opted for geology, earning his A.B. in 1951. His advanced study was done at Harvard University, where he won an M.A. in geology in 1952 and his Ph.D. in the same field in 1955. But his education was gained at great personal cost: he was never to see his father again, and it would be thirty years before he could visit his mother, trapped behind the Chinese Communist bamboo curtain.

As early as the time of his Ph.D., Zen was an acknowledged master of the geology of New England. An early stint as assistant professor at the University of North Carolina also brought him into contact with the geology of the Appalachian Mountains. By 1959, he was a geologist for the U.S. Geological Survey, a position he held until 1989. In the 1960s he conducted field mapping of the stratigraphy and structure of western Vermont, solving the long-standing problem of the tectonic origin of those rocks. Other early research and papers that won him scientific renown include those on the thermodynamics of so-called mix-layered minerals and of multisystems of rocks. His research into the petrology or origin and structure of granites and plutonic rocks also formed a major focus of his work in those years. In 1986, he was awarded the Arthur L. Day Medal from the Geological Society of America for his outstanding work in applying thermodynamics and physical chemistry to the problems of geology. Five years later, he was recognized by the Mineralogical Society of America, winning its Roebling Medal for his career-long work in the field of mineralogy.

In 1990, Zen became an adjunct professor at the University of Maryland and turned his attention from pure research to helping to train a future generation of committed geologists. He was married to Cristina Coney Silber, a geologist and school teacher, from 1967 to 1982.

SELECTED WRITINGS BY ZEN:

Periodicals

American Mineralogist, Metamorphism of Lower Paleozoic Rocks in the Vicinity of the Taconic Range in West-Central Vermont, Volume 45, 1960, pp. 129–175.

Geological Society of America Bulletin, Stratigraphy and Structure in the Vicinity of the Taconic Range in West-Central Vermont, Volume 72, 1961, pp. 293–338.

American Journal of Science, Some Topological Relationships of N+3 Phases, I. General Theory; Unary and Binary Systems, Volume 264, 1966, pp. 401–427.

The American Mineralogist, The Phase-Equilibrium Calorimeter, the Petrogenic Grid, and a Tyranny of Numbers, Volume 62, 1977, pp. 189–204.

Geologic Society of America Memoir, Exotic Terranes in the New England Appalachians, Volume 158, 1983, pp. 55–81.

Annual Review of Earth and Planetary Sciences, Phase Relations of Peraluminous Granitic Rocks and Their Petrogenic Implications, Volume 16, 1988, pp. 21–51.

American Journal of Science, Phanerozoic Denudation History of the Southern New England Appalachians Deduced from Pressure Data, Volume 291, 1991, pp. 401–424.

FURTHER READING:

Periodicals

Kieffer, Susan W., *American Mineralogist,* Presentation of the Roebling Medal of the Mineralogical Society of America for 1991 to E-an Zen, July/August, 1992, pp. 863–864.

McPhee, John, *New Yorker,* Travels of the Rock, February 26, 1990, pp. 108–117.

Skinner, Brian, J., *Geological Society of America Bulletin,* Presentation of the Arthur L. Day Medal to E-an Zen, July, 1987, pp. 136–138.

Other

Zen, E-an, *Interview with J. Sydney Jones,* conducted February 10, 1994.

Sketch by J. Sydney Jones

Frits Zernike
1888–1966
Dutch physicist

Frits Zernike won the 1953 Nobel Prize in physics for his invention of the phase-contrast microscope, an instrument which enabled scientists to study living tissue samples under magnification for the first time. Zernike's background in statistical mathematics and thermodynamics was responsible for his groundbreaking discovery. A conventional microscope utilizes ordinary light, and under these instruments living tissues, particularly transparent ones, are not visible unless stained. Yet staining usually kills the specimen or produces artifacts that are impossible to differentiate from the specimen. The phase-contrast microscope utilizes a diaphragm and a diffraction plate. The diaphragm funnels light into a cone, which is focused on the specimen; the diffraction plate is placed between the lenses, changing the speed of the light if the specimen has diffracted the light. The phase-contrast technique can reveal variations in opacity as well as variations in the thickness of transparent objects.

Born on July 16, 1888, in Amsterdam, Zernike was the son of two mathematicians, Carl Frederick August Zernike and Antje Dieperink Zernike. He was recognized while still young for his mathematical abilities. He received both his B.S. and his Ph.D. in physics from the University of Amsterdam, and he worked at an astronomical laboratory while pursuing his graduate studies. His doctoral thesis, "Critical Opalescence, Theoretical and Experimental," quickly established him as a leader in his field. In 1915 he was appointed lecturer in theoretical physics at the University of Groningen. In 1920, he was promoted to professor, and he remained at Groningen for the rest of his career.

Glitch in Telescopes Leads to New Microscope

It was while working in the field of astronomy that Zernike first discovered the advantages of phase-contrast techniques. Irregularities on the surfaces of the curved mirrors of telescopes were a common problem at that time; these mirrors sometimes produced "ghost" images and Zernike hypothesized that they were caused by out-of-phase wavelengths. If he could somehow bring direct and diffracted images back into phase, perhaps these aberrations would disappear. He developed a glass plate with tiny grooves etched in it to be placed in the focal plane of the telescope, and he called this a "phase plate." His experiment worked: when looking through the phase plate, the out-of-phase areas became clearly visible. Zernike published these findings in 1934, and by 1935 he was applying these same principles to microscopes, which he knew had optical problems that were similar to telescopes. He inserted a phase strip into the focal plane of a microscope and immediately it brought the direct and the diffracted beams into phase.

Although the practical applications of Zernike's findings seem obvious now, it was some years before he could find a manufacturer for a phase-contrast microscope. He first approached a German company, Carl Zeiss, in 1932. "They understood the theoretical background but did not think the practical use would be great," Zernike recalled in an interview when he won the Nobel Prize. "They said if it was practical they already would have developed it." Finally, in 1941, Carl Zeiss agreed to produce the instrument. But it was not until American troops arrived in Germany in 1945 and discovered photomicrographs taken by a phase-contrast microscope that Zernike's instrument received worldwide attention. When he won the Nobel Prize in 1953, the phase-contrast microscope was cited as being a key to insights into cancer research.

Unlike many instrument makers, Zernike worked first from theoretical principles and then moved to practical applications. "Perhaps Dr. Zernike's most outstanding characteristic," said the author of his *New York Times* obituary, "was his ability to blend theory with experiment." Though the phase-contrast microscope is considered his crowning achievement, Zernike is also known for other work. Early in his career he invented the Zernike galvanometer, an instrument used to detect and measure small electrical currents. The Zernike polynomials are a method he developed regarding the wave theory of light and are widely used by mathematicians. He also made many improvements in infrared and ultraviolet spectroscopy, as well as in the construction of the electromagnet.

Although Zernike stayed at his alma mater for his entire career, he was a visiting professor of physics at the Johns Hopkins University in Baltimore in 1948. In 1950 he was elected to the Royal Microscopical Society of London,

and he was presented with the Rumford Medal of the British Royal Society in 1952.

Zernike married Dora van Bommel van Vloten in 1929. The couple had two children; his wife died in 1944. In 1954, Zernike remarried, to L. Koperberg-Baanders. He retired in 1958 and died in Groningen on March 10, 1966.

SELECTED WRITINGS BY ZERNIKE:

Periodicals

Monographs of the National Royal Astronomical Society, Diffraction Theory of the Knife-Edge Test and Its Improved Form, the Phase-Contrast Method, Volume 94, 1934, p. 377.
Physica, The Propagation of Order in Cooperative Phenomena, Volume 7, 1940, p. 565.
Les prix Nobel en 1953, How I Discovered Phase Contrast, Stockholm, 1953, pp. 107–114.

FURTHER READING:

Periodicals

New York Times, March 16, 1966, p. 45.

Sketch by Dorothy Barnhouse

Karl Ziegler
1898–1973
German chemist

Karl Ziegler had a long and distinguished career in diverse areas of chemistry. Although he is considered an organic chemist, he applied the methods and principles of inorganic, physical, and analytical chemistry to his research problems. He thought of himself as a chemist who carried out "pure" research, but his greatest contribution was a discovery that led to a revolution in "applied" research and was of great benefit to industry. This breakthrough related to catalysts—substances that provoke a chemical reaction—and Ziegler's work became the foundation of the modern plastics industry. The discovery and application of the "Ziegler catalysts" were rewarded with lucrative licensing fees and the 1963 Nobel Prize in chemistry, which Ziegler shared with **Giulio Natta**, an Italian chemist who significantly extended Ziegler's work.

Ziegler was born on November 26, 1898, in Helsa, Germany, to Luise (Rall) and Karl Ziegler, a Lutheran minister. As a youth he showed an early interest in chemistry, and had a laboratory at home. In 1916 he matriculated at the University of Marburg, from which his father had graduated, and was so advanced in his studies that he was able to complete his Ph.D. in 1920, when he was only twenty-one. His thesis adviser was Karl von Auwers, a noted organic chemist of his time. Ziegler remained at Marburg as a lecturer until 1925, then spent a year as a visiting lecturer at the University of Frankfurt. In 1926 Ziegler moved to the University of Heidelberg, receiving a promotion to professor the following year. He remained at Heidelberg until 1936, when he was appointed professor and director of the Chemical Institute at the University of Halle. In 1943 Ziegler accepted the directorship of the Kaiser Wilhelm Institute (later known as the Max Planck Institute) for Coal Research in Müllheim, located in Germany's Ruhr valley. Ziegler agreed to the appointment on condition that he could work on any research project of his choice and not be limited to the chemistry of coal. It was at Müllheim that he discovered the catalyst that brought him great renown, but the discovery was a natural consequence of research which he had begun as a graduate student and developed over his long career.

From 1923 to 1943 Ziegler concentrated his research on free radicals (atoms or groups of atoms having one or more unpaired electrons), organometallic compounds and their reactions with double bonds, and the synthesis of large rings, which are cyclic compounds of molecules. He was primarily interested in the fundamental aspects of structural chemistry, such as the strength of the carbon-carbon bond. He studied the nature of free radicals while looking for compounds whose bonds could be broken easily to form a trivalent species, or one containing a carbon atom bound to three other substances. Usually free radicals exist only briefly and rapidly react to form normal tetravalent compounds—carbon most often has a bonding capacity of four—but Ziegler found many examples of complex free radicals that could survive and be manipulated like ordinary compounds, as long as reactive species such as oxygen were excluded.

In the course of his work on free radicals, Ziegler investigated the organic derivatives of reactive metals, such as sodium and potassium, and later, lithium. With a chemical composition similar to that of the organomagnesium compounds explored earlier by French chemist and Nobel Prize–winner **Victor Grignard**, lithium proved to be extremely useful in organic synthesis. Unlike Grignard's reagent, however, Ziegler found that certain organopotassium compounds could add to a carbon-carbon double bond to make a more complex organopotassium compound. Ziegler applied the reaction to butadiene, a compound that contains two double bonds, and found that the butadiene molecules could form long chains.

As this research progressed, Ziegler considered the problem of joining the ends of long chain molecules to form large rings. This problem had considerable practical importance, for example, in the synthesis of the natural perfume base, muscone. Ziegler eventually used a strong base—a material that accepts protons in solution—with a long-chain

compound in very high dilution in order to prepare a large-ring ketone, a compound with fourteen to thirty-three carbons.

Discovery of Polymerization Catalysts Revolutionizes the Chemical Industry

When Ziegler moved to the Institute for Coal Research in 1943, he continued the lines of research he had earlier developed. Ziegler tried many experiments to add lithium hydride to the carbon-carbon double bond, but the reaction was slow and unsuccessful. The compound lithium aluminum hydride was reported by Schlesinger at the University of Chicago in 1947, and Ziegler tried this as a substitute for lithium hydride in 1949. This was successful, and led Ziegler to the conclusion that the aluminum was the vital component. Ziegler found that organoaluminum compounds reacted with double-bond compounds at one hundred degrees centigrade to produce long chains of carbons attached to the aluminum atom. The organoaluminum compounds could be converted into long-chain alcohols (alcohols are characterized by a hydroxyl, or oxygen-hydrogen, group attached to a hydrocarbon chain) by allowing air into the reaction, and these alcohols were useful in the formulation of detergents.

In the course of the investigation of organoaluminum reactions in 1953, one experiment delivered a product that did not contain the expected long chains. The reaction had been carried out in an autoclave—an apparatus suited to special conditions such as high or low pressure or temperature—and careful analysis showed that the autoclave had been previously used in a reaction that contained nickel, with small traces of nickel salts remaining. Ziegler and his colleagues investigated the addition of other metal salts and found that in contrast with nickel, which caused the reaction to fail, certain salts dramatically improved the reaction. When ethylene, the simplest compound containing a carbon-carbon double bond, is bubbled into a hydrocarbon solvent containing a very small amount of an organoaluminum compound and titanium tetrachloride (a volatile liquid compound used now chiefly in skywriting and smoke screens because it fumes in moist air), there is formation of polyethylene (a long, straight hydrocarbon chain). The reaction conditions are very mild, consisting of atmospheric pressure and room temperature.

Polyethylene had been previously produced by the British company Imperial Chemicals Industries, but their method required temperatures up to two hundred degrees centigrade and pressures up to two thousand atmospheres. The ICI polyethylene had shorter chains, and the chains were branched; the substance was waxy and products made from it were soft and easily deformed. On the other hand, Ziegler's polyethylene was hard and rigid, and could be drawn into fibers. Many useful products could be made from Ziegler's low-pressure polyethylene, starting from inexpensive, abundant starting materials. Ziegler refined the process and investigated other catalyst systems. Chemical companies worldwide showed immediate interest in Ziegler's discovery and paid for the right to use it. Among those who extended Ziegler's work was Natta, a chemist at the University of Milan, who showed how the geometry of the polymer could be controlled by the catalyst, and made different polypropylenes, whose physical properties were determined by their molecular geometries.

The discovery of the Ziegler catalysts had a profound effect on the course of chemical research and development. Industrial and academic chemists turned their attention to the wide area of organometallic chemistry in order to understand the fundamental chemistry and to discover useful catalysts for polymerization and other commercial reactions. In Ziegler's Nobel lecture, he showed a world map that indicated large chemical plants that were producing polyethylene and other products based on his research only ten years after his initial discovery. Ziegler became wealthy as a result of his research, and when he was seventy years old, he established the Ziegler Fund for Research with ten million dollars. Ziegler had no political connections with the Nazi government, and he was welcomed at the Institute for Coal Research because his work could continue in the postwar period without interference from the Allies. After resurrecting the German Chemical Society in 1949, Ziegler served as its first president. He retired from the institute in 1969 after bringing great prestige and funding to it.

Ziegler had a long and happy marriage to Maria Kurz, whom he married in 1922. His daughter Marianne was a physician and his son Erhart was a physicist. Ziegler was able to enjoy himself outside the laboratory; among his hobbies were collecting paintings and hiking in the mountains. Ziegler died on August 12, 1973, after a short illness.

SELECTED WRITINGS BY ZIEGLER:

Books

Advances in Organometallic Chemistry, A Forty Years' Stroll through the Realms of Organometallic Chemistry, Volume 6, edited by F. G. A. Stone and R. West, Academic Press, 1968, pp. 1–17.
Nobel Lectures: Chemistry, 1963–1970, Consequences and Development of an Invention, Elsevier, 1972.

FURTHER READING:

Books

Bonnesen, Peter V., *Nobel Laureates in Chemistry, 1901–1992,* Karl Ziegler, edited by L. K. James, American Chemical Society, 1993, pp. 449–455.
Boor, J., Jr., *Ziegler-Natta Catalysts and Polymerization,* Academic Press, 1979.
Lagrone, Craig P., *The Nobel Prize Winners: Chemistry,* Karl Ziegler, Volume 3, edited by F. N. Magill, Salem Press, 1990, pp. 744–754.

Periodicals

Eisch, J. J., *Journal of Chemical Education,* Karl Ziegler: Master Advocate for the Unity of Pure and Applied Research, Volume 60, 1983, pp. 1009–1014.

Sketch by Martin R. Feldman

Norton Zinder
1928–
American molecular geneticist

Norton Zinder is a molecular geneticist and John D. Rockefeller Jr. Professor of molecular genetics at Rockefeller University in New York City. He also serves as the university's dean of graduate and postgraduate studies. Zinder is known primarily for his research during the late 1940s and early 1950s, when he discovered a new mechanism of genetic transfer called bacterial transduction. This process refers to the transfer of genetic material between bacteria through bacterial viruses. The discovery has shed new light on the location and behavior of bacterial genes. Zinder is the recipient of numerous awards and honors, including the 1962 Eli Lilly Award in Microbiology and Immunology from the American Society of Microbiology.

Norton David Zinder, the older of two boys, was born on November 7, 1928, in New York City to Harry Zinder, a manufacturer, and Jean (Gottesman) Zinder, a homemaker. He attended New York City public schools, graduating from the prestigious Bronx High School of Science, and went on to attend Columbia University, where he received his B.A. in biology in 1947. The following year, at the recommendation of Francis Ryan, a professor of zoology at Columbia and in whose laboratory he had worked, Zinder commenced his graduate career at the University of Wisconsin. There, he studied under American geneticist **Joshua Lederberg**, who had already discovered genetic conjugation (or "mating") a few years earlier and who would win a Nobel Prize in 1958 for his viral and bacterial research. Zinder focused his research on microbial genetics (the study of the genetics of microorganisms), at a time when the field was relatively new and when many basic phenomena were as yet undiscovered.

In 1946, Lederberg had researched mating in *Escherichia coli*—a bacterium that is found in the intestinal tract of animals and which can cause bacterial dysentery. Zinder wished to continue Lederberg's investigations, and he chose to study the closely related genus of *Salmonella*—bacteria that cause illnesses such as typhoid fever or food poisoning in humans and other warm-blooded animals. For his work, Zinder needed to obtain large numbers of mutant strains,

Norton Zinder

which were, at the time, acquired by randomly testing the survivors among bacteria that had been treated with mutagens, or agents that increase both the chance and extent of mutation. Zinder, however, wanted to experiment with a different method of acquisition: He knew that mutant bacteria will not grow in a nutritionally deficient medium and that antibiotic penicillin will kill only growing bacteria. So, he was able to collect bacteria into an environment that was nutritionally inadequate, then kill any normal bacteria by administering penicillin.

Discovers Genetic Transduction

Zinder obtained large numbers of mutant bacteria using this method, and he began his experiments to investigate conjugation in *Salmonella;* however, instead of observing conjugation, he stumbled upon a different method of genetic transfer in bacteria: genetic transduction. As Zinder continued his research, he determined that genetic material is transferred from one bacterial cell to another by means of a phage, or a virus that invades the bacterial cell, assumes control over the cell's genetic material, reproduces, then eventually destroys the cell. Zinder's discovery of this genetic transfer has led to further studies into the mapping and behavior of genes found in bacteria. For example, Milislav Demerec and other researchers at New York's Cold Spring Harbor Laboratory later found that the bacterial genes that regulate biosynthetic steps are grouped in what have become known as "operons," a term coined in 1960 to describe closely linked genes that function as an integrated whole.

In subsequent investigations, Zinder and his team also discovered the F2 phage, very small in size and the only virus known to contain RNA (ribonucleic acid) as its genetic substance. The researchers ascertained that the RNA generated by the virus contains codes for specific amino acids—the building blocks of protein molecules—as well as signals to control the termination and initiation of protein chains.

Zinder received his M.S. in genetics in 1949 from the University of Wisconsin and married Marilyn Estreicher in December of that same year; the couple eventually had two sons, Stephen and Michael. In 1952 Zinder completed his Ph.D. in medical microbiology, then accepted the post of assistant professor at Rockefeller University (then Rockefeller Institute for Medical Research). By 1964 he had become a full professor of genetics, and approximately ten years later he was named John D. Rockefeller Jr. Professor of Molecular Genetics; in 1993 he was appointed dean of graduate and postgraduate studies. The primary focus of Zinder's research has been in the molecular genetics of phages.

In addition to his positions at Rockefeller, Zinder also has been associated with other institutions. In the mid–1970s he began lengthy affiliations with the science departments of Harvard University, Yale University, and Princeton University, and, beginning in the same period, he also worked in the viral cancer program at the National Cancer Institute. In 1988 he assumed the position of chair of the program advisory committee for the National Institute of Health (NIH) human genome project, and remained in that capacity for three years. He has served in editorial capacities for scientific journals, such as *Virology* and *Intervirology,* and has published numerous articles in professional journals.

Throughout his career Zinder has received several honors, including the United States Steel Award in Molecular Biology from the National Academy of Sciences in 1966, the Medal of Excellence from Columbia University in 1969, and an honorary doctorate of science from the University of Wisconsin in 1990. He was named a fellow of the American Academy of Arts and Sciences, and is associated with such organizations as the National Academy of Sciences, the American Society of Microbiology, Genetics Society of America, the American Society of Virology, and HUGO (Human Genome Organization).

SELECTED WRITINGS BY ZINDER:

Books

RNA Phages, Cold Spring Harbor Laboratory Press, 1975.

Periodicals

Journal of American Chemical Society, Concentration of Biochemical Mutants of Bacteria with Penicillin, Volume 70, 1948, p. 4267.

Journal of Molecular Biology, Physical Map of Defective Interfering Particles of Bacteriophage F1, Volume 111, 1977, pp. 395–414.

Scientific American, The Genome Initiative: How to Spell 'Human,', July, 1990, p. 128.

Sketch by Kala Dwarakanath

Rolf M. Zinkernagel
1944–
Swiss immunologist and virologist

Rolf M. Zinkernagel

Rolf M. Zinkernagel joined the ranks of the Nobel laureates in 1996 because of his relatively early work with colleague **Peter Doherty** defining the system by which the immune system identifies friend and foe. His work since then has built upon this discovery, revealing how the thymus gland selects only white blood cells that react properly to virus-infected cells and investigating the complex interplay by which viruses and their hosts co-evolve.

Zinkernagel has also been a vocal proponent of the promise of biotechnology in his native Switzerland. He worries that the conservatism of his countrymen may lead to the stifling of the fledgling Swiss biotechnology industry.

Zinkernagel and his ophthalmologist wife, Kathrin, live in Zumikon, Switzerland, near Zurich, where he is head of the Institute of Experimental Immunology, and she practices medicine. Their adult children, Christine, Annelies, and Martin, are all in various stages of physician training.

A Rich, Busy Childhood

Zinkernagel was born on January 6, 1944, in Basel, Switzerland. His father was a biologist and had the distinction of being both the first Ph.D. and one of the few biologists at the time hired by the Swiss pharmaceutical giant J.R. Geigy AG. His mother, who came from the French-speaking Jura mountains region of Switzerland, came from a family with ties to the Swiss watch-making and banking industries. She became a lab technician when she moved to Basel, where she met Zinkernagel's father.

Zinkernagel attended the Mathematisch-Naturwissenschaftliches Gymnasium, the same secondary school that had educated both his father and father-in-law. While there, he pursued a great number of hobbies, including exploration of

prehistoric human settlements near Basel with a chemist friend of his father's, cabinet-making and smithing, dancing, and alpine mountaineering. He also voluntarily studied Latin for four years—not a requirement of his school, but prerequisite to studying law or medicine at the time. He traveled to Scandinavia, France, and England as a teen, spending a year in England in order to learn English.

Zinkernagel went to the University of Basel in 1962, deciding to study medicine rather than chemistry—his other great interest—because the former profession offered the possibility of clinical or private practice as well as research. He met his wife when they were both medical students; the two married in 1968, two weeks after their final board examinations. In 1970 the university accepted his M.D. dissertation. Rejected by the World Health Organization for travel to Africa to study and treat leprosy because of lack of experience, the couple worked for the next three years in Switzerland.

To Australia—and to Immunology

In 1969 Zinkernagel's work in the surgery department of a hospital in Basel failed to spark his interest. He began looking around for other possible career paths. From 1970 to 1973 he worked as a postdoctoral fellow at the University of Lausanne, Switzerland, in a laboratory studying the process by which the immune system kills virus-infected cells. Zinkernagel's project, trying to monitor the destruction of bacterial cells preloaded with radioactive chromium-51, was frustrating because the method never worked properly on the bacteria—but it gave him experience with a number of experimental techniques that were to prove crucial for his Nobel-winning research.

In 1972 Robert Blanden of the John Curtin School of Medical Research, Canberra, Australia, came to the Swiss university to teach a World Health Organization course on immunology. Intrigued by the course and encouraged by senior researchers at Lausanne, Zinkernagel applied for a fellowship with Blanden at the Curtin school. Thanks to a two-year Swiss Foundation for Biomedical Fellowships grant, Zinkernagel and his young family—Christine was two, and Annelies not yet one—moved to Australia in 1973. While at the Curtin school, Zinkernagel earned a Ph.D. in immunology, finishing his dissertation in 1975.

A fortuitous accident led Zinkernagel to team up with another young postdoctoral fellow at the Curtin school, Peter Doherty. While the Blanden laboratory was cramped for space, Doherty had room in his assigned lab. Thanks in part to their shared love of operatic music—and Zinkernagel's penchant for singing it aloud while working—Zinkernagel began to work with Doherty on how white blood cells called killer T cells identify virus-infected host cells to attack. "He was tolerable, but loud," according to Doherty.

Friend or Foe?

At the time, immunologists were very interested in a group of genes collectively called the major histocompatibility complex, or MHC. These genes, clustered together in the DNA sequence, encode a series of proteins called the MHC antigens, which determine whether a transplanted organ will be accepted or rejected by a recipient. If the MHC genes of the donor and the recipient match, the organ survives; if they do not, the organ is attacked by the recipient's immune system and dies.

A number of researchers had guessed that the rejection of MHC-mismatched organs was essentially the same process as the killing of virus-infected cells by killer T cells. Zinkernagel and Doherty demonstrated that this was true, and that the MHC antigens were necessary for killer T cells to tell friend from foe. But when they investigated further, they found something very unexpected; most immunologists had expected that when virus-infected cells and killer cells were poorly MHC matched, the immune cells' killing response would be strongest, much as in badly matched transplants. But the opposite was true. In order to get proper T-cell killing of the virus-infected cells, Zinkernagel and Doherty discovered, the cells' MHC regions had to match.

The two had discovered that T cells—indeed, the immune response in general—can only recognize viral proteins when they are displayed in the context of properly matched MHC antigens. The immune system, which had evolved to recognize "self" from "other" did not react most strongly to "other," but to a third state, "altered self." This discovery finally put transplant rejection into biological context. The body does not purposely reject mismatched organs because they are different, it rejects them because it

mistakenly identifies the mismatched MHC antigens as "self" antigens that have been altered by interaction with viral proteins. The finding also opened the way to better methods for heading off transplant rejection, for creating vaccines, and for further unraveling the workings of immunity; vulnerability to certain infections; and autoimmune disease, where the body mistakenly attacks its own tissues.

Recognition—and a Chance to be Heard

Zinkernagel's and Doherty's work together took place in a fairly short amount of time between 1973 and 1974. By 1976, both were moving on, with Zinkernagel going to the Scripps Clinic Research Institute in La Jolla, California, as an associate—a rank roughly equal to an assistant professor at a university. There he studied whether or not the thymus gland—long known to play a role in the "maturation" of infection-fighting white blood cells—used MHC antigens to select which white blood cells would mature and which would die before being released to the bloodstream. The work once again proved seminal, providing the first evidence that the thymus only allows killer cells that react against slightly altered self MHC antigens to survive. This helped explain how and why killer T cells recognize altered-self antigens most strongly. The thymus prevents autoimmune disease by killing off killer cells that would otherwise attack healthy tissues and prevents a too-weak immune response by destroying those that would fail to attack any but the most profoundly changed self antigens.

Zinkernagel became a member—the equivalent of a full professor—at Scripps in 1979. But later that year he returned to Switzerland, to take an associate professorship at the University of Zurich, followed by a full professorship in 1988. During that period, his work with Doherty began to receive growing international recognition, with an Ehrlich Prize in Germany in 1983 and a Gairdner Foundation International Award in Canada in 1986. In 1992 Zinkernagel was named head of the Institute of Experimental Immunology in Zurich and also received the Christoforo Colombo Award in Italy, to be followed by an Albert Lasker Medical Research Award—often a prelude to a Nobel—in 1995.

Zinkernagel's and Doherty's Nobel Prize for Physiology or Medicine came in 1996. Zinkernagel has since used the award as a platform from which to speak out on the threat posed by what he has said is "the Swiss lack of willingness to take risks." Conservative Swiss investors, he has argued, do not fully appreciate the importance of high-risk venture investments like those necessary to establish a biotechnology industry. Worse, he has said, his country's strong animal welfare movement threatens to kill what little biotechnology Switzerland has with over-regulation. While he applauds his country's progressive laws to ensure animal welfare and is in favor of increased government oversight of the use of genetic engineering and transgenic animals, he worries that unless Swiss voters are properly educated about the risks and promise of biotechnology, outright bans will ensue.

SELECTED WRITINGS BY ZINKERNAGEL:

Periodicals

"Cytotoxic T Cells Learn Specificity for Self H-2 During Differentiation in the Thymus." *Nature* (January 19, 1978): 251-253.

(With P.C. Doherty) "Immunological Surveillance Against Altered Self Components by Sensitized T Lymphocytes in Lymphocytic Choriomeningitis." *Nature* (October 11, 1974): 547-548.

(With P.C. Doherty) "The Discovery of MHC Restriction." *Immunology Today* (January 1997): 14-17.

Other

"Rolf M. Zinkernagel." September 29, 1997. http://www.nobel.sdsc.edu/laureates/medicine-1996-2-autobio.html (November 25, 1997).

FURTHER READING:

Periodicals

Benowitz, Steven. "New Nobel Laureates Speak Out for Increased Research Funding." *The Scientist* (November 11, 1996): 1, 4-5.

Other

"David Baron Reports that the Latest Nobel Prize Goes to Rolf Zinkernagel and Peter Doherty." Audio Recording, October 7, 1996. http://www6.realaudio.com/contentp/npr/nc6o07.html (November 25, 1997).

"Research for Life." April 23, 1997. http://www.unizh.ch/upd/unileute/portraet/zinkernagel-le.html (November 25, 1997).

"The Nobel Prize in Medicine 1996." October 7, 1996. http://www.nobel.se/announcement-96/medicine96.html (November 25, 1997).

Sketch by Kenneth Chiacchia

Walter Henry Zinn
1906–2000
Canadian-born American physicist

Walter Henry Zinn

participation in the Manhattan Project and the conception and invention of the atomic bomb, as well as a lifelong career for Zinn. After World War II, Zinn continued his research into atomic energy, creating the world's first breeder reactor and acting as Argonne National Laboratory's first director. His work revolutionized the way energy is harnessed and used today.

Walter Zinn was originally from Kitchener, Ontario, Canada, born on December 10, 1906. After receiving his B.A. (1927) and M.A. (1929) from Queen's University in Ontario, he moved to the United States in 1930 to continue his higher education at Columbia University. Eight years later he became a naturalized American citizen in 1938. During that same period, Zinn married his first wife in 1933, received his Ph.D. in 1934, and began to pursue his lifelong interest in atomic energy.

Verifies Fission and Lays Groundwork for Atomic Bomb

Between 1932 and 1941, Zinn taught at the City College of New York, first as an instructor and then as an assistant professor. It was during this time that he and his colleague, Leo Szilard, conducted their experimentation on the possibility of atomic fission. In 1939 they successfully illustrated how uranium, when placed under pressure, will undergo fission, its atomic structure breaking apart to release a large amount of energy.

Because of his groundbreaking work with fission, Zinn moved to the University of Chicago's Manhattan Engineer-

Walter Henry Zinn's scientific endeavors dramatically changed the world. He, along with his colleague **Leo Szilard**, began his exploration of atomic fission at Columbia University. That same exploration led to his

ing District's Metallurgical Laboratory in 1942. It was there that Zinn worked with colleagues on the Manhattan Project, which created the atomic bomb.

Designs First Breeder Reactor

After World War II, Zinn continued his work at the Metallurgical Laboratory, but he switched his focus to the development of nuclear power reactors. In 1944 Zinn successfully started "the world's first heavy-water-moderated nuclear reactor" known as Chicago Pile 3 (CP-3).

Two years later, the Manhattan Engineering District's Metallurgical Laboratory was officially changed to Argonne National Laboratory, and named Zinn as its first director. One year later in 1947, Zinn was approved by the Atomic Energy Commission, Argonne's sponsor, to build the first breeder reactor. Unlike the reactorthat produces energy from uranium-235 fission, the breeder reactor attains energy while at the same time converting uranium-238 to o more uranium-235. It makes more energy than it needs, thereby making nuclear energy a potential fuel source. Known as experimental breeder reactor 1 (EBR-I) or "Zinn's Infernal Pile" (ZIP), the breeder reactor produced its first electricity in 1951, when it lit up four light bulbs.

Zinn also was key in establishing the National Reactor Testing Station (now, Idaho National Engineering Laboratory), a reactor proving ground. He also set up the Naval Reactor Division at Argonne in 1948, and in 1949 he discovered that the water-cooled reactor is most appropriate type of reactor for naval use. After resigning as director of Argonne in 1956, Zinn held a position as special consultant to the Joint Congressional Committee on Atomic Energy. He was also a special member of the President's Scientific Advisory Committee and president of the General Nuclear Engineering Corp. from 1956-64. In 1959 he was appointed vice president of Combustion Engineering Inc., a position he held until 1971.

Zinn was a member of the National Academy of Science, the National Academy of Engineering, and the American Nuclear Society, as well as being a fellow of the American Physics Society. Zinn received a special commendation from the U.S. Atomic Energy Commission in 1956. He was the recipient of the Atoms for Peace Award in 1960 and the Enrico Fermi Award in 1969.

Zinn died on February 14, 2000 in Clearwater, Florida, at the age of 93.

FURTHER READING:

Books

A Biographical Encyclopedia of Scientists. Bristol: Institute of Physics Publishing, 1994.

Asimov, Isaac. *Asimov's Biographical Encyclopedia of Science and Technology: The Lives and Achievements of 1510 Great Scientists from Ancient Times to the Present*. Garden City, NY: Doubleday & Co. Inc., 1982.

Other

Argonne National Laboratory. "Argonne Highlights." (September 27, 1996). http://www.anl.gov/OPA/history/ (December 3, 1997).

Sketch by Jacqueline L. Longe

Hans Zinsser
1878–1940
American bacteriologist

Hans Zinsser was one of the leading bacteriologists and immunologists in the United States during the first half of the twentieth century. His work in advancing the understanding of typhus fever as well as a number of fundamental features of immunology remains central to this day. Zinsser was born on November 17, 1878, in New York City, and grew up in a household where German was the primary language that was spoken. Both of his parents had emigrated from Germany: His father, August Zinsser, was a wealthy manufacturing chemist originally from the Rhineland, and his mother, Marie Theresa (Schmidt), was from the Black Forest region, an area long dominated by French tradition. For this reason, the young Zinsser soon became fluent in a second language: French.

The youngest of August and Marie's four sons, Zinsser did not start formal schooling until age ten. At that time he was sent to a private school in New York City operated by Julius Sachs, and only then did Zinsser begin using English as his first language. The school emphasized the liberal arts, an area of learning especially valued by Zinsser, who had the fortune of spending some portion of every one of his first twenty years of life visiting the art galleries and concert halls of Europe. In 1895, at age seventeen, Zinsser entered nearby Columbia University, where he was intent on studying literature and pursuing a writing career. Studying under comparative literature specialist George Edward Woodberry, the already broadly educated Zinsser showed great promise in the writing of poetry. In an article in *Memoirs of the National Academy of Sciences,* Zinsser's principal biographer, Simeon Burt Wolbach, noted that the "world of things and thoughts" had occupied Zinsser until that time. Although his intellectual life was about to change, Zinsser remained an accomplished poet and essayist as well as lucid writer of scientific prose for the remainder of his more than sixty years. On his deathbed, after battling leukemia for the final two years of his life, he wrote his last sonnet. The poem, which was published posthumously in his collection *Spring, Summer and Autumn,* ends with the lines: "Then, ageless, in your heart I'll come to rest / Serene and proud as when you loved me best."

Enters the Field of Bacteriology

It was only after his tutelage under biologists **Edmund Beecher Wilson** and Bashford Dean during his junior year at Columbia that Zinsser realized that the life sciences would be his career. He went on to Columbia's College of Physicians and Surgeons in 1899, deciding to devote his career to the application of his interest in biology to real human problems. Earning both an M.A. and an M.D. in 1903, he interned at Roosevelt Hospital, then began to practice medicine. He left that vocation after a short while, however, when Columbia offered him a post as instructor in bacteriology. In the meantime, he had married Ruby Handforth Kunz in 1905.

Zinsser taught bacteriology for a short time at Columbia and teamed with Philip Hanson Hiss, Jr., with whom in 1910 he coauthored *A Textbook of Bacteriology,* which has become a standard microbiology text. Simultaneously, he served as assistant pathologist at New York's St. Luke's Hospital. The same year *A Textbook of Bacteriology* was released, Zinsser moved his wife and first child, Gretel, to Palo Alto, California, to accept a position as associate professor of bacteriology and immunology at Stanford University. There, he set up a bacteriology laboratory with the most minimal of equipment in some space borrowed from the anatomy department. In 1913, Zinsser returned to Columbia University, where he concentrated his research in the field of immunology.

Encounters an Outbreak of Typhus

As a professor of bacteriology and immunology at Columbia, Zinsser experienced a decade that was both exciting and dismaying. In 1915, in the midst of World War I, Zinsser served first as a member of the Red Cross Typhus Commission and later as an officer in the U.S. Army Medical Corps. Arriving in Serbia in 1915, Zinsser had his first field contact with an epidemic of typhus—a disease that is caused by the family of bacteria known as rickettsia, and is characterized by stupors, delirium, high fevers, severe headaches, and dark rashes. Approximately one hundred and fifty thousand cases of typhus existed at the Belgrade front, with a fatality rate of about sixty to seventy percent. During their experiences in the Eastern Front, the scientists in the commission began to gain a rudimentary understanding of the bacteriology and pathology of the disease. For his contributions during the war, Zinsser was awarded the U.S. Distinguished Service Medal, the French Legion of Honor, and the Order of Sava, a major Serbian citation.

In 1918, Zinsser left the U.S. Army Medical Corps as a lieutenant colonel, and continued his professorial duties at Columbia, where he specialized in immunology. In particular, Zinsser focused on discovering a way to immunize patients against the chronic and contagious disease syphilis. Though he did not succeed in his quest to discover a successful method of immunization, he did contribute to the existing knowledge of spirochete, a type of bacteria that causes syphilis and relapsing fevers. In addition, Zinsser continued to study typhus, since he had became an expert on military sanitation, especially with regards to typhus, during his service in the war. He wrote articles and books on the subject in the course of his career, and during his lifetime took a number of trips to distant lands to study epidemic typhus or cholera—a diarrheal disease caused by bacteria. Among his expeditions were excursions to the Soviet Union in 1923, to Mexico in 1931, and to China in 1938, where he lectured at the Peiping, Beijing, Medical College. His Columbia years came to an end in 1923 when, at the age of forty-five, he was offered a teaching position at Harvard University Medical School. Within two years he was named the Charles Wilder Professor of Bacteriology. Zinsser remained in Boston for the remainder of his life. The Zinsser family, along with their second and last child, Hans Handforth Zinsser (who later graduated from Columbia's College of Physicians and Surgeons), lived in a house in the city and traveled often to their country farm in Dover, Massachusetts. The farm became a retreat and entertainment site for Zinsser's colleagues and his medical students.

By 1930, Zinsser had decided to concentrate his studies on typhus fever research, and began a lengthy friendship with **Charles J. H. Nicolle**, the Nobel Prize–winning French physician and bacteriologist who discovered that typhus is transmitted by body lice. During the 1930s, Zinsser was able, either alone or with a variety of co-workers, to aid in the understanding of the cause of the several forms of typhus, including Brill's disease, named for American physician Nathan Edwin Brill, who investigated the malady. Zinsser was able to prove that the disease is caused by the microorganism *Rickettsia prowazekii* as opposed to *Rickettsia mooseri,* as was commonly believed, and hypothesized that Brill's disease is a form of recrudescent (or renewing) typhus. His theory was confirmed by later studies, and the disease has since been renamed Brill-Zinsser's disease. In addition, Zinsser worked on a vaccine against typhus and assisted in conceiving of a way to prepare the vaccine commercially, thus making the treatment available to large numbers of people. These endeavors have guaranteed him a place in the history of bacteriology and medicine.

In addition to his significant contributions to bacteriology, Zinsser also made advancements in the field of immunology. He discovered that it is not possible to create a grand conceptual unification for an understanding of the phenomenon of allergic reaction. Near the beginning of the twentieth century, Austrian pediatrician Clemens von Pirquet and Hungarian pediatrician Bela Schick, then leading figures in immunology, sought to explain allergic reactions as if all were antibody-mediated. They also believed that an allergic reaction was a typical step in the recovery process.

Zinsser showed that certain forms of bodily responses to infection, including those involving the body's reaction to tuberculin (a substance that was later, and to this day, used in the test for tuberculosis infection), are fundamentally different from other types of allergic responses.

In several books and papers, Zinsser detailed his scientific studies in the fields of bacteriology and immunology; among the most well known of these volumes is his 1935 work *Rats, Lice and History*. An examination of the history of typhus, the book intermixes philosophy and wit along with scientific information. The book became a best-seller and was praised by several literary critics. Zinsser delved into his private life with his 1940 autobiography, *As I Remember Him: The Biography of R. S.* Made up of some of the author's thoughts regarding living with leukemia— the disease that eventually caused his death— *As I Remember Him* was a popular book whose somewhat odd subtitle was derived from Zinsser's use of a pseudonym for his literary writings. In these writings he often referred to himself as R. S. There is disagreement as to what R. S. stood for: Some say it meant "Romantic Self"; others believe that it was derived from a German author, Rudolf Schmidt, who in 1908 had written on pain and its significance in medicine.

During his lifetime, Zinsser won numerous awards and was actively involved in many scientific societies, such as serving as president of the American Association of Immunologists in 1919 and of the Society of American Bacteriologists in 1926. His major honors include the receipt of honorary doctorates from Columbia University in 1929, Western Reserve University in 1931, Lehigh University in 1933, Yale University in 1939, and Harvard University in 1939. Among his other accolades are his elections to the Harvey Society and Sigma Xi. His published articles number more than 270.

Zinsser possessed a life-long devotion to personal fitness—enjoying activities ranging from horseback riding to hounds (at which he was expert) to shooting. "Throughout his life," Wolbach reported in *Memoirs of the National Academy of Sciences*, "he carried the aura of youth." Zinsser died of leukemia in his native New York City on September 4, 1940.

SELECTED WRITINGS BY ZINSSER:

Books

A Textbook of Bacteriology, D. Appleton, 1910.
Infection and Resistance, Macmillan, 1914.
Laboratory Course in Serum Study, [New York], 1916.
Typhus Fever with Particular Reference to the Serbian Epidemic, Harvard University Press, 1920.
Rats, Lice and History, Little, Brown, 1935.
As I Remember Him: The Biography of R. S., Little, Brown, 1940.
Spring, Summer and Autumn, (poems), Knopf, 1942.

Periodicals

Archives of Internal Medicine, The Bacteriology of Rheumatic Fever and the Allergic Hypothesis, Volume 42, 1928, pp. 301–309.
American Journal of Hygiene, Varieties of Typhus Fever and the Epidemiology of the American Form of European Typhus Fever (Brill's Disease), Volume 20, 1934, pp. 513–534.

FURTHER READING:

Periodicals

Wolbach, Simeon Burt, *Memoirs of the National Academy of Sciences,* Biographical Memoir of Hans Zinsser: 1878–1940, Volume 24, 1947, pp. 323–360.

Sketch by Donald J. McGraw

Richard Zsigmondy
1865–1929
German colloidal chemist

Although trained as an organic chemist, Richard Zsigmondy earned fame in the field of colloidal chemistry, the study of fine dispersions of a material in a solution of another substance. Colloids had been well known and widely used for centuries, but at the dawn of the twentieth century very little was known about their physical and chemical nature. To learn more about this class of materials, Zsigmondy invented a number of tools, including the ultramicroscope, with which he was able to study colloids more closely. Such equipment allowed Zsigmondy to make a number of fundamental discoveries about the composition and properties of colloids. For this work he was awarded the 1925 Nobel Prize in chemistry, the first and one of the few times this award has been given for research on colloids.

Richard Adolf Zsigmondy was born in Vienna on April 1, 1865. His father, Adolf Zsigmondy, a dentist and an inventor of surgical instruments, and his mother, the former Irma von Szakmáry, oversaw their four sons' home experiments in chemistry and physics. After Zsigmondy graduated from high school in 1883, he enrolled at the Vienna Technische Hochschule, where he majored in chemistry. At the time, the Hochschule emphasized organic chemistry, which eventually became Zsigmondy's major field of study. However, he also became interested in the colorization of glasses, and he collaborated with a Prague chemist in some original research at a nearby glass factory.

In 1887 Zsigmondy completed his studies at the Hochschule and began a graduate program in organic chemistry.

Some disagreement among scholars surrounds the conditions of Zsigmondy's doctoral work. Most authorities say that he attended the University of Munich and was granted his Ph.D. in organic chemistry in 1885. In one of the most complete biographies available, however, George Fleck in the American Chemical Society's *Nobel Laureates in Chemistry, 1901–1992,* claims that Zsigmondy did his research on chlorine derivatives at the Munich Technische Hochschule, which "was the basis for the doctor of philosophy degree awarded to Zsigmondy by the University of Erlangen in December 1889."

Interest in Glass Colorization Leads to Research on Colloids

After receiving his doctorate, Zsigmondy became an assistant to A. A. Kundt at the University of Berlin's Institute of Physics. Kundt, an authority on the colorization of glass by inorganic materials, further encouraged Zsigmondy's interest in this field. In 1893 Zsigmondy became qualified to teach and accepted a job as privatdozent at the Technische Hochschule in Graz. He joined the Schott Glass Manufacturing Company in Jena, Germany, in 1897; there he continued his work on the colorization of glass and invented a product known as *Jena milk glass* that was later to attain wide commercial popularity.

Zsigmondy's work with colored glass led to an increased interest in colloids, which are often responsible for the colorization of glassy materials. Colloids are mixtures of two substances that do not form a solution, but that do not separate even after standing for long periods of time. For example, if one were to add powdered iron to water, the iron would not dissolve, but would remain suspended for some period of time. Eventually, however, the iron would settle at the bottom of the container.

Under certain conditions, however, the iron can be made into such fine particles that, although still not dissolved, remain in suspension essentially forever. The science of colloidal chemistry is devoted to a study of the ways in which such mixtures can be made, of their properties, and of the ways the particles can be made to settle out.

A fundamental problem with colloidal research is that, although not of atomic size, colloidal particles are too small to be seen with ordinary light microscopes. Direct observation of such particles was therefore impossible before Zsigmondy's time. The one method that was (and is) commonly available for the study of colloids relies upon the so-called Tyndall effect. The Tyndall effect occurs when colloidal particles scatter light shined through a mixture. A common example of this effect is the scattering of light that occurs when a beam of light shines through a smoky room.

Invents the Ultramicroscope for the Study of Colloids

Zsigmondy concluded that an instrument could be developed that makes use of the Tyndall effect. In this instrument, called the ultramicroscope, light is reflected off particles not in the same direction as the incident light, as in a conventional microscope, but at right angles to the incident beam.

From 1900 to 1907 Zsigmondy's work was supported by his family's own fortune, and he pursued his research without any official professional affiliation. During this time he was invited, however, to make use of the superb facilities at the Zeiss Optical Company in Jena for his research on the ultramicroscope. There he collaborated with Zeiss physicist H. F. W. Siedentopf; together, the two men produced the first microscope of Zsigmondy's design, with which he soon made a number of discoveries about colloidal materials. For example, in 1898 Zsigmondy discovered that the valuable dye known as Cassius purple is actually a suspension of colloidal gold and stannic acid particles. In 1907 Zsigmondy returned to academia as assistant professor of inorganic chemistry and director of the Institute for Inorganic Chemistry at the University of Göttingen. Twelve years later he was promoted to full professor, a post he held for the rest of his life. Zsigmondy died from arteriosclerosis at his home in Göttingen on September 24, 1929.

Zsigmondy was married to Laura Luise Müller in 1903; the couple had two daughters. Zsigmondy's work was recognized by his election to the scientific academies of Göttingen, Vienna, Uppsala, Zaragoza, Valencia, and Haarlem. He was awarded honorary doctorates from the University of Königsberg and the Technische Hochschules at Vienna and Graz. Throughout his life, Zsigmondy's leisure-time passions were hiking and mountain climbing.

SELECTED WRITINGS BY ZSIGMONDY:

Books

Über Kolloid-Chemie: mit besonderer Berücksichtigung der anorganischen Kolloide, J. A. Barth, 1906.

Colloids and the Ultramicroscope: A Manual of Colloid Chemistry and Ultramicroscopy, translated by J. Alexander, John Wiley, 1909.

The Chemistry of Colloids, translated by E. B. Spear, John Wiley, 1917.

Das kolloide Gold, Akademische Verlagsgesellschaft, 1925.

Colloid Chemistry: Theoretical and Applied, "The Immersion Ultramicroscope, and "Membrane Filters and Their Uses," edited by J. Alexander, The Chemical Catalog Company, 1926.

FURTHER READING:

Books

Fleck, George, *Nobel Laureates in Chemistry, 1901–1992,* Richard Zsigmondy, edited by Laylin K. James, American Chemical Society and The Chemical Heritage Foundation, 1993, pp. 151–157.

Gillispie, Charles Coulson, editor, *Dictionary of Scientific Biography,* Volume 14, Scribner, 1975, pp. 632–634.

Madden, Paul, *The Nobel Prize Winners: Chemistry,* Richard Zsigmondy, Volume 1, 1901–1937, edited by Frank N. Magill, Salem Press, 1990, pp. 271–276.

Sketch by David E. Newton

Konrad Zuse
1910–1973
German computer scientist

Konrad Zuse was one of the most honored figures in the history of computing, with his influence on computing in Britain and America abated only because of World War II. In 1938, in Germany, Zuse built a binary calculator, the Z1. A young engineering student without knowledge of similar inventions being built simultaneously in other parts of the world, Zuse created several computers that equaled in some respects and surpassed in many ways the capabilities of American-built computers of the same generation. With the war intervening, it was not until several years later that Zuse's inventions were known outside Germany.

Born in 1910 in Berlin-Wilmersdorf, Zuse grew up in East Prussia, where his family moved shortly after his birth. He attended school in Braunsberg, experiencing an early education that revolved around a curriculum based on the classics and Latin. By his mid-teens he had developed a fascination for engineering and in 1927, at the age of seventeen, he enrolled at the Technical University (Technische Hochschule) in Berlin. He graduated eight years later with a degree in civil engineering.

Develops Computer to Facilitate Job

While at engineering school, Zuse became disillusioned by the "long and awful" calculations he had to perform, according to David Ritchie in *The Computer Pioneers.* Some equations were so tedious it would take the better part of a year to solve on a desktop calculator. Upon graduation he went to work at the Henschel Flugzeugwerke

(aircraft factory) in Berlin, where he was a stress analyst, studying the amount of stress an airplane in flight could stand before it began to break apart. Because of the extreme difficulty Zuse came across working with differential equations, he knew he would have to build a machine that could automatically do his calculations.

The biggest problem Zuse found when making the initial sketches for his machine was not in the calculations themselves, but in the steps in between—the recording and transferring of intermediate results. And, as the equations became larger, the transfer became more difficult. Getting those intermediate results from one part of a problem to another was Zuse's main task. He considered several options before arriving at the idea of creating a calculator with a mechanical keyboard. In fact, twenty years after the war, Zuse admitted in a speech which is quoted in *The Computer Pioneers,* "I did not know anything about computers, nor had I heard about the early work of Charles Babbage." Babbage was a contemporary of Zuse who also made early discoveries in the field of computing.

Zuse's ideal computer contained an arithmetic unit and storage unit, a selection mechanism to link the two, and a control unit that would be directed by punched tape and would deliver instructions to the selection mechanism and arithmetic unit. Once he had finalized his computer design, he devoted full time to its realization, using his parents' living room as his workshop.

Although he was a competent draftsman and skilled mechanic, he was relatively ignorant when it came to electrical engineering. He also knew very little about how to go about constructing a mechanical calculator. With his lack of knowledge Zuse was able to approach his project without the burden of conventional ideas. Later, after the war, he said, "Thus—unprejudiced—I could go new ways," according to Ritchie in *The Computer Pioneers.*

Since Zuse was more familiar with binary arithmetic—math based on a two digit system rather than ten—he decided to make his machine a binary device. Zuse's reasoning was that if he didn't have to represent ten numbers when two would work, why should he? A major influence on him was the writings of Gottfried Wilhelm Leibniz, who several centuries earlier imagined the entire universe reduced to binary values. In fact, one of Zuse's reports about his work was entitled, "Hommage to Leibniz."

The computer that Zuse designed and built, with the help of friends, had a mechanical memory unit that used movable pins in slots to indicate, by their position, zeroes and ones. Because of his use of the binary approach, the memory space was surprisingly compact, occupying about a cubic meter. Zuse's first computer was produced in 1938 when he connected his mechanical memory with a crude mechanical calculating unit.

With the help of friends and a supply of secondhand telephone relays, Zuse built his second computer, the Z2 computer, using electromechanical relays. Although the Z2's relays were problematic, making it less reliable than the Z1, it sparked the interest of the German Experimental Aircraft Institute, or Deutsche Versuchanstalt für Luftfahrt (DVL). The problem of trying to overcome flutter, a shivering of aircraft wings, demanded extensive calculations and the DVL was not equipped to handle the tasks. The Z2 was seen as a possible solution to the DVL's perplexing problem.

Zuse received money from the DVL for the design and manufacture of a relay computer. He began work on the Z3 while still using his parents' living room. The Z3, with two thousand relays and the capability to multiply, divide, or extract a square root in only three seconds, was completed in 1941. The Z3 was extremely compact (occupying only the volume of a closet) and had a sophisticated push-button control panel enabling the user to carry out operations with the touch of a finger. A single keystroke would convert decimal numbers into binary and, with another keystroke, switch them back again.

Zuse even created an innovative programming notation that included the now familiar symbols ≥ (greater than or equal to) and ≤ (less than or equal to). He used punched motion picture film for input. In addition to designing and building a sophisticated yet compact computer, Zuse, with the Z3, also created the first computer to achieve automatic control of a sequence of calculations. A person was no longer needed to continually punch in numbers. Zuse's computer could automatically carry out a string of calculations.

In fact, Zuse became a software pioneer before the concepts of software and hardware were fully developed. As noted in *The Computer Pioneers,* Zuse remarked in a postwar speech to an American audience, "In the early forties nobody knew the difference between hardware and software. We concentrated ourselves on purely technological matters, both logical design and programming."

Enhanced Computer Aids in War Effort

Although the Z3 was totally destroyed in 1944 when an Allied bomb fell on the apartment building where the Zuses lived, he did produce another computer, the S1, that was a non-programmable version of the Z3 that was used to design German glider bombs, unmanned aircraft that carried high explosives and were carried aloft by bombers. Directed to their targets by radio control, the bombs were usually dropped on British ships. In fact, the British feared glider bombs more than almost any other aerial weapon because, since it was pilotless, it could not be disabled. During the last two years of the war, glider bombs were used against Allied shipping in the Mediterranean. Zuse's S1 assisted in plotting a glider bomb's actual flight path as well as its deviations. With those factors in place the control surfaces on the glider bomb's wings and tail could be adjusted to ensure a steady flight and a direct hit.

With the Allied armies moving toward Germany from the west and the Russians advancing from the east, Zuse finished the Z4 an even more advanced mechanical comput-

er. To escape damage from Allied bombs he kept moving the Z4 around Berlin. By 1945 Zuse moved the Z4 to the university town Göttingen, a fair distance west of Berlin. The computer was left with the Experimental Aerodynamics Institute, or Aerodynamische Versuchanstalt (AVA). As the Allies continued to advance, Zuse, once again, moved the Z4, this time to Hinterstein, a small Alpine village, where he hid it in a barn.

Although Zuse felt he needed to keep his computer from harm's way, his brilliant work was also hidden from the rest of the world until years after Germany surrendered. In fact, it wasn't until French troops discovered Zuse and the Z4 in Hinterstein that word of the computer reached the British and Americans.

Observers who saw the Z4 in operation were amazed at what Zuse had accomplished. Without any knowledge of other, previous computer designs to assist him, as well as no information about contemporaneous computer projects in the United States and Britain, Zuse had designed and built his computers practically from scratch. In 1951, Zuse demonstrated the Z4 in Zurich, where one observer, quoted in *The Computer Pioneers,* wrote, "I could not believe it."

There were several contributing factors in addition to the isolation of his work at Hinterstein as to why Zuse's wartime achievements took so long to be recognized. The Z4 looked more like a typesetting machine than the huge American machines. Also, Zuse resented the Allies so he did not cooperate with their inquiries about his machines.

It was only well after the war that Zuse learned about other computer scientists such as **Howard H. Aiken** and his team at Harvard, who worked extensively on technological development during the war years. Although they had constructed computers larger than Zuse thought possible, it was Konrad Zuse who had brought computer design farther than they had.

After the war Zuse continued to design calculating machines and in 1949 established a small computer company, Zuse KG, that developed into a leading manufacturer of small scientific computers. He remained with the firm until 1966. After retirement, he remained as a consultant to the firm but devoted most of his remaining years to painting, his lifelong hobby. He died in 1973.

FURTHER READING:

Books

Augarten, Stan, *Bit by Bit,* Ticknor & Fields, 1984.

Fang, Irving E., *The Computer Story,* Rada Press, 1988.

Ritchie, David, *The Computer Pioneers,* Simon & Schuster, 1986.

Slater, Robert, *Portraits in Silicon,* Massachusetts Institute of Technology Press, 1987.

Wulforst, Harry, *Breakthrough to the Computer Age,* Scribner, 1982.

Periodicals

Golden, Frederic, *Time,* Big Dimwits and Little Geni-
    uses, January 3, 1983, pp. 30–32.

Sketch by Dorothy Spencer

Vladimir Zworykin

Vladimir Zworykin
1889–1982
American physicist and engineer

Vladimir Zworykin is best remembered for developing the iconoscope and the kinescope, two inventions for which he became known as "the father of television." During his lifetime he obtained more than 120 patents on a wide variety of electronic devices and applied many of the principles from his work with television to microscopy, leading to the development of the electron microscope.

Vladimir Kosma Zworykin was born to Kosma and Elaine (Zworykin) Zworykin on July 30, 1889, in Mourom, Russia. His early years were spent in Mourom, where his father owned and operated a fleet of river boats on the Oka River. He was educated locally before studying electrical engineering at the St. Petersburg Institute of Technology (also known as Petrograd Institute of Technology). In St. Petersburg, he studied with professor Boris Rosing, who maintained that cathode ray tubes, with their ability to shoot a stream of charged particles, would be useful in the development of television. This belief contrasted with efforts at the time to use mechanical systems based on a variety of synchronized moving parts. Although Rosing's ideas could only be demonstrated by transmission of crude geometric images in his laboratory in St. Petersburg, these early experiments inspired much of Zworykin's later successful work on the television.

After receiving his degree from St. Petersburg in 1912, Zworykin entered the prestigious College de France in Paris, where he studied X-ray technology under the well-known French physicist **Paul Langevin**. With the outbreak of World War I in 1914, he returned to Russia and spent the war years as a radio officer in the Russian signal corps. During the war Zworykin married Tatiana Vasilieff, a union that produced two children. At the war's end in 1918, he left Russia and traveled widely before emigrating with his family to the United States in 1919. When he arrived in the U.S., Zworykin obtained a position as a bookkeeper for the financial agent of the Russian embassy.

Television Is Born

In 1920 Zworykin was invited to join the research laboratories at Westinghouse to work on the development of radio tubes and photoelectric cells (small devices whose electrical properties are modified by the action of light). While at Westinghouse, Zworykin earned his Ph.D. in physics at the University of Pittsburgh, writing his dissertation on the improvement of photoelectric cells. It was the concept of television, however, that most excited him, and in December 1923 he filed a patent application for his iconoscope, an invention that would revolutionize the development of television (although the actual patent was not granted until 1938). Until this time most television research involved mechanical systems. These relied on a rapidly rotating, perforated disk. The perforations were arranged in a spiral which could be quickly rotated. Light was transmitted from a photoelectric device behind the disk through the holes to form a series of successive parallel lines on a viewing screen. Unfortunately, the amount of light transmitted for each picture was very small, making the pictures quite dim and lacking in detail.

Zworykin's landmark iconoscope was an attempt to reproduce the human eye electronically. In human vision, light enters the eye through the iris, passes through a lens, and focuses an image on the retina, which registers colors via photosensitive receptor cells known as cones and light intensities via cells called rods. The optic nerves of the eye transmit this information to the brain in the form of electrical impulses which register as an image for the viewer. The iconoscope, like the eye, used a lens to focus an image on a signal plate of mica, covered with tiny dots of photoelectric cells (corresponding to and simulating the rods and cones of the retina). An electron beam (corresponding to and simulating the optic nerves) scanned the signal plate from top to bottom in parallel lines detecting the electrical emissions. This formed the picture. This system was more sensitive than any mechanical system then being explored and greatly reduced the amount of light necessary to produce a clear picture.

To reconstruct the transmitted image, Zworykin needed a special kind of cathode-ray tube which could send a steady stream of electrons to the signal plate. The kinescope was his ingenious solution, an idea whose essential elements were suggested by Scottish physicist A. A. Campbell Swinton in 1908 and amplified in an address to the Roentgen Society of London in 1911. Until Zworykin's efforts, however, a series of technical barriers had prevented a practical demonstration of Swinton's ideas. The kinescope, or picture tube, corresponded to the brain in human vision. An electron beam is applied to an electrode grid (invented in 1906 by the American Lee DeForest) with modulation occurring through the use of electromagnetic fields. With the addition of the kinescope, for which Zworykin filed a patent in 1924, television as we know it was now feasible.

In 1924, the year Zworykin gained American citizenship, he demonstrated his new system to Westinghouse executives. As he later wrote in an article in *American Magazine,* "1 was terribly excited and proud. After a few days I was informed, very politely, that my demonstration had been extremely interesting, but that it might be better if I were to spend my time on something 'a little more useful'." Apparently, Zworykin was too forthcoming about the technological problems still to be surmounted even as he persisted in pleading his cause with management. Westinghouse decided not to pursue Zworykin's research, a decision they surely lived to regret many times over in subsequent years as a whole industry developed around this new communications medium.

In 1929 Zworykin, still determined to prove the worth of his ideas, found a receptive audience at Radio Corporation of America (RCA) and was hired away from Westinghouse as associate research director of the RCA electronic research laboratory in Camden, New Jersey. The story is told that when RCA's president, the famous scientist-administrator David Sarnoff, asked Zworykin how much it would cost to perfect his system, he replied, "About $100,000." Sarnoff later said, as quoted in the *New York Times,* "RCA spent $50 million before we ever got a penny back from TV." The same year that Zworykin moved to RCA, he filed his first patent for color television. It took the end of World War II, however, with the lifting of restrictions on manufacturing of receivers to fuel explosive growth in television communications. As a result of the quality of his efforts at RCA, Zworykin was elevated to director of electronic research in 1946 and to vice president of the laboratories division in 1947, a position he held in an emeritus capacity until his death.

Turns to New Ventures

A man of many interests, Zworykin began work with G. A. Morton in 1930 on the infrared (electron) image tube, which converted infrared rays into visible light. This device enabled humans to see in the dark and became the basis for the Sniperscope and Snooperscope used during World War II and all subsequent night sighting instruments.

Believing that the refinement of television could be left to fellow engineers, Zworykin then sought to apply television technology to microscopy. Under his leadership the electron microscope was developed by James Hillier and others at the RCA labs. This device enabled researchers to see objects much smaller than was possible with a conventional microscope and revolutionized scientific understanding of the fine structure of matter, especially in the fields of molecular and cell biology. The number of scientific applications for this technology continue to multiply. Zworykin's remaining patents consisted of such inventions as the electric eye used in security systems and automatic door openers, electronically-controlled missiles and automobiles, a clock which operated without moving parts, and a device which enabled the blind to read print—a very early precursor to textual recognition systems which combine light-based technologies with electronics and microprocessors.

During World War II, Zworykin served on the Scientific Advisory Board to the U.S. Air Force and on a number of committees of the National Defense Research Council which advised the U.S. government on scientific contributions to the war effort. In the early years of the Cold War, Zworykin collaborated with **John Neumann** of the Institute for Advanced Study at Princeton University to lay the conceptual groundwork for a computer sophisticated enough to open the possibility of accurate weather forecasting—an application whose possibilities were not lost on the American military command.

Zworykin was honored with numerous awards during his lifetime. The first major award he received was the Morris Liebmann Memorial prize given him in 1934 for his television contributions by the Institute of Radio Engineers. The American Institute of Electrical Engineers bestowed its highest honor, the Edison Medal, on Zworykin in 1952 citing his "outstanding contributions to the concept and development of electronic components and systems." In 1967 he was awarded the National Medal of Science by the National Academy of Sciences for his work in television, science, and engineering and the application of science to medicine. Among other tributes, he was elected to the National Academy of Sciences in 1943, was one of the earliest inductees into the newly founded National Academy of Engineering in 1965, and was honored by the French Legion of Honor.

With his first marriage ended in divorce, Zworykin married Katherine Polevitsky in 1951. He retired from RCA in 1954 at which time he was named an honorary vice president and technical consultant for the company. He was appointed director of the Medical Electronics Center at the

Rockefeller Institute for Medical Research (now Rockefeller University), where he worked for a number of years in an attempt to broaden the range of electronically-based applications in medicine.

Zworykin died July 29, 1982, one day before his 93rd birthday. He is best remembered for his pioneering work in the development of television, a technology which has evolved into a major shaper of cultures and events around the world. Ironically, as quoted in his *New York Times* obituary, when asked to comment on the content of American television in an interview in 1981, Zworykin replied, "Awful."

SELECTED WRITINGS BY ZWORYKIN:

Books

Television: The Electronics of Image Transmission, Wiley, 1940, 2nd edition, 1954.
Electron Optics and the Electron Microscope, Wiley, 1946.

Photoelectricity and Its Applications, Wiley, 1949.
Television in Science and Industry, Wiley, 1958.

FURTHER READING:

Books

Current Biography 1949, H. W. Wilson, 1950, pp. 654–56.
Parker, Sybil P., editor, *McGraw-Hill Modern Scientists and Engineers,* Volume 3, McGraw Hill, 1980.

Periodicals

Abramson, A., *Journal of the Society of Motion Picture and Television Engineers,* Pioneers of Television, July, 1981, pp. 579–90.
Thomas, Robert McG., Jr., *New York Times Biographical Service,* Vladimir Zworykin, Television Pioneer, Dies at 92, August, 1982, p. 1119.

Sketch by Dennis W. and Kim A. Cheek

Selected Biographical Sources

African American Scientists, Capstone Press, 1996.

Asimov, Isaac, *Asimov's Biographical Encyclopedia of Science and Technology: The Lives and Achievements of 1510 Great Scientists from Ancient Times to the Present Chronologically Arranged,* 2nd revised edition, New York: Doubleday, 1982.

Blacks in Science: Ancient and Modern, edited by Ivan Van Sertima, New Brunswick, NJ: Transaction Books, 1983.

Dash, Joan, *The Triumph of Discovery: Women Scientists Who Won the Nobel Prize,* Englewood Cliffs, NJ: Julian Messner, 1991.

Dunlap, Jr., Orrin E., *Radio's One Hundred Men of Science: Biographical Narratives of Pathfinders in Electronics and Television,* New York: Harper, 1944.

Feldman, Anthony, *Scientists and Inventors,* New York: Facts on File, 1979.

Gaillard, Jacques, *Scientists in the Third World,* Lexington: University Press of Kentucky, 1991.

Hispanic Scientists, Capstone Press, 1996.

Larousse Dictionary of Scientists, edited by Hazel Muir, Larousse, 1996.

Lives in Science, New York: Simon and Schuster, 1957.

McGraw-Hill Modern Men of Science: 426 Leading Contemporary Scientists, New York: McGraw-Hill, 1966-68.

McGraw-Hill Modern Scientists and Engineers, New York: McGraw-Hill, 1980.

McGrayne, Sharon Bertsch, *Nobel Prize Women in Science: Their Lives, Struggles, and Momentous Discoveries,* Secaucus, NJ: Carol Publishing Group, 1993.

Native American Scientists, Capstone Press, 1996.

Out of Their Minds: The Lives and Discoveries of 15 Great Computer Scientists, Springer-Verlag, 1995.

A Passion to Know: 20 Profiles in Science, New York: Scribner, 1984.

Pioneers of Science in America: Sketches of Their Lives and Scientific Work, revised and edited by William J. Youmans, New York: Arno Press, 1978.

The Scientific 100: A Ranking of the Most Influential Scientists, Past and Present, Citadel Press, 1996.

Scott, Michael Maxwell, *Stories of Famous Scientists,* London: Barker, 1967.

Siedel, Frank, and James M. Siedel, *Pioneers in Science,* Boston: Houghton, 1968.

The Twentieth-Century Sciences: Studies in the Biography of Ideas, New York: Norton, 1972.

Van Wagenen, Theodore F., *Beacon Lights of Science: A Survey of Human Achievement from the Earliest Recorded Times,* New York: Thomas Y. Crowell, 1924.

Weisgerber, Robert A., *The Challenged Scientists: Disabilities and the Triumph of Excellence,* New York: Praeger, 1991.

Women Scientists in America: Before Affirmative Action, 1940-1972, Johns Hopkins University Press, 1995.

Autobiographical Collections

The Excitement and Fascination of Science: A Collection of Autobiographical and Philosophical Essays, Palo Alto, CA: Annual Reviews, 1965-78.

Scientists Who Believe: Twenty-One Tell Their Own Stories, edited by Eric C. Barrett and David Fisher, Chicago: Moody Press, 1984.

Studying Animal Behavior: Autobiographies of the Founders, edited by Donald A. Dewsbury, Chicago: University of Chicago Press, 1989.

Historical Collections

Elliott, Clark A., *Biographical Dictionary of American Science: The Seventeenth through the Nineteenth Centuries,* Westport, CT: Greenwood Press, 1979.

Engstrand, Iris W., *Spanish Scientists in the New World: The Eighteenth-Century Expeditions,* Seattle: University of Washington Press, 1981.

Gascoigne, Robert Mortimer, *A Historical Catalogue of Scientists and Scientific Books: From the Earliest Times to the Close of the Nineteenth Century,* New York: Garland Pub., 1984.

The Golden Age of Science: Thirty Portraits of the Giants of 19th-Century Science by Their Scientific Contemporaries, edited by Bessie Zaban Jones, New York: Simon and Schuster, 1966.

Hutcgubgs, D., and E. Candlin, *Late Seventeenth-Century Scientists,* 1st edition, Oxford, NY: Pergamon Press, 1969.

Kohler, Robert E., *Partners in Science: Foundation Managers and Natural Scientists, 1900-1945,* Chicago: University of Chicago Press, 1991.

Late Eighteenth-Century European Scientists, 1st edition, edited by Robert C. Olby, Oxford, NY: Pergamon Press, 1966.

Lenard, Philipp Eduard Anton, *Great Men of Science: A History of Scientific Progress,* translated from the second German edition by H. Stafford Hatfield, New York: Macmillan, 1933.

Murray, Robert H., *Science and Scientists in the Nineteenth Century,* New York: Macmillan, 1925.

North, J., *Mid-Nineteenth-Century Scientists,* 1st edition, Oxford, NY: Pergamon Press, 1969.

Dictionaries and Encyclopedias

The Biographical Dictionary of Scientists, edited by Roy Porter, Oxford: Oxford University Press, 1994.

Biographical Encyclopedia of Scientists, edited by Richard Olsen and Roger Smith, Marshall Cavendish, 1998.

Concise Dictionary of Scientific Biography, New York: Scribner, 1981.

Howard, Arthur Vyvyan, *Chambers's Dictionary of Scientists,* New York: Dutton, 1961.

Directories

American Men and Women of Science, 1998-99, 20th edition, New York: R. R. Bowker, 1998.

Cassutt, Michael, *Who's Who in Space: The International Space Year Edition,* Boston: Prentice Hall, 1993.

Ireland, Norma, *Index to Scientists of the World from Ancient to Modern Times: Biographies and Portraits,* Boston: Faxon, 1962.

Pelletier, Paul A., *Prominent Scientists: An Index to Collective Biographies,* 3rd edition, New York: Neal-Schuman, 1994.

Who's Who in Computer Education and Research: U.S. Edition, edited by T. C. Hsiao, Latham, NY: Science and Technology Press, 1975.

Who's Who in Science and Engineering, 1998-1999, 4th edition, edited by Kristin A. Eckes, New Providence, NJ: Marquis Who's Who, 1997.

Who's Who in Technology, 7th edition, edited by Kimberley A. McGrath, Detroit, MI: Gale Research Inc., 1995.

Who's Who in Science in Europe: A Biographical Guide in Science, Technology, Agriculture, and Medicine, Essex, England: Longman, 1995.

Who's Who of British Scientists, 1980-81, New York: St. Martin's, 1981.

Who's Who of Nobel Prize Winners, 3rd edition, edited by Bernard S. Schlessinger and June H. Schlessinger, Phoenix, AZ: Oryx Press, 1996.

Field of Specialization Index

Acoustic Design
Harris, Cyril **2**: 960

Aerodynamics
Prandtl, Ludwig **4**: 1804

Aeronautical Engineering
Bondar, Roberta L. **1**: 241
Draper, Charles Stark **2**: 589
Durand, William F. **2**: 605
Flügge-Lotz, Irmgard **2**: 745
Fokker, Anthony H. G. **2**: 747
Harris, Wesley L. **2**: 961
Heinkel, Ernst **2**: 988
Hunsaker, Jerome C. **2**: 1092
Johnson, Clarence L. **3**: 1146
Ochoa, Ellen **4**: 1668
Piasecki, Frank **4**: 1767
Shurney, Robert E. **4**: 2041
Sikorsky, Igor I. **4**: 2046
Stever, H. Guyford **4**: 2131
van der Wal, Laurel **5**: 2290
von Kármán, Theodore **5**: 2310
von Mises, Richard **5**: 2313
Widnall, Sheila E. **5**: 2401
Williams, O. S. **5**: 2436
Orville Wright **5**: 2480

Aerospace Engineering
Alcorn, George Edward **1**: 18
Armstrong, Neil **1**: 69
Bluford, Guion S. **1**: 227
Brill, Yvonne Claeys **1**: 292
Gutierrez, Orlando A. **2**: 924
Harris, Wesley L. **2**: 961
Johnson, Barbara Crawford **3**: 1145
Korolyov, Sergei **3**: 1258
Liepmann, Hans Wolfgang **3**: 1394
MacGill, Elsie Gregory **3**: 1446
Rockwell, Mabel M. **4**: 1897
Rogers, Marguerite M. **4**: 1902
Ross, Mary G. **4**: 1914
Tereshkova, Valentina **5**: 2202
Tsiolkovsky, Konstantin **5**: 2256
von Braun, Wernher **5**: 2307
Wu, Y. C. L. Susan **5**: 2485

Agriculture
Brown, Lester R. **1**: 307
Carver, George Washington **1**: 373
Evans, Alice **2**: 680
Khush, Gurdev S. **3**: 1218
Sanchez, Pedro A. **4**: 1972
Swaminathan, M. S. **4**: 2164
Tsao, George T. **5**: 2255

Algebra
Baxter, Agnes **1**: 144
Birkhoff, Garrett **1**: 197
Blum, Lenore **1**: 229
Cartan, Henri Paul **1**: 370
Falconer, Etta Zuber **2**: 690
Fenchel, Käte **2**: 706
Gelfond, Aleksandr Osipovich **2**: 826
Hazlett, Olive Clio **2**: 982
Hermite, Charles **2**: 997
MacPherson, Robert **3**: 1455
Maddison, Ada Isabel **3**: 1456
Nash, John Forbes **4**: 1614
Nelson, Evelyn **4**: 1626
Neumann, Hanna **4**: 1631
Noether, Max **4**: 1649
Oleinik, Olga **4**: 1680
Schafer, Alice T. **4**: 1980
Stanley, Richard **4**: 2106
Szegö, Gabor **4**: 2167
Wheeler, Anna Johnson Pell **5**: 2380

Algebraist
Bari, Ruth Aaronson **1**: 128

Analysis
Keen, Linda **3**: 1198
Klein, Christian Felix **3**: 1233
Lindemann, Carl Louis Ferdinand von **3**: 1400
Macintyre, Sheila Scott **3**: 1447
Merrill, Helen Abbot **3**: 1520
Scott, Charlotte Angas **4**: 2002

Analysis, combinatorial
Pless, Vera **4**: 1782

Analysis, mathematical
Askey, Richard **1**: 75

Cartwright, Mary Lucy **1**: 372
Chang, Sun-Yung Alice **1**: 392
Szegö, Gabor **4**: 2167

Anatomy
Alcala, Jose **1**: 17
Banting, Frederick G. **1**: 118
Barr, Murray Llewellyn **1**: 134
Cobb, William Montague **1**: 426
Crosby, Elizabeth Caroline **1**: 492
Dart, Raymond A. **2**: 522
Dubois, Eugène **2**: 598
Fell, Honor Bridget **2**: 705
Hoyle, Fred **2**: 1073
Keith, Arthur **3**: 1199
Lloyd, Ruth Smith **3**: 1412
Papanicolaou, George **4**: 1705
Romer, Alfred Sherwood **4**: 1906
Sabin, Florence Rena **4**: 1953
Scharrer, Berta **4**: 1985
Straus, Jr., William Levi **4**: 2147
Trotter, Mildred **5**: 2252
Vallois, Henri-Victor **5**: 2280
Weidenreich, Franz **5**: 2357

Anthropology
Dart, Raymond A. **2**: 522
Diggs, Irene **2**: 569
Keith, Arthur **3**: 1199
Leakey, Louis **3**: 1330
Leakey, Richard E. **3**: 1336
Lévi-Strauss, Claude **3**: 1379
Parker, Arthur C. **4**: 1707
Stewart, Thomas Dale **4**: 2134
Weidenreich, Franz **5**: 2357

Applied Mathematics
Antonelli, Kay McNulty Mauchly **1**: 58
Birkhoff, Garrett **1**: 197
Oleinik, Olga **4**: 1680

Astrophysicists
Hewitt, Jacqueline N. **2**: 1017

Astronomy
Adams, Walter Sydney **1**: 6
Baade, Walter **1**: 93
Babcock, Horace W. **1**: 96

Banks, Harvey Washington **1**: 117
Brown, Robert Hanbury **1**: 311
Cannon, Annie Jump **1**: 347
Clemence, Gerald M. **1**: 422
Davis, Jr., Raymond **2**: 530
de Sitter, Willem **2**: 555
Eddington, Arthur Stanley **2**: 620
Faber, Sandra M. **2**: 685
Geller, Margaret Joan **2**: 830
Gold, Thomas **2**: 866
Hertzsprung, Ejnar **2**: 1004
Hill, George William **2**: 1031
Hogg, Helen Sawyer **2**: 1052
Hubble, Edwin **2**: 1081
Humason, Milton L. **2**: 1091
Jeffreys, Harold **3**: 1129
Kuiper, Gerard Peter **3**: 1282
Leavitt, Henrietta **3**: 1338
Le Cadet, Georges **3**: 1342
Lemaître, Georges **3**: 1365
Lin, Chia-Chiao **3**: 1399
Lippmann, Gabriel **3**: 1404
Massevitch, Alla G. **3**: 1479
Maunder, Annie Russell **3**: 1487
Maury, Antonia **3**: 1488
Minkowski, Rudolph **3**: 1547
Moulton, Forest Ray **3**: 1591
Nicholson, Seth Barnes **4**: 1638
Oort, Jan Hendrik **4**: 1685
Osterbrock, Donald E. **4**: 1694
Payne-Gaposchkin, Cecilia **4**: 1730
Reber, Grote **4**: 1854
Roman, Nancy Grace **4**: 1905
Rubin, Vera Cooper **4**: 1926
Russell, Henry Norris **4**: 1938
Sagan, Carl **4**: 1956
Sandage, Allan R. **4**: 1973
Shapiro, Irwin **4**: 2017
Shapley, Harlow **4**: 2019
Slipher, Vesto M. **4**: 2069
Stefanik, Milan Ratislav **4**: 2119
Taylor, Jr., Joseph H. **5**: 2191
Tombaugh, Clyde W. **5**: 2244
van de Kamp, Peter **5**: 2286
Voûte, Joan George Erardus Gijsbert **5**: 2318
Whipple, Fred Lawrence **5**: 2385
Wilson, Robert Woodrow **5**: 2456

Astrophysics

Banks, Harvey Washington **1**: 117
Breit, Gregory **1**: 280
Burbidge, E. Margaret **1**: 319
Burbidge, Geoffrey **1**: 321
Carruthers, George R. **1**: 363
Chandrasekhar, Subrahmanyan **1**: 387
Dirac, Paul **2**: 573
Friedmann, Aleksandr A. **2**: 783
Giacconi, Riccardo **2**: 834

Goldreich, Peter **2**: 874
Hale, George Ellery **2**: 939
Hewish, Antony **2**: 1014
Hulse, Russell A. **2**: 1090
Lizhi, Fang **3**: 1410
McAfee, Walter S. **3**: 1494
Milne, Edward Arthur **3**: 1542
Moore, Charlotte E. **3**: 1566
Osterbrock, Donald E. **4**: 1694
Parker, Eugene Newman **4**: 1709
Penzias, Arno **4**: 1749
Ride, Sally **4**: 1884
Russell, Henry Norris **4**: 1938
Ryle, Martin **4**: 1946
Spitzer, Jr., Lyman **4**: 2103
Taylor, Jr., Joseph H. **5**: 2191
Wilson, C. T. R. **5**: 2443
Zel'dovich, Yakov Borisovich **5**: 2510

Atmospheric Science

Farman, Joseph C. **2**: 691
Gadgil, Sulochana **2**: 800

Atomic/Nuclear Physics

Abelson, Philip Hauge **1**: 1
Breit, Gregory **1**: 280
Charpak, Georges **1**: 397
Chu, Steven **1**: 411
Cockcroft, John D. **1**: 428
Ghiorso, Albert **2**: 831
Jensen, J. Hans D. **3**: 1136
Kastler, Alfred **3**: 1190
Kinoshita, Toichiro **3**: 1226
Kurchatov, Igor **3**: 1285
Mulliken, Robert S. **3**: 1599
Oppenheimer, J. Robert **4**: 1689
Rutherford, Ernest **4**: 1942
Segrè, Emilio **4**: 2007
Stern, Otto **4**: 2128
Wheeler, John Archibald **5**: 2381
Wu, Chien-Shiung **5**: 2484

Bacteriology

Avery, Oswald Theodore **1**: 85
Behring, Emil von **1**: 154
Bordet, Jules **1**: 245
Ehrlich, Paul **2**: 637
Evans, Alice **2**: 680
Fibiger, Johannes **2**: 716
Fleming, Alexander **2**: 734
Flexner, Simon **2**: 739
Gajdusek, D. Carleton **2**: 803
Gross, Carol **2**: 912
Hobby, Gladys Lounsbury **2**: 1042
Koch, Robert **3**: 1240
Lancefield, Rebecca Craighill **3**: 1298
Landsteiner, Karl **3**: 1309
McCarty, Maclyn **3**: 1497
Moore, Ruth **3**: 1569

Moulton Browne, Barbara **3**: 1593
Nicolle, Charles J. H. **4**: 1639
Northrop, John Howard **4**: 1655
Poindexter, Hildrus A. **4**: 1788
Reed, Walter **4**: 1856
Robbins, Frederick **4**: 1890
Szent-Györgyi, Albert **4**: 2169
Twort, Frederick **5**: 2268
Vedder, Edward Bright **5**: 2296
Waksman, Selman **5**: 2327
Williams, Anna W. **5**: 2428
Zinsser, Hans **5**: 2520

Biochemistry

Abelson, Philip Hauge **1**: 1
Abraham, Edward P. **1**: 3
Ames, Bruce N. **1**: 40
Anderson, W. French **1**: 54
Anfinsen, Christian Boehmer **1**: 56
Axelrod, Julius **1**: 88
Bachrach, Howard L. **1**: 98
Baltimore, David **1**: 114
Berg, Paul **1**: 169
Bergström, Sune Karl **1**: 175
Blackburn, Elizabeth H. **1**: 209
Bloch, Konrad **1**: 220
Blout, Elkan R. **1**: 226
Boyer, Herbert W. **1**: 264
Boyer, Paul D. **1**: 266
Bressani, Ricardo **1**: 287
Brown, Rachel Fuller **1**: 310
Butenandt, Adolf **1**: 333
Cech, Thomas R. **1**: 376
Chain, Ernst Boris **1**: 381
Chance, Britton **1**: 386
Chargaff, Erwin **1**: 393
Cohen, Stanley **1**: 436
Cohen, Stanley N. **1**: 437
Cohn, Mildred **1**: 440
Cori, Carl Ferdinand **1**: 462
Cori, Gerty T. **1**: 464
Daly, Marie M. **2**: 513
Dam, Henrik **2**: 516
Deisenhofer, Johann **2**: 547
Doisy, Edward A. **2**: 580
Domagk, Gerhard **2**: 585
du Vigneaud, Vincent **2**: 609
Edelman, Gerald M. **2**: 623
Emerson, Gladys Anderson **2**: 662
Euler-Chelpin, Hans von **2**: 679
Fischer, Edmond H. **2**: 720
Fischer, Emil **2**: 722
Folkers, Karl A. **2**: 749
Fox, Sidney W. **2**: 763
Govindjee, **2**: 900
Hanafusa, Hidesaburo **2**: 949
Hevesy, Georg von **2**: 1012
Hill, Robert **2**: 1033
Hinshelwood, Cyril N. **2**: 1036

Holley, Robert William **2**: 1055
Hopkins, Frederick Gowland **2**: 1062
Huber, Robert **2**: 1085
Jencks, William P. **3**: 1134
Jones, Mary Ellen **3**: 1162
Kendall, Edward C. **3**: 1206
Khorana, Har Gobind **3**: 1216
Kornberg, Arthur **3**: 1256
Koshland, Jr., Daniel E. **3**: 1260
Kossel, Albrecht **3**: 1262
Krebs, Edwin G. **3**: 1269
Krebs, Hans Adolf **3**: 1271
Leloir, Luis F. **3**: 1363
Li, Choh Hao **3**: 1390
Lipmann, Fritz **3**: 1401
Lynen, Feodor **3**: 1438
Martin, A. J. P. **3**: 1478
McCollum, Elmer Verner **3**: 1502
Meyerhof, Otto **3**: 1527
Michel, Hartmut **3**: 1528
Miller, James A. **3**: 1535
Milstein, César **3**: 1544
Mitchell, Peter D. **3**: 1552
Moore, Stanford **3**: 1570
Mullis, Kary **3**: 1601
Needham, Joseph **4**: 1621
Neufeld, Elizabeth F. **4**: 1629
Nirenberg, Marshall Warren **4**: 1642
Nishizuka, Yasutomi **4**: 1644
Northrop, John Howard **4**: 1655
Ochoa, Severo **4**: 1669
Olden, Kenneth **4**: 1677
Oparin, Aleksandr Ivanovich **4**: 1687
Pert, Candace B. **4**: 1756
Perutz, Max **4**: 1757
Petermann, Mary Locke **4**: 1761
Porter, Rodney **4**: 1798
Pregl, Fritz **4**: 1806
Ramey, Estelle R. **4**: 1842
Ratner, Sarah **4**: 1851
Roberts, Richard J. **4**: 1892
Rodbell, Martin **4**: 1898
Roelofs, Wendell L. **4**: 1901
Ružička, Leopold **4**: 1945
Samuelsson, Bengt **4**: 1970
Sanger, Frederick **4**: 1976
Schally, Andrew V. **4**: 1983
Seibert, Florence B. **4**: 2009
Sheldrake, Rupert **4**: 2026
Singer, Maxine **4**: 2060
Skou, Jens C. **4**: 2065
Smith, Michael **4**: 2077
Sørensen, Søren Peter Lauritz **4**: 2093
Stanley, Wendell Meredith **4**: 2108
Stein, William Howard **4**: 2120
Steitz, Joan Argetsinger **4**: 2125
Sumner, James B. **4**: 2154
Sutherland, Earl **4**: 2157
Synge, Richard **4**: 2165

Szent-Györgyi, Albert **4**: 2169
Tatum, Edward Lawrie **5**: 2179
Theorell, Axel Hugo Teodor **5**: 2215
Tildon, J. Tyson **5**: 2231
Tsao, George T. **5**: 2255
Vernadsky, Vladímir Ivanovich **5**: 2299
Virtanen, Artturi Ilmari **5**: 2303
Wald, George **5**: 2329
Walker, John E. **5**: 2332
Wang, James C. **5**: 2339
Warburg, Otto **5**: 2343
West, Harold Dadford **5**: 2373
Wood, Harland G. **5**: 2465

Biology

Alvariño, Angeles **1**: 36
Arber, Werner **1**: 63
Astbury, William **1**: 76
Avery, Oswald Theodore **1**: 85
Beltrán, Enrique **1**: 163
Booker, Walter M. **1**: 244
Carson, Rachel **1**: 366
Chang, Min-Chueh **1**: 391
Cloud, Preston **1**: 423
Cobb, Jewel Plummer **1**: 425
Cohen, Stanley N. **1**: 437
Cohn, Zanvil **1**: 441
Commoner, Barry **1**: 448
Cox, Geraldine V. **1**: 481
Dallmeier, Francisco **2**: 510
Diacumakos, Elaine **2**: 558
Djerassi, Carl **2**: 574
Dobzhansky, Theodosius **2**: 576
Dole, Vincent P. **2**: 583
Dubos, René **2**: 601
Earle, Sylvia A. **2**: 614
Fell, Honor Bridget **2**: 705
Goldstein, Avram **2**: 880
Gould, Stephen Jay **2**: 895
Govindjee, **2**: 900
Horn, Michael Hastings **2**: 1067
Hubel, David H. **2**: 1083
Isaacs, Alick **3**: 1109
Jacob, François **3**: 1116
Janzen, Dan **3**: 1123
Johannsen, Wilhelm Ludvig **3**: 1143
Just, Ernest Everett **3**: 1170
Keller, Evelyn Fox **3**: 1202
Koehl, Mimi A. R. **3**: 1246
Konishi, Masakazu **3**: 1254
Lancaster, Cleo **3**: 1297
Laveran, Alphonse **3**: 1325
Leopold, Estella Bergere **3**: 1372
Levi-Montalcini, Rita **3**: 1377
Li, Ching Chun **3**: 1389
Lillie, Frank Rattray **3**: 1397
Lovejoy, Thomas Eugene **3**: 1428
Lovelock, James E. **3**: 1430
Lwoff, André **3**: 1435

MacArthur, Robert H. **3**: 1442
Maynard Smith, John **3**: 1490
Mayr, Ernst **3**: 1492
Medawar, Peter Brian **3**: 1510
Merrifield, R. Bruce **3**: 1518
Nabrit, Samuel Milton **4**: 1609
Osborn, Mary J. **4**: 1692
Palade, George **4**: 1701
Pardue, Mary Lou **4**: 1706
Perutz, Max **4**: 1757
Pincus, Gregory Goodwin **4**: 1777
Puck, Theodore T. **4**: 1821
Ray, Dixy Lee **4**: 1853
Russell, Frederick Stratten **4**: 1937
Sager, Ruth **4**: 1959
Sanford, Katherine Koontz **4**: 1975
Sharp, Phillip A. **4**: 2021
Silbergeld, Ellen Kovner **4**: 2049
Spemann, Hans **4**: 2097
Sperry, Roger W. **4**: 2100
Stahl, Franklin W. **4**: 2104
Stevens, Nettie Maria **4**: 2130
Sturtevant, A. H. **4**: 2152
Sutton, Walter Stanborough **4**: 2160
Tan Jiazhen, **5**: 2176
Taylor, Stuart **5**: 2194
Thompson, D'Arcy Wentworth **5**: 2220
Turner, Charles Henry **5**: 2265
Wieschaus, Eric F. **5**: 2412
Wilson, Edmund Beecher **5**: 2446
Young, J. Z. **5**: 2496

Biomathematics

Cardús, David **1**: 353

Biomedical Engineering

Cohen, Stanley N. **1**: 437
Estrin, Thelma **2**: 676
Greatbatch, Wilson **2**: 905
Hounsfield, Godfrey **2**: 1070
Jarvik, Robert K. **3**: 1124
Jemison, Mae C. **3**: 1133
Kolff, Willem Johan **3**: 1250
Kouwenhoven, William B. **3**: 1266
Lee, Raphael C. **3**: 1351
Micheli-Tzanakou, Evangelia **3**: 1530

Biophysics

Bronk, Detlev Wulf **1**: 298
Chance, Britton **1**: 386
Cohn, Mildred **1**: 440
Deisenhofer, Johann **2**: 547
Hartline, Haldan Keffer **2**: 963
Hauptman, Herbert A. **2**: 967
Hodgkin, Alan Lloyd **2**: 1043
Neher, Erwin **4**: 1624
Quimby, Edith H. **4**: 1830
Rich, Alexander **4**: 1867
Sakmann, Bert **4**: 1964

Stoll, Alice M. **4**: 2140
Szilard, Leo **4**: 2172
Wilkins, Maurice Hugh Frederick
   5: 2425

Botany

Adams, Roger **1**: 5
Arber, Agnes **1**: 62
Borlaug, Norman **1**: 249
Chase, Mary Agnes (Meara) **1**: 398
Diener, Theodor Otto **2**: 568
Earle, Sylvia A. **2**: 614
Eastwood, Alice **2**: 615
Engler, Adolph Gustav Heinrich **2**: 664
Ferguson, Margaret Clay **2**: 709
Johannsen, Wilhelm Ludvig **3**: 1143
Khush, Gurdev S. **3**: 1218
King, Louisa Boyd Yeomans **3**: 1224
Leopold, Estella Bergere **3**: 1372
Marie-Victorin, Frère **3**: 1476
Mexia, Ynes **3**: 1526
Parker, Charles Stewart **4**: 1708
Skoog, Folke Karl **4**: 2063
Todd, Alexander **5**: 2241
Tswett, Mikhail **5**: 2261
Vries, Hugo de **5**: 2319
Weber-van Bosse, Anne Antoinette
   5: 2351
Went, Frits **5**: 2370

Calculus

Young, William Henry **5**: 2499

Cellular Biology

Claude, Albert **1**: 416
Cobb, Jewel Plummer **1**: 425
Cohn, Zanvil **1**: 441
de Duvé, Christian **2**: 539
Farquhar, Marilyn G. **2**: 694
Nirenberg, Marshall Warren **4**: 1642
Olden, Kenneth **4**: 1677
Petermann, Mary Locke **4**: 1761
Sheldrake, Rupert **4**: 2026

Chemical Engineering

Bird, R. Byron **1**: 195
Dicciani, Nance K. **2**: 561
Greenewalt, Crawford H. **2**: 907
Hawkins, W. Lincoln **2**: 975
Johnson, Marvin M. **3**: 1150
Katz, Donald L. **3**: 1195
Le Beau, Désirée **3**: 1340
Lewis, Warren K. **3**: 1387
Little, Arthur D. **3**: 1407
Patrick, Jennie R. **4**: 1714
Sioui, Richard H. **4**: 2063
Tsao, George T. **5**: 2255

Chemistry

Anderson, Gloria L. **1**: 51
Arrhenius, Svante August **1**: 71
Astbury, William **1**: 76
Aston, Francis W. **1**: 77
Axelrod, Julius **1**: 88
Baeyer, Johann Friedrich Wilhelm Adolf
   von **1**: 101
Bartlett, Neil **1**: 135
Barton, Derek H. R. **1**: 137
Beckman, Arnold **1**: 149
Bergius, Friedrich **1**: 173
Berkowitz, Joan B. **1**: 176
Blodgett, Katharine Burr **1**: 222
Bosch, Karl **1**: 255
Brady, St. Elmo **1**: 269
Brønsted, Johannes Nicolaus **1**: 300
Brooks, Ronald E. **1**: 302
Brown, Herbert C. **1**: 305
Buchner, Eduard **1**: 315
Burger, Alfred **1**: 323
Calvin, Melvin **1**: 342
Carothers, Wallace Hume **1**: 356
Castro, George **1**: 376
Chance, Britton **1**: 386
Claude, Georges **1**: 418
Cooke, Lloyd M. **1**: 455
Coolidge, William D. **1**: 458
Corey, Elias James **1**: 461
Cornforth, John **1**: 468
Cram, Donald J. **1**: 483
Curie, Marie **1**: 497
Davis, Jr., Raymond **2**: 530
Davis, Marguerite **2**: 530
Debye, Peter **2**: 538
de Gennes, Pierre-Gilles **2**: 545
Diels, Otto **2**: 565
Djerassi, Carl **2**: 574
Drickamer, Harry G. **2**: 595
Eigen, Manfred **2**: 642
El-Sayed, Mostafa Amr **2**: 653
Ernst, Richard R. **2**: 672
Ferguson, Lloyd N. **2**: 707
Fieser, Louis F. **2**: 717
Fischer, Emil **2**: 722
Fischer, Ernst Otto **2**: 724
Fischer, Hans **2**: 725
Flory, Paul **2**: 743
Fraser-Reid, Bertram Oliver **2**: 774
Fukui, Kenichi **2**: 791
Garrod, Archibald **2**: 813
Ghiorso, Albert **2**: 831
Giauque, William F. **2**: 837
Good, Mary L. **2**: 886
Grignard, François Auguste Victor
   2: 911
Haagen-Smit, A. J. **2**: 927
Haber, Fritz **2**: 928
Hackerman, Norman **2**: 930

Hahn, Otto **2**: 933
Hall, Lloyd Augustus **2**: 942
Hammond, George S. **2**: 947
Harden, Arthur **2**: 953
Hassel, Odd **2**: 965
Haworth, Walter **2**: 976
Herschbach, Dudley R. **2**: 998
Hevesy, Georg von **2**: 1012
Hill, Henry A. **2**: 1032
Hinshelwood, Cyril N. **2**: 1036
Hodgkin, Dorothy Crowfoot **2**: 1044
Hoffmann, Roald **2**: 1049
Houdry, Eugene **2**: 1069
Joliot-Curie, Irène **3**: 1158
Julian, Percy Lavon **3**: 1166
Karle, Isabella **3**: 1181
Karle, Jerome **3**: 1183
Karrer, Paul **3**: 1188
King, Reatha Clark **3**: 1225
Kistiakowsky, George B. **3**: 1231
Kolthoff, Izaak Maurits **3**: 1253
Kuhn, Richard **3**: 1281
Langmuir, Irving **3**: 1314
Lauterbur, Paul C. **3**: 1324
Le Beau, Désirée **3**: 1340
Lee, Yuan T. **3**: 1354
Lehn, Jean-Marie **3**: 1362
Lester, Jr., William Alexander **3**: 1375
Lewis, Gilbert Newton **3**: 1383
Libby, Willard F. **3**: 1391
Lipscomb, Jr., William Nunn **3**: 1406
Lovelock, James E. **3**: 1430
Marcus, Rudolph A. **3**: 1471
Massie, Samuel P. **3**: 1481
McCollum, Elmer Verner **3**: 1502
McConnell, Harden **3**: 1503
Merrifield, R. Bruce **3**: 1518
Midgley, Jr., Thomas **3**: 1533
Miller, Stanley Lloyd **3**: 1537
Moissan, Henri **3**: 1557
Molina, Mario **3**: 1559
Morley, Edward Williams **3**: 1582
Müller, Paul **3**: 1598
Mulliken, Robert S. **3**: 1599
Nakanishi, Koji **4**: 1611
Natta, Giulio **4**: 1617
Nernst, Walther **4**: 1626
Noddack, Ida Tacke **4**: 1646
Norrish, Ronald G. W. **4**: 1654
Olah, George A. **4**: 1676
Onsager, Lars **4**: 1682
Ostwald, Friedrich Wilhelm **4**: 1695
Pauling, Linus **4**: 1724
Pedersen, Charles John **4**: 1737
Pennington, Mary Engle **4**: 1744
Polanyi, John C. **4**: 1789
Ponnamperuma, Cyril **4**: 1793
Porter, George **4**: 1796
Pregl, Fritz **4**: 1806

Taylor, Frederick Winslow **5**: 2188

Electrical Engineering

Armstrong, Edwin Howard **1**: 67
Ayrton, Hertha **1**: 91
Baird, John Logie **1**: 105
Boykin, Otis **1**: 268
Bundy, Robert F. **1**: 319
Chestnut, Harold **1**: 402
Cho, Alfred Y. **1**: 406
Edgerton, Harold **2**: 626
Flanagan, James L. **2**: 732
Fleming, John Ambrose **2**: 736
Forrester, Jay W. **2**: 754
Haus, Hermann **2**: 968
Hewlett, William **2**: 1018
Kilby, Jack St. Clair **3**: 1221
Marconi, Guglielmo **3**: 1468
Nishizawa, Jun-ichi **4**: 1643
Ochoa, Ellen **4**: 1668
Packard, David **4**: 1699
Peden, Irene Carswell **4**: 1736
Rigas, Harriett B. **4**: 1887
Rockwell, Mabel M. **4**: 1897
Sinclair, Clive Marles **4**: 2057
Steinmetz, Charles P. **4**: 2124
Terman, Frederick **5**: 2203
Tesla, Nikola **5**: 2206
Tien, Ping King **5**: 2230
Trump, John G. **5**: 2254
Weber, Ernst **5**: 2351
Whinnery, John R. **5**: 2384
Williams, Frederic C. **5**: 2433
Zadeh, Lotfi Asker **5**: 2503

Embryology

Hamburger, Viktor **2**: 944
Mintz, Beatrice **3**: 1551
Spemann, Hans **4**: 2097
Wilmut, Ian **5**: 2441
Wilson, Edmund Beecher **5**: 2446

Endocrinology

Guillemin, Roger **2**: 918

Engineering

Alcorn, George Edward **1**: 18
Alexander, Archie Alphonso **1**: 21
Alexanderson, Ernst F. W. **1**: 24
Ammann, Othmar Hermann **1**: 42
Armstrong, Edwin Howard **1**: 67
Armstrong, Neil **1**: 69
Ayrton, Hertha **1**: 91
Baird, John Logie **1**: 105
Bishop, Alfred A. **1**: 200
Bluford, Guion S. **1**: 227
Bosch, Karl **1**: 255
Boykin, Otis **1**: 268

Brill, Yvonne Claeys **1**: 292
Bundy, Robert F. **1**: 319
Bush, Vannevar **1**: 328
Cambra, Jessie G. **1**: 345
Carrier, Willis **1**: 361
Chestnut, Harold **1**: 402
Cho, Alfred Y. **1**: 406
Clarke, Edith **1**: 415
Conway, Lynn Ann **1**: 454
Crosthwait, Jr., David Nelson **1**: 494
Dalén, Nils **2**: 509
Daniels, Walter T. **2**: 517
de Forest, Lee **2**: 542
Dicciani, Nance K. **2**: 561
Douglas, Donald W. **2**: 588
Draper, Charles Stark **2**: 589
Drucker, Daniel Charles **2**: 597
Durand, William F. **2**: 605
Dyson, Freeman J. **2**: 610
Edgerton, Harold **2**: 626
Estrin, Thelma **2**: 676
Evans, James C. **2**: 681
Fitzroy, Nancy D. **2**: 731
Fleming, John Ambrose **2**: 736
Flügge-Lotz, Irmgard **2**: 745
Fokker, Anthony H. G. **2**: 747
Ford, Henry **2**: 752
Forrester, Jay W. **2**: 754
Fukui, Kenichi **2**: 791
Gilbreth, Frank **2**: 846
Gilbreth, Lillian **2**: 848
Goethals, George W. **2**: 865
Goldmark, Peter Carl **2**: 872
Gourdine, Meredith Charles **2**: 897
Greatbatch, Wilson **2**: 905
Greenewalt, Crawford H. **2**: 907
Groves, Leslie Richard **2**: 915
Gutierrez, Orlando A. **2**: 924
Harmon, E'lise F. **2**: 959
Harris, Wesley L. **2**: 961
Hawkins, W. Lincoln **2**: 975
Heinkel, Ernst **2**: 988
Henderson, Cornelius Langston **2**: 994
Hewlett, William **2**: 1018
Hicks, Beatrice **2**: 1024
Hounsfield, Godfrey **2**: 1070
Hubbard, Philip G. **2**: 1078
Hunsaker, Jerome C. **2**: 1092
Iverson, F. Kenneth **3**: 1112
Jansky, Karl **3**: 1120
Jarvik, Robert K. **3**: 1124
Jemison, Mae C. **3**: 1133
Jewett, Frank Baldwin **3**: 1139
Jobs, Steven Paul **3**: 1141
Johnson, Barbara Crawford **3**: 1145
Johnson, Clarence L. **3**: 1146
Johnson, Marvin M. **3**: 1150
Juran, Joseph M. **3**: 1168
Katz, Donald L. **3**: 1195

Kettering, Charles Franklin **3**: 1211
Kilby, Jack St. Clair **3**: 1221
Kolff, Willem Johan **3**: 1250
Korolyov, Sergei **3**: 1258
Kuhlmann-Wilsdorf, Doris **3**: 1280
Latimer, Lewis H. **3**: 1316
Le Beau, Désirée **3**: 1340
Lee, Raphael C. **3**: 1351
Lewis, Warren K. **3**: 1387
Liepmann, Hans Wolfgang **3**: 1394
Little, Arthur D. **3**: 1407
MacGill, Elsie Gregory **3**: 1446
Marconi, Guglielmo **3**: 1468
Matthews, Alva T. **3**: 1483
Micheli-Tzanakou, Evangelia **3**: 1530
Midgley, Jr., Thomas **3**: 1533
Morgan, Arthur E. **3**: 1575
Nichols, Roberta J. **4**: 1637
Nishizawa, Jun-ichi **4**: 1643
Ochoa, Ellen **4**: 1668
Patrick, Jennie R. **4**: 1714
Peden, Irene Carswell **4**: 1736
Piasecki, Frank **4**: 1767
Pressman, Ada I. **4**: 1811
Qöyawayma, Alfred H. **4**: 1827
Quate, Calvin F. **4**: 1829
Reid, Lonnie **4**: 1862
Rickover, Hyman G. **4**: 1881
Rigas, Harriett B. **4**: 1887
Rockwell, Mabel M. **4**: 1897
Rogers, Marguerite M. **4**: 1902
Ross, Mary G. **4**: 1914
Shurney, Robert E. **4**: 2041
Sikorsky, Igor I. **4**: 2046
Sioui, Richard H. **4**: 2063
Sorensen, Charles E. **4**: 2091
Sperry, Elmer **4**: 2098
Steinman, David B. **4**: 2123
Steinmetz, Charles P. **4**: 2124
Stever, H. Guyford **4**: 2131
Taylor, Frederick Winslow **5**: 2188
Tereshkova, Valentina **5**: 2202
Terman, Frederick **5**: 2203
Terzaghi, Karl **5**: 2205
Tesla, Nikola **5**: 2206
Thomas, Martha Jane Bergin **5**: 2219
Tien, Ping King **5**: 2230
Timoshenko, Stephen P. **5**: 2232
Trump, John G. **5**: 2254
Tsiolkovsky, Konstantin **5**: 2256
van der Wal, Laurel **5**: 2290
von Braun, Wernher **5**: 2307
von Kármán, Theodore **5**: 2310
von Mises, Richard **5**: 2313
Whinnery, John R. **5**: 2384
Whittle, Frank **5**: 2398
Wickenden, William E. **5**: 2400
Widnall, Sheila E. **5**: 2401
Williams, Frederic C. **5**: 2433

Metallurgical Engineering

Metallurgy

Meteorology

Microbiology

Bordet, Jules **1**: 245
Claude, Albert **1**: 416
Cobb, Jewel Plummer **1**: 425
Cohn, Zanvil **1**: 441
Colwell, Rita R. **1**: 446
de Duvé, Christian **2**: 539
d'Hérelle, Félix **2**: 557
Dubos, René **2**: 601
Ehrlich, Paul **2**: 637
Evans, Alice **2**: 680
Farquhar, Marilyn G. **2**: 694
Fibiger, Johannes **2**: 716
Fleming, Alexander **2**: 734
Flexner, Simon **2**: 739
Friend, Charlotte **2**: 784
Gajdusek, D. Carleton **2**: 803
Griffith, Frederick **2**: 910
Gross, Carol **2**: 912
Hay, Elizabeth D. **2**: 978
Hazen, Elizabeth Lee **2**: 981
Hershey, Alfred Day **2**: 1000
Hobby, Gladys Lounsbury **2**: 1042
Huang, Alice Shih-hou **2**: 1077
Koch, Robert **3**: 1240
Kornberg, Arthur **3**: 1256
Lancefield, Rebecca Craighill **3**: 1298
Landsteiner, Karl **3**: 1309
MacLeod, Colin Munro **3**: 1452
Moore, Ruth **3**: 1569
Nicolle, Charles J. H. **4**: 1639
Nirenberg, Marshall Warren **4**: 1642
Noguchi, Hideyo **4**: 1651
Northrop, John Howard **4**: 1655
Olden, Kenneth **4**: 1677
Petermann, Mary Locke **4**: 1761
Pierce, George Edward **4**: 1770
Poindexter, Hildrus A. **4**: 1788
Reed, Walter **4**: 1856
Robbins, Frederick **4**: 1890
Rowley, Janet D. **4**: 1924
Salk, Jonas **4**: 1967
Sheldrake, Rupert **4**: 2026
Sutton, Walter Stanborough **4**: 2160
Szent-Györgyi, Albert **4**: 2169
Varmus, Harold E. **5**: 2294
Waksman, Selman **5**: 2327
Williams, Anna W. **5**: 2428
Wright, Almroth Edward **5**: 2474
Zinsser, Hans **5**: 2520

Microscopy
Zworykin, Vladimir **5**: 2526

Mineralogy
Fersman, Aleksandr Evgenievich **2**: 713
Goldschmidt, Victor **2**: 879
Vernadsky, Vladímir Ivanovich **5**: 2299

Model Theory
Blum, Lenore **1**: 229
Nelson, Evelyn **4**: 1626

Molecular Biology
Altman, Sidney **1**: 31
Ames, Bruce N. **1**: 40
Arber, Werner **1**: 63
Bachrach, Howard L. **1**: 98
Benzer, Seymour **1**: 167
Bishop, J. Michael **1**: 201
Blackburn, Elizabeth H. **1**: 209
Brenner, Sydney **1**: 283
Crick, Francis **1**: 487
Delbrück, Max **2**: 549
Fedoroff, Nina V. **2**: 700
Franklin, Rosalind Elsie **2**: 772
Gilbert, Walter **2**: 844
Huxley, Hugh Esmor **2**: 1097
Itakura, Keiichi **3**: 1111
Klug, Aaron **3**: 1234
Kramer, Fred Russell **3**: 1268
Luria, Salvador Edward **3**: 1433
Meselson, Matthew **3**: 1522
Monod, Jacques Lucien **3**: 1561
Nomura, Masayasu **4**: 1653
Perutz, Max **4**: 1757
Smith, Hamilton O. **4**: 2075
Stahl, Franklin W. **4**: 2104
Stanley, Wendell Meredith **4**: 2108
Szent-Györgyi, Albert **4**: 2169
Tonegawa, Susumu **5**: 2247
Watson, James D. **5**: 2347
White, Raymond L. **5**: 2392

Mycology
Hazen, Elizabeth Lee **2**: 981

Natural Science
Adamson, Joy **1**: 8
Bailey, Florence Merriam **1**: 104
Dobzhansky, Theodosius **2**: 576
Janzen, Dan **3**: 1123
Noble, G. K. **4**: 1645
Rothschild, Miriam **4**: 1918
Schaller, George **4**: 1981
Sheldrake, Rupert **4**: 2026
Thompson, D'Arcy Wentworth **5**: 2220

Naval Architecture
Gibbs, William Francis **2**: 841

Neural Science
Cooper, Leon **1**: 459

Neurobiology
Axelrod, Julius **1**: 88
Hamburger, Viktor **2**: 944

Hubel, David H. **2**: 1083
Kandel, Eric R. **3**: 1177

Neuroendocrinology
Leeman, Susan E. **3**: 1356

Neurohistology
Ramón y Cajal, Santiago **4**: 1843

Neurology
Berger, Hans **1**: 172
Bondar, Roberta L. **1**: 241
Fuller, Solomon **2**: 794
Gajdusek, D. Carleton **2**: 803
Leeman, Susan E. **3**: 1356
Moniz, Egas **3**: 1560
Prusiner, Stanley B. **4**: 1818

Neurophysics
Granit, Ragnar Arthur **2**: 901

Neurophysiology
Sherrington, Charles Scott **4**: 2030

Neuroscience
Pert, Candace B. **4**: 1756
Snyder, Solomon H. **4**: 2080

Neurosurgery
Barber, Jr., Jesse B. **1**: 122

Nuclear Engineering
Bishop, Alfred A. **1**: 200
Dyson, Freeman J. **2**: 610
Rickover, Hyman G. **4**: 1881

Nuclear Physics
Fowler, William A. **2**: 761
Rainwater, James **4**: 1834

Number Theory
Cartan, Élie Joseph **1**: 369
Chung, Fan R. K. **1**: 413
Selberg, Atle **4**: 2013
Taussky–Todd, Olga **5**: 2186
Vallée–Poussin, Charles Jean Gustave Nicolas de la **5**: 2279

Number theory
Erdős, Paul **2**: 667
Fredholm, Erik Ivar **2**: 777
Gelfond, Aleksandr Osipovich **2**: 826
Landau, Edmund **3**: 1303
Méray, Hugues Charles Robert **3**: 1517

Nutrition
Edwards, Cecile Hoover **2**: 632
Kittrell, Flemmie Pansy **3**: 1232

Manton, Sidnie Milana **3**: 1467
Mayr, Ernst **3**: 1492
Morgan, Ann Haven **3**: 1574

Noble, G. K. **4**: 1645
Odum, Eugene Pleasants **4**: 1672
Schaller, George **4**: 1981

Thompson, D'Arcy Wentworth **5**: 2220
Tinbergen, Nikolaas **5**: 2234
Wilson, Edward O. **5**: 2448

Gender Index

Female

Adamson, Joy
Ajzenberg-Selove, Fay
Alexander, Hattie
Alvariño, Angeles
Anastasi, Anne
Andersen, Dorothy
Anderson, Gloria L.
Antonelli, Kay McNulty Mauchly
Apgar, Virginia
Arber, Agnes
Auerbach, Charlotte
Avery, Mary Ellen
Ayrton, Hertha
Bailey, Florence Merriam
Baker, Sara Josephine
Bari, Nina
Bari, Ruth Aaronson
Bascom, Florence
Baxter, Agnes
Bell Burnell, Jocelyn Susan
Bellow, Alexandra
Berkowitz, Joan B.
Bernstein, Dorothy Lewis
Bishop, Katharine Scott
Blackburn, Elizabeth H.
Blau, Marietta
Blodgett, Katharine Burr
Bondar, Roberta L.
Brill, Yvonne Claeys
Brown, Rachel Fuller
Browne, Marjorie Lee
Burbidge, E. Margaret
Caldicott, Helen
Cambra, Jessie G.
Canady, Alexa I.
Cannon, Annie Jump
Carothers, E. Eleanor
Carson, Rachel
Cartwright, Mary Lucy
Chang, Sun-Yung Alice
Chase, Mary Agnes (Meara)
Chinn, May Edward
Chung, Fan R. K.
Clarke, Edith
Clay-Jolles, Tettje Clasina
Cobb, Jewel Plummer
Cohn, Mildred

Colborn, Theodora E.
Colmenares, Margarita
Colwell, Rita R.
Conway, Lynn Ann
Conwell, Esther Marly
Cori, Gerty T.
Cowings, Patricia S.
Cox, Geraldine V.
Cox, Gertrude Mary
Crosby, Elizabeth Caroline
Curie, Marie
Daly, Marie M.
Darden, Christine
Daubechies, Ingrid
Davis, Margaret B.
Davis, Marguerite
Diacumakos, Elaine
Dicciani, Nance K.
Dick, Gladys (Henry)
Diggs, Irene
Dresselhaus, Mildred S.
Earle, Sylvia A.
Eastwood, Alice
Edinger, Tilly
Edwards, Cecile Hoover
Edwards, Helen T.
Ehrenfest-Afanaseva, Tatiana
Ehrlich, Anne Howland
Einstein-Marić, Mileva
Elion, Gertrude Belle
Emerson, Gladys Anderson
Esau, Katherine
Estrin, Thelma
Evans, Alice
Faber, Sandra M.
Falconer, Etta Zuber
Farquhar, Marilyn G.
Farr, Wanda K.
Fasenmyer, Mary Celine
Fedoroff, Nina V.
Fell, Honor Bridget
Fenchel, Käte
Ferguson, Margaret Clay
Fieser, Mary Peters
Fisher, Elizabeth F.
Fitzroy, Nancy D.
Flügge-Lotz, Irmgard
Fossey, Dian

Franklin, Rosalind Elsie
Freitag, Herta Taussig
Friend, Charlotte
Gadgil, Sulochana
Galdikas, Birute Marija Filomena
Gardner, Julia Anna
Gayle, Helene Doris
Geiringer, Hilda
Geller, Margaret Joan
Gentry, Ruth
Giblett, Eloise R.
Gilbreth, Lillian
Goeppert-Mayer, Maria
Goldberg, Adele
Goldhaber, Gertrude Scharff
Goldring, Winifred
Good, Mary L.
Goodall, Jane
Granville, Evelyn Boyd
Gross, Carol
Guthrie, Mary Jane
Hamilton, Alice
Hardy, Harriet
Harmon, E'lise F.
Harvey, Ethel Browne
Hay, Elizabeth D.
Hay, Louise Schmir
Hayes, Ellen Amanda
Hazen, Elizabeth Lee
Hazlett, Olive Clio
Healy, Bernadine
Herzenberg, Caroline L.
Hewitt, Jacqueline N.
Hibbard, Hope
Hicks, Beatrice
Hobby, Gladys Lounsbury
Hodgkin, Dorothy Crowfoot
Hoffman, Darleane C.
Hogg, Helen Sawyer
Hollinshead, Ariel Cahill
Hopper, Grace
Horstmann, Dorothy Millicent
Huang, Alice Shih-hou
Hyde, Ida H.
Jackson, Shirley Ann
Janovskaja, Sof'ja Aleksandrovna
Jemison, Mae C.
Johnson, Barbara Crawford

Johnson, Katherine Coleman Goble
Johnson, Virginia E.
Joliot-Curie, Irène
Jones, Mary Ellen
Karle, Isabella
Keen, Linda
Keller, Evelyn Fox
Kelsey, Frances Oldham
King, Helen Dean
King, Louisa Boyd Yeomans
King, Reatha Clark
Kittrell, Flemmie Pansy
Knopf, Eleanora Bliss
Koehl, Mimi A. R.
Krieger, Cecilia
Krim, Mathilde
Kuhlmann-Wilsdorf, Doris
Kuperberg, Krystyna
L'Esperance, Elise Depew Strang
Ladd-Franklin, Christine
Lancaster, Cleo
Lancefield, Rebecca Craighill
Leakey, Mary
Leavitt, Henrietta
Le Beau, Désirée
Leeman, Susan E.
Lehmann, Inge
Lehmer, Emma Trotskaya
Leopold, Estella Bergere
Levi-Montalcini, Rita
Litvinova, Elizaveta Fedorovna
Lloyd, Ruth Smith
Logan, Myra A.
Long, Irene D.
Lonsdale, Kathleen
Lubchenco, Jane
Maathai, Wangari
Macdonald, Eleanor Josephine
MacGill, Elsie Gregory
Macintyre, Sheila Scott
Macklin, Madge Thurlow
Maddison, Ada Isabel
Malone–Mayes, Vivienne
Manton, Sidnie Milana
Margulis, Lynn
Massevitch, Alla G.
Matthews, Alva T.
Maunder, Annie Russell
Maury, Antonia
Maury, Carlotta Joaquina
McClintock, Barbara
McDuff, Margaret Dusa
Meitner, Lise
Mendenhall, Dorothy Reed
Merrill, Helen Abbot
Merrill, Winifred Edgerton
Mexia, Ynes
Micheli-Tzanakou, Evangelia
Miller, Elizabeth C.

Mintz, Beatrice
Moore, Charlotte E.
Moore, Ruth
Morawetz, Cathleen Synge
Morgan, Ann Haven
Moulton Browne, Barbara
Nelson, Evelyn
Neufeld, Elizabeth F.
Neumann, Hanna
Nice, Margaret Morse
Nichols, Roberta J.
Noddack, Ida Tacke
Noether, Emmy
Nüsslein-Volhard, Christiane
Ocampo, Adriana C.
Ochoa, Ellen
Ogilvie, Ida H.
Oleinik, Olga
Osborn, Mary J.
Panajiotatou, Angeliki
Pardue, Mary Lou
Patrick, Jennie R.
Patrick, Ruth
Payne-Gaposchkin, Cecilia
Peden, Irene Carswell
Pellier, Laurence Delisle
Pennington, Mary Engle
Penry, Deborah L.
Perey, Marguerite
Pert, Candace B.
Péter, Rózsa
Petermann, Mary Locke
Peterson, Edith R.
Pierce, Naomi E.
Pless, Vera
Polubarinova-Kochina, Pelageya
  Yakovlevna
Pressman, Ada I.
Prichard, Diana García
Profet, Margie
Quimby, Edith H.
Ramart-Lucas, Pauline
Ramey, Estelle R.
Randoin, Lucie
Ratner, Sarah
Ray, Dixy Lee
Rees, Mina S.
Reichmanis, Elsa
Richards, Ellen Swallow
Ride, Sally
Rigas, Harriett B.
Robinson, Julia
Rockwell, Mabel M.
Rogers, Marguerite M.
Roman, Nancy Grace
Ross, Mary G.
Rothschild, Miriam
Rowley, Janet D.
Rubin, Vera Cooper

Rudin, Mary Ellen
Russell, Elizabeth Shull
Sabin, Florence Rena
Sager, Ruth
Sanford, Katherine Koontz
Schafer, Alice T.
Scharrer, Berta
Scott, Charlotte Angas
Seibert, Florence B.
Shaw, Mary
Shockley, Dolores Cooper
Silbergeld, Ellen Kovner
Simon, Dorothy Martin
Singer, Maxine
Slye, Maud
Solomon, Susan
Spaeth, Mary
Sparling, Rebecca H.
Steitz, Joan Argetsinger
Stevens, Nettie Maria
Stoll, Alice M.
Stott, Alicia Boole
Stubbe, JoAnne
Taussig, Helen Brooke
Taussky–Todd, Olga
Telkes, Maria
Tereshkova, Valentina
Tesoro, Giuliana Cavaglieri
Tharp, Marie
Thomas, Martha Jane Bergin
Trotter, Mildred
Uhlenbeck, Karen
van der Wal, Laurel
van Straten, Florence W.
Vassy, Arlette
Velez–Rodriguez, Argelia
Waelsch, Salome
Weber-van Bosse, Anne Antoinette
Weertman, Julia
Weiss, Mary Catherine Bishop
Wexler, Nancy
Wheeler, Anna Johnson Pell
Widnall, Sheila E.
Williams, Anna W.
Williams, Cicely Delphin
Williams, Heather
Witkin, Evelyn Maisel
Wright, Jane Cooke
Wu, Chien-Shiung
Wu, Y. C. L. Susan
Xide, Xie
Yalow, Rosalyn Sussman
Young, Grace Chisholm
Young, Lai-Sang

Male

Abelson, Philip Hauge
Abraham, Edward P.
Adams, Roger

Adams, Walter Sydney
Adrian, Edgar Douglas
Ahlfors, Lars V.
Aiken, Howard
Aki, Keiiti
Alcala, Jose
Alcorn, George Edward
Alder, Kurt
Aleksandrov, Pavel S.
Alexander, Archie Alphonso
Alexanderson, Ernst F. W.
Alfvén, Hannes Olof Gösta
Alikhanov, Abram Isaakovich
Allen, Jr., William E.
Alpher, Ralph Asher
Altman, Sidney
Alvarez, Luis
Amdahl, Gene M.
Ames, Bruce N.
Ammann, Othmar Hermann
Anders, Edward
Anderson, Carl David
Anderson, Don L.
Anderson, Philip Warren
Anderson, W. French
Anfinsen, Christian Boehmer
Appleton, Edward
Arber, Werner
Armstrong, Clay M.
Armstrong, Edwin Howard
Armstrong, Neil
Arrhenius, Svante August
Artin, Emil
Askey, Richard
Astbury, William
Aston, Francis W.
Atanasoff, John
Atiyah, Michael Francis
Auger, Pierre V.
Avery, Oswald Theodore
Axelrod, Julius
Ayala, Francisco J.
Baade, Walter
Babcock, Horace W.
Bachrach, Howard L.
Backus, John
Baeyer, Johann Friedrich Wilhelm Adolf
  von
Baez, Albert V.
Bahcall, John Noris
Baird, John Logie
Baker, Alan
Bakker, Robert T.
Ballard, Robert Duane
Baltimore, David
Banach, Stefan
Banks, Harvey Washington
Banting, Frederick G.
Bárány, Robert

Barber, Jr., Jesse B.
Bardeen, John
Barghoorn, Jr., Elso Sterrenberg
Barkla, Charles Glover
Barnard, Christiaan Neethling
Barnes, William Harry
Barr, Murray Llewellyn
Bartlett, Neil
Barton, Derek H. R.
Basov, Nikolai
Batchelor, George
Bateson, William
Bayliss, William Maddock
Beadle, George Wells
Beckman, Arnold
Becquerel, Antoine-Henri
Bednorz, J. Georg
Begay, Fred
Behring, Emil von
Békésy, Georg von
Bell, Gordon
Bell, John Stewart
Beltrán, Enrique
Benacerraf, Baruj
Benzer, Seymour
Berg, Paul
Berger, Hans
Bergius, Friedrich
Bergström, Sune Karl
Bernays, Paul
Berner, Robert A.
Berners-Lee, Tim
Bernstein, Richard B.
Berry, Leonidas Harris
Bers, Lipman
Best, Charles Herbert
Bethe, Hans
Bhabha, Homi Jehangir
Binnig, Gerd
Bird, R. Byron
Birkhoff, Garrett
Birkhoff, George David
Bishop, Alfred A.
Bishop, J. Michael
Bjerknes, Jacob
Bjerknes, Vilhelm
Black, Davidson
Black, James
Blackett, Patrick Maynard Stuart
Blackwell, David
Blobel, Günter
Bloch, Felix
Bloch, Konrad
Bloembergen, Nicolaas
Blout, Elkan R.
Bluford, Guion S.
Blum, Lenore
Blumberg, Baruch Samuel
Bodmer, Walter F.

Bohr, Aage
Bohr, Niels
Bolin, Bert
Bondi, Hermann
Booker, Walter M.
Borcherds, Richard Ewen
Bordet, Jules
Borel, Émile
Borlaug, Norman
Bormann, Frederick Herbert
Born, Max
Bosch, Karl
Bose, Satyendranath
Bothe, Walther
Bott, Raoul
Bovet, Daniel
Bowie, William
Boyer, Herbert W.
Boyer, Paul D.
Boykin, Otis
Brady, St. Elmo
Bragg, William Henry
Bragg, William Lawrence
Brans, Carl Henry
Branson, Herman
Brattain, Walter Houser
Braun, Karl Ferdinand
Breit, Gregory
Bremermann, Hans-Joachim
Brenner, Sydney
Breslow, Ronald C.
Bressani, Ricardo
Bridges, Calvin B.
Bridgman, Percy Williams
Brockhouse, Bertram Neville
Broecker, Wallace S.
Bromley, D. Allan
Bronk, Detlev Wulf
Brønsted, Johannes Nicolaus
Brooks, Ronald E.
Brouwer, Luitzen Egbertus Jan
Browder, Felix
Brown, Herbert C.
Brown, Lester R.
Brown, Michael S.
Brown, Robert Hanbury
Bucher, Walter Herman
Buchner, Eduard
Bullard, Edward
Bundy, Robert F.
Burbidge, Geoffrey
Burger, Alfred
Burkitt, Denis Parsons
Burnet, Frank Macfarlane
Burton, Glenn W.
Bush, Vannevar
Butement, William
Butenandt, Adolf
Cahn, John Werner

Cairns, Jr., John
Calderón, Alberto P.
Callender, Clive O.
Calvin, Melvin
Cantor, Georg
Cardona, Manuel
Cardozo, W. Warrick
Cardús, David
Carlson, Chester
Carothers, Wallace Hume
Carrel, Alexis
Carrier, Willis
Carroll, Lewis
Carruthers, George R.
Carson, Benjamin S.
Cartan, Élie Joseph
Cartan, Henri Paul
Carver, George Washington
Castro, George
Cech, Thomas R.
Chadwick, James
Chain, Ernst Boris
Chamberlain, Owen
Chamberlin, Thomas Chrowder
Chance, Britton
Chandrasekhar, Subrahmanyan
Chang, Min-Chueh
Chang, Te-Tzu
Chargaff, Erwin
Charnley, John
Charpak, Georges
Chaudhari, Praveen
Cherenkov, Pavel A.
Chestnut, Harold
Chew, Geoffrey Foucar
Child, Charles Manning
Cho, Alfred Y.
Chomsky, Avram Noam
Chu, Paul Ching-Wu
Chu, Steven
Church, Alonzo
Claude, Albert
Claude, Georges
Clay, Jacob
Clemence, Gerald M.
Cloud, Preston
Cobb, William Montague
Cockcroft, John D.
Cocke, John
Cohen-Tannoudji, Claude
Cohen, Joel Ephraim
Cohen, Paul
Cohen, Stanley
Cohen, Stanley N.
Cohn, Zanvil
Coifman, Ronald Raphael
Commoner, Barry
Compton, Arthur Holly
Condon, Edward U.

Cooke, Lloyd M.
Cooley, Denton Arthur
Coolidge, William D.
Cooper, Leon
Corey, Elias James
Cori, Carl Ferdinand
Cormack, Allan M.
Cornforth, John
Coster, Dirk
Coulomb, Jean
Courant, Richard
Cournand, André F.
Cousteau, Jacques
Cox, Elbert Frank
Cram, Donald J.
Cray, Seymour
Crick, Francis
Cronin, James W.
Crosthwait, Jr., David Nelson
Crutzen, Paul J.
Culler, Glen Jacob
Curie, Pierre
Curl, Jr., Robert Floyd
Cushman, David Wayne
Dale, Henry Hallett
Dalén, Nils
Dallmeier, Francisco
Dalrymple, G. Brent
Daly, Reginald Aldworth
Dam, Henrik
Daniels, Walter T.
Dansgaard, Willi
Dantzig, George Bernard
Dart, Raymond A.
Dausset, Jean
Davidson, Norman R.
Davis, Jr., Raymond
Davisson, Clinton
DeBakey, Michael Ellis
de Broglie, Louis Victor
Debye, Peter
de Duvé, Christian
de Forest, Lee
de Gennes, Pierre-Gilles
Dehmelt, Hans
Deisenhofer, Johann
Delbrück, Max
Deligné, Pierre
Dennis, Jack B.
de Sitter, Willem
d'Hérelle, Félix
Diamond, Jared Mason
Diaz, Henry F.
Dicke, Robert Henry
Diels, Otto
Diener, Theodor Otto
Dijkstra, Edsger W.
Dirac, Paul
Djerassi, Carl

Dobzhansky, Theodosius
Doherty, Peter C.
Doisy, Edward A.
Dolby, Ray Milton
Dole, Vincent P.
Domagk, Gerhard
Donaldson, Simon
Douglas, Donald W.
Draper, Charles Stark
Drew, Charles R.
Drickamer, Harry G.
Drucker, Daniel Charles
Dubois, Eugène
Dubos, René
Dulbecco, Renato
Durand, William F.
Durrell, Gerald
du Vigneaud, Vincent
Dyson, Freeman J.
Eagle, Harry
Eccles, John C.
Eckert, J. Presper
Eddington, Arthur Stanley
Edelman, Gerald M.
Edgerton, Harold
Edison, Thomas Alva
Ehrenfest, Paul
Ehrlich, Paul
Ehrlich, Paul R.
Eigen, Manfred
Eijkman, Christiaan
Einstein, Albert
Einthoven, Willem
Eisner, Thomas
El-Sayed, Mostafa Amr
Eldredge, Niles
Elsasser, Walter M.
Elton, Charles Sutherland
Enders, John F.
Engler, Adolph Gustav Heinrich
Enskog, David
Erdös, Paul
Erlang, Agner Krarup
Erlanger, Joseph
Ernst, Richard R.
Esaki, Leo
Estes, William Kaye
Euler, Ulf von
Euler-Chelpin, Hans von
Evans, James C.
Ewing, William Maurice
Fabry, Charles
Fairbank, William
Farman, Joseph C.
Farnsworth, Philo T.
Fauci, Anthony S.
Favaloro, René Geronimo
Feigenbaum, Edward A.
Feigenbaum, Mitchell

Ferguson, Lloyd N.
Fermi, Enrico
Fersman, Aleksandr Evgenievich
Feynman, Richard Phillips
Fibiger, Johannes
Fieser, Louis F.
Fischer, Edmond H.
Fischer, Emil
Fischer, Ernst Otto
Fischer, Hans
Fisher, Ronald A.
Fitch, Val Logsdon
Flanagan, James L.
Fleming, Alexander
Fleming, John Ambrose
Flexner, Simon
Florey, Howard Walter
Flory, Paul
Fokker, Anthony H. G.
Folkers, Karl A.
Forbush, Scott Ellsworth
Ford, Henry
Forrester, Jay W.
Forssmann, Werner
Fowler, William A.
Fox, Sidney W.
Fraenkel, Abraham Adolf
Fraenkel-Conrat, Heinz
Franck, James
Frank, Il'ya
Fraser-Reid, Bertram Oliver
Fréchet, Maurice
Fredholm, Erik Ivar
Freedman, Michael H.
Frenkel, Yakov Ilyich
Friedman, Jerome
Friedmann, Aleksandr A.
Frisch, Karl von
Frisch, Otto Robert
Fujita, Tetsuya Theodore
Fukui, Kenichi
Fuller, Richard Buckminster
Fuller, Solomon
Gabor, Dennis
Gadgil, Madhav
Gagarin, Yuri A.
Gajdusek, D. Carleton
Gallo, Robert C.
Gamow, George
Garrod, Archibald
Gasser, Herbert Spencer
Gates, Bill
Gates, Jr., Sylvester James
Gaviola, Enrique
Geiger, Hans
Gelfond, Aleksandr Osipovich
Gell-Mann, Murray
Ghiorso, Albert
Giacconi, Riccardo

Giaever, Ivar
Giauque, William F.
Gibbs, Josiah Willard
Gibbs, William Francis
Gilbert, Walter
Gilbreth, Frank
Gilman, Alfred Goodman
Glaser, Donald
Glashow, Sheldon Lee
Glenn, Jr., John H.
Goddard, Robert H.
Gödel, Kurt Friedrich
Goethals, George W.
Gold, Thomas
Goldhaber, Maurice
Goldmark, Peter Carl
Goldreich, Peter
Goldschmidt, Richard B.
Goldschmidt, Victor
Goldstein, Avram
Goldstein, Joseph L.
Golgi, Camillo
Gomez-Pompa, Arturo
Gorer, Peter
Goudsmit, Samuel A.
Gould, Stephen Jay
Gourdine, Meredith Charles
Gourneau, Dwight
Govindjee
Gowers, William Timothy
Granit, Ragnar Arthur
Greatbatch, Wilson
Greenewalt, Crawford H.
Grier, Jr., Herbert E.
Griffith, Frederick
Grignard, François Auguste Victor
Grothendieck, Alexander
Groves, Leslie Richard
Guillaume, Charles-Edouard
Guillemin, Roger
Gullstrand, Allvar
Gutenberg, Beno
Guth, Alan
Gutierrez, Orlando A.
Haagen-Smit, A. J.
Haber, Fritz
Hackerman, Norman
Hadamard, Jacques
Hahn, Otto
Haldane, John Burdon Sanderson
Hale, George Ellery
Hall, Lloyd Augustus
Hamburger, Viktor
Hammond, George S.
Hanafusa, Hidesaburo
Hannah, Marc R.
Hansen, James
Harden, Arthur
Hardy, Alister C.

Hardy, Godfrey Harold
Harris, Cyril
Harris, Wesley L.
Hartline, Haldan Keffer
Hassel, Odd
Hauptman, Herbert A.
Haus, Hermann
Hausdorff, Felix
Hawking, Stephen
Hawkins, W. Lincoln
Haworth, Walter
Heezen, Bruce C.
Heimlich, Henry Jay
Heinkel, Ernst
Heisenberg, Werner Karl
Hench, Philip Showalter
Henderson, Cornelius Langston
Henry, John Edward
Henry, Warren Elliott
Hermite, Charles
Herschbach, Dudley R.
Hershey, Alfred Day
Hertz, Gustav
Hertzsprung, Ejnar
Herzberg, Gerhard
Hess, Harry Hammond
Hess, Victor
Hess, Walter Rudolf
Hevesy, Georg von
Hewish, Antony
Hewlett, William
Heymans, Corneille Jean-François
Heyrovský, Jaroslav
Higgs, Peter Ware
Hilbert, David
Hill, Archibald V.
Hill, George William
Hill, Henry A.
Hill, Robert
Hille, Bertil
Hinshelwood, Cyril N.
Hinton, William Augustus
Hitchings, George H.
Ho, David Da-I
Hodgkin, Alan Lloyd
Hoffmann, Roald
Hofstadter, Robert
Holdren, John P.
Holley, Robert William
Holmes, Arthur
Hooft, Gerardus 't
Hopkins, Frederick Gowland
Horn, Michael Hastings
Houdry, Eugene
Hounsfield, Godfrey
Houssay, Bernardo
Hoyle, Fred
Hrdlička, Aleš
Hubbard, Philip G.

Hubbert, M. King
Hubble, Edwin
Hubel, David H.
Huber, Robert
Huggins, Charles B.
Hughes, John
Hulse, Russell A.
Humason, Milton L.
Hunsaker, Jerome C.
Hutchinson, G. Evelyn
Huxley, Andrew Fielding
Huxley, Hugh Esmor
Huxley, Julian
Hyman, Libbie Henrietta
Imes, Elmer Samuel
Ioffe, Abram F.
Isaacs, Alick
Itakura, Keiichi
Iverson, F. Kenneth
Jacob, François
Jansky, Karl
Janzen, Dan
Jarvik, Robert K.
Jason, Robert S.
Jeffreys, Alec John
Jeffreys, Harold
Jeffries, Zay
Jencks, William P.
Jensen, J. Hans D.
Jerne, Niels K.
Jewett, Frank Baldwin
Jobs, Steven Paul
Johannsen, Wilhelm Ludvig
Johnson, Clarence L.
Johnson, Jr., John B.
Johnson, Joseph Lealand
Johnson, Marvin M.
Johnson, William Summer
Johnston, Harold S.
Joliot-Curie, Frédéric
Jones, Fred
Jordan, Ernst Pascual
Josephson, Brian D.
Julian, Percy Lavon
Juran, Joseph M.
Just, Ernest Everett
Kadanoff, Leo P.
Kamerlingh Onnes, Heike
Kan, Yuet Wai
Kandel, Eric R.
Kapitsa, Pyotr
Karle, Jerome
Karlin, Samuel
Karp, Richard M.
Karrer, Paul
Kastler, Alfred
Kates, Robert W.
Kato, Tosio
Katz, Bernard

Katz, Donald L.
Kay, Alan C.
Keith, Arthur
Kemeny, John G.
Kendall, Edward C.
Kendall, Henry W.
Kendrew, John
Kettering, Charles Franklin
Kettlewell, Bernard
Kety, Seymour S.
Khorana, Har Gobind
Khush, Gurdev S.
Kilburn, Thomas M.
Kilby, Jack St. Clair
Kimura, Motoo
Kinoshita, Toichiro
Kinsey, Alfred
Kishimoto, Tadamitsu
Kistiakowsky, George B.
Klein, Christian Felix
Klug, Aaron
Knudsen, William Claire
Knuth, Donald E.
Koch, Robert
Kocher, Theodor
Kodaira, Kunihiko
Köhler, Georges
Kohn, Walter
Kolff, Willem Johan
Kolmogorov, Andrey Nikolayevich
Kolthoff, Izaak Maurits
Konishi, Masakazu
Kontsevich, Maxim
Kornberg, Arthur
Korolyov, Sergei
Koshland, Jr., Daniel E.
Kossel, Albrecht
Kouchner, Bernard
Kountz, Samuel L.
Kouwenhoven, William B.
Kramer, Fred Russell
Krebs, Edwin G.
Krebs, Hans Adolf
Krogh, August
Kroto, Harold Walter
Kuhn, Richard
Kuiper, Gerard Peter
Kurchatov, Igor
Kurtz, Thomas Eugene
Kurzweil, Raymond
Kusch, Polycarp
Lamb, Jr., Willis E.
Land, Edwin H.
Landau, Edmund
Landau, Lev Davidovich
Landsberg, Helmut E.
Landsteiner, Karl
Langevin, Paul
Langlands, Robert P.

Langmuir, Irving
Latimer, Lewis H.
Lattes, C. M. G.
Laub, Jakob Johann
Laue, Max von
Laughlin, Robert B.
Lauterbur, Paul C.
Laveran, Alphonse
Lawless, Theodore K.
Lawrence, Ernest Orlando
Leakey, Louis
Leakey, Richard E.
Lebesgue, Henri
Le Cadet, Georges
Leder, Philip
Lederberg, Joshua
Lederman, Leon Max
Ledley, Robert Steven
Lee, David M.
Lee, Raphael C.
Lee, Tsung-Dao
Lee, Yuan T.
Leevy, Carroll
Leffall, Jr., LaSalle D.
Lehn, Jean-Marie
Leloir, Luis F.
Lemaître, Georges
Lenard, Philipp E. A. von
Leopold, Aldo
Leopold, Luna
Lester, Jr., William Alexander
Levi-Civita, Tullio
Lévi-Strauss, Claude
Lewis, Edward B.
Lewis, Gilbert Newton
Lewis, Julian Herman
Lewis, Warren K.
Li, Ching Chun
Li, Choh Hao
Libby, Willard F.
Liepmann, Hans Wolfgang
Likens, Gene Elden
Lillie, Frank Rattray
Lim, Robert K. S.
Lin, Chia-Chiao
Lindemann, Carl Louis Ferdinand von
Lipmann, Fritz
Lippmann, Gabriel
Lipscomb, Jr., William Nunn
Little, Arthur D.
Lizhi, Fang
Loeb, Jacques
Loewi, Otto
London, Fritz
Lorentz, Hendrik Antoon
Lorenz, Edward N.
Lorenz, Konrad
Lorius, Claude
Lovejoy, Thomas Eugene

Lovelock, James E.
Luria, Salvador Edward
Lwoff, André
Lynen, Feodor
Lynk, Miles Vandahurst
MacArthur, Robert H.
MacDonald, Gordon
MacKinnon, Roderick
Mac Lane, Saunders
MacLeod, Colin Munro
Macleod, John James Rickard
MacPherson, Robert
Maillart, Robert
Maiman, Theodore
Maloney, Arnold Hamilton
Mandel'shtam, Leonid Isaakovich
Mandelbrot, Benoit B.
Marchbanks, Jr., Vance H.
Marconi, Guglielmo
Marcus, Rudolph A.
Margulis, Gregori Aleksandrovitch
Marie-Victorin, Frère
Markov, Andrei Andreevich
Martin, A. J. P.
Massey, Walter E.
Massie, Samuel P.
Masters, William Howell
Matuyama, Motonori
Mauchly, John William
Maynard Smith, John
Mayr, Ernst
McAfee, Walter S.
McCarthy, John
McCarty, Maclyn
McCarty, Perry L.
McCollum, Elmer Verner
McConnell, Harden
McMillan, Edwin M.
McMullen, Curtis T.
Mead, George Herbert
Medawar, Peter Brian
Méray, Hugues Charles Robert
Merrifield, R. Bruce
Meselson, Matthew
Metchnikoff, Élie
Meyerhof, Otto
Michel, Hartmut
Michelson, Albert
Midgley, Jr., Thomas
Miller, James A.
Miller, Stanley Lloyd
Millikan, Robert A.
Milne, Edward Arthur
Milnor, John
Milstein, César
Minkowski, Hermann
Minkowski, Rudolph
Minot, George Richards
Minsky, Marvin

Mitchell, Peter D.
Mittermeier, Russell
Mohorovičić, Andrija
Moissan, Henri
Molina, Mario
Moniz, Egas
Monod, Jacques Lucien
Montagnier, Luc
Moore, Raymond Cecil
Moore, Stanford
Mordell, Louis Joel
Morgan, Arthur E.
Morgan, Garrett A.
Morgan, Thomas Hunt
Mori, Shigefumi
Morley, Edward Williams
Morrison, Philip
Moseley, Henry Gwyn Jeffreys
Mössbauer, Rudolf
Mott, Nevill Francis
Mottelson, Ben R.
Moulton, Forest Ray
Muller, Hermann Joseph
Müller, K. Alex
Müller, Paul
Mulliken, Robert S.
Mullis, Kary
Munk, Walter
Murphy, William P.
Murray, Joseph E.
Nabrit, Samuel Milton
Nagata, Takesi
Nakanishi, Koji
Nambu, Yoichiro
Nash, John Forbes
Nathans, Daniel
Natta, Giulio
Ne'eman, Yuval
Neal, Homer Alfred
Needham, Joseph
Néel, Louis
Neher, Erwin
Nernst, Walther
Newell, Allen
Newell, Norman Dennis
Nicholson, Seth Barnes
Nicolle, Charles J. H.
Nier, Alfred O. C.
Nirenberg, Marshall Warren
Nishizawa, Jun-ichi
Nishizuka, Yasutomi
Noble, G. K.
Noether, Max
Noguchi, Hideyo
Nomura, Masayasu
Norrish, Ronald G. W.
Northrop, John Howard
Novikov, Sergei
Noyce, Robert

Nozoe, Tetsuo
O'Neill, Gerard K.
Oberth, Hermann
Ochoa, Severo
Odum, Eugene Pleasants
Odum, Howard T.
Oeschger, Hans
Olah, George A.
Olden, Kenneth
Oldham, Richard Dixon
Ondetti, Miguel A.
Onsager, Lars
Oort, Jan Hendrik
Oparin, Aleksandr Ivanovich
Oppenheimer, J. Robert
Osheroff, Douglas D.
Osterbrock, Donald E.
Ostwald, Friedrich Wilhelm
Packard, David
Palade, George
Panofsky, Wolfgang K. H.
Papanicolaou, George
Parker, Arthur C.
Parker, Charles Stewart
Parker, Eugene Newman
Parsons, John T.
Patel, C. Kumar N.
Patterson, Claire
Patterson, Frederick Douglass
Paul, Wolfgang
Pauli, Wolfgang
Pauling, Linus
Pavlov, Ivan Petrovich
Peano, Giuseppe
Pearson, Karl
Pedersen, Charles John
Peebles, Phillip James Edwin
Peierls, Rudolf
Peirce, Charles Sanders
Penrose, Roger
Penzias, Arno
Perl, Martin L.
Perrin, Jean Baptiste
Perutz, Max
Pettersson, Hans
Phelps, Michael E.
Phillips, William D.
Piasecki, Frank
Piccard, Auguste
Pierce, George Edward
Pilbeam, David R.
Pimentel, David
Pinchot, Gifford
Pincus, Gregory Goodwin
Planck, Max
Plotkin, Mark
Pogue, William Reid
Poincaré, Jules Henri
Poindexter, Hildrus A.

Polanyi, John C.
Pólya, George
Ponnamperuma, Cyril
Pople, John A.
Porter, George
Porter, Rodney
Poulsen, Valdemar
Pound, Robert
Powell, Cecil Frank
Powless, David
Prandtl, Ludwig
Pregl, Fritz
Prelog, Vladimir
Press, Frank
Prigogine, Ilya
Prokhorov, Aleksandr
Prusiner, Stanley B.
Puck, Theodore T.
Punnett, R. C.
Purcell, Edward Mills
Qöyawayma, Alfred H.
Quarterman, Lloyd Albert
Quate, Calvin F.
Quinland, William Samuel
Rabi, I. I.
Rainwater, James
Ramalingaswami, Vulimiri
Raman, C. V.
Ramanujan, S. I.
Ramón y Cajal, Santiago
Ramsay, William
Ramsey, Frank Plumpton
Ramsey, Norman Foster
Rao, C. N. R.
Raven, Peter Hamilton
Reber, Grote
Reddy, Raj
Reed, Walter
Reichstein, Tadeus
Reid, Lonnie
Reines, Frederick
Revelle, Roger
Rice, Stuart Alan
Rich, Alexander
Richards, Jr., Dickinson Woodruff
Richards, Theodore William
Richardson, Lewis Fry
Richardson, Owen W.
Richardson, Robert C.
Richet, Charles Robert
Richter, Burton
Richter, Charles F.
Rickover, Hyman G.
Risi, Joseph
Ritchie, Dennis
Robbins, Frederick
Roberts, Lawrence
Roberts, Richard J.
Robinson, Robert

Rock, John
Rodbell, Martin
Roddy, Leon Raymand
Roelofs, Wendell L.
Rohrer, Heinrich
Romer, Alfred Sherwood
Romero, Juan Carlos
Röntgen, Wilhelm Conrad
Rosenbluth, Marshall N.
Ross, John
Ross, Ronald
Rossby, Carl-Gustaf
Rous, Peyton
Rowland, F. Sherwood
Rubbia, Carlo
Runcorn, S. K.
Ruska, Ernst
Russell, Bertrand
Russell, Frederick Stratten
Russell, Henry Norris
Russell, Loris Shano
Rutherford, Ernest
Ružička, Leopold
Ryle, Martin
Sabatier, Paul
Sabin, Albert
Sagan, Carl
Sakharov, Andrei
Sakmann, Bert
Salam, Abdus
Salk, Jonas
Samuelsson, Bengt
Sanchez, David A.
Sanchez, Pedro A.
Sandage, Allan R.
Sanger, Frederick
Satcher, David
Schaller, George
Schally, Andrew V.
Schawlow, Arthur Leonard
Schick, Bela
Schneider, Stephen H.
Schou, Mogens
Schrieffer, J. Robert
Schrödinger, Erwin
Schultes, Richard Evans
Schwartz, Melvin
Schwarz, John Henry
Schwinger, Julian
Seaborg, Glenn T.
Segrè, Emilio
Seitz, Frederick
Selberg, Atle
Semenov, Nikolai N.
Serre, Jean-Pierre
Shannon, Claude
Shapiro, Irwin
Shapley, Harlow
Sharp, Phillip A.

Sharp, Robert Phillip
Sheldrake, Rupert
Shepard, Jr., Alan B.
Shepard, Roger N.
Sherrington, Charles Scott
Shockley, William
Shoemaker, Eugene M.
Shokalsky, Yuly Mikhaylovich
Shtokman, Vladimir Borisovich
Shull, Clifford Glenwood
Shurney, Robert E.
Siegbahn, Kai M.
Siegbahn, Karl M. G.
Sierpiński, Waclaw
Sikorsky, Igor I.
Simmons, Jr., Howard Ensign
Simon, Herbert A.
Simpson, George Gaylord
Sinclair, Clive Marles
Singer, I. M.
Sioui, Richard H.
Skoog, Folke Karl
Skou, Jens C.
Slater, John Clarke
Slipher, Vesto M.
Smale, Stephen
Smalley, Richard Errett
Smith, Hamilton O.
Smith, Michael
Snell, George Davis
Snyder, Solomon H.
Soddy, Frederick
Solberg, Halvor
Sommerfeld, Arnold
Sommerville, Duncan McLaren Young
Sorensen, Charles E.
Sørensen, Søren Peter Lauritz
Spedding, Frank Harold
Spemann, Hans
Sperry, Elmer
Sperry, Roger W.
Spitzer, Jr., Lyman
Stahl, Franklin W.
Stanley, Richard
Stanley, Wendell Meredith
Stark, Johannes
Starling, Ernest H.
Starr, Chauncey
Starzl, Thomas
Staudinger, Hermann
Stefanik, Milan Ratislav
Stein, William Howard
Steinberger, Jack
Steinman, David B.
Steinmetz, Charles P.
Steptoe, Patrick
Stern, Otto
Stever, H. Guyford
Steward, Frederick Campion

Woodwell, George M.
Wozniak, Stephen
Wright, Almroth Edward
Wright, Louis Tompkins
Wright, Orville
Wright, Sewall
Wright, Wilbur
Yang, Chen Ning
Yau, Shing-Tung

Young, J. Z.
Young, William Henry
Yukawa, Hideki
Zadeh, Lotfi Asker
Zamecnik, Paul Charles
Zeeman, E. C.
Zeeman, Pieter
Zel'dovich, Yakov Borisovich
Zen, E-an

Zernike, Frits
Ziegler, Karl
Zinder, Norton
Zinkernagel, Rolf M.
Zinn, Walter Henry
Zinsser, Hans
Zsigmondy, Richard
Zuse, Konrad
Zworykin, Vladimir

Nationality/Ethnicity Index

Roberts, Lawrence **4**: 1891

Robinson, Julia **4**: 1894

Rock, John **4**: 1896

Rockwell, Mabel M. **4**: 1897

Rodbell, Martin **4**: 1898

Roddy, Leon Raymand **4**: 1900

Roelofs, Wendell L. **4**: 1901

Rogers, Marguerite M. **4**: 1902

Roman, Nancy Grace **4**: 1905

Romer, Alfred Sherwood **4**: 1906

Rosenbluth, Marshall N. **4**: 1912

Ross, John **4**: 1913

Ross, Mary G. **4**: 1914

Rous, Peyton **4**: 1919

Rowland, F. Sherwood **4**: 1922

Rowley, Janet D. **4**: 1924

Rubin, Vera Cooper **4**: 1926

Rudin, Mary Ellen **4**: 1928

Russell, Elizabeth Shull **4**: 1935

Russell, Henry Norris **4**: 1938

Russell, Loris Shano **4**: 1940

Sabin, Albert **4**: 1950

Sabin, Florence Rena **4**: 1953

Sagan, Carl **4**: 1956

Sager, Ruth **4**: 1959

Salk, Jonas **4**: 1967

Sanchez, David A. **4**: 1971

Sanchez, Pedro A. **4**: 1972

Sandage, Allan R. **4**: 1973

Sanford, Katherine Koontz **4**: 1975

Satcher, David **4**: 1979

Schafer, Alice T. **4**: 1980

Schaller, George **4**: 1981

Schally, Andrew V. **4**: 1983

Schawlow, Arthur Leonard **4**: 1987

Schneider, Stephen H. **4**: 1990

Schrieffer, J. Robert **4**: 1993

Schultes, Richard Evans **4**: 1996

Schwartz, Melvin **4**: 1998

Schwarz, John Henry **4**: 1999

Schwinger, Julian **4**: 2001

Seaborg, Glenn T. **4**: 2004

Segrè, Emilio **4**: 2007

Seibert, Florence B. **4**: 2009

Seitz, Frederick **4**: 2011

Shannon, Claude **4**: 2016

Shapiro, Irwin **4**: 2017

Shapley, Harlow **4**: 2019

Sharp, Phillip A. **4**: 2021

Sharp, Robert Phillip **4**: 2023

Shaw, Mary **4**: 2024

Shepard, Jr., Alan B. **4**: 2027

Shepard, Roger N. **4**: 2029

Shockley, Dolores Cooper **4**: 2033

Shockley, William **4**: 2033

Shoemaker, Eugene M. **4**: 2035

Shull, Clifford Glenwood **4**: 2040

Shurney, Robert E. **4**: 2041

Sikorsky, Igor I. **4**: 2046

Silbergeld, Ellen Kovner **4**: 2049

Simmons, Jr., Howard Ensign **4**: 2050

Simon, Dorothy Martin **4**: 2051

Simon, Herbert A. **4**: 2053

Simpson, George Gaylord **4**: 2054

Singer, I. M. **4**: 2059

Singer, Maxine **4**: 2060

Sioui, Richard H. **4**: 2063

Skoog, Folke Karl **4**: 2063

Slater, John Clarke **4**: 2067

Slipher, Vesto M. **4**: 2069

Slye, Maud **4**: 2071

Smale, Stephen **4**: 2072

Smalley, Richard Errett **4**: 2073

Smith, Hamilton O. **4**: 2075

Snell, George Davis **4**: 2078

Snyder, Solomon H. **4**: 2080

Solomon, Susan **4**: 2086

Sorensen, Charles E. **4**: 2091

Spaeth, Mary **4**: 2094

Sparling, Rebecca H. **4**: 2095

Spedding, Frank Harold **4**: 2096

Sperry, Elmer **4**: 2098

Sperry, Roger W. **4**: 2100

Spitzer, Jr., Lyman **4**: 2103

Stahl, Franklin W. **4**: 2104

Stanley, Richard **4**: 2106

Stanley, Wendell Meredith **4**: 2108

Starr, Chauncey **4**: 2113

Starzl, Thomas **4**: 2114

Stein, William Howard **4**: 2120

Steinberger, Jack **4**: 2121

Steinman, David B. **4**: 2123

Steinmetz, Charles P. **4**: 2124

Steitz, Joan Argetsinger **4**: 2125

Stern, Otto **4**: 2128

Stevens, Nettie Maria **4**: 2130

Stever, H. Guyford **4**: 2131

Steward, Frederick Campion **4**: 2133

Stewart, Thomas Dale **4**: 2134

Stibitz, George R. **4**: 2135

Stoll, Alice M. **4**: 2140

Stommel, Henry **4**: 2142

Straus, Jr., William Levi **4**: 2147

Stubbe, JoAnne **4**: 2151

Sturtevant, A. H. **4**: 2152

Sumner, James B. **4**: 2154

Suomi, Verner E. **4**: 2156

Sutherland, Earl **4**: 2157

Sutherland, Ivan **4**: 2159

Sutton, Walter Stanborough **4**: 2160

Szent-Györgyi, Albert **4**: 2169

Szilard, Leo **4**: 2172

Tapia, Richard A. **5**: 2177

Tarski, Alfred **5**: 2178

Tatum, Edward Lawrie **5**: 2179

Taube, Henry **5**: 2183

Taussig, Helen Brooke **5**: 2184

Taylor, Frederick Winslow **5**: 2188

Taylor, Jr., Joseph H. **5**: 2191

Taylor, Moddie **5**: 2192

Taylor, Richard E. **5**: 2193

Taylor, Stuart **5**: 2194

Teller, Edward **5**: 2197

Temin, Howard **5**: 2200

Terman, Frederick **5**: 2203

Terzaghi, Karl **5**: 2205

Tesla, Nikola **5**: 2206

Tesoro, Giuliana Cavaglieri **5**: 2210

Tharp, Marie **5**: 2211

Theiler, Max **5**: 2213

Thomas, E. Donnall **5**: 2217

Thomas, Martha Jane Bergin **5**: 2219

Thompson, Kenneth Lane **5**: 2222

Thurston, William **5**: 2228

Tien, Ping King **5**: 2230

Tildon, J. Tyson **5**: 2231

Timoshenko, Stephen P. **5**: 2232

Ting, Samuel C. C. **5**: 2235

Tishler, Max **5**: 2239

Tombaugh, Clyde W. **5**: 2244

Townes, Charles H. **5**: 2250

Trotter, Mildred **5**: 2252

Trump, John G. **5**: 2254

Tsao, George T. **5**: 2255

Tsui, Daniel Chee **5**: 2259

Turner, Charles Henry **5**: 2265

Tuve, Merle A. **5**: 2266

Uhlenbeck, George **5**: 2271

Uhlenbeck, Karen **5**: 2272

Urey, Harold **5**: 2273

Van Allen, James **5**: 2281

Van de Graaff, Robert J. **5**: 2283

van der Wal, Laurel **5**: 2290

Van Vleck, John **5**: 2291

van Straten, Florence W. **5**: 2291

Varmus, Harold E. **5**: 2294

Vedder, Edward Bright **5**: 2296

von Braun, Wernher **5**: 2307

von Mises, Richard **5**: 2313

von Neumann, John **5**: 2315

Waelsch, Salome **5**: 2323

Wahl, Arnold C. **5**: 2326

Waksman, Selman **5**: 2327

Wald, George **5**: 2329

Wang, An **5**: 2338

Wang, James C. **5**: 2339

Washington, Warren M. **5**: 2345

Watkins, Jr., Levi **5**: 2346

Watson, James D. **5**: 2347

Weertman, Julia **5**: 2353

Weinberg, Robert A. **5**: 2360

Weinberg, Steven **5**: 2362

Weiss, Mary Catherine Bishop **5**: 2365

Weller, Thomas **5**: 2368

Went, Frits **5**: 2370

West, Harold Dadford **5**: 2373

Wetherill, George West **5**: 2374

Bosnian

Prelog, Vladimir **4**: 1807

Brazilian

Lattes, C. M. G. **3**: 1317

British

Borcherds, Richard Ewen **1**: 244
Carroll, Lewis **1**: 362
Gowers, William Timothy **2**: 901
Pople, John A. **4**: 1795
Stokes, George Gabriel **4**: 2138

Canadian

Avery, Oswald Theodore **1**: 85
Banting, Frederick G. **1**: 118
Barr, Murray Llewellyn **1**: 134
Baxter, Agnes **1**: 144
Best, Charles Herbert **1**: 187
Black, Davidson **1**: 207
Bondar, Roberta L. **1**: 241
Brill, Yvonne Claeys **1**: 292
Brockhouse, Bertram Neville **1**: 293
Daly, Reginald Aldworth **2**: 514
d'Hérelle, Félix **2**: 557
Fraser-Reid, Bertram Oliver **2**: 774
Giauque, William F. **2**: 837
Herzberg, Gerhard **2**: 1006
Hogg, Helen Sawyer **2**: 1052
Hubel, David H. **2**: 1083
Kelsey, Frances Oldham **3**: 1203
Lillie, Frank Rattray **3**: 1397
MacArthur, Robert H. **3**: 1442
MacGill, Elsie Gregory **3**: 1446
MacLeod, Colin Munro **3**: 1452
Marcus, Rudolph A. **3**: 1471
Marie-Victorin, Frère **3**: 1476
Nelson, Evelyn **4**: 1626
Polanyi, John C. **4**: 1789
Pound, Robert **4**: 1800
Rigas, Harriett B. **4**: 1887
Risi, Joseph **4**: 1887
Russell, Loris Shano **4**: 1940
Smith, Michael **4**: 2077
Spedding, Frank Harold **4**: 2096
Taube, Henry **5**: 2183
Taylor, Richard E. **5**: 2193
Vollenweider, Richard **5**: 2304
Wilson, J. Tuzo **5**: 2451

Canadian-born American

Bromley, D. Allan **1**: 296
Eastwood, Alice **2**: 615
Langlands, Robert P. **3**: 1313
Peebles, Phillip James Edwin **4**: 1738
Zinn, Walter Henry **5**: 2519

Chinese

Chang, Min-Chueh **1**: 391
Cho, Alfred Y. **1**: 406
Fischer, Edmond H. **2**: 720
Huang, Alice Shih-hou **2**: 1077
Kan, Yuet Wai **3**: 1176
Lee, Yuan T. **3**: 1354
Li, Ching Chun **3**: 1389
Li, Choh Hao **3**: 1390
Lin, Chia-Chiao **3**: 1399
Lizhi, Fang **3**: 1410
Tan Jiazhen, **5**: 2176
Tien, Ping King **5**: 2230
Tsao, George T. **5**: 2255
Tsui, Daniel Chee **5**: 2259
Wang, An **5**: 2338
Wang, James C. **5**: 2339
Wu, Y. C. L. Susan **5**: 2485
Xide, Xie **5**: 2487
Yau, Shing-Tung **5**: 2493
Young, Lai-Sang **5**: 2497
Zen, E-an **5**: 2511

Chinese-born American

Chang, Sun-Yung Alice **1**: 392
Chang, Te-Tzu **1**: 393
Ho, David Da-I **2**: 1040

Chinese-born Canadian

Tsui, Lap-Chee **5**: 2259

Colombian

Ocampo, Adriana C. **4**: 1667

Croatian

Mohorovičić, Andrija **3**: 1556
Ružička, Leopold **4**: 1945

Cuban

Diaz, Henry F. **2**: 560
Gutierrez, Orlando A. **2**: 924
Sanchez, Pedro A. **4**: 1972

Cuban-born American

Velez–Rodriguez, Argelia **5**: 2298

Czechoslovakian

Heyrovský, Jaroslav **2**: 1022
Hrdlička, Aleš **2**: 1076
Stefanik, Milan Ratislav **4**: 2119

Danish

Bohr, Aage **1**: 234
Bohr, Niels **1**: 235
Brønsted, Johannes Nicolaus **1**: 300
Dam, Henrik **2**: 516
Dansgaard, Willi **2**: 518
Erlang, Agner Krarup **2**: 669

Fibiger, Johannes **2**: 716
Hertzsprung, Ejnar **2**: 1004
Jerne, Niels K. **3**: 1137
Johannsen, Wilhelm Ludvig **3**: 1143
Krogh, August **3**: 1277
Lehmann, Inge **3**: 1360
Mottelson, Ben R. **3**: 1590
Poulsen, Valdemar **4**: 1799
Schou, Mogens **4**: 1991
Sorensen, Charles E. **4**: 2091
Sørensen, Søren Peter Lauritz **4**: 2093

Dutch

Bloembergen, Nicolaas **1**: 224
Brouwer, Luitzen Egbertus Jan **1**: 303
Clay, Jacob **1**: 419
Clay-Jolles, Tettje Clasina **1**: 421
Coster, Dirk **1**: 469
Crutzen, Paul J. **1**: 494
Debye, Peter **2**: 538
de Sitter, Willem **2**: 555
Dijkstra, Edsger W. **2**: 570
Dubois, Eugène **2**: 598
Ehrenfest, Paul **2**: 634
Ehrenfest-Afanaseva, Tatiana **2**: 635
Eijkman, Christiaan **2**: 643
Einthoven, Willem **2**: 651
Fokker, Anthony H. G. **2**: 747
Goudsmit, Samuel A. **2**: 893
Haagen-Smit, A. J. **2**: 927
Hooft, Gerardus 't **2**: 1061
Kamerlingh Onnes, Heike **3**: 1174
Kolff, Willem Johan **3**: 1250
Kolthoff, Izaak Maurits **3**: 1253
Kuiper, Gerard Peter **3**: 1282
Lorentz, Hendrik Antoon **3**: 1421
Oort, Jan Hendrik **4**: 1685
Skou, Jens C. **4**: 2065
Tinbergen, Nikolaas **5**: 2234
van der Meer, Simon **5**: 2287
van der Waals, Johannes Diderik
    5: 2288
Voûte, Joan George Erardus Gijsbert
    5: 2318
Vries, Hugo de **5**: 2319
Weber-van Bosse, Anne Antoinette
    5: 2351
Went, Frits **5**: 2370
Zeeman, Pieter **5**: 2508
Zernike, Frits **5**: 2512

Dutch-born American

van de Kamp, Peter **5**: 2286

Egyptian

El-Sayed, Mostafa Amr **2**: 653

Weidenreich, Franz **5**: 2357

Weinberg, Wilhelm **5**: 2363

Weizsäcker, Carl F. Von **5**: 2366

Weyl, Hermann **5**: 2376

Wiechert, Emil **5**: 2403

Wieland, Heinrich **5**: 2404

Wien, Wilhelm **5**: 2406

Willstätter, Richard **5**: 2438

Windaus, Adolf **5**: 2458

Wittig, Georg **5**: 2463

Ziegler, Karl **5**: 2513

Zsigmondy, Richard **5**: 2522

Zuse, Konrad **5**: 2524

German-born American

Ajzenberg-Selove, Fay **1**: 14

Blobel, Günter **1**: 216

Bremermann, Hans-Joachim **1**: 282

Elsasser, Walter M. **2**: 659

Kusch, Polycarp **3**: 1290

Scharrer, Berta **4**: 1985

German-born Danish

Fenchel, Käte **2**: 706

German-born English

Bodmer, Walter F. **1**: 233

Peierls, Rudolf **4**: 1739

Greek

Micheli-Tzanakou, Evangelia **3**: 1530

Panajiotatou, Angeliki **4**: 1703

Papanicolaou, George **4**: 1705

Guatemalan

Bressani, Ricardo **1**: 287

Hispanic American

Alvarez, Luis **1**: 33

Baez, Albert V. **1**: 102

Cardona, Manuel **1**: 351

Cardús, David **1**: 353

Castro, George **1**: 376

Colmenares, Margarita **1**: 445

Dallmeier, Francisco **2**: 510

Diaz, Henry F. **2**: 560

Gutierrez, Orlando A. **2**: 924

Molina, Mario **3**: 1559

Ocampo, Adriana C. **4**: 1667

Ochoa, Ellen **4**: 1668

Pimentel, David **4**: 1774

Romero, Juan Carlos **4**: 1908

Sanchez, Pedro A. **4**: 1972

Tapia, Richard A. **5**: 2177

Hungarian

Erdös, Paul **2**: 667

Gabor, Dennis **2**: 797

Goldmark, Peter Carl **2**: 872

Kemeny, John G. **3**: 1205

Lenard, Philipp E. A. von **3**: 1368

Péter, Rózsa **4**: 1760

Pólya, George **4**: 1791

Stefanik, Milan Ratislav **4**: 2119

Teller, Edward **5**: 2197

von Kármán, Theodore **5**: 2310

Hungarian-born American

Olah, George A. **4**: 1676

Pólya, George **4**: 1791

Schick, Bela **4**: 1988

Szegö, Gabor **4**: 2167

Telkes, Maria **5**: 2195

Indian

Bhabha, Homi Jehangir **1**: 193

Bose, Satyendranath **1**: 256

Chaudhari, Praveen **1**: 399

Gadgil, Madhav **2**: 799

Gadgil, Sulochana **2**: 800

Govindjee **2**: 900

Haldane, John Burdon Sanderson **2**: 936

Khorana, Har Gobind **3**: 1216

Khush, Gurdev S. **3**: 1218

Ramalingaswami, Vulimiri **4**: 1836

Raman, C. V. **4**: 1837

Ramanujan, S. I. **4**: 1839

Rao, C. N. R. **4**: 1850

Reddy, Raj **4**: 1855

Ross, Ronald **4**: 1914

Swaminathan, M. S. **4**: 2164

Indian-born American

Chandrasekhar, Subrahmanyan **1**: 387

Patel, C. Kumar N. **4**: 1712

Irish

Bell, John Stewart **1**: 158

Bell Burnell, Jocelyn Susan **1**: 160

Maunder, Annie Russell **3**: 1487

Oldham, Richard Dixon **4**: 1679

Walton, Ernest **5**: 2335

Irish-born English

Burkitt, Denis Parsons **1**: 324

Stott, Alicia Boole **4**: 2144

Israeli

Fraenkel, Abraham Adolf **2**: 765

Ne'eman, Yuval **4**: 1618

Italian

Bovet, Daniel **1**: 261

Dulbecco, Renato **2**: 604

Fermi, Enrico **2**: 710

Giacconi, Riccardo **2**: 834

Golgi, Camillo **2**: 884

Krim, Mathilde **3**: 1275

Levi-Civita, Tullio **3**: 1375

Luria, Salvador Edward **3**: 1433

Marconi, Guglielmo **3**: 1468

Natta, Giulio **4**: 1617

Peano, Giuseppe **4**: 1733

Rubbia, Carlo **4**: 1925

Segrè, Emilio **4**: 2007

Tesoro, Giuliana Cavaglieri **5**: 2210

Volterra, Vito **5**: 2306

Italian-born American

Levi-Montalcini, Rita **3**: 1377

Jamaican-English

Williams, Cicely Delphin **5**: 2429

Japanese

Aki, Keiiti **1**: 15

Esaki, Leo **2**: 673

Fujita, Tetsuya Theodore **2**: 789

Fukui, Kenichi **2**: 791

Hanafusa, Hidesaburo **2**: 949

Itakura, Keiichi **3**: 1111

Kato, Tosio **3**: 1193

Kimura, Motoo **3**: 1222

Kinoshita, Toichiro **3**: 1226

Kishimoto, Tadamitsu **3**: 1230

Kodaira, Kunihiko **3**: 1244

Konishi, Masakazu **3**: 1254

Matuyama, Motonori **3**: 1484

Mori, Shigefumi **3**: 1580

Nagata, Takesi **4**: 1610

Nambu, Yoichiro **4**: 1613

Nishizawa, Jun-ichi **4**: 1643

Nishizuka, Yasutomi **4**: 1644

Noguchi, Hideyo **4**: 1651

Nomura, Masayasu **4**: 1653

Nozoe, Tetsuo **4**: 1660

Tomonaga, Sin-Itiro **5**: 2246

Tonegawa, Susumu **5**: 2247

Uyeda, Seiya **5**: 2277

Yukawa, Hideki **5**: 2500

Japanese-born American

Nakanishi, Koji **4**: 1611

Kenyan

Maathai, Wangari **3**: 1441

Korean

Pedersen, Charles John **4**: 1737

Latvian

Anders, Edward **1**: 44

Ostwald, Friedrich Wilhelm **4**: 1695

Latvian American
  Bers, Lipman **1**: 186

Liberian
  Fuller, Solomon **2**: 794

Lithuanian
  Klug, Aaron **3**: 1234

Lithuanian-Canadian
  Galdikas, Birute Marija Filomena **2**: 805

Mexican
  Baez, Albert V. **1**: 102
  Beltrán, Enrique **1**: 163
  Gomez-Pompa, Arturo **2**: 886
  Molina, Mario **3**: 1559

Native American
  Begay, Fred **1**: 154
  Chinn, May Edward **1**: 405
  Gourneau, Dwight **2**: 899
  Horn, Michael Hastings **2**: 1067
  Powless, David **4**: 1803
  Qöyawayma, Alfred H. **4**: 1827
  Ross, Mary G. **4**: 1914
  Sioui, Richard H. **4**: 2063
  Williamson, James S. **5**: 2437

New Zealand
  Rutherford, Ernest **4**: 1942
  Wilkins, Maurice Hugh Frederick
    5: 2425

New Zealand-born Australian
  Butement, William **1**: 332

Norwegian
  Bjerknes, Jacob **1**: 203
  Bjerknes, Vilhelm **1**: 205
  Giaever, Ivar **2**: 836
  Goldschmidt, Victor **2**: 879
  Hassel, Odd **2**: 965
  Selberg, Atle **4**: 2013
  Solberg, Halvor **4**: 2084
  Størmer, Fredrik **4**: 2143

Pakistani
  Salam, Abdus **4**: 1965

Polish
  Banach, Stefan **1**: 116
  Charpak, Georges **1**: 397
  Curie, Marie **1**: 497
  Hoffmann, Roald **2**: 1049
  Karlin, Samuel **3**: 1185
  Kuperberg, Krystyna **3**: 1284
  Mandelbrot, Benoit B. **3**: 1463

  Reichstein, Tadeus **4**: 1860
  Rickover, Hyman G. **4**: 1881
  Schally, Andrew V. **4**: 1983
  Sierpiński, Waclaw **4**: 2045

Polish-American
  Bari, Ruth Aaronson **1**: 128

Polish-born Canadian
  Krieger, Cecilia **3**: 1273

Portuguese
  Moniz, Egas **3**: 1560

Prussian
  Michelson, Albert **3**: 1531

Romanian
  Juran, Joseph M. **3**: 1168
  Palade, George **4**: 1701

Romanian-American
  Bellow, Alexandra **1**: 162

Russian
  Aleksandrov, Pavel S. **1**: 20
  Alikhanov, Abram Isaakovich **1**: 27
  Bari, Nina **1**: 127
  Basov, Nikolai **1**: 140
  Breit, Gregory **1**: 280
  Cantor, Georg **1**: 349
  Cherenkov, Pavel A. **1**: 401
  Dobzhansky, Theodosius **2**: 576
  Esau, Katherine **2**: 675
  Fersman, Aleksandr Evgenievich **2**: 713
  Frank, Il'ya **2**: 771
  Frenkel, Yakov Ilyich **2**: 780
  Friedmann, Aleksandr A. **2**: 783
  Gagarin, Yuri A. **2**: 801
  Gamow, George **2**: 809
  Gelfond, Aleksandr Osipovich **2**: 826
  Ioffe, Abram F. **3**: 1107
  Janovskaja, Sof'ja Aleksandrovna
    3: 1119
  Kapitsa, Pyotr **3**: 1179
  Karrer, Paul **3**: 1188
  Kistiakowsky, George B. **3**: 1231
  Kolmogorov, Andrey Nikolayevich
    3: 1252
  Kontsevich, Maxim **3**: 1255
  Korolyov, Sergei **3**: 1258
  Kurchatov, Igor **3**: 1285
  Landau, Lev Davidovich **3**: 1305
  Litvinova, Elizaveta Fedorovna **3**: 1409
  Mandel'shtam, Leonid Isaakovich
    3: 1462
  Margulis, Gregori Aleksandrovitch
    3: 1473

  Markov, Andrei Andreevich **3**: 1477
  Massevitch, Alla G. **3**: 1479
  Metchnikoff, Élie **3**: 1524
  Minkowski, Hermann **3**: 1546
  Novikov, Sergei **4**: 1657
  Oleinik, Olga **4**: 1680
  Oparin, Aleksandr Ivanovich **4**: 1687
  Pavlov, Ivan Petrovich **4**: 1728
  Polubarinova-Kochina, Pelageya
    Yakovlevna **4**: 1790
  Prigogine, Ilya **4**: 1813
  Prokhorov, Aleksandr **4**: 1817
  Sabin, Albert **4**: 1950
  Sakharov, Andrei **4**: 1961
  Semenov, Nikolai N. **4**: 2014
  Shokalsky, Yuly Mikhaylovich **4**: 2037
  Shtokman, Vladimir Borisovich **4**: 2039
  Sikorsky, Igor I. **4**: 2046
  Tamm, Igor **5**: 2175
  Tereshkova, Valentina **5**: 2202
  Timoshenko, Stephen P. **5**: 2232
  Topchiev, Alexsandr Vasil'evich **5**: 2249
  Tsiolkovsky, Konstantin **5**: 2256
  Tswett, Mikhail **5**: 2261
  Veksler, V. I. **5**: 2297
  Vernadsky, Vladímir Ivanovich **5**: 2299
  Waksman, Selman **5**: 2327
  Zadeh, Lotfi Asker **5**: 2503
  Zel'dovich, Yakov Borisovich **5**: 2510
  Zworykin, Vladimir **5**: 2526

Russian American
  Lehmer, Emma Trotskaya **3**: 1361

Russian-born English
  Uvarov, Boris Petrovich **5**: 2276

Scottish
  Fleming, Alexander **2**: 734
  Isaacs, Alick **3**: 1109
  Keith, Arthur **3**: 1199
  Macintyre, Sheila Scott **3**: 1447
  Macleod, John James Rickard **3**: 1453
  Sommerville, Duncan McLaren Young
    4: 2090
  Thompson, D'Arcy Wentworth **5**: 2220
  Watson-Watt, Robert **5**: 2349
  Wilson, C. T. R. **5**: 2443

Singaporean
  Lim, Robert K. S. **3**: 1398

Slovenian-born American
  Haus, Hermann **2**: 968

South African
  Barnard, Christiaan Neethling **1**: 130
  Brenner, Sydney **1**: 283

Subject Index

References to individual volumes are listed in **boldface**; numbers following a colon refer to page numbers. **A boldface** page number indicates the full entry for a scientist.

American Telephone and Telegraph Company (AT&T) **3:** 1139, 1140

americium **2:** 832; **4:** 2006

Ames test

Ames, Bruce N. **1: 40**; **4:** 1816

amines, aromatic **5:** 2405

amines, sympathomimetic **1:** 88

amino acid automated analyzer **3:** 1571

amino acids **1:** 2, 32, 57, 147, 169; **2:** 624, 722, 1062; **3:** 1343, 1537, 1538, 1570; **4:** 1798, 1851, 2093, 2165, 2166; **5:** 2260, 2304

amino acids, isolation of **3:** 1570

Ammann, Othmar Hermann **1: 42**

ammonia, synthesis of **2:** 928

ammonia, synthetic **1:** 255, 418

amniocentesis **3:** 1275

AMP **5:** 2332

amphibians **4:** 1645

amplidyne **1:** 24, 25

amplifier, magnetic **1:** 24

Amundsen, Roald **4:** 2084

anaerobic glycolysis **3:** 1527

analgesics **4:** 2033

analogs, purine **2:** 1039

analysis **1:** 186, 260

analysis of variance **2:** 729

analysis, classical **5:** 2299

analysis, complex **1:** 75, 282; **3:** 1198

analysis, functional **1:** 163; **3:** 1546; **4:** 1742; **5:** 2187, 2381

analysis, global **1:** 260

analysis, harmonic **1:** 163; **5:** 2365

analysis, higher **5:** 2306

analysis, mathematical **1:** 197

analysis, nonlinear **4:** 1614

analysis, numerical **4:** 2168

analysis, singles method **3:** 1389

analysis, structural **1:** 5, 6

analytic theory **2:** 826

analyzer, retarding potential **3:** 1237, 1238

anaphylaxis **4:** 1876, 1877

Anastasi, Anne **1: 43**

anatomy **1:** 207; **2:** 599; **3:** 1200, 1412; **4:** 1986

anatomy, racist characterizations of **1:** 427

ancient pollen **2:** 528

Anders, Edward **1: 44**

Andersen, Dorothy **1: 46**

Andersen, Per **2:** 966

Anderson localization **1:** 54

Anderson, Carl **1:** 211; **4:** 1690

Anderson, Carl David **1: 47**, 383, 420; **2:** 573, 1010; **4:** 2008; **5:** 2501

Anderson, Don L. **1: 50**

Anderson, Ernest C. **3:** 1392

Anderson, French **2:** 558

Anderson, Gloria L. **1: 51**

Anderson, Philip **2:** 1026

Anderson, Philip Warren **1: 53**; **3:** 1165, 1588

Anderson, Rudolph J. **1:** 393

Anderson, Thomas **2:** 551

Anderson, W. French **1: 54**

Anderson, Weston A. **2:** 672

Ando, T. **5:** 2313

Andor Systems **1:** 39

androgens **2:** 1088

Andromeda Galaxy **3:** 1592

Andronov, A. A. **3:** 1463

androsterone **1:** 333; **4:** 1946

anemia **5:** 2389

anemia, pernicious **3:** 1605, 1606; **5:** 2387

anemia, sickle-cell **1:** 55; **3:** 1176

anemias, hereditary **4:** 1935

anemometer, hot wire **2:** 1079

anesthesia **1:** 244

anesthesiology **1:** 60

Anfinsen, Christian Boehmer **1: 56**; **3:** 1571; **4:** 2120

angina pectoris **1:** 208

angiocardiography **3:** 1148; **4:** 1869

angiography **2:** 699

angioplasty **2:** 534

angiotensin **4:** 1909

Ångstrom, Anders **1:** 239

Angstrom spot **1:** 76

animal behavior **2:** 608

animal breeding **3:** 1224

animal regeneration **4:** 1609

animal tropism **3:** 1413

animals **2:** 607

animals, care and preservation of **2:** 607

animals, ethical treatment of **2:** 890

Annals of Mathematics **3:** 1456

anorexia nervosa **5:** 2507

Anson, M. L. **4:** 1656

Antarctic ice pack **4:** 1736

Antarctica **2:** 691

anthocyanins **4:** 1895; **5:** 2242, 2438, 2440

anthraquinone **5:** 2243

anthrax **3:** 1241

anthropic principle in cosmology **5:** 2379

anthropology **2:** 522; **5:** 2498

anthropology, forensic **4:** 2134

anthropology, physical **4:** 2147

anthropometry **2:** 1076

anti-aromatic compounds **1:** 286

anti-cancer drugs **2:** 1059

antibiotic, antifungal **2:** 981

antibiotics **1:** 3, 310, 441; **2:** 749, 1042; **3:** 1116; **4:** 1877; **5:** 2240, 2328

antibiotics, development of **4:** 1692

antibiotics, resistance of bacteria to **1:** 23

antibodies **1:** 165; **2:** 623, 784; **3:** 1137, 1138, 1247, 1309, 1310, 1311, 1343, 1544; **4:** 1656, 1798, 1877

antibodies, active sights **2:** 624

antibody diversity **5:** 2247

anticosmon **2:** 547

antielectrons **2:** 547

antiferromagnetism **4:** 1623

antifungals **1:** 310

antigen **3:** 1137, 1138

antigens **1:** 86, 87, 165, 326; **2:** 525, 623, 892, 1058; **3:** 1299, 1309, 1310, 1311, 1545; **4:** 1798, 1877; **5:** 2408, 2518

antigens, relation to antibodies **1:** 231

antihistamines **1:** 261; **2:** 575

antihypertensives **3:** 1363, 1364

antilogisms **3:** 1294

antimatter **2:** 573; **4:** 2008

antimicrobials **2:** 1042

antimony **4:** 2137

antimutagens **4:** 1612

antineutrons **1:** 383

Antioch Plan **3:** 1576

antioxidants **2:** 943

antiparticles **1:** 383

antiprotons **1:** 383; **2:** 633; **4:** 2007; **5:** 2288

antisense DNA **5:** 2506

antiseptics **2:** 735

antistatics **5:** 2210

antitoxins **1:** 155; **5:** 2440

Antonelli, Kay McNulty Mauchly **1: 58**

ants **4:** 1772

aortocoronary artery bypass **2:** 534

apes **4:** 1773

Apgar Score **1:** 59

Apgar, Virginia **1: 59**

Aplysia **3:** 1177

apocholic acid **5:** 2242

apoenzymes **5:** 2215

Apollo 15 **4:** 1666

Apollo lunar module **5:** 2436

Apollo lunar voyages **2:** 512

Apollo missions, automatic guidance system in **2:** 591

Apollo moon program **4:** 1914

Apollo program **2:** 1007; **5:** 2309

Apollo space missions **3:** 1145

Apollo space program **1:** 402

Appalachian Mountains, geology of **5:** 2512

Appell, Paul **1:** 247

appendicitis **4:** 1822

Apple I computer **3:** 1142

Apple II computer **3:** 1142

Appleton, Edward **1: 61**; **3:** 1120

Appleton, Sir Edward Victor **5:** 2350

Appleton-layer **1:** 61

Applied and Computation Harmonic Analysis **2:** 525

applied mathematics **1:** 186; **2:** 825; **3:** 1163; **5:** 2314

applied research **4:** 1617

applied science **1:** 468

Bari, Ruth Aaronson **1: 128**

Barkla, Charles Glover **1: 129**, 271;
　4: 2044

Barnard, Christiaan Neethling **1: 130**;
　4: 2115

Barnard's Star **5:** 2286

Barnes, William Harry **1: 133**

Barnett, Miles **1:** 61

Barr body **1:** 134

Barr, Murray Llewellyn **1: 134**

Barrbody **1:** 134

Barré-Sinoussi, Françoise **3:** 1565

Barringer Crater **4:** 2036

Barron, D. H. **4:** 2147

Bartee, Thomas **1:** 198

Bartlett, Neil **1: 135**

Barton, A. W. **1:** 317

Barton, Derek H. R. **1: 137**; **2:** 965;
　4: 1808, 1923

Bartonellosis **4:** 1651, 1652

baryons **2:** 854

Bascom, Florence **1: 139**; **3:** 1236

bases **1:** 300, 301

BASIC computer programming language
　3: 1205, 1286, 1288

basic rocket equation **5:** 2258

basic science **1:** 468

basilar membrane **1:** 157

Basov, Nikolai G. **1:** 140, 225; **3:** 1459;
　4: 1817, 1987; **5:** 2251

Batchelor, George **1: 141**

Bates, Robert W. **4:** 1778

Bateson, William **1: 142**; **4:** 1822, 2161

batholiths **5:** 2511

bathyscaphe **4:** 1769

battery, lifetime **2:** 906

Bauer, L. A. **1:** 281

Baumann, Eugen **3:** 1207

Baxter, Agnes **1: 144**

Baxter, Gregory Paul **2:** 719

Bayesian statistical analysis **1:** 212

Bayliss, William Maddock **1: 145**; **2:** 507;
　4: 1729, 2112

bazooka **2:** 858

Bcell **3:** 1230

BCS theory of superconductivity **1:** 123,
　125, 460; **4:** 1993

Beadle, George Wells **1: 147**, 233; **2:** 623;
　3: 1345, 1500, 1580; **5:** 2179

bean plants **3:** 1143

Beaverbrook, William Maxwell Aitken,
　Lord **5:** 2241

Beck, Guide **2:** 821

Becker, Hans **1:** 380; **3:** 1157, 1159

Beckman Center **1:** 150

Beckman Helipot **1:** 150

Beckman Instruments **1:** 149, 150

Beckman Laser Institute and Medical Clinic
　1: 150

Beckman, Arnold **1:** 149; **4:** 2094

Beckman, J. W. **2:** 837

Becquerel, Antoine-Henri **1: 151**, 498

Becquerel, Henri **1:** 501; **4:** 1943

Becquerel's rays **1:** 152

Bednorz, J. Georg **1: 153**, 409; **3:** 1597;
　4: 1850

bee dance **2:** 787

Beebe, William **1:** 367

beetles **2:** 1063

Begay, Fred **1: 154**

Beginner's All-Purpose Symbolic Instruction
　Code (BASIC) **3:** 1205

behavior **3:** 1177

behavior, animal **5:** 2234

behavior, embryonic **2:** 945

behavior, insect **2:** 653

behavioral biology **1:** 168

Behring, Emil von **1: 154**

Beijerinck, M. **4:** 2108

Békésy, Georg von **1: 156**

Bell Burnell, Jocelyn Susan **1: 160**;
　2: 1014; **5:** 2191

Bell Laboratories **3:** 1139

Bell Telephone Laboratories **3:** 1140

Bell X–2 rocket plane **2:** 858

Bell, Alexander Graham **2:** 630; **3:** 1301,
　1316, 1387

Bell, Gordon **1: 157**

Bell, John **3:** 1165

Bell, John Stewart **1: 158**

Bell, Julia **2:** 938

Belling, John **3:** 1500

Bellow–Furstenberg Theorem **1:** 162

Bellow, Alexandra **1: 162**, 162

Bellow, Saul **1:** 162

Bell's theorem **1:** 158

Beltrán, Enrique **1: 163**

Beltsville project **1:** 117

Belzer, Folker O. **3:** 1266

Bémont, G. **1:** 501

Benacerraf, Baruj **1: 165**; **2:** 526; **4:** 2079

Bendall, Fay **2:** 1034

Benford, Gregory **2:** 923

Benioff, Hugo **2:** 1091

Bennett, Harry **4:** 2092

Bennett, Willard **5:** 2284

benthic ecosystems **4:** 1748

benthic organisms **4:** 1748

benzene **4:** 2050

benzene molecule **4:** 1726

Benzer, Seymour **1: 167**, 284; **2:** 550

benzyne **4:** 2050

Berg, Otto **4:** 1646

Berg, Paul **1: 169**, 264, 265; **2:** 845;
　4: 1978, 2061

Bergen school of meteorology **1:** 205;
　3: 1423

Bergenstal, D. M. **2:** 1088

Berger, Hans **1: 172**

Bergeron, Tor **4:** 2085

Bergius, Friedrich **1: 173**, 255, 256;
　5: 2440

Bergius-Willstätterprocess **5:** 2440

Bergletter **1:** 170

Bergmann, Max **2:** 763; **3:** 1570; **5:** 2505

Bergström, Sune Karl **1: 175**, 222; **2:** 678;
　4: 1970; **5:** 2293

Beria, Lavrentii **3:** 1180

beriberi **1:** 286; **2:** 644, 954; **5:** 2296

Bericht über der Entwicklung der
　algebraischen Funktionen **4:** 1650

Bering Strait **4:** 2134

berkelium **2:** 832; **4:** 2006

Berkowitz, Joan B. **1: 176**

Berman, Robert **2:** 973

bermudagrass, coastal **1:** 327

Bernal, Desmond **4:** 1757

Bernal, J. D. **2:** 1045; **3:** 1209, 1313;
　4: 1793

Bernal's, J. D. **2:** 773

Bernard, Claude **3:** 1527

Bernays, Paul **1: 177**; **3:** 1451

Berner, Robert A. **1: 178**

Berners-Lee, Tim **1: 180**

Bernhard, Carl Gustaf **5:** 2414

Bernstein, Dorothy Lewis **1: 182**

Bernstein, Julius **2:** 1043

Bernstein, Richard B. **1: 183**

Berry, Clifford **1:** 78

Berry, Leonidas Harris **1: 185**

Bers, Lipman **1: 186**

Berson, Solomon **2:** 919; **5:** 2490

Berthelot, Marcellin **4:** 1949

Berthelot, Pierre **5:** 2373

Bertrand, G. **2:** 679

berylliosis **2:** 958

Berzelius, Jöns **5:** 2242

Best, Carles Herbert **1:** 118, 119, 120, **187**;
　3: 1454

beta decay **1:** 27; **2:** 711; **4:** 1722, 1723,
　2042; **5:** 2197, 2484, 2485

beta particle **5:** 2432

beta spectra **1:** 27

beta-alanine **3:** 1538

beta-carotene **3:** 1189, 1281

beta-endorphin **3:** 1391

betaglobulin gene **3:** 1551

betaradiation studies **3:** 1514

betarays **2:** 870

Betelgeuse **2:** 941; **3:** 1479

Bethe, Hans **1:** 30, **190**, 218; **2:** 611, 621,
　762, 811, 1073; **3:** 1494; **4:** 1740, 2096;
　5: 2315, 2366

Bethe-Bloch expression **1:** 218

Bethe-Feynman formula **1:** 192

Bethecoupler **1:** 192

bevatron **3:** 1329; **4:** 2008

dipole theory **4**: 1684

Dirac, Paul **1**: 49, 219, 383, 389, 467; **2**: 573, 611, 710, 893; **3**: 1163, 1226, 1291, 1296, 1297; **4**: 1690, 1740, 1994, 2001, 2008; **5**: 2247, 2500

direct current (DC) **2**: 543

direct method **2**: 967

direct-current electricity **5**: 2207

direct-current motor **5**: 2207

directed panspermia **1**: 490

Dirichlet problem in mathematics **5**: 2411

Dirichlet, Johann Peter Gustav Lejeune **1**: 282; **5**: 2279

dirigibles **2**: 588

"dirty snowball" model **5**: 2386

disaccharides **2**: 976, 977

disarmament **1**: 192, 238, 340

disc valve **5**: 2341

discharge tube **5**: 2336

discriminant analysis **2**: 729

disease, genetic **2**: 814

diseases, brain **2**: 804

diseases, genetic **3**: 1552

diseases, hereditary **4**: 2022

diseases, tropical **4**: 1788

disk seal triode **5**: 2384

disordered states **1**: 53

displacement analysis **5**: 2238

Displacement Law of atomic decay **4**: 2083

dissipative structures **4**: 1813, 1814

dissociation **4**: 1627

dissociation, electrolytic **1**: 71, 72

distance functions **2**: 776

distillation **3**: 1387, 1388

Distributed System for Collaborative Information Processing and Learning (DISCIPLE) **2**: 733

diuretics **3**: 1415

divergence difficulties **5**: 2247

divergent series summation **1**: 372

diving saucer **1**: 477

Dixon, H. B. **2**: 953

Djerassi, Carl **2**: 574; **3**: 1154

DNA **1**: 81, 233; **2**: 527, 1000; **3**: 1127, 1268; **4**: 1867, 2125; **5**: 2260, 2392, 2442, 2505

DNA molecules **1**: 412

DNA renaturation **2**: 528

DNA sequencing **3**: 1188

DNA, structure **4**: 2021

Dobrolowski, Kazimierz **2**: 511

Dobzhansky, Theodosius **2**: 576; **3**: 1389, 1493; **4**: 1726, 2153; **5**: 2479

Dochez, Alphonse **3**: 1299

Dodge, Harold **3**: 1168

Doell, Richard **2**: 512; **5**: 2302

Doering, William E. von **2**: 719; **3**: 1302; **5**: 2470

Doermann, A. H. **4**: 2105

Doherty, Peter C. **2**: 578; **5**: 2517

Doisy, Edward A. **1**: 333; **2**: 516, 580

Dokuchaev, V. V. **5**: 2299

Dolby, Ray Milton **2**: 582

Dole, Vincent P. **2**: 583

Dolly **5**: 2441

Domagk, Gerhard **1**: 261; **2**: 585

Donald, Hugh **3**: 1512

Donaldson, Simon **2**: 587; **5**: 2493

Donnan, Frederick G. **2**: 1023

Doob, Joe **1**: 213

Doppler effect **2**: 820; **4**: 2069, 2110

Doppler radar **2**: 791

Doppler, Johann Christian **4**: 2110

Dornberger, Walter **5**: 2308

double helix **1**: 170; **5**: 2340

double refraction, theory of **4**: 2140

double resonance **3**: 1190

double-arm spectrometer **5**: 2236

double-focusing mass spectrometer **4**: 1640

doublet lines **5**: 2271

Douglas Aircraft **2**: 588

Douglas Aircraft Company, Inc. **2**: 588

Douglas SBD dive bombers **2**: 589

Douglas World Cruiser aircraft **2**: 588

Douglas, Donald W. **2**: 588, 1093

Douglass, Frederick **4**: 1719

Dounce, Alexander L. **4**: 2155

D'Ovidio, Enrico **4**: 1733

down bursts **2**: 790

downdrafts **2**: 790

Down's syndrome **1**: 135, 232

drag, induced **4**: 1805

drainage **3**: 1576

Drake, Frank **4**: 1957

Dramamine **2**: 723

Dransfeld, Klaus **2**: 548

Draper, Charles Stark **2**: 589

Dresselhaus, Mildred S. **2**: 592

Drew, Charles R. **2**: 594

Drickamer, Harry G. **2**: 595

Driesch, Hans **3**: 1579

drinking water **5**: 2464

Driza, Gothard J. **4**: 1808

Drosophila **4**: 1661; **5**: 2413

Drosophila subobscura **3**: 1491

Drucker, Daniel Charles **2**: 597

drug addiction **2**: 584

drug design, rational **2**: 1039

drug, medicinal **3**: 1593

drug-approval process **3**: 1593

drugs, medicinal **5**: 2239

drugs, psychoactive **1**: 89

drugs, synthetic **2**: 722

Druyan, Ann **4**: 1957, 1958

Druyer, Gwendolyn Kay **1**: 157

dry copying **1**: 353, 354

Du Bois-Reymond, Emil Heinrich **3**: 1263

du Pont, Irenree **2**: 908

du Toit, Alex **5**: 2356

du Vigneaud, Vincent **1**: 440; **2**: 609

Dubbelman, C. P. **3**: 1251

Dubois, Eugène **2**: 598

DuBois, W. E. B. **2**: 569

Dubos, René **1**: 441; **2**: 601; **5**: 2328

Dubrova, Yuri **3**: 1129

Duchenne muscular dystrophy **5**: 2393

Ducrey's Bacillus **4**: 1639

Duddell's, W. **4**: 1800

Duffin, Richard J. **1**: 260

Duffin-Bott theorem **1**: 260

Dulbecco, Renato **1**: 114, 115; **2**: 604; **5**: 2200, 2201, 2248, 2360

Dumanoski, Dianne **1**: 444

Dumas, Frédéric **1**: 477

dumdum fever **3**: 1326

Dunn, Leslie **5**: 2323

Dunning, J. R. **4**: 1641

Dunoyer, Louis **4**: 2128

Durand, William F. **2**: 605

Durrell, Gerald **2**: 607

Dussoix, Daisy **1**: 64

dyes **2**: 1034; **4**: 1841

dyes, saturable **4**: 2094

dynamic allocation **4**: 1892

dynamical systems **1**: 199; **4**: 2072, 2073

dynamids **3**: 1369

dynorphins **2**: 880

dysentery **2**: 739

Dyson, Freeman J. **2**: 610; **4**: 1663

Dysphagia Foundation **2**: 988

E. coli bacteria **1**: 2, 32, 170, 265; **2**: 844; **4**: 2105; **5**: 2181, 2515

E-layer **1**: 61

Eagle, Harry **2**: 613

Eagle's growth medium **2**: 613

Earle, Sylvia A. **2**: 614

Earth **3**: 1430

earth metals, rare- **4**: 2096

Earth, composition of **2**: 879

Earth, core of **1**: 318; **3**: 1130, 1360; **4**: 1679; **5**: 2404

Earth, crust of **1**: 264; **2**: 713; **5**: 2404

Earth, interior heat flow **1**: 317, 318

Earth, ionosphere of **3**: 1237

Earth, mantle of **5**: 2404

Earth, origin of **1**: 384

earthquake **2**: 684; **4**: 1679

earthquake prediction **4**: 1810

earthquakes **1**: 15; **2**: 921; **3**: 1308, 1360, 1556, 1557; **4**: 1879, 1880, 1881

earthquakes, propagation of **1**: 471

Earth's atmosphere **2**: 659, 686, 692

Earth's crust **2**: 683; **5**: 2303

Earth's interior **4**: 1809

Earth's magnetic field **2**: 659; **4**: 1709; **5**: 2302

Eastwood, Alice **2**: 615

Eastwood, Arthur **2**: 910

Eberhardt, W. H. **3**: 1406

Eccles, John C. **2**: 508, **616**, 1043, 1044, 1096; **3**: 1194; **4**: 2032

ecdysone hormone **1**: 334; **2**: 1085

echinoderms **3**: 1569

Eckert Scientific International Corporation **2**: 620

Eckert, J. Presper **2**: **618**, 1065; **3**: 1485; **5**: 2316

Eckert, W. J. **1**: 422

eclipses, solar **1**: 117; **3**: 1487

ecological damage assessment **1**: 481

ecological niche **2**: 1094

ecology **1**: 448; **2**: 800; **4**: 1672; **5**: 2471, 2472

ecology, animal **2**: 660

ecology, plant community **5**: 2396

economic systems **4**: 2073

economics, agricultural **1**: 307

ecosystem **1**: 335; **3**: 1493; **4**: 1673; **5**: 2471

ecotoxicology **1**: 336

ectoplasm **3**: 1171

Eddington, Arthur Stanley **1**: 7, 389; **2**: 556, 573, 574, **620**; **3**: 1366, 1542; **4**: 1731, 1814, 2103

Edelman, Gerald M. **1**: 165; **2**: **623**; **4**: 1798

edge effect **3**: 1429

Edgerton, Harold **1**: 477; **2**: **626**, 908

Edinger, Ludwig E. **2**: 628

Edinger, Tilly **2**: **627**

Edison effect **2**: 543, 629, 631, 738

Edison, Thomas Alva **1**: 24; **2**: 542, **629**, 738, 753; **3**: 1212, 1301, 1315, 1316, 1387, 1471; **4**: 1628; **5**: 2207

Edlefsen, Niels E. **3**: 1329

education, mathematics and physics **5**: 2298

education, philosophy of **5**: 2395

Edwards, Cecile Hoover **2**: **632**

Edwards, George **3**: 1168

Edwards, Helen T. **2**: **633**

Edwards, Robert G. **4**: 2127

Effler, Donald R. **2**: 699

Efroimson, V.P. **4**: 1962

Egami, Fujio **4**: 1612

Eggerer, H. **1**: 469

Ehrenfest, Paul **1**: 281; **2**: **634**, 635, 636, 710, 893; **3**: 1306, 1540; **5**: 2271

Ehrenfest-Afanaseva, Tatiana **2**: **635**, 650

Ehrlich, Anne Howland **2**: **636**

Ehrlich, Paul **1**: 155, 253; **2**: 507, 585, **637**, 735; **3**: 1188, 1525

Ehrlich, Paul R. **2**: **640**

Eichhorn, Heinrich **5**: 2286

eigen–values, theory of **2**: 778

Eigen, Manfred **2**: **642**; **4**: 1654, 1796

eight-fold way **2**: 828

Eijkman, Christiaan **2**: 530, **643**, 1062, 1064

Eilenberg, Samuel **3**: 1450, 1451

Einhorn, Alfred **5**: 2439

Einstein rings **2**: 1017

Einstein, Albert **1**: 7, 140, 142, 159, 193, 238, 248, 253, 256, 259, 275, 291, 371, 412, 433, 451; **2**: 536, 555, 563, 621, 634, 636, **645**, 650, 668, 712, 766, 783, 797, 819, 820, 853, 859, 972, 1003, 1013, 1074, 1090; **3**: 1163, 1205, 1312, 1318, 1320, 1366, 1369, 1375, 1376, 1383, 1421, 1422, 1532, 1540, 1542, 1546, 1583, 1586, 1600; **4**: 1614, 1628, 1647, 1731, 1753, 1779, 1781, 1787, 1801, 1817, 1944, 1995, 2002, 2018, 2021, 2042, 2088, 2128, 2162, 2172, 2173; **5**: 2191, 2197, 2227, 2229, 2251, 2298, 2337, 2343, 2358, 2378, 2411, 2418, 2461, 2493, 2494

Einstein-de Sitter model **2**: 556

Einstein-Marić, Mileva **2**: 636, **650**

einsteinium **2**: 833; **4**: 2006

Einthoven, Willem **2**: **651**

Eisner, Thomas **2**: **652**

El niño **2**: 560

El-Sayed, Mostafa Amr **2**: **653**

elastic collision **3**: 1208

elastic scattering **1**: 184

elasticity **3**: 1458

elasticity, theory of **5**: 2232, 2306

elastin **4**: 2120

Eldredge, Niles **2**: **654**, 895

electric arc furnace **3**: 1557, 1558

electric arc lamps **1**: 91

electric automobile starter **3**: 1212

electric eye **5**: 2527

electric light bulb **1**: 458

Electric Power Research Institute (EPRI) **4**: 2113, 2114

electrical bottle **4**: 1720, 1721

electrical current **1**: 151; **4**: 2034

electrical current, flow of **2**: 631

electrical distribution systems **1**: 402

electrical engineering **2**: 1018

electrical fields **3**: 1541

electrical metal-fiber brushes **3**: 1280

electrical standards **4**: 2149

electricity **1**: 409; **3**: 1211

electricity, behavior in gases **5**: 2226

electricity, effects on living tissue **3**: 1351, 1352

electricity, high voltage **5**: 2208

electro weakforce **4**: 1925

electro-mechanical computational devices **3**: 1486

electro-plating **4**: 1744

electrocardiography, principles of **2**: 651

electrochemistry **2**: 929, 930

electrodynamic theory **3**: 1422

electrodynamics **1**: 257

electrodynamics, quantum **2**: 587; **3**: 1226

electroencephalogram **1**: 10, 172

electroencephalography **1**: 9

electrogas dynamics **2**: 897

electrokinetic ultrafiltration **4**: 2166

electrolyte activity **1**: 301

electrolytes **1**: 301; **2**: 539

electrolytic dissociation **2**: 538, 539; **4**: 1696

electromagnet **3**: 1420

electromagnetic fields **4**: 2001

electromagnetic force **4**: 1965

electromagnetic oscillations **3**: 1462

electromagnetic quanta **1**: 258

electromagnetic radiation **1**: 129, 225; **2**: 564, 1017; **3**: 1421; **4**: 1801; **5**: 2508

electromagnetic radiation, amplification of **1**: 141

electromagnetic theory **3**: 1421; **4**: 1878; **5**: 2352, 2384

electromagnetic waves **1**: 26, 140; **3**: 1462; **4**: 2088

electromagnetic waves, propagation **4**: 1736

electromagnetics **2**: 838, 968

electromagnetism **1**: 219; **4**: 1613, 1943; **5**: 2191, 2287, 2362, 2462

electromagnetism, theory of **4**: 1910; **5**: 2508

electrometer **4**: 1944

electromotive force method **4**: 2093

electron **2**: 596; **3**: 1163, 1589

electron and positron pairs, production of **5**: 2236

electron capture detector **3**: 1430

electron deceleration **4**: 2088

electron diffraction **1**: 190; **2**: 966; **5**: 2224

electron micocopy **2**: 1098

electron micrograph auto radiography **2**: 978

electron microscope **2**: 694, 798; **4**: 1702, 1931, 1932, 2172; **5**: 2287

electron microscope, holographic **2**: 798

electron microscope, prototype **2**: 797

electron microscope, scanning **4**: 1932

electron neutrino **4**: 1998, 1999

electron orbitals **2**: 792; **4**: 1723, 1994

electron orbitals, symmetry of **2**: 1049

electron scattering **2**: 532

electron spectroscopy for chemical analysis (ESCA) **4**: 2042

electron spin **2**: 893; **4**: 1723, 1833; **5**: 2271

electron spin resonance (ESR)spectrometer **1**: 449

electron theory **3**: 1319, 1421

electron theory ofmetals **1**: 236

electron-transfer reactions **3**: 1471, 1472

Mendel, Lafayette B. **4**: 2009

Mendeleev, Dmitri Ivanovich **2**: 713, 714; **3**: 1585; **4**: 1646, 1845; **5**: 2299

mendelevium **2**: 833; **4**: 2006

Mendelian genetics **4**: 1823, 1962

Mendelian genetics, mathematical laws of **5**: 2364

Mendelian selection **2**: 729

Mendelism **2**: 577

Mendel's, Gregor **4**: 1822

Mendenhall, Dorothy Reed **3**: **1516**

meningitis, cerebrospinal **2**: 739, 740

meningitis, Flexner serum for treatment of **2**: 739

meningitis, group B **3**: 1300

meningitis, influenzal **1**: 22, 23

Menkin, Miriam F. **4**: 1896

Men'shov, D. E. **1**: 127

menstruation **1**: 391

mental illness **2**: 794

mental retardation **1**: 134

mental rotation **4**: 2030

Meny, Robert G. **5**: 2231

Menzel, Donald **4**: 1731

Méray, Hugues Charles Robert **3**: **1517**, 1517

Mercalli, Giuseppe **4**: 1880

6-mercaptopurine (6MP) **2**: 657, 1039

Mercury **2**: 875; **4**: 2049

mercury–197 isotope **4**: 1878

Mercury capsule **4**: 2027

mercury poisoning **4**: 2137, 2138

mercury vapor lamp **1**: 34

mercury-delay lines **3**: 1219

Mering, Jacques **2**: 773

Mering, Oscar von **1**: 118

meromorphic functions **1**: 11; **3**: 1245

Merriam, Clinton **1**: 104

Merrian, G. F. **1**: 333

Merrifield, R. Bruce **3**: **1518**

Merrifield, Richard E. **4**: 2051

Merrill, Helen Abbot **3**: **1520**, 1520

Merrill, Winifred Edgerton **3**: **1521**, 1521

Mertz, Edwin T. **1**: 288

Meselson, Matthew **1**: 32, 64, 284; **3**: **1522**; **4**: 2104

mesometeorology **2**: 789

mesons **1**: 27, 28, 47, 49, 211; **2**: 854; **3**: 1208; **5**: 2500

mesons, production of **3**: 1318

mesothelioma **2**: 896

mesotron **1**: 49

Mesozoic era **2**: 812

messenger ribonucleic acid (mRNA) **1**: 64, 170, 283, 284, 377; **2**: 844, 1056; **3**: 1116, 1118, 1217, 1523, 1561, 1563; **4**: 1653, 1893, 2022

messenger RNA **5**: 2506

Messier, Charles **4**: 1974

metabolic cycle **3**: 1273

metabolic energy production **3**: 1401

metabolic process **3**: 1272

metabolism **2**: 514, 749, 953, 1062; **3**: 1135, 1439; **4**: 1851

metabolism, cholesterol **1**: 308

metabolism, intermediary **1**: 221; **3**: 1271, 1273

METAFONT typeface-design system **3**: 1238, 1239

metal corrosion **2**: 930

metal manufacturing **2**: 931

Metal Mike steering control system **4**: 2099

metallic beryllium **4**: 2138

Metallurgical Laboratory **1**: 452

metallurgy, high temperature **4**: 2095

metals **2**: 724, 931

metals passivation **3**: 1151

metals, grain size in **3**: 1131, 1132

metals, noble **1**: 136

metals, properties of **3**: 1280

metals, transition **3**: 1589

Metchnikoff, Élie **1**: 246, 441; **2**: 639; **3**: **1524**; **4**: 1639

Meteor Crater **4**: 2036

meteorites **1**: 44, 45; **3**: 1538; **5**: 2374

meteorological research stations **4**: 2119

meteorology **1**: 239, 471; **2**: 687, 921; **3**: 1130, 1155, 1307, 1423, 1486; **5**: 2291, 2345, 2354

meteorology, atmospheric dynamic **1**: 205

meteorology, theoretical **2**: 783

meteors **5**: 2385

methadone **2**: 583

methadone maintenance programs **2**: 584

methadone, treatment for addiction **2**: 584

methemoglobinemia drug **1**: 88

methionine **2**: 609, 632

methotrexate **4**: 1692

methyl groups **2**: 609, 610

methylalcohol, production of **1**: 256

methylprednisolone steroid **3**: 1266

metric spaces **2**: 776

metric transitivity **1**: 197

metrical topology **1**: 12

metrization **1**: 20

metrology **2**: 917

mevalonic acid **2**: 749

mevinolin **2**: 883

Mexia, Ynes **3**: **1526**

Meyer, Hans **3**: 1415

Meyer, Victor **4**: 2082

Meyerhof, Otto **2**: 930, 1030, 1064; **3**: 1402, **1527**; **4**: 1670; **5**: 2330

MHC antigens **2**: 579

mice, funny foot **4**: 1936

mice, laboratory **4**: 1935

Michaelis, Leonor **1**: 449; **4**: 2094

Michaelson-Morley experiment **3**: 1321

Michel, Hartmut **2**: 548, 1086; **3**: **1528**

Micheli-Tzanakou, Evangelia **3**: **1530**

Michelson, Albert **2**: 687; **3**: 1139, 1328, 1422, **1531**, 1539, 1582; **5**: 2509

micro analysis **4**: 1806

micro bursts **2**: 789, 790

micro evolution **2**: 878

micro gravity **4**: 2041

micro lithography **4**: 1860

micro neurosurgery **2**: 944

micro pipettes **4**: 1625

micro seismic disturbances **2**: 921

microbes **4**: 1877

microbial nutrition **3**: 1561

microorganisms **1**: 302, 303

microphone, condenser **3**: 1161

microscope, electron **1**: 417; **5**: 2526, 2527

microscope, phase-contrast **5**: 2512

microscope, transmission **4**: 1932

microscopes **4**: 1829

Microsoft Company **2**: 817

Microsoft Disk Operating System (MS-DOS) **2**: 817

microsomes **1**: 417; **2**: 540; **4**: 1702

microspheres **2**: 764

microspheres, electical properties of **2**: 764

microsurgery **4**: 2097, 2098

microtonometer **3**: 1277

microwave amplification **5**: 2250, 2251

microwave early-warning system **1**: 35

microwave electron devices **5**: 2384

microwave electronics **1**: 406; **5**: 2384

microwave radar **4**: 2068

microwave radiation, high-power **3**: 1180

microwave signals **3**: 1312

microwave spectroscopy **1**: 504; **3**: 1296

microwaves **4**: 1829; **5**: 2230

Mid-Atlantic Ridge **2**: 684, 985; **5**: 2211

Mid-Ocean Dynamics Experiment **4**: 2142

mid-ocean ridges **5**: 2301, 2452

midbrain **2**: 1012

Midgley, Jr., Thomas **3**: **1533**

Midland man **4**: 2134

midocean ridges **2**: 1009

Miescher, Johann Frederick **3**: 1263

Miki, Kunio **2**: 548

Miledi, Ricardo **3**: 1194

military codes, World War II **4**: 2017

Milky Way galaxy **4**: 1685, 1710, 2019, 2020, 2069

Milledge, Judith **3**: 1420

Miller Mathematics Improvement Program **2**: 904

Miller, Elizabeth C. **3**: **1535**

Miller, Frederick R. **1**: 118

Miller, James A. **3**: **1535**

Miller, John A. **3**: 1566

Miller, John R. **3**: 1472

Miller, Paul **4**: 1906

PEDAGOGICAL STANDARDS:
Social studies teachers should possess the knowledge, capabilities, and dispositions...

1. Learning and Development *...to provide learning opportunities that support learners' intellectual, social, and personal differences.*	Chapters 1, 2, 4
2. Differences in Learning Styles *...to create learning experiences that fit the different approaches to learning of diverse learners.*	Chapters 2, 4
3. Critical Thinking, Problem Solving, and Performance Skills *...to use a variety of instructional strategies to encourage student development of critical thinking, problem solving, and performance skills.*	Chapter 8
4. Active Learning and Motivation *...to create learning environments that encourage social interaction, active engagement in learning, and self-motivation.*	Chapter 6
5. Inquiry, Collaboration, and Supportive Classroom Interaction *...to create learning environments that encourage techniques that foster active inquiry, collaboration, and supportive instruction in the classroom.*	Chapter 6
6. Planning Instruction *...to plan instruction based on understanding of subject matter, students, the community, and curriculum goals.*	Chapter 5
7. Assessment *...to use formal and informal assessment strategies to evaluate and ensure the continuous intellectual, social, and physical development of learners. They should be able to assess student learning using various assessment formats, including performance assessment, fixed response, open-ended questioning, and portfolio strategies.*	Chapter 7
8. Reflection and Professional Growth *...to develop as reflective practitioners and continuous learners.*	Chapter 1, For Your Portfolio
9. Professional Leadership *...to foster cross–subject matter collaboration and other positive relationships with school colleagues, and positive associations with parents and others in the larger community to support student learning and well-being.*	Chapters 12, 13

To access authentic videos to support material in this text, visit MyLabSchool, click on Courses and then Social Studies Methods. Then find resources for:

- Chapter 5, Planning for Social Studies Teaching and Learning (Module 1 in MyLabSchool)

- Chapter 6, Strategies for Social Studies Teaching and Learning (Module 2 in MyLabSchool)

- Chapter 7, Assessing Social Studies Learning (Module 4 in MyLabSchool)

- Chapter 13, Social Studies and the Literacy Connection (Module 3 in MyLabSchool)

eighth edition

Teaching and Learning
Elementary Social Studies

Arthur K. Ellis

Seattle Pacific University

PEARSON

Boston • New York • San Francisco
Mexico City • Montreal • Toronto • London • Madrid • Munich • Paris
Hong Kong • Singapore • Tokyo • Cape Town • Sydney

Editor: Kelly Villella Canton
Editorial Assistant: Angela Pickard
Senior Development Editor: Virginia L. Blanford
Marketing Manager: Krista Clark
Production Administrator: Annette Joseph
Editorial-Production Service: Omegatype Typography, Inc.
Manufacturing Buyer: Megan Cochran
Composition and Prepress Buyer: Linda Cox
Electronic Composition: Omegatype Typography, Inc.

For related titles and support materials, visit our online catalog at www.ablongman.com.

Between the time Website information is gathered and then published, it is not unusual for some sites to have closed. Also, the transcription of URLs can result in typographical errors. The publisher would appreciate notification where these errors occur so that they may be corrected in subsequent editions.

Library of Congress Cataloging-in-Publication Data

Ellis, Arthur K.
   Teaching and learning elementary social studies / Arthur K. Ellis. — 8th ed.
      p. cm.
   Includes bibliographical references and index.
   ISBN 0-205-48394-1
   1. Social sciences—Study and teaching (Elementary)   I. Title.

   LB1584.E39 2007
   372.83—dc22

                                                           2005056457

Printed in the United States of America

10   9   8   7   6   5   4   3   2   1   RRD-VA   11   10   09   08   07   06

Credits appear on page 409, which constitutes an extension of the copyright page.

Brief Contents

Contents

chapter 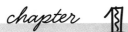 **Social Studies Education: Definitions and Rationales   2**

chapter  **Diversity, Multiculturalism, and Pluralism in the Social Studies Classroom   22**

chapter **5** *Planning for Social Studies*
Teaching and Learning **84**

chapter **6** *Strategies for Social Studies*
Teaching and Learning **116**

chapter **Making History Come Alive   204**

chapter **10** *Exploring Our Geographic World:*
Maps, Globes, and Graphics   228

chapter  *Teaching and Learning Values, Character Education, and Moral Development*   *268*

chapter **12** *Social Studies and Curriculum Connections: Integrated Studies*   *298*

chapter **13** *Social Studies and the
Literacy Connection   322*

chapter **14** *Children in a Democracy: Teaching and
Learning Responsible Citizenship   342*

chapter **15** *Reflective Thinking: The Essence of Social Studies   374*

Features

keys to . . .

in the classroom

current events

sample lessons

Preface

elcome to the eighth edition of *Teaching and Learning Elementary Social Studies.* Although this edition contains many changes from previous editions, it remains dedicated to the proposition that teachers and children are gifted in their potential to engage in depth in the great and abiding themes of social studies. This new edition is based on several assumptions about (1) the nature and purpose of social studies, (2) teachers and teaching, and (3) children and how they learn. The book represents my attempt to integrate constructivist philosophies of active teaching and learning with the essential knowledge, basic skills, and positive values required of the citizens of a healthy, diverse, pluralistic democracy.

What's New in This Edition

While I have attempted to keep the best of prior editions current and updated, new material is abundant. I have focused on providing materials and content that are really useful.

- *Classroom activities and lesson plans.* Much of what is new takes the form of activities and lessons that provide both guidance and resources for new teachers. Classroom activities and anecdotes, those "teachable moments," are presented as features labeled **In the Classroom. Sample Lessons,** which follow a standard lesson plan format, appear at the ends of many chapters and illustrate how to transfer chapter content into the classroom.

- *New and expanded topics.* In this edition you will find **a new chapter (Chapter 2) on multicultural teaching and learning.** Our diverse, pluralistic society cries out for teachers who are informed and sensitive to our incredibly rich and varied society, and the information in this chapter is critical to becoming an effective teacher. You will also find **complete chapters on history and geography,** the twin anchors of the social science disciplines. No child should leave elementary school without a thorough grounding in each of these subject areas.

- *Web references.* Given the exponential growth of information and access to it through the Internet in recent years, I have included **a wide variety of websites** designed to further your access to good ideas for teaching and learning. The knowledge explosion is very real. New "pages" are added to our cumulative history each day. News is reported in 24-hour cycles. The pace of change accelerates.

- *Current Events boxes.* Current events teaching ideas, which were grouped into an independent chapter in earlier editions, are now found throughout the book in features labeled **Current Events.** I think this makes sense because it models the way in which I encourage you to teach current events as an ongoing unit throughout the school year. Almost every lesson you teach can be enhanced by including references to current events.

- *Keys to . . .* These features provide quick snapshots of key concepts throughout the text. They will help you focus on the most important aspects of the content you are learning.

- *Standards correlations.* More and more, standards created by various professional organizations are defining the way we teach. A chart on the inside front cover of this book links content from this text to the standards created by the National Council for the Social Studies (NCSS) for both content and pedagogy in elementary social studies. You will also find expanded references to the standards throughout the book as appropriate and, most important, a nine-page section at the end of the book that provides an **overview of standards** for teaching the social studies.

- *And an atlas!* Packaged with every copy of this book is a copy of the *Allyn & Bacon Atlas for Elementary Social Studies*—an invaluable resource for every new teacher. Created by Maps.com under the editorial guidance of Allyn & Bacon, the atlas includes a wide variety of useful maps, as well as suggestions for teaching the five themes of geography. I hope that every reader of this book finds this atlas useful.

What This Book Is All About

Maintaining the balance between theory and practice is never easy, but I am convinced that this new edition presents each to its best advantage. The pages of the text explain, illustrate, and encourage developmentally appropriate practice, engaged and exploratory learning, and reflective thought and action. A host of practical lessons are found throughout the book, ready for you to use directly or to adapt to your circumstances as needed. A central purpose of the book is to address and nurture the strategies and tactics necessary to achieve these social studies goals (see also the figure):

- *Participatory citizenship.* From Aristotle's time to the twenty-first century, the idea of the participating citizen has been a dream and an ideal. Citizenship is not an abstract concept. It is the life to which each of us is called.

- *Knowledge of our world.* Having knowledge of the world we live in equips us with what Abraham Lincoln called "the mystic chords of memory." Our knowledge of history, geography, and civics provides the foundation of a good life. Knowledge of our world serves at once as a tool for problem solving and as an end in itself.

- *Self-realization and self-regulation.* Every child represents a promise. Our task as teachers is to be true to that promise. The unique qualities of each individual begin to show their promise in an environment where freedom and discipline are brought into harmony.

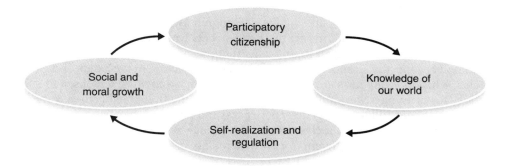

• *Social and moral growth.* Classrooms and schools are social settings, filled with potential for moral growth. To the extent that your own classroom is truly social, it has the potential to be truly moral.

Teaching and Learning Elementary Social Studies is organized around the following themes:

1. *Integration.* The theme of integration recurs throughout the text. Just as life itself is best when it is integrated, connected, and experienced, so must the lives that teachers and children live together be integrated. Integration begins with people. Subject matter will follow. Children come to school seeing a world connected, but that world is all too often subsequently disconnected for them in the name of school learning. Social studies, more than all other subjects, has the potential to capitalize on this strength of childhood. *Social studies* (note the term *social*) is the obvious connecting centerpiece of school life. Of course, history can be separated from geography, and it often is, but time and place are naturally connected. Just ask any child.

2. *Inquiry and discovery.* Children are born inquirers. They make important discoveries daily. They spend much of their time attempting to figure out the nature of things. They are the ultimate question askers. They are on a quest to organize, adapt to, and explore their world. This inquisitive nature is one of several gifts children bring to an educational setting. In this sense, they have much in common with the historian, the geographer, the anthropologist, and other social scientists. Good teachers understand the unquenchable readiness of young learners to observe, record, classify, compare, and hypothesize. These are the very tools of inquiry, discovery, and exploration. Such an inclination must be nurtured and refined through meaningful experiences, as concepts, skills, and values develop in spiral-like fashion in the minds of the young. I have attempted in the pages that follow to illustrate how teachers can model inquiry and discovery as facilitators of learning.

3. *Creative expression.* Emerging brain research supports what good teachers have always thought: that childhood is a time of great creativity. A Japanese proverb says, "It is like the springtime to be a child." We know that nature is at its creative best in spring, when flowers bloom, trees blossom, and the earth renews itself. Childhood is a time of artistry, philosophy, and big ideas. Children love to draw, sing, dance, play, and make things. In fact, children are our best teachers when it comes to seeing the relationship between constructivism and constructionism. The natural inclinations of childhood become the essence of the social studies curriculum in the hands of a gifted teacher. This book supports creative expression through activities, lessons, and suggestions for creating a world of exploration based on multiple intelligences, varying styles, developmentally appropriate experiences, and practical, hands-on learning. It is an axiom of school life that classrooms where teachers take childhood expression seriously are qualitatively different from ordinary classrooms, simply because they are so inviting.

4. *Interest.* The doctrine of interest was proposed in the first century by Roman educator Quintilian, who suggested that children should be allowed to pursue their interests in learning and that they not be force fed things they do not care about. Twentieth-century philosopher Alfred North Whitehead wrote, "There can be no mental development without interest." But what if children express no interest in certain things you think are important for them to learn? I have attempted to show how you can have it both ways. The goal of self-realization implies that children should learn what they want to learn, but you can lead them to want to learn matters of educational significance by creating interest. Social studies is above all a practical subject. It is at its best when children are doing. We know they prefer activity over passivity, involvement over boredom, friendship over isolation, and opportunity over restraint. Social studies has not always fared so well when students are asked to list their favorite subjects. My goal is to work with you to make it special.

5. *Democracy.* Children need to experience democracy firsthand throughout the elementary school years, and social studies is the proving ground of that experience. Our nation is a pluralistic, diverse society. Our world is a place of fascinating similarities and differences to be discovered. Social studies provides splendid opportunities for experiences in tolerance, respect, civil society, and awareness of self in the context of others. Resolving conflicts, making decisions, working and playing together, creating community, learning to lead as well as to follow, having active involvement, and caring for the common good are fundamental aspects of the education of young citizens. Of all the subjects in the school curriculum, only social studies focuses directly on education for democracy. Children learn what they live, and I am confident that in your classroom, they will live as citizens in a democracy.

6. *Reflection.* Activity, experience, collaboration, and investigation are crucial, to be sure, but they are not sufficient unto themselves. Without reflection, there is a lack of coherence, experiences become random, and growth does not realize its potential. In a reflective classroom, the pace is slower, ideas are studied in greater depth, the opportunity for student voice is greater, and time is devoted to a search for meaning. I have included a number of strategies to promote reflective thinking, including "I learned" statements, "Key Idea Identification," "Thinking Aloud," and "The Week in Review," just to name a few. These very practical strategies will enable you to create an atmosphere of reflection in ways that make such practice a seamless part of teaching, learning, and assessment.

7. *Community and beyond.* The Greek word *paideia* is translated approximately as "learning from the culture." Ours is a rich and diverse society that has much to offer the young beyond the confines of the classroom and school. *Paideia* includes both the local community and the world beyond. Local resources take the form of museums, libraries, parks, galleries, and resource people. Global resources are found in such technologies as the Internet, films, newspapers, and other means of reaching out to a global society. Your social studies headquarters is the classroom, but to the extent that you can get your students involved in the world beyond the classroom, you will have achieved the elusive goal of making the world itself a living laboratory for exploration.

The children you teach were born in the twenty-first century. Given the advances in health and medicine, you can be assured that many of them will live to be 100 years old or more. Your work with them is done at the early stage of their lives. You have the honor and privilege of being there at the beginning, of playing a role in shaping their growth and development, of making of them what they are and will become.

You will model the themes just set forth. Children will look to you for guidance, and they will view you as a model of behavior. Each act of kindness, of civility, of support on your part reverberates through the present and the future. As you create the conditions for their present learning, you help to set the conditions for what is yet to come over their lifetime. You have the best job in the world!

> *In all your teaching, show integrity.*
> —Paul the Apostle

Acknowledgments

This book is far better than it might have been because of the involvement of some people to whom I wish to express my appreciation. I especially wish to acknowledge the work of John J. Cogan and L. JoAnne Buggey, both of the University of Minnesota; Allen Glenn, University of Washington; Cherie Major, University of Idaho; Naomi Peterson, Indiana University; Patricia Hammill; and Richard Scheuerman—colleagues whom I respect a great deal.

Thanks as well to Kent Freeland, Morehead State University; Timothy Lintner, University of South Carolina–Aiken; Marcia Mayo, Georgia Southwestern State University; Paul Nagel, Northwestern State University; and Russell Thatcher, Oklahoma Panhandle State University, who reviewed the manuscript—their insights proved to be very helpful. Ginny Blanford, Senior Development Editor, provided the kind of leadership an author dreams of. Finally, I wish to thank my family for all their love and kindness.

A. E.

Supplements and Learning Aids

To help you get the most out of *Teaching and Learning Elementary Social Studies,* Eighth Edition, a number of useful supplements are available for students and instructors.

For the Instructor

- The **Instructor's Manual with Test Items** provides a variety of instructional tools, including chapter summaries, student objectives, activities and discussion questions, vocabulary, test questions, and reflections inspired by the text. (Available from Allyn & Bacon's Instructor Resource Center. Ask your sales representative about access to this site.)

For Students

- The *Allyn & Bacon Atlas for Elementary Social Studies,* packaged with every copy of this text, offers a collection of maps and activities that every new elementary social studies teacher can use in the classroom—a terrific value-added component with every new book!

For Instructors and Students

- **MyLabSchool** is Allyn & Bacon's supersite for prospective teachers, where the classroom comes to life! From videoclips of teachers and students interacting to sample lessons, portfolio templates, and standards integration, Allyn & Bacon brings your students the tools they'll need to succeed in the classroom—with content easily integrated into your existing course. Check out the Social Studies Methods Course within MyLabSchool for resources specific to social studies teaching, including videos, lesson plans, and cases. Available as a website with protected access or within CourseCompass (Allyn & Bacon's course management system), this program provides students with powerful insights into how real classrooms work and a rich array of tools that will support them on their journey from their first class to their first classroom. (Talk with your Allyn & Bacon sales representative about the CourseCompass version, about packaging MyLabSchool with your text, or about how students can purchase access to MyLabSchool online.)

mylabschool
Where the classroom comes to life!

About the Author

Arthur Ellis is Professor of Education and Director of the International Center for Curriculum Studies at Seattle Pacific University.

Before that, he was Professor of Education at the University of Minnesota. Dr. Ellis was an elementary and middle school teacher in Oregon and Washington before completing his doctorate at the University of Oregon.

He also holds honorary doctorates from the Russian Academy of Education and is a Corresponding Professor at two universities in Russia. He also is a Corresponding Professor at Zhejiang University in China. Several of his books have been translated and published in Russian and Chinese versions.

The totem pole or story pole in the photograph was created by the famous Native American carver Abner Johnson, a member of the Tlingit Nation of the Northwest Coast of North America.

Teaching and Learning
Elementary Social Studies

Social Studies Education

Definitions and Rationales

In this chapter, we will explore these themes:

key concepts

- The meaning of *social studies*
- The rationale for social studies education
- Social studies curriculum patterns
- The environment for social studies learning
- The roles of the teacher

"Would you tell me, please, which way I ought to go from here?"

"That depends a good deal on where you want to get to," said the Cat.

"I don't much care where—," said Alice.

"Then it doesn't matter which way you go," said the Cat.

"—so long as I get somewhere,*" Alice added as an explanation.*

"Oh, you're sure to do that," said the Cat, "if you only walk long enough."

—Lewis Carroll, *Alice's Adventures in Wonderland* (1865)

I invite you to accompany me on a journey in celebration of childhood, filled with wonder—a journey that will lead us to a realm of discovery, adventure, teamwork, and excitement. It is the journey into the world of social studies.

You know as well as I do why you decided to become a teacher: You dream of making a difference in the lives of children. And social studies is the study of human beings; it is where the dream comes true. We learn about ourselves, our friends, our neighbors, and even people whom we might not otherwise know. We learn about the past, the present, and even the future. We learn that there is strength in diversity but that the common bonds of humanity make us, finally, one.

This chapter is a beginning, designed to chart our course. As a Chinese proverb tells us, "The journey of a thousand miles begins with a single step." In this chapter, we will take that first step together.

s we begin our journey, let's take a moment to look at the journeys of two characters from children's fiction: Alice in *Alice's Adventures in Wonderland* and Dorothy in *The Wonderful Wizard of Oz*. Each met a rather bizarre set of folks as she tried to find her way—Alice out of Wonderland and Dorothy to the Emerald City. Their experiences were different, to be sure. Poor Alice had no clear goal and kept asking for directions from highly unreliable characters. Dorothy knew where she was headed and had only to follow the Yellow Brick Road, but she had to avoid the obstacles put in her path to get there. Alice was in a state of perpetual uncertainty; Dorothy knew all along exactly what needed to be done.

We might say that Alice was working her way through a maze, while Dorothy had a map. Alexander Pope, an English writer and philosopher, once observed that learning should be a map, not a maze. A well-taught social studies curriculum is just that: a map that helps make sense of the human experience.

Social studies is the study of human beings. Specifically, social studies focuses on human activities in the past, present, and emerging future. It is the study of other people, places, and events across time and space. At the same time, it is direct life experience in what it means to be a citizen, a participant, and a self-realized individual. In other words, you don't just *learn* social studies as a school subject; you *take part* in it. In that sense, social studies demands of teachers and students a deeper level of knowledge. It demands knowledge lived, not just information studied.

The skills and ideas learned in social studies should be put to direct and practical use in the form of classroom and school governance, of realizing one's unique potential, of growing awareness of others and concern for their welfare, and for free and full participation in the group. Abraham Lincoln's well-chosen phrase "of the people, by the people, and for the people" goes to the very heart of an uplifting social studies experience. My task in this book is to facilitate your journey, not to give you easy answers but to challenge you and your students to rise to the occasion of making social studies eminently rewarding, enjoyable, and worthwhile.

Although the term *social studies* was coined in the second decade of the twentieth century, it was not until 1993 that a final version or official definition was ratified by the National Council for the Social Studies (NCSS). Of course, there was no hurry; but, on the other hand, it's nice to know what this area of the curriculum is officially all about. Just imagine: You may have gone through some of your school years studying an area of the school curriculum that had not been officially defined. Horrors! So, at long last, here it is:

> *Social studies* is the integrated study of the social sciences and humanities to promote civic competence. Within the school program, social studies provides coordinated, systematic study drawing upon such disciplines as anthropology, archaeology, economics, geography, history, law, philosophy, political science, psychology, religion, and sociology, as well as appropriate content from the humanities, mathematics, and natural sciences. The primary purpose of social studies is to help young people develop the ability to make informed and reasoned decisions for the public good as citizens of a culturally diverse, democratic society in an interdependent world.

Certain elements of this definition are particularly appealing. Notice the commitment to integrated studies. This makes good sense when the subject matter is people. Notice also the emphasis on civic duty, the public good, and the individual as decision maker, as well as the attention paid to democracy, cultural diversity, and interdependence. In my opinion, this is good and noble rhetoric. Any teacher who takes these ideas seriously will no doubt do worthwhile things with children. My only reservation with this definition, although perhaps it's implied, is the lack of a statement about the personal fulfillment of the individual. I firmly believe that social studies can do much to help a child along the road to self-realization, through the soaring vision found in biographies, the arts, and music; through the great mysteries unlocked for a child who discovers the world of maps, stories, and histories; and, most of all, in the wonderful realm of group activities, projects, and shared experience.

Nevertheless, the official definition of social studies represents a useful point of departure, a place from which to begin the journey. After all, it wouldn't be social studies in a democracy if we all agreed on every aspect of this wonderful area of the curriculum. But more and more, the curriculum is governed by standards set by associations such as the NCSS, state departments of education, and even the federal government through laws such as the No Child Left Behind Act. Take a few moments to study the Keys to an Exemplary Social Studies Program, based on NCSS standards. We will spend the course of this book attempting to bring these ideas to life.

 ## Keys to an Exemplary Social Studies Program

An exemplary social studies program should involve social studies teachers and curriculum that engage students according to the following criteria:

The Teacher

- Demonstrates both scholarship and expertise in the curriculum
- Participates in all aspects of the development of the curriculum, including setting goals and objectives, implementation, evaluation, and revision
- Uses sound instructional theory and practice

The Curriculum

- Is guided by thoughtfully selected as well as clearly stated and defined goals and objectives
- Is based on sound scholarship from the content areas relative to the social studies
- Sets high expectations for students and uses a variety of systematic and valid measures to assess student performance
- Relates appropriately to the age, maturity, interests, and needs of the students for whom it is designed

- Incorporates effective instructional strategies and techniques that engage students directly and actively in the learning process both in and out of the classroom
- Provides valid evidence that the outcome of the program is consistent with the stated goals and objectives
- Is consistent with the 10 thematic strands identified by NCSS Curriculum Standards for Social Studies (see Figure 3.1 on page 43)

The Students

- Critically examine significant content, issues, and events from a variety of perspectives
- Participate actively in their school community and world
- Engage in focused systematic observations and comprehensive decisions
- Understand democratic principles and participate in the democratic process

Source: Adapted from criteria outlined by the National Council for the Social Studies Curriculum Awards, available at www.ncss.org/awards/curriculum.html.

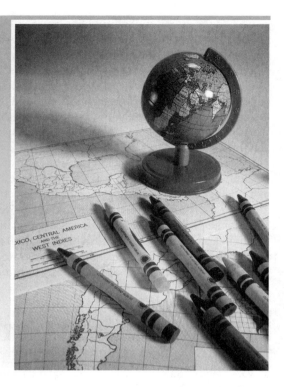

The goals of social studies encompass a wide range of knowledge, skills, and values.

A Rationale for Social Studies Education

From time to time, someone will question the validity of social studies as an elementary school subject. Some critics would prefer to see social studies replaced with history, geography, and perhaps civics as separate subjects. At another extreme are those who feel that social studies ought to be combined with science and taught as environmental studies.

The first group argues that social studies is a watered-down form of several subjects brought together under the umbrella of "people-related" topics and that history and geography, in particular, suffer as a result. These critics point to the widespread historical and geographic illiteracy among today's students. The second group complains that it is unrealistic to expect elementary teachers (especially at the primary level) to have to prepare lessons in both social studies and science when there is so much reading, language, spelling, math, and so forth that must be covered. If social studies and science were combined, they argue, the teacher would have more time in the day and would probably do a better job of teaching the combined subject.

Both of these criticisms of social studies are reasonable, and they ought to be considered fairly. I agree with futurist Alvin Toffler's point that *every* subject in the school curriculum ought to be continually reexamined and not taken for granted. It is, therefore, healthy to question the appropriateness of social studies or any other subject.

Some elementary school teachers teach social studies each day with great earnestness; and some teachers, feeling considerable pressure to produce results in other areas, say they work social studies in when and where they can. So it goes. Of course, social studies has been around as a school subject for some time (since about 1918), so it does have the force of tradition behind it. Therefore, the search for a rationale may lead teachers initially to say: Why wouldn't we have social studies? We've always had it! After all, social studies is largely an adapted, interdisciplinary form of two subjects, history and geography, that have been considered important for centuries.

Our search for a rationale begins with the premise that a number of unique characteristics of social studies must be identified—things that only social studies can do for young learners. Social studies supports at least five critical areas of learning (see Figure 1.1), listed here in no particular order:

- *Citizenship*: *Social studies provides a forum for children to learn about and practice democracy.* From ancient Athens, to the English Magna Carta, to the councils of the Iroquois nation, to the Constitution of the United States, to Martin Luther King Jr.'s "I Have a Dream" speech, the idea of participatory government and freedom for the individual represents one of humankind's noblest achievements. Surprisingly few people in the world today have the opportunity to live in democratic societies. This precious heritage

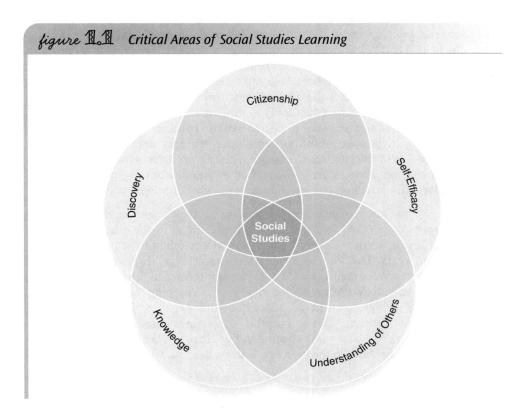

figure **1.1**   *Critical Areas of Social Studies Learning*

of Americans is, as Thomas Jefferson said, "renewed with each succeeding generation." The rights and responsibilities of adults living in a democratic society include freedom of speech, worship, assembly, the press, and so on. You have the privilege—and mandate—to set those rights and responsibilities in motion through stories, activities, discussions, and projects with the children you teach.

• *Discovery: Social studies is designed to help children explain their world.* Jean Piaget wrote that the two most important tasks of childhood are organization and adaptation. By *organization,* he basically meant the ability to understand and classify things with respect to how they work. For example, a child's initial insights into the U.S. economic system or to the location of continents on the world map represent examples of organization. *Adaptation* refers to the process of accommodating oneself to one's environment. A child who enters school has already adapted considerably to the environment through speech, dress, rules at home, and so forth, but school is designed to expand such adaptation greatly through formal learning processes. These processes are intellectual, social, emotional, and physical. A good social studies program provides insights to one's history, culture, and landscape—in short, to the world and how it works. Jerome Bruner wrote that most of what happens appears as chaos to children because they don't understand how things work. An effective teacher replaces chaos with understanding.

• *Self-concept: Social studies can help children along the road to positive self-development.* People who reflect on their school days often speak about teachers who really affected their lives. One teacher characteristic inevitably comes to the fore in such conversations—something like: "He [She] showed a personal interest in me." The research literature in effective teaching frequently uses the term *pervasive caring* as an important characteristic of good teachers. Thus, both anecdote and research bear testimony to the teacher who cares. Because social studies is the area of the curriculum dedicated to the study of human beings, it lends itself quite naturally to the care and nurturing of the individual child. After all, you would not want to be accused of spending time teaching children about community helpers, economic systems, other cultures, and so on without first tending to the needs of the children in your own classroom. Unless the lives of the children you come in contact with daily are touched by you in a positive way, they will be hard pressed to learn anything meaningful about the lives of others.

• *Knowledge: Social studies should help children acquire a foundational understanding of history, geography, biography, and the social sciences.* It is difficult to say exactly how much knowledge of history or of the other disciplines children ought to acquire in their elementary school years. The sources of children's knowledge are several, and school alone will not account for their knowledge of the world. Indeed, teachers carry far too heavy a burden when they assume responsibility for *all* learning that children achieve. The best access to knowledge is found in listening and speaking, reading and writing, and observing and recording. You will need to give serious consideration to how you will build the knowledge base most effectively. But clearly, you are the one who is responsible for teaching children the basics of history, geography, and citizenship.

• *Understanding of others: Social studies ought to promote in children a genuine sense of the social fabric.* Children come to school from increasingly smaller families. The one-parent, one-child family is not uncommon. Opportunities for give and take within the family structure are lessened not only because there are fewer family members but also because people within a family spend less time interacting with each other in task-related activities (chores, etc.) than they used to. But the social needs and potential of human beings remain constant. The question is: What will you do to promote a sense of others in your classroom? From the day they enter school, children need to be supported and guided in their attempts to cooperate, share, and contribute. A sense of others includes respect for and tolerance of the child at the adjoining desk, an openness to alternative points of view, a willingness to take part in group efforts, and an expanding view of the community as not merely something the child is a part of but as something he or she can make better through participation in it. Cooperative learning ideas introduced over the past few decades offer virtually unlimited possibilities for you to develop the social fabric with your social studies program as its centerpiece.

Social Studies Curriculum Patterns

Let's come back to the idea of social studies as the study of human beings. First, social studies is the only curriculum subject with people as its subject matter. People are often considered in language arts and science, but in social studies, people remain the constant focus. Social studies deals directly with the basic needs of human beings: food, clothing, shelter, belonging, security, and dreams. Everyone, everywhere, throughout history has had these needs, but it takes a good teacher to help students understand and recognize these needs in themselves and in others. For a snapshot of a typical K–6 social studies curriculum, see Figure 1.2.

Social studies, like other subjects of the elementary school curriculum, is designed to be taught in increments, or in a developmental sequence. This means that instruction proceeds from the simple to the complex, from the familiar to the remote, from the known to the unknown. Thus, kindergarten and first-grade students spend much social studies time studying self-awareness and families because these two topics have a sense of relevance and immediacy to young children. In time, the horizons widen to neighborhoods, communities, cities, regions, the nation, and the Western and Eastern hemispheres. Such a progression from self to the world in the study of people is known as the *widening horizons* or *expanding environments curriculum.*

Integrated with the idea of widening horizons is a second thought. Called the *spiral curriculum,* it is designed to enhance such key factors as reinforcement of knowledge and ideas, concept and skill development, and transfer of learning. Thus, even though self-awareness and family studies are found in the early primary years, they are not abandoned as topics of later study. They are too important to set aside. Instead, the spiral curriculum calls for introducing concepts and skills at simple levels, to be pursued at deeper levels of sophistication each time they are revisited. Therefore, sixth-graders ought to be capable of conducting relatively sophisticated neighborhood studies if the concept of a neighborhood has been sequentially reinforced in a variety of settings over the years.

The other facet of the spiral curriculum that needs to be developed is the early introduction of topics that experts once thought were beyond young children. Through television, young children are aware of elections, space travel, unemployment, and

figure **1.2**   *Outline of Social Studies Content*

Kindergarten

Tools for learning about the world: maps, photos, globe

The *individual* and others

Living in a family

Going to school

Changes in seasons, animals, people

Need for food, clothing, shelter

Need for rules

Different places to live

Grade 1

Tools for learning about the world: maps and photos

The individual and the family

Needs of families:
  Food
  Clothes
  Shelter

Families in neighborhoods

Living in the United States

Grade 2

Tools for learning about the world: map, photos, graphs

Setting for *communities:* the earth, North America, the United States

Large and small communities made up of neighborhoods

Community services

Different kinds of work in communities

Rules in communities

Communities long ago in our country

Celebrating holidays in communities

Grade 3

Tools for learning about the world: maps, photos, graphs, time lines, diagrams, tables

How to study a particular community

Representative communities in the United States:
    Cities, towns, and suburbs
    Farms and ranches
    Fishing communities

Need for rules

Communication

Grade 4

Tools for learning about the world: maps, photos, time lines, diagrams, tables

Forest *regions* in Washington state, Hawaii, Puerto Rico, Russia, Amazon Basins

Desert regions in southwestern United States, Africa, Arabian Peninsula

Plains regions in central and coastal United States, China, Kenya, Australia

Mountain regions in Colorado, West Virginia, Switzerland

Interdependence of regions

Materials for learning about one's own state

Grade 5

Tools for learning about the world: maps, graphs, photos, time lines, diagrams, tables

Ways of learning about the past

Chronological history of the *United States*

An overview of the geography of the United States

Geography of:
    New England states
    Middle Atlantic states
    Southeast states
    South Central states
    North Central states
    Mountain West states
    Pacific states

History and geography of Canada and Latin America

Grade 6

Tools for learning about the world: maps, photos, graphs, time lines, diagrams, tables

Beginnings of Western Civilization:
    Mesopotamia and Ancient Egypt
    Ancient Greece
    Ancient Rome and the Roman Empire

Geography and history of:
    Western Europe
    Eastern Europe and Russia
    Middle East and North Africa
    Africa south of the Sahara
    South Asia, East Asia, and Australia

Source: Adapted from *The World and Its People* (Glenview, IL: Silver Burdett).

global conflicts. It would be folly to ignore these national and global events; they can, at the very least, be treated impressionistically.

Thus, the widening horizons and spiral curricula work in concert. Let's take a look at each idea in greater detail.

The Widening Horizons Curriculum

The widening horizons philosophy states that the study of human beings should begin with examples from the local environment. Thus, first-graders might find themselves learning about the family and the neighborhood. Certainly, these are two aspects of humanity that are within the realm of the daily experience of young learners. Each day, they interact with family members. They walk or ride through neighborhoods on the way to school, and they play there during their free time. Thus, when thoughts about families and neighborhoods are presented in the classroom, students can relate them to their own life experiences.

After a study of the family and the neighborhood, students expand their horizons to the community, the city, the state, the region, the United States, and finally the wider world. Each new area of study is an outgrowth of those that preceded it. In moving from the close and familiar examples of people to those further away and more remote in terms of experience, students are following what seems to be a logical progression. Notice the relationship between the specific curriculum topics illustrated in Figure 1.2 and the widening horizons graphic shown in Figure 1.3.

Even though it remains essentially intact as the dominant curricular pattern for elementary social studies, the widening horizons approach has its detractors. In a simpler era, when travel and television were less influential for some and nonexistent for others, perhaps it was reasonable to expect children to learn more gradually about worldwide events. But much has changed since the widening horizons curriculum was proposed half a century ago. Further, not one shred of empirical evidence has ever been

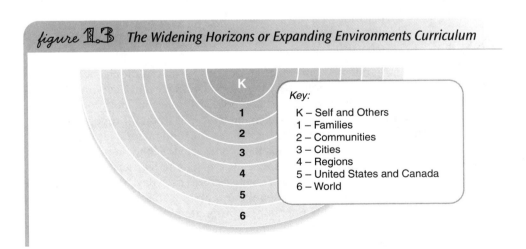

figure **1.3** *The Widening Horizons or Expanding Environments Curriculum*

Key:

K – Self and Others
1 – Families
2 – Communities
3 – Cities
4 – Regions
5 – United States and Canada
6 – World

Two young geographers compare the Eastern and Western regions of the United States.

produced to substantiate its structure. Obviously, it is difficult for very young children to understand events that occur in remote corners of the globe or that occurred centuries ago. But we know that they are indeed interested in other peoples and other times and that there is much they can understand through stories, film, and play. The other side of this issue is that older children ought to study families and neighborhoods. Those are not exclusively topics for primary school children to study. If they were, sociologists, geographers, and historians wouldn't study them.

The Spiral Curriculum

Perhaps the most intriguing new curricular approach to social studies is the spiral curriculum. The basic idea of the spiral curriculum is that within each discipline of the social sciences there exists a basic structure, composed of concepts and processes, that can be adapted for use in the teaching of elementary social studies. Proponents of this point of view suggest that the social sciences contain the fundamental ideas (concepts) and procedures (processes) a learner needs to become an independent problem solver.

The presentation of ideas from social science to young learners can be accomplished in a number of ways, including 50-minute lectures each day, but why would any teacher want to do that? The key to the spiral curriculum is to identify and teach real social science concepts in a developmentally appropriate way. Thus, children are recognized and respected as *young* learners who need active experience in order to build up their *schema,* or knowledge base, yet meaningful content is not sacrificed. Therefore, you can expect that I will keep reminding you of terms such as *experience, activities,* and *inquiry.* The concepts you will teach remain essentially the same from kindergarten to sixth grade. That is how the spiral works. Teachers and students keep revisiting the same important ideas at increasingly sophisticated levels over time. This makes it easier for a school faculty to work together to articulate the curriculum. Of course, the content is different each year, but the ideas or concepts are the same. Chapter 9 is important in this regard because it introduces and explains these key concepts.

Here is a brief example of how the spiral curriculum works (see Figure 1.4). Perhaps you wish to teach children the historical concept of the *oral tradition,* which is the handing down of life activities and patterns through the spoken word (stories, reminiscences, and so on). It is an important source of knowledge of the past, especially knowledge of everyday life patterns. A primary teacher might introduce the concept by asking children if they know stories about their parents' or grandparents' childhoods. The teacher then shares a family story or two that was told (and perhaps retold) to him or her, working a little geography into the story, showing where incidents took place (perhaps in another state). Later that day, as the children prepare to go home, the teacher hands out a letter for parents, which asks them to share a story from their childhood with their child. When the children return to school, the teacher asks them to discuss and draw pictures about something from their parents' childhood stories. The teacher takes time to explain the idea of traditions, relating this experience to larger, shared traditions such as Thanksgiving, as well as stories about famous people from history. After the stories are collected and illustrated, the class prepares to compile them into a history book. The teacher introduces the rich oral traditions of certain Native American tribes and other groups that depended more on the spoken than the written word.

Now all of this is rather simple and introductory, which is exactly the right idea. This teacher has done a good job of setting the stage for the concept of the oral tradition to emerge. As students progress through the year and through the grades beyond, the concept is revisited time and again in different contexts. It is compared and contrasted

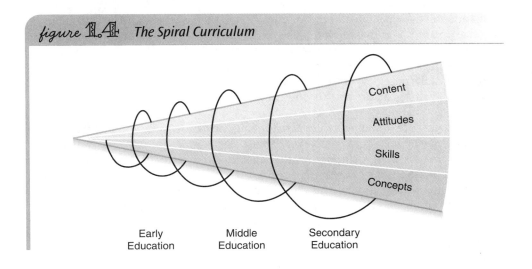

figure 1.4 *The Spiral Curriculum*

Content

Attitudes

Skills

Concepts

Early
Education

Middle
Education

Secondary
Education

with the written tradition and other ways of preserving the past. Students become historians who investigate and re-create the past through stories handed down. They write plays, put on pageants, listen to storytellers and guest speakers, read the work of other historians, and build the concept deeper and deeper. Philosopher Jean-Jacques Rousseau wrote more than two centuries ago, "Teachers, teach less, and teach it well." This is the essence of the spiral approach to the curriculum: to identify a few key concepts and to teach them well with depth.

The Environment for Social Studies Learning

For effective social studies learning to take place, the environment must be conducive to free and open inquiry. The chemistry or mix of basic ingredients is something that will be examined later, but for now, here is a brief look at several aspects of a supportive social studies learning environment: a constructivist environment for learning, productive and reflective thinking, and provisions for differences in learners. Many states provide guidelines or frameworks for what and how students should learn. See, for example, the California Framework in Figure 1.5.

A Constructivist Environment for Learning

Most teachers would agree that students should become increasingly self-sufficient and less dependent on direct supervision as they progress through the grades. Curiously, however, it is not uncommon to find that precisely the opposite occurs. A certain type of teacher—the teacher whose presence dominates the classroom, who passes judgment on every pupil response, who always decides who will or will not be called on, who asks questions that have "right" and "wrong" answers, and who reduces the students' concept of learning to paper and pencil, read and recite, listen and give back—causes students to become directly dependent on him or her and not on their own latent powers.

Eventually, students construct their own knowledge. Teachers must make a conscious attempt to help students become confident in their own abilities by assuming less directive postures and by seeing themselves in the role of facilitators of learning and not dispensers of information. A teacher must be open to the students' views even when those views fail to coincide with the teacher's own. A teacher must ensure that students acquire the skills necessary to survive and prosper as inquirers.

The following goals are directed toward the creation of a constructivist environment:

- To recognize that human beings actively construct knowledge and that they should not be viewed merely as passive receivers
- To teach a research methodology that enables children to look for information to answer questions they have raised, and to use the conceptual framework developed in the course (e.g., to apply the concept of system to new areas)
- To help youngsters develop the ability to use firsthand sources—both the materials provided and the materials they gather in their communities—as evidence from which to develop hypotheses and draw conclusions

figure **1.5** *The California Framework for History and the Social Sciences: A Graphic Illustration of the Goal Structure of the Social Studies*

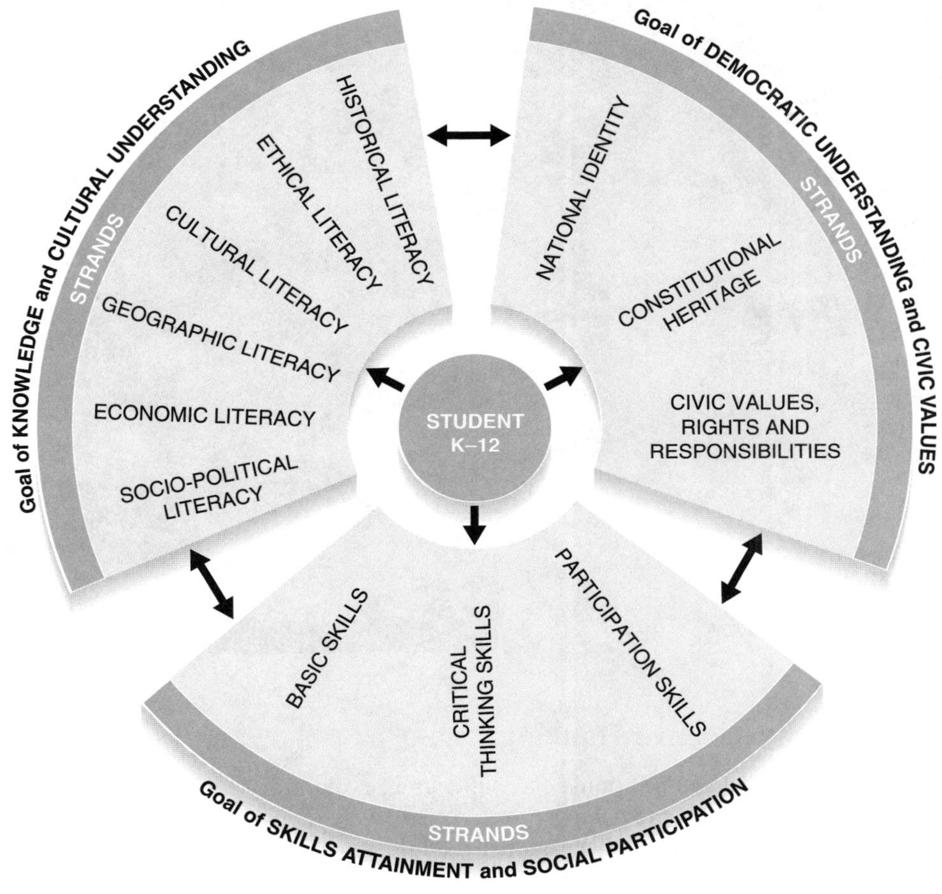

Source: The History–Social Science Framework for California Public Schools (Sacramento: California State Department of Education, 1998).

- To conduct classroom discussions in which youngsters learn to listen to others as well as to express their own views
- To legitimize the search—that is, to give sanction and support to open-ended discussions where definitive answers to many questions are *not* found
- To encourage children to reflect on their own experiences
- To create a new role for the teacher, in which he or she becomes a resource rather than an answer giver
- To utilize people in the community as resources

"Butterfly and Flower" by 6-year-old child.

Productive, Reflective Thinking

A social studies classroom should be a challenging, exploratory environment. It should be a place of excitement and energy, of movement and collaboration. It should be physically, socially, and intellectually attractive to children. Ideally, a child walking by your classroom will feel a genuine desire to come in.

Asking *questions* is at the heart of the matter:

- Can you sketch a map of your room at home?
- How is *longitude* different from *latitude?*
- Why do people around the world live in such different kinds of homes?
- In what ways have you grown this year?
- What does it mean to be a good citizen?
- How is learning together different from learning alone?
- What did you learn about history today?
- Could you teach someone at home something you learned today?
- What causes conflict between people?
- How can our class use creative ways to teach the rest of the school about safety issues on the playground?

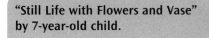
"Still Life with Flowers and Vase" by 7-year-old child.

- How much television do I watch? How else do I spend my time? How else could I spend my time?

Good questions lead to exploration, research, discovery, and activity. As the year progresses, you should see growth and development in your students' ability to ask and answer important questions. They need to learn the difference between a *memory question* (What is the capital of Argentina?) and an *exploratory question* (What do you think should be done to improve our environment?). Questions and problems ranging from the lowest to the highest levels of thinking are important—and the key is balance.

An active learning environment provides the greatest opportunities for reflective thinking by children. Children's play, construction, games, drawing, music, reading, writing, acting, and movement take on great meaning when the children are asked to reflect on them, to discuss purpose, learning, enjoyment, and growth. It is one thing to build a colonial village and quite another to reflect on people's lives then and now. But building the village is crucial because it gives a concrete, experiential point of reference for reflection.

Provisions for Learner Differences

Every teaching situation involving two or more students contains a number of learner differences; these may be intellectual, experiential, social, emotional, preferential, or developmental. To provide for these differences while presenting a cohesive program is one of the great challenges of teaching social studies—or any other subject, for that matter. Even if a teacher had diagnostic instruments available for determining which particular learning situation would suit which particular student(s) at which particular time, there would be no way to guarantee delivery of the many possible alternatives. The more reasonable course of action, given present possibilities, is to become acquainted with each student as a person with unique needs, interests, and learning styles rather than as a potential reservoir of information, and to provide for a variety of different learning styles.

For example, for a primary class studying the Japanese family, typical alternative activities might include viewing a film on family life in Japan, inviting a Japanese person to visit the classroom, preparing and eating food similar to that eaten by people in Japan, role-playing various roles in the Japanese family, putting together a photomural of life in Japan from magazine pictures, listening to the teacher read about various tasks performed in a Japanese household, writing letters to children in a Japanese school, and making charts on differences and similarities between our lives and those of the Japanese. Although this type of planning certainly does not provide for every type of individual difference, it does provide the variety necessary to ensure that a number of basic skills are developed while different interests are taken into account.

The Roles of the Teacher

As a school subject in the context of the school day, social studies is one of a number of subjects you teach. It therefore must compete for your energy and time on your schedule with reading, mathematics, science, and language. You are, of course, expected to teach all these subjects well.

Following are 12 roles of the social studies teacher. They span the range of expectations held for you as measures of competence. How competent are you? Your skills as a social studies teacher can hardly be viewed apart from your competencies as a teacher in general. But social studies is fundamental as a school subject because of its commitment to the fulfilled person, the informed citizen, and the contributing individual. To the extent that these ideals become reality for your students, they will improve their performance throughout the entire curriculum. Check yourself against these 12 roles as you reflect on your performance as a teacher of elementary social studies. Each role is explained in greater detail in various portions of this book.

1. *Use a variety of teaching strategies.* Variety accomplishes at least two things. First, it makes learning more enjoyable because it resists the boredom of a set, highly predictable routine. Second, it increases your chances of reaching the wide range of learning styles found in every classroom. Think for a moment of the possibilities: small-group discussion, whole-class discussion, committee work, drama, construction, drawing, films, speakers, silent reading, problem solving, and so on.

2. *Build bridges to other subjects.* Social studies is inherently interdisciplinary. It is possible to make logical and useful connections between social studies and almost any other subject. Cultural areas such as art and music, skill areas such as reading and

A good teacher cares deeply about children's freedom, interests, belongingness, and dreams.

math, and inquiry areas such as science are all natural subjects for integration with social studies. When you build these bridges, you achieve a natural reinforcement of subject matter, you make learning seem more real, and you present students with many opportunities to experience learning transfer.

3. *Teach to the real world.* Applications ought to be built into every lesson. The best applications tie school learning into the real world. The subject matter of social studies is people, so you should be able to apply ideas about individuals and groups of any size to the real world of your students.

4. *Emphasize hands-on experiences.* Most children of elementary age are in stages of intuitive and concrete learning. Such direct, active experiences as making things, investigating, and play can form the basis for learning more remote and abstract ideas.

5. *Keep the focus on people.* Human beings are the subject matter of social studies. Sometimes those people live far away or existed long ago. Do not forget that you have a group of human beings in your classroom. Provide time for sharing, for cooperating, for expressing feelings, and for caring about each other. Research shows a steady decline in students' concepts of themselves as learners as they progress through the school years. Resolve to turn that around.

6. *Gather materials.* It's true that a good social studies teacher is a scrounge. You need to be on the alert for copies of used *National Geographic,* old maps, books, pictures, construction materials, games, and any other materials you can beg, borrow, or purchase reasonably. When your friends know it is for a worthy cause, they may be able to help.

7. *Encourage reflective thinking.* The value of experience increases to the extent that children reflect on it. They need to talk about, plan, assess, and thoughtfully consider the conceptual, moral, and social aspects of the time you and they spend together learning. Are the children learning ideas? Are the experiences purposeful and socially redeeming? Are lives being improved?

8. *Teach values.* Integrity, trust, cooperation, respect, and dignity can be modeled, talked about, and expected in your classroom. Do not shy away from these basic values. Instead, take every opportunity to explore them with your students.

9. *Give students freedom.* It is a curious fact that freedom is encouraged and expected in our Western societies, but we give little of it to the students in our schools. Where will they learn to use freedom in a responsible way? Give your students a certain amount of free time, perhaps on one day a week, just to see what they will do with it. If you have developed a rich environment and modeled learning well, they will use it productively.

10. *Create a sense of place.* If your students must spend six hours a day in your room, make it a challenging, attractive place to be. Do not overlook the value of displays, bulletin boards, interest centers, game tables, reading corners, and privacy areas. It does not take much to make a place magic for a young child.

11. *Promote success.* Many of your children will have an almost desperate need to experience success. Some will view themselves as largely unsuccessful. For a few children, you may need to scale down the amount and difficulty of the work. For others, you may have to intensify the complexity of the work. All people need to experience success or they tend to give up, become apathetic, and cease to learn.

12. *Reward excellence.* If you seriously consider these roles, you will have some amazing outcomes in social studies. Do not let the fine work of your students go unnoticed. Inform them of their progress. Let parents know how well their children are doing. Display your students' work in the hallway or media center. Promote a sense of public recognition and appreciation for excellence.

Summary

Social studies is the study of human beings. The purpose of social studies in the elementary school curriculum is to introduce children to the world of people. Your task as a teacher of social studies is to make this world come alive. You need to share with children the excitement and creativity that are generated by inquiry, projects, cooperative efforts, integration of the arts, and other imaginative strategies. It isn't easy. It takes much thought and energy to move away from a worksheet-centered, read-around-the-room, emotionless approach to this subject.

The challenge of this first chapter has been to open up to you the world of possibilities inherent in the social studies curriculum. Think of yourself as an explorer on the edge of a great adventure as you approach this complex, intriguing subject. As you catch a glimpse of the vision of what social studies can become in the hands of a caring teacher, you are on the threshold of limitless possibilities.

Explorations

Reflect On . . .

1. Compare a recently published elementary social studies textbook with one at the same level that was published a few years ago. Make your own inferences about the changes that have taken place in the social studies curriculum. What might be some reasons for these changes?

2. Try to imagine a classroom where social studies was being taught really well. What would it look like? What would it feel like? How would you describe the teacher's behavior? In what kinds of activities and experiences would the students be involved?

In the Field

3. Talk to elementary school children about what they are doing in social studies. Try to piece together the scope and sequence of the social studies curriculum from their perspective. How much do you think these students understand about how their social studies program is organized? About its goals?

4. Interview an elementary school teacher who has taught for five or more years. Ask what changes have occurred in the curriculum. What does he or she see as the most important reasons for these changes?

For Your Portfolio

5. Review several new social studies programs. (You can do this online through publishers' catalogues.) Analyze the content of each program to see which one best suits your perspective. If you are currently teaching, see what it would take to get that program implemented in your classroom.

Continuing the Journey: Suggested Readings

The National Council for the Social Studies (NCSS) is the primary professional organization for social studies educators. You can find a wealth of useful material by visiting the organization's website (www.ncss.org) and looking at the "Publications" list. Here are a few that you will want to explore:

Laughlin, M., ed. (1996). *Meeting the standards: Social studies readings for K–6 educators.* Washington, DC: NCSS.
Useful background knowledge for teachers who wish to know the whys and wherefores of the standards.

Task Force for Social Studies Standards. (1994). *Expectations of excellence: Curriculum standards for social studies.* Washington, DC: NCSS.
This book spells out the standards. It is a must in any good curriculum library.

Yell, M., Scheurman, G., & Reynolds, K. (2004). *A link to the past: Engaging students in the study of history.* Washington, DC: NCSS.
An excellent primer for involving teachers and their students as historians.

Social Education. This is the official journal of the NCSS.

Social Studies and the Young Learner. This NCSS journal is devoted to the theory and practice of elementary social studies.

chapter 2

Diversity, Multiculturalism, and Pluralism in the Social Studies Classroom

In this chapter, we will explore these themes:

key concepts

- Diversity in the United States and in the classroom
- The role of social studies education in promoting pluralism and diversity
- The teacher's cultural sensitivity
- Preparing children for a diverse world

Working with children is the easiest part of education for democracy, because children are still undefeated and have no stake in being prejudiced.

—Margaret Halsey

The young citizens whom you teach or will teach represent an increasingly diverse society. The United States has historically been a nation of immigrants; only Indians, or Native Americans, can lay claim to being indigenous inhabitants of this land. In a sense, the nation is an ongoing experiment, constantly testing whether peoples of wide-ranging cultural, ethnic, and religious backgrounds can live together in harmony. Today, the premise of this experiment is being tested even more rigorously than in the past. Minorities are becoming majorities, and divisions between peoples appear wider and deeper than ever.

As the United States grows culturally more diverse, the need for developmentally appropriate education designed to help children understand, tolerate, and appreciate cultural differences becomes increasingly critical. One of your tasks as a social studies teacher is to create conditions in your classroom that lead to greater understanding, increased tolerance, and a deepened sense of appreciation toward others.

The life of an elementary teacher is challenging, difficult, and complex. On some days, you will wish you had done certain things differently. On the worst days, teaching may hardly seem worthwhile and you may wonder whether you've chosen the right career. But on the good days, those doubts will fade away. There is probably no other profession that brings with it so many rewards. The rewards of teaching come in many forms. And often, the rewards are unexpected. The great investigator of childhood growth and development, Jean Piaget, once noted that all genuine learning is spontaneous. It happens in the moment. The rewards of joy, accomplishment, sharing, persistence, teamwork, and a job well done seem to happen along the way.

Teaching social studies is one way to ensure that these rewards will come your way. Why is this so? Social studies is learning about human activity, and the best way to learn about human activity is to make sure that every child you teach feels that he or she is truly part of the daily life of the classroom. In other words, experience is the best teacher. If the experience is one that is positive, uplifting, respectful, and sensitive, then children will feel included. And this is where cultural sensitivity begins: with *inclusion*. Each child must be included. There is no room for exclusion.

Think of yourself as the conductor of a fine symphony orchestra. This is a useful metaphor for the role of the teacher. You are the leader of a talented group of individuals whose success depends on their ability to work together. The members of the orchestra *must* work together—in concert, to be exact. To be *in concert* means to be in harmony. Here is the key to a fine orchestra: In order to produce beautiful music, the orchestra must be a collection of very different musicians playing very different instruments dedicated to producing the same piece of music together. Each instrument (percussion, brass, woodwinds, and strings) has its certain beauty when played alone, but when all the instruments are played together, something much greater happens. In other words, diversity in harmony produces the best effect.

Just as diversity strengthens an orchestra, diversity has the potential to make your classroom a better place to work and play. Each child is needed because in the best social studies classrooms, teamwork is a daily occurrence. It is obvious that different instruments are needed in order to complete the requirements of a symphony performance. Notice that I said the different instruments are *needed,* not just *tolerated.* This is the transformation achieved by great teachers. Every child feels *needed.* When a child tells a parent, "I need to go to school today because we're working together on our project" (or words to that effect), we have a glimpse of a teacher who has transformed the culture of the classroom from passive to active, from one of restriction to one of opportunity, from one where attendance is required to one where children desire to be there.

Diversity in the United States and in the Classroom

American society has always been diverse, even in the earliest days of settlement. That our society has become and will continue to become more pluralistic and diverse is obvious in any number of ways, from the numbers reflected in the official U.S. government census to the proliferation of ethnic cuisine in regional restaurants to the multitude of languages heard on the streets of any large city. The evidence is all around us. A child hanging onto a parent's hand at the local grocery store will see shelves stocked with products from all over the world, representing a range of ethnicities (Hispanic, Thai, Caribbean, South Asian, Chinese—an endless array!) that probably would not have been there even a decade ago. Clothing, architecture, films, television, music— all reflect the growing diversity of this nation.

It is one thing, however, for a society to be diverse and another for it to provide equal opportunity for all its members. Public education has long been seen as a venue for "melting" the various ethnicities together. In the nineteenth century, educational leaders such as Horace Mann, often considered the "father" of American public education, led the way for schools to offer daily opportunities for children to work and play together across economic, religious, and social barriers. Mann was convinced that a democratic society could survive and prosper only if it were truly integrated. Thus, one major purpose of schooling was born: to become a crucible of democracy. It was a noble dream, one that today places schools and teachers in a more strategic role than Mann might ever have imagined.

As a teacher, you are a major player in this great democratic experiment. The National Council for the Social Studies (NCSS, 1994) says that "social studies teachers should possess the knowledge, capabilities, and dispositions to organize and provide instruction at the appropriate school level for the study of culture and cultural diversity" (p. 18). And the NCSS is clear about its expectations for learners, for teachers, and for classrooms (see Figure 2.1).

---

figure **2.1**   *NCSS Standards*

1.1 Culture and Cultural Diversity. Candidates in social studies should possess the knowledge, capabilities, and dispositions to organize and provide instruction at the appropriate school level for the study of culture and cultural diversity.

1.2 Time, Continuity, and Change. Candidates in social studies should possess the knowledge, capabilities, and dispositions to organize and provide instruction at the appropriate school level for the study of time, continuity, and change.

1.3 People, Places, and Environment. Candidates in social studies should possess the knowledge, capabilities, and dispositions to organize and provide instruction at the appropriate school level for the study of people, places, and environment.

1.4 Individual Development and Identity. Candidates in social studies should possess the knowledge, capabilities, and dispositions to organize and provide instruction at the appropriate school level for the study of individual development and identity.

1.5 Individuals, Groups, and Institutions. Candidates in social studies should possess the knowledge, capabilities, and dispositions to organize and provide instruction at the appropriate school level for the study of individuals, groups, and institutions.

1.6 Power, Authority, and Governance. Candidates in social studies should possess the knowledge, capabilities, and dispositions to organize and provide instruction at the appropriate school level for the study of power, authority, and governance.

1.7 Production, Distribution, and Consumption. Candidates in social studies should possess the knowledge, capabilities, and dispositions to organize and provide instruction at the appropriate school level for the study of production, distribution, and consumption of goods and services.

1.8 Science, Technology, and Society. Candidates in social studies should possess the knowledge, capabilities, and dispositions to organize and provide instruction at the appropriate school level for the study of science, technology, and society.

1.9 Global Connections. Candidates in social studies should possess the knowledge, capabilities, and dispositions to organize and provide instruction at the appropriate school level for the study of global connections and interdependence.

1.10 Civic Ideals and Practices. Candidates in social studies should possess the knowledge, capabilities, and dispositions to organize and provide instruction at the appropriate school level for the study of civic ideals and practices.

But when a single classroom may include students from eight or ten different ethnic or cultural backgrounds, students whose first language is not English, and students with a variety of disabilities, then what does it mean to be able to "provide instruction at the appropriate school level"? In the past, children from minority backgrounds, second-language English speakers, children with disabilities, and children from lower socioeconomic backgrounds were often relegated to second-class citizenship in the classroom. In the second half of the twentieth century, great strides were made toward achieving equality and inclusion. But there is a long distance still to go.

A wide range of thought and activity can exist within the framework of rules, norms of behavior, and law. This fact leads to two values you will definitely want to emphasize in teaching social studies to children: (1) diversity and differences and (2) respect for individual rights. Rosa Parks was a true pioneer of the twentieth-century Civil Rights movement. Her courage stands as a testament to the positive effects one individual can have in a democratic society (see Figure 2.2). Democratic societies, such as those in the United States and Canada, place great value on the uniqueness of the

figure 2.2   *Rosa Parks: A Person of Dignity and Courage*

Rosa Parks died in October of 2005 at the age of 92. She died in Detroit, where she had lived for some years. She was an old woman, and it is quite possible that many young people living today do not even know who she was or what she did a half century ago that was so remarkable. What she did that took so much courage and determination has become commonplace in today's world. She took a seat on a city bus on her way home from work.

Rosa Parks lived in Montgomery, Alabama, for much of her life, and it was in that city more than 50 years ago that she performed a simple act of courage that helped change the world. On her way home from work she took a seat in a section of a city bus reserved for white people. The rule of the day in that city and throughout much of the American South was that white people sat in one section and colored people sat in an area reserved for them in the back of the bus.

When a white male passenger asked—or told—her to move, she refused. This act of defiance made headlines. By sitting where she did not "belong" she had broken the rules, violated the established norm of behavior, and otherwise made of herself a nuisance. The police were called to arrest her. This action proved to be the catalyst for the more than year-long Montgomery Bus Boycott, a watershed in the annals of American civil liberties.

What Rosa Parks did was at once outrageous and reasonable. It was outrageous because it was against the law. It was reasonable because she acted in defiance of a bad law, one that simply had to change.

Rosa Parks was in many ways an ordinary person. She gave no famous speeches, wrote no best-selling books, ran for no political office. She is best remembered today as a person who merely wanted to be treated equally, with dignity and respect. In that sense, Rosa Parks takes her place as a citizen of the United States who truly understood what it means to be a citizen.

individual and on personal freedom to pursue a path of self-determination in life. In a democracy, differences must not only be tolerated, but they must also be respected. Any truly democratic society is diverse in any number of ways.

Children need to learn through your teaching and your example that a genuine emphasis on the rights of individuals means accepting the rights of those who may be different from oneself. This lesson seems obvious, but nowhere should these primary values be more evident than in your classroom. The children you teach will vary greatly, perhaps with respect to race/ethnicity, religion, socioeconomic status, intelligence, motivation, and self-concept. You will have diversity within your classroom because classrooms are microcosms of society. To what extent will you tolerate, appreciate, and celebrate these differences? Will you show as much respect for the poor child as you show for the well-to-do child? Will you be as tolerant toward the slow learner as you are toward the student who catches on quickly to everything you assign? Will the child whose behavior is often less than socially desirable be welcome in your classroom, or will that child have to find compassion elsewhere? These are the real issues you must resolve every day of your teaching career.

The Role of Social Studies Education in Promoting Pluralism and Diversity

Social studies plays a dual role in promoting diversity and pluralism. First, the classroom climate must be one of respect, dignity, caring, and support for every child. This expectation is or should be true about every aspect of the school day and is not unique to the social studies. Second (and this role *is* unique to social studies education), social studies is the study of the contributions, traditions, and world views of people from all backgrounds, cultures, races/ethnicities, language groups, and religions. In other words, social studies is the study of humankind.

Children in costume celebrate the Chinese New Year. Such experiences bring cultural understanding to life.

One specific goal of social studies education is to create awareness of and appreciation for others. We study ancient civilizations not merely to build up the information needed to pass tests but to gain an understanding of the human adventure over time. We study other cultures in order to discover that there are many ways in which to organize families, communities, and whole societies. There is no room for condescension: We do not think in terms of *inferior* and *superior* or even *strange* and *familiar.* We simply seek to understand the differences. This is part of the long-term process of helping children to grow into reflective, caring citizens.

Cultural Sensitivity in Social Studies Curricula

Banks and Banks (2001) define four levels of curriculum that represent how diversity content is typically taught in the social studies classroom. Their model is hierarchical, thus offering a map to teachers who truly wish to teach meaningful content while ensuring balance and fairness toward different points of view, particularly on sensitive issues. In this sense, the model represents growth and development on the part of the teacher. The four levels that Banks and Banks define include the following:

1. *The contributions approach.* At this level, students are exposed to information that generally lacks a conceptual frame. Holidays, special occasions, food, and famous people are emphasized without providing a larger context. Typically, the textbook sets the course of the curriculum.

2. *The additive approach.* Here, the basic structure of the curriculum still does not change; it remains textbook coverage. However, the teacher adds a conceptual framework and thematic teaching that set the various holidays and personalities within a larger context of social struggle. Cultures outside the mainstream—Native American, African, East Asian, and so on—may be featured.

3. *The transformational approach.* At this level, teachers begin to introduce fundamental change into the curricular structure. Students are encouraged to examine ideas, events, and issues from divergent perspectives. Christopher Columbus's voyage to the New World, for example, may be seen not simply from the European standpoint as a great step forward but also as a dangerous intrusion from a Native American one. Similarly, a study of the westward expansion may look at this movement from both the pioneer and Native American perspectives. Concepts such as *conflict* and *tolerance* are studied reflectively.

4. *The social action approach.* This level represents a fundamental change from "learning about" to making decisions, conducting investigations, and engaging in social action. It is a problem-solving, reflective thinking approach to the social studies curriculum in which students are supported in their efforts to make a difference in the world. Knowledge and skills become tools for change rather than serving as ends in themselves. See, for example, how Canadian students were successful in removing Styrofoam containers from the British Columbia Ferry System (pp. 129–130).

The Banks and Banks (2001) model is intended to provide a means for teachers (and schools) to examine the level of cultural sensitivity in their social studies programs. But it

Students participate in a lively debate over school uniforms. Such experiences allow young people to learn to deal with different opinions in a civil manner.

is also a useful way of thinking about teaching and learning in general. Although you may be constrained by district, state, or even federal standards and guidelines from implementing the curriculum of your choice, I encourage you to study the Banks model carefully as you prepare lessons, units, and ongoing experiences for the children you teach.

Creating a Culturally Responsive Learning Environment

All of us desire to create classroom environments where children feel welcome, engaged, and appreciated for who they are. This is especially so in the case of social studies, because in social studies, the subject matter and the experience are ideally one. We don't just study citizenship, we engage in it. We don't just tell children about tolerance, we practice it together. The gap between what we teach and what we live must be closed if social studies is to come to life in any meaningful way. But how does this happen in day-to-day practical classroom life?

Hamilton (2000, 2004) offers a number of insights designed to promote a *culturally responsive learning environment.* Her ideas are simple yet profound. Put into practice, they have the potential to create a truly democratic community in miniature. The classroom becomes a place where diversity is seen as positive and where pluralism is celebrated along the way. Specifically, Hamilton identifies five practices that involve such important concepts as interest, relevance, collaboration, meaning, community, trust, and openness. These concepts come to life as they are actually lived by students who are then challenged to reflect on the quality of their experience.

Hamilton's (2000, 2004) ideas work at a variety of levels of growth and development, but I have attempted to capture and expand on them here with an emphasis on the elementary level social studies experience:

- *Coursework based on human needs and childhood interest.* When students feel their basic needs of safety, belonging, and curiosity are being met, they are ready for the challenges of ideas that are relevant to their lives, challenges that are developmentally appropriate and of interest.

- *Teaching as a collaboration with learners.* This involves nurturing students to believe in their own ideas and to express them in an accepting, caring environment. It also involves a search for meaning in what is being taught and learned, raising issues of honesty, value, and worth. The image of a great coach comes to mind—a coach who cares about young people, who holds them to standards, and who wants the best for the individuals and the team.

- *A community of learners who share and work together in a spirit of collaboration.* John Dewey thought an elementary classroom was at its best when it was a miniature community in which democracy, in the full sense of the term, came to life. Integration of subject matter is a wonderful thing, but integration of people who care and share is even more profound.

- *The development of a classroom environment that is blame free and based on trust and transformation.* I have seen such classrooms, and they are a beauty to behold. Such classrooms are overwhelmingly positive, polite, trusting places. Not only do the individuals in them grow and prosper, but so does the group. This kind of environment seems to blossom more readily where there is esprit de corps, where projects are being carried out, and where real-world applications are being made.

- *The development of classrooms where students are treated equally and invited to address behaviors and policies that are prejudicial.* In such a classroom, communication is real and fairness and justice are not abstract concepts but part of the expectations of daily life. Few teachers practice prejudicial behaviors consciously, and few teachers encourage such behaviors on the part of their students. Rather, such unfortunate behaviors more often arise when conscious attempts to ensure fairness and justice are not routinely part of the discussion of daily life. What is the key to this? The key is to adhere faithfully to the first four ideas found in this list.

Cultural Sensitivity: The Teacher as Learner

What can the teacher do to create a more culturally sensitive classroom climate? How does the social studies teacher contribute to the growth and development of future citizens, who will take their places in an increasingly pluralistic society? How do you as a teacher encourage your students to view diversity as positive?

These are not easy questions, and much is at stake in their answers. The very survival of our democracy depends on the attitudes that our children take into the future. If they are willing to embrace and even celebrate a society where all members are equal, where all members are treated with respect, and where each has an equal opportunity to succeed, then and only then is there hope for our success as a nation and a people. In a day when so much is demanded of teachers in terms of the development of student skills and knowledge and when that development is evaluated frequently by state and federally mandated tests, let us not lose sight of the fact that attitudes are equally important.

Here is an opportunity for you to assess your own attitudes and potential to succeed in a classroom environment where diversity is found. Research (Diller & Moule, 2005; Haberman, 1996) has shown that certain traits are related to success in teaching, especially success in teaching diverse student populations. Take a moment to respond to the statements in Figure 2.3 about teacher characteristics. For each statement, consider certain priorities in social studies teaching and respond "Yes," "No," or "Not sure." After you have done so, continue reading to examine the research results related to success in working with diverse student groups.

Did you answer "Yes" to most or all of the survey questions? "Yes" answers demonstrate cultural sensitivity. Research studies have shown that the qualities represented in these questions are shared by effective teachers in diverse, pluralistic school environments. No matter how you may have answered the questions, however, there is always room for improvement in your work with children. The best teachers are lifelong learners filled with the desire to be the best they can possibly be. Take the time to discuss the questions in this survey with your colleagues. They are far from trivial.

Haberman (1996) reports that the characteristics illustrated in the statements in the survey in Figure 2.3 are most likely to enhance cross-cultural teaching and learning. Diller and Moule (2005) identify four key teacher traits that are likely to enhance the successful interaction of teachers and culturally diverse students: care, dialogue, passionate pursuit, and openness to learning. What do these characteristics mean to you? To me, they identify a teacher who truly cares about each student; who creates an environment where everyone is encouraged to speak and to listen politely and thoughtfully when others speak; who brings energy, joy, and a sense of wonder to activities and experiences; and who is a model of lifelong learning.

One of the joys of teaching is found in the experience of humility. Some teachers discover this sooner than others. No matter how much you know or think you know,

---

figure **2.3**   *A Survey of Teacher Characteristics*

1. I believe the social studies teacher is responsible for engaging all students in purposeful learning experiences.   YES   NO   NOT SURE
2. I believe it is important for the social studies teacher to try to establish meaningful rapport with all students.   YES   NO   NOT SURE
3. I believe it is important for the social studies teacher to place emphasis on nurturing and coaching children to learn, supporting their curiosity and creative expression.
   YES   NO   NOT SURE
4. I believe that children with difficult home lives deserve teachers who are willing to persist and offer emotional and academic support even when it appears difficult to do so.
   YES   NO   NOT SURE
5. I believe it is important for the teacher to place greater emphasis on children's efforts at school rather than on their seeming academic ability.   YES   NO   NOT SURE
6. I believe it is important for teachers to reflect on and learn from their own mistakes.
   YES   NO   NOT SURE

Source: Adapted from Haberman, 1996.

you can always be taught by your students. Teaching and learning are truly reciprocal. Sometimes it is difficult to know who is teaching whom—whether the teacher is teaching the students or the students the teacher. John Dewey (1916) acknowledged this many years ago when he wrote that the best classroom is one where the teacher becomes a learner and the learners become teachers.

During my own third year of teaching, I found myself in a new school and district, one quite different, in many ways, from the one in which I had spent my first two years. During the first week, I disciplined a child for some misbehavior that I no longer remember. I always tried to speak privately later in the day to any child I had disciplined; it seemed then, as it does now, a reasonable thing to try to talk privately after feelings had subsided. When I asked the child, whose name was John, if he wanted to talk about the incident, he told me that he felt I was picking on him because of his race. I was completely surprised. It hadn't occurred to me that race might have played a role in my actions. But I realized that John may have seen the incident differently. We had different perspectives on the same event. It was the beginning of the year, and we knew very little about each other.

I realized that John's interpretation of our interaction may have reflected his own experience, which had taught him to feel that way. By calling that to my attention, he was teaching me. If we consider John's misbehavior as a miniature historical event, isn't it reasonable to assume that more than one perspective exists? Just as eyewitnesses saw the Battle of Lexington differently, so John and I saw our interaction differently.

John was polite and expressed himself clearly. We got to know each other better as a result of our conversation. I realized that I needed to earn his trust—that he was not going to simply hand it to me because I was an adult authority figure. In fact, my role as an adult and authority may have made me harder to trust than a peer. This was the beginning of a wonderful teacher–student relationship, for which I take very little credit. John's own civility and patience made this interaction more congenial than some (and I do not mean to suggest that because he was polite, he deserved to be heard, whereas a student who responded more belligerently would be less worthy of concern). Our task is to take students as they come to us and to treat them with dignity and honor, even in the most difficult situations. So the next time you sit down to plan a lesson, don't overlook the possibility that you might be planning a learning experience for yourself as well as for your students.

Preparing Children for a Diverse World

The challenge of preparing children to take their places as citizens in a pluralistic society never ends. It is a journey more than a destination. One of the key principles of the UNESCO Earth Charter reads, "Honor and support the young people of our communities, enabling them to fulfill their essential role in creating sustainable societies." When we are called on (in the same document) to "eliminate discrimination in all its forms, such as that based on race, color, gender, sexual orientation, religion, language, and national, ethnic, or social origin," we begin to realize the enormity of the task. But as the old cliché goes, "No one said teaching was ever going to be easy."

Two ideas are worth bearing in mind as you prepare your students to be thoughtful citizens. The first has to do with the day-to-day social and moral fabric of school life. The children you teach are there to learn from you, in all the ways that such a trust implies.

Our American society is plural-istic and culturally rich.

Children's learning process begins with or is founded on how they are treated routinely, every day, day in and day out. It is often the little incident that makes the difference: the casual exchange, the small smile, the encouraging remark, the cheerful hello. Your students are watching you and learning from your actions. No doubt in your reading methods class, you have learned that the more often your students see you read, the more they will value reading. In the same way, your students will notice how you treat them and how you treat others. They will look to you for guidance, reassurance, fairness, and leadership in its many manifestations. Remember always that children live what they learn and learn what they live. Your attitudes and behaviors will be contagious. Kindness, firmness, openness, caring, nurturing, and curiosity will spread through a classroom; they cannot be stopped. In the religion and philosophies of India, this is known as *karma*.

The second idea to keep in mind in preparing your students to become thoughtful, participant citizens in a diverse world is related to both the child and the curriculum. The social studies curriculum is about more than simply *covering* a course of study that represents a typical scope and sequence. It is also about *uncovering* and *recovering*. What do I mean? Simply this: The act of discovery consists of uncovering previously un-known knowledge and ideas. Childhood is a time of discovery, and discovery at its best involves uncovering new ideas and recovering early knowledge.

The child who learns that Columbus sailed to the New World and opened two con-tinents to European settlement and conquest also needs to learn that the native peoples of those continents probably viewed that historical event from the perspective of being overrun and oppressed. Likewise, the child who learns about the freedom and oppor-tunity sought by early settlers in this country needs to learn that while many achieved this American dream, many others did not. We can only discover what we can uncover. And at some point, children discover that history is often recorded and published by those who were empowered in any given historical situation—by those who held the upper hand. In their journey of discovery, they need your help in uncovering the some-times hidden evidence of diverse perspectives.

Beyond that, children discover that neither naïveté nor cynicism has much to offer. The conceptual secrets to be discovered are balance, openness, and reason. The human experience is filled with hope and wonder, just as it is filled with deceit and despair. Wisdom, that undervalued commodity in our world today, comes slowly, incrementally. Poet T. S. Eliot wrote of the hierarchy of information, knowledge, and wisdom. Our knowledge is only as good as our information. What knowledge is of most worth? Moreover, our adventure toward wisdom depends greatly on what we already know. Somewhere along the way on the journey from information to wisdom, we begin to put knowledge together into meaningful structures called *concepts*. It doesn't happen overnight. The quality of our knowledge and ultimately our wisdom becomes a product of the quality of our experience. This is the joy, the high moral ground, of teaching and learning with children. Use their time and yours well, and great things will happen.

Summary

Few issues are more vital to the preservation and improvement of a democratic society than the issue of respect for differences. The United States has been a nation of diversity since its founding. Even in colonial times, American society was probably the most diverse in the world. Diversity enriches a nation and its people. Democracy demands multiple perspectives in order to remain dynamic. The genius of the American nation is not that it is simply a homogeneous racial or ethnic enclave, rooted in traditions that cannot be changed, but that it is a nation dedicated to equality, opportunity, and freedom for all its peoples, regardless of their heritage. This has caused us to be a forward-looking nation, one that embraces pluralism and celebrates diversity.

One of the privileges of being an elementary teacher is that you are entrusted by the public to nurture young lives. I can imagine no greater honor. But with trust and honor come duty and obligation. The young citizens who come to your classroom each day are watching you, imitating you, and seeing in you what it means to be a responsible, caring adult. As you model respect, dignity, trust, and hope in their presence, you send them a powerful message of right and proper conduct in a civil society. In social studies, children will learn the history, geography, and civics of their country and of other countries. This is necessary, valuable, and appropriate. But the lessons learned will have little meaning if they are not lived by you and your students.

As you create conditions for community, tolerance, freedom, and opportunity in your classroom, you sow the seeds of a democratic, civil society that will bloom for years to come. Never underestimate your influence. As Henry Adams wrote, "A teacher affects eternity."

Explorations

Reflect On . . .

1. What do you consider to be the most important qualifications for a teacher who works with children of different cultural and racial/ethnic backgrounds? Why? What might a prospective teacher do to ensure that he or she will enter the classroom with those qualifications intact?

2. Social studies is the only curricular area that has human beings as its subject matter. Given the pressing educational issues related to diversity,

what are the implications of this for the way your students study history, geography, civics, and the other social studies disciplines?

In the Field

3. Visit a local elementary school (or the one in which you are teaching), and select a unit or chapter from the social studies textbook that is in use at any level that interests you. Look for evidence of sensitivity to race/ethnicity, age, gender, and so on. What grade would you give this material for cultural sensitivity? Why? At what level of the Bankses' hierarchy does the material seem to fit?

4. Consider your own heritage. Create a family tree that identifies your ancestors and notes where

they came from. In what ways do you think your own heritage has affected you? What do you perceive as the benefits and limitations that your heritage provides you as a teacher? If any of your relatives are teachers, ask them how they feel their heritage has affected their teaching, if at all.

For Your Portfolio

5. Plan a learning experience for an extended activity called "What Is an American? Who Is an American?" Create an interdisciplinary experience that includes the visual arts, music, and drama, along with civics, history, geography, and the other social sciences.

Continuing the Journey: Suggested Readings

Danker, A. C. (2003). Multicultural social studies: The local history connection. *Social Studies, 94*(3), 111–117. *Practical ways to acknowledge diversity in the local community.*

Diller, J., & Moule, J. (2005). *Cultural competence: A primer for educators.* Belmont, CA: Wadsworth. *This book serves as a useful introduction for teachers who wish to increase their own sensitivity to multicultural issues.*

Ellermeyer, D., & Chick, K. (2003). *Multicultural American history: Through children's literature.* Minneapolis: Greenwood. *A cornucopia of good reading that connects U.S. history to literature for young people.*

Gillan, M. M., & Gillan, J. (1999). *Growing up ethnic in America.* New York: Penguin Books. *A sensitive portrayal of a minority perspective.*

Haberman, M. (1996). Selecting and preparing culturally competent teachers for urban schools. In J. Sikula, T. Buttery, & E. Guyon (Eds.), *Handbook of research on teacher education* (2nd ed.). New York: Macmillan. *A research-based analysis of findings and implications that all teachers need to know.*

Hamilton, M. H. (2000). Creating a culturally responsive learning environment for African American students. In M. Magolda (Ed.), *Teaching to promote intellectual and personal maturity: Incorporating students' worldviews and identities into the learning process* (pp. 45–54). San Francisco: Jossey-Bass. *A kid's view of history with regard to treatment of minorities.*

Hamilton, M. H. (2004). *Meeting the needs of African American women: New directions for student services.* San Francisco: Jossey-Bass. *This book provides useful insights to complex issues. Hamilton provides clarity and direction applicable to a variety of situations at different levels*

McCall, A. L. (2002). That's not fair! Fourth graders' responses to multicultural state history. *Social Studies, 93*(2), 85–91. *The ideas found here are practical and profound. This is an excellent beginning reference for any teacher who values sensitivity to others.*

Scott, C., Gargan, A., & Zakierski, M. (1997). *Managing diversity-based conflicts among children.* Bloomington, IN: Phi Delta Kappa Educational Foundation. *Ideas and techniques for conflict resolution with children in pluralistic settings.*

Wheat, B., & Robinson Kapavik, R. (2005). The civil rights movement: A humanities rainbow. *Social Studies and the Young Learner, 17*(1), 15–16. *This article will help teachers of elementary-age students communicate positive ideas of diversity and pluralism.*

Setting Standards

The Knowledge Base for Social Studies

In this chapter, we will explore these themes:

key concepts

- The nature of knowledge
- The NCSS standards as a guide to the knowledge base
- What children should know
- The social science disciplines
- Current events

Knowledge is of two kinds. We know a subject ourselves, or we know where we can find information upon it.
—Samuel Johnson

The central question of this chapter—What should elementary students know and be able to do?—is not an easy question to answer, and discussing it raises a considerable amount of controversy. We can begin our quest with the content, concepts, and methods of elementary social studies. They are derived primarily from history, geography, and the social sciences. Social studies is both integrative and broad in scope by its very nature. After all, when the subject matter is human beings and their interaction with the environment, then we have a wide-ranging course of study. This is both a strength and weakness of this area of the curriculum. It is a strength because human behavior takes so many forms over time and place that we are never at a loss for interesting material. The weakness may be that there is so much to learn that it seems, at times, overwhelming. Children are all too easily overwhelmed by names, dates, facts, and so on. The secret is to bring meaning to knowledge. Good teachers have always known that.

You can see from the 1775 Samuel Johnson quote (by the way, he wrote the first dictionary of the English language) that there is an age-old perception of the differences people have in mind when they speak about knowledge. In a nutshell, the argument is over whether knowledge is strictly content, strictly process, or, as Dr. Johnson suggests, both. A recurring issue in teaching and learning social studies is that of what and how much children should know about history, geography, and the social sciences. It is easy to find critical commentaries regarding how little today's students know, especially compared to students of generations past. Similarly, it is not particularly difficult to find commentaries arguing that the amount of content knowledge someone has is insignificant. This argument holds that the important thing is that people have process skills that enable them to locate and use knowledge when needed. Each of these arguments contains a certain measure of truth and a good dose of exaggeration.

Keys to Progressive Education

- Learning how to learn is at the heart of the matter. Students need to learn how to deal with unknown outcomes and challenges. In this sense, knowledge is seen as dynamic and ever changing rather than as static.
- Subject matter does not represent an end in itself; rather, it provides the raw material for learning and is relevant when it can be put to use. Textbooks, lectures, and formal examinations are considered artificial; true learning takes place when real problems of living are engaged and subject matter is used as a tool or instrument for learning.
- Experience is the key to productive learning. Learning should be active, exploratory, and socially engaged. A school should be a miniature democracy, a community where citizenship is learned through experience.
- Learner interest is significant. Human beings learn best when they have the opportunity to study those things that interest them most.
- Project learning is productive because of its practical, problem-solving, creative, social, and open-ended attributes.
- Real-world connections provide a sense of relevance and enable students to feel that they are taking part in public life.
- Reflective thinking should accompany active learning to provide a sense of purpose, balance, and assessment.
- The *process* of education should take precedence over the *product*. Learning represents continuous growth and is a complex enterprise.

Actually, the content versus process debate will probably never be completely solved, simply because it hinges so much on opinion and philosophy of teaching and learning. Let me illustrate the point by asking you to examine the two boxes that follow: Keys to Progressive Education and Keys to Essentialist Education. They present the basic arguments from the progressive (process orientation) and essentialist (basic skills and knowledge) points of view, respectively. Take a moment to consider each and whether you favor one perspective more than the other or whether perhaps you see certain advantages in each.

The Nature of Knowledge

Who was the first president of the United States? Who is the woman whose profile has recently appeared on a U.S. coin? How many time zones does the United States have? Which state is bordered by more states than any other? What were the principal causes of the Civil War?

Perhaps you think I'm trying to draw you into a game of Trivial Pursuit. No, on the contrary, I'm merely bringing up an issue that has become one of paramount debate in recent years—that of what and how much children ought to know as a result of their experiences with elementary social studies. At the heart of this matter is the process/ product controversy, the essence of which is whether greater emphasis should be placed on *how* to learn or *what* to learn. Everyone agrees that both are important, but the argument is focused more on where the appropriate balance lies than on anything else.

Keys to Essentialist Education

- The true purpose of education is intellectual and academic, not social and emotional.
- Education should be rigorous and demanding. The teacher's role is that of scholar who challenges students to reach higher levels of academic achievement.
- Academically talented students should especially be challenged because they represent the nation's future talent pool in a meritocratic society.
- The core disciplines, such as history and geography, should represent the essence of the curriculum. Activities in peer relations, life adjustment, and so on should be downplayed.

- Standards are necessary, as are standardized tests of achievement. Standards help teachers and students focus on essential knowledge and skills.
- Educational fads—such as learning styles, self-esteem curricula, and so on—are distractions from the real issue, which is to provide each student with the basic skills and knowledge necessary to achieve in life.
- Traditional forms—including textbooks, examinations, grades, graded schools, standards for promotion, and the like—are of proven worth and should be maintained.

What do you think about this? Perhaps your opinion is influenced by your own experience with social studies during your school years. Maybe you were the type of person who enjoyed learning the names of rivers and mountains, about the way people made a living in distant lands, or about life in ancient times. Maybe you weren't. Take a moment to write briefly your own recollections of social studies, especially how you felt about it.

_____

_____

_____

_____

Whether your memories were positive, negative, or mixed is no doubt influenced by (1) your attitude toward the subject matter itself, (2) the kinds of experiences you had in learning the subject matter, and (3) who taught you. In most cases, the subject matter itself is the least important of the three considerations. One person may remember studying Latin America and how boring it was. Another person may remember studying Latin America and how much fun it was when the class got to fix a Latin American meal and how kind and enthusiastic the teacher was about things. Elements such as these tend to interact and influence how a person feels, not just about social studies but about school learning in general.

Each of us has a certain amount of portable knowledge of history, geography, and the like. This knowledge belongs to us, and we carry it around with us inside our heads. It is committed to memory. Of course, memory fits into two categories: long term and short term. Some things we seem to remember all our lives, and other things, well, we just hope we can remember them for the big test! But whatever we know, we had to *acquire* the knowledge because we weren't simply born with it.

Knowledge Received

There are three ways that people know what they know. The first way, and the most common, is *knowledge received*. People receive knowledge from many sources: lecture, explanation, story, sermon, song, textbook, film, and so on. The point is that the knowledge first belongs to someone else, and it is then transmitted to another through some medium. This is essentially a passive view of knowledge acquisition. That, however, can be misleading because the level of a person's motivation will determine his or her level of involvement. Perhaps you can recall being told a story when you were a child and your own imagination was participating actively along with the storyteller. Knowledge received implies that experts are at the source and novices who need to know something are on the receiving end. The expert may be a lecturer, the author of a textbook, a gifted storyteller, or whatever, but the point is that the relationship between the expert and the learner is unequal. Another point worth considering about knowledge received is that it is secondhand knowledge. The learner generally trusts the accuracy of the authority because the learner is dependent on the expert source of information.

Most of your knowledge and mine is knowledge received. We didn't create it, and we probably had no way to verify it; rather, we tend to trust its accuracy. For example, you may know some things about life in ancient Greece or colonial America. It is likely that you received that knowledge from some source or perhaps a number of sources. It is important for a teacher to convey to students that no text on any subject is entirely accurate. There is no such thing as complete accuracy; only degrees of accuracy are found.

Knowledge Discovered

A second way people know what they know is *knowledge discovered*. This means of knowing is quite different from knowledge received. The implication of knowledge discovered is that some thing, event, circumstance, or whatever exists that you do not know about; however, by applying yourself, you can find out. In a nutshell, the difference between these first two forms is as simple as the difference between being told by someone else and finding out for yourself.

In essence, this changes the learning equation fundamentally. The center of gravity shifts to the learner. The teacher, or other expert source, becomes a facilitator. This puts the teacher in an extremely important role because he or she must arrange the environment for learning in such a way as to be challenging, motivating, and filled with possibilities. Discovery learning assumes that students will investigate, experiment, use trial and error, and reach conclusions for themselves. Thus, in their quest for knowledge, students become historians, geographers, and so on.

The teacher who involves students in knowledge discovered must create a rich environment, know when to ask questions, know when to lend support and cues, and, most difficult of all, know when not to intervene. All this raises teaching to a higher art form.

Students study a scale model of Stonehenge that they built. Concepts such as scale and proportion develop deeply when hands-on experience is combined with reflection.

Knowledge Constructed

The third way people know what they know is *knowledge constructed.* Here, there is no assumption of the prior existence of certain knowledge; that is, being told or even finding out will not work at this level. At a simple level, imagine an empty lot with little on it. You decide to build a house there. You change things as a result of your effort. Now knowledge of a house in that part of town is common—others know about it, too. Knowledge constructed implies the building of new structures, the writing of new stories or accounts, the reassembling of existing knowledge into new forms, and so on. Creativity and originality are keys to knowledge constructed, although the creativity may exist within an already developed pattern. Projects, plays, building, and drawings are examples of knowledge constructed.

Knowledge of this third kind also exists as a social construction. Children working together will talk about what they are doing. They will make decisions, have agreements and disagreements, organize themselves, socialize, reflect, and find themselves linked to something greater than that which exists when people work alone. Thus, a far more subtle kind of knowledge emerges. It is a knowledge of friendship, collaboration, and teamwork. This kind of knowledge must be experienced in order for it to be real. To deny this kind of knowledge to children in the name of teaching social studies would be ironic, to say the very least.

Russian psychologist Lev Vygotsky noted the importance of language and thought as dependent on each other for their development. When children work together on a project, a mural, a play, or a construction activity, they will have the opportunity to express their ideas and feelings during the process. They are engaged in constructing knowledge as they talk and listen to each other. The importance of this can hardly be underestimated. When people express themselves verbally in connection with their involvement in an activity, they have the possibility to reach higher levels of consciousness about what they are doing. They can reflect, decide, evaluate, and employ a range of metacognitive strategies that are not available to the person working alone.

In summary, it is fair to say that all three ways of knowing are strategic and complementary. People simply cannot discover or create everything they need to know, so received knowledge plays a vital role in human development. On the other hand, knowledge received must be balanced with knowledge discovered and constructed. The wise teacher understands the relationship among all three and uses all three. When President Thomas Jefferson sent Lewis and Clark on their three-year expedition to the West of North America, he chose them because they were well read and had received knowledge from multiple sources over the years. He also chose them because he knew they were discoverers, and, indeed, they discovered many plants, animals, rivers, mountain passes, and so on along the way. But Jefferson also knew these expedition leaders would construct new knowledge of the West as a result of their experiences. Their maps, charts, and descriptions created new knowledge of a landscape known well perhaps to certain Native Americans but hardly at all to European Americans. Today, their journal accounts are considered to be one of the great epic stories of the nineteenth century.

A gifted teacher is aware that the well-known journeys of discovery found in text and film are qualitatively no different from the journeys of discovery that his or her students are involved in as they learn about their world and construct both personal and collective meanings of it.

The National Council for the Social Studies Standards as a Guide to the Knowledge Base

The past decade has seen the development of national standards in all the major areas of school curriculum. The standards for social studies were completed under the aegis of the National Council for the Social Studies (NCSS) in 1994. The standards serve as a general framework for the knowledge and experiential basis of social studies. The purpose of the standards is not, as some have feared, to create a national curriculum. Rather, the intent is to establish a sense of direction and a goal structure.

The NCSS notes that the standards should support three intended outcomes. Let's take a look at each of these.

First, the standards should serve as a framework for K–12 social studies program design through the use of 10 thematic strands. As illustrated in Figure 3.1, 10 thematic strands represent broad categories of teaching and learning and are meant to provide only the most general sense of coverage. However, they convey the essence of the spiral curriculum concept of visiting and revisiting a few key ideas from kindergarten through twelfth grade.

The 10 key strands from the NCSS standards represent powerful ideas about human behavior. As you examine them carefully, you will see that they are concept statements

figure **3.1**   *NCSS Standards: Ten Key Strands*

I. Culture

Human beings create, learn, and adapt culture. Human cultures are dynamic systems of beliefs, values, and traditions that exhibit both commonalities and differences. Understanding culture helps us understand ourselves and others.

II. Time, Continuity, and Change

Human beings seek to understand their historic roots and to locate themselves in time. Such understanding involves knowing what things were like in the past and how things change and develop— allowing us to develop historic perspective and answer important questions about our current condition.

III. People, Places, and Environment

Technological advancements have insured that students are aware of the world beyond their personal locations. As students study content related to this theme, they create their spatial views and geographic perspectives of the world; social, cultural, economic, and civic demands mean that students will need such knowledge, skills, and understandings to make informed and critical decisions about the relationship between human beings and their environment.

IV. Individual Development and Identity

Personal identity is shaped by one's culture, by groups and by institutional influences. Examination of various forms of human behavior enhances understanding of the relationships between social norms and emerging personal identities, the social processes which influence identity formation, and the ethical principles underlying individual action.

V. Individuals, Groups, and Institutions

Institutions exert enormous influence over us. Institutions are organizational embodiments to further the core social values of those who comprise them. It is important for students to know how institutions are formed, what controls and influences them, how they control and influence individuals and culture, and how institutions can be maintained or changed.

VI. Power, Authority, and Governance

Understanding of the historic development of structures of power, authority, and governance and their evolving functions in contemporary society is essential for the emergence of civic competence.

VII. Production, Distribution, and Consumption

Decisions about exchange, trade, and economic policy and well-being are global in scope and the role of government in policy making varies over time and from place to place. The systematic study of an interdependent world economy and the role of technology in economic decision making is essential.

VIII. Science, Technology, and Society

Technology is as old as the first crude tool invented by prehistoric humans, and modern life as we know it would be impossible without technology and the science which supports it. Todays technology forms the basis for some of our most difficult social choices.

IX. Global Connections

The realities of global interdependence require understanding of the increasingly important and diverse global connections among world societies before there can be analysis leading to the development of possible solutions to persisting and emerging global issues.

X. Civic Ideals and Practices

All people have a stake in examining civic ideals and practices across time, in diverse societies, as well as in determining how to close the gap between present practices and the ideals upon which our democratic republic is based. An understanding of civic ideals and practices of citizenship is critical to full participation in society.

Source: Expectations of Excellence: Curriculum Standards for Social Studies, Bulletin 89, Fall 1994, Washington, DC: NCSS.

from history, geography, and the social sciences. They are a logical place for you to begin thinking about the spiral curriculum and its potential to build a schema for young learners. These ideas need to be emphasized and reemphasized each year at increasing levels of sophistication. The standards are, in fact, the cornerstone of the social studies goal structure. As you plan lessons, units, and experiences, you should seriously consider them. I would go so far as to say that every social studies experience should relate to one or more of the strands. The point that must be underscored, however, is that the ideas need to be taught and learned in developmentally appropriate ways.

Second, the NCSS standards serve as a guide for curriculum decision making by providing performance expectations regarding knowledge, processes, and attitudes essential for all students. At one level, decisions about what textbooks to adopt, which materials to use, and so on should focus on the knowledge, processes, and attitudes exemplified in the 10 concept statements. The hope is that commercial textbook companies and experimental projects alike will take the standards into account so that a measure of commonality will emerge. This is not to say that every program should look alike, especially in a day of site-based decision making. Rather, the point is that educators can begin to address the fundamental questions of (1) What knowledge of history, geography, and social science should children possess? (2) What skills of critical thinking and problem solving should children attain? and (3) What values of citizenship and self-fulfillment are basic to positive growth and development for children in a democratic society?

Third, the NCSS standards should provide examples of classroom practice to guide teachers in designing instruction to help students meet performance expectations. As you design lessons and units, you will want to take into account the performance expectations implied in the strands. In order to give you a clearer idea of this, Figures 3.2 and 3.3 illustrate at the primary and middle grades, respectively, *performance expectations* (i.e., what should students know and be able to do as a result) and *classroom examples* showing how teachers can bring the NCSS standards to life.

What Should Children Know?

The years that have marked the bridge between the closing of the twentieth century and the opening of the twenty-first century have been a time of great contention over the knowledge base that children ought to possess, not just in social studies but in all content areas. Part of the problem is the sheer explosion of the base itself; today, there is more to know than ever before. Another aspect of the problem is the fundamental transformation in the ways in which knowledge is stored, received, and made available. This is particularly an issue with regard to the advent of video, computer technologies, and electronic databases. The book, which has been the staple of knowledge stored, is being challenged by the new technologies, and no one knows for sure what it all means. One thing is certain, however: We are witnessing a return of graphic and pictorial forms (which were dominant in centuries past) to a world of education that has been dominated by print.

Who has the better sense of the events surrounding the American Revolution: the child who has read the book *Johnny Tremain* or the child who has seen the film? Who knows more about city government: the child who has read the text or the child who

figure **3.2**   *Standard VII: Production, Distribution,*
and Consumption—Primary Grades

Social studies programs should include experiences that provide for the study of *how people organize for the production, distribution, and consumption of goods and services,* so that the learner can:

Performance Expectations
a. give examples that show how scarcity and choice govern our economic decisions;
b. distinguish between needs and wants;
c. identify examples of private and public goods and services;
d. give examples of the various institutions that make up economic systems such as families, workers, banks, labor unions, government agencies, small businesses, and large corporations;
e. describe how we depend upon workers with specialized jobs and the ways in which they contribute to the production and exchange of goods and services;
f. describe the influence of incentives, values, traditions, and habits on economic decisions;
g. explain and demonstrate the role of money in everyday life;
h. describe the relationship of price to supply and demand;
i. use economic concepts such as supply, demand, and price to help explain events in the community and nation;
j. apply knowledge of economic concepts in developing a response to a current local economic issue, such as how to reduce the flow of trash into a rapidly filling landfill.

Focus on the Classroom: Standards into Practice

Performance Expectations: e, i

At the beginning of a unit on economic specialization in production, Mark Moran's early primary class is divided into two teams of cookie makers. Both teams make gingerbread cookies. One team works as an assembly line, each person having a special job—rolling out the dough, cutting the basic shape, making the almond mouth, locating raisin buttons, etc. The second team works as individuals, each person creating his or her own gingerbread cookies. Both teams have the same supplies to work with.

After they have finished baking their cookies, the students examine the cookies and identify the advantages and disadvantages of each method of producing cookies. Ideas that emerge relate to division of labor, pride, creativity, independence, specialization, and quality control.

Students subsequently prepare summaries in writing about how they produced their cookies. Moran evaluates the quality of the student writing by determining how accurate the students are in detailing the production process and the extent to which evidence of key concepts is present.

In the weeks that follow this lesson, students examine other situations involving assembly line production, including a field trip to a local plant where pickup trucks are assembled.

Source: From *Expectations of Excellence: Curriculum Standards for Social Studies* (p. 65), Bulletin 89, Fall 1994, Washington, DC: NCSS. © National Council for the Social Studies. Reprinted by permission.

figure **3.3**   *Standard I: Culture—Middle Grades*

Social studies programs should include experiences that provide for the study of *culture and cultural diversity,* so that the learner can:

Performance Expectations
a. compare similarities and differences in the ways groups, societies, and cultures meet human needs and concerns;
b. explain how information and experiences may be interpreted by people from diverse cultural perspectives and frames of reference;
c. explain and give examples of how language, literature, the arts, architecture, other artifacts, traditions, beliefs, values, and behaviors contribute to the development and transmission of culture;
d. explain why individuals and groups respond differently to their physical and social environments and/or changes to them on the basis of shared assumptions, values, and beliefs;
e. articulate the implications of cultural diversity, as well as cohesion, within and across groups.

Focus on the Classroom: Standards into Practice
Performance Expectations: a, c, d, e
The fifth grade students in Rose Sudmeier's class are sharing the stories behind their names in small groups. In constructing a "native culture" in their classroom, they have studied the place/environment, including descriptions, vocabulary development, visual presentations, and survival in the environment. This process led to a look at the people living in that place. They are now talking about naming traditions in general and how they came to be named.

The class researches the tools, food, and other survival necessities that would be needed in their place. They then begin to discuss what the people might do at night when it was dark or during the day when work was done and how traditions, such as the naming tradition, might be passed on. At this point, Sudmeier brings in her colleague, Dave Trowbridge, and his geography class from the high school, which has been studying traditions, storytelling, art, and music of the Northwest Coastal Indian tribes.

The high school students visit the fifth grade class on two different days, showing the elementary students how to do basic dance steps and how to make dancing masks. They also tell them stories of various legends and play musical tapes. The fifth graders continue their study for another three days on their own. The high school students plan a return visit for the end of the week, when they also invite the fifth graders to be their guests in a potlatch. At the potlatch, the high schoolers entertain the fifth graders with stories and then have them join them in dances and use the masks they had shown them how to make. In keeping with the potlatch tradition, the guests receive small gifts from the high school students at the end.

As an evaluation tool, Sudmeier has the children keep journals in which they write about their culture, traditions they started, poetry they wrote about their environment, and reflections on their participation in the various activities. She looks for the journals to be thoughtfully written, expressing positive views, accurate in the information presented, creative, and reflective.

Source: From *Expectations of Excellence: Curriculum Standards for Social Studies* (p. 79), Bulletin 89, Fall 1994, Washington, DC: NCSS. © National Council for the Social Studies. Reprinted by permission.

has played the simulation *Sim City*? Who knows more about the U.S. space program: the child who has read several books on its history or the child who uses the Internet and World Wide Web to access the daily activities of NASA? I don't think these are trivial questions. Of course, the easy answer to each one is that teachers want children to access knowledge through multiple sources and experiences.

Setting aside for now *how* someone gains knowledge of history, geography, government, and so forth, let's return to the question of what a child completing elementary school ought to know. A number of prominent educators have addressed this question, most notably philosopher Mortimer Adler in his book *The Paideia Proposal* (1982), and professor of English E. D. Hirsch Jr. in his book *Cultural Literacy* (1987). I recommend that you examine both books, and because Hirsch went a step further with his *Core Knowledge Series,* books that define a knowledge base for elementary children in all disciplines, you might want to look more deeply into his work. *The Core Knowledge Series K–8* (Hirsch, 1991–2005) develops content material for the social studies under the headings of Geography, World Civilization, and American Civilization. Other sources exist, certainly, but for the serious seeker of a knowledge base in elementary social studies, Hirsch's materials are probably the best place to start. In fact, it would be beneficial to you to compare Hirsch's *Core Knowledge Series* with the contents of textbooks available from publishers such as Scott-Foresman, Macmillan, McGraw-Hill, Harcourt, and so on.

This is not the place to attempt to document everything children should know based on the social studies experience. However, I will attempt to give the flavor of such a quest—in this case, a list of the historical fiction that children should have read or have had read to them about one period in American history (late colonial to Revolutionary America, 1685–1785) by the time they finish the elementary school years, which was developed for the NCSS in the mid-1990s (see Figure 3.4). Consider what titles might be added today. This is not to say, however, that other books of high quality pertaining to that time period should not also be read. Part of the problem with making lists is the predictable possibility that others might disagree. Welcome to democracy!

Thus far, we have considered the broad guidelines of the NCSS curriculum standards as well as the knowledge base and a recommendation to research Adler's and Hirsch's viewpoints on such. The final portion of this chapter is devoted to an examination of the basic structure of history, geography, and the social science disciplines. These are the knowledge-generating scholarly disciplines from which social studies subject matter is derived.

The Social Science Disciplines

The social science disciplines of anthropology, economics, geography, history, sociology, and political science form the foundation of the elementary social studies curriculum. The social sciences are those areas of scholarly inquiry that focus in a systematic way on the study of human behavior. Social studies is that area of the elementary school curriculum that focuses on the activities of human beings.

A background in the social sciences is vital, because one task you face as a social studies teacher is to present social science to young learners in a meaningful way. Social studies is, of course, more than simplified social science. It is, above all, about the

figure 3.4 *Recommended Books on the Late Colonial and American Revolutionary Periods (1685–1785)*

Avi	*The Fighting Ground*
	Night Journeys
Caudill, Rebecca	*The Far-Off Land*
Clapp, Patricia	*I'm Deborah Sampson: A Soldier in the War of the Revolution*
	Witches' Children: A Story of Salem
Collier, James Lincoln,	*Jump Ship to Freedom*
and Collier, Christopher	*My Brother Sam Is Dead*
	War Comes to Willy Freeman
Forbes, Esther	*Johnny Tremain*
Fritz, Jean	*The Cabin Faced West*
	Will You Sign Here, John Hancock?
Gauch, Patricia	*This Time, Tempe Wick?*
Lasky, Kathryn	*Beyond the Burning Time*
Lawson, Robert	*Ben and Me*
	Mr. Revere and I
Monjo, F. N.	*King George's Head Was Made of Lead*
O'Dell, Scott	*Sarah Bishop*
Petry, Ann	*Tituba of Salem Village*
Rinaldi, Ann	*A Break with Charity: A Story about the Salem Witch Trials*
	The Fifth March: A Story of the Boston Massacre
Speare, Elizabeth George	*The Sign of the Beaver*
	The Witch of Blackbird Pond

Source: Adapted from Judith Irvin, John Lunstrum, Carol Lynch-Brown, and Mary Friend Shepard, *Enhancing Social Studies through Literacy Strategies,* Bulletin 91, 1995, Washington, DC: NCSS.

students themselves—their present needs, their possible futures, and their growing awareness of themselves and others around them. But the methods and ideas of social science can and should contribute to the intellectual and social growth of students.

Anthropology

WHAT IS ANTHROPOLOGY?   Anthropology has been characterized as the study of culture or the scientific study of human beings. Such a definition is obviously rather broad in scope and hardly serves to distinguish it from other social sciences. Oliver (1964) writes:

> Anthropologists occasionally cast their glance over Western Civilization, but they are mainly concerned with the history of "historyless" peoples, with the economics of communities without price-fixing market institutions, with government and politics in "stateless" societies, with social relations in places where kinship usually outweighs occupation, with the psychology of non-Westerners, with the anatomy and physiology of the whole range of mankind and its primate relatives. (p. xii)

Thus, anthropologists incorporate elements of behavior, economics, political science, sociology, psychology, and other social sciences into their investigations. Although some anthropologists focus on Western and other technologically advanced societies—particularly on such aspects of those societies as education, vocations, religion, and families—such investigations are usually considered to be in the domain of the sociologist. The anthropologist is more commonly identified with studies of the cultural norms of so-called preliterate and emerging societies.

WHAT DO ANTHROPOLOGISTS DO? Anthropologists study cultures. They develop case histories of various tribal and ethnic groups, as well as descriptive accounts of the mores and patterns of different groups. Their data sources include the writings of previous investigators, plus artifacts, informants, and eyewitness accounts. Because their concern is with the concept of culture, anthropologists are generally interested in developing a total, interrelated picture of a society rather than in dealing exclusively with its economic patterns, power structure, or any other facet of that society's existence. In this respect, anthropology has been termed an *integrative science.*

Anthropologists investigate cultures using one or more of the following methods:

1. *Indirect observation.* Anthropologists pursuing indirect observation use maps, census data, the writings of previous investigators, the examination of artifacts, and interviews with informants. Indirect observation is useful for developing historical accounts of cultures and validating information obtained by other methods.

2. *Direct observation.* Anthropologists using direct observation spend time with their subjects, observing them and taking notes as they go about the business of living their lives. This method uses such tools as the camera, tape recorder, and field notebook.

3. *Participant observation.* Participant observation also depends on the investigator spending time with subjects. However, participant observers make an attempt to join their group and thereby become as inconspicuous as possible. The participant investigator often attempts to learn the language and customs of a group in order to gain some degree of acceptance. This approach was used rather effectively by an investigator who actually married the chief of a tribal group during the course of her work in Indonesia.

SELECTED ANTHROPOLOGICAL CONCEPTS Certain terms and ideas can help define the conceptual structure of anthropology.*

- *Acculturation.* The changes resulting when two cultures make contact with one another (e.g., the changes in European and Native American societies following the voyages of Columbus).
- *Artifacts.* Objects produced by human beings, as opposed to natural objects. Artifacts provide clues to a group's values, economic system, technological orientation, and so forth.
- *Culture.* The personality or way of life of a group of human beings; the particular set of characteristics that unify a group and make it distinguishable from other

*Selected social science concepts appearing throughout this chapter are adapted from *Selected Learner Outcomes for Social Studies* (St. Paul, MN: Minnesota State Department of Education, 1981, 1986).

groups. The attributes of culture include language, technology, religion, food, clothing, shelter, traditions, and ideas.

- *Diffusion.* The flow of ideas, traits, and tools from one culture to another. Racial characteristics, for example, are diffused as one culture marries into and mingles with another.
- *Enculturation.* Those learning experiences a person has as a result of his or her culture. The home and school are agents of enculturation.
- *Innovation.* The introduction of new ideas, traits, and tools into a culture as a result of invention, discovery, or diffusion.
- *Personality.* Traits, behaviors, and habits a person acquires as a result of membership in and interaction with a particular culture.
- *Role.* The status of a member of a particular culture and the resulting behavior exhibited by or expected of that person in a given situation.
- *Traditions.* Customs and beliefs of a culture that are transmitted from one generation to succeeding generations.

Keys to Anthropology

- All people have universal cultural traits, including the following:

  Language
  Technology
  Social organization
  Political organization
  Moral and legal sanctions
  Religion or philosophy
  Creative activities—art, music, dance...
  Ways of resolving differences

  Methods of protection
  Leisure activities
  Methods of education or enculturation

- All elements of culture, whether explicit or implicit, are integrated.
- A change in one aspect of culture influences the total pattern of culture.
- Cultural change may occur by diffusion, invention, and innovation.

Economics

WHAT IS ECONOMICS?   Economics focuses on the production and consumption of goods and services. Economists are concerned with human and material resources. Calderwood, Lawrence, and Maher (1970) write:

> Economics is concerned with all of society and with the activities of the various groups and institutions it contains—consumers, businessmen, farmers, workers, savers, investors, corporations, and federal, state, and local government. It is a social science.
>
> Economics is concerned not only with the individual parts of our economy—the consumer, the business, the union, and the market for a particular product (which we call microeconomics)—but also with the sum of these parts that together constitute the economic system of a country; that is, how the individual parts relate to form a whole. Economics is also concerned with the functioning of the economy, with how fast it is growing, and how vulnerable it is to inflation or depression (which we call macroeconomics). (p. 4)

Maher (1969) defines *economics* in terms of the basic economic concept of scarcity of resources and the attendant problems of their allocation:

> Ever since the spell of abundance was broken in the Garden of Eden, individuals and nations alike have confronted the fact of scarcity. It is for this reason that there are economic problems and an economic science. Scarcity means that there are not enough of the goods and services around to satisfy human wants. These goods and services are scarce because the materials from which they are made are insufficient. Thus, there is scarcity of both the resources used in production—land, machinery, equipment, and labor—and the final products into which these resources are transformed. Because of scarcity, there is a need to use to best advantage both the resources and the things produced—to economize. Economics is the science of economizing. (p. 1)

WHAT DO ECONOMISTS DO?   Economists analyze the use of various resources. Their analyses are designed to deal with the problems arising due to the scarcity of material and technical resources. Such analyses result in recommendations regarding the kinds of choices that ought to be made in order to optimize the production and consumption of goods and services. Choices must be made among alternatives, whether those choices involve buying a bracelet versus going to a movie, going to Disney World versus paneling the family room, or spending government money for foreign aid versus spending it for domestic vocational education. Economists attempt to clarify and define objectives for persons, families, and nations in order to make them better able to understand the consequences of various uses of resources. Maher (1969) provides a simple example of an economic analysis of a situation:

> The land in a pea patch together with the farmer's labor, his shovel, his hoe, and some seed are *resources.* (Sunshine and rain are resources too, but the farmer has little control over them nor does he pay to use them.) Next, the *production* process includes plowing, planting, weeding, and harvesting the peas. The *output,* of course, is the peas—if everything has gone well. But a bushel of peas is not the end of the whole activity. Rather, the satisfaction of hunger is the objective. For this satisfaction to take place, another process intervenes, namely, the process of *consumption.* When the peas are consumed, the *objective* is satisfied. (p. 1)

The economist is faced with analytical questions regarding the allocation of resources. This abiding problem of deciding how best to use resources faces all types of economic systems: barter, capitalist, communist, socialist, and so forth. Calderwood and associates (1970) illustrate the analytical questions facing the economist:

1. How shall the economy use (allocate) its productive resources to supply the wants of its people? In commonsense terms, *what* shall be produced and *how?*
2. How fast shall the economy grow, and how shall it obtain reasonably stable growth, avoiding both depression and inflation? In other words, *how much* shall be produced in total, and how many resources shall be devoted to increasing future capacity rather than to producing goods for current consumption?
3. How shall the economy distribute money incomes, and through them the goods and services it produces, to the individual members and groups in society? For whom shall the goods be produced?

SELECTED ECONOMIC CONCEPTS   These are the basic concepts that underlie the field of economics.

- *Allocation of goods and services.* *Goods* are materials produced for consumption, and s*ervices* are skills or abilities sold to consumers. Different methods can be used to allocate goods and services. People acting individually and collectively through government must choose which methods to use to allocate goods and services. Related concepts include *supply* and *demand.*

- *Consumer.* A person or group that uses goods and services.

- *Corporation.* A company in which people invest money and share profits and losses.

- *Cost/benefit ratio.* Effective decision making in economics requires comparing the cost of doing something with the benefit derived from the same action. Most choices involve doing a little more or a little less; few choices are all or nothing.

- *Division of labor.* Assigning specific tasks to workers so each does a part of a total job.

- *Gain from trade.* Voluntary exchange occurs only when all participants expect to gain. *Trade* refers to the exchange of goods, services, and money that occurs among individuals or organizations within a nation, individuals or organizations in different nations, or between nations themselves. Related concepts include *exports, imports, barter,* and *tariffs.*

- *Incentives.* People respond predictably to positive and negative incentives, or rewards and punishments.

- *Producer.* The person or company that manufactures or creates a product.

- *Profit.* The net income derived from the sale of goods and services.

- *Scarcity.* Productive resources are limited; therefore, people cannot always have all the goods and services they want. Instead, they must choose some things and give up others.

- *Supply and demand.* *Supply* is the amount of goods and services available for consumption; *demand* is the need for and ability to purchase goods and services. The balance between these two forces at any give time influences prices and ultimately the stability of an economy.

Keys to Economics

- The individual plays three roles in economic life: worker, consumer, and citizen.
- The general social/political/economic environment affects the individual's economic opportunities and well-being.

- An individual's economic choices and behaviors may affect the system as a whole.
- The market system is the basic institutional arrangement through which production and distribution of goods and services are determined in a free economy.

Geography

WHAT IS GEOGRAPHY?   Like anthropology, geography is a broad and integrative discipline. Its basic concepts are concepts of space. Greco (1966) writes that geography

> is not defined by subject matter but its method or the way it looks at things. . . . Geography, as a chorological or spatial science, strives for an architecture of description in segments of space or areas. . . . It is a synthetic areal science which utilizes the ecological aspects of all the systematic sciences—physics, biotic, or societal. . . . Explaining area differentiation is the quest of the geographer. Space, the chorology of phenomena, is his principal concern. (p. 3)

In addition to their basic concern for describing space, geographers focus on the dynamics and interactions of variables at a particular place. Harper and Schmudde (1973) provide insight into the concept of an interconnected system:

> Four variables should provide us with a basic understanding of life at any place, if we know how to relate them. They are (1) the operation of the earth environment, (2) the culture or cultures of the people living there, (3) the technological know-how possessed by the group, and (4) the ties between the people at that place and those in other areas. These are the components, or variables, with which geographers commonly work. If we are to learn to think geographically, we need to analyze each of the components and understand why they vary from place to place. (p. 56)

Harper and Schmudde stress further the importance of recognizing the relationships among the four components cited, rather than dealing with each of them in isolation. Thus, a case is made for viewing geography and geographic inquiry from a conceptual perspective—destroying the outmoded, stereotyped view of geography as a study of isolated subjects such as landforms, capital cities, and crops.

A young geographer puts the finishing touches on her map of the school grounds.

WHAT DO GEOGRAPHERS DO? Geographers develop descriptions of regions or places and investigate special topics involving spatial interactions. The two major types of inquiry that geographers pursue involve regions of the world, such as the Amazon rain forest and the Pacific Northwest of the United States, and special topics, such as migration patterns and urban settlement.

Geographic methods include analyzing existing maps; developing new maps (see Figure 3.5), graphs, and charts; interpreting aerial and other photographs; using statistical techniques to analyze data; and developing descriptions of places or phenomena.

figure **3.5**   *A Child's Perspective: Map of Shelton View Elementary School*

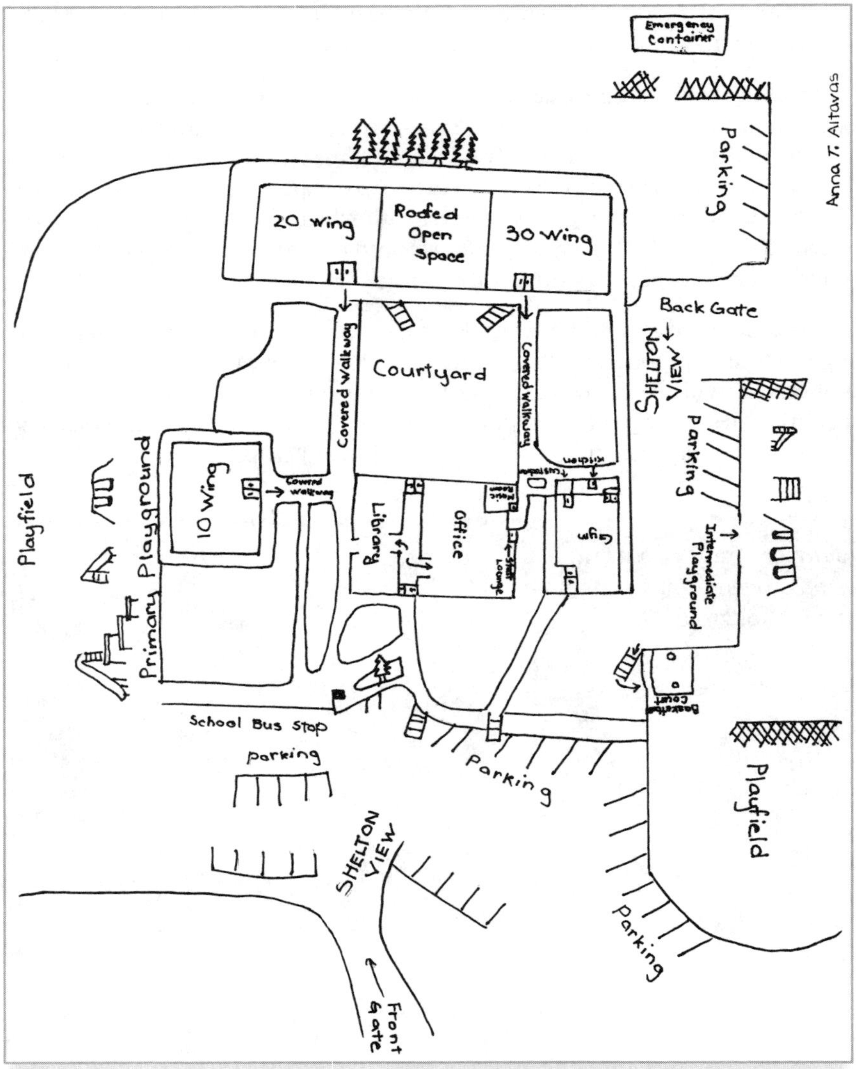

SELECTED GEOGRAPHIC CONCEPTS   These selected terms and ideas help form the conceptual structure of geography.

- *Areal association.* The relationship of phenomena on the earth's surface to one another, such as the relationship among soil, climate, and vegetation in a particular place.
- *Central place.* The focal point of a region. The central place of a region contains the specializations and services necessary to the function of that region. For example, Omaha, Nebraska, serves as a central place for the surrounding cattle country of that region.
- *Region.* An area on the earth's surface that has common properties—such as topography, climate, and soils—and that is bound together by a common focus in a particular central place. For example, the region of the Pacific Southwest has its focus in Phoenix, Arizona.
- *Situation.* The location of a place in relation to other places and the degree to which those other places are accessible. Thus, the situation of a particular place may change with the building of a railroad or with new developments in air transportation. A city such as Seattle, Washington, is in a more favorable trade situation now than it was 30 years ago. Its specific location on the earth's surface is unchanged, but the development of more efficient transportation systems makes it more accessible to Japanese as well as East Coast markets.
- *Spatial interaction.* The functional relationship between and among phenomena in a particular place. For example, textiles may be manufactured where cotton, water sources, a population of workers, and transportation networks for shipping are all available.

Keys to Geography

- Location of people and economic activities are influenced by external factors and internal value choices.
- Environmental conditions place restrictions on cultural choices.
- Nature and culture are interlocking components of the ecosystem.
- Movement of cultures from subsistent economies and self-sufficient communities toward surplus-oriented, interdependent cultures means an increased technology, trade, migration, and communication network.
- Highly specialized and specifically adapted livelihood forms have limited potential for cultural change. (Nomadic pastoralism and hunting societies are becoming extinct.)

History

WHAT IS HISTORY?   Of all the sciences that focus on human behavior, history is perhaps the broadest in scope. In fact, because its subject matter encompasses past events (and current events as they unfold and rapidly become history) in all areas of human endeavor, there is the persistent question of whether history is a science or merely a collection of stories of the past and the unfolding present. If one benchmark of a scientific endeavor is predictive capability, then history certainly does not qualify as a science to the same extent that economics or psychology does. Krug (1967) writes:

> History is concerned with the totality of human experience, past and present. . . . It is past politics, past economics, past science, past society, past religion, past civilization— in short, past everything. . . . History written today records not only the story of kings, rulers, wars, and conquests, but also how men grew wheat and corn, how they sold their wares, built their homes, worshiped their gods, and how they lived and how they died. It is because of its concern with the totality of human experience that history, unlike many of the social sciences, has loosely defined boundaries. (p. 4)

Expanding on this view, Ward (1971) notes:

> History in its original meaning, everyone agrees, is inquiry. . . . History is inquiry into myths and folk stories that grandmothers tell. It is inquiry to find truer explanations for existing institutions and situations. It is also inquiry for the sake of inquiry, for mankind is a very interesting phenomenon. All in all, history is inquiry into the heritage and burden that society would lay on us, an inquiry that frees us to select and learn from it. (p. 30)

An obvious point of distinction between history and the other social sciences lies in the primary focus of historical studies on the past, a concern that plays only a supportive role in the other social sciences. On the other hand, history shares with the other social sciences the function of seeking explanations of human interactions as they are exemplified by institutions and situations through processes of inquiry. Collingwood (1946) lists four characteristics of history that could well be applied to other social sciences:

1. that it is scientific, or begins by knowing something and tells what it knows.
2. that it is humanistic, or asks questions about things done by men at determinate times in the past.
3. that it is rational, or bases the answers which it gives on grounds, namely, appeal to evidence.
4. that it is self-revelatory, or exists in order to tell man what man is by telling him what man has done. (p. 18)

WHAT DO HISTORIANS DO?   Historians pose questions about human interaction in current and past events, seek appropriate sources of data, and attempt to develop explanations and inferences to answer those questions. Krug (1967) writes that "a historian starts his inquiry basically with three questions: 'What happened? How did it happen? Why did it happen?'" (p. 5) Such questions could, for example, serve as a guide to historical inquiry into the clashes between the executive and legislative branches of government during the Watergate inquiry.

Historians seek sources of data in a variety of places: museums, libraries, repositories, attics, archives, film depositories, and, of course, the field, where they may search for and use documents and other artifacts. Historical data consist of letters, paintings, photographs, films, charters, compacts, census tracts, financial records, household utensils, weaponry, statuaries, literature, people—there is an endless and ever growing supply of sources. Unfortunately, historians have less control over the situations they investigate than psychologists, for example. As a result, the data sources that are preserved and located often seem to be available on a random basis. Historians work with sources they can locate, which means that priceless sources of data are often irretrievably lost or destroyed.

Keys to History

- Change has been a universal characteristic of all human societies.
- A knowledge of the past is necessary to understand present and future events.
- No historical events have resulted from a single cause.
- The leadership of certain individuals has had a profound influence on the course of history.
- Interpretations of the past are constantly changing as new data and trends result in altered perspectives.

Sociology

WHAT IS SOCIOLOGY?   Sociology is the study of groups and the subsequent norms of behavior that human beings exhibit as a result of their group memberships. Thus, the subject matter of sociology consists of such groups as the family, the ethnic group, the tribe or band, the society, and the nation. The subject matter of sociology also focuses on groups within larger groups—for example, suburban dwellers, business executives, migrant workers, communal groups, heads of households, or drug users.

The subject matter of sociology traditionally has been found in complex, modern, industrial societies. This distinguishes it from the subject matter of anthropology, which is often identified with preliterate cultures. Both sociology and anthropology are specialized branches of the same science, however (Rose, 1965).

Sociology involves more than the mere description of groups and their resultant norms of behavior. It also involves the examination and analysis of changes that occur in group structures (e.g., changing patterns in family structures) and a study of the relationships that exist among group members and among groups (Rose, 1965). Group behaviors, called *norms,* are, as Perrucci (1966) writes, clues to "the things that people invest emotional interest in—things they want, desire, consider as important, desire to become, and enjoy" (p. 3).

The effects of groups on individual behavior—processes of socialization as exemplified by speech patterns, clothing styles, choices of food, recreation, for example— are of special interest to the sociologist. Kinch (1971) writes: "An individual is not born with a culture; he must acquire it through a process called *socialization.* In studying sociology, sociologists look at the significant points of contact between the individual and his society and the mechanisms by which he learns or acquires his culture" (p. 3).

WHAT DO SOCIOLOGISTS DO?   Sociologists spend their time studying groups. They ask analytical questions about groups and group behavior that can be answered through data gathering. The sociologist gathers data through means similar to those employed by the anthropologist: direct observation, indirect observation, interviews, and examination of the writings of other social scientists. In addition, sociological research has made extensive use of the questionnaire as a data-gathering instrument. Like other social scientists, the sociologist poses researchable questions, hypothesizes, selects appropriate sources of data, gathers and processes the data, and makes inferences or statements about the data.

SELECTED SOCIOLOGICAL CONCEPTS   Here are a few selected terms and basic ideas from sociology.

- *Integrated group.* A group in which members interact and communicate with one another and in which positions of dominance and hierarchy are established—such as a family, club, or classroom.
- *Nonintegrated group.* A group in which members are basically interchangeable with one another and in which lines of communication and interaction are not clearly established. A group of people waiting in line for the theater or a group of people shopping in a store are examples.
- *Norms.* Generalizable (to most members of any given group) patterns of behavior. Norms may be found in clothes, food, and shelter, for example.
- *Socialization.* Those things that happen to an individual as a result of his or her contacts with society and the influences that society has on the life of that individual.
- *Values.* Those beliefs that people internalize and act on as a result of their group experiences—for example, success, punctuality, generosity, and frugality.

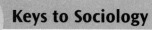

Keys to Sociology

- Norms define the boundaries of social interaction.
- Differentiation of social roles is based on sex, age, kinship, and occupation.
- Complex, technological societies tend toward greater stratification.
- Social interaction involves cooperation, conflict, assimilation, and accommodation.

- Each society develops institutions to aid the socialization of its members.
- Socialization is the process by which the individual becomes a functioning member of society.
- Human survival depends on living in groups.

Political Science

WHAT IS POLITICAL SCIENCE?   Like the other social sciences, political science has no clear-cut, one-sentence definition. However, a central focus of political science is on governing processes and the power structure found in those governing processes. As the name implies, political science involves the study of human behavior as it relates to political systems, governments, laws, and international relations. Easton (1966) writes:

> In defining political science, we are seeking concepts to describe the most obvious and encompassing properties of the phenomena we wish to describe. The idea of a *political system* proves to be an appropriate and indeed unavoidable starting point in this search. Certain kinds of activity are more prominently associated with political life than others; for example, governmental organizations, pressure groups, voting, and parties. They are, of course, part of the whole social process and, therefore, they are also relevant to systems other than political. Recurrent relationships among parts of the system suggest that the elements of political life have some form of determinate relationships. The task of research is to discover what they are. (p. 1)

Thus, Easton argues that an emphasis should be placed on systems, which means essentially that the political sphere is an interrelated, dynamic set of interactions among people and the power that they exercise or that is exercised on them.

The systems approach to political science provides a rather comprehensive definition of the discipline; other definitions are more restrictive. Watkins (1960) writes: "The proper study of political science is not the study of the state or of any other specific institutional complex, but the investigation of all associations insofar as they can be shown to exemplify the problem of power" (p. 140). Although such a definition highlights the key political science concept of *power* and is useful in that regard, it fails to distinguish with any great degree of clarity between political science and other social sciences such as anthropology, sociology, and history, all of which are concerned with power. However, it does supplement Easton's (1966) definition, because power serves as the organizing concept in a dynamic political system.

WHAT DO POLITICAL SCIENTISTS DO?   Political scientists attempt to determine the existence of and analyze the relationships among the people and institutions that make up political systems. Senn offers two methods by which political scientists derive explanations for human behavior in political systems: explanations by purpose or intention and probability explanations. A statement of the basic premises of these two methods is excerpted here from Senn's (1971) book *Social Science and Its Methods*:

> *Explanation by purpose or intention.* This method explains in terms of aims, plans, goals, or intentions. Whenever human beings are studied, the social scientist must take into account the fact that they have wills and change their future.
>
> Social scientists know that whenever human behavior must be explained, either in terms of the individual or in terms of groups, the plans, intentions, and goals of

individuals themselves must be taken into account. We call this explanation by purpose.

Explanation by purpose is commonly used in two situations. First, a social scientist may ask a person what his purposes or intentions are or were when the purpose of the action the social scientist is attempting to explain is not clear. . . . Secondly, this kind of explanation is sought when the social scientist is ignorant of the connections between the actions of the group and the goals of the individual.

Probabilistic explanation. Probabilistic explanations occur when a social scientist says, "If a country is attacked, it is likely that it will defend itself." . . . Probabilistic explanations use terms of probability, not certainty, and the degree to which the premises follow is sometimes called the degree of confidence, and is sometimes given as a percentage.

Example: three out of four first voters select a candidate from the same party supported by their parents. . . . Therefore, we can conclude that the chances are three out of four that John (a first-time voter) will vote Democratic as his parents did. (pp. 145–154)

Political scientists are interested in more than the mere description of human behavior in response to political systems. Although they may attempt to develop an accurate description of human behavior—for example, voting patterns in an off-year election—such a description may serve as a prelude to the development of explanations of the purposes or intentions of voters in voting the way they did. This information could well be translated into a prediction of how voters, given certain profiles, might vote in future elections.

SELECTED POLITICAL SCIENCE CONCEPTS   Here are a few selected terms and basic ideas from political science.

- *Authority.* The binding powers held by persons and/or laws over other persons. In a democracy, persons in a position of authority are either elected or appointed by elected officials and are therefore ultimately responsible to the people.
- *Government.* The officials, laws, and institutions that are responsible for maintaining social control and functions in a society.
- *Power.* Influence held by individuals or groups over others. Persons holding power in a democratic society are bound by existing laws and the right of voters to recall such laws. Within these constraints, persons holding positions of power may determine the behavior of others. For example, Congress exercised its constitutional power in passing legislation reducing highway speed limits to 55 miles per hour and more recently raising them to 65 miles per hour and higher. The executive branch exercises power by enforcing such a law.
- *Political system.* The set of interactions among persons, institutions, processes, and traditions by which a society is governed, or "a set of interactions, abstracted from the totality of social behavior, through which valued things are authoritatively allocated for a society" (Easton, 1966, p. 5).

Keys to Political Science

- The study of politics and government includes the study of the institution of government and how individuals behave as citizens.
- Democracy is government in which the decision making is in the hands of the people, who make their demands known through voting, political parties, and pressure groups.

- Democracy seeks to protect the rights of individuals and minority groups, although its actions are based on majority opinion.
- Citizenship in a democracy is the exercise of duties, responsibilities, and privileges, as a reasoned and functional act of political behavior.
- Political systems exist to make binding authoritative decisions for all citizens.

Criteria for Successful Current Events Sessions

Obviously, no set of suggestions is going to give you the perfect news period or current events session. You need to examine the following suggestions and decide for yourself how and to what extent they meet the needs of your unique situation. My purpose is to give you some general guidelines, which you and your students may find helpful as you strive to improve this important facet of the social studies curriculum.

DETERMINING WHETHER NEWS IS IMPORTANT A basic question to consider in selecting a news item for reporting and analysis is the following: To what extent is the news story of lasting importance? Sensational events, such as vehicle accidents and bizarre crimes, may be given considerable attention by the press and capture the fancy of a child looking for something to report on Monday morning, but these are often not items of lasting importance and generally do not provide material for analysis by students. This is not to say that such topical events should never be reported. Rather, it is to say that students should learn not to be misled about what is newsworthy. Here are two strategies designed to help students consider the ultimate newsworthiness of items from the newspaper:

1. Select a newspaper from several years ago. You can probably borrow a copy from a library. Have the students list some headlines you have selected from the newspaper in order of their size. The largest headline is number 1, the second largest is number 2, and so on. Then let small groups (or the entire class) list the headlines in the order of their importance today (in the students' opinion). Figure 3.6 illustrates this procedure. Examine the figure and do your own ranking.

2. Select a current newspaper and let students predict which stories will be of importance 1 year from now, 5 years from now, and 100 years from now.

figure **3.6**   *Newspaper Headlines to Be Ranked*

Mets Take Division Lead
With Win Over Washington

Chinese Bid for
U.S. Oil Giant

Stuffing Kids With TV
Ads for Fatty Foods

Illiteracy in America

Thieves Get
Another Picasso

Supreme Court Justice Resigns

Tonight's TV Listings

Of course, the newspaper is only one source of news. These strategies could be applied to radio, television, and online newscasts as an independent investigation for intermediate-age students.

SEPARATING FACTS FROM OPINIONS   Whether disseminated by the Internet, newspapers, magazines, television, radio, or word of mouth, news contains both factual and opinion-oriented information. Most newspapers attempt to separate factual news from such opinion-oriented items as editorials and letters to the editor. However, rather than assume students know that (or even that it is true, for that matter), let students apply simple content analyses to articles and arrive at their own decisions as to whether articles are fact or opinion oriented.

Figure 3.7 is a letter typical of the mixtures of fact and opinion one finds in the newspaper. Can you tell fact from opinion? Use the Content Analysis Guide below the letter to review each statement.

CONSIDERING OTHER PERSPECTIVES   Earlier, chronological perspective was alluded to as a measure of how important a news item might be. Cultural, attitudinal, and/or geographical perspectives are also worth noting. For example, a college newspaper's report on a campus demonstration might be very different from the portrayal of the same event by a city newspaper. Papers from different regions of the United States may have different editorial opinions and different ways of reporting events. You can and should occasionally order newspapers from other cities around the country.

Also, other nations often see news of the United States from a different perspective. I recall talking to a man who returned to the United States from Europe during the

figure **3.7** *A Letter to the Editor*

To the Editor: Last Saturday a protest march was held on the Village Green. The newspapers and television reported that more than 2,000 people took part in the protest. I wasn't one of them. The people who do this kind of thing are bums. They shouldn't be allowed to live in our country. No arrests were made. A police captain was quoted as saying it was a peaceful demonstration. Well, we are sick and tired of people with beards carrying signs. The police should have put them in jail.

F. D. Jones
Midville

Take the following test. Put an *F* in front of each sentence you think is probably factual and an *O* in front of each sentence you think is probably the writer's opinion.

Content Analysis Guide

_____**1.** Last Saturday a protest march was held on the Village Green.
_____**2.** The newspapers and television reported that more than 2,000 people took part in the protest.
_____**3.** I wasn't one of them.
_____**4.** The people who do this kind of thing are bums.
_____**5.** They shouldn't be allowed to live in our country.
_____**6.** No arrests were made.
_____**7.** A police captain was quoted as saying it was a peaceful demonstration.
_____**8.** Well, we are sick and tired of people with beards carrying signs.
_____**9.** The police should have put them in jail.

Here is how I marked them. You may or may not agree, but your reasons for a response are crucial. (1) Fact; this could be verified. (2) Fact; the numbers could be wrong, but I assume the writer is right. (3) Fact; I take the writer's word for it. (4) Opinion; this is a sweeping inference. The writer uses an emotion-laden term. (5) Opinion; our country guarantees people the right to protest. (6) Fact; I assume this is accurate—at least it could be verified. (7) Fact; same reason as for Number 6. (8) Opinion; inference is too sweeping. Everyone may not feel that way. (9) Opinion; I disagree. It would have been of questionable legality.

World Trade Organization (WTO) "riot" in Seattle. He commented that the coverage in newspapers was quite extensive and (in his opinion) much more sympathetic to the cause than that in American papers he had seen. At any rate, cities in Canada, England, New Zealand, and other countries in which English-speaking newspapers are prevalent should be kept in mind as sources of news reporting that may offer alternatives to prevailing national views.

In this vein, Spanish-language newspapers, both domestic and foreign, are a valuable alternative news source if children speak Spanish, are learning it as a second language, or are studying countries in which Spanish is the national language. Newspapers from around the world are available from Multinewspapers, Box DE, Dana Point, CA 92629. Many can be downloaded from the Internet, as well.

CURRENT EVENTS

Today's News Media

Ben Bradlee, editor of the *Washington Post* during the Watergate scandal, once told his staff reporters that their job was to write "the first rough draft of history." He was right. Some years ago, I spent several days working in the archive room of a major university library, reading through old issues of the *San Francisco Chronicle.* I was reading my way through issues from 1943 when I came across a small article buried in the back pages about a young U.S. Navy lieutenant whose PT boat had been torpedoed and sunk. The lieutenant, one John F. Kennedy, had helped his crew reach the shore of a Pacific island. There it was: the rough draft of a story that would become part of the presidential campaign some 20 years later.

Imagine what Ben Bradlee might say today about history's rough draft, with 24/7 news channels (MSN, CNN, CNBC) and websites attached to every major news source, not to mention constantly streaming web logs, or blogs. News coverage is now around the clock, and the sheer quantity of it is overwhelming. This is literally a time of information explosion.

The danger at the beginning of this new century is not that we do not have enough access to news and information but rather that we have too much. Whereas only a few years ago, the front page of the *New York Times* more or less dictated what we would see on the network newscasts, television news channels now fill their time with anything they can find—often because they have video to accompany the story, not because the story itself is important. Moreover, the content on cable news channels is often determined by the political outlook of the channel's owner rather than by fact.

As a result of all this, our job as teachers has become even more important: We need to help our students learn to listen and watch critically, to sort out fact from opinion, and to differentiate the true priorities of society from those constantly repeated on the nightly news. I urge you to make current events and news reporting an integral part of your social studies curriculum. Encourage your students not only to be aware of the news but also to distinguish the superficial from the significant and opinion from truth. And in the spirit of this book, encourage your students to participate—to be reporters themselves. Students can report daily on news stories. They can explore newspapers for longer features and analyses on issues such as global warming and the election of a new pope. They can compare how stories are treated in one medium versus another— perhaps on a cable channel versus a network or a newspaper.

USING A THEME APPROACH   The daily newspaper carries a little bit of everything: the signing of an international treaty to limit the production of nuclear weapons, a recipe for pineapple-upside-down cake, a summary and analysis of the Super Bowl game, an editorial on the hazards of chlorine in drinking water, the arrest of an alleged hijacker, tomorrow's weather forecast, and the latest cartoon adventures of Garfield. Therefore, what news to report can be confusing to a child.

The study of current events creates the awareness that is necessary for good citizenship.

A solution to this problem is to let the students (with some help from you) select themes in the news and current events. When a theme has been selected, news reports are given for a week at a time on that theme. This approach will do two things for your study of current events. First, it will free students from wondering whether the news they have selected is fit to report. Second, it will allow sufficient coverage of a topic for students to develop an analysis of it. Possible themes include the following:

Air Pollution
Water Pollution
New Stadium Proposal
Controversial New Freeway
Presidential Election
Bond Issues (New Swimming Pool, Park, School, etc.)
Space Travel
School Consolidation

International Treaties
The Economy
School Busing
Agricultural Conditions
Traffic Problems
Labor Conditions
Transportation Issues
Other Countries

Summary

Anthropology, economics, geography, history, sociology, and political science all involve the study of human beings. Therefore, all these areas are, by definition, included in social studies. This chapter described the structure of each of these social sciences and highlighted terms and key ideas from each. The key ideas listed with each discipline in this chapter make good concept statements on which to develop lessons, activities, and even units of instruction. Go back and skim them, and you will see what I mean. Of course, when you select a key idea, you must do two things: (1) attach it to some appropriate content and (2) develop it by using an activity appropriate to certain age levels.

Explorations

Reflect On . . .

1. Make a list of differences between social studies and social science. Make a list of similarities between social studies and social science. Which list is longer? Why?
2. Think about the concept of change. Identify an example of change for each of the social science disciplines.

In the Field

3. Examine an elementary social studies series. Try to determine which social science disciplines are stressed at each level.

4. "Geography and history should receive far more emphasis in elementary studies than the other social sciences." Do you agree or disagree with that statement? Why or why not? Talk to an elementary school teacher and ask the same question.

For Your Portfolio

5. Use one of the key ideas listed in this chapter and develop a lesson based on it.

Continuing the Journey: Suggested Readings

Berkowitz, C. (2002). I like those other cultures now. *Social Education, 66*(6), 353–359.
Provides a helpful means of thinking and acting toward differences. The author helps readers to enlarge their perspectives on other cultures.

Boehm, R., & Rutherford, D. (2004). Implementation of national geography standards in the social studies: A ten-year retrospective. *Social Studies, 95*(6), 228–231.
The authors take a 10-year look at geography standards and how they have fared.

Branson, M. (2005). The connection between civic and economic education. *Teacher Librarian, 32*(3), 26–29.
An interdisciplinary perspective on two areas of social studies that unfortunately often go unconnected.

Coles, R. (2000). *The political life of children.* Boston: Atlantic Monthly Press.
Wonderful insights from the acclaimed author who has written on the moral life of schools, the moral life of childhood, and so on.

Fertig, G. (2005). Teaching elementary students how to interpret the past. *Social Studies, 96*(1), 2–9.
A must read for teachers who are serious about enabling their students to become young historians.

Hirsch, E. D. (1991–2005). *The core knowledge series K–8.* New York: Delta.
Hirsch is often criticized by those who think he is interested in nothing more than facts, dates, names, and so on, but personally, I think you will find these books a good addition to your professional library.

McArthur, J. (2004). Involving preservice teachers in social studies content standards: Thoughts of a methods professor. *Social Studies, 95*(2), 79–81.
Ideas for empowering future teachers and getting them to think reflectively about the role of content in social studies.

National Council for the Social Studies. (1994). *Curriculum standards for social studies: Expectations of excellence.* Washington, DC: Author.
A classic and required reading for anyone who wants to take social studies seriously.

Park, M. (2000). *Introducing anthropology: An integrated approach.* Mountain View, CA: Mayfield.
A useful primer on anthropology and its conceptual links to other disciplines.

www.ncss.org
The website of the National Council for the Social Studies (NCSS), the official professional organization of social studies teachers in the United States and Canada.

www.socialstudies.org
This website links to many other websites featuring information on standards, activities, lessons, units, and the like.

Developmentally Appropriate Social Studies

Theory and Practice

In this chapter, we will explore these themes:

key concepts

- Time-tested social studies practices
- Setting conditions for meaningful learning
- Children's natural tendencies
- Encouraging high achievement
- Encouraging thoughtfulness
- Encouraging creativity

> *There is a time for everything.*
> —Ecclesiastes

The term *developmentally appropriate practice* has gained considerable currency in recent years. For the social studies teacher, it represents a commitment to the idea that as children grow and develop, they respond differently to content, concepts, skills, and values. Psychologist Jerome Bruner noted many years ago that you can teach anybody anything, if you do it in an intellectually honest way. By that, he meant that we sometimes confuse *subject matter* with *method*. Young children are perfectly capable of learning sophisticated ideas, but as social studies teachers, you and I must be insightful enough to create the appropriate conditions for that learning.

Teachers can learn a great deal from the research that has been conducted in the areas of developmental psychology and learning theory. Learning theorists made enormous progress in the twentieth century, furnishing educators with new insights into how children think and learn. The scope and sequence of the social studies curriculum, the materials that are used, and the teaching strategies that are employed are all crucial components of an appropriate social studies program. Once you have accounted for these factors, you are ready to go—right? Well, perhaps not quite. Let's not overlook the need to understand the developmental dimension of the students in your classroom.

The finest materials, the most innovative teaching strategy, and the most interesting content become useful and meaningful only when they match the learner and his or her ability to accommodate them. To take into account the growth and development of the young learner is to recognize at the outset that not all children grow and develop at the same rate. The obvious differences in physical size should serve as a reminder that differential rates of growth also occur in the social, emotional, and intellectual dimensions. Our teaching needs to accommodate this.

Time-Tested Social Studies Practices

The worlds of educational theory and classroom teaching can sometimes seem so unrelated that we might think of them as different planets. Research, the myth contends, takes place under controlled, pristine conditions, while the real world of the classroom is unpredictable and chaotic. There may be some truth to this, but to think of research and practice as unrelated is to create a false dichotomy. In a book on social studies methods, our purpose is not to delve into specific theories of learning; rather, it is to know to what extent theory can inform and improve practice.

In the following sections, I identify several general conclusions from theories of teaching and learning that I think you will find quite useful in your teaching. If you take them seriously and act on them, you will be pleased with the results.

The Doctrine of Interest

The *doctrine of interest* is actually a very old idea that states that children should study those things that interest them most. However, this idea is easily misunderstood as an invitation to chaos and superficiality. The fact is that human beings respond more deeply to learning when they find the topic rewarding, compelling, fascinating, and worth wondering about. I think you already know this from your own experience. Children love stories, projects, activities, and games. Social studies at its best involves these very things.

Here are three keys to creating interest:

1. Show genuine interest in your students. Call them by name. Get to know their interests.
2. Be enthused about the material you teach. Make it exciting. Model joy and wonder.
3. Give your students choices within a structured framework. Students respond to making choices.

Active Learning

You don't need to have dedicated your entire life to a study of Jean Piaget's research to know that children need to move, to play, to use their five senses in learning. They want to create, explore, discover, build, talk, act, sing, dance, pretend, draw, paint, play, and perform. This does not mean that no time should be provided for other forms of learning, such as reading, writing, and listening. Of course it should be. But you should not ignore children's need for activity. Freedom of movement is closely related to freedom to learn. Make your social studies classroom a place of activity.

Project Learning

Human beings thrive on projects. Ask grown people what they remember most about their good school experiences, and you will find they talk about the projects they did. Why? Projects create purpose. They call for collaboration, planning, building, and authentic assessment.

It is useful for children to read about life in the Renaissance, but doing a project of putting on a Renaissance fair will bring the Renaissance to life. Projects call on us to apply our knowledge. You can put the *social* back in *social studies* by involving your students in group projects where team building, friendship, and esprit de corps become realities. My favorite rooms to visit are those where you find cardboard, paint, tools, and lots of children's work in evidence.

Parent Involvement

I can hardly exaggerate how important it is for you to involve your students' parents in their learning. Take every step you can to do so. Achievement will increase, and discipline problems will diminish. Involve parents in student assignments and homework. Call them occasionally to let them know how their child is doing. Send letters home informing parents of topics of study, explaining how they can help, inviting them to performances, and so on. Don't allow them to forget or be unaware of what is going on at school. Research has shown that when parents feel involved in the life of the school, academic achievement shows real gains (Michigan Department of Education, 2001).

Team Building

From the first day of school on, think of your class as a team. Really believe it. Give your students social experiences working in groups. Your classroom needs to be a place of social activity where kids talk to each other, depend on and support one another, and develop friendships. Social studies should be, above all, a time of working together, making decisions, and reflecting on teamwork. If I could visit your classroom, I'd hope to hear the hum of voices and see a little world of civility, caring, sharing, and democracy in action.

Encouraging Individuals

The corollary to team building is building up individuals. Take opportunities to talk with each child. Ask how things are going. Suggest a book to read. Mention something you know he or she is interested in. Offer a compliment on something he or she did that was good, useful, right, or supportive. Never assume that just because a child is not acting out or causing problems that everything is fine. You are the adult: Reach out, care for, and support each child. The genuine interest you show will be contagious.

Reflection

It is tempting to try to cover too many topics, too many pages in the book. The problem with doing so is that little knowledge takes hold at a deeper level. You and your students end up like academic nomads, always moving on. It is better to go more deeply into subjects, to take time to reflect on what the students are learning, and to encourage them to share their thoughts and feelings with you and their classmates. Give students time at the end of each lesson and at the end of the week to look back, to search for key ideas and meaningful experiences, and to consider what they have learned.

These principles of teaching and learning provide the foundation of a meaningful social studies curriculum. Memorize them. Make them part of your routine. If you act on them, your life as a teacher will be more rewarding, your students will learn more, and you will find yourself increasingly receiving that ultimate childhood compliment: "Can we keep working on this just a little longer? Please, can we?" I've seen it happen.

Setting Conditions for Meaningful Learning: Concept Learning

Concept development is a basic principle of developmentally appropriate practice. *Concepts* are abstract knowledge structures that we use to organize large amounts of information. For example, a child learns about cars, airplanes, trains, and bicycles. In time, the child realizes that these are forms of transportation. Thus, the child has formed the concept of *transportation.* Transportation becomes an abstract concept or an intellectual tool belonging to the child. Of course, the child's concept is not as fully developed as that of, say, the director of transportation systems for a large city. But the groundwork has been laid.

The important thing to keep in mind about concept development is that your students are developing memories, or *schemas,* that they store in order to keep track of things. In other words, they are comparing, contrasting, classifying, and categorizing—all important skills in social studies. The child who has developed a schema for the concept of *transportation* is able to put a cruise ship or a skateboard into that category. Experience and reflection are the keys to concept development.

Let's say you decide to teach a lesson or series of lessons on the concept of *conflict resolution.* We will begin with the assumption that this is an important topic in social studies. It transcends time and space; that is, conflicts have existed throughout history, and we can imagine that people will have conflicts in the future, as well. Further, conflicts do not happen merely in one setting. They have happened and will continue to

An intuitive teacher knows when to lead and when to step aside.

happen in a wide variety of places. Finally, conflicts happen at different levels and on different scales. Conflicts happen among preschoolers, and conflicts happen among great nations.

Conflict resolution can be taught at different levels, but how we go about teaching it and our expectations for how students might learn about it will differ by age level. In a *spiral* social studies curriculum, important topics and content are studied again and again in different contexts as students grow and develop. The idea is that each successive time a topic such as conflict resolution is studied, it can be studied at an increased level of sophistication, since the children have been previously exposed to it. The quality of the experience, therefore, is the key to improved learning. The question is not whether there is one definite place in the social studies curriculum to study conflict resolution but whether the experience has meaning to learners.

Consider the two following scenarios: (1) fifth-grade students studying the American Revolution are presented with a world-class example of conflict and how it was resolved, and (2) first-grade students are led by their teacher into a small-scale study of conflict resolution following a quarrel on the playground. In the first instance, the teacher is able to build the concept into the course of study using the content students are already studying. The teacher capitalizes on the opportunity to have the students examine an important idea in the context of studying a historical event. In the second example, the teacher takes advantage of an incident that happens with the children and helps them examine and reflect on it. Large scale or small scale, textbook history or life experience, close to home or long ago and far away, the idea is the same. The difference is found in thoughtful judgment of what is developmentally appropriate for the grade level.

Let's listen as two teachers reflect on this matter. The grade levels differ, but the teacher in each case is doing something significant: building an important concept.

in the classroom   The American Revolution (Fifth Grade)

We had just read about the Battles of Lexington and Concord and the beginnings of the American Revolution. We had connected these battles to literature by reading Ralph Waldo Emerson's poem "Concord Hymn." The students were really interested in this important moment in American history. I asked the class, "Could these battles have been avoided? Could the American colonists and the British have resolved their conflict in any other way?"

I was amazed at the students' answers. One said she thought that when a conflict becomes so heated, it is a good idea to try to arrange a time to talk about it, to see if there might be some way to avoid fighting. Other students also gave their opinions at the time. I told the class to do some research, think about the questions, talk to their parents about the topic, and do some reading and writing. We would have a follow-up discussion two days later.

When the students and I took up the matter again two days later, they were ready with some ideas. One student said that when conflict is avoided, then it doesn't get into the history books so easily. Therefore, we don't always know the names of the heroes who helped to avoid war. Another student said that her parents told her about the Cuban missile crisis of 1962. She said the president of the United States and the premier of the Soviet Union had agreed to a peaceful means of resolving a conflict that seemed to be headed toward war. Others pointed out that sometimes in history, war has been unavoidable, or so it seemed.

My point was not to have the students rewrite history but to examine an event and raise the question of whether there might have been alternative solutions to what actually happened.

in the classroom   Playground Politics (First Grade)

Several students returned from recess in an angry mood. They had been quarreling over a playground ball and who should get to use it. The quarrel resulted in some pushing and shoving, which had to be broken up by the playground supervisor.

I could tell that this was not the time to say "OK class, open your spelling books." We needed to talk about the incident, not to ignore it. It turned out that the quarrel was between students only from my class, so that simplified things in one sense. It was our problem, our conflict, and we needed to resolve it.

I quickly set up a "courtroom" in the classroom. I told the students I would play the part of the judge and the class members who were not involved would be the jury. Each student who was involved was allowed to state his or her case without interruption. Then the jury and I could ask questions. When all those directly involved had stated their cases and answered our questions, I asked the jury to decide what should be done. By now, the

students were enjoying the activity so much that all tempers had cooled off. (Maybe they just didn't want to do spelling, but I think it was that they were genuinely involved in our deliberation.)

The decision of the jury interested me a lot. They decided that the conflict arose because of some misunderstanding of whose turn it was to have the ball. They "sentenced" the students on both sides to shake hands and say they were sorry the conflict happened. The students seemed eager to do so, and the incident was defused.

I thought later that evening about what we did as a class. It was spontaneous. I certainly did not plan to hold court in my classroom that day. It wasn't in my lesson plans. I also thought about how the situation might have gotten out of hand. I realized I was shaking as I thought that. But it didn't get out of hand. I learned a lot about my students that day. I think they learned some valuable things, as well.

A couple of days later, I brought the incident up just to see if they wanted to reflect on it. Well, yes, they did want to. We sat on the floor in a circle, and I gave each person in turn a chance to talk. I was so proud of my students. They not only found a peaceful way to resolve a conflict, but they also showed me something about the moral growth of children.

Legendary explorer Marco Polo reached the islands of the East Indies late in the thirteenth century. When he came to the islands of Sumatra, Java, and Borneo, he noticed certain wild animals living there. Here is an excerpt from his diary, which documents how he told the story to a fellow prisoner some years later when they both were serving time in jail in the city of Venice, Italy:

> There are wild elephants in the country and numerous unicorns, which are very nearly as big. They [the unicorns] have hair like that of a buffalo, feet like those of an elephant, and a horn in the middle of the forehead, which is black and very thick. They do no mischief with the horn, but with the tongue alone, for this is covered all over with long and strong prickles, and when savage with any one they crush him under their knees and then rasp him with their tongue.

Perhaps you grew up as I did, believing that unicorns are imaginary animals found in fairy tales. They are shown in fairy tales as being white, not black as Marco Polo described them. They look like a horse with a cone-shaped horn on its forehead, and they do not have feet like an elephant. What animal, then, did Marco Polo see? We know now that the animal he encountered was a rhinoceros.

The problem for Marco Polo, a mere teenager at that time, was that his *schema,* or background knowledge, did not permit him to understand that this was, to him at least, a new animal. However, his schema did include a belief that unicorns were real animals, not just animals found in fairy tales. His belief in imaginary animals outweighed his ability to believe that he had encountered a different mammal. So, concepts can be based on misunderstanding. Marco Polo did a good job of relating the supposed unicorn to the buffalo and elephant, two creatures that are indeed related to the rhinoceros. But he used familiar attributes to reach a faulty conclusion.

The point of this story is that developmentally appropriate learning takes into account prior knowledge and the quality of the learning experience. Marco Polo had no one available to teach him, so he merely depended on his prior knowledge, which in this case was based on misinformation. For the social studies teacher, the message is clear. The more you are able to provide conditions for rich experiences and meaningful learning, the richer each child's schema will become. In other words, the more you already know about a subject, the more you will be able to learn about it. It is as simple as the old saying "The rich get richer . . ."

Figure 4.1 illustrates the importance of schema, even in everyday life. In this cartoon, the joke is funny only to readers who know that Isaac Newton is supposed to have discovered the law of gravity when he observed an apple fall from a tree and who also know what a dangling participle is. Also, the cartoon lampoons those teachers who "can't see the forest for the trees." Creating schema as the foundation for knowledge—so that we can draw on our prior knowledge as we learn more—is the essence of learning.

figure 4.1   *The Importance of Schema*

Young Isaac's teacher finds it difficult to tolerate
the lad's tendency to dangle a participle

Source: Arthur Ellis and Maria Ellis.

Children's Natural Tendencies

John Dewey (1899) wrote a book called *The School and Society* more than 100 years ago. Much of what he noted has been validated over time, but curiously, many of his better ideas continue to elude our grasp at the level of school practice. I wish to spend a little time illuminating some of his thoughts as guides to productive teaching and learning in social studies. His ideas are quite powerful, but like most truly powerful ideas, they are also rather simple. They serve as reminders to us—reminders of certain foundational elements needed to support the growth and development of young learners.

Dewey referred to these natural tendencies of children as "instincts" because his own observation and reflection led him to conclude that they tend not only to be universal but qualities that we do not have to teach because they are already there. I like to think of them as gifts of childhood. These tendencies are gifts to us as teachers. We only need to act on them. Sadly, some teachers see these tendencies not as opportunities but as problems to be overcome. Keep these four tendencies in mind for every lesson you teach:

CURRENT EVENTS

Focus on Holidays and Special Occasions

Holidays and special occasions are of great interest to children. Because they love to celebrate these events, holidays and special occasions offer splendid opportunities to introduce history, geography, and cultural diversity. For younger children, awareness is created through celebrating or noting a particular holiday, with the context of its origin and significance provided by the teacher. For students in the middle grades, holidays can prompt good independent study projects, historical investigations, and drama and music projects, as well as times for celebration.

Focusing on the following holidays and special occasions can provide a means of discussing current events and calendar keeping throughout the school year:

New Year's Day	Mother's Day
Martin Luther King Jr.'s Birthday	Father's Day
Valentine's Day	Citizenship Day
Presidents' Day	American Indian Day
Black History Month	Canada Day
March of Dimes Week	American Independence Day
Brotherhood Week	Labor Day
Conversation Week	Columbus Day
Kindness to Animals Week	Fire Prevention Day
Earth Week	Veterans Day
St. Patrick's Day	Halloween
Citizenship Day	Thanksgiving (Canadian)
Arbor Day	Thanksgiving (U.S.)
May Day	

The following websites provide useful information about holidays and festivals:

www.kidsdomain.com	www.infoplease.com
www.yahooligans.com	www.falcon.jmu.edu

1. *Conversation.* Surprise, children like to talk. They want to talk. They spend much of their early childhood asking questions, chattering, and developing the art of conversation. When they come to school, they find themselves in group settings that unfortunately are not always supportive of this tendency. In my own teaching at the college level, I often find myself reflecting on the difference between my classroom when I am lecturing and students are supposedly listening and my classroom when I involve my students in an activity of some kind. Everything changes. Time passes more quickly. People are sharing their thoughts. Problems are being solved. Language develops. Of course, there is a time to talk and a time to listen. Balance is the key, but the evidence shows that students are not given enough time to talk to one another during the school day.

2. *Construction.* Yes, I'm saying your room ought to become a construction zone. Kids need to build things, to take things apart, to work as little artists, architects, engineers,

Children are naturally curious. They want to learn. Our task is to nurture the possibilities.

builders, and designers. They learn this way. You need manipulatives, equipment, and interest centers in your classroom. The construction needs to be related to topics of study, and social studies offers virtually unlimited opportunities in this regard. Maps, models, puppet theatres, dioramas, and villages are waiting to be built. This is constructivism in its most literal sense. Children are natural constructivists. Take advantage of the opportunity.

3. *Inquiry.* Curiosity, discovery, and good old poking around all come rather naturally to children. Your job and mine is to use this instinct to good advantage. This means involving students in problem-solving activities, in asking good questions, in seeking answers to questions posed, and in finding out on their own as opposed to being told. Much of what people learn comes from being told, reading, and so on, but this type of learning takes on deeper meaning when it relates to our one's own inquiry. The knowledge is useful. Knowledge discovered is always more powerful because it is knowledge owned by the inquirer. Self-confidence deepens when we learn to depend on ourselves.

4. *Artistic expression.* Every child is an artist—so is every adult, for that matter—but we sometimes seem to forget that. Our artistic interests take different forms, but we all have an ability to express ourselves creatively. In social studies, artistic expression takes on such forms as drawing, painting, sculpting, making models, writing play scripts, producing plays, role-playing, keeping a journal, writing stories, writing and playing music, sewing, cooking, recreating historical characters, making videos, building villages, creating time lines, and so on.

These four tendencies, viewed as solutions to making social studies come alive, handed to us by children as gifts, need to become imbedded in practice. Conversation, construction, inquiry, and artistry ought to be the essence of the day-to-day routine in your classroom. You and your students should come to expect this as a matter of course. Classrooms where these things happen regularly are places of active learning, places of freedom of movement and expression, and places where opportunity prevails over restraint.

Encouraging High Achievement

Every student can be a higher achiever in the sense that every individual can always do better. From the struggling child who can barely read to the child who regularly achieves the highest grades, the challenge is one of self-improvement. But what is different about highly successful students? Can we identify the salient characteristics of those children who do well in school and in life in general? And can the classroom teacher who knows about those characteristics foster them in all students? It is a bit of a challenge, but good teaching, though never easy, brings its own rewards.

Researcher Howard Johnston (1995) has investigated the patterns or characteristics of higher achievers and has identified eight such characteristics. You can take full advantage of these findings through social studies experiences and throughout the entire curriculum for that matter. The point is that some children already exhibit the attributes. But for the good teacher, this is not enough. We want to extend the opportunities to all our students. As you read through the Keys to High Achievement, challenge yourself to think of ways in which you could ensure that all your students and their parents become aware of these characteristics.

Keys to High Achievement

Higher-achieving students have these qualities:

- *Hold more conversations with adults.* You can give assignments that require children to interview other teachers, their parents, and people in the neighborhood. These are modest ideas, but they represent a beginning.
- *Develop skills and interests outside school (hobbies, drama, sports, music, etc.).* Anything you can do to encourage your students to take up hobbies, to become involved in school music programs, or to join after-school clubs will pay great dividends. Some teachers go so far as to start after-school extracurricular groups, such as drama clubs, chess clubs, and the like.
- *Have more consistent life patterns.* Start the process by sending letters home to parents urging them to provide definite times and places to do homework, place restrictions on the amount of television time, and encourage family activities related to social studies and other curricular areas.
- *Spend time planning for the future.* Students need to think, draw, write, and talk about their futures. They need to talk with responsible adults and older students about how to go about planning for life beyond the present moment.
- *Are involved in academically challenging activities.* You need to set whole-class challenges as well as challenges for each individual student. Contracts, work plans, and goal setting represent concrete means of doing this.
- *Have purpose within their families (chores, responsibilities, etc.).* Again, there is nothing like a letter home to parents encouraging them to find tasks, chores, and meaningful responsibilities that enable your students to feel as though they are contributing to family life.
- *Spend more time in supervised settings (home, church, clubs, sports, etc.).* Children need models of positive adult leadership. This is crucial to their development as fully functioning individuals and as citizens of the community.
- *Spend more time reading.* Set the tone. Talk to your students about the many books you read. Talk about going to the library and looking for good material learning. Require each of your students to read at least 30 books per year.

Source: Adapted from Johnston, 1995.

Now that you have had a chance to read through the list, you need to ask yourself whether you can play a significant role in encouraging the traits of high achievers in *all* your students. Notice that money, expenses, and so on are not issues here. What does come through is a sense of a more ordered, consistent, supervised, and adult-connected childhood. Nurturing is the key. Children need love, structure, and patience.

In a perfect world, all the kids you teach would already exhibit these characteristics, and your job would be far easier than in fact it is. But short of that, you can begin by informing the parents of your own students. They need your help. Good information in invaluable. You might be surprised how many parents are perfectly willing to try to improve their child's opportunities to become a better student and a better person.

Encouraging Thoughtfulness

As you walk down the halls of a school and look into the classrooms, you get different feelings about each one. Why is it that some are inviting and others are not? Why is it that some are places of thoughtfulness, reflection, and coherence and others simply are not? And why is it that you find yourself thinking that you'd like to be a student in this classroom but you're not so sure about that one?

Onosko and Newmann (1994), two eminent researchers, have identified certain attributes of classrooms where thoughtfulness prevails. The work in this area by Berliner and Biddle (1997) is also very useful to teachers who wish to make their classrooms places of reflection and deeper thought. Here are a few ideas around which you can build a foundation of thoughtfulness for social studies.

- *Treat students' ideas and contributions with respect.* It is a fragile thing to be a student. Students respond to encouragement, to civil behavior, and to kindness. They tend to pass it along to others. You need to make it clear through your behavior that you welcome ideas from your students. You want them to feel that they can contribute. More than this, you want them to feel that their contributions are genuinely *needed* in order to make this a better place. It takes a gifted teacher to create such an atmosphere.

- *Encourage students to justify their contributions.* Just as you want your students to feel free to contribute their ideas, so too will you want them to think through what they are doing and to learn to make a case for their efforts. They need this. Think of it as having high expectations, of asking each student to do his or her best work. When students are required to analyze and assess their own ideas, they become more reflective in their own practice. Administrators, parents, and the general public expect this of you as a teacher, and you should expect it of your students.

- *Maintain sustained involvement with a smaller number of topics.* A criticism of teaching in U.S. schools is that we tend to try to cover too many topics, resulting in superficial treatment of subject matter. The saying "Less is more" is certainly true. Depth of coverage is the key. One teacher spent a great deal of time with her class studying the Hopi nation. The class built a model village. They made kuchina dolls. They assumed Hopi names during the study. They made food from Hopi recipes. They wrote letters to the Hopi nation, asking for information. They did a great deal of reading. Another teacher, thinking this was too much attention to one group, had his students cover all the Native American nations of North America. Think about it.

- *Plan challenging activities.* Psychologist Lev Vygotsky described the *zone of proximal development* as the space between which a child can learn on his or her own and in which a child can learn with guidance. This is the realm of challenge for a learner. The challenge for the teacher is to figure out what experiences students need to truly challenge their intellectual and social skills. In this sense, a good teacher is like a good coach, observing, diagnosing, and advising. A perfect example of this happens when a teacher says to a student, "You know, there's a book I've been thinking about that I'd love to have you read." Such a comment, given lovingly and sincerely, has all the qualities of personalizing, of showing interest, and of expressing desire to help a young person grow.

- *Exhibit coherence, continuity, and a progression of ideas in your lessons.* *Coherence* means that things stick together; they make sense; they are thought out. You'll find that your teaching achieves greater coherence if you involve the students in planning. *Continuity* means that one day flows naturally from the day before and so on. It implies a plan from beginning to end, with flexibility along the way. You begin to achieve continuity when you are willing to slow down the process and ask your students to reflect on meaning, purpose, and interest. We talk about a *progression of ideas* in the sense of a spiral; that is, we have a few powerful ideas and we keep returning to them with new examples that allow children to probe them in greater depth over time.

Thoughtfulness begins with you. As you model this behavior, your students will begin to get the idea. Talk about the books you are reading. Talk about the things you are learning. Convey to your class a sense of excitement about your own journeys of discovery. Take time to reflect with individuals and with the class as a whole. Take time to find out how students feel, what they think, and what they are interested in. And above all, don't fall victim to the coverage mentality. Take the advice of the great philosopher Alfred North Whitehead, who said simply, "Don't try to teach too much."

Encouraging Creativity

In this book and from other sources, you will learn about constructivism, multiple intelligences, learning styles, thinking styles, individual differences, and other characteristics of learners that speak to their uniqueness. I wish to close this foundational chapter by addressing the issue of creativity—a topic dear to the heart of social studies. It has been observed that creative people have an ability to make the familiar strange and the strange familiar. What does this mean to you? What does this have to do with teaching and learning social studies? I won't tell you because I think your own sense of creativity will enable you to answer the question. For now, let's explore some fundamentals to making your classroom a place where creativity is encouraged and found.

- *Give children freedom and space.* A school and the classrooms within a school should be places of opportunity over restraint, places of freedom over coercion. In recent times, we have seen a shift in the business world from top-down, authoritarian management to relaxed, playful atmospheres in which people are encouraged think for themselves, show initiative, and take chances with ideas. This is a remarkable change, and believe me, businesses would not do this if they weren't getting good results.

- *Encourage projects.* Please forgive me if I begin to sound like a broken record to you at some point because my feelings are so strong on this matter. Projects help us apply knowledge; they get us beyond learning information for information's sake. Projects are something we *do*. They involve construction, building, performing, and, above all, teamwork. A class play or pageant; a display of maps, drawings, and models; a neighborhood cleanup campaign; the "adoption" of a nearby retirement home—all are examples of ways to involve students in something bigger than any individual can do alone. Philosopher Jurgen Habermas has raised the question "What happens when interest in performance is not accompanied by corresponding participation?" The answer is disaster. Projects are about participation.

- *Encourage reading good literature.* Active learning does not mean that we do not read and write. Reading biographies, histories, novels, and poetry are essential to the growth and development of learners. Children watch too much television, and they do not read enough. As I mentioned earlier, there is no reason to think in terms of anything less than each of your students reading one book a week (at least 30 per year) as a goal, regardless of their age. Beyond reading, students should write every day. We get good at what we practice, especially with expert help. Two of the best ways for people to expand their horizons are friendship and books. Working and playing together, reading good literature, and writing about your ideas represent fast tracks to improved achievement and social/moral growth.

- *Encourage the arts and music.* Don't even think about putting together a social studies unit devoid of drawing, sketching, mapping, designing, painting, sculpting, drama, and singing. These are not frills. They are essentials. Your students need to listen to good music and to study good artwork. They need to draw every day, because learning to draw is the best way of learning to see and create. The arts can bring a social studies program to life, whether at the level of appreciating good work done by experts or at the level of childhood performance.

Social studies is the study of human beings. Human beings are natural creators. It's what we do. It is difficult even to imagine the potential creativity lying dormant in a typical class of 25 to 30 students. Your task is to unleash it, to nourish it, to encourage risk taking, and to help each child find his or her unique gifts. As you support your students in their creative efforts, you will find your own creativity coming to the surface. It will manifest itself undeniably in the variety of lessons you teach and in the freedom you give yourself and your students to explore, to dream, and to discover the pleasures of learning together.

Summary

My purpose in this chapter has been to introduce the underlying foundational aspects of teaching and learning social studies. Much of the rest of this book is devoted to coverage of these same basic themes in greater depth. Thus, the book itself is based on the idea of the spiral curriculum. Using the spiral, we will limit ourselves to a few powerful ideas that we will study over and over. You don't want too many themes, too many ideas. When that happens, you are left with a laundry list. Your own teaching should be limited to a small number of truly important ideas, skills, and values that you and your students return to over and again. Instead of going down the tempting road of broad and superficial coverage, we will continue to pursue these themes with expanded analysis; with numerous examples of activities, lessons, and units; and with strategies for planning, teaching, learning, and assessment.

Explorations

Reflect On . . .

1. I made the statement that drawing, mapping, drama, painting, singing, and so on are not frills in a good social studies program. To what extent do you agree?
2. Who should plan the social studies curriculum? Should students be involved in planning, and if so, to what extent?

In the Field

3. Engage a fellow educator in a reflective discussion on the nature of childhood learning. What are the priorities?

4. Some people will say that if you give children freedom to engage each other in conversation and to move about the room, then management problems will inevitably result. Do you agree? Talk with an elementary school teacher. Does he or she agree? Why or why not?

For Your Portfolio

5. Download at least two social studies lesson plans or activities from the Internet that do not include active movement. Modify them to allow students to converse, work in teams, or create art or graphics.

Continuing the Journey: Suggested Readings

Berliner, D., & Biddle, B. (1997). *The manufactured crisis*. White Plains, NY: Longman.
A still-cogent argument about the strengths of American public education.

Eco, U. (1998). From Marco Polo to Leibniz. In *Serendipities: Essays in language and lunacy* (pp. 53–76). New York: Harcourt Brace.
Eco is one of the foremost essayists of our time. His ideas are worth reading for the intellectual stimulation and also for the clear prose style he uses to communicate with the reader who is willing to join him in profound thought.

Joyce, B., Weil, M., & Calhoun, E. (2004). *Models of teaching* (7th ed.). Boston: Allyn & Bacon.
Provides helpful illustrations of a wide range of teaching models, including cooperative learning, inquiry, simulations, nondirective teaching, and values study.

Kelly, M., & Battle-Bailey, L. (2004). Interactive homework for increasing parent involvement and student achievement. *Childhood Education, 81*(1), 36–41.
Ideas for partnering with parents and connecting the home to school.

Mueller, A., & Fleming, T. (2001). Cooperative learning: Listening to how children work at school. *Journal of Educational Research, 94*(5), 259–266.
A study of student behaviors and engagement in group practices.

Onosko, J., & Newmann, F. (1994). Creating more thoughtful learning environments. In J. Mangieri & C. Block (Eds.), *Creating powerful thinking in teachers and students*. Fort Worth, TX: Harcourt Brace.
Ideas for establishing a reflective atmosphere in the classroom.

Planning for Social Studies Teaching and Learning

In this chapter, we will explore these themes:

key concepts

- Teachers as decision makers
- Planning for long-range goals
- Planning lessons and activities
- Teaching concepts, skills, and values
- Teaching and learning with units in social studies
- Developing a unit plan

*Mix a little foolishness with your serious plans;
it's lovely to be silly at the right moment.*
　　　　—Horace (65 B.C.)

A good plan is much like a good map: It can help you get where you want to go. But a good plan is always a flexible document, open to possibilities along the way. In this chapter, we will investigate a set of specific ideas designed to help improve your planning for social studies learning.

Ancient Roman poet Horace noted that although planning is often a serious matter, it doesn't hurt to add a little humor or perhaps have a little fun along the way. This is wise counsel, indeed, when we remember that we're working with children. I suspect that Horace is also telling us that timing is everything when he uses the phrase *the right moment*. Three centuries before Horace, Greek philosopher Plato made it clear that the work of childhood is play. We should keep this in mind, as well. After all, we're helping to build lifelong memories and attitudes, so why not make them good ones?

A plan represents an organized way of thinking about the future. The future is unknown, but we still make plans because by doing so, we can at least have something to say about the future. The alternative is not appealing: To let the future merely happen is to place ourselves at the mercy of events. We know that one of the attributes of higher-achieving students is that they make plans for both the near and distant future. Likewise, an attribute of effective teachers is that they plan carefully and flexibly, always building in variety and choice for their students. A good plan not only guides your actions, but it also allows you to reflect on what you did against some standard. A good plan exists in the future, present, and past in that it is at once a forecast, an experience, and a retrospective. A plan is speculative when it is drawn up, in motion when it is implemented, and history after it happens.

A plan for learning is therefore an enabling device that does three things:

1. Helps you think about what needs to be accomplished and why
2. Guides you and your students through experiences in much the same way a map guides a traveler
3. Provides a frame of reference for deciding to what extent the experience was meaningful

Careful planning empowers you. It makes you a true professional. Careful planning helps distinguish the teachers who do it from those who, content with mediocrity, merely make their way through textbooks with no strategic vision, occasionally hitting on a good activity here and there. That's not teaching; that's monitoring.

Teachers as Decision Makers

Teachers need to make several basic decisions as they plan for instruction. Those decisions relate to content, activities of the teacher, and activities of the learner.

First of all, you must make decisions about the content of your social studies program. I recommend a developmental approach to the teaching of content. This means that your instruction should proceed from what students already know and are able to do toward knowledge and skills beyond their present understanding. Thus, you will want to sequence your instruction from simple to complex. Facts can lead to concepts, which can in turn lead to generalizations. This progression happens, however, only if you are willing to make the connections. The same thing is true in the teaching of skills. Simple skills, such as measuring distance, can lead to more complex skills, such as accurately estimating distance and size.

Decision making about content also has another dimension. Suppose two fifth-grade teachers are each assigned to teach about the United States as the central focus of the social studies curriculum. One teacher might give more emphasis to history; the other might choose to emphasize geography. One might spend more time on the colonial era, concentrating on the family; the other might spend more time emphasizing settlement patterns in the New World. The point is that teachers have a great deal of autonomy within a prescribed curriculum, especially in social studies (as opposed to mathematics), where little agreement exists on what constitutes minimal content coverage of people, places, and events.

The second area in which you will make instructional decisions concerns the activities of the learners. What will your students actually do during social studies? Will they read? Orally? Silently? What will they read? Textbooks? Biographies? Original documents? Will they engage in discussion? If so, with whom? Will you lead the discussion, or will students discuss ideas in small groups? Will your students be expected to listen as you lecture to them? Will they take notes? Will you have your students observe, do surveys, make maps, and draw pictures? Will they construct villages, put on plays, and tape news programs? Will they work individually? Cooperatively? Whatever your students do in social studies will be the result of the decisions you have made. One thing is certain: How students spend their time will have a great effect on both their attitudes and their achievements in social studies.

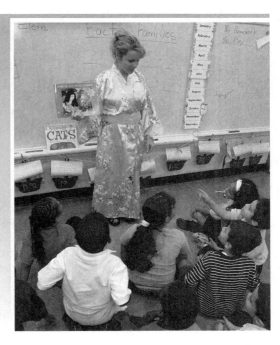

A teacher in Japanese costume models role play while teaching her students, creating a powerful effect.

You will also make instructional decisions about your own conduct, or the activities of the teacher. As you plan for your behavior in the instructional process, keep in mind these principles of learning: motivation, retention, and transfer.

Motivation

Motivation is a powerful tool in the learning process. Consider yourself, for example: How motivated are you to be the best teacher possible? It's probably true that the level of your motivation will dictate the extent to which you succeed, assuming, of course, that you possess the basic abilities.

Here is something to keep in mind regarding motivation: A student's most powerful motivation to learn a school subject comes from his or her prior success in that subject. In other words, "Nothing succeeds like success." Successful experiences are those in which students feel a sense of involvement, mastery, enjoyment, and challenge. The question for you is: How can I make sure that my students succeed?

Retention

How well do you remember what you hear, see, and experience? The ability to recall information and events is retention at its simplest level. At a higher level, retention means how well you are able to use what you have learned. The key to memory and application is the learner's level of involvement in the learning process. I once worked for the National Science Foundation developing problem-solving units and training teachers to use the units in elementary classrooms. We discovered that the teachers behaved in their own classrooms essentially as we did when we taught them. If we lectured to them, they lectured to

Whatever decisions you make about your instructional approach, I urge you to make current events and news reporting an integral part of your social studies curriculum. Encourage your students to be aware of the news, to learn to distinguish the superficial from the significant, and, in the inquiry spirit of this book, to become reporters themselves.

their students. If we got them actively involved, they involved their students. The old saying "I hear and I forget; I see and I remember; I do and I understand" comes to mind.

Few of us retain all or even very much of what we learn. Our memories are less than perfect, and we may not have fully understood what we were taught in the first place. As a teacher, your responsibility is to attempt to maximize students' *retention* of key ideas, skills, and values. Facts, names, dates, and places taught as items of specific knowledge are short-term memory items, at best. Long-term retention comes from active involvement in the learning process and emphasis on connections among ideas.

Transfer of Learning

The ability to transfer learning is the ability to take what we have learned in one situation and use it in another situation. Obviously, specific facts taught without any meaningful context have little potential for transfer. Such skills as observing, recording, and communicating, however, have unlimited transfer value. Concepts also transfer well. The child who internalizes such concepts as *supply and demand, cause and effect,* and *interdependence* has learned ideas that will apply in a variety of situations, now and in the future. Learning experiences should use facts and information as *tools* for thinking, rather than as ends in themselves. When this occurs, the potential for transfer greatly increases.

You also can promote the transfer of learning by making connections between and among the subjects you teach. Challenge yourself, for example, to use ideas from mathematics in social studies. If your students are learning to make graphs in math, give them the opportunity to graph such social science data as high and low temperature readings for a week. If your students are learning to write letters in language arts, have them send real letters to cities around the country, asking for information about climate, commerce, recreation, and agriculture. If your students are learning about perspective and shading in art, apply these concepts to student-constructed maps.

Planning for Long-Range Goals

The decisions you make about content, your students' activities, and your activities will be reflected in your planning for classroom activities. Generally, when you think of planning, daily lesson plans come to mind. Planning is so much more than that, however. Planning encompasses long-range goals as well as short-term objectives.

It is useful to think of the chunks of instruction for which you are responsible. In a global sense, you are responsible for the entire year. This is your largest chunk. Full-year planning is, by its very nature, quite general. For example, you will want to come up with four or five long-range goals for the year. Such goals might include "Developing a miniature democracy in my classroom," "Imparting a knowledge of the geography of the United States," or "Being committed to enhancing the self-concept of each child."

Long-range goals are not written in instructional terms, nor are they meant to be achieved quickly. The advantage to developing long-range goals is that they give you a sense of structure, a sort of intellectual scaffold from which to view learning in a meaningful, long-term perspective. You should know what your long-range goals are, and you should share them with your students. By discussing them from time to time, you and your class will be able to make reflective judgments about how well you are progressing. A useful frame of reference for thinking about long-range goals for your social studies program is to consider your students' academic needs, their social development, and their personal fulfillment. By including your students in planning, you will begin to get a far better sense of who they really are. The Keys to Developing a Successful Unit will be useful as you plan units for your own classroom.

Keys to Developing a Successful Unit

- Choose a suitable topic—for example, "Colonial Life," "Inventions and Discoveries," "Space and Place," "A Renaissance Fair," "The Age of Exploration," "Pioneer Life and Times," "Hopi Culture," "Japanese Families," or "A Better Community."
- Spend time reading about and researching the topic. Announce the topic to the class, and tell them to find out what they can in order to prepare for a planning meeting.
- Bring the class together for a discussion of the possibilities. Involve the students in planning.
- Collect resource materials (e.g., books, magazines, websites, etc.), and establish centers or focal points of learning.
- Develop and distribute a list of types of activities related to the topic. The types should include (a) academic, (b) construction, and (c) social. The expectations should be for each student to show evidence of reading, writing, drawing, building, teaching, and performance.
- Develop strategies for involving the home. It is crucial that parents take part in some meaningful way.

- Meet with students to establish their personal goals and responsibilities.
- Meet with the whole class daily for times of sharing and team building.
- Encourage freedom, responsibility, creativity, and teamwork.
- Allow time for reflection. Ask: What are we learning?
- Involve resource people (e.g., librarians, artists, authors, scientists, professionals, workers, parents, service groups, retired people, etc.).
- Ensure that student work is presented, published, displayed, performed, and otherwise shared beyond the classroom.
- Plan assessment strategies that will show evidence of academic, personal, social, and citizenship growth. Include students in the assessment process, and expect them to assume responsibility for much of the assessment.
- Celebrate the experience in some meaningful way—for example, a party, a performance, or a similar activity.

Planning Lessons and Activities

Every lesson plan can be analyzed using two distinct criteria: mechanics and substance. Let's look at each individually.

Mechanics

To analyze the *mechanics,* think of placing a sort of template over the lesson that represents the procedures one reasonably ought to follow to obtain measurable, effective results. Generally, these procedures are thought of as steps, although there is no need to follow them slavishly in linear fashion. The steps come principally from the ideas about learning developed in the psychological literature, which include needing to establish purpose and key ideas, motivating students to learn, providing continuity in the learning process, and supporting concept development, transfer of learning, and reflective thinking.

A typical lesson includes six basic components, which are generally thought of as steps in lesson development: key idea, instructional objective, motivation (an anticipatory "set" or introduction), activity, assessment, and reflection or closure. Let's look at these individually.

1. *Key idea.* The key idea is the social science concept or generalization you want the students to learn. It represents the single most important thought or idea of the lesson. (See Chapter 3 for sample of key ideas from each of the social sciences.) For example, a key idea from history is "Our interpretations of the past change as new information is discovered." The key idea is the centerpiece of the lesson. Without it, you merely have an activity. With it, you have something special: an idea about human behavior.

2. *Instructional objective.* The instructional objective is the portion of the lesson plan that establishes its intent and proposed outcome. It is the means of operationalizing the lesson's key idea. The instructional objective must be clearly stated. It should tell what the students will do (e.g., discuss, list, classify, draw) under what conditions (e.g., small-group work, independent study). Students also need to know the intended purpose of the lesson. What should they know, feel, or be able to do as a result of the lesson?

3. *Motivation.* This stage is known variously as the *anticipatory set* or the *lesson introduction.* At this point of the lesson, you want to arouse students' attention, capture their imagination, or indicate how today's lesson is connected to yesterday's lesson. You are putting the activity into context and making it meaningful to your students. Motivation is a crucial issue early in the lesson because at this stage, you create the appropriate mental set and accompanying desire to learn. You can use any number of ways to motivate your students. You can try to make the lesson interesting or appealing, you can try to convince your students of the lesson's importance, or you can decide to use such extrinsic motivators as grades or special favors. In most cases, an interesting introduction designed to gain the students' attention will be sufficient.

4. *Activity.* This step represents the major teaching/learning focus of the lesson. At stake is the ratio of teacher activity to student activity: the behaviors of the teacher and students, the management of the activity and materials, the explanations and information offered by the teacher, the tasks given to the students, and the additional help given to the students who need it. Obviously, for one adult to lead the behaviors and learning attempts of 30 children is a very complex task. Be sure that students understand specifically what they will be doing during the lesson. Providing clear directions is crucial to the lesson's success. Will students work together or alone? Will they make things? Do seat work? Help your students carry out the assignment. Move around the room, providing assistance as needed. Ask questions, probe, clarify, maintain order, and reassure. Of course, the nature and amount of guidance will vary with such factors as student age, ability, motivation, and the nature of the task itself.

5. *Assessment.* You have a key idea and a learning objective. Your instructional activity has been designed to develop the key idea through experience. Now comes the question of assessment: What did the students learn? How will you know what they learned? What will you do to find out what they learned? All assignments need some pulling together, some summarizing, or some means of looking back. In some cases, a brief discussion will be adequate. In other cases, you will need to analyze the students' work together. In still other instances, you will give a quiz or test. Part of your instructional strategy should be to allow time for students to look reflectively on their work. If you don't, you may inhibit their chances of retaining key ideas and thus limit the lesson's potential to achieve transfer of learning.

6. *Reflection.* At this stage, you and your students have the opportunity to revisit what you have accomplished. You need to spend some time reviewing what has been learned and how it is connected to what has gone before and what is yet to come. Clarify any extended expectations. This is also the time to elicit ideas about the lesson from your students. What do they think they have learned? There will also be times when you assign homework in connection with a lesson. When you do, be certain you are clear about what students are to do at home and what they will be expected to turn in. Remember that they are on their own, so it is not appropriate to expect them to develop new skills. They will continue or build on their classwork.

Together, these steps give you a structure or framework for lesson planning. Don't think of them, however, as comprising a lockstep recipe, in which you must account for every point each time you work with students. The steps are based on known principles of effective learning. Sample Lessons 5.1 and 5.2, at the end of this chapter, illustrate the mechanics of lesson planning more concretely. Read them carefully to see how the steps are fleshed out.

Substance

The other fundamental aspect of a lesson besides mechanics is *substance,* or what is learned. A knowledge of the mechanics of lesson planning is useful because it gives you a framework within which to work. But the framework is of little value unless the substance of the lesson is worthwhile. The substance of social studies lessons is found in four bases: content, concepts, skills, and values.

1. *Content.* The content of a lesson is the knowledge that you have decided is necessary for students to learn. In elementary social studies, the content of the curriculum comes primarily from the social sciences. The most dominant influences of social studies content are history and geography, but economics, government, psychology, anthropology, and sociology are also significant. As you consider lesson content in the planning stages, ask yourself questions to clarify this area of concern: What is important about this content? How is it necessary to students? What information, knowledge, and understanding should students gain from this lesson?

2. *Concepts.* The content of a lesson will be adapted to the ideas or concepts that you want to emphasize. (The teaching of concepts is detailed in the next section.) At the planning stage, consider these issues: What idea or ideas about human behavior are inherent in this lesson? What kinds of questions need to be raised? To what extent will the students be stimulated intellectually? Will they share their ideas? Are the ideas in this lesson transferable to other experiences?

3. *Skills.* As you plan the actual instruction for your lesson, consider what skills you want to reinforce or teach. A later section of this chapter gives specific recommendations addressing this concern. In planning, ask yourself questions such as these: What methods and skills will the students use? Are the skills in this lesson transferable? (see Figure 5.1). Are students becoming increasingly independent in their problem solving?

4. *Values.* To be complete, your planning should take into account the values that will be part of the lesson. Again, some suggestions for doing this are given later in this chapter. As you plan, however, ask yourself: What will the students learn about themselves? Will they be exposed to the values of others? Will they have a chance to share their values?

figure 5.1   *A Sixth-Grader's Drawing of Herself Preparing to Make a Sketch of the School She Attends. The Skill of Perspective Taking Is Fundamental to Map Making.*

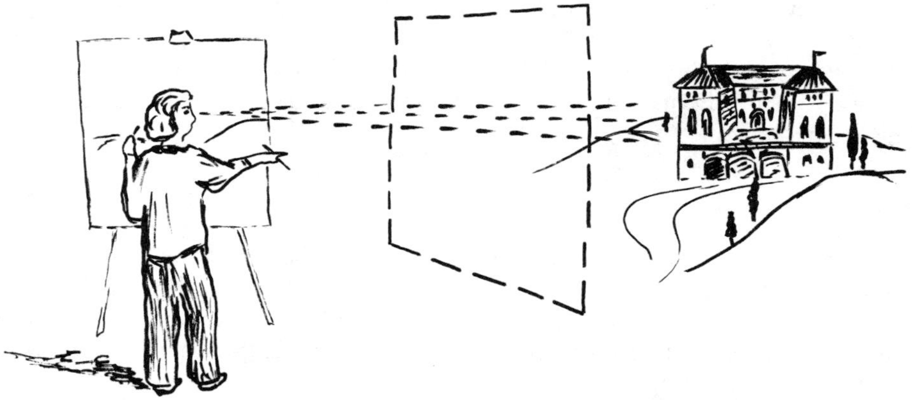

Obviously, not every lesson you teach will provide definitive answers to all the questions suggested here. However, every lesson ought to form part of a total context of instructional experience designed to take all these questions into account. Regardless of whether your philosophy of lesson planning tends to be formal or informal, you need to ensure that your social studies instruction is based on a purposeful rationale, rather than on merely covering topics or spending what is supposedly the appropriate amount of time with social studies. The teaching of concepts, skills, and values is considered in greater detail in the next sections of this chapter.

Teaching Concepts

Concepts in social studies are ideas about human activity. They transcend time and space, and they transfer to new situations. For example, the economic concept of *supply and demand* can be used to understand any economic system, anywhere, at any time. For example, people living in caves faced issues of supply and demand: They had to eat, and they had to gather or hunt in order to suppy their demand. But the concept of supply and demand also applies to modern capitalist societies, and it will be an important concept to understand if people establish a base on the moon in the future.

The power of concepts over mere facts and information is that concepts are intellectual tools that can be applied in an endless variety of settings. They provide us with generalizable ways of dealing with reality. Anthropologists make extensive use of the concept of *culture*. Sociologists attempt to identify and describe *norms of behavior*. Figure 5.2 provides a list of concepts commonly taught in elementary social studies.

figure 5.2   *Concepts Commonly Taught in Elementary Social Studies*

Adaptation	Diffusion	Norms	Social interaction
Artifacts	Diversity	Organizations	Socialization
Areal association	Enculturation	Patterns	Space
Assimilation	Environment	Power	Spatial interaction
Behavior	Family	Probability	Supply and demand
Cause/Effect	Governance	Problems	Systems
Change	Groups	Resources	Technology
Communication	Interdependence	Roles	Time
Community	Land use	Rules	Tools
Conflict	Life cycle	Scarcity	
Cooperation	Markets	Seasons	
Culture	Needs/Wants	Self	

Concepts are ideas, not terms whose definitions are to be memorized. There-fore, concepts are learned only through meaningful experiences that are revisited by reflective thinking. Only when people reflect on what they have done or seen do they begin to analyze, to see relationships, to make connections.

Developing Concepts

There are many ways to develop any given concept. However, as just noted, direct ex-perience and reflection on that experience are two proven techniques for concept build-ing with elementary-age children. Let's look at two scenarios that illustrate effective ways to get children to think conceptually.

The first lesson, for primary-age children, features a problem-centered experience with *supply and demand,* in which the teacher asks students to think reflectively and then to generalize to larger and different problems. This is a very effective way of teaching concepts.

The second lesson uses *webbing,* or *mind maps.* In it, the teacher and class begin their discussion with an organizing concept of theme—in this case, the concept of *cul-ture.* Concepts have attributes or characteristics that define them. In the case of culture, some of those attributes are food, clothing, shelter, customs, work, religion, and tech-nology (see Figure 5.3). Notice the progression from the more abstract webbing, which identifies a kind of rubric of cultural attributes that could be applied to any study (for example, ancient Athens, a medieval village, our community, and so on) to the specific application shown in Figure 5.4, which shows the webbing applied to the Pilgrims of colonial America.

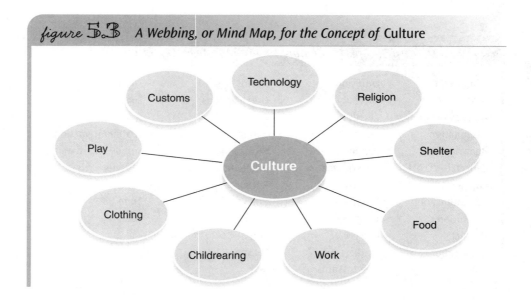

figure 5.3   *A Webbing, or Mind Map, for the Concept of* Culture

figure **5.4** A Webbing, or Mind Map, for the Concept of Culture *in the Context of the Culture of the Pilgrims*

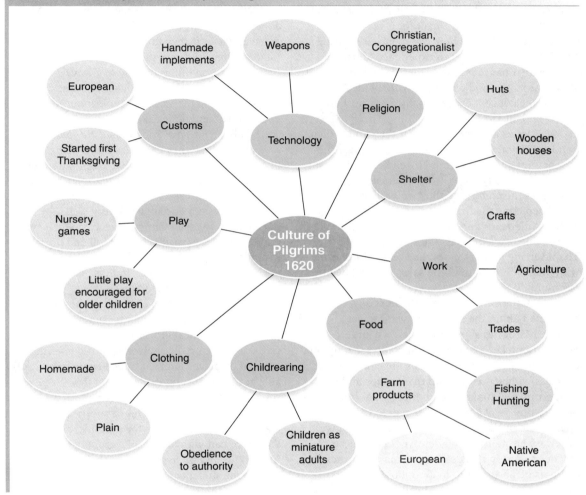

- Handmade implements
- Weapons
- Christian, Congregationalist
- European
- Huts
- Religion
- Customs
- Technology
- Wooden houses
- Started first Thanksgiving
- Shelter
- Nursery games
- Play
- Culture of Pilgrims 1620
- Crafts
- Work
- Agriculture
- Little play encouraged for older children
- Food
- Trades
- Homemade
- Clothing
- Childrearing
- Farm products
- Fishing Hunting
- Plain
- Obedience to authority
- Children as miniature adults
- European
- Native American

in the classroom **Teaching Supply and Demand through Problem Solving**

Ms. Jones, a first-grade teacher, wants to develop the economic concept of *supply and demand* with her students. Since concepts are ideas, not isolated facts, they always transcend time and space. Supply and demand certainly qualifies as a concept be-

cause there were supply-and-demand problems in prehistoric times, in ancient Egypt, in the Middle Ages, and in our present society, and there will no doubt be such problems in the future. Thus, we can see that supply and demand is not limited to any one place or any one time; rather, it transcends time and space.

At this point, we know that our first-grade teacher has selected a useful social science concept. But is this concept too difficult for 6-year-olds to comprehend? This is where experience is crucial. Ms. Jones must develop an experience for these children that has meaning to them. She thinks about the matter and comes up with an idea to introduce the concept experientially. Let's peek in as she sets up the experience.

Ms. Jones asks the students if they know what holiday is coming up this month. Right away, she has their attention. It is mid-November, and the students immediately answer "Thanksgiving." Ms. Jones asks the children if they would like to make a mural depicting the first Thanksgiving held by the Native Americans and the Pilgrims. Of course they would! She reads the class the story of the first Thanksgiving and discusses the events of that time with them. "Tomorrow," she says, "we will begin our mural."

When the children arrive the next day, they are excited about the mural and want to get started. Ms. Jones shows the class two large pieces of butcher paper, each taped up securely on either side of the room. She tells the children that the class will be divided into two groups and that each group will make its own mural. Then she says, "Jenny, why don't you go over to the paper on this side of the room and get started." Jenny stands up hesitantly and goes over to the piece of butcher paper. In front of her are many brushes and pots of poster paint in a rainbow of colors. Ms. Jones tells Jenny to go ahead and asks the rest of the class to come over to the other side. Twenty-two children crowd around the second piece of butcher paper. There is one paintbrush and one baby food jar filled with brown paint. The teacher tells the children to go ahead and make their mural.

Confusion reigns. Finally, someone says, "This isn't fair. It won't work." Others echo those sentiments. Ms. Jones asks the children if they have any ideas about how this situation could be improved. They suggest that half the kids should go to each

mural site and that the paint jars and brushes should be equally distributed. The teacher agrees, and the students make two great murals.

When the murals have been completed, Ms. Jones reminds the children of the problem they faced and asks if they think their solution was satisfactory. One child asks the teacher why all of this happened when things otherwise always go so smoothly. The teacher explains that it was done on purpose to help the students think about *resources,* both human and material. The children and Ms. Jones talk about *equal* and *unequal distribution of resources* (although they don't use those terms, at least at first). Ms. Jones explains that when the supply is too great for the demand (poor Jenny) or when the demand is too great for the supply (poor rest of the class), the system doesn't work very well. She asks the students to recall Christmases past when every child wanted a particular toy or doll and the supply simply wasn't great enough. Yet usually within a few months, the demand all but disappeared and the supply was more than adequate.

Ms. Jones also talks about the water supply and the demand for water in the summer. She explains how the local grocer knows how much cold cereal to stock on the shelves. She discusses the amount of playground space and equipment available at the school and explains that that is one reason that recess occurs at different times for different classes. She solicits examples of supply and demand from the students—for example, experiences they have had with toys or playground equipment (thirty kids and three playground balls). Last, she assigns the students the task of asking their parents if they can think of examples from life at home. The students are to report on these examples the following day.

To reconstruct this example of concept development, Ms. Jones took the students through the experience→mind→meaning continuum. An experience shared by the entire class provided a common point of reference. The teacher then helped the students to reflect on and process the experience, and she developed the meaning of the concept by providing and soliciting from the children other examples of supply and demand.

This supply-and-demand lesson raises an important point in teaching and learning social studies: Why go to all this trouble in order to introduce an economic concept to a group of 6-year-olds? Why not just read the definition from a dictionary or some other source, if you really think the term is important? First, relatively little extra work was involved, assuming that the teacher was going to have the children make Thanksgiving murals anyway. What the teacher did was to capitalize on an every-day situation and teach a concept from it. Second, you can't teach concepts by reading words from the dictionary. At best, you can teach vocabulary that way, but the method isn't very efficient, given what is known about short-term memory learning. The experience itself was the key, and the reflective thinking and mental processing of the process were also instrumental. This teacher taught the students a concept in such a way that they will probably always remember it.

in the classroom **Defining *Culture* through Webbing**

One of the most fundamental social science concepts is that of *culture*. The sociological or anthropological definition of *culture* is "the sum total of ways of living built up by one group of human beings and transmitted from one generation to another." But what you have just read is a definition of a term. For culture to become a concept and not just a term, you will have to develop appropriate experiences for your students.

The *webbing* approach represents a graphic strategy for developing conceptual schemes. A webbing, or mind map, enables students to bring meaning to information at both the content and conceptual levels. Marzano and Arredondo (1986) suggest that the use of webbing and other graphic approaches can lead students to generate new meaning about the material they study in several important ways:

- Webbing permits and often encourages non-linear thinking.
- Webbing can be used to synthesize complex information from diverse sources efficiently, helping students to identify patterns and relationships that are otherwise difficult to comprehend.

- Webbing helps the user generate information about the structure of the whole and the relationships among its parts that may not have been clear in the original, nongraphic information.

The webbing shown in Figure 5.3 illustrates how one might begin to imagine the attributes of the concept of *culture*. If culture is about the ways that a group of people live, then it would logically include their food, clothing, shelter, customs, and so on. The webbing in Figure 5.3 contains nine attributes of culture; certainly, others could be added. But this webbing is fairly abstract because it contains no specific content about a certain group of people. In that sense, it could be used as a starting point to describe any culture.

The second webbing, shown in Figure 5.4, illustrates how the attributes of the concept of *culture* can be applied to a specific cultural group—in this case, the Pilgrim settlers of Plimoth Plantation in the 1620s.

Here is a challenge for you: Identify some aspect of human activity—past or present, near or far, small or large scale. See if you can take the concept of *culture* and apply it as a webbing to the group or society you have chosen.

Keep in mind that concepts are *ideas*. Thus, in the first scenario, if you were asked what the main idea of the lesson is, your response would be that it is the concept of *supply and demand*. In the second scenario, the main idea is the concept of *culture*. Teachers are sometimes criticized for their failure to teach conceptually. This will not happen if you approach each experience by asking yourself: What is the main idea or concept I want the children to learn?

Teaching Skills

Skills are the *methodological tools* of social science. Being able to use them effectively sets a student free to investigate problems independently. If concepts are ideas about human behavior, then investigative skills are the primary means to further develop and expand those ideas. Social studies instruction often supports a wide variety of skill development:

- *Observing.* Observing phenomena, events, and interactions, both alone and with a partner; eyewitnessing; listening
- *Recording.* Recalling information and observations; photographing; mapping, drawing, and illustrating; tape recording; listing and writing
- *Describing.* Creating written, oral, photographic, and graphic descriptions; identifying attributes
- *Defining.* Defining terms and procedures; developing precise meanings; communicating; stating problems
- *Measuring.* Using standard measures and developing one's own measures; counting and quantifying data; using mathematical computations; developing rating scales; using and developing map scales
- *Estimating.* Guessing distance and size; using experience to make informed guesses
- *Classifying.* Grouping and categorizing; differentiating and labeling
- *Comparing / Contrasting.* Noting differences and similarities; identifying attributes; describing
- *Data gathering.* Identifying and selecting data sources; determining appropriate methods; conducting surveys, historical studies, experiments, and interviews
- *Data processing.* Quantifying data; performing graphic analysis; mapping; making charts; writing summaries
- *Communicating.* Communicating orally, in writing, and through pictures and graphics; engaging in group activities; expressing oneself
- *Constructing.* Building models and dioramas; drawing relief maps and murals; creating displays and exhibits
- *Analyzing.* Discriminating; categorizing; finding patterns; identifying attributes; detecting structures
- *Synthesizing.* Planning; producing; documenting; theorizing; developing systems
- *Hypothesizing.* Guessing in an educated way; developing hunches; testing assumptions
- *Inferring.* Making statements from data; reaching conclusions; making decisions
- *Predicting.* Determining relationships; forecasting outcomes; correlating variables
- *Generalizing.* Conceptualizing; identifying supportive data; testing relationships; finding patterns; summarizing

Collaborative learning works best in an open environment built on trust.

- *Evaluating.* Making judgments and decisions; determining validity; detecting errors and fallacies
- *Question posing.* Developing questions; identifying researchable problems; defining terms
- *Verifying.* Checking sources; validating ideas and sources; referring to authority

Effective teachers plan on incorporating a variety of skills in their lessons. Doing so helps keep students interested and offers them a panoply of ways to process, interpret, apply, and share what they learn. Consider the foregoing list carefully. Every lesson you teach should incorporate one or more of these skills. Let me give you an example of how skills can be put to use.

in the classroom Teaching Estimation

Take your class out to the play area of the school. Be sure they bring along some basic tools, such as pencils, pads, and rulers. Have the students work in pairs. Their task is to *estimate* the distance from one end of the play area to the other. Expect wild guesses. This is fine. Remember that children are imaginative.

Next, have the partners work together to measure the length of each person's stride. Depending on the age level, you can teach them about the average length of one of their strides by mathematically averaging 10 strides.

Finally, have the students step off the length of the play area by counting the number of strides from one end to the other end. Now they have *measured* the length. See Figure 5.5, in which a student describes the work she and her partner did in this activity.

figure 5.5   *Students Write about Measuring Distance*

Jason and I worked togeather.
First we guessed the distance across
the play-ground. We learned our
guesses were wrong but we didn't
know that them. We both laught.
Jason stepted ten times each
time we measered his stride

His average stride is 32mm
It took Jason 180 stride to cross
the playground. So, the playgound
is 5760 mm or 57.6 meters.
My guess was 1000 meters so I
learned something about
istimation!!
Shanda!!

Teaching Values

The values that we teach in elementary social studies fall into three distinct but related categories, each of which is important to children's growth and development: behavioral, procedural, and substantive. Your task is to ensure that all three are being learned along the way, not just in social studies but throughout the school experience.

English philosopher John Locke noted that teaching and learning can be approached at the simple level of just one variable, as illustrated by the teacher who says, "I teach social studies." What we do can also be approached by addressing several variables, as does the teacher who says, "I teach social studies, but I also teach children to be good citizens and to be critical thinkers." So, when we think of teaching values, skills, and concepts, we can see that good teachers always think in terms of several variables. It is all a part of the art of teaching that separates mediocre teachers from those teachers who aspire to excellence.

Let's consider the three categories of values:

- *Behavioral values* are related to conduct in the classroom and at school. They are what we might consider values of good citizenship. Behavioral values include having respect for others, showing politeness and kindness, taking turns, obeying rules, showing initiative, sharing ideas, and cooperating in group efforts, to name a few. A classroom is a crowded place, and behavioral values are at the heart of the matter of civility.

- *Procedural values* include inquiry, scientific thinking, critical thinking, problem solving, rational thought, perseverance, hard work, organization, and respect for evidence. These are the values we want children to acquire as they study, do their homework, and investigate problems. Procedural values represent the methods of the geographer, historian, and social scientist and are obviously closely connected to the skills mentioned earlier.

- *Substantive values* are those beliefs acquired by individuals as a result of their experiences and feelings about what is true and important. Such values include an individual's ideas of what is enjoyable and not enjoyable, what is right and wrong, and what is worthwhile and wasteful in life. So, if you and I disagree over which season of the year is the best, we can say we have a difference of substantive values. When people express religious differences, it is usually because of their differences in substantive values. One thing you can be sure of is that you will find a wide range of substantive values among students in any class you teach. In a pluralistic society, teachers need to show tolerance and appreciation for differences if they are to expect this from the children they teach.

Values are a part of every lesson and every experience at school, whether we want them to be or not. A teacher's behavior is on constant view by the students. The best way to approach values is at a level of consciousness, in which you determine to teach all three types of values and to organize reflective thinking sessions in which you and your students search for meaning in the social studies experience.

Perhaps you never thought of it this way before, but your values will determine whether you think children should work alone or together in certain situations. Your values will determine how much respect you show to children, especially those whose values seem to be different from your own. Your values will determine whether you can tolerate the messiness of projects and childhood activities. Your values and those of your students will determine to what extent your classroom is a miniature civil society, in which courtesy, politeness, and respect for others are built into the routine. Figure 5.6 is an essay written by a student from that type of classroom, reflecting on what he likes about school.

figure **5.6**   *A Second-Grader's Essay: "I Like School"*

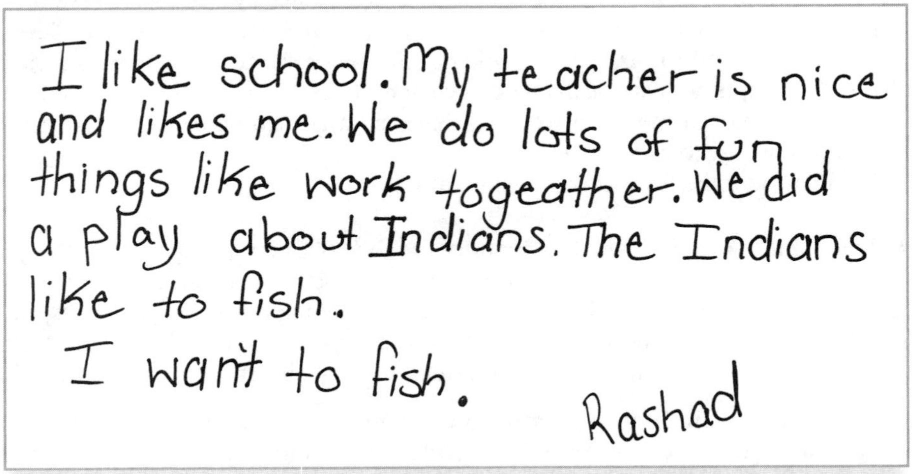

> I like school. My teacher is nice and likes me. We do lots of fun things like work togeather. We did a play about Indians. The Indians like to fish.
> I want to fish.
>
> Rashad

Planning and Developing Units

Unit instruction is a useful approach to most teaching and learning situations because it concentrates your efforts and those of your students on a central theme, organizing idea, or set of concepts. The effect of such a focus is to promote systematic learning toward clearly defined objectives, thus keeping you from falling into the trap of teaching nothing more than activities, worksheets, or pages from a textbook.

What Is a Unit?

A *unit* is a sequential progression of lessons directed toward the development of a theme. Unit themes are developed through articulating content, concepts, skills, and values. The term *unit* implies oneness or wholeness, as opposed to fragmentation. In other words, a unit has integrity; it holds together. Thus, a unit will describe its sense of coherence and oneness.

In social studies, common unit titles might include "Choosing Our Leaders," "Early Explorers," "The Pilgrims," "Minority Rights," "Learning about Latitude and Longitude," and "The Gold Rush." Of course, your textbook and district or state guides provide other sources of information regarding what material (and therefore what unit topics) you are to cover at your given grade level.

How Long Should a Unit Be?

How many days of instruction should be allocated to each unit? There is no predetermined amount of time that must be allocated for any given unit. You, as the instructional expert, need to make that decision on the basis of what needs to be covered in the course of the school year. For instance, if you must cover seven major topical areas in social studies in one school year and a school year is thirty-six weeks long, calculating a simple average will suggest that you should spend about five weeks on each unit. However, that is only an average figure, and various factors are involved.

Much depends on how your units are designed—whether they are based on large themes or smaller, more focused topics. For example, the "Transportation Revolution" could be presented independently as a week-long unit, or it could be taught as part of a broader unit on the United States. A week-long unit on the "Settlers of Massachusetts Bay Colony" could provide a brief overview of the lives of the early colonists in New England; a more comprehensive unit might cover life and times in all 13 original colonies. The same information might also be part of a "Thanksgiving" unit for first grade.

Some teachers prefer to restrict unit length, as narrowing the focus allows more units to be covered in a single year. However, some teachers prefer to keep their unit topics more broadly focused and to develop and teach longer units. A broader focus might support a unit titled "The Movement West," while a narrower focus might support several smaller units, such as "Life on the Prairie," "The Trail of Tears," "Texas, the Lone-Star State," and "Settling the Oregon Country."

Although teaching narrow topics can keep the content focused and manageable, doing so may tend to present learning in small, compartmentalized packages that do not reflect reality. And although broad units can provide a more comprehensive and thus realistic overview, they take seemingly forever to teach and so the focus may well be lost. Developing a *balance* between the two and making connections from one unit to another are among the many challenges facing the instructional expert.

Developing a Unit Plan

In developing a unit, you should always follow these six steps: Set unit goals in context of goals for the year, create an overview, develop objectives, develop a block plan, identify resources, and create an instructional design. Let's explore each of these steps.

SET GOALS IN CONTEXT   The first step in developing a unit is to think of it in terms of your goals for the entire year. You will need to answer such questions as these: Where does this topic logically fit in the flow of my instruction? What skills and knowledge are prerequisite to the skills and knowledge in this unit? And most important, What should children at this level know and be able to do as a result of this year's experience?

CREATE AN OVERVIEW   The second step in the development of a unit is to write the unit overview, which contains a rationale and a brief statement of content. The purpose of a written rationale is to state why you are teaching a particular unit. How is the unit crucial in the process of children's learning in the social studies? This is not terribly difficult to do because people generally agree with the concepts that children must learn to live as social beings in a civilized world and that learning about citizenship, government, history, and geography is necessary to function effectively as a citizen of the world. The statement of content may be written in paragraph form, but more often a table-of-contents format is used. The table of contents tells what topics you intend to teach. (Many teachers map out a plan—a table of contents—for the entire year.)

DEVELOP UNIT OBJECTIVES   Write the objectives for the unit in clear terms; that is, make each objective specify exactly what is expected of the children in performance terms. Thus, while a statement such as "The children need to develop greater capabilities in the area of critical thinking" is fine as part of your rationale, it is probably better stated as a long-term goal than as a unit objective. Here are some examples of clear objectives. Note that each specifies *who* (the child) does *what* (identifies, categorizes, etc.):

- The students are able to identify the symbols used on a map.
- The students can verbally define, recognize, and draw latitude and longitude lines on both a globe and a map.
- The students can locate and identify the four major directions (north, south, east, west) and develop a map key to explain the directional symbols on a map.
- The students can identify examples of cooperative, competitive, and independent learning.
- The students can identify examples of prejudice and bias.
- The students can cite examples of tolerance, justice, and fairness.

When you develop your set of unit objectives, be sure to consider the range of intellectual endeavor, from knowledge and comprehension through such higher levels as application and analysis. Bloom's (1984) *Taxonomy of Educational Objectives* is a useful guide for writing unit objectives. As shown in Figure 5.7, this taxonomy (cognitive domain) is a hierarchical construct that is divided into six increasingly complex levels. Take a few moments to consider each level. Remember that your unit objectives should reflect a representative distribution of each level.

Although you need to develop unit objectives at all six levels, you will write more objectives for knowledge and comprehension than you will for the higher categories. There are two reasons for this: (1) Knowledge and comprehension represent the most basic skills and are therefore fundamental to the learning enterprise, and (2) the complexity of tasks at such levels as synthesis and evaluation means that those assignments will usually be of much longer duration.

It is important that you recognize the necessity of developing unit objectives using clear terms and all the levels of Bloom's taxonomy. These objectives will serve to guide your day-to-day instruction, and they will form the basis for writing test items and other means of evaluating students' progress. Thus, there is a natural axis that runs from planning through instruction to assessment:

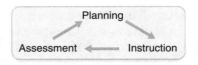

DEVELOP A BLOCK PLAN   The fourth step in developing a unit is to create a block plan. A block plan is a unit calendar, in which the scope and sequence of the unit are

figure 5.7 *Bloom's Revised Taxonomy of Educational Objectives*

1. *Remembering.* The issue is recall of information. At this level, it is important that children remember what they have read, were told, or observed. This level is crucial because if children do not possess basic skills in social studies, they are hardly in a position to later carry out meaningful or creative analyses of issues with a social or international scope.

2. *Understanding.* Your objective for children at this level is to ensure that they can explain ideas. It is one thing, for example, to be able to list and identify the requirements necessary to run for president (knowledge) but quite another to be able to explain why these requirements might be important (comprehension).

3. *Applying.* Objectives developed at the application level have as their purpose something practical: actual usage. The issue at this level is whether the child can use such things as skills and concepts in new situations. For example, in spelling, one needs to know how to spell words for a spelling test (knowledge), to define words for a vocabulary test (comprehension), and to use those words appropriately in an explanation or story (application).

4. *Analyzing.* Objectives written at the analysis level are designed to enable children to see relationships, make comparisons and contrasts, and look for patterns. *Analysis,* as the term implies, is an attempt to break down whole entities into their component parts. For example, in a study of communities, you might want the children to identify how various communities (e.g., urban, suburban, rural) function differently to meet the needs of the people living within them or perhaps to identify how daily life might differ among those communities.

5. *Evaluating.* Objectives for the evaluation level include those that encourage children to form their own points of view or to express their ideas on issues. For evaluation to be adequate, this level need not always take the form of the traditionally expected written test. Drawings, stories, and a class panel discussion in which the children explain and support individual opinions can all be considered in evaluation. At the evaluation level, divergent thinking is encouraged and differences of opinion are to be expected.

6. *Creating.* This level requires critical analysis as well as insight, out-of-the-box thinking, and an ability to see things from fresh perspectives. Students are called on to design, construct, plan, produce, and generate new ideas and/or products.

Source: Adapted from Bloom, 1984. In the 1990s a team of psychologists led by Lorin Anderson revised Benajmin Bloom's Taxonomy of Educational Objectives in order to make it more adaptable to classroom needs (www.rite.ed.qut.edu.au/oz-teachernet).

laid out on a grid where each square represents one lesson. The filled-in squares show at a glance what will be taught when. Once you have chosen a unit topic that fits logically into your year's sequence of social studies instruction (whatever the level or focus—history, geography, community, or citizenship) and you have developed a set of instructional objectives to guide your teaching, you will be ready to sketch your block plan for the unit. Figure 5.8 illustrates a block plan for a unit on "Consumer Research."

IDENTIFY UNIT RESOURCES   It is quite possible that most of the units you develop and teach will depend heavily on textbooks and your accompanying teacher's guide both for content and direction. When this is the case, the textbook and teacher's guide will be your primary resources. However, even the teacher who takes a textbook-oriented approach to

figure **5.8**   *Consumer Research (Economics) Unit: Simple Block Plan*

Monday	Tuesday	Wednesday	Thursday	Friday
Introduction. Discuss quality of products.	Watch film: *Seeing through Commercials.*	Begin testing products.	Do product testing.	Complete graphs, charts.
Present consumer research findings.	Discuss and reflect on product testing.	Write letters to companies.	Prepare advertisements for hypothetical products.	Present advertisements to class.
Analyze videotaped commercials.	Do survey research; skills lesson.	Prepare consumer surveys.	Conduct consumer surveys at primary grades.	Conduct consumer surveys at upper grades.
Analyze survey results. Prepare graphs and displays.	Reflect on pros and cons of consumerism.	Debate topic of advertising on children's television.	Write stories on creative ideas for consumer guidance.	Have test on unit material.

his or her units should go beyond the given, finding and developing additional source material. A textbook and teacher's guide can give basic direction, but only you, the instructional expert, can design, arrange, and implement the presentation. It is up to *you* to enhance the material and develop a unit that reflects your special style and expertise, as well as the needs of the children in your classroom.

As you consider the development of a unit of instruction (particularly one that goes beyond a series of textbook assignments), you will find it necessary and helpful, as well as challenging, to seek and collect resources that not only help strengthen your own background on the topic but also provide resource material for the children to use throughout the course of study.

CREATE AN INSTRUCTIONAL DESIGN   This section discusses the various elements involved in the development of instruction. It summarizes much of the information just discussed and also provides a guide as you embark on your personal journey of instructional design.

After you have planned your unit, follow these steps:

1. *Time your unit.* Think of your unit in terms of a period of time you must fill from beginning to end. Think of the whole as being made up of segments. Ask yourself: What do I have to cover? Make a list. Then ask yourself: What do the children need to know? Make a list of that, as well.

2. *Design and build a framework of ideas.* Decide how to structure or present those segments. Decide exactly *what* you want to do (the approach you will use in the unit), and then decide *how* you want to do it (the variety of means you will choose to utilize). Remember that the saying "Variety is the spice of life" refers to instructional design, too!

3. *Brainstorm your plan.* Go through an informal planning process, moving energetically from idea, to process, to possibilities, to product. Remember: The creative process is messy! Map out ideas visually, or make lists of them. Dream, think, and imagine. It *will* begin to come together.

4. *Organize your ideas.* The unit needs to be formally organized, so from your outline of ideas or list of themes, activities, and approaches, decide how to do the following:

- Develop your specific lesson plans
- Prepare your lecture notes, assignments, and cooperative and individual activities
- Develop and prepare your handouts
- Develop and prepare assignments
- Prepare your classroom to reflect the focus of study in the unit

5. *Calendarize your design.* Organize your unit into a time frame. Decide what you plan to do on a day-to-day basis (including adequate time for children to complete assignments, etc.).

6. *Teach that unit!* First, get the attention of your students by giving them a sneak preview. Next, hit them with the hard stuff: Challenge them, raise their expectations, and explain the need to conquer certain academic material before moving on. Then, proceed through the organized design of instruction. Order and organization are not boring concepts. It's up to *you* to bring your unit to life!

in the classroom An Archaeology Unit

A unit on archaeology can provide an excellent opportunity to practice a variety of skills and teaching methods. It is also an ideal unit for integrating different areas of the curriculum: history, certainly, but also geography and science; language arts writing and presentation skills; artistic skills (as students create "artifacts" and record "finds" on sketch pads and graph paper); and even skills in mathematics, as children measure their dig areas and take depth measurements onsite. A unit on archaeology also lends itself (as do so many teaching units) to a wide variety of instructional strategies. For example, this unit incorporates cooperative learning, video presentations, creative group storytelling, direct instruction, and a good many hands-on activities outside the regular classroom environment. Critical thinking and decision making are also part of this unit of study, and most of it is conducted by the children while working in dig teams.

Exact instructions on how to teach a unit on archaeology are *not* included here; they are for you, the professional, to assemble and design. However, a good many guidelines are provided to get you started as you explore various ideas, and they might spark you into adding your personal touches to the unit. I encourage you to use the suggestions offered to start your own journey toward filling in the framework. A presentation outline is provided for your reference, but it will be up to you to fill in the blanks and research the content. Reading through the unit materials that follow will present some of the possibilities of what might be done with the children in your unique classroom. For instance, Figure 5.9 shows a sample webbing that you and your students might develop.

Refer to the block plan (Figure 5.10) for ideas and a possible sequence, and remember that the unit can easily be adapted to the age of the children

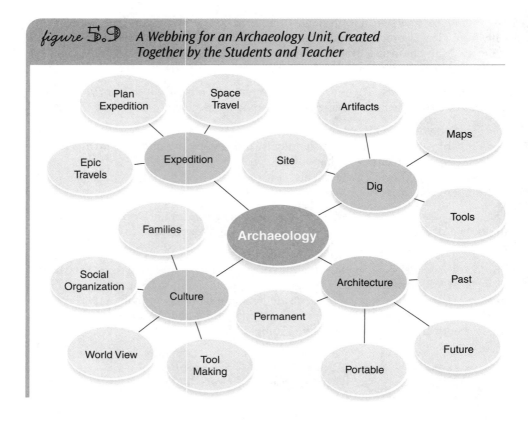

figure **5.9**   *A Webbing for an Archaeology Unit, Created Together by the Students and Teacher*

you teach. Obviously, depending on grade level, certain adjustments will have to be made in terms of content, length, and the explanation and execution of the actual "big dig event" (i.e., the excavation). This particular block plan is designed for a 20-day unit, but given your particular circumstances, you may choose to use some of the ideas and teach an abbreviated unit. For example, you might arrange a simulated dig in a sandbox or in a number of sand-filled cartons in your classroom, or you might decide to teach a similar unit but with less comprehensive preparation and fewer after-dig activities.

Be creative in your use of resources. There are many possibilities for obtaining items that can be used in the dig, from your school's art department to the broken items in the storage room of a nearby art or import store. "Artifacts" can come from the most unexpected places. Also keep in mind that vast community resources are available—volunteers you might ask to assist in preparing the imaginary excavation and to serve as observers at each team's dig area. Research your library and social studies publications for information on archaeological terms and for illustrations of the process of excavating. Again, many resources are available. You simply need to locate them.

With some effort and the application of your instructional design expertise to this model, you and your students can gain much from an archaeological experience—a motivating way to teach units in social studies.*

figure 5.10 *Archaeology Unit: Sample Block Plan*

Monday	Tuesday	Wednesday	Thursday	Friday
INTRODUCTION: Springboard Tell true stories of discovery Share an artifact Show opening segment *Raiders of the Lost Ark* Start logs	Give hint of upcoming BIG DIG Team Assignment Distribute presentation outline: *HOW do archaeologists actually work?* Reflective thinking Log entries	Garbage can analogy (classroom demonstration and home experiment) Present basic terminology Write letters to museums/universities	VIDEO: *King Tut's Tomb* Discuss Howard Carter Talk about thrill of discovery *(use circle discussion)*	STORY IN THE ROUND: *The Mystery Dig* (must use archaeology terms learned on Wed; group activity) Introduce idea of field notes
GUEST SPEAKER: Archaeologist from the Children's Museum	TOPIC: Social Scientists (handout, section 2) Class discussion CREATE A POSTER (individual activity): Illustrating and defining one social scientist	SNEAK PREVIEW of big excavation activity Talk about roles and what kinds of things they can expect to be doing CREATE DIG TEAMS Make posters	LIBRARY (cooperative and individual activity): Locate and copy photos, drawings, symbols to assist students in preparing artifacts for dig (art class tomorrow)	ART ROOM (cooperative team activity): Prepare individually designed shards ("artifacts") to be used for the BIG DIG Activity *Prepare Hallway Exhibits (use posters made by class)*
ARMCHAIR TRAVEL: Teacher slide presentation of her travels to Greece (Mycenae, Delphi, Santorini) Share real stories about archaeologists (Handout, section 3)	PREPARE DIG FOLDERS (cooperative team activity): Select team name; assemble information; illustrate digging methods on graph paper	ORAL REVIEW of terms, social scientists, steps, and dig methods Talk about FIELD and LAB experts *Students give briefings*	DISTRIBUTE TEAM PACKET for the BIG DIG EVENT: Review all in detail; HOW will it work; time for questions, ideas, clarifications	GROUP DECISION MAKING (cooperative team meetings) *Getting Ready for the BIG DIG Event!*
THE BIG DIG EVENT (onsite) Videotaping	Groups meet to PREPARE presentations Share ideas from logs	BIG DIG EXCAVATION TEAM PRESENTATIONS	DIG TEAMS CREATE CLASSROOM DISPLAYS for Parent-Friendship Night	REFLECTION: Watch video of dig and discuss experience

Young anthropologists experience the process/inquiry approach firsthand as they work on a dig at an actual site.

**Presentation Outline Introduction:
Mysteries and Antiquities from the Past**

I. Historical Records
  A. What *is* history?
  B. What is history based on?
  C. Types of historical records:
    1. Material remains
    2. Written accounts (primary and secondary sources)
II. Social Scientists
  A. Archaeologist
  B. Cartographer
  C. Geographer
  D. Linguist
  E. Political scientist
  F. Sociologist
  G. Economist
  H. Psychologist
  I. Historian
  J. Anthropologist
III. Some Real "Indiana Jones" Experts
  A. The Leakey family (Louis, Mary, and Richard)
  B. Heinrich Schliemann
  C. Your teacher (well, sort of . . .)
IV. Archaeology: Getting to Work
  A. The dig
  B. Plan of work: six steps, from start to finish
  C. Methodology (main ones only; there are others)
    1. Trench
    2. Quadrant
    3. Squares
    4. Numbered squares

V. Experts and Specialists Involved
   A. In the field
      1. Surveyor
      2. Geologist
      3. Photographer
      4. Draftsperson
      5. Preparator
   B. In the lab
      1. Geochemist
      2. Paleontologist
      3. Physical anthropologist
      4. Petrologist
      5. Palynologist

The Dig

WHEN: Select a specific day; arrange it with school officials if necessary.

WHERE: Somewhere on the school campus; look for the marked site!

EQUIPMENT: YOUR TEAM PACKET

- Graph paper.
- Recording material: paper, pencil, marking pen, clipboard.
- Plastic bags that zip close and a shoebox (for the finds).
- Very important: a toothbrush and a spoon. (Each member of the digging team will need both.) These are the only pieces of digging equipment you can use. Archaeologists work slowly and carefully, not wanting to damage potential finds.

OPTIONAL EQUIPMENT: Optional (but potentially helpful in your presentation) is a digital camera to record the stages of discovery and the finished work. (An artist might choose to bring additional equipment to assist in record keeping and documentation.)

CLOTHING: Jeans, sweatshirt, gloves—this is going to be messy!

BASIC TEAM INSTRUCTIONS: You will have to make some decisions together. By the time you locate the excavation site (as soon as possible after fourth period), you should already have decided on the method you will use first and what role each member of the team will play in the actual dig. (We have some time in class before the dig, and you can make your decisions at that time.) Begin digging immediately after you have located your site. All sites will be well marked. Have an alternative method ready, in case the one you select does not work out. An archaeologist would be sure to dig very carefully, as there is always a chance that carelessness will destroy a priceless antiquity. You have no idea what you may find (but believe me—there is something there!), so wield that toothbrush and spoon *very* carefully!

Be sure to keep very careful records of everything you do and everything you find. Remember, you are maintaining a complete record of your dig for next week's presentation.

PROCEDURE: As soon as you come across the edge of something, carefully work your way around it and it will begin to emerge. Your team may have chosen to have members take turns at various tasks, or you may have divided the work evenly so that you each play the same role throughout the dig. However you chose to organize yourselves to accomplish your goal, make sure that all of the following tasks are covered:

- Some members will be engaged in the actual process of digging.
- Someone might use a camera to record stages of discovery.
- Keep track on graph paper of exactly where on the site finds have been located, and illustrate for each the exact method of digging used (trench, quadrant—check your class notes for the different types of methods).
- Be sure to record (draw) each piece as it emerges.
- Maintain a journal of the activity onsite.

When You Have Recovered the Artifact or Antiquity

- Identify and describe. Prepare written copies and graphs—all records of your process.
- Reconstruct and preserve. As archaeologists, your job is to reconstruct and preserve the item(s). Hang on to your sketches and the items themselves. (Put broken bits back together, if possible.)

NOW THAT THE DIG IS OVER, THIS IS YOUR JOB: Let's hope you have kept careful records of everything you accomplished and what you found as it happened. You have been maintaining a complete record of the dig to use in next week's presentation to the museum curator (that's me!)—the sponsor of the dig. As part of the presentation, your team will be sharing the methods and procedures your team chose to use; you will be telling the story of your dig and showing the physical results. (Remember, notes and quick sketches made onsite can be tidied up before the presentation.) During the next few days (and any time you and your team members arrange to meet together), work on your curator (teacher!) presentation, which is due next week. Other noted archaeologists (your classmates) will observe. We're excited to see what you have to share! As part of your presentation, your team will do these two things:

- Share the methods and procedures your team chose to follow.
- Tell the story of your dig and show the results. (Remember, sketchy notes and drawings made onsite can be tidied up before the presentations.)

The Content of Your Presentation

- Decide who will report what.
- As a team, explain the find and the process you followed. Remember, the final job of an archaeologist is to report findings.
- Organize your information so that it will tell the story of your experiences. (Remember the Howard Carter and King Tut video we saw). Unfold the facts gradually. Tell about the methods you used and why you chose them. Take the rest of the class through each step as you share graphs and/or posters with us.
- Show us the reconstructed item (glue is fine). Describe it carefully; tell us what you know.
- Do some research: Can you date the item? Where did it probably come from? What was it used for? Get us excited!

You can mount your sketches and photos on posterboard so we can see everything as you present. Or perhaps you have a better, more creative idea for presenting. (Video? Computers?) Remember to keep *quality* in mind. Don't be sloppy in your presentation, or the curator may not hire you next time!

Finally, hand in an official half-page summary on the Curator Conclusion Form. The whole team should have contributed to this, and the names of all team members should appear on the sheet. What are your conclusions?

(Hey, even Indiana Jones had to start this way!)

---

*My thanks to Shirley Riley for her contributions to this archaeology unit.

Summary

"Teachable moments"—those serendipitous events that sometimes allow you to support your students' learning in totally unexpected ways—are delightful and rewarding. But the vast majority of what your students learn in your classroom will be the result of what you bring to them. And the more carefully you plan, the deeper and more wide ranging their learning will be. Careful planning of units and lessons will en-sure that your instruction meets the goals you set for it—that students understand the content and concepts you envision, that they master the skills you intend, and that they develop the values you incorporate.

Your textbooks and other programs can furnish you with existing lesson and unit plans. It would be exhausting (and counterproductive) for you to attempt to develop all your own lessons and units. In some instances, however—for example, in developing local topics—you will need to make your own lesson plans. But whether you are using plans created by others or developing your own, you should always perceive an underlying rationale designed to expand students' knowledge (content), ideas (concepts), investigative skills (processes), and attitudes and beliefs (values).

Explorations

Reflect On . . .

1. It has been suggested that teachers often teach facts and information, rather than concepts and ideas, in social studies. Why do you think this might be the case? What can you suggest to improve the conceptual aspect of lesson planning?

2. Some teachers might argue that planning takes away from the more creative aspects of teaching—that it inhibits spontaneity in learning. What are the arguments for and against planning social studies lessons? What is your position on planning?

In the Field

3. Examine the teacher's edition of an elementary social studies textbook, and try to find at least five suggested activities that you think would lend an added dimension to social studies lesson plans. Share those ideas in a small-group discussion of effective planning.

For Your Portfolio

4. Develop a one- or two-page lesson plan on the topic of "the importance of reading biographies of key people in American history." Include a few excerpts from actual biographies as part of the material for your lesson plan. Share your plan with several others who have attempted this same activity. What did you learn from them? What did they learn from you?

Continuing the Journey: Suggested Readings

Ellis, A. (2004). *Exemplars of curriculum theory.* Larchmont, NY: Eye on Education.
This book explains three models of curriculum (learner centered, society centered, and knowledge centered) with real-world examples of each.

Gardner, H. (2000). *The disciplined mind.* New York: Penguin.
The guru of the multiple intelligence theory writes an intriguing book on underlying purposes of learning.

Joyce, B., Weil, M., & Calhoun, E. (2006). *Models of teaching* (8th ed.). Boston: Allyn & Bacon.
An explanation of four families of teaching with models of each. An excellent source for expanding a teacher's repertoire.

Kinnucan-Weisch, K. (1999). Strategic teaching and strategic learning in first grade. *Reading Horizons, 40,* 3–21.
A useful source of ideas and techniques for working with primary-age learners.

Olson, K., & Kovalik, S. (1999). *Integrated thematic instruction: Classroom stages of implementation.* New York: Classroom Books for Education.
A practical guide for integrating separate subjects around conceptual themes.

Sternberg, R. (1999). *Thinking styles.* Cambridge: Cambridge University Press.
A review of theory and research into a strategic topic.

Wasley, P. (1999). Developing a repertoire. *Childhood Education, 77,* 276–279.
The title of this useful article speaks for itself.

SAMPLE LESSON 5.1   *What Season Is It?*

AGE LEVEL: Primary

KEY IDEA: Each season of the year has its own unique characteristics.

INSTRUCTIONAL OBJECTIVE: Students will explore the local environments to observe, record, and gather evidence to show what season it is.

SET: Begin by showing the students a calendar (preferably one with pictures that illustrate the seasons). Ask the following questions to stimulate class discussion:

1. What is a calendar for?
2. Why do we need to keep track of time?
3. How is a calendar like a clock? How is a calendar different from a clock?
4. Calendars keep track of days, weeks, months, and years. Each year is divided into four seasons. Can anyone tell me the names of the four seasons?

INSTRUCTION: Write the names of the four seasons on the board. Ask the students to list various characteristics of each season (e.g., winter might have rain or snow). Write their responses on the board until there is a good list under each season—for example:

Winter	*Spring*	*Fall*	*Summer*
rain	flowers	leaves	blue sky
snow	baseball	football	sunshine
skiing	green grass		vacation

Next, tell the students, "We are going to pretend that we don't know what season it is. We are going to go outside together to see if you can find *evidence* (define) to prove what season it is." Take the class outside, and see how many examples the children can find to show what season it is (e.g., leaves, weeds, kids on the playground playing football). Bring any tangible examples back to the classroom for display.

REFLECTION/ASSESSMENT: Ask the class, "If someone asked us what season it is, how could we prove our answer (with evidence)?"

CLOSURE: Have students complete these statements: "The evidence we found outside shows that it is _____ (name season). When you go home today, I'd like to have you tell someone at home how you proved it was _____ (season). Also, I'd like to have you bring any new evidence that you can to prove that it is _____."

SAMPLE LESSON 5.2   *Aleut Maps**

AGE LEVEL: Intermediate

KEY IDEA: Distances can be measured in units of space or time. Each culture has invented units of space and time to keep track of those dimensions.

INSTRUCTIONAL OBJECTIVE: Students will construct and use Aleut maps to measure distances on the playground.

SET: Begin by asking students to estimate the following distances or other distances they can think of:

1. The length of a football field
2. The distance from their home to school
3. The height of the classroom door

Next, ask the following questions:

1. How long does it take you to get to school? Can the trip to school be measured using either distance or time?
2. How does using a map help you get from one place to another?
3. How is a map like a plan? A record? A story? A picture?

INSTRUCTION: Tell the students that in times past, when an Aleut hunter or fisherman would leave the village by kayak, he would paddle close to the shore as he voyaged from bay to bay, sometimes going great distances. Because the route was uncharted and bays have a way of looking alike, the Aleuts had to have a method of keeping track of how far they were from their home village. They came up with a simple but ingenious way of doing this: They would take a stick with them, carving a notch in the stick each time they entered a new bay. So, five notches meant five bays away from home.

Tell the children that they are going to make Aleut maps. Give each group of two students a stick (e.g., tongue depresser, Popsicle stick) and a pencil. Take the class out to the playground, and have each pair of students make their way around the edge of the playground, making a mark on their stick for each notable tree, fence post, or whatever they pass.

REFLECTION/ASSESSMENT: Ask the students how such a system of keeping track of distances is similar to or different from the measures they are used to. Give each pair of students time to process this, asking them to make notes. Then discuss insights with the full class.

CLOSURE: Assign students the homework task of making an Aleut map that measures distances at home or in their neighborhoods.

*Aleuts (pronounced "Al-ee-utes") are native people of the Aleutian Islands and the western part of the Alaska peninsula. The traditional Aleut culture is a hunting and fishing culture. They are a resourceful people who are skilled kayak builders and sailors. Their culture is ancient and has been traced back to at least 2000 B.C.

Strategies for Social Studies Teaching and Learning

In this chapter, we will explore these themes:

- Research about social studies teaching and learning
- Direct instruction strategies
- Indirect instruction strategies

To see a child learn is to see a miracle unfold.
—Anna Rosewell
To make social studies interesting, make it social.
—Allysia, sixth-grade student

Research in effective teaching has shown that using a variety of learning experiences is far superior to repetitive, highly predictable, paper-and-pencil-type lessons. We learn best by doing.

Teaching and learning strategies can be divided into two broad and related categories: direct teaching and indirect teaching. Both are necessary. Proper balance is the key.

ocial studies instruction demands alternatives, not only in terms of the content learned by students but also—and equally important—in terms of *how* students go about learning. Some evidence exists that social studies is one of the least-liked subjects in the curriculum (Goodlad, 1984). We simply can't have that! It is especially important that students be motivated by a variety of experiences in social studies and that those experiences be designed to reach students whose interests and needs vary—not only from student to student but from day to day, as well.

The alternatives presented here are not meant to be an exhaustive list of the possibilities inherent in teaching social studies. Rather, they are designed to serve as models. In the pages that follow, each learning alternative is explained and accompanied by examples. Some examples are oriented to primary school–age students; others are oriented to intermediate school–age students.

What Research Says about Social Studies Teaching and Learning

A number of studies have been conducted over the years in which students have been given an opportunity to voice their opinions about social studies. Schug and colleagues (1984) explored the question of how students thought social studies teaching and learning might be improved. The following list shows the preferences that students expressed about social studies learning:

1. Group projects
2. Field trips
3. Less reading
4. Role-play and simulations
5. Class activities
6. Independent work
7. Class discussion
8. Student planning
9. Less lecture
10. Challenging learning experiences
11. Clear examples

Schug's useful study provided insights to the childhood perspective on social studies. However, it was conducted more than 20 years ago, and much has happened since then. What do children think *today?*

In order to answer this question, I conducted a survey, asking children to list ways in which they think social studies could be improved. With a few notable exceptions, the outcomes are remarkably similar to those Schug found. Admittedly, my survey did not involve a random sample, so the results are difficult to generalize. However, I do think they are representative in many ways. Here are the findings:

- Group projects
- Field trips
- Drama and role-play
- Games
- Computer activities
- Construction and hands-on activities
- Animals
- Environment
- Student interest

- Drawing and maps
- Less reading (especially textbooks)

Clearly, the lists are more alike than different. Still, in the more recent list, we see the importance of the computer and its influence on childhood learning and the idea emerging that animals should be studied. Interest in the computer is easy to explain, given the incredible advances in technology in the past twenty-odd years. But the idea of studying animals makes little sense at first glance, since social studies is the study of human beings. Maybe the children know something intuitively that many adults have not considered. When the great psychologist Jerome Bruner put together an experimental social studies program for children many years ago, he was very clear about the idea that in order to understand human behavior, it is necessary to contrast and compare it with the behavior of various animal groups. The second list also shows concern for the environment, a hopeful sign that today's young people take environmental studies seriously.

In yet another study, Fouts (1989) used a questionnaire/survey of students to determine their perceptions of what creates a positive attitude toward social studies. As shown in Figure 6.1, he characterized the findings under positive and negative attitudes.

If you check out the results of these various studies, the obvious and very compelling message from students is that they wish to be actively involved. They also want to work with others, and they would appreciate a certain amount of variety. Now it is up to us to channel these interests in meaningful ways. The evidence is clear that *how* we teach does make a difference. Every now and then, research and common sense come together.

Research in effective teaching supports the use of a variety of teaching strategies. It is useful to vary your strategies in teaching social studies for two reasons. First, students

figure **6.1** *Results of Survey on Attitudes toward Social Studies Instruction*

More Positive Attitudes	More Negative Attitudes
• Variety of teaching strategies are used; classroom routines often vary.	• Heavy reliance on a few teaching strategies; classroom routine seldom varies.
• Teacher is involved with students; knows students personally; is perceived as having caring attitude.	• Teacher perceived as aloof and noninvolved with students; perceived as noncaring by students.
• Classroom rules and expectations are fair, clear, and equitable; consistent enforcement of expectations by teacher.	• Classroom rules and expectations are arbitrary and unclear; poor communication and possible favoritism by teacher.
• Students are actively involved in diverse learning activities; structure of class and assignments requires active student participation.	• Students play passive learning roles; are simply recipients of information and content.
• Positive and frequent student–student interaction; high student support and cooperation.	• Very limited student–student interaction; students usually work in competitive environment.
• Teacher is continually striving to show relevance of subject matter and content; creates interest in subjects by using various strategies.	• Teacher relies on innate importance of subject matter; makes little attempt to show relevance or develop interest.

Source: Based on Fouts, 1989.

respond differently to various ways of teaching. One student learns effectively through silent reading, but another does not. One student benefits from direct instruction and clear explanations; another benefits from hands-on, self-directed activity. Of course, learners should not be typecast and exposed to only single strategies. You indicate a degree of sensitivity to individual needs when you provide for a wide range of learning styles.

The second reason to use varied approaches is simply for the sake of variety itself. Just as people prefer to vary their diets and other routines, students (and you!) benefit from variety in instruction. A class will be more interesting and appealing when students can look forward to discussions, hands-on projects, games, demonstrations, role-plays, and other strategies. Following a monotonous, predictable routine reduces both motivation and retention of ideas.

Direct Instruction Strategies

Direct instruction, or *expository learning,* is defined as the transmission of knowledge from a source to a receiver. The source of knowledge can vary widely to include teachers, textbooks, films, lectures, records, tapes, trade books, and encyclopedias. The receiver, of course, is the student. Although direct instruction is generally associated in social studies with the transmission of *content* information about events, eras, regions, families, tribal groups, cities, governments, and so forth, it can also be used to impart skills or offer explanations, such as how to read a map or how to write an information-seeking letter.

Those who believe in inquiry and student-involvement approaches to social studies learning are often mistakenly labeled as opponents of expository learning. But in fact, effective teachers always use both direct and indirect instructional approaches in an effort to meet the needs of all the students in their classes. Viewed as one of several viable alternatives, direct instruction can be an effective and stimulating way to learn. Perhaps its greatest strength (as well as its greatest potential weakness, if overdone) is its efficiency. Because direct instruction provides students with information, they are spared the inconvenience of having to discover everything themselves. In reality, none of us would be very far along in our academic development if we were forced to discover on our own everything we needed to learn.

We'll examine three direct instruction strategies: lecture or teacher presentation, class discussion, and demonstration. In each instance, the teacher is directly in charge of the instructional process and the students are challenged to acquire information.

Teacher Presentation

The idea of lecturing or presenting directly to young children may at first seem preposterous, particularly in light of what we have learned from the constructivist movement. Of course, long, didactic presentations are inappropriate. The idea of a well-constructed teacher presentation, however, used in concert with other more involving strategies, can make a lot of sense.

For example, primary students who were investigating the safety of a crosswalk near their school and who had been involved in a number of experiential activities were perfectly willing to listen as the teacher told them how professional traffic personnel do similar investigations. Intermediate students who were producing a product to sell needed to hear their teacher tell them about supply and demand, inventory, advertising, profit and loss, and other economic concepts. These presentations were given in meaningful contexts to students who were able to apply the information. Students who were to prepare a Mexican meal in the context of their study of that country were quite eager to hear their teacher present a talk on Mexican geography, agriculture, and customs. The students' felt need to learn makes all the difference in the world, as demonstrated by these examples.

Presentations should be reasonably brief, well thought out on your part, and focused on key ideas or concepts. It is important to use numerous examples of the concepts you stress and to make as many real-world applications as you can. Stories also make presentations more appealing to children and adults alike. You should encourage active listening by having students take notes, if they can. It also helps students to have listening partners, with whom they can discuss information as you pause from time to time in your presentation. The Keys to Effective Teacher Presentations provide concrete suggestions for making your presentations successful. Study them carefully, and try to use them when you plan presentation lessons.

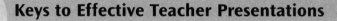

Keys to Effective Teacher Presentations

- *Remember who your audience is.* These are children of elementary school age. Their attention span is short. Try to make your presentations appealing and contextual.
- *Prepare an outline.* Have just a few key points. Keep in mind the idea that "Less is more."
- *Use examples.* Illustrations help people understand and remember. Use multiple examples to make a key point.
- *Speak clearly.* Pronounce your words clearly, speak at a moderate to slow speed, and be sure that you can be heard in the back of the room.
- *Provide an introduction.* Begin with a brief preview of what you plan to say. Build a frame of reference—especially try to relate the topic to previous learning.
- *Emphasize concepts and generalizations.* These are what you really want to teach and what you really want your students to remember. Show how the concepts relate to one another as you proceed.

- *Pause.* Give your students time to think, to write, or to discuss with a partner.
- *Be enthusiastic.* Communicate with your attitude that you think this material is well worth learning.
- *Use props.* Models, transparencies, pictures, diagrams, and so on will bring your presentations to life. These visuals provide variety and support different learning styles.
- *Provide change.* Move around the room. Ask for questions or comments. Pose a question or two. Have students draw illustrations of what they have learned to this point.
- *Summarize.* Remember the adage "Tell them what you are going to tell them, tell them, and then tell them what you have told them." It really works.
- *Assess.* Give the students an opportunity to discuss with a partner what they have learned. Have them draw or write about the topic. With older children, you may even want to give a brief quiz.

Whole-class discussion is an example of direct instruction.

Class Discussion

Class discussion may not seem like a direct teaching strategy, but keep in mind that the teacher is responsible for structuring the flow of the interaction and for directing the students' involvement and participation. The secret to effective class discussion is organization. A well-organized discussion has four basic components: a base of information, a central focus, effective questions, and a supportive classroom environment.

1. *Information base.* Information is essential to a purposeful exchange of ideas and points of view. Be sure to get that point across to your students. Even good questions will not rescue a discussion that's floundering because you didn't give students sufficient information on which to build answers.

2. *Central focus.* Provide a central focus of discussion. In a whole-class discussion, you should ensure that the questions keep coming back to the key issues. You can facilitate this by writing out your questions in advance and gently reminding students that extraneous information, while often interesting, is not useful in the process of examining ideas in depth.

3. *Effective questions.* As you develop questions for discussion, use Bloom's (1984) taxonomy to ensure that your questions include knowledge and understanding of the issue and allow for applications to the real world. You also need to include higher-level questions that ask students to analyze, synthesize, and evaluate. The level of the questions you ask sets the tone for the level of thinking by the students. The pacing of your questions is also important. Casual observation in elementary classrooms leads to the obvious conclusion that teachers are trying to teach students to be impulsive in providing answers. Seldom does one encounter a classroom discussion in which the wait-time between a teacher's questions and the students' answers exceeds a few seconds.

4. *A supportive environment.* You probably know from your own experience that it is risky to speak up in front of a group. Children need to know that you are there to support them, to challenge them in a nurturing way. The more they realize that trust and support are foundational elements of your classroom, the more they will be willing to express themselves and to respect the ideas of others.

Demonstration

A demonstration lesson represents a direct teaching strategy in which the teacher models the behaviors of presentation, analysis, and synthesis. The student's role is that of observer and recorder of information and/or skills. Demonstrations, often wrongly called "experiments," are in fact carefully rehearsed situations in which the teacher knows the outcome. Demonstrations are most effective when followed by corresponding student activities. Thus, a teacher demonstrating a measuring technique for determining distance on a map would expect the class to use the same technique in a follow-up activity. Or if the class were going to conduct an experiment in product testing, the teacher might demonstrate the appropriate techniques for testing a given product.

Application is the key to a demonstration's worth. If something is worth demonstrating to the students, it is also worth the teacher's time to engage them in a direct application of the skill or activity. Demonstration is an efficient strategy because it allows the teacher to illustrate procedures and to communicate information at the same time. The danger of the demonstration strategy lies in the passive role of the students, who may or may not understand the concept or skill the teacher is demonstrating. The solution is to accompany the demonstration with an application by the class. Ideally, the students will perform exactly the same activity the teacher has demonstrated in much the same way he or she demonstrated it. In some cases, however, that is not possible. For example, you might demonstrate the working of a volcano, and the student follow-up might consist of completing a diagram or drawing of a volcano. Or you might demonstrate the flow of wealth in the U.S. economic system using a chart, and the follow-up might consist of students keeping records of the money they spend. The Keys to Effective Direct Instruction will help you understand the strengths of this approach.

What are some of the other strategies that you ought to consider in addition to direct instruction? Let's explore them right now.

Keys to Effective Direct Instruction

- Direct instruction usually involves whole-class instruction. Basically, the teacher is the presenter or explainer, and the students are the receivers of information.
- Direct instruction need not be passive learning. It is best to have students involved through questions, note taking, drawing, constructing, and so on, either as an accompaniment or follow-up to a teacher presentation.
- You don't have to do all the talking. Even though a high teacher profile is basic to direct instruction, remember that a textbook, film,

filmstrip, video, website, or guest speaker can also deliver information.
- Timing and pacing are crucial to the success of direct instruction. Children will learn more from you when you lecture or present to them for just a brief time period than when you take a long time to tell them the same thing. If you have too much information, break it up into two presentations.
- Direct instruction works best in social studies when you use other teaching/learning strategies, as well. Too much of anything is not good.

Indirect Instruction Strategies

Indirect instruction is an approach that reorganizes classroom activities in such a way that students take responsibility for much of their own learning. Indirect instruction, which generally draws on the constructivist principles of learning, has been called "democratic learning" because it emphasizes such experiences as student leadership and initiative, group interdependence, shared decision making, and reflective thinking. In the classic *Democracy and Education,* educational philosopher John Dewey (1916) presented his vision of a classroom as a miniature democracy where children participate actively and purposefully. His vision seems even more crucial today.

The teacher's role in indirect instruction is that of facilitator of learning. The teacher often works behind the scenes to prepare the intellectual, social, and moral environment. One goal is the development of a classroom environment where children feel free to express themselves, to explore actively, and to work together. The teacher ensures that the needed materials and strategies are in place and expects the individual student or the class, depending on the nature of the activity, to assume ownership and responsibility for learning. The teacher questions, suggests, and mediates. A teacher who is accustomed to being the center of attention, direction giver, or autocratic leader often finds this role very difficult.

The student's role is that of active learner. Students are expected to inquire, discover, discuss, plan, act on, and evaluate ideas. The ratio of student-to-student interaction is much higher in classes where indirect instruction takes place. Students seldom sit in straight rows for their work, simply because this configuration is not conducive to working together. Thus, students find themselves playing the role of people who are responsible—morally, intellectually, and socially—for their own learning and that of their fellow students. Figure 6.2 shows certain contrasts between direct and indirect instruction.

Indirect instruction typically means that the student takes on a more active, participatory role while the teacher shifts from the role of director or leader to that of facilitator. Although it may appear that the teacher is doing little except monitoring student involvement during any given activity, the fact is that effective indirect teaching

figure **6.2** *Contrasts between Direct and Indirect Instruction*

Direct Instruction	Indirect Instruction
• Students play passive role	• Students play active role
• Teacher serves as director	• Teacher serves as facilitator
• Students receive knowledge	• Student generalizes knowledge
• Answers to questions are predetermined	• Answers to questions are discovered by students
• Promotes convergent thinking	• Promotes divergent thinking
• Learning consists chiefly of recall and explanation	• Learning consists chiefly of analysis, synthesis, and judgment

can involve a good deal of behind-the-scenes preparation preceding the lesson itself. In fact, the better the planning, the more the teacher sometimes seems to fade from view. I have visited exploratory classrooms where you have trouble even locating the teacher when you first enter—and then you spot her kneeling beside a cluster of desks, helping children with some project.

As noted earlier, indirect teaching and learning generally reflect a constructivist approach. *Constructivism* is based on the theory that we all construct our own knowledge; no one else can do that for us. Constructivist learning is active, engaged, generally hands on, and reflective. See Figure 6.3 for a list of the attributes of constructivist teaching and learning.

The following sections explore 10 different indirect teaching and learning strategies, each of which exemplifies attributes of constructivism. Each strategy places the teacher in the role of facilitator of learning and the student in the role of investigator, inquirer, discoverer, constructor, and so on. The process of learning is emphasized as much as the product, and students are invariably actively engaged.

Role-Play

Role-play is an exceptionally versatile strategy used in drama, simulation, play, games, and, of course, counseling. Essentially, role-play is a projective technique in which the role-player either "becomes" someone else or pretends to be performing a task that is different from what he or she usually does. An example of the former could be a student role-playing Martin Luther King Jr. or Harriet Tubman. An example of the latter could be a student pretending to be a nurse, fire fighter, or store clerk.

Role-play comes naturally to children, who do it without ever having heard the term. They use role-play intuitively as a means of learning. It is part of their exploratory nature. A young child becomes a truck driver in a sandbox. Several children play house on a Saturday afternoon. Children pretend to be famous movie stars or popular entertainers. They become traders and bankers in games they play. However, with the exception of the few who go on to try out for the high school play, role-play is often left behind with early childhood. This is unfortunate, because role-play is a viable way

figure **6.3** *Attributes of Constructivist Learning in Social Studies*

- Emphasis on creativity and hands-on construction
- Emphasis on multiple ways to represent learning
- Real-world connections in meaningful contexts
- Collaboration and team building
- Emphasis on project learning
- Learner inclusion in determining activities
- Emphasis on freedom and opportunity over coercion and restraint
- Emphasis on performance outcomes of work
- Thoughtful reflection on experiences

Students can take an active role in learning history by donning costumes and role-playing characters from the period.

to teach and to learn. It helps a child get beneath the surface of learning and begin to explore moods, feelings, and values.

I once had a grant with Harlan Hansen, a nationally known specialist in early childhood education, that enabled us to develop a curriculum for children in kindergarten through second grade. We used an interest-centers approach to learning, and one of the centers that Harlan installed in a first-grade classroom was a shoe shop. It wasn't much on the surface—just a countertop in a corner of the room with a sign saying "Shoe Shop" and a bunch of donated, mostly worn-out shoes. But what was special about that shop was the role-playing the girls and boys did there. The children took turns being the clerk or the customer. Here is a typical exchange at the Shoe Shop:

Clerk: Hello, may I help you?
Customer: Yes, I'd like to buy a pair of shoes.
Clerk: Oh, what kind of shoes would you like?
Customer: Well, I would like some brown shoes.
Clerk: Brown shoes? Yes, we have some. Here, would you like to try these on?
Customer: Okay. *(Child puts on the shoes with assistance from the clerk.)*
Clerk: How do they feel?
Customer: They're fine. I'll take them.
Clerk: Okay. That will be ten dollars.

Customer:	Here is your money.
Clerk:	Thank you.
Customer:	Good-bye.
Clerk:	Good-bye.

The civility of this exchange seems remarkable for first-graders, yet it is typical of the role-play children are capable of when they are given the chance. Don't underestimate the power of role-play or consign it to the dustbin of "child's play." Language development and gaining a sense of others' perspectives are two of the consistent outcomes of role-play. This strategy can be meaningfully integrated into your social studies program, as the example in the next paragraph illustrates.

The poster reproduced in Figure 6.4 advertises farmland for sale in Illinois in the 1860s and suggests a role-play activity related to the study of the westward movement. In the activity, students are assigned the roles of various family members who live on a farm in the eastern United States during the days of the westward expansion of the country. The father in the family is excited about the opportunities for a new chance out West (Illinois, in this case)—things haven't been so good on the present farm. Other members of the family react to the proposed move in several different ways. The mother isn't sure; she would have to give up a great deal. A sickly daughter fears the move. An older son thinks it would be a great opportunity.

I have used this role-play activity a number of times. The dynamics are fascinating. What emerges are the feelings, hopes, and fears that the pioneers must have known. In other words, the activity humanizes history because the role-players (and audience, if there is one) begin to think about actual lives and how people were affected by such changes. Of course, the role-play works best when knowledge of the westward movement is applied. Role-play furnishes the social studies teacher with a perfect intersection of cognition and affect.

One last thought about role-play: You should model it to your class occasionally. Try teaching your students about Sacagawea, George Washington, astronaut Sally Ride, or simply an early American by dressing up like the person and talking to your students as though that is who you are. You will have to do a little background reading about your character, of course, but I think you'll be pleased with the effect your little performance will have on your class. It's fun, and social studies ought to be fun. Don't you agree?

Interest Centers

The interest-centers approach to teaching and learning social studies is primarily a child-centered, exploratory way to get children involved in self-directed, autonomous behavior. Interest centers do not depend on such well-known phrases as "All right, class, take out your books and turn to page 59." Rather, students do different activities of their own choosing.

The key to successful interest centers is to make them meaningful, appealing, and self-sustaining. In order for centers to be meaningful, they should reflect the purposes of your social studies program. Ask yourself: What am I trying to teach my students

figure 6.4   *Poster Advertising Illinois Farmland in the 1860s*

An artifact such as this poster provides a springboard for student role-play.

that they could learn essentially on their own at a center? To make your centers appealing, try to put yourself in a child's position. Games, maps, puzzles, activities, computers, videos, and so on are highly attractive to a child, especially when organized in an attractive way. For example, it doesn't take much to make a reading center appealing—a small rug, some beautiful posters, a table covered with wonderful books, and you're ready to go. The children's imagination will supply the rest of what your center needs. To be self-sustaining, a center must be a place where a child can function successfully and independently. If your presence is constantly needed at a center, it is probably too difficult or ambiguous for the students to understand. Remember: One of the reasons for having centers is to give students a sense of autonomy, not a sense of dependence. The key concept in the interest-centers approach is freedom of choice.

A teacher who uses interest centers is dedicated to the idea that in an attractive, purposeful environment, students make meaningful use of their time based on the pursuit of knowledge and ideas of their own choosing. The teacher has to do much behind-the-scenes work, establishing the centers and providing resources and other types of materials. And during center time, the teacher moves about the room and is available to the children. The roles of the teacher include support person, sympathetic listener, mediator of ideas, and arranger of possibilities.

The teacher assumes a low profile, being careful not to talk too much, not to give too many directions, and not to tell the children how to do things unless it's absolutely necessary. Again, the term *facilitator* is appropriate in this context. A good facilitator is someone who works behind the scenes to make things function as smoothly as possible. The main drawback of being a good facilitator is that it makes the work look so easy. Have you ever watched a really accomplished talk-show host do his or her job? The better the host is, the more people like us are apt to think, "I could do that. It looks so easy." Well, facilitating is not so easy.

The role of students in interest-centers instruction is that of active explorers. The students are decision makers who choose freely from among an array of attractive ways of spending time. They are learning and expressing a great variety of content and concepts in a variety of ways, and they are enjoying their learning.

Group Investigations and Projects

Imagine a group of students who, with their teacher's guidance and support, decide to do something about the environment where they live. Imagine further that these students take up the challenge of asking the school board to ban the use of styrofoam cups and other containers by the schools in their district. This is exactly what happened in Victoria, British Columbia, when some sixth- and seventh-grade students at James Bay School decided to seek such a ban.

The work of these students first came to my attention one fall morning as I drove along the interstate listening to a Canadian radio station. The announcer mentioned the work the James Bay students were trying to accomplish, and I was quite impressed that young people would take up such a challenge. I decided to write them a letter seeking more information about the project, and they replied promptly (see Figure 6.5).

figure 6.5 *Correspondence Concerning a Group Project*

JAMES BAY
COMMUNITY SCHOOL

140 Oswego Street
Victoria, B.C.
V8V 2B1

384-7184

Dr. Arthur K. Ellis, Professor
Seattle Pacific University
Seattle, Washington

Dear Dr. Arthur Ellis:

Your letter about the styrofoam project arrived at James Bay Community School on November 14. We want you to know that it was grade 6/7 students that were working on the project not grade 5/6. We got started when the question "How does dumping garbage affect our environment?" was raised. We decided we had the power to change our environment. Our first step was to write letters. We wrote to places like grocery stores and the B.C. Ferry Corporation. Later on we talked about writing to government officials and the school board.

Our first response was from the school board who wanted a presentation. In our presentation we talked about what styrofoam is doing to our environment. We also talked about the recycling program that we started in our school and and asked if they would recycle papers in the school district. In the end they passed both motions. We did not know that a spokesman from C FAX radio station was sitting silently at another table taking in bits of our presentation.

The B.C. Ferry Corporation then responded by buying a new type of styrofoam cups with out the Chloro Fluoro Carbons

A student in our class came up with the name S.P.O.E.—Students Protecting Our Environment. Some of us are still carrying on with the project.

The news media asked us if they could get a picture of S.P.O.E. for an article in a magazine.

Thank you for your interest in Students Protecting Our Environment.

Sincerely,
Grade 6/7 class of
J.B.C.S.

Warren Walbaum
K R
Zach Whitmarsh
Corine Wilson

CURRENT EVENTS

Focus on Strategies

Take a strategic view of teaching current events. By doing this, you accomplish more than merely covering stories in the news or, worse yet, falling prey to the unsystematic show-and-tell approach to news reporting by children who are given little leadership. Here is a sampling of proven strategies for emphasizing the productive use of the daily newspaper, television and radio, and Internet news sites:

1. *Read from news sources to your students.* Take a few minutes each morning or at some convenient time of the school day to read to your students from the newspaper, websites, magazines, and the like. This gives you the opportunity to focus on stories of importance and those items in the news related to your current course of study. This time is crucial because it provides students with a model of an adult thoughtfully going through the news and reflecting with them on the significance of different stories.

2. *Headlines and their significance.* Newspapers, websites, magazines, and other sources of the news carry headlines of different sizes and locations. A front-page, above-the-fold headline in bold type is considered to indicate a lead story, especially if it is a "banner" headline, stretching across the width of the front page. But headlines are written under the pressure of deadlines. One strategy that allows your students to show their comprehension is to challenge them to rewrite headlines, improving on them from their reading of a story. A second strategy is to present the class with the headlines from a current newspaper. Ask students to work in groups of two to determine what they think will be the long-term significance of each of the various stories. Ask them to rank order the stories and defend their choices.

3. *Special topics.* A special-topics approach to the news takes into account students' interest and motivation. Teams of students can take responsibility for reporting on special topics that appear in the news, including the following: animals, politics, weather, disasters, major countries, science, medicine, military, transportation, and trade.

4. *Categories in the news.* Newspapers, magazines, the Internet, and even the evening newscast all carry stories by departments or categories; for example, the news is often broken up into international, national, regional, and local. Then there are special sections for sports, weather, business, life-style, travel, comics, classified ads, and so on. Give your students choices of categories, and allow them to become "experts" in those categories by reading and analyzing particular sections. This strategy takes advantage of student interest. One child may be interested in sports, another in the comics, and so forth.

5. *Advertising and want ads.* It is a useful exercise in economics to go through a newspaper or magazine looking at the advertising and want ads. The daily newspaper carries grocery ads, department store ads, and advertising of other kinds. A historical perspective can be reached by comparing prices now with those found in an old newspaper. A similar comparison can be made of jobs, salaries, and the like listed in the want ads, using a current newspaper and one from the past.

Cross-age tutoring experiences are rewarding for both younger and older students.

There is something very compelling about positive social action mounted by a group of concerned citizens. It seems to address the very heart of democracy. This is especially true when those citizens are young people who are still in the process of learning how democracy works. The efforts of the students to ban styrofoam use were successful, by the way, but they had to do a considerable amount of work in order to achieve their goal. I'm sure they learned that one has to present evidence and do background work in order to present one's case clearly and persuasively to elected officials.

The James Bay project exemplifies the spirit of group investigation. A group project is an effort by a class—or a whole school—to make a difference in their world. The exciting thing about group investigation is that issues abound in every locality in democratic societies such as Canada and the United States. The teacher just needs to be sensitive to the issues and willing to do the work it takes to keep the students' effort going, ensuring that it is a positive, purposeful effort.

Students of any age can conduct group investigations. I've seen first-graders investigate a potentially dangerous crosswalk near the school and make it safer, possibly saving a life. I've seen third-graders investigate the playground equipment at their school and make it safer and more creative. I've also seen intermediate-grade students make their school cafeteria a more appealing and sane place to eat lunch. You ought to try the approach—it works!

The role of the teacher in group investigation is complex. He or she must facilitate group processes, keep the focus on the problem to be solved, ensure that *all* students are involved actively, help the students locate appropriate resources and information, and evaluate the group's progress as it conducts its investigation. Some teachers find this overwhelming and fall back on traditional seat work assignments.

Admittedly, it does take a lot of energy to guide a group of children through an investigation, but the rewards of seeing students grow and learn to work effectively with each other are considerable.

Independent Study and Presentations

It goes without saying that children need to learn to work together, but they also need to find out what they can do largely on their own. Children learn interdependence when they collaborate as well as when they work alone. In life we need both. Independent study can be conducted as a solo investigation or as a piece of a larger group investigation. It is ideal for invoking the *doctrine of interest,* which states that students should study what they are personally interested in.

When a student studies something he or she is curious about or wants to learn more about or simply chooses for whatever reason to study something, a powerful energy is already in place: *motivation.* When teenagers get to take driving lessons, we typically do not have to worry about their motivation to learn. They bring that commodity along with them. When a young child asks a parent if he or she can bake some cookies, we know that motivation is already in place. And when a child learns to ride a bicycle, painful as it is, the child typically won't stop until he or she can do it, no matter how long it takes. The motivation is there.

So, what I am saying to you is, let students decide for themselves some of the things they want to study. The following scenarios demonstrate the role you can play in providing independent study opportunities for your students.

in the classroom **Finding Students' Interests**

In a primary-grade class, the teacher asked the students what seasons, games, and activities interested them the most. The students volunteered their ideas while the teacher wrote them on the board. When the board was filled with ideas, the teacher talked with the students about how they could learn more about the topics of their choice. The teacher gave each student three tasks to carry out:

1. To talk with his or her parent(s) about the topic and have them help write down some of the things they discussed
2. To draw a picture showing something he or she learned or enjoyed about the topic
3. To tell the class about his or her findings

This assignment involved the home. It also asked the child to inquire on his or her own and to express himself or herself artistically. Finally, it gave each child an experience with presentation skills. As simple as this independent study is, consider that it involved choosing freely, carrying out a task, talking to an adult, and presenting before an audience.

In an intermediate-level class that was studying Native Americans, the teacher showed the class a large map that illustrated the locations of various nations on the North American continent. The teacher spent a little time telling the class about various tribal groups, including information about their customs, habits, food, and shelter. The teacher stressed the idea that each nation had its own unique identity and way of life.

The independent study flowing from this overview/introduction was to challenge each student to make a booklet and accompanying display on one of the Native American nations. Each student chose a different nation and did research, including writing letters to people of the nation to learn of modern-day life, reading accounts of tribal life in the past, and learning as much as possible in order to become an "expert." As the study progressed, the room began to fill up with maps, pictures, drawings, artifacts, stories, letters, and so on. Each student reported his or her findings to the class during a culminating activity, and a number of students taught a "lesson" on their chosen nation to a class of younger students in the school.

In both of these cases, the teacher played the role of facilitator, helping students with sources of information and providing guidance when they needed it. But in both cases, the ultimate responsibility for learning was with the individual students.

Reflective Thinking

Reflective-thinking activities are designed to give learners the opportunity to be philosophical—to consider, discuss, and argue issues. Reflective-thinking sessions are often used to help students analyze certain tasks they have performed. This strategy is also involved in situations where the teacher wants students to speculate on how a certain chain of events might take place under certain conditions.

Reflective thinking and inquiry share the idea of active student involvement in problems and questions. They differ as learning strategies in that inquiry learning is predicated on the notion that sufficient data will enable a student to answer a question or solve a problem, whereas reflective thinking often deals with questions that cannot be answered solely by data. The following questions provide a simple contrast:

Inquiry question: How do messages flow in our school?
Reflective-thinking question: What are the advantages of written versus oral messages?

The first question can be answered on the basis of data gathered, whereas the second may be a matter of opinion. The following examples demonstrate how reflective thinking can be implemented in your classroom, as does Sample Lesson 6.1 at the end of the chapter.

in the classroom **An Incident in Human Behavior**

A teacher told her third-grade class the following story:

> Mary, a third-grader, checked a book out of the library. When school was over, she took the book home to read. On the way home, Mary's friends asked her to play outside. So Mary ran into her house, changed into play clothes, left the book on a chair in the living room, and went outside to play. Her brother Tim, who was 3 years old, found the book and colored on the pages with crayons. The book was ruined.

The teacher then asked the class this question: "How many people could we name who *might* be responsible?" The class listed Mary, her mother, her father, Tim, Mary's teacher, and the librarian. The teacher did not ask the students to reach conclusions about responsibility at this point. She just told the students to think about it and that they would discuss it the next day.

During a discussion period the next day, the teacher asked the students to tell who they thought was responsible. Here are some responses:

- "Mary is responsible. She shouldn't have left the book where her little brother could get it."
- "Her brother is 3. He shouldn't be coloring in books. A 2-year-old might."
- "Her mother didn't watch her little brother very carefully."
- "The teacher shouldn't let kids take books home."

Some students took issue with certain responses. Others supported their classmates' reasoning. Others had asked their parents and gave their parents' opinions. The teacher then asked, "How do we know the right answer?" One student said, "Some families are different, so it might not be the same for everyone."

The teacher asked another question: "What should be done, now that the book is ruined?" Some students had ready answers, while others made such suggestions as "We could ask the librarian what she thinks about it."

in the classroom **Looking Forward and Looking Back**

The Roman god Janus (for whom the month of January is named) could look forward into the future and back into the past. So can we, at least to some extent. Many learners (not just children) tend to be impulsive when it comes to carrying out an assignment. Reflective thinking can improve one's work substantially.

Let's say that you want your students to make maps of the school and play area. Prior to the activity itself, allow your students to meet in groups of two or three to think and plan about the qualities of a good map. Depending on the age of the pupils, you may want to list some key terms on the board,

including *scale, key, cardinal directions, color, perspective, accuracy,* and so on. Following the activity of making maps, give your students an opportunity to talk about the assignment, including such issues as these: What was difficult about it? What did you learn? What would you tell someone who was going to make such a map?

Having before-and-after sessions like this raises students' levels of consciousness about their work. In doing so, they practice *metacognition,* or thinking about thinking. It's time consuming but eminently worthwhile.

Brainstorming

One proven method for tapping into the creativity of a group is brainstorming. It is particularly useful at those times when the teacher wants to give students an opportunity to think expansively about a problem, activity, project, or the like. Brainstorming in problem solving, for example, typically is done early in the process. If your class is studying economics and the children have decided to manufacture a product that they will then market, you might begin with a brainstorming session in which you allow students to think of as many possibilities as they can. Eventually, you and the children will decide on a single product to manufacture, but for now, you want to let the creative potential of the students flower.

There are three essential elements of brainstorming, and you must honor all three for the process to work effectively. First, there is the rule of *quantity over quality.* This means that you want the children to come up with as many possibilities as they can— the more, the merrier. The second rule is *no judgments.* There will be plenty of time later to decide if an idea is practical, achievable, whatever. For now, refrain from judging; to do otherwise kills creative instincts. The third rule is *inclusion*. Everyone in the class needs to feel welcome to take part, not just the more vocal or more opinionated students.

Two alternative grouping possibilities are available, and I suggest you use them both from time to time. First, there is the whole-class group with the teacher at the chalkboard. Students simply speak up while you record their ideas. Generally speaking, you will have no trouble filling an entire board with suggestions. A follow-up session can be devoted to discussing the feasibility of the various suggestions. The second procedure is to put students in small groups of three or four and allow them to brainstorm. Each group will need a recorder or some way of keeping track of their ideas. The class then comes back together for a time of sharing.

The last thing to keep in mind is how much you want to structure the process. Freeform brainstorming allows people to speak up spontaneously. Its advantage is obvious—the spontaneous nature of the process. Its disadvantage is that the more vocal, outgoing types will dominate, while others will be reluctant to compete. Structured brainstorming is a process whereby a group (class or small group) actually gives each person a turn either to make a suggestion or to pass. The great advantage is that everyone has an equal opportunity to participate; the disadvantage is some slight loss of spontaneity. Try both approaches.

Creative Expression

Social studies offers great potential for students to express themselves creatively in a variety of ways. Although consuming knowledge, inquiring into problems, and discussing ideas are important uses of students' time in social studies, it is also important that they be given opportunities to build, act, draw, paint, and photograph as means of involving themselves in learning and sharing. See the Keys to Creativity for guidelines on encouraging creative thinking among your students.

Keys to Creativity

The teacher's behavior is crucial in establishing conditions that are conducive to creativity. The following suggestions are designed to help you establish a creative climate in your classroom:

- Give freedom and space.
- Promote discovery learning.
- Create a playful atmosphere.
- Encourage projects.
- Allow students to make choices.
- Bring interesting things to class.

- Be a good listener and sounding board.
- Give open-ended assignments.
- Encourage students to help each other.
- Encourage fresh perspectives on ordinary things.
- Model and encourage trust and respect.
- Encourage student initiative and risk taking.
- Have a sense of humor.
- Give unusual assignments.
- Encourage involvement with good literature and the arts.

Here are some examples of creative expression by students:

- A second-grade class presented a slide show to the PTA, illustrating their work on improving the safety of a crosswalk near the school.
- A sixth-grade class constructed a diorama in the school showcase, illustrating life in a medieval manor during their study of a unit on life in the Middle Ages.
- A student constructed a model of the school playground and presented his recommendations for improving its use during recess periods.
- A group of fifth-grade students made puppets and presented shows to kindergarten and first-grade classes on the topic of school safety.
- A third-grade class put together a directory of mini–field trips in the local area that students could take with their parents.
- Some sixth-graders developed and constructed a simple game designed to teach cardinal directions. They mass produced the game and made copies available to children in the lower grades.

What kinds of products do creative students produce? There are some you might expect—poems, stories, drawings, paintings. But there are also others that might not immediately come to mind—murals, booklets and instruction pamphlets, models, puppet shows, games, plays, dioramas, radio and television programs, photographs, and a wide range of computer-assisted slide shows and websites. The following example tells about students becoming "journalists" and writing newspaper stories about nursery rhymes.

in the classroom Nursery Rhyme Newspaper Stories

One way to support children's creative instincts is to let them write newspaper stories about nursery rhymes. Give each child a nursery rhyme (find nursery rhyme books in your school or local library), and ask him or her to write a newspaper article about the story the rhyme tells. Here is an example of how one child wrote up the story of "Jack and Jill":

> Jack and Jill went up the hill,
> to fetch a pail of water.
> Jack fell down and broke his crown,
> and Jill came tumbling after.
>
> Now up Jack got and home did trot,
> as fast as he could caper.
> He went to bed and covered his head
> with vinegar and brown paper.

"Youngsters Hurt in Tragic Fall"
by Shandra, Room 17 (5th Grade)

Jack and Jill, both aged 10, were injured today when they fell while running down the hill from the town well. Witnesses said they tripped over each other in their hurry to bring the pail of water back to the Old Washerwoman. Jack apparently broke his crown. He ran home and covered his head with vinegar and brown paper and is expected to make a full recovery. Jill needed no treatment. Safety Officer Billy Bones said that children should *never* run down the hill because it is too steep. Concerned citizens will meet at Town Hall on Friday night to discuss this important safety issue. Officer Bones will lead the opening flag salute. Both Jack and Jill said this sure has been a lesson to them, and from now on, they will *walk* down the hill. The Old Washerwoman said in an interview that maybe she had been working the children too hard and that is why they fell. No charges are expected to be filed in the case.

Content Analysis

Because so much of what people learn and know comes from secondary sources, it is important to develop the skill of content analysis. Content analysis is a means of examining content more closely than if one merely wanted to know what it stated. Content analysis raises such questions as interpretation of meaning, significance of material, and even accuracy or bias. It is also a way for students to take information presented globally and break it into categories that are more manageable.

The content that students can analyze can come from any source: a film, story, textbook, newspaper, website, and so forth. Practice at content analysis should make students more critical thinkers and critical readers. The interpretive activities involved in content analysis enable students to construct meaning as they read, view, or listen to information. Take some time to consider the following examples, as well as Sample Lesson 6.2.

in the classroom Nursery Rhymes

Nursery rhymes have the potential for content analysis at several levels. In that respect, they are appropriate content at both the primary and intermediate levels. At the primary level, you might focus on the sequence of events within a nursery rhyme. After memorizing "Humpty Dumpty," for example, you might ask the children to draw a series of pictures showing what actually happened. Figure 6.6 illustrates a young child's sequence content analysis of the nursery rhyme.

At the intermediate level, you can use the same content to get at different things. Here are two possibilities:

1. Have students write about what they think the message really is in the story of "Humpty Dumpty." The literal meaning is obvious: He fell off the wall. But is there a moral to the story?
2. "Humpty Dumpty" was written in a historical context. Have students investigate the origins of this nursery rhyme. Does it portray an actual king? What were the conditions that led to his fall? What were the consequences?

in the classroom Textbooks

All textbooks, by definition, contain content. A very useful exercise in content analysis for a team of intermediate-level researchers is to take two social studies textbooks designed for their particular grade level and to compare and contrast them. A good place to start is the books' tables of contents; then look at the indexes.

Ask the students to focus on these questions: To what extent are the two books alike and different in coverage? How difficult and how interesting is the writing in each book? How do the illustrations compare? How complete and how fair is the coverage each book gives to certain cultural groups? To women? To minorities? Which of the two texts do you prefer?

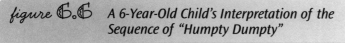

figure **6.6**   *A 6-Year-Old Child's Interpretation of the Sequence of "Humpty Dumpty"*

Humpty Dumpty sat on a wall....

Humpty Dumpty had a great fall.

All the king's horses and all the king's men....

Couldn't put Humpty Dumpty together again.

Differentiated Assignments

Often, assignments are given to the whole class, as though all the students have the same needs and the same learning styles. In fact, they do not. If you provide choices for children, they have an opportunity to practice decision making and to fulfill your requirements while serving their own interests. Of course, not every assignment needs to be differentiated, but many should be, if only to provide variety.

The idea behind differentiated assignments is to give students choices. In a true differentiated assignment, there are a number of ways each student might achieve this goal. Learning style, interest, and motivation are factors that will guide the student's choice of activities. In most cases, a differentiated assignment will take several days for each student to complete because of the research, construction, drama, and other activities involved. Time should also be allowed for class presentations, because much additional learning will take place as the children share what they have learned. The following examples show how you can offer differentiated assignments in your classroom.

in the classroom **The Pioneer Treks***

The teacher's goal in this example is for students to learn about the westward expansion of the United States across the Great Plains and on to the territories of California and Oregon. As you examine the following assignment options, keep in mind Howard Gardner's (1983) *multiple-intelligences theory,* as well as what you know about student learning styles:

- Find a book that has a picture of a covered wagon in it. Sketch a copy of the covered wagon.
- As the covered wagon trains moved along the trail, they would stop for the night. Find a picture of a covered wagon encampment, and draw a sketch of it.
- Using craft sticks, cloth, glue, and other materials, make a model of a covered wagon.
- Most families that traveled west had to leave many of their possessions behind. Prepare a list of the things you think a family might have had to leave behind and a list of things a family would have needed to take with them on the trail.
- Write a fictional story about a family and their decision to leave the eastern United States and move west.
- Draw a map that illustrates the Oregon Trail, the California Trail, and the Mormon Trek.
- The westward movement of the pioneers must have seemed strange from the perspective of the various native peoples through whose territory they traveled. Write a story explaining the westward movement from a Native American point of view.
- Read the book *The Children of the Covered Wagon,* by Elizabeth Carr. Present a brief oral report to the class on the life of children in a wagon train, as described in this book.
- Pretend you are a child journeying west on a wagon train. Write a letter to a friend who stayed behind, telling him or her about life on a wagon train.

- Some people who went west went to the gold fields of California and Colorado. Draw a sketch of a gold-mining camp.
- Write a song about life along the trail.
- What job would you have liked to have on a wagon train? Wagon master? Scout? Write a paragraph telling what job you would have liked and why.
- Look through the index of a book on the westward movement. Find a topic that looks interesting to you and research it, using this book and other sources.
- Find a play about pioneer days or the westward movement. Round up enough students to put it on, and present it to a primary-grade class in your building.
- Make a salt/flour map of the westward movement. Show the major trails, forts, and other important features.
- Find out what songs were sung along the trail by the pioneers. Learn a song and teach it to the class.
- How fair do you think the westward movement was to the Native Americans? Do some research into this question, and report your findings to the class.
- What was the typical diet along the trail? Find out and (with the teacher's help) prepare a meal for the class to eat.
- Where will pioneers go in the future? Under the oceans? To the Antarctic? To outer space? Do some research and write a report on future pioneer efforts.
- Look through the school district's film catalog for a good film on the westward movement. Ask your teacher to order the film you select. Preview it so that you can introduce it to the class for showing.

*Thanks to Anne DeGallier for many of the differentiated assignment options for this activity.

in the classroom Archaeology

Using differentiated assignments helps ensure that you will reach children who have a variety of learning styles and preferences. The type of differentiated assignment illustrated here, which includes three modes of learning (verbal, activity, production), is really a template that you can use for any unit or area of instruction. Just change the focus of the assignment to whatever content you are teaching.

Direct each student to choose *any two* assignments from *each list,* for a total of *six* assignments.

List A: Verbal

- Read one of the books on our Unit Resource List.
- Write a letter to a museum that asks how curators do their work.
- Read an article on archaeology from *National Geographic* or *Smithsonian* magazine, and write a report on it.
- Write an essay on archaeology. Be sure to include at least three references.
- View a video on archaeology (select one from the video list), and write a report on it.
- Write a short play or skit about an actual archaeological expedition.
- Write a story about a fictional archaeological expedition.

List B: Activity

- Make a model of an ancient dwelling.
- Construct a diorama of life in an ancient setting.
- Draw a series of pictures that illustrate an archaeological dig.
- Use clay and sticks to make a model of an ancient city.
- Make a reproduction of an artifact from ancient times.
- Draw sketches of several ancient tools.
- Use magazine pictures to make a collage of an archaeological expedition.
- Make a time capsule filled with artifacts from our culture.
- Tour a local museum, and draw pictures of the exhibits.

List C: Production

- Help stage a play about an archaeological expedition.
- Do a role-play in which you become an actual archaeologist who tells about his or her work.
- Prepare and present a group presentation on an actual archaeological expedition.
- Prepare and teach a lesson on archaeology to another class.
- Have a discussion on archaeology at home with your family members.
- Be an archaeologist. Carry out your own expedition using artifacts from your home or neighborhood.
- Visit a garage sale or yard sale. Pretend that you are an archaeologist and the items for sale are artifacts.

Jigsaw/Peer Teaching and Cooperative Learning

The jigsaw strategy, developed by Elliot Aronson (1997), is an interesting combination of cooperative learning and individualistic goal structure. The idea of this teaching/learning strategy is that each student in a cooperative learning group of, say, three students is responsible for peer teaching his or her companions a portion of the material that they all need to learn. Thus, each student teaches one-third of the information, skills, or whatever and is taught two-thirds of that content. It is important that students do their best to teach their compatriots, because all the members of the group are depending on each other. This truly creates a "We're in this together" mentality.

The jigsaw strategy is illustrative of the broader idea of *cooperative learning,* which is dedicated to the idea of having civil conversations and working together in an atmosphere of mutual interest and collaboration. Cooperative learning is based on the idea of shared goals. If you and I want the same thing, why don't we work together to achieve it? The work of such theorists as Lev Vygotsky, Jean Piaget, and Jerome Bruner points to the need for children to express themselves civilly in social situations for language and thought to codevelop.

Johnson and Johnson (2004), pioneers in this area, cite cumulative research findings that support cooperative learning. Positive outcomes include the following:

- Higher achievement and better retention
- Growth in moral and cognitive reasoning
- Enhanced motivation to learn
- Improved attitude toward school and school subjects
- Improved attitude toward teachers
- Enhanced self-esteem
- Greater liking of one another

The teacher's role is to act as a consultant, mediator, and facilitator in keeping the process going forward. The teacher also serves as a strategist who carefully considers who should work with whom. He or she teaches students the skills needed to work together, helping them know when to listen, when to talk, how to be supportive, how to ensure participation by all, and so on. The teacher creates an atmosphere in which students are able to construct knowledge, reflect on what they are learning, practice good citizenship, and build one another up in an academically and socially supportive atmosphere.

Keys to Cooperative Learning

Cooperative learning is based on these six principles:

- Positive interdependence
- Small groups (two or three students)
- Face-to-face interaction

- Individual accountability
- Development of small-group skills
- Time for reflection and analysis

Source: Based on Johnson, Johnson, & Holubec, 2002.

The student's role is to work with others to achieve common goals. Many students today come from small families, where there is little of the give and take that occurs with a clan of brothers and sisters. These students need to learn to share, give, listen, care, and experience the transcendent moments of life that come only when people are part of something larger than themselves. When students come to learn the skills of co-operation, the projects, productions, committee work, and other experiences found at the heart of social studies are greatly facilitated.

I'm convinced that peer teaching is one of the best ways for children to learn. Piaget noted that children are more effective than most adults realize in teaching each other, especially if teachers provide some structure and support. This is so, he claimed, because of a language issue—namely, greater syntactic compatibility is found within the peer group than exists when, for example, adults talk to children. What this means in simple terms is that adult language is far more complex than children's language; therefore, a child talking to another child does not take linguistic shortcuts, use sophisticated terminology, or assume years of experience. John Dewey noted that one of the biggest problems in teaching is the false assumption by teachers of experience on the part of students.

All of this in no way diminishes the importance of your role as a teacher. It does, however, shift the center of gravity from you to the students, making your job one of organizer and facilitator of learning, rather than lecturer or presenter. See the following example of how to use cooperative learning.

in the classroom The American Revolution

You can use the jigsaw or cooperative learning method to help students understand three events that took place leading up to the American Revolution: the Boston Tea Party, the Battle of Lexington, and Paul Revere's ride. Break the class into groups of three, and assign each group the responsibility of learning about all three events. Using the jigsaw strategy, have one student within each group study one of the events thoroughly. Provide enough time for students to study their respective events. Then convene the small groups and ask each student to teach the other two members of his or her group about the event assigned.

You will need to coach your students in techniques for making the information they present interesting, significant, and involving. With practice, the students will improve their teaching, especially if they have learned a variety of teaching strategies from what you have modeled.

Simulations

Simulations are attempts to represent and model social systems, often through the medium of a game. Those social systems may be economic, political, spatial, or cultural, or they may be some sort of combination of systems. *Reality* is the key word in simulation activities. If students are to learn how a market system or a governing system works, then it is important that they not only play the roles and use the processes but also that those roles and processes accurately reflect the reality of the system they are intended to represent.

Of course, in every simulation, some compromise must be reached between the attempt to represent the reality of the system and the limitations imposed by such factors as the age and maturity of the students, the resources available, the size of the classroom, and the constraints of time. Oversimplifying processes and interactions in order to make a simulation easier or more exciting can be dangerous. Developing an effective simulation requires making wise choices about which elements of reality need to be included in order to make the activity valid and which elements can be factored out as extraneous to the fundamental processes involved.

Thus, in any social system you choose to model or in any simulation you select for use in social studies, it is crucial for you to determine whether the elements included accurately represent the ideas you think children should learn. One way to ensure this is to determine exactly what your learning and valuing objectives are and to choose or develop a simulation on that basis. Sample Lesson 6.3 provides a simulation that's not tied to any particular unit of study that you can use in the classroom. In adition, two commercially developed examples of simulations are described in the following examples.

in the classroom Starpower

Starpower has been used extensively in age groups ranging from third grade to college graduates and business personnel. It is designed to set up a three-level, low-mobility socioeconomic society, in which the low group remains low in power and the high group remains high in power and ultimately is allowed to make the rules for continuing the game. The middle group isn't sure what to think. The wealthy power group generally makes rules that maintain its own wealth and power rather than benefit the poorer groups. The dramatic parallels with real-life society are missed by few participants. Participation and interest are reliably high, with most participants becoming highly emotionally involved.

Although recommended for 18 to 35 participants, Starpower has been successfully used with groups as small as 13 and as large as 70 or 80. The use and abuse of power demonstrated by the game is particularly appropriate to a number of factions in today's society. Discussion during the debriefing of the highly stimulating activity is frequently intense and heated, even for fifth- and sixth-graders. Although the facilitator's guide recommends a 50-minute period for playing Starpower, experience dictates that a 3-hour time block should be allowed, excluding preparation time of about 30 minutes. At least 1 hour should be allowed for debriefing and discussion, since emotionally charged topics often come up and should be dealt with thoroughly during the course of the debriefing.

During the game, interaction among the participants is spirited, basically cooperative within each of the three groups, and allowed to occur naturally, with little or no outside control on what is said or what roles are portrayed. The roles of the three groups are allowed to develop naturally along the lines dictated by the power structure involved. Overall, this is an excellent simulation that is highly recommended for fourth grade or higher.

in the classroom **Bafá Bafá**

In this simulation, participants are divided into two groups. Each group is taught certain rules and develops its own culture. Then visitors are exchanged between the groups to experience the foreign culture instituted by the other group. The game helps students understand the meaning of the term *culture* in graphic and physical ways, how cultural misunderstandings and miscommunications occur, and how stereotypes and prejudice evolve.

Although the simulation may at first seem complex to participants, after a few minutes of practice at their given culture, participants generally find the experience enjoyable, exciting, and interesting. The cultural exchange and subsequent debriefing provide many opportunities for eliciting cultural stereotypes and misunderstandings and provide for an emotional understanding of what it is like to be a visitor to another culture. Bafá Bafá also helps illustrate that values are culture laden and that no culture is necessarily better but merely different. This understanding is essential to increasing world harmony in a modern, technological society.

This is an excellent cross-cultural simulation that has been used successfully with Peace Corps volunteers, teachers, and legislators, as well as students. It is highly effective in creating an understanding of cultural attitudes and cultural norms.

Computer Simulations

Simulations have taken a great leap forward with the advent of videodiscs, video and computer games, and the whole theory of computers as learning environments in themselves. The early days of so-called drill-and-kill computer programs have come and gone. Those programs have been replaced by exciting ways to access and interact with stored knowledge.

The videodisc encyclopedia is a good example. A child reading about the origins of World War II can virtually watch and listen to President Franklin D. Roosevelt's speech to the nation following the attack on Pearl Harbor in 1941. Or a child using videodisc technology can suddenly find himself or herself on the banks of the Zambesi River in Africa, surveying the landscape.

At a heightened interactive level, computer simulations allow learners to take part in making decisions, solving problems, and otherwise applying their knowledge and skills to situations where they have consequences. Computer simulations range from those suitable for one or two students at a time to whole-class simulations. At their best, they represent situations much like those that students will encounter in real life. One of the first computer simulations to achieve widespread popularity was Oregon Trail. It is perhaps primitive by the standards of the new generation of simulations, but it remains no doubt one of the most played school-related simulations. Students take on roles of pioneers traveling west and must make decisions regarding food supplies, safety, health, and various other issues all along the trail. The idea is to survive and reach the Oregon Territory. Three of the most widely used and successful computer simulations of recent times are Where in the World Is Carmen Sandiego?, Sim City, and Science 2000.

● *Where in the World Is Carmen Sandiego?* This game begins with the whole class playing; the game is projected from the computer onto a large monitor or screen (see Figure 6.7). The students practice observation, note taking, and other skills needed to capture the wily criminal, Carmen Sandiego. The teacher guides the class at first, teaching students to use reference materials that they will need for tracking and apprehending the criminal. Because Carmen Sandiego travels all over the world, geographic

figure **6.7**   *Where in the World Is Carmen Sandiego?*

Discover *Where in the World Is Carmen Sandiego?*, where the chase first began in popular computer software games by Broderbund Software.

Learn about countries and cultures as you search for the elusive Carmen in beautiful locations rich with history, culture, and music. Software, animated adventures on DVD, and other Carmen products are available worldwide.

Where in the World Is Carmen Sandiego? was also a PBS television game show for kids that built knowledge of geography. It was on the air for five seasons and nominated for seven Emmys, which it won in 1995 and 1996.

As they chase Carmen Sandiego and her gang through countries around the globe, or through all fifty United States and Washington, DC, kids learn about geography and cultures. Carmen has also been known to challenge kids to learn more about history, music, and the solar system.

Carmen Sandiego began her career in 1985 as an original character in an innovative detective software game that broadened kids' knowledge of languages. Over seven million copies have been sold for use in schools and homes worldwide.

knowledge builds as the game proceeds. In time, students work in pairs to solve the problem and to prepare a report about the state or region they have researched.

● *Sim City.* This and a related simulation, Sim Earth, place students in the roles of planners and builders of cities. They must take into account the systems that cities depend on, including transportation, water, industry, communications, recreation, and housing. Problems occur along the way that must be solved, whether they be traffic congestion, water supply, or inadequate residential zoning. The complexities introduced in Sim City give students a far more sophisticated sense of urban planning, development, and maintenance than they could obtain in a less interactive way.

● *Science 2000+.* This thematic curriculum uses hypertext databases connected to videodiscs. Students encounter problems found in real life, including pollution, fragile ecosystems, water supplies, soil conditions, climate factors, and so on. The approach is based on cooperative group learning in which students take on roles ranging from farmers, developers, elected officials, and law enforcement personnel to naturalists and representatives of the Environmental Protection Agency. The rich databases enable the students to access information that's useful in representing their positions and reaching decisions made in the best interests of society.

Observations on Indirect Instruction

The strengths of the indirect instructional strategies are exemplified by the contrasts between direct and indirect instruction. Although the contrasts seem on the surface to be heavily weighted in favor of indirect instruction, keep in mind that it is not practical for students to learn from any one strategy exclusively. Knowledge of events, eras, and places and explanations of spatial, cultural, and economic systems, which are certainly major objectives of a social studies program, are often better suited to direct teaching.

Perhaps the major contribution of indirect learning is that it gives students opportunities to become involved in the processes used in forming knowledge. Such intimate contact with knowledge formation gives learners an important perspective as they read, see, and hear what others have to show and tell them about human beings through books, films, lectures, websites, and other sources of information. But when the subject lends itself to indirect learning, the rewards of this democratic learning strategy are great both for the facilitator/teacher and for the active, independent learners.

Summary

This chapter defined and illustrated the wide range of approaches you might use to teach and students might use to learn social studies. Two categories, direct and indirect instruction—each with numerous

permutations—were discussed. The search for curricular balance in teaching and learning is particularly important. Keep in mind as you combine lessons into units that students need a certain amount of meaningful reception learning balanced with a certain amount of construction of knowledge and meaning on their own part. Also keep in mind the social aspect of social studies. Whenever possible, students should learn and work together. A final thought is that yet another kind of balance should be sought: one that ensures students will learn through verbal modes, through construction and related activities, and through productions and presentations they carry out themselves.

Explorations

Reflect on . . .

1. Choose a key idea or concept from one of the social sciences—for example, the concept of *culture* from anthropology. Consider what three instructional strategies you might use to teach this concept. Try to achieve balance in your choice of strategies.

2. Discuss with a partner, a small group, or your whole class the issue of how a teacher might decide how much time to devote to particular strategies in teaching social studies.

In the Field

3. Try teaching one or more of the In the Classroom lessons or activities illustrated in this chapter, either in a student-teaching environment or to your peers.

4. Get a copy of the teacher's guide for a social studies textbook being used in an elementary school. How many teaching/learning alternatives does it suggest? How might you enhance the unit or otherwise improve on it using the suggestions found in this chapter?

For Your Portfolio

5. For the activity or lesson that you taught in item 3 above, write about what worked and didn't work. Would you choose a different strategy if you were to teach this content again?

Continuing the Journey: Suggested Readings

Bolen, J. (1999). Taking students seriously. *Social Studies and the Young Learner, 11*(1), 6–8.
Good advice for relating to students in meaningful ways. The journal itself is an essential resource for the elementary social studies teacher.

Lederer, J. (2000). Reciprocal teaching of social studies in inclusive classrooms. *Journal of Learning Disabilities, 33*(1), 91–106.
Useful advice for teachers on how to be sensitive to increasing diversity in classrooms; in this case, the topic is learning disabilities.

Marzano, R. (2000). Twentieth century advances in instruction. In R. Brandt (Ed.), *Education in a new era* (pp. 67–96). Washington, DC: Association for Supervision and Curriculum Development.
An overview of teaching and learning techniques with research-based foundations.

Matthews, D. (1999). What we are learning about how children learn, and what this means for teachers. *Education Canada, 39*(1), 35–37.
An insightful article on childhood learning and how teachers can make the most of it.

www.compsimgames.mining.com
Features simulations and games for children.

www.creativeteachingsite.com
Contains many useful ideas for elementary social studies teachers; includes features on simulations, games, interactive learning, and the like.

SAMPLE LESSON 6.1 *Settlement of the United States*

AGE LEVEL: Intermediate

KEY IDEA: History is affected by a variety of factors, some random.

INSTRUCTIONAL OBJECTIVE: Students will develop alternatives that might have occurred given a changed historical circumstance.

SET: Begin by asking the question below on a Monday morning and telling students that the class will spend about 15 minutes on Friday discussing their responses. Post this question on the board:

> In what ways would the United States be different if it had been settled west to east instead of east to west?

Tell students they may discuss the question with parents or friends during the week.

INSTRUCTION: On Friday, ask students to give their responses to the question, and write their responses on the board. Here are some answers provided by a fifth-grade class to this question:

- "We'd have a different language. Maybe Chinese."
- "People would have come mainly from Asia."
- "The capital city would probably be in the West."
- "We'd have easterns instead of westerns on TV."
- "We probably wouldn't be here."
- "The western areas would probably have a larger population."
- "The high mountains of the West would have been a barrier to early expansion."
- "There might be several countries where Canada and the United States are today."

REFLECTION/ASSESSMENT: Ask students to comment on one another's responses. Which ones seem the most realistic? Why?

CLOSURE: Point out that sometimes the historical events we take for granted are the result of random circumstances, such as the fact that Europeans landed on this continent before (or perhaps with different motives than) Asians.

SAMPLE LESSON 6.2 *The Zuni Culture*

AGE LEVEL: Intermediate

KEY IDEA: Most cultures are founded on central cultural concepts, which are observed through various behaviors and rituals.

INSTRUCTION OBJECTIVES: Students will identify concepts followed by the Zuni Indians and describe how they observe those concepts.

SET: Have students read the following narrative about the Zuni and study the accompanying picture.

Zuni

In the fine craftsmanship of their turquoise and silver jewelry, in the fabulous designs of their dance masks and in their wealth of ceremonial observances, the Zuni Indians have displayed a creative spirit which has brought great beauty to their desert home.

The Zuni now occupy an area along the Zuni River, south of Gallup, New Mexico. Their old home was a terraced, stone and adobe

A visual description of Zuni life.

pueblo on a hill overlooking the river. Originally they lived primarily by agriculture, raising corn, beans, squash and chiles. During the last hundred years, or so, Zuni Indians developed skills as jewelry-makers—and are now famous for this work.

Zuni use a variety of jewelry designs—deer, butterflies, eagles, dance figures in flat relief and more—in which turquoise stones are individually set or arranged in mosaics. Different colors of stone, shell and coral pieces, delicately elaborate designs and silverware trim often distinguish Zuni creations. Jewelry-making has joined agriculture as their important economic activities.

The artistry expressed by the jewelry-makers was traditionally found in the fertile imagery of the abundant religious dances and ceremonials of the Zuni. Kiva groups, priesthoods, fraternities and medicine societies played important roles in preserving sacred traditions and observances. For it was through proper attention to ritual and prayer that rain, fertility and a joyful life were granted by the gods.

Religious dances were not diversions from a rigorous life, but a highly important unifying element in the Zuni harmony with life. Dances were held often throughout the year, except during the crucial planting and harvest seasons.

Masks became a vital element in these dances. The Zuni were renowned for the skill in construction, imagination in design and the sheer variety of their masks. They were bizarre, often grotesque creations, symbolically painted and, at times, impressively large. The masks used for the Shalako festival after the harvest were as much as three meters (nine feet) high and enclosed the men who danced within them.

The Zuni sun priest set the dates for the dances. In the summer, rain dances were held. In winter, members of the Wood Fraternity—men and women—performed the dances of the sword swallowers. With great dexterity they combined dancing with swallowing red-colored swords made of juniper and decorated with feathers. Their rites lasted for several days. The medicinal powers of the Wood Fraternity were said to have been most useful for treating sore throats.

The climax of the year was the Shalako ceremonial, held in November or December. This was a symbolic representation of the Zuni's creation and migration to their homeland. Dancers completely enveloped in huge, awe-inspiring masks personified the Shalako, divine messengers from the rain gods who devoted prayers to the happiness and fruitful life of the Zuni.

Preparations for this festival went on throughout the year. Participants honored special rites to prepare themselves for their roles. As the great time approached, special houses built for the Shalako were decorated, great amounts of bread baked and meals readied. Finally a masked, nude youth painted black with red, yellow, blue and white spots, representing the fire-god, appeared carrying a burning cedar brand. He was followed by a Council of Gods and finally, by the six Shalako. These figures were striking, enormous masks with eagle-feather headdresses, turquoise faces with rolling, bulging eyes, clacking beaks, and accents of long black hair and ravens' feathers. These marvels were received in their houses where they danced through the night. Truly, the gods seemed to be among their people.

The Zuni have preserved much of their heritage to this day. Many of their dances survive.*

INSTRUCTION: Ask students to consider the concepts list that follows. First, have students decide how the Zuni observe the concepts. Second, have students decide how they themselves observe the concepts.

Culture Concepts	How the Zuni Observe Them	How I Observe Them
Food	_____	_____
	_____	_____
Shelter	_____	_____
	_____	_____
Seasons	_____	_____
	_____	_____
Religion	_____	_____
	_____	_____
Festivals	_____	_____
	_____	_____
Ceremonies	_____	_____
	_____	_____
Heritage	_____	_____
	_____	_____
Artistry	_____	_____

CLOSURE: Ask students to read entries from their lists aloud, and write these on the board.

REFLECTION/ASSESSMENT: Have students discuss whether they could identify their own cultural concepts from the lists that the class has developed. What do students in the class have in common with one another? What differences are there among students? Is it possible to draw comparisons between the classroom culture and Zuni culture?

EXTENSION: Have students take their lists home and talk with their parents about the cultural traditions of their own ethnic groups.

*Text and image from Price Stern Sloan, Incorporated. Reprinted by permission.

SAMPLE LESSON 6.3   *The Bicycle Path*

AGE LEVEL: Intermediate

KEY IDEA: The role of special interests in making public decisions.

INSTRUCTIONAL OBJECTIVE: Students will demonstrate understanding of the role of a particular participant in a public decision-making process.

SET: While showing students the map below, explain that the town plans to build a bicycle path from Lower Town to the Little Red Schoolhouse that will enable the children who live in Lower Town to ride their bikes to school. Explain that several obstacles lie along the way from Lower Town to the school, including hills, swamps, roads, and houses, and that various groups are concerned about these obstacles:

- The City Engineers do not want to build the path over hills because doing so raises construction costs.
- The Wildlife League does not want the path built through swamps because it might harm animal habitats.
- The Safety Commission does not want the path to cross streets because that would be dangerous to young bikers.
- The Housing Commission does not want the path built through people's homes and yards.

INSTRUCTION: Divide the class into four groups, and assign each group one of the four roles listed above (City Engineers, Wildlife League, Safety Commission, or Housing Commission). Explain that the object of the game is for each group to draw a path from *any* of the southernmost squares to any of the northernmost squares and to acquire the least number of points. For each square that a path passes through, the group must add 5 points. In addition, the group must add 5 points to their total for each square they enter that causes problems for their particular role: for example, the City Engineers must add 5 points for every square with hills; the Wildlife League must add 5 points for every square with swamps; the Safety Commission must add 5 points for every square with streets; and the Housing Commission must add 5 points for every square with houses. Thus, for the Engineers, a square with hills in it adds 10 points—5 for the square and 5 for the hill. Give students enough time to complete the task.

CLOSURE: Have a spokesperson for each group talk about why the route they have established is more appropriate than the other routes. Allow the groups time to negotiate. Can the groups together establish a route for the path that is least objectionable to the town as a whole? Which group created the path that accumulated the least points?

EXTENSION: Assign the students to investigate a local issue that is controversial. Ask them to try to identify the particular interests of each group involved and how those interests are reflected in the group's position on the issue.

Lower Town

⌒ = hill

≈ = swamp

≈ = road

chapter 7

Assessing Social Studies Learning

In this chapter, we will explore these themes:

key concepts

- An overview of assessment
- Integrated assessment strategies
- The importance of assessing assessment
- Testing and assessment
- Portfolio assessment
- Assessing your own effectiveness
- Standards and achievement

I guess I lost track of time.
   —A child's self-assessment of why
she came back late from recess

Assessment. Tests. Grades. Report cards. Do these terms bring joy to your heart? Is this why you decided to go into teaching? Maybe not.

Well, now that I've cheered you up with these opening remarks, let me just mention that assessment is more complex in social studies than in, say, spelling. I think you already know that. Social studies assessment calls on the imagination to seek out grand strategies that can be integrated with teaching and learning as a seamless whole. When you elevate assessment to this level, it becomes something to anticipate with, yes, a sense of joy, rather than a sense of dread. It becomes part of the "big picture" of teaching and learning.

We have a basic human need to know how we are doing. Most of us want to make progress in life, and most of us know that assessment, at its most meaningful, is really just a way of showing how we're doing so that we can improve. I think there is a discussion in this—one between you and your students. It could bear real fruit if it is an open, honest discussion of feelings and dreams and even fears.

It is easy to forget that social studies is about more than history and geography and civics. It is about the very life of the classroom. In that sense, if you were to assess yourself as a social studies teacher, you might make one of the self-test questions: "Have I talked with the kids about why assessment is necessary?"

Meaningful assessment is an integral part of effective planning and teaching. At its best, assessment is ongoing and reflective, meant to help make improvements along the way. Still, a problem exists at the level of childhood education because it in never easy to determine what young children know using either traditional or innovative measures. We know that their thinking abilities typically transcend their abilities to read and write. I firmly believe that the students in your class are learning a lot. The issue is how to capture it.

This chapter addresses that very issue. The major focus is authentic, integrated assessment strategies. In that sense, many of the techniques I will propose are themselves activities for teachers and students in the spirit of teaching, learning, and assessment as seamless whole.

An Overview of Assessment

Assessment is best perceived as a natural and logical part of the teaching/learning process. Try not to think of it as something set apart or as a kind of outside event. Perceptions of assessment as integrated into the routine of school life are not easily held, given the experiences we've all had with tests through the years. Let's consider three key questions about assessment: Why should we assess? What should we assess? How should we assess?

Why Assess?

My guess is that assessment is not one of the leading reasons you got into teaching. Most of the teachers I know and have known over the years, myself included, don't particularly enjoy assigning grades, even though they have come to accept that part of the job as a necessary part of school life. Assessment certainly has its critics—probably more than any other aspect of teaching. Common complaints include such comments as "It takes the joy our of teaching" and "It hurt me to give out the report card to that child." Many people feel that nothing takes the joy out of learning more than a test.

There is some merit to that sentiment, especially where young children are concerned. Children are often not testwise and may not understand school assessment purposes in general. They tend to see the world as a whole, and only gradually do they begin to perceive that there are activities and there are test. As this unfortunate dualism becomes a reality, some children, often high achievers, fall prey to learning not for its own sake but for getting good grades. Others find assessment traumatic, worrisome, or lacking in meaning.

Of course, there is another side to this argument. I could tell you stories about the look of joy on the face of a child who has done something very hard, very well. There are compelling reasons for assessing student progress. First of all, students need to know how they are doing. Their parents need and want to know, as well. And you need to know to what extent your students are learning important ideas, skills, and content. Your own concerns will range from the professional to the personal as you consider your students' progress. Finally, there is the role of assessment as a means of getting students to take learning seriously, to realize that accountability is a fact of life.

What Should Be Assessed?

The question of what to assess is not as simple as it may seem at first glance. You can't assess everything. This argues for a strategic use of assessment. In social studies, we can start with the standards as our long-term goal structure. From there, we should consider the age level and the specific course of study at a particular grade. Within that structure lie the various units you will teach during the year. And finally, we come to the day-to-day experiences. So when we arrive at the place where you and your students are involved concretely in reading, discussing, writing, constructing, and otherwise performing in some meaningful manner, we can reflect on the idea that goals, plans, activities, and assessment make up our social studies curriculum. Further, we can reflect on the idea that each of these separate pieces must be joined together in ways that make sense. Figure 7.1 shows the flow among these pieces.

How Should We Assess?

Let's say, for example, that one of your unit teaching objectives is: "Students will develop a sense of chronology or time order." This objective fits NCSS Standard II, "Time, Continuity, and Change" (see Chapter 3). Obviously, your plans will call for activities that

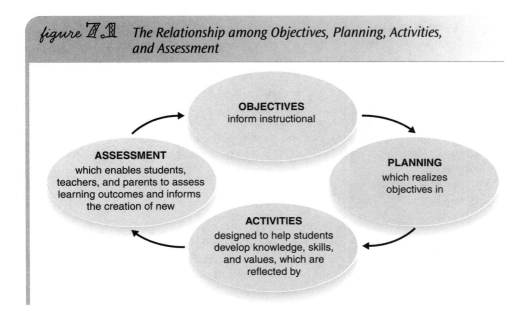

figure **7.1**   *The Relationship among Objectives, Planning, Activities, and Assessment*

OBJECTIVES
inform instructional

PLANNING
which realizes
objectives in

ACTIVITIES
designed to help students
develop knowledge, skills,
and values, which are
reflected by

ASSESSMENT
which enables students,
teachers, and parents to assess
learning outcomes and informs
the creation of new

give your students opportunities to develop their sense of time. Such activities might include having students make time lines of their lives to date with speculation about their lives into the future or family trees showing parents, grandparents, and other relatives. Another activity might include a whole-class project on the history of the community and how local history fits into state, national, and world history. Assessments might include writing or otherwise explaining how time lines or family trees work. The point is that goals, objectives, plans, activities, and assessments should be aligned.

So when you think of how you should assess, think of how you should teach, how your students should learn, and keep the assessment procedures in line with experiences. A balanced curriculum will contain a balance of experience, including reading, writing, listening, speaking, constructing, inquiring, and performing. In addition, keep in mind that some experiences are individualistic and some are collaborative. A balanced curriculum leads naturally to balanced assessment.

See what you think of the teacher's use of assessment in the following scenario.

in the classroom Assessing a Lesson

Mr. Hayward, a fourth-grade teacher, brought a large number of Brazilian artifacts to class one day. He placed them on a display table in a corner of the room. The students eagerly examined the artifacts and asked their teacher many questions. He said he would rather let them guess about the artifacts for a while. On the next day, Mr. Hayward gave two artifacts each to small groups of four and asked the groups to consider the following questions: (1) How are the two artifacts alike and different? (2) Who might use them? (3) What uses might they have? (4) How many uses can you suggest for them? On the third day, he told the name and use of each artifact and explained that the items were from Brazil. He told the class that they would be involved in a unit on Brazil and he just wanted them to be inquirers. He said he was pleased with their guesses and their active involvement.

To evaluate the outcome of this experience, Mr. Hayward gave the class a test in which he selected 20 of the artifacts, numbered them, and asked the students to write the name and use of each artifact beside its number on a sheet of paper.

How fair do you think this test was to the learners? What might have been a more fair evaluation?

In my opinion, Mr. Hayward was not totally fair because he tested only for the third day's experience. Before that, he had the students hypothesizing, probing relationships, communicating in groups, and making inferences. After they engaged in these high-level activities, he tested the students only on their ability to recall. If you feel the evaluation was fair, as Mr. Hayward obviously did, I think you made a very common error: You defended an assessment strategy that is attractive because the test is easily developed, easily scored, and provides an objective progress check. Unfortunately, the students deserved more in this case.

This scenario illustrates the use of an essentially invalid test. For an assessment to be *valid,* it must be a representative measure of the material that was taught. Mr. Hayward had three days of instruction, but his test measured only the learning that took place during a portion of that time. He used an inquiry-teaching strategy but not an inquiry-testing strategy.

What could Mr. Hayward have done to make his assessment strategy valid? He overlooked a simple procedure, which, if followed, helps ensure that assessments provide accurate reflections of potential learning outcomes. Objectives, activities, and assessment must parallel one another. Take a moment to study Figure 7.1.

For a portion of the inquiry activity, Mr. Hayward might have stated the following objective: "Students will be able to state ways in which two artifacts are alike and different." The statement of such an objective, clearly present in the activity in which the students were involved, would have helped focus the assessment. Obviously, another objective was the following: "Students will be able to list the name and use of each artifact." As we saw, the teacher taught toward that objective and tested for it.

Following are a sample objective, some activities, and a test item that Mr. Hayward might have used to assess learning outcomes other than recall of information:

- *Objective.* Students will be able to state ways in which two artifacts are alike and different.
- *Activities.* Students discuss and record similarities and differences between two artifacts in small groups. Student groups share their analyses with the class. The teacher helps students consider the physical properties, form, and potential uses of artifacts.
- *Sample assessment.* The teacher gives groups two new artifacts and asks them to record differences and similarities.

You may be wondering about the propriety of such a group assessment procedure. Remember that the students learned in groups. They should therefore be given some opportunity to illustrate how effective that strategy was. This is not to say that all group activities need to be tested in groups. However, some provision should be made for such a procedure if for no other reason than students should sense that you have confidence in group activities as a way to learn effectively. Do the exercise in Figure 7.2 to see how you feel about assessment of social studies learning.

---

figure **7.2**   *An Assessment Survey*

Let's consider two questions: (1) Should children's learning in social studies be evaluated? and (2) Why or why not? To answer the first question, place a check at the point on the continuum that describes your feelings.

| Elementary students should *never* be assessed in social studies. They should just enjoy it and learn what they will. Tests are evil. | Low key assessment is okay but not formal tests. | Some form of assessment is necessary—not always in the form of tests. A wide variety of measures should be used. | Formal tests are necessary, but other measures can be used to supplements assessment by tests. | Elementary students *must* be assessed by formal tests, better grades are necessary in order to assess student progress, and only formal assessment procedures can give reliable grades. |

Integrated Assessment Strategies

For the teacher of elementary social studies, authentic, integrated assessment strategies are completely necessary. They accomplish several important teaching/learning goals at once: They enable you to get a clearer picture of how well you are teaching. They provide both you and your students with a far clearer idea of how well you and they are learning. They promote a reflective atmosphere in which you and students begin to become more consciously aware of what is being learned and how meaningful it is. (This is known as *metacognition,* or thinking about thinking.) And they help provide a classroom experience that is itself more integrated and seamless.

I can tell you this: If you use these strategies faithfully, two things of great and lasting significance will happen. First of all, student achievement will increase. You will definitely see improvement on standardized tests. Second, the social/moral fabric of life in your classroom will improve. Your classroom will be a better place for you and your students, and citizenship will be something real, not just an academic study.

Writing about Learning

"I LEARNED" STATEMENTS   This is a simple and durable strategy that you should use often. At the end of an activity or lesson, ask your students to write down (or tell you if they are too young) something they learned. When you have your students write down what they learned and turn in their papers, you have given each of them the opportunity to think about the experience and to reflect on it. You will also notice that the aggregate of what gets turned in is an excellent measure of what your students thought was significant. Don't be disappointed if the first time you try this, many students don't write or say anything. Why should they? No one has ever asked them such a question. They will get the idea in time. Use "I learned" statements a couple of times a week—in other words, often enough to keep the students thinking that you just might ask them following any given experience.

KEY IDEA IDENTIFICATION   At the close of a lesson or activity, ask your students to explain—preferably in writing, if they can—what they think was the key idea. Researcher John Goodlad (1984) has faulted teachers for failing to teach ideas. That can't happen if you teach your lessons with a key idea in mind and you ask your students to identify it. Don't worry if they identify something other than what you were looking for or if different students identify different key ideas. That becomes the essence of a good discussion. By using this strategy from time to time, you will raise your own level of consciousness about the importance of ideas in learning while you raise your students' consciousness.

THE WEEK IN REVIEW   This is a small-group assessment strategy best done on every Friday afternoon. Place students in groups of two or three, and challenge them to look back over the week with the idea of identifying some of the most important things the class did and learned. Each group should submit a written statement or verbally explain their findings. When the students know that they will always reflect back on the week, they begin to think about what they are doing and learning, especially if you remind them that on Friday, they will do the Week in Review. It makes a great way for you to begin on Monday. You start the week by saying, "Well, here were the big stories from last week. Let's see what happens this week."

SEARCH FOR MEANING   One of the most important assessment strategies you can utilize is to search for meaning in learning. From time to time, you need to ask your students to write (or tell) you what they are learning that is meaningful to them. This takes trust on your part and theirs, but I guarantee you that it is rewarding.

Ideally, all learning should be meaningful, but we know that is not always the case. However, as a search for meaning becomes a part of the goal structure for you and your students, meaning will begin to develop if for no other reason than that you and they are looking for it.

CLEAR AND UNCLEAR WINDOWS   Have you ever tried to look through a window that was dusty, dirty, or foggy? You can't see much, can you? Or have you ever noticed a child whose glasses are so smudged that you wonder how he or she can see anything?

Sometimes, social studies can be that way for some students. Why not ask your students now and then how clear things are? Give them an opportunity to show you by putting things that they understand in a clear window and things that are hard for them in an unclear window. Here is an example of Sarah's windows:

Sarah

Clear Window	Unclear Window
I loved doing the rol play, It was fun to be a astonott.	I hav trubbel reading the book. It was to hard for me.

RECORD KEEPING   Record keeping uses Skinnerian reinforcement techniques and, at the same time, turns a measure of responsibility over to the student. In order to carry out accurate individualized record keeping, your students will need to record the assignments they have completed, the scores or grades they received on each assignment, the pages they have read, the films they have seen, the books they have read, the projects they have participated in, the maps they have made, and so forth.

It sounds complicated, doesn't it? It's not, though, if you have your students record each item as soon as they complete it or as soon as you return it to them. I would also encourage you to have your students make a brief notation beside each entry. The notation should include the main idea or most important point of the activity. Here is an example:

Noah M.
Social Studies Record

Date	Assignment	Grade	Note
Mon. 6th	Film on traffic safety		Don't just depend on cars to stop for you.
Tue. 7th	Worksheet on traffic safety	100%	Rights and responsibilities of pedestrians
Wed. 8th	Make map of crosswalks by Oak Point School	A	My map shows what the crosswalks look like, only flat.

I guess every teacher wants to teach his or her students ways of becoming more responsible. Record keeping is a tangible way to do that. It is also a kind of metacognitive strategy, because it enables students to increase their awareness of the work being done in social studies.

SELF-REPORTING   An obvious but often overlooked assessment strategy is to have students assess their own progress. It's their work, after all. Why not let them help to assess it? Self-reporting gives students an opportunity to be analytical about their own progress. A good self-report should deal with both the strengths and weaknesses of progress as viewed by the student.

Because self-analysis is rarely encouraged in school settings, you will have to be patient at first. In fact, some students may even consider self-reporting inappropriate. But what, after all, is the purpose of learning if it is not to encourage independence on the part of the learner? I think that in time, you will be gratified with the ability students develop in this area. Following is an example of a self-report turned in by a fourth-grade student:

February 10
Mark Goldberg

I liked learning about the feudal economy. I'm glad we don't have it anymore though. The best thing I did was when Jason, Maria, and me made the feudal manor out of cardboard. I really did a lot of work and so did everyone. We showed where the lord of the manor lived and where the serfs were. The poor serfs loved holidays. So do I! Do you know where we got most of our information? We got it out of a book called *Life in Medieval Times*. Part of it was hard to understand.

QUESTION AUTHORING   This seldom-used strategy can provide brilliant insights to your students' sense of what is important and just how curious they have become about learning. Simply ask the children to write down (do this orally with young children) any questions they would like to ask about the content and experience in general.

This activity provides you with a context for telling the class about higher-level questions. In time, if you are patient, you will see a tremendous improvement in the nature of the children's questions. Also, many of the questions they raise will help you with your teaching because the children are, in effect, acting as diagnosticians for you.

JOURNAL ENTRIES One of the greatest improvements in teaching and learning in recent years has been the idea of student journals. Although journals serve a variety of purposes, they are quite useful as an assessment tool. Encourage students to make entries about the subject matter they are studying, including their feelings about it as well as their thoughts and ideas. Their entries will provide them with an ongoing record of their perceptions of social studies. You should collect student journals periodically and make brief comments of encouragement and support.

SPOT-CHECK INVENTORIES The spot-check inventory is a simple strategy that allows you to obtain from your students a brief synthesis about what they think they have learned during a particular amount of time. To do a spot-check inventory, merely stop whatever is going on at a given time (class discussion, group work) and ask each student to list several things that he or she has learned during the activity. Be patient and allow students to become better at this metacognitive strategy over time.

Younger children will simply have to tell you what they have learned as you list their thoughts on the board. Older children can write down their own lists to share with the class. A useful alternative to the listing approach is to have students write a paragraph or essay telling what they have learned. The example in Figure 7.3 was written by a Scottish girl, Diane, age 9, after a discussion about life in America.

THANK-YOU There is a powerful idea known as *serial reciprocity*. Simply put, it means that if someone does something kind, helpful, or thoughtful for you, you need to pass it along. This is different from merely giving back directly to the person who helped you. It goes around and comes around.

This is an assessment technique that will in time make your classroom a truly civil place to be. It is based on the notion that in a classroom, everyone is a teacher in one way or another. We can all help each other. Make it part of the routine to encourage students to write or draw thank-you notes and notes of appreciation to each other. You might be surprised how many come your way!

Talking about Learning

PYRAMID DISCUSSIONS Have you ever thought of class discussion as assessments? Probably not, if for no other reason than that most class discussions involve only the teacher and a handful of more talkative students. But what if you wanted everyone to discuss and reflect? Here's how you can do it.

Begin by asking or writing on the board one or two important questions related to what your students should be learning. Place students in groups of two and have them discuss the questions. When the groups of two have had a chance to discuss, place students in groups of four and have them discuss the same questions. Groups of eight come next, discussing the same question. Then go to the whole class.

figure **7.3** *A Scottish Child's Essay on Her Knowledge of America*

> Diane McCaldin
>
> What I Know About America
>
> In America the peple take diprent than us. And they have a hoter conchry. It is a very nice place in the world. It is the place were we get all our food from. In America thay have enomus sky skrepers that are biger than our flats and houses. And if you go to America for your holidays your will get a gret suntan, you mite get sun strok. And in America brlyons of films are made. And best of all is Wolt Disny land were all the chilarend go to all the carrictars lice Donld Duck

> and Miky mouse and goofy are good. And all the grat houses. Thay have lovely firnisher in them. And if you are hungry in the midst of your trip you can go in a place which ther is a speecer that you speec in what you want. And in a minit you will get your food you want and you mit ask for a milk shak. Or a chocklet bispet. And you want feel hungry any more.
>
> good by

This accomplishes two things. First of all, everyone has a chance to talk. Second, if the questions are important, then the students should have the chance to consider and reconsider them. By the time you reach whole-class discussion, everyone will have had an opportunity to think through something important.

I CAN TEACH We've all heard the expression "The best way to learn something is to teach it." There is some profound wisdom in the saying, for teaching involves expression and performance, two commodities often sadly lacking in school learning. So, the assignment is for the students to teach an idea, skill, or some content they have learned in social studies to someone else. Typically, you would ask your students to teach one of their parents or a brother or sister. This accomplishes the goal of having your students revisit what you taught them from a different perspective, that of a teacher.

CURRENT EVENTS

Focus on Assessing Critical-Thinking Skills

One easy way to evaluate both literacy and critical-thinking skills is to ask students to give occasional oral reports on current events. Emphasizing themes in the news encourages students to do in-depth investigating and reporting and discourages them from reporting on the many sensational and bizarre events that are reported. A focus on a given theme also creates a conceptual framework for students, and many themes create an exciting potential for learning.

You may want to post a "Theme of the Week" on the bulletin board and ask students to focus on it as they report the news. Some themes are so powerful that you will find yourself returning to them several times during the school year. Here are some suggested themes:

- *Energy:* conservation, production, supply and demand, new developments, controversial issues
- *Air and/or Water Issues:* supplies, sources, pollution, clean-up efforts, exhaust, run-off, conservation
- *Helping People:* volunteer efforts, clubs, organizations, heroes, service people, advice columns, leaders.
- *Transportation:* inventions, energy-saving ideas, mass transit, modes of travel, space flight, travel by water, air, and land
- *Climate and Weather:* droughts, disasters, tourism, ideal places, clothing, shelter

Here are some websites that students may want to explore:

    www.ecologyactioncenter.org
    www.eia.doe.gov/kids
    www.mhwest.com/NTCSC
    www.kidsnet.au/kidscategories/kids
    www.whyfiles.org/021climate

Doesn't anybody worry about the day when the stream might run dry?

Editorial cartoons furnish students with excellent nonverbal material for the analysis and display of current events topics.

Source: Arthur Poinier, courtesy of *The Detroit News.* Reprinted by permission.

CHOICES AND FEELINGS   At the end of a lesson or at the end of a week, give your students a few minutes to reflect on the choices they were able to make in social studies. Did they get to decide anything? What was it? How do they feel about how things are going? Let them express their feelings in a conversation with you or a brief note.

CIRCLE MEETINGS   The circle meeting is a very helpful way to gauge the class's feelings and thoughts about how things seem to be going. Everyone's seat, including yours, is arranged in a circle. You begin the meeting by telling about what you have been trying to accomplish and how you think it is going. After your introduction, simply go around the circle and give each child an opportunity either to say something or to pass, if he or she does not wish to talk. Don't be discouraged if, at your first try, the children do not offer up gems of wisdom and insight. They will, in time, if you are patient and supportive.

This technique, which draws on Lev Vygotsky's ideas of social intelligence, is one of the surest ways of getting at the truth of things based on the group's collective perceptions and impressions. Primary school–age children take to this format naturally. By the intermediate grades, some children have become reluctant to speak up in a group setting. Your job is to overcome that unfortunate phenomenon.

Circle meetings take anywhere from 10 minutes to an hour, depending on how deeply the class gets into the matters at hand. Once a week is probably a good target for circle meetings.

THINKING ALOUD   The simple technique of thinking aloud is one of the best ways to prevent the "in one ear and out the other" syndrome that seems to haunt children's learning of social studies (not to mention other subjects!). This should be a 5- to 10-minute activity in which you ask students to talk and listen with partners about what they are learning. Sometimes you may want to place a question or two on the board for the pairs to discuss. However, if you leave the discussion open, you will find that you get a wider range of student input. It is useful to have a whole-class discussion following the thinking-aloud session, in which students can volunteer aspects of their talks together.

Illustrating Learning

LEARNING ILLUSTRATED   At least once a week, you should ask your students to draw pictures or make maps of interesting or important things that they have learned recently in social studies. Their drawings and maps make excellent displays, and they should find their way into the students' portfolios in time. It is important to remember that some children who may not be adept verbally are actually learning a lot, and this provides one way for them to show it.

DISPLAYS   It has been noted that doing schoolwork is like preparing for an athletic event or a drama production that never happens. You just *prepare*. Imagine spending time rehearsing a play and never putting it on. Doesn't that strike you as strange? But this is what happens with schoolwork all the time. Perhaps this is one reason it seems unreal to some children.

You might be surprised at the number of nursing homes, hospitals, clinics, restaurants, shopping malls, stores, and so on that would welcome the chance to display your students' work. Parents and children alike are proud when they see student work put on public display. By the way, it is very good public relations for the school.

Students combine historical and geographical inquiry as they participate in a project tracing the origins of their ancestors.

Keys to Getting Parents Involved

Parents send their children to you, hoping that you will do a good job of teaching them. In most cases, they are extremely interested in how their children are doing. Report cards give parents a sense of a child's progress, but only a general sense. Here are several strategies you can use to inform parents of the progress their children are making in social studies:

- *Send a note home.* If someone in your class did a nice job on an assignment, worked effectively in a group, or whatever, send a brief note home that explains to the parents what happened.
- *Make a phone call.* You and your students' parents are busy people. But a one-minute phone call in the evening for the purpose of telling a child's parent that he or she is doing very well (it helps to be specific) in social studies doesn't take very much of anyone's time, and it will be appreciated.
- *Have a conference.* In most schools, conferences are held once or twice a year for the purpose of reporting pupil progress. It is important to be prepared for such an important meeting. First, don't sit behind your desk at a conference; it is too threatening and official. Rather, sit at a table with the parent. Try to be positive; remember, you are discussing the parent's own child. If you do have some negative comments, be sure that they are specific and that they are not a personal attack against the child. Balance any negative comment with something positive. Perhaps the most important thing at a conference is to have numerous examples of the child's work. Parents are impressed with maps, artwork, and so forth. Above all, express genuine interest in the child. That won't be hard, because you really do care.

Assessing Assessment: Why Is It Important?

Perhaps at this point you are thinking something like, "OK, Arthur, those may be good metacognitive strategies for assessing student learning, but where on earth am I supposed to find the time for them?" I have an answer for you. The saying "Less is more" is really quite profound. As applied to education, it has been attributed to Theodore Sizer, a leader in the school restructuring movement. But the idea is actually rather an old one, dating back at least to Jean-Jacques Rousseau, who wrote in the preface to his book *Emile*, "Teachers, teach less and teach well." A so-called coverage mentality is self-defeating. The more you try to cover, the less your students will learn and retain. The strategies I have presented here are time consuming, but they have several advantages.

1. *They will facilitate language development.* This one of the most important goals of teaching. As Piaget, Vygotsky, and others have pointed out, children need to reflect and talk about about what they are learning. Speech and thought co-develop; they are not separate functions. So, by giving children time to talk about, draw about, and reflect in general on what they are learning, you actually create a more efficient system.

2. *They build opportunities for citizenship.* This is one of the major goals of social studies. The participating citizen is basic to our democratic way of life. The kinds of activities and conversations you focus on during assessment of learning represent fundamental practice in speaking one's mind and in publicly expressing oneself.

3. *If you are patient, you will begin to see a group intelligence start to emerge.* This is something that simply cannot happen when people are denied the opportunity to reflect on and talk about ideas publicly. So, yes, it does take time. Anything worthwhile takes time.

My advice is to take these strategies seriously and integrate them into your teaching. It will mean less talking time for you and more for the children, but since their growth and development is at stake, it is well worth it.

Testing and Assessment

The assessment procedures described to this point are essentially unobtrusive; that is, they are designed to be integrated into the flow of instructional activities. The idea is to create a seamless whole. Tests, on the other hand, are typically perceived by students as disconnected events that they must prepare for and that often cause nervous discomfort.

Formal tests are a fact of classroom life, but you should use them sparingly and strategically. Make a sincere effort to help your students understand that the purpose of such testing is to identify where they still need instruction—not to embarrass them! This is not easy to do. Some educators feel that testing causes problems of trust between students and teachers. That may be somewhat extreme, but the point is valid. Children are natural learners. They like to explore, create, talk, and do projects. They do not always understand the adult agenda that mandates accountability measures that they would not choose to participate in: namely, formal tests.

Part of your task as a social studies teacher is to help children understand the role that accountability plays in their learning. Tests help us, as teachers, know how our students are doing and what progress they are making, as well as what they are not learning and what needs to be revisited. More and more, tests are mandated by state and federal law. But when you move from authentic, integrated assessment into the realm of formal tests, proceed with caution.

Let me tell you a story. Recently, a fourth-grade teacher told me that her son had come home from school after a long day of taking statewide standardized tests. She asked how things had gone. She could tell her son was upset. He told her that he hadn't had time to finish the test. Sympathetic, she reassured him that we often can't complete tests because the questions are difficult. He said no, it wasn't that the questions were hard. He knew the answers. What had taken time was filling in all the circles. He explained, "The teacher told us we had to fill in each circle for a right answer with our pencil, and we couldn't go outside the lines." This boy had spent a lot of time filling in each circle completely and then carefully erasing all the places where his pencil had strayed outside the line. That was why he didn't finish the test.

It's easy for adults to forget that children are not testwise. It's also easy to forget how literally they take what we say. And it's easy to forget how much children worry over getting things right.

I'm not arguing that children should not be tested, although I do think the current fad for standardized testing is not particularly helpful to learning in many cases. (Do you ever wonder how children managed to grow up into contributing, thoughtful, responsible adults in the days before standardized testing existed? It's a pretty good bet that George Washington and Abraham Lincoln never took a multiple-choice test in their lives. Neither did Jane Austen or Thomas Edison.)

We live in an era of testing, and that is a reality you must face. But you can do everything in your power to make testing more humane and children less anxious. Review the most important foundations of assessment in the Keys to Humane Assessment.

Keys to Humane Assessment

- *A teacher's first job is to care.* You are there because you care about children. You want the best for them. Never lose sight of the fact that great teachers make it their central concern to care for their students, to make them whole.

- *Social studies is about human beings.* Always make it a point to treat the human beings in your classroom with respect, care, and support.

- *Students need to understand the purpose of tests.* When you do formal testing of your students, explain that the purpose is not to punish them but to help them and their parents get a better idea of what is going on in the classroom. You want to identify what children have learned and plan for future learning.

• *Students need to be prepared.* Be as certain as you can that the children in your classroom are prepared to take a test—not only by reviewing the content that will be covered but also by explaining test procedures and strategies. Maintain a firm, friendly classroom atmosphere, one where learning is prized. Help children understand exactly what is expected of them when they do take tests.

• *The classroom needs to be a safe place.* Help your students understand that your classroom is a place where they can relax, be comfortable, and feel free to share concerns. If they are worried about tests, make sure they know they can express that worry.

• *Model the importance of learning.* Be certain that each lesson and each activity contains important knowledge, skills, and values. And take the time to reflect on important concepts with your students. You might be surprised how well prepared they are for formal tests as a result. The prepared mind always has the advantage!

Essay Tests: Extended-Response Questions

In social studies assessment, an *extended-response question* requires the student to write an answer that explains his or her position, reasoning, and conclusions. A good extended response contains something more than the correct answer. In fact, students are sometimes given credit for their reasoning, even if they have certain facts wrong. Often, extended-response answers include interpretations of data, identifications of relationships, analyses of problems, and so on. The one thing that all extended responses have in common is that they require the student to supply information, rather than merely pick an alternative, as with a true-false or multiple-choice question.

You should have at least two purposes in asking extended-response questions: (1) You want to gain some idea of how much each student knows, and (2) you want to help students learn to present their ideas in a logical, coherent manner. To accomplish these two goals, extended-response questions should have these qualities:

1. *Be focused on main ideas.* Because they require providing developed answers to a few global questions, rather than a wide range of specific knowledge, extended-response questions should always review the main ideas you have covered in instruction. When you prepare for a unit, identify the main ideas you wish students to learn; then write extended-response test questions that parallel those ideas. Consider these examples of good and bad test questions:

Poor: What caused the fight between Peter and James? (This question seeks recall of a specific event.)

Better: Peter and James fought over who would take Bob's paper route. List some reasons such conflicts happen. Explain how you think this conflict might have been avoided. (This question seeks students' understanding of the concept of *conflict*.)

2. *Be designed to elicit higher-level thinking.* Lower thought levels, such as recall, are more easily tested by objective tests. Again, consider some examples:

Poor: Why were Iroquois longhouses made of wood? (This question seeks lower-level information that could readily be incorporated into a higher-level question.)

Better: Do you think an Iroquois longhouse is more like an apartment building or a one-family house in our culture? Why? (This question gives students an opportunity to choose between alternative answers and seeks criteria in defense of the answer they select.)

3. *Be written in clear, unambiguous language.* Children need to know what is expected of them. One way to ensure that your questions will be reasonably clear is to list the criteria you will use in judging student responses. Compare the following:

Poor: Discuss the causes of the American Revolution. (This question invites rambling answers and does not specifically seek alternative perspectives on the issue.)

Better: (a) List two reasons the American colonists felt they should break away from England. Do you think these were good reasons? Why or why not? (b) List two reasons the English wanted to keep the American colonies. Do you think these were good reasons? Why or why not? (The questions are broken down so specific criteria can be applied. The questions guide students toward developing reasons that reflect alternative perspectives.)

Objective Tests: Selected-Response Questions

Three types of items for objective tests are (1) true-false, (2) multiple choice, and (3) matching. These types of items have certain common characteristics. For instance, tests containing such items are easily scored. Also, a relatively high number of questions can be included on a test, thus ensuring adequate representation of topics and ideas. Elementary students who lack the capability to develop an essay that conveys their true understandings of a topic are often able to demonstrate their understanding by discriminating among alternative answers. Also, objective tests are potentially fairer than essay tests, in that they prevent teachers from favoring student responses on the basis of penmanship, personality, and other essentially irrelevant variables.

Perhaps the greatest potential shortcoming of objective tests involves the tendency teachers have to develop questions that seek answers based only on recall or explanation. This is certainly a difficult obstacle to overcome, and having a certain number of lower-level questions is acceptable on an objective test. However, if you taught higher-level thinking during a social studies unit, you should logically attempt to assess whether your students profited from that instruction.

Let's examine the three types of objective test items and strategies for their effective development.

TRUE-FALSE Following are some suggestions for developing true-false test items for social studies:

1. Statements should be entirely true or entirely false.

   Poor: The population of California grew rapidly as settlers moved east during the gold rush of 1849.

   Better: The population of California grew as settlers moved west during the gold rush of 1849.

2. Include only one idea or thought in a true-false item.

   Poor: Producers offer both goods and services in our economy, and consumers help regulate supply and demand.

   Better: Producers offer both goods and services in our economy.

3. Use terms that are clear and unambiguous.

   Poor: Trading things is better than buying and selling them.

   Better: Trading goods and services is more common than using money in our country.

MULTIPLE CHOICE Multiple-choice items permit inclusion of a wider range of possible answers to items than do true-false items. Obviously, a person responding to multiple-choice items has less chance of surviving questions on the basis of guesswork. It is important that the test writer attempt to keep all potential responses plausible and ensure that the stems to each item are parallel.

   Poor: Persons everywhere have unlimited wants and limited resources. James and Heidi are persons who live in different countries.
   a. James and Heidi have unlimited wants and limited resources.
   b. James lives on the moon and Heidi lives in Switzerland.
   c. Heidi is a young girl.

   Better: Persons everywhere have unlimited wants and limited resources. James and Heidi are persons who live in different countries.
   a. James and Heidi have unlimited wants and limited resources.
   b. James and Heidi can have all their material wants fulfilled.
   c. James and Heidi must produce all the goods that they consume.

Portfolio Assessment

One of the most promising ideas to come along in recent years is authentic assessment of learning. The term *authentic assessment* implies that the assessment of student learning should be more reality based. This is not to say that standard paper-and-pencil tests are of no value; rather, it is to say that the more natural forms of assessment are not only less threatening to children but also make more sense to them. Perhaps the best-known approach to authentic assessment is *portfolio assessment*.

The idea of children putting together and keeping track of their own portfolios comes from such professional areas as architecture and art. An architect keeps a folder or portfolio of his or her sketches, designs, plans, drawings, photographs, ideas, and so on. The architect will show the work to interested people who will then decide if they want him or her to do architectural work for them. It is a way of showing what one has accomplished and is capable of doing.

For children in social studies classes, the building of a portfolio makes good sense. A good portfolio will contain a variety of entries that provide a record of authentic student accomplishments. Here are some suggestions for what a portfolio should contain:

- Daily work samples; ordinary papers that are part of the daily routine
- Various data entries—for example, research notes, graphs, and surveys
- Student writing samples, such as essays and stories
- Rough drafts of work in progress
- Finished products, final drafts, and papers turned in for final grading
- Group or cooperative efforts that illustrate the work of several students
- Sample journal entries
- Reflections, such as "I learned" statements
- Tests, exams, and so on
- Major projects or pictures of displays
- Teacher comments and feedback
- Creative thoughts, ideas, insights, and personal-growth reflections

Each child is responsible for building and maintaining his or her own portfolio. Of course, some teacher guidance and support is necessary, especially with younger children, but it is important that children assume as much responsibility as they can for their portfolio. Sometimes we are tempted to include only a child's very best work in a portfolio. But good portfolios demonstrate progress and real learning. These suggestions can help students assemble materials for genuinely useful portfolios:

- A sample that reflects a problem that was difficult for you
- Work that shows where you started to figure it out
- A sample that shows you reached a solution
- A sample that shows you learned something new
- A sample of incomplete work and where it will lead
- Two items of which you are proud
- An example of something that did not work out well

Several interesting moral issues arise in connection with the keeping of portfolios. For example, whose property is the portfolio? Should the school keep it and pass it along to next year's teacher? Is it a private possession to be viewed only by the child and the teacher? Who decides what goes into the portfolio? Remember, a portfolio can, at most, hold a mere sample of the child's work. Should only his or her best work be included? These are important moral issues for you and your students to discuss.

My own position on ownership is that the portfolio belongs to the child and is his or hers to take home at year's end. Does the teacher have the right to examine the portfolio? I think, yes, he or she does, but I hope that the trust level is such in your classroom that the child wants you to see the portfolio. Actually, portfolios are wonderful to share with parents at conference time. As for the last question: What should go into the portfolio? I think it's the child's decision.

Assessing Your Own Effectiveness

When people think of assessment, such things as tests, conferences, and report cards typically come to mind. I've attempted to persuade you in this chapter that there is much more to assessment, even though those things are important. I do want to impress on you how meaningful informal assessment strategies can be. I hope that you will use them often.

Let's now take the process of assessment a step further. How do you, the teacher, know whether you are doing an effective job of teaching your subject? Read the Keys to Being an Effective Assessor, which provide some strategies that will help you probe deeper than most teachers ever go in assessing the effectiveness of their instruction.

These strategies are metacognitive strategies, in that they enable you to think reflectively about your work. I'll pose them as questions for you to answer from time to time. In fact, I guarantee you that if you tape these questions to the top of your desk and read them occasionally, your teaching will improve. Use these questions to shape your thoughts about social studies teaching. Ask them of yourself often. Take them seriously, but have fun with them as well. Relax and enjoy social studies. After all, as I told you earlier, social studies is about people, so it's a pretty exciting subject to teach.

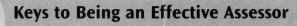

Keys to Being an Effective Assessor

- Am I trying to learn more about the content I'm teaching? What books have I read lately?
- Am I talking with the children about how they feel about the material we are studying? Am I genuinely interested in their thoughts about social studies? Do I seek to know their interests?
- Are my lessons organized appropriately? Are we studying ideas in depth, or are we just covering the material?
- Do I attempt to make connections? Do I relate social studies to other areas of the curriculum? Do I attempt to build continuity from one day to the next?
- Am I teaching key ideas and concepts and not just information? What are some of those ideas?
- What values are the students and I exploring? Do we have conversations that take us

into depth? When was the last time the children and I really explored feelings?
- Am I developing lessons and activities that allow for many ways to learn? Are my students involved in making things, talking to each other, and doing cooperative projects, artwork, music, role-play, drama, and so on?
- Am I getting the students involved in making decisions and participating in democratic processes? Does my class ever get involved in the community?
- Am I making real readers out of my students? Do they read biographies, historical fiction, stories about other lands, and so forth?
- Would I want to be in this classroom if I were a child? Is this room an interesting place to come to every day?

Standards and Achievement

Beginning in the 1990s and continuing into the first decade of the twenty-first century, teachers have found themselves in an age of standards and assessment. The No Child Left Behind legislation, passed in 2002, has been called by some No Child Left Untested. Considerable anxiety has been expressed by child-centered teachers, who feel not only that childhood should be a time of exploration, wonder, and joy, not rigorous testing, but also that overtesting encourages "teaching to the test," not true learning.

Can assessment work effectively? The key is to integrate assessment into the everyday classroom routine as organically as possible. I am convinced that using the 20-odd integrated assessment strategies presented in the first part of this chapter will go a long way toward ensuring that children both learn and enjoy learning.

The most powerful means of integrating informal assessment procedures into the routine of classroom life is reflective thinking. Reflective thinking causes both teachers and students to slow down, to go back over what has been taught, and to search for meaning. By returning to an activity or lesson, students revisit it with a fresh perspective. Take, for example, the "I can teach!" strategy, which asks the student to teach to someone else what he or she learned in social studies that day. The student will need to go back over the material learned, organize it, and think about what to emphasize. The child's role, in other words, will change from student to teacher. This approach supports learning through the power of repetition, insight, and altered perspective.

Figure 7.4 shows an assessment activity from the Michigan State Social Studies Assessment for the fifth grade called "Colonial Comparison." Students are presented with pictures of the interior and exterior of a typical colonial house of the 1700s, where various items are labeled with letters of the alphabet, and then asked to answer multiple-choice questions. Let's assume that you want to use the "I can teach!" strategy with this material. You might ask your students to teach this lesson at home and report back on their experiences the next day. Your students will not only need to know what the items in the picture are and how they are used, but they will also need to be able to explain which answers are correct and why. By adding this task to their learning, you will be well on the way both to ensuring that their learning meets appropriate standards and to preparing your students for the more complex kinds of reasoning that will be required of them by the new generation of assessments.

Most of the new generation of standards and accompanying assessments are based on learning at three levels: knowledge, understanding, and application. See, for example, Figure 7.5, which shows an assessment framework from the National Assessment of Educational Progress (NAEP). The terminology used in these materials may vary from state to state, but you will typically find these three concepts embedded in every set of standards.

Knowledge

Students are always expected to be able to recall information. Assessments for knowledge typically include *what, when,* and *where* questions. The idea behind them is that

figure **7.4**   *An Assessement Activity Using Graphics and Multiple-Choice Questions*

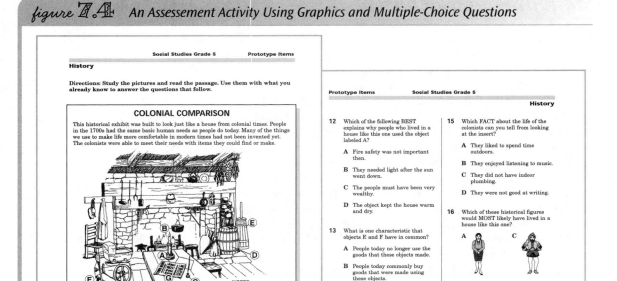

Source: Michigan Department of Education, Michigan Educational Assessment Program (MEAP). Reprinted by permission.

students must possess a certain amount of basic information—a basic *schema,* as we talked about in earlier chapters—to be able to build on what they already know and comprehend, analyze, synthesize, and apply new social studies concepts.

Understanding

Assessment of understanding often calls on students to tell *why,* or to explain the information they possess. It is one thing to know the location of a city (*where*), but it is another to explain the reasons the city might have been built where it is (*why*).

Application

Assessments that measure whether students can apply their knowledge and understanding of a certain topic typically ask them to support their conclusions, reason

figure **7.5**   *Elements of the NAEP Geography Assessment Framework*

Cognitive Dimension	Content Dimension		
	Space and Place	**Environment and Society**	**Spatial Dynamics and Connections**
Knowing	Where is the world's largest tropical rain forest?	What mineral resources are often extracted by strip mining?	What factors stimulate human migrations?
Understanding	Why are tropical rain forests located near the equator?	Explain the effects of strip mining and shaft mining on the landscape.	Explain the motivations of modern-day Mexicans and Cubans for immigrating to the United States.
Applying*	Support the conclusion that tropical rain forests promote wide species variation.	How can both economic and environmental interests be reconciled in an area of strip mining?	Compare current settlement and employment patterns of Cuban and Mexican immigrants in the United States.

Note: Example questions are illustrative only and not meant to represent the full array of assessment content.
*Applying = A range of higher-order thinking skills.
Source: National Assessment Governing Board (1994, 2001).

through an issue, make contrasts and comparisons, transfer knowledge from one situation to another, and provide a reasoned analysis of an issue.

Although educators are concerned about too much "teaching to the test," the curriculum can often follow readily from the frameworks created by various standards and assessments. For example, the NAEP's U.S. History Framework (NCES, 1994, 2001) stresses the use of themes as a way of thinking about history. Theme 2 is "The Gathering and Interactions of Peoples, Cultures, and Ideas." An associated question asks:

1. What were the family patterns, religious practices, and artistic traditions of Native Americans, Western Europeans, and West Africans on the eve of Columbus' voyage?

Questions for Theme 3, "Economic and Technological Changes and Their Relations to Society, Ideas, and the Environment," include the following:

1. How did Europeans, Native Americans, and West Africans live and make a living on the eve of Columbus' voyage?
2. How did European inventions and technological developments (particularly in navigation and armament) lead to exploration and early conquest? What individuals and groups contributed to these developments?

Can you begin to imagine the unit objectives that might flow from these questions? How about stimulating classroom activities? Engaging in drama, construction, music, foods, dance, artwork, and so on is the key to blending child-centered experiences with the demands placed on teachers and students by the standards and testing movement.

Summary

Assessment of student learning in some form is necessary. If you are planning social studies experiences that focus on content, concepts, processes, and values, you and your students will certainly want to obtain some measure of their progress. The most effective way to assess student progress is to use a variety of measures.

Perhaps you have strong feelings about formal tests for children. If you feel they are harmful or ineffective, then you will need to depend more heavily on such unobtrusive measures as checklists, observations, and interviews. If you favor the use of formal tests, you will have to justify their use as an effective means of finding out how much learners really know. The balance you achieve among the various assessment measures available to you will be a function of your teaching style and the ages and capabilities of the students you teach.

Explorations

Reflect On . . .

1. Write an "I learned" statement about something you have learned in this chapter. Share it with a classmate.
2. Interview some elementary school students to find out their attitudes toward testing and being tested. What, if anything, do their responses tell you about the relationship between student success and attitude toward tests?

In the Field

3. Collect student social studies work from several classrooms. See what inferences you can make about what is happening in those classrooms.

4. Make a list of 10 different social studies activities. Have the children in a classroom rank order them from most to least favorite.

For Your Portfolio

5. Make a list of some of the things that children might do in social studies that cannot readily be evaluated. Then figure out ways to evaluate the outcomes of those activities. Keep the results in your portfolio.

Continuing the Journey: Suggested Readings

Alderman, M. (2004). *Motivation for achievement: Possibilities for teaching and learning* (2nd ed.). Mahwah, NJ: Erlbaum.
Illustrates theory and practice of techniques for enhancing students' desire to achieve.

Ellis, A. (2001). *Teaching, learning, and assessment together: The reflective classroom.* Larchmont, NY: Eye on Education.
Provides more than 20 tested strategies for creating a reflective classroom in which teaching, learning, and assessment are combined into a seamless whole. Emphasizes formative assessment ideas.

National Assessment Governing Board. (2001). *Frameworks for history, civics, geography.* Washington, DC: National Assessment of Educational Progress.
A clear presentation of goal structures and purposes in these areas of social studies; a crucial roadmap for valid assessment. Available online at www.nagb.org.

Neisworth, J., & Bagnato, S. (2004). The mismeasure of young children. *Infants and Young Children, 17*(3), 198–213.
A sensitive portrayal of how children are subjected to tests and measures that have little to do with their real lives.

Smith, D. (2005). Accountability for academics and social responsibility through service learning. *Middle School Journal, 36*(4), 20–25.
A clear focus on the need to combine achievement with citizenship.

www.kidsource.com
Features excellent resources for assessment and a host of other teaching/learning ideas. See, in particular, the feature on assessment of young children by noted researcher Lillian Katz.

chapter 8

Inquiry, Discovery, and Problem Solving

Children as Researchers

In this chapter, we will explore these themes:

key concepts

- Inquiry, discovery learning, and problem solving
- Three types of inquiry research
- Assessment and inquiry
- Metacognition and inquiry

These children can do wondrous things,
if only we would let them.
   —Akmed Akbar

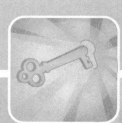

Children are natural researchers. They begin life that way. Just watch a toddler some-time, as the little one goes about researching the environment. Observe as the child uses *sense realism,* as Aristotle himself described it: observing, touching, listening, tast-ing, and smelling. *Sensory learning* is the beginning of the inquiry/discovery process. In this chapter, we will examine several different methods of social science research; specifically, we will see how children can readily use the methods of the social science researcher.

An interesting chapter called "The Science of Deduction" appears early in Arthur Conan Doyle's *A Study in Scarlet;* it describes the methods of crime detection used by the world's greatest detective, Sherlock Holmes. Holmes observes, smells, tastes, listens carefully, does chemical analyses, makes notes, and gathers bits and pieces of evidence. He sifts through his findings mentally, reflecting on their possible meanings. He spends time thinking aloud with his associate, Dr. Watson, who marvels at Holmes's ingenuity. Using all these strategies, Holmes is able to put the evidence together—almost like someone assembling a jigsaw puzzle without having the cover to the box to look at. In time, when a sufficient number of puzzle pieces have fallen into place, Holmes reaches his conclusion and solves the crime.

The only problem with this description is that the author, Conan Doyle, has confused *deduction* with *induction*. Holmes's methods are, in fact, inductive.

Inquiry and discovery methods and social science research procedures, in general, are based on inductive reasoning. *Induction* is the process whereby information and evidence are pieced together to the point that reasonable conclusions, based on evidence or data, can be reached. These conclusions then result in making inferences about some time, place, event, or phenomena. We often call this *inquiry*. Inquiry and inductive reasoning go together in social science problem solving.

Inquiry, Discovery Learning, and Problem Solving

Are there differences among the terms *inquiry, discovery,* and *problem solving?* Yes, but the differences are subtle.

• *Inquiry* is an investigative process based on the examination of evidence, often using questioning, hypothesis testing, and other means of information or data gathering. Typically, the inquirer reaches a conclusion based on the evidence and then makes inferences. Inquiry is generally the method of choice for the historian, geographer, anthropologist, economist, and sociologist. The conclusions based on inquiry are always accepted tentatively and open to revision when new evidence is offered.

• *Discovery learning* is the search for something. (Of course, some discoveries are completely accidental, but that is another matter.) In history, geography, and the social sciences, discovery implies a search that results in bringing something to light—new information of some kind. Distinctions are sometimes made between "big D" *Discovery* and "small d" *discovery*. For example, the discoveries made by Christopher Columbus in the New World changed the world (for better or worse, depending on one's point of view) and are therefore "big D" Discoveries, while the discovery made by a child that the native people of the Pacific Northwest were quite peaceful is a "small d" discovery, since this knowledge is already available to historians. Regardless of these differences in scope, the process of the discovery is the same: An investigation takes place, and an idea emerges.

• *Problem solving* is the process of attempting to answer a question in some systematic way. Typically, the problem solver tries to resolve some doubt, come to some solution, or satisfy those involved to the best extent possible. Problem solving is closely related to inquiry and discovery in that it attempts to bring to light an answer that enables us to know more, do more, or have greater insight. For school purposes, problems can be thought of as real or contrived. As we will discuss later in this chapter, *real prob-*

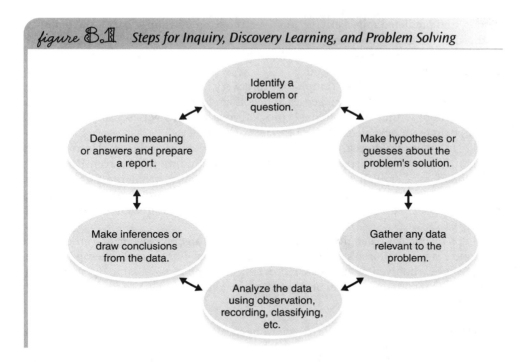

figure **8.1** *Steps for Inquiry, Discovery Learning, and Problem Solving*

lems involve the issues that arise naturally in school life and that a thoughtful teacher turns into social studies content. *Contrived problems* are those that are not directly part of students' lives but that are beneficial to their growth and development.

Inquiry, discovery learning, and problem solving are far more alike than they are different. They all involve active learning. They typically (but not always) require some teamwork, they work best when students utilize good information, and they all teach a disciplined way of reasoned thinking and acting. They generally share the steps that I have placed in a circular diagram (see Figure 8.1) to emphasize that they are not necessarily linear, resulting in a final outcome. Rather, as John Dewey once noted, the purpose of problem solving is *more* problem solving. Sample Lesson Plan 8.1, found at the end of this chapter, illustrates the inquiry, discovery, and problem-solving processes.

The Tradition of Inquiry

The inquiry tradition is an ancient one, dating back at least to Aristotle, who emphasized the use of the five senses in learning. In fact, although John Dewey is generally credited with the idea of "learning by doing," Aristotle himself wrote, "It is in doing that we learn best."

Sensory experience is fundamental to discovery learning, and all people employ it, at least in casual fashion, on a daily basis. If, for example, you decide to go for a walk, step outside, and realize you had better go back in the house for a coat, you are using sensory learning. You *felt* the chill or damp, or you *looked* at the sky, *saw* threatening clouds, and predicted rain. Perhaps you *heard* the wind whistling around the buildings or through the trees. Some people say they can *smell* rain in the air. These sensory experiences, of course, are direct encounters with the environment—a hallmark of discovery learning.

The teacher who wants to emphasize discovery learning capitalizes on the built-in tendency for people to use their senses to help them learn. The keys to discovery learning in a school setting are twofold: (1) provide your students with sensory experiences and (2) help them develop the skills of systematic inquiry.

Fortunately, children are natural inquirers. They excel at the art. Unfortunately for them, most teachers spend no time on problem finding whatsoever. It is simply overlooked as a skill in school life. On the other hand, from the first day they enter school, children are given problems to solve. These "problems," which are actually exercises, appear in seemingly unlimited quantities in their workbooks and textbooks.

Let's see what we can do to remedy that. I think a good place to start the process of inquiry is with children's stories and nursery rhymes. For example, Aesop (620–560 B.C.), a slave who lived in ancient Greece, collected and wrote a large number of animal fables that contained moral problems within them. Consider the story of the moles and porcupine:

> Once a porcupine asked a group of moles if he could live with them in their safe, snug, warm underground tunnels. Feeling sorry for the porcupine, the moles agreed to let him live with them. But the porcupine's quills stuck the moles, making them uncomfortable when they tried to sleep.

What is the problem in this fable? Can you offer a solution?

In the Gospel of Luke, Jesus tells the parable of the good Samaritan:

> A man was going down from Jerusalem to Jericho when he fell into the hands of robbers. They robbed and beat him, leaving him half dead. A priest going down the road saw the hurt man but crossed over to the other side to avoid him. Another man came along, and he too passed by the hurt man. But a Samaritan traveling the road stopped to help the hurt man. He bandaged his wounds, put the man on his donkey, and took him to an inn to take care of him. The next day, he gave the innkeeper two silver coins and asked him to care for the hurt man. He said if there were more expenses, he would pay for them when he returned from his business.

Can you state the problem or key issue in the story?

Stories, parables, nursery rhymes, and other tales have been used for centuries to help children frame problems, think about right actions, and consider moral issues. I encourage you to draw on the wealth of stories that already exist in folklore, fable, myth, and legend to find and solve problems with the children you teach.

Real and Contrived Problems

Now let's look at a few of the characteristics that distinguish *contrived* and *real* problem solving in the inquiry process. A contrived problem may deal effectively with the inquiry process; however, it is imposed on learners by the teacher or the program. A contrived problem does not arise directly from the life experiences of the students. Obviously, textbooks and other social studies programs cannot anticipate and make provision for the real problem that may confront a given group of students located in a particular geographic/economic/social setting at a particular time.

Proponents of real problem solving point out that because the learners are attempting to deal with an issue that they helped to develop and that is part of their lives, the learning process has more meaning. Proponents of contrived problem solving point out, on the other hand, that many worthwhile issues in historical, economic, and anthropological inquiry might never come to the learners' attention if they had not been guided into them by a creative teacher working with a good program. Rather than take sides in an either/or dichotomy, let's assume that both approaches have their merits. Note the steps of inquiry process in the following two examples.

in the classroom A Contrived Problem

Before the formal introduction of a unit on Japan, a fourth-grade teacher brought a number of Japanese artifacts to the classroom. He divided the class into research teams of five students each. He gave each team three artifacts, which he asked them to spend a few minutes examining and discussing. He then placed the following questions on the board for each team to answer:

1. How would you describe each artifact?
2. How are the artifacts alike and different?
3. Are these artifacts like any tools that we use?
4. What uses would you guess these artifacts might have?
5. Who might use these artifacts?

The small groups of students discussed the questions and recorded their answers. As the discussion progressed, the teacher moved around the room and helped students focus on their analysis of the artifacts. When the discussion groups had completed their tasks, each group was given an opportunity to present its conclusions. When each group made its presentation, students from other groups were allowed to ask questions about the artifacts and their possible uses.

Later, each group developed a chart based on its speculations about the artifacts, and the chart and accompanying artifacts from each group were displayed in various areas of the room. The teacher asked the students to treat the statements on the charts as hypotheses that they would either accept or reject as the unit progressed and more information was acquired.

Thus, in this lesson, students were given a *problem.* The teacher *gathered appropriate data sources,* which the students examined. The students then *processed the data* through oral discussion and the development of their charts. The charts contained the students' *inferences,* which were to be treated as *hypotheses* that could later be verified.

in the classroom A Real Problem

One morning, members of a second-grade class were excitedly telling their teacher and each other about a near accident that had occurred at a pedestrian crossing next to their school. A primary-age child had nearly been struck by a car as she was crossing the street. The students exclaimed that the intersection was dangerous, especially during the winter months when ice and snow were present.

The teacher asked the students if they would like to conduct an investigation of the intersection to see how dangerous it really was and to see if they could suggest ways to make it safer. The class agreed that this would be a worthwhile project.

The class wrote a *statement of the problem* as follows: "How can our school crossing be made safer?" With the teacher's help, the class decided to use the following *data sources* in their research: a model of the intersection; the intersection itself; other students in the school; school staff members, including teachers, custodians, the principal, and the secretary; local residents; photographs of the intersection; and drivers who use the intersection. Working all together as well as in teams over the course of several weeks, the class *gathered data* through interviews, observation of traffic flow, timing the speed of cars near the intersection, and taking pictures of pedestrian, bicycle, and automobile traffic at peak crossing times before and after

school. The students *processed their data* with a photo essay of the intersection, summaries of interviews, drawings of the intersection depicting the various problems they had discovered, and charts showing the volume of foot, bicycle, and auto traffic at peak hours. They *made the following inferences:*

1. The crossing is dangerous, especially for younger children, and a safety awareness campaign is needed.
2. Four safety patrol students should be placed on duty rather than two, the present number.
3. Larger, more visible warning signs should be posted along the streets leading to the intersection.
4. The crosswalk lines should be repainted.

The students' report was given to the school principal and to the police department. They were pleased to see that all four of their recommendations were enacted.

Differences and Similarities

Although these examples of contrived and real problems are intended as models, rather than exhaustive explanations of the possibilities inherent in each approach, let's take a moment to review their differences and similarities as teaching strategies.

The most obvious point of contrast is that the intersection investigation came directly from the life experiences of the students, whereas the artifact lesson was imposed on students at least partly to broaden their life experiences. A second contrast is found in the ways in which the students dealt with the steps in the inquiry process. In the artifact lesson, the statement of the problem, the selection of data sources, the means of gathering and processing data, and the making of inferences were predetermined by the teacher. In the intersection problem, the structure of the inquiry problem was much less obvious. A third contrast involves the outcomes of the students' findings. The intersection investigators were able to effect changes in the community. The artifact investigators were given an opportunity to become actively involved in previewing a forthcoming social studies unit.

The two examples also have similarities. Both used the steps in the inquiry process presented at the beginning of this section. In each case, students moved through a progression from problem statement to inference making. Second, both problems provided for a high degree of student interaction. Third, both problems provided for the development of the following skills: observation, description, problem definition, classifying, decision making, hypothesizing, verifying, and inference making. Fourth, in each lesson the teacher played the role of facilitator, guiding but not dictating to the students. A further similarity is the active involvement of the students. Finally, both lessons had transfer value; that is, they had the potential to be used by learners as models for investigating and solving problems in many situations other than the actual lesson situation. The next section expands on the idea of transfer of learning.

Reflective Thinking as a Follow-Up to Inquiry

Perhaps either of the foregoing inquiry examples could be justified on the grounds of student motivation and active involvement. But it should be emphasized that problems such as these have an inherent potential for helping students make applications of their learning that are generalizable beyond the specific problem. A useful strategy to facilitate learning transfer is a short *reflective thinking session,* held either at the conclusion of a given lesson or on the following day before the introduction of new material.

Three Types of Inquiry Research

Historians and archaeologists attempt to reconstruct past events and eras. Anthropologists observe and try to describe cultural aspects of human behavior. Sociologists deal with the behavior of groups. Psychologists conduct experiments with human subjects in an effort to expand our knowledge of human responses and behavior.

What do these investigators have in common? They share a common subject matter—human beings—as well as a respect for evidence and a desire to increase the world's knowledge of human behavior. In each case, their investigations represent attempts to answer questions by seeking appropriate sources of data, gathering and processing data, making inferences, and reaching conclusions about human behavior. Differences exist as well. The historian cannot replicate a situation, as a psychologist often can, nor can the historian mail questionnaires to subjects in many cases.

In the next few sections, we'll look at descriptive research, survey research, and experimental research. Many illustrations are provided of ways these inquiry methods can be implemented in the classroom, turning your children into researchers and active learners. As you read about the investigations, try to view them from the dual perspective of teacher and researcher.

Descriptive Research

Descriptive research, as the term implies, has as its purpose the description of human behavior, primarily through observation. Groups and/or individuals are the descriptive researchers' data sources. For example, it has been common practice for anthropologists to live among tribal groups in order to make direct observations of their behavior. Such a method of investigation is known as *participant observation* because the investigator plays the dual role of participant in the daily life of a group and observer of that group.

Another form of descriptive research is *direct observation.* One can observe without actually becoming involved in a situation. Although participation puts the observed at greater ease and thus produces a more natural situation, it may make the observer less objective because of personal involvement in the activities of a group.

A young inquirer makes a careful descriptive study of the Sacagawea dollar coin.

Another type of descriptive research is *indirect observation*. This often involves the use of such data as pictures, artifacts, written accounts, books, and maps. Of course, someone engaged in direct or participant observation might also use such tools as the camera, tape recorder, and field notes as aids to ensure the accuracy and permanence of his or her record keeping.

Another means of gathering information for use in descriptive research is the technique of *interviewing informants*. Members of a group often are a valuable source of data. In addition to observing their behavior, an investigator can obtain information by interviewing them—asking individuals questions about leadership, customs, rapport, and so on within the group.

As an illustration, let's see how the four descriptive research techniques of participant observation, direct observation, indirect observation, and interviewing informants might be used in investigating the activities and behavior of a Cub Scout pack. As a participant observer, you would join the Cub Scout pack, attend meetings, and take part in the rituals and activities. You would, in effect, become one of the group. As a direct observer, you would watch the pack at its meetings but refrain from taking part. In addition to keeping notes, you might photograph and tape record events. As an indirect observer, you might examine crafts made by members of the pack. You might also examine minutes of meetings, the *Cub Scout Handbook,* and other relevant artifacts. As an investigator interviewing informants, you would seek out one or more members of the pack and ask such questions as: How do you usually spend your time in meetings? and Who do you think are some leading members of the group?

Obviously, to do a thorough study of the scout pack, it would be advisable to use all the foregoing techniques, because (1) to use all four would provide a greater and

Young social scientists observe artifacts and record their findings.

more varied base of information and (2) the different approaches might provide cross-checks on the validity of the information obtained.

As is the case with all social science research, descriptive research attempts to answer questions or solve problems by gathering and processing data and making inferences from those data. The following sections illustrate various techniques students might use in doing descriptive research.

OBSERVATION   Observation can take many forms and should be used as often as it takes to see real improvement in the children's ability to observe systematically, a very valuable skill. Here is one example: Take the class out to the playground or to some interesting scene near the school. Each student should have a pencil and a sketch pad. The idea is to let the students look at the scene for a couple of minutes or so. Then ask them to turn around and sketch or map what they saw. A variation on this theme is to ask students to write down a description of what they saw. Older students, of course, can and should do both. After students have finished their descriptions, ask them to turn around and check their work against what they see. How accurate was it?

Another example of this form of descriptive research is to have students make a drawing of an object such as a vase, a toy, or whatever. The brain begins to function elaborately in such a situation. The concentration, the careful observation, and the attempt to render what you see brings out subtleties that are too easily overlooked in casual observation. I suggest that you put on a recording of Mozart or Haydn when you do this activity. I think you'll find the students will like it. Finally, another variation is to describe the music. See the activity called The Five Senses Game for other possibilities.

INTERVIEWING   The interview, as a descriptive research tool, provides investigators with an informant's perspective on a group or event. Obviously, investigators could add validity to their research by interviewing more than one group member. Also, it is important that investigators consider a member's status within a group. For example, the perspective of the president of a club is likely to be different from that of a member with lower status who attends meetings only occasionally. When an interview is expanded to include larger numbers of respondents, it becomes a *questionnaire*. Figure 8.2 illustrates an interview situation in which a third-grade investigator questioned a 4-year-old about her membership in a YMCA group.

To summarize, the task of the descriptive researcher is to pose a question or problem about human behavior and to attempt to answer that question by gathering data through observation and/or interviewing. Thus, descriptive researchers add to the existing base of knowledge of human behavior through their investigations.

COMMUNITY STUDY   The community study descriptive investigation can become a whole-class project. The object of the study is to describe the community around the school. Students can work in teams to develop their descriptions. Among the descriptive research tools they might use are drawings, maps, photographs, and interviews. The following elements of the community would be worth describing:

Types of trees	Streets
Parks	Churches/temples
Businesses	Vacant lots
Houses/apartments/condominiums	Playgrounds

figure **8.2**   *The Interview Guide*

I talked to Robyn . Age 4 . She belonged to YMCA .

She goes there 2 times a week. This is how she feels about it ☺ .

Her favorite things to do at YMCA are swimming and gym .

I asked her if she thought other 4 year olds would like to be in.

She said Yes .

Comments. She likes to go there.

MAP MAKING   Map making begins with observation and description. In fact, a map is a spatial (as opposed to verbal) description of a place. Make sure everyone has a notebook or sketch pad and a pencil and ruler, and take your class outdoors. If you can find one, choose an elevated spot, such as a hillside, and put the children to work sketching what they see. Don't be too concerned with some of the details at first. Things like which way is north and how does one draw to scale can come along gradually. The key is to observe and describe, not in words but using a spatial approach (drawing) to description. I guarantee that you will gain some new insights regarding students' abilities. Some of the children who don't shine verbally will surprise you with their spatial abilities.

in the classroom   The Five Senses Game

The Five Senses Game, which takes on many variations, can be played as often as you like. It takes its cues from the work of Francis Bacon and before that from Aristotle, who were both convinced that sensory learning was the foundation of scientific inquiry. I would recommend that you try the game with your class as a whole, at least for starters. If you have a primary class, you may have to do most of the note taking. Older children can do their own.

The key idea of this game is the ability to *describe*. It is useful to isolate one of the senses each time you play the game. If you decide to emphasize the sense of touch, you can take your students outside and ask them to identify various objects in the environment they would like to touch—for example, a leaf, a mud puddle, a worm, grass, bark, the air, the side of the building, and so on. The idea is to draw out of your students descriptive terms related to texture, feel, and touch. You can do the same for the other senses: sight, hearing, smell, and taste. (You may want to elicit taste descriptions in the classroom using some things to eat that you have brought.)

Survey Research

Taking a survey is a means of gaining information about groups of persons. Often, an investigator will be interested in discovering the attitudes, preferences, or opinions held by large numbers of people concerning particular ideas or issues. This precludes the possibility of mere observation because of the difficulties posed by such factors as time and distance.

Assume, for example, that a student investigator at Washington Elementary School wishes to assess the attitudes of the students at the school toward some newly installed playground equipment. Although it might prove instructive to observe who uses it, it could be difficult to provide observation coverage during the many recess periods throughout the school day. Additionally, an observer would probably see only students who chose to use the equipment, thus failing to tap the attitudes of nonusers who might have a preference for different kinds of equipment. Thus, the survey offers an alternative to the observation/descriptive approach.

The student researcher should bear in mind three important considerations when conducting surveys: (1) what to measure, (2) how to measure, and (3) whom to measure.

A young sociologist conducts survey research.

The question of *what* to measure needs to be defined with precision. For example, a surveyor who wishes to determine how students feel about school assemblies must decide exactly what it is about student attitude toward the assemblies it is important to know. Consider the following two questions:

1. What do you think of school assemblies?
2. Are you in favor of school assemblies?   yes   no

Although Question 1 may provoke interesting responses, it is a vague question and thus it may be difficult to quantify the responses. Question 2 is more precisely defined, and it allows one to quantify the responses given to it. Figure 8.3 illustrates the processed data for Question 2.

The question of *how* to measure involves the idea of *sampling*. A survey researcher need not ask all the students at the school whether they favor school assemblies in order to make valid inferences about the opinions of students at the school. Rather, an effective method is to sample student responses from the school's population. These are three different sampling techniques:

1. *Simple random selection.* If our school has a student population of 500 and we wish to sample 10 percent, or 50 students, we need only ensure that the 50 we choose are selected on the basis of pure chance.
2. *Stratified random selection.* Because we might wish to ensure equal numbers of primary and intermediate students, we could take room lists and randomly select three students from each room in the school.

figure 8.3   *Students Favoring and Opposing School Assemblies*

3. *Stratified selection.* To do a stratified sampling, a researcher would take, for example, every tenth name from room lists. This might be useful if we wished to ensure equal boy/girl representation, in which case we would use separate boy/girl lists.

All three procedures provide fairness in the selection of samples and allow investigators to make inferences about a population without interviewing every person in that population.

The question of *whom* to measure is important because survey researchers need to ensure that their samples adequately represent the various types of groups and/or individuals found in the population. Thus, in a student preference poll, it may be crucial to ensure that primary-age as well as intermediate-age students are given an opportunity to respond and that teachers, clerks, custodians, and cooks are not included.

Let's consider two examples of surveys done by elementary classes. The first, a playground equipment survey, was conducted by a second-grade class. The second, a Halloween survey, was conducted by a fifth-grade class.

in the classroom   **A Playground Investigation**

Students in a second-grade class had experienced a number of problems with the use of the playground equipment at their school. They wondered if students in other classrooms were having similar difficulties. Among the problems the class listed were the following:

1. Some things are too crowded, so we don't get to use them.
2. People get hurt on some of the equipment.
3. We would like to have some new equipment.

The students randomly chose five students from each room in the school and asked them the following questions:

1. Have you ever been hurt while using playground equipment at school?

   yes   no

   If so, on which piece of equipment?

   _____

2. Do you ever have to wait to use playground equipment?

   never   sometimes   often

3. Would you like to have some new playground equipment?

   yes   no

   If so, give the name of the new equipment.

   _____

4. Are you a boy or a girl? _____

5. What grade are you in? _____

The results of the survey indicated that few children had ever been hurt using the playground equipment. However, 83 out of 110 students indi-cated that they often had to wait to use equipment. The most asked for piece of new equipment was a tetherball pole. Two such poles were installed at the principal's request after he had reviewed the students' findings.

in the classroom **A Halloween Study**

Students in a fifth-grade class were interested in the question of who trick-or-treats. To investigate the question for their school's population, they devised a questionnaire:

Trick or Treat Survey Form

_____ Boy _____ Girl _____ Age

Do you plan to trick-or-treat on Halloween this year?

_____ Yes _____ No

The class decided to try each of the three sampling procedures described in this chapter to see if different results would be obtained. Here are their results:

	Random Sample		Stratified Sample		Stratified/Random Sample	
	Boys	Girls	Boys	Girls	Boys	Girls
Yes	13	10	12	13	12	12
No	1	2	0	1	1	1

In addition, the father of one of the students agreed to gather age and gender data from the trick-or-treaters who came to his house that Halloween. (All the students were busy trick-or-treating themselves!) That information is collated in this bar graph:

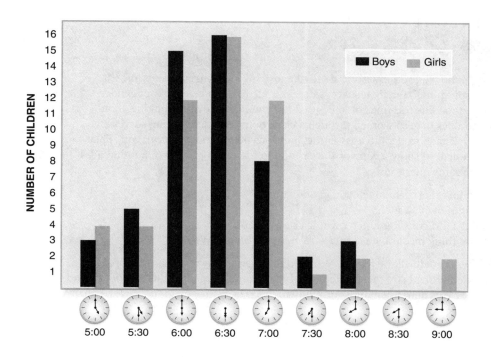

On the basis of their survey work, the class made the following inferences:

- Trick-or-treating is popular among all age groups at our school.

- From 6:00 to 7:00 P.M. is the prime trick-or-treating time.
- There don't seem to be many differences between the trick-or-treat habits of boys and girls.

Students need to understand that for the results of a survey to have real meaning, their work in gathering, recording, and graphing data must be accurate. The next example shows an effective way to develop students' survey skills by conducting a weather station survey.

in the classroom   A Weather Station Survey

Assign each child in class the task of recording the high temperature and low temperature in a major U.S. city for two weeks. The temperatures are given in most daily papers every day, so you need to be certain the class has access to the weather page. One child can take Seattle, another Phoenix, another Houston, another Cleveland, and so on.

When they are finished, use the graphs to make an impressive display in your classroom.

Of course, an additional outcome of the weather stations survey is the introduction of geographic concepts and how geography affects weather and climate. Here are some questions you will want to consider with the class:

CURRENT EVENTS
Focus on Gender Roles

Cartoons, political or otherwise, can provide insights into current issues and provide inspiration for student surveys. Look at the cartoon below about gender roles. A cartoon like this one could be used to stimulate students' thinking about current attitudes toward women through a classroom or wider-ranging survey.

First, ask each student to answer the questions below about the cartoon. Then ask each student to show a copy of the cartoon to his or her parents or another adult and ask the same questions.

1. What does this cartoon tell you about women?
2. Can a girl own a ranch?
3. Should a girl consider ranch owning as an occupation?
4. Do you think most ranch owners are men or women? Why?

Finally, tabulate all the results. What do the answers say about how people feel about women's roles? Are there differences between how your students responded and how their parents and other adults responded?

Little Bo Peep had lost her sheep and couldn't tell where to find them— So when she grew up and had her own ranch, she hired someone to take care of lost sheep for her.

Reprinted by permission of Allen Glenn.

- How does latitude affect temperature?
- Does closeness to large bodies of water have an effect on temperature (Seattle versus Minneapolis, for example)?
- How do mountains affect temperature?

With younger students, you may wish to do the project together as a class, selecting only four or five cities. With older students, you may wish to include international temperatures.

A survey can serve more of a purpose than mere information gathering. Sometimes, the results of a survey can help people take positive action. If you send your surveyors (your students) out around the school environment to look for potential problems, they can no doubt come up with a list of them: litter, vandalism, faulty playground equipment, pollution, noise, dangerous intersections, and the like. Thus, your students' survey can serve as the basis of a list of concerns that they can survey the whole school about. Then they can determine the rank order of the student body's concerns and try to involve the whole school in taking positive action to remedy the situation.

Getting a whole elementary school mobilized to study and correct a pressing problem is a wonderful experience. Having an impact beyond that is even more wonderful. That's what happened in the following example.

in the classroom Consumerism

This example of a child researcher using survey techniques is from Evelyn Kaye's (1974) book *The Family Guide to Children's Television*. An 11-year-old girl named Dawn Ann Kurth from Melbourne, Florida, became interested in advertising to children because of her younger sister:

My sister Martha, who is seven, had asked my mother to buy a box of Post Raisin Bran so that she could get a free record that was on the back of the box. It had been advertised several times on Saturday morning cartoon shows. My mother bought the cereal, and we all (there are four children in our family) helped Martha eat it so she could get the record.

It was after the cereal was eaten and she had the record that the crisis occurred. There was no way the record would work.

Martha was very upset and began crying and I was angry too. It just didn't seem right to me

that something could be shown on TV that worked fine and people were listening and dancing to the record and when you bought the cereal, instead of laughing and dancing, we were crying and angry.

Dawn had been chosen with 35 other students at Meadowlane Elementary School to do a project in any field they wanted. She decided to find out how other children felt about deceptive advertising. She began by watching television one Saturday morning. She clocked 25 commercial messages during one hour, 8:00 to 9:00, not counting ads for shows coming up or public service announcements. She also discovered that during shows her parents liked to watch there were only 10 to 12 commercials each hour, which surprised her.

Dawn devised the following questionnaire and asked 1,538 children the following questions (answer these questions yourself):

1. Do you ask your mother to buy products you see advertised on TV?

      yes   no

2. Did you ever buy a product to get the free bonus gift inside?

      yes   no

3. Were you satisfied?

      yes   no

4. Write down an example.

      _____

      _____

5. Do you believe that certain products you see advertised on TV make you happier or have more friends?

      yes   no

6. Please write an example.

      _____

      _____

7. Did you ever feel out of it because your mother wouldn't buy a certain product?

      yes   no

8. Did you ever feel your mother was mean because she wouldn't buy the product you wanted?

      yes   no

Dawn got the following responses to her questionnaire: (1) yes 1,203; no 330. (2) yes 1,120; no 413. (3) yes 668; no 873. (5) yes 1,113; no 420. (7) yes 802; no 735. (8) yes 918; no 620.

Dawn's teacher sent the results of Dawn's work to a local paper, the kind known as an advertising shopper that carries a few stories of local interest. To their surprise, Dawn was invited to testify before a U.S. Senate committee that was investigating the effects of advertising on children. In her testimony, she explained her concerns and how she conducted her research. Her work is now part of the *Congressional Record*.

Source: From *The Family Guide to Children's Television* by Evelyn Kaye, text copyright © 1974 by Action for Children's Television, Inc. Used by permission of Pantheon Books, a division of Random House, Inc.

Experimental Research

In social science, experimentation involves the manipulation of variables to determine whether a particular treatment has an effect. In its simplest form, this generally means that subjects are placed in control and experimental groups and an assessment is made at the end of the experiment to see which group receives a higher average score on a test or performs better according to some other criterion. Commonly, the experimental group is given a special or "experimental" treatment, whereas the control group is given "other" (perhaps traditional) treatment. Experimental treatments often involve a special group of lessons or a special way of teaching those lessons. For example, an experimenter might wish to know whether learning pioneer history through stories (the experimental treatment) is as effective as learning history from the textbook (the control treatment).

The next two examples engage students in experiments about products: first, paper towels and then, a health drink.

in the classroom **The Great Paper Towel Experiment**

Here is an example you can try with a class of students. It's an experiment I've done many times with children, and I can tell you they do a remarkably good job.

Begin the session by asking the class if anyone has ever bought a product that he or she thought was very good. Perhaps students will tell about bicycles, toys, or video games. Give them plenty of time to tell about what makes a product good. Then ask them if they have ever had a product that was not so good. Let the children reflect on what makes a product not so good.

Tell the class that they are going to become experimenters who do research on products. Of course, their scientific work may take several days, and they will want to be very careful that they do a good job. The first product they will examine is paper towels. You will need to get three rolls of paper towels, each a different brand. You will also need a little bit of equipment: rulers, water, oil, containers, and calculators.

Place the students in groups of three, and have them begin their plans for how they will conduct their research. Be sure to tell them that their challenge is to determine which of the towels is the best buy, second best, and third best. When the groups are ready to proceed, let them go ahead and begin their testing. (Your job is that of coach, to make sure the students are considering how good their tests are.)

When the tests are completed and each group has its ranking of the towels, you can put all the data on the board to see how the groups' results compare. This will be a time of discussion as each group reports to the class.

Of course, there are many other products to test: brands of popcorn, orange juice, crayons, peanut butter, or other products the children may suggest. Your research may lead to letter writing, analyses of advertising, or even suggestions for improvements in various products.

in the classroom **Health Drink Design**

This problem-solving experiment challenges students to invent and advertise a new health drink. Working in small groups of about five, students will need to test various formulas, figure ways to keep

costs down, and plan a promotional campaign for their product. You will need to supply such raw materials as fruit, juices, and kitchen measuring instruments.

Assessment and Inquiry

Part of the process of inquiry is being able to understand and apply the information that is gathered. Students not only need to understand how to conduct research; they also need to understand how to analyze it, comprehend the results, and use their analysis to form opinions or make decisions.

Moreover, as the emphasis on assessment continues at every level of American education, we are starting to see the analysis and application of survey results in various assessment tools. Even standardized tests can require that students understand the process of inquiry, including how to comprehend and apply results. Figure 8.4 is part of the Michigan State Social Studies Assessment for the fifth grade. In this test item,

figure 8.4 An Assessment Activity Using Survey Research

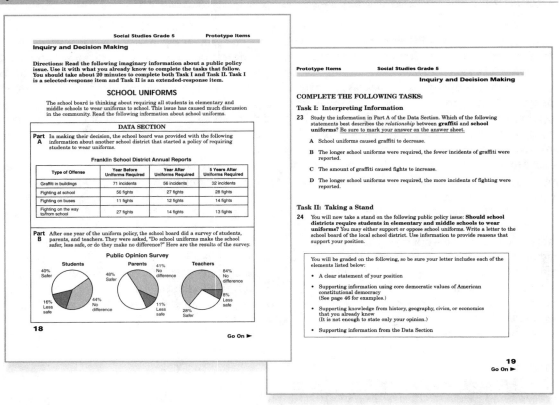

Source: Michigan Department of Education, Michigan Educational Assessment Program (MEAP). Reprinted by permission.

students are asked to interpret the results of a survey and then to form an opinion based on those results.

Metacognition and Inquiry

As students become inquirers, discoverers, and problem solvers, they can also explore the process of their own learning. Thinking about one's own learning and knowledge is called *metacognition.* With virtually any of the projects we have talked about in this chapter, the simple act of reflecting on the results can provide an added dimension to the learning experience. Let me give you some examples.

Earlier in this chapter, we looked at the strategy of observation. A simple way for you to extend any observation activity is to have students try it both alone and in groups or pairs: How effectively do they observe on their own, as opposed to observing with a partner? Try this: One day, ask students to observe a painting for five minutes. Then remove the painting and ask each student first to draw a picture of it and then to write down everything he or she can recall about the painting—colors, size, subject matter, composition. The following day, using a different painting, put the students into pairs and ask them to observe for five minutes, during which time they may discuss what they are seeing. Then ask them, as you did the day before, to draw and write about what they observed. Did talking about the painting with a partner improve their ability to re-member it? Or did having a partner simply distract them from the task at hand? You can't generalize too much from this brief exercise, but repeating it several times might allow your class to reach firmer conclusions.

Here's another possible experiment with a metacognitive element: Does listening to classical music help a person think better as he or she studies? Some experts think it does (and, of course, most teenagers will argue that listening to rock, rap, or heavy metal will do the same), but most feel there is not enough evidence to support this conclusion. Try something like playing a Mozart or Haydn piece in the background during a spelling les-son each day for a week. Then give a quiz on the words studied. The following week, have the daily lessons without the music and then give the quiz. Are the quiz results any differ-ent? (This not only gives you an opportunity for studying the learning process, by the way, but also provides you with a good time to teach students how to compute an average score for the class.) Finally, compare attitudes. Whether or not there was a difference in quiz scores, did students find studying with music or without music more enjoyable? Do all the students agree? Which do they prefer? What might be some weaknesses in this study?

Summary

This chapter illustrated a number of ways in which children can themselves become social science re-searchers. All too often, children are exposed only to the results and conclusions of the research of others. They therefore gain little insight into the processes of producing knowledge. By allowing them to conduct descriptive, survey, and experimental research, you give your students the opportunity to move toward the forefront of knowledge. A student who has helped to develop new knowledge is in a far better position to consume knowledge because he or she understands what is involved in gathering the origi-nal ideas from which conclusions are made.

No school-age child is too young or immature to conduct research of the kind described in this chap-ter. Allowances must be made for students' abilities to work independently of the teacher as they mature. Younger students often profit from whole-class in-vestigations supervised by the teacher. So, whether your students are primary or intermediate or perhaps older than that, get them involved as inquiring, curi-ous researchers.

Explorations

Reflect on . . .

To review what you have just read about the use of social science research methods in elementary social studies, take the following quiz:

1. Indicate whether you think each of the following research problems would best lend itself to de-scriptive, survey, or experimental methods.

a. _____ A study to determine which of two ways of studying our spelling words produces higher average test scores.

b. _____ A study in which investigators observe the flow of the school lunch lines in order to determine whether improvements could be made.

c. _____ A study to determine local residents' preferences concerning topics the PTA might present at its monthly meetings during the school year.

Problem (a) is experimental. Investigators could randomly assign students in the classroom (or classrooms) to two groups, each of which would study the same spelling list in a different fashion for a certain time period—perhaps 15 minutes per day for four days. Both groups would then be tested on the fifth day to determine which received the higher average score.

Problem (b) is descriptive. Observing, photographing, mapping, and drawing the flow of traffic through the lunch lines in order to recommend improved procedures would make this a descriptive study. However, you might have thought of experimenting with alternate flow routes, staggered serving times, and so on. Also, investigators could certainly survey students, teachers, and lunchroom personnel to see if they had ideas for improving the lunch line service.

Problem (c) is survey. Students could make a valuable contribution to the PTA or other parent group by consulting with the group's leadership about potential offerings for that year and then surveying community interest in proposed topics.

2. Explain the differences among the following types of sample selection: simple random selection, stratified random selection, stratified selection.

In the Field

3. Choose any one of the three methods of research presented in this chapter, and develop a possible investigation at a grade or age level of interest to you. Use the following form to outline your proposed study.

Topic: _____

Problem or question to be investigated: _____
_____

Data sources: _____
_____

For Your Portfolio

4. Carry out an investigation, from problem posing to conclusion. Use the methods of inquiry and discovery in much the same way you would want students to use them. Make maps, charts, and illustrations and also write up your results. By doing this, you will have an artifact showing your own knowledge of how inquiry works.

Continuing the Journey: Suggested Readings

American Academy of Pediatrics. (2005). *The smart parent's guide to kids' TV.* Elk Grove, IL: Author. *Wise advice for limiting, assessing, and selecting programs for kids.*

Janzen, R. (1995). The social studies conceptual dilemma: Six contemporary approaches. *Social Studies, 86*(3), 134–140. *This article challenges the reader to think through a variety of social studies emphases.*

Kellett, M. (2005). *Children as researchers.* Thousand Oaks, CA: Sage. *This book identifies both topics and procedures for carrying out research by children.*

Lintner, T. (2005). A world of difference: Teaching tolerance through photographs in elementary schools. *Social Studies, 96*(1), 34–37. *A good example of the exciting use of original source material.*

Maxim, G. (2003). The local cemetery: Exploring a primary source. *Social Studies and the Young Learner, 15*(4), 21–23.
Children become historians doing first-person field work.

Merryfield, M. (2004). Elementary students in substantive culture learning. *Social Education, 68*(4), 270–274.
The concept of culture so central to social studies comes alive in this article.

SAMPLE LESSON 8.1 — *The $1.50 Inquiry*

This lesson plan will involve your students in an inquiry activity that has potential to extend itself in a number of ways into history, geography, economics, and anthropology. To carry out this lesson, you will need enough nickels so that each child in your classroom can have one. Always provide drawing paper, notebook paper, and pencils.

PURPOSE: Students will learn the skills of observing, recording, classifying, and inference making as they examine an artifact (a nickel). Students will practice the communication skills of speaking, listening, drawing, and writing.

PROCEDURE:

1. Give each of your students a nickel, and ask them to spend some time observing it and taking notes about what they see. Tell them to write down anything they think is important about the artifact. Each student should work alone at this stage of the lesson.
2. Ask each student to draw two pictures of the nickel: one of the coin's head and the other of the tail.
3. Place students in groups of two, and ask them to research and discuss the following questions:

   - What different inscriptions do you find? (Liberty, date, five cents, etc.)
   - Whose face is on the nickel? (Thomas Jefferson)
   - What is the drawing on the back side? (Lewis & Clark's flatboat)
   - Who were Jefferson, Lewis, and Clark? (third president; nineteenth-century explorers of the American West)
   - What does *e pluribus unum* mean? (Latin for "one out of many") What is the significance of this Latin phrase for the United States? (one nation out of many states)
   - What kinds of things do you learn about an artifact by drawing it?

4. Have each pair of students put their findings into categories and label the categories (for example, "Words or Phrases," "Pictures").

CLOSURE: Ask each student individually to write as many "I learned" statements as he or she can about the activity.

REFLECTION: Ask students to share their "I learned" statements, and record them on the board. Have the class discuss what they learned.

EXTENSIONS:

- Make an illustrated poster portraying today's activity.
- Research the origin of the United States' motto: *e pluribus unum.*
- What is a nickel made of? What other materials have coins been made of over the centuries?
- Make a brief report on Lewis and Clark and their expedition of 1804–1806.
- Make a report on the life of Thomas Jefferson.
- Compare a nickel from the 1990s with a new nickel. How are they alike and different? Illustrate the differences.
- Interview an older, retired person. Ask him or her what a nickel would buy years ago.

Making History Come Alive

In this chapter, we will explore these themes:

key concepts

- The nature of history
- Why young people should study history
- The power of storytelling as history
- Using historical sources
- Children as historians

The future is here now, and the past is full of actual deeds, real history.
   —Patricia Hampl

The children we teach in elementary school don't have much of a past themselves, of course. But, they still refer to the past surprisingly often. Talking with children about the past is instructive. Their thoughts serve as reminders that they are, in fact, historians. Young children are especially good at oral history. They love to tell about things they have done, places they have been, and sights they have seen. They also never tire of hearing the stories of adults—parents, grandparents, aunts and uncles, and even just friends. "Tell me about when you were little," they ask.

The *Random House College Dictionary* defines *history* as the record of past events, especially in connection with the human race. Others define *history* simply as a record of everything that has happened.

These two definitions are more alike than different: Both define history as a record of the past (although the second encompasses more), and both acknowledge the potential for change, because the record of the past is itself constantly changing. New discoveries happen daily. Here are two examples:

- On the western coast of Mexico, historians and archaeologists have unearthed large stone heads with features that appear to be Chinese. Who created these heads? Do they suggest that there was contact between Old World and New World civilizations long before Christopher Columbus?
- In 2005, a collection of ancient manuscripts was rediscovered in storage at Oxford University in England. Some of the manuscripts are as much as 2,000 years old and would previously have been indecipherable. But new technologies now make the print legible to scholars.

What Is History?

Let us accept the definition of *history* as a record of the past. But what exactly do we mean by the word *record?* Surely, text qualifies—the written record. So does film, a more recent innovation. But what about artifacts? Cave drawings? And what about the writings whose origins have been disputed or even proven false? What about religious writings, which were produced sometimes centuries after the events they recorded, but are now taken as perfect fact?

Our libraries and museums are outstanding repositories of history, making it readily available to us. Old books, ancient maps, and exhibits can bring the past to life in wondrous ways, thus stimulating the childhood imagination. But should we include as history the stories handed down from one generation to the next?

The family is the social unit that young students relate to most intimately. Alex Haley, author of the Pulitzer Prize–winning book *Roots: The Saga of an American Family,* wrote, "In every conceivable manner, the family is link to our past, bridge to our future." Haley's book traces the history of a family (a fictionalized reality) from its African roots, through its arrival in the United States via the slave trade, to its eventual growth into a diverse African American family. Like Haley's creation, every family has a history, a set of stories, a saga. In recent years, oral history—which is often about everyday life, as it was lived by ordinary people—has become a respected and legitimate form of historical inquiry.

Is yesterday's newspaper history? Are old television reruns history? What role do the Internet and the World Wide Web play in keeping the historical record? History is all around us, from the statue in the park to the evening program on the History Channel. But that may be a very real problem for us and especially for our children: the overload of information that we face in today's world.

How does a teacher know what history is of most worth? Fortunately, most social studies curricula are grounded in a scope and sequence designed to help you with this. To some extent, the district and state in which you teach will help you make decisions about what comprises history. But beyond that, your own professional judgment must come into play. No two teachers teach in the same contextual setting. In fact, local studies often provide the richest opportunity for searching and researching the past with your students.

Why Should Young People Study History?

For some of us, World War II was the stuff of our childhood. We remember hearing radio newscasts in our parents' cars; perhaps we even remember our fathers going off to war. For others, the cold war looms large in our memories. Bomb drills were conducted in school, where we were asked to hide under our desks to escape nuclear annihilation. And for others, the memories are of Vietnam—all those people in the streets, all that long hair. For those of us with these memories, it can be hard to understand that the first Gulf War is a distant memory for today's high school students and that for the next generation of elementary school children, the 9/11 attacks on New York and Washington will be as unreal and far away as Hiroshima.

Why do children need to understand history? One answer to this question is that history is a fluid continuum. The present in which we live is also the future of the past and the past of the future. Children living in the present can benefit greatly from understanding the past—the sense of continuity, the inheritance, the traditions, the changes, and the reminders that are all around them.

Historian Peter Stearns (1993, 2006) writes, "History should be studied because it is essential to individuals and to society." Stearns goes on to list these six reasons that we should study history:

1. *History helps us understand people and societies.* History is our "laboratory" of the past. It shows us how people solved problems in the past. We can learn from their behaviors, whether good or bad.

2. *History helps us understand change and how society came to be.* The children we teach are changing every day. Their own history bears evidence of physical, mental, emotional, and social growth. And just as individuals change, so do families and even societies change. Sample Lesson 9.1, for example, helps students understand the Civil War from different viewpoints.

3. *History is important in our own lives.* Reading biographies, works of historical fiction, and other histories informs us not only about other people but also about ourselves. In learning about the lives of others, we can also reflect on our own lives.

4. *History contributes to moral understanding.* History provides examples of human behavior. We learn about courage, honesty, perseverance, and integrity from the stories of those who have gone before us.

5. *History provides identity.* One of the important questions of childhood is: Who am I? When children construct family trees, research their genealogy, and hear stories from parents and grandparents, they gain a greater, deeper sense of self.

6. *Studying history is essential for good citizenship.* The rights and responsibilities we enjoy today did not just happen. They came about because of the contributions of caring and courageous leaders from the past. The habits of heart and mind that characterized persons from years past become part of us when we learn of their dedication and sacrifice.

Henry Ford once suggested that "History is bunk." But in fact, history is a noble subject, filled with human behavior at its best as well as its worst. History reminds us that we have obligations to citizenship, morality, identity, and heritage. As philosopher George Santayana famously wrote, "Those who do not learn from the past are condemned to repeat it."

The Power of Storytelling as History

Encouraging students to learn history should not be difficult. In fact, learning about the past can be one of the most exciting and engaging activities you will undertake with your students. In part, that's because history is so much about stories, which almost all children enjoy both telling and hearing.

A teacher in traditional African costume teaches his students.

Surely, your family has stories about its history that you heard over and over again as a child. Those stories became part of who you are. They are your history. In the largest sense, history is simply storytelling. Some of the best historians—or at least, the ones who have had the most impact on our understanding of history—have been story-tellers. The stories they tell are of adventure and hardship, love and cruelty, and an entire range of human emotions. They touch us deeply.

As children study history, it becomes important that they learn about sources. Some of the most exciting sources available are children's trade books, especially biographies and works of historical fiction, although these also pose some challenges. Children must learn, of course, how to tell fact from fiction. Historical fiction, in particular, can be challenging in this respect. But a classroom stocked with a wealth of good children's books, both nonfiction and fiction, can go a long way toward learning history.

Perhaps the very best way to learn history is through *primary sources:* texts, images, and artifacts produced at the same time the events being recorded took place. Although original primary sources are often available only through libraries and museums, fac-similes can almost always be found, especially with the electronic help of the Internet and World Wide Web.

Of course, the most common resource for learning history in most elementary school classrooms is the social studies textbook. Many textbooks are engagingly written; even so, support from trade books and primary sources can only make learning more exciting. Let's take a look at some of the resources available to you.

Biographies

A biography tells the story of someone's life and times. Children in the intermediate grade levels are especially ready for biographies. The life stories of people like Martin Luther King Jr., Abraham Lincoln, Jane Addams, Marie Curie, and George Washington can be particularly inspirational for young readers. But be sure to find well-written trade books for your classroom. (See the end of this chapter for websites that provide lists of appropriate, high-quality children's books.) You have only to contrast a well-written biography with a typical social studies textbook to know why I make this suggestion!

Primary-age children depend more on oral forms of learning than older children do, so your own role as a storyteller is significant as a means of teaching and learning about the past. When teachers role-play certain persons from the past by dressing in period costume and becoming that person, children watch and listen with rapt attention. And just in case you think storytelling is only for the young, I can tell you about a friend of mine, a high school history teacher, who electrified his classes by showing up dressed as Andrew Jackson and being him for the entire day.

Historical Fiction

Learning to differentiate fact from fiction is an important skill, especially when students read books in which the authors have included both real and fictitious characters. Help your students understand how historical fiction works. Good historical fiction provides examples of real settings—for example, everyday life in colonial America, the suffering of the soldiers in the American Revolution, the hardships endured on the American frontier. Historical fiction can create context, setting, characterization, and plot in ways designed to attract young readers, who might well find textbook accounts less appealing than fictionalized ones.

Using Historical Sources

Most of what children learn at school about history comes from what are known as *secondary sources:* textbooks, workbooks, encyclopedias, websites, and even biographies and works of historical fiction. Secondary sources are fine, up to a point. Their primary limitation is that they provide the reader with already formed conclusions. The best contribution of secondary sources is to provide the context and background for children's inquiry into primary sources. *Primary sources,* which are original texts and artifacts, are filled with potential, not with conclusions. The reader, not the writer, must analyze, synthesize, and draw conclusions.

Children need to know and have access to primary sources as well as secondary sources and to understand the differences between them. The two types of sources are not opposed one to another; rather, they have a symbiotic relationship when teachers use them wisely.

Again, primary sources include materials such as interviews, newspapers, letters, diaries, journals, drawings, maps, paintings, photographs, artifacts, and even stories told to children by adults inside or outside their families. Only when children and teachers use primary sources do they *become* historians. This is the excitement of discovery, the excitement of doing one's own thinking and reaching one's own conclusions.

To understand the differences between primary and secondary sources, consider the two excerpts that follow. The first, dated November 20, 1805, is from the journal of Captain Meriwether Lewis of the Lewis and Clark expedition of 1804–1806. It was written some two centuries ago, when the expedition was camped at a site where the

Columbia River meets the Pacific Ocean, and it includes Lewis's reflections about a day on which his party had encountered several parties of Chinook Indians.

> It rained during the course of the night. A hunter dispatched to kill some food, returned with eight ducks on which we breakfasted. We then followed the course of the bay [where the Columbia meets the Pacific Ocean]. As we went along the beach we were overtaken by several Indians who gave us dried sturgeon and wapato roots.
>
> We met several parties of Chinooks returning from the camp and two of them were chiefs. We went through a ceremony of giving to each a medal and a flag to the most distinguished. . . . One of the Indians had a robe made of two sea otter skins which was the most beautiful fur we had ever seen. The owner at first resisted every attempt to part with it but length could not resist the offer of a belt of blue beads which Sacagawea wore around her waist. (Scheuerman & Ellis, 2004, pp. 162–163)

Reading this excerpt might lead to any number of possible activities. You might begin your inquiry by having students draw pictures of what they think this scene must have been like. From there, you might challenge your young historians to reflect on how this scene would have been considered differently by the Chinook or perhaps by Sacagawea herself, either in drawings or in words. The journal excerpt is rich in possibilities for research by students into native clothing, foods such as the wapato root and sturgeon, and the relationships between various Native American tribes.

Now consider how a textbook treats the same moment from the Lewis and Clark expedition:

> Lewis and Clark explored much of what is today the Columbia River region. They established a camp near the mouth of the Columbia River. While they were there, they hunted for food and traded with the local Indians. Their camp was near the beach of the Pacific Ocean so this made it possible for them to live off fish, birds, and other animals. The Indians were especially fond of bright beads, and Lewis and Clark were able to trade beads for robes and skins. They also gave medals and a flag to the Indian leaders. (Scheuerman & Ellis, 2003, p. 24)

Here, we have much the same scene, but we have traded a narrative account, written by the explorer himself, for information that, while accurate, has little character or sense of adventure. Of course, a good teacher could give many of the same follow-up assignments suggested for the original source material, but students might find less to inspire their creations.

In 1863, President Abraham Lincoln delivered the Gettysburg Address, the most famous speech in American history, on the battlefield at Gettysburg, Pennsylvania, where only months before, the decisive battle of that great armed conflict between the Union and the Confederacy had taken place. No television cameras were present, no tape recordings were made, and conflicting reports of the speech itself and how it was received were filed by different newsmen. Figure 9.1 presents what is thought to be the most accurate version of the address.

Note that the speech is only 10 sentences long. It contains only 271 words. It is hardly the length of an essay that a child of 10 or 12 might write. Most of the words are simple and common. What makes this speech so powerful? What ideas are found in it? What values does it contain?

figure 9.1   *The Gettysburg Address*

Four score and seven years ago our fathers brought forth on this continent a new nation, conceived in Liberty, and dedicated to the proposition that all men are created equal.

Now we are engaged in a great civil war, testing whether that nation or any nation so conceived and so dedicated, can long endure. We are met on a great battlefield of that war. We have come to dedicate a portion of that field, as a final resting place for those who here gave their lives that that nation might live. It is altogether fitting and proper that we should do this.

But, in a larger sense, we can not dedicate—we can not consecrate—we can not hallow—this ground. The brave men, living and dead, who struggled here, have consecrated it, far above our poor power to add or detract. The world will little note, nor long remember what we say here, but it can never forget what they did here. It is for us the living, rather, to be dedicated here to the unfinished work which they who fought here have thus far so nobly advanced. It is rather for us to be here dedicated to the great task remaining before us—that from these honored dead we take increased devotion to that cause for which they gave the last full measure of devotion—that we here highly resolve that these dead shall not have died in vain—that this nation, under God, shall have a new birth of freedom—and that government of the people, by the people, for the people, shall not perish from the earth.

Abraham Lincoln

The Gettysburg Address could be used to prompt a whole-class inquiry, in which you lead the class through the investigation. To begin, ask your students to illustrate each of the 10 sentences. Have some students memorize the speech, or even a sentence from it, and deliver it as a role-play. Have others look up any unknown words and report their meanings. Still others can investigate the context of the time Lincoln spent before and after delivering the speech. Using the library or the Internet, some might be able to find contemporary news articles about the address or other instances in which Lincoln's powerful language echoed. See, for example, prior uses or variations of the famous phrase "government of the people, by the people, for the people," as discovered by Lincoln scholar William Barton in 1930 (see Figure 9.2). And of course, you will want to have a class discussion or two devoted to the meaning of the speech.

figure 9.2   *Previous Versions of "Of the People . . ."*

- "a government of all the people, by all the people, for all the people."—Theodore Parker, at an antislavery convention in Boston, May 20, 1850
- "the people's government, made for the people, made by the people, and answerable to the people."—Daniel Webster, January 26, 1830
- "a government made by ourselves, for themselves, and conducted by themselves."—John Adams, 1798
- "I am in favor of democracy . . . that shall be of the people, by the people, for the people." —Attributed to Cleon, 420 B.C.

For how many speeches would this activity be possible? Not many, I think, which may explain some of the power of Lincoln's words. Regardless, make sure that your students have access to the actual words of historical figures, along with contemporary accounts of historical events and other primary sources. History will be so much richer for them! That point is well proven in the following example.

in the classroom   Thomas Jefferson and Meriwether Lewis

Students must be exposed to original source materials as they conduct inquiry. Far too often, even university-level students read only textbooks and other secondary interpretations—the academic equivalents of frozen dinners! Original resource materials, such as the following exchange of letters between Thomas Jefferson and Meriwether Lewis, represent rich text—*real* food for learners!

First, have your students read the letters that follow. You may want to read the letters to your class or have members of the class role-play (in costume, perhaps!) and read them aloud. You may need to explain certain words (*relinquish,* for example) and phrases, and walk students through difficult passages, but that's what real teaching and learning are all about. Don't worry: The students can understand the ideas. Trust them. If you don't believe me, go back and read the quote at the beginning of this chapter!

Jefferson to Lewis

Washington, February, 23, 1801

Dear Sir

The appointment to the Presidency of the U.S. has rendered it necessary for me to have a private secretary, and in selecting one I have thought it important to respect not only his capacity to aid in the private concerns of the household, but also to contribute to the mass of information which it is interesting for the administration to acquire. Your knowledge of the Western country, of the army and of all its interest & relations has rendered it desirable for public as well as private purposes that you should be engaged in that office. In point of profit it has little to offer; the salary being only 500. D. which would scarcely be more than an equivalent for your pay & rations, which you would be obliged to relinquish while withdrawn from active service, but re-

taining your rank & right to rise. But it would be an easier office, would make you know & be known to characters of influence in the affairs of our country, and give you the advantage of their wisdom. You would of course save also the expense of subsistence & lodging as you would be one of my family. If these or any other views which your own reflections may suggest should present the office of my private secretary as worthy of acceptance you will make me happy in accepting it. It has been solicited by several, who will have no answer till I hear from you. Should you accept, it would be necessary that you should wind up whatever affairs you are engaged in as expeditiously as your own & the public interest will admit, & adjourn to this place and that immediately on receipt of this you inform me by letter of your determination.

It would also be necessary that you wait on General Wilkinson & obtain his approbation, & his aid in making such arrangements as may render your absence as little injurious to the service as may be. I write to him on this subject. Accept assurances of the esteem of Dear Sir your friend & servant.

Th. Jefferson

Lewis to Jefferson

Pittsburg, March 10, 1801

Dear Sir,

Not until too late on Friday last to answer by that day's mail did I receive your much esteemed favor of the 23rd Ult. In it you have thought proper so far to honor me with your confidence, as to express a wish that I should accept the office, nor were further motives necessary to induce my compliance, than that you Sir should conceive that in the discharge of the duties of that office, I could be serviceable to my country, or useful to yourself Permit me here, sir, to do further justice to my feelings by expressing the lively sensibility with which I received this mark of your confidence and esteem.

I did not reach this place on my return from Detroit until late on the night of the 5th instant, five

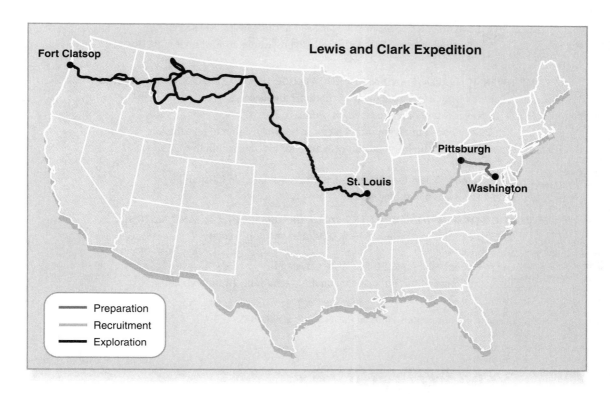

days after the departure of General Wilkinson. My report therefore on the subject of your letter was immediately made to Colonel Hamtramck, the commanding officer at this place. Not a moment has been lost in making the necessary arrangements in order to get forward to the City of Washington with all possible despatch. Rest assured I shall not relax in my exertions. Receive I pray you, sir, the most undisassembled assurance of the attachment and

friendship of your most obedient, & very humble servant,

Meriwether Lewis

Next, use a discussion guide, like the one below, to help students understand and evaluate the historical information in these letters.

Discussion Guide

DIRECTIONS: Please check each statement that you can support and be prepared to cite your evidence from your reading and experience.

DEFINITIONS AND KNOWLEDGE:

_____ 1. President Jefferson invited Meriwether Lewis to be his private, presidential secretary.

_____ 2. President Jefferson liked Lewis's knowledge of the western country and the army.

_____ 3. Jefferson pointed out that Lewis could serve his country and also get to know important people.

_____ 4. Jefferson offered to make Lewis a member of his family, which meant Lewis would receive both food and lodging.

_____ 5. Lewis retained his rank in the army.

_____ 6. Lewis accepted Jefferson's invitation to become his private secretary.

_____ 7. Lewis had to travel from Pittsburgh, Pennsylvania, to Washington, DC, to accept the position.

COMPREHENSION (RELATE AND APPLY KNOWLEDGE TO EXPERIENCES AND CONCEPTS):

_____ 1. Jefferson was a good judge of character and loyalty.

_____ 2. Lewis was honored to serve his country.

_____ 3. Salary was not an important factor in Lewis's decision to take the job.

_____ 4. Lewis gave up his opportunity to advance his rank within the militia.

_____ 5. It took 15 days for Jefferson's letter to reach Lewis in Pittsburgh.

_____ 6. Lewis was a humble servant.

EVALUATION (JUDGMENTS ABOUT THE VALUE OF IDEAS, OBJECTS, AND ACTIONS):

_____ 1. He profits most who serves best. (Arthur Sheldon—Rotary International)

_____ 2. Honor lies in honest toil. (Grover Cleveland)

_____ 3. Nothing endures but personal qualities—nothing. (Walt Whitman)

Source: Thanks to Jim Worthington, Ph.D., for the discussion statements.

Children as Historians

Historical research represents an attempt to put together the pieces of the past. Because such research deals with events that have already happened, it is often difficult to find precise and accurate reports. Historical researchers cannot control the events they wish to recapture; more often than not, they cannot even find enough information to document all the facts of an occurrence, much less all the inferences. Historical events such as the assassination of Martin Luther King Jr., the Watergate affair, the 9/11 attacks, and the events leading up to the invasion of Iraq illustrate the difficulties involved in attempting to reconstruct details of the past. The problems involved in even a relatively simple investigation, such as finding out about one's grandparents or reconstructing one's hairstyles, illustrate the difficult task of the historian!

"Finding" history can be one of the most engaging activities young children ever undertake. Let's look at some ways in which your students can become historians. All the following examples of historical inquiry and discovery are meant to serve as models for the kind of active, hands-on, experiential teaching and learning I encourage you to do with your students. As you read the following sections, picture yourself and your class engaging in just such activities. I think that if you do, you will agree that history is intellectually and socially stimulating.

Oral Histories

Oral histories involve interviews with real people—older relatives or friends, perhaps, or the recorded voices of historical figures. This approach is particularly suited to young

A young historian and his good friend from another generation.

learners because it emphasizes interviews, rather than letters, documents, and other written records. Any number of oral history experiences can become part of your teaching: interviews with a town historian, with older members of the community, with members of certain ethnic or cultural groups, or simply with family members, fellow students, or older students in the same school.

One class studying family structures tried to reconstruct the daily life of a grandmother when she was the age of the class members. The teacher began by asking how many students knew one or both of their grandmothers and then where those grandmothers lived. About half the students knew a grandmother, and about half of them could say where she had been born or lived as a girl. The teacher then made lists on the board based on the students' guesses about what their grandmothers might have studied in school, what games they might have played, what they might have eaten, how they might have traveled, and so on.

Finally, the teacher said, "We've made lots of guesses about our grandmothers' lives. How do you think we could find out if we are right?" Immediately, the children responded, "We could ask our mothers. They might know" and "We could ask our grandmothers!"

As a result of this discussion (and in response to a note that the children drafted and the teacher sent home with each of them), two grandmothers visited the classroom. The students asked the grandmothers questions based on the categories they had established (School, Games, Food, Transportation, Clothes, Work), and the grandmothers' responses were recorded next to the students' guesses. In addition, each grandmother spent time teaching the class one game she had played as a child. When the interview was over, the students spent some time comparing their guesses with the

---

figure 9.3   **A Grandmother Information Sheet**

My Grandmother's Name	Wilma Pederson
Her Place of Birth	Grand Rapids, Mich.
Games She Played	Hopscotch, Tag, Run-Sheep-Run, Baseball
Her Schoolwork	Reading, Numbers, Artwork, Writing
Her Chores at Home	Set the Table, Watch Her Brother, Do Errands
Food She Ate	Fruit, Vegetables, Meat, Cereal, Bread, Potatoes, Sweets

---

answers their grandmothers had given. They were pleased to find that some of their guesses were right—and surprised that some were very wrong!

The next day, the teacher asked the students whether *all* grandmothers would have given the same answers to their questions. The students didn't think so. In order to find out, they decided to take home information sheets for their grandparents, parents, or guardians to fill out (see Figure 9.3).

Personal Histories

Every child has a history, and every child's history is interesting and worth studying. One way for students to learn about the structure and premises of historical documentation is for them to create histories of their own lives.

I suggest that from time to time, you have your students write autobiographical sketches (see Figure 9.4). In time, these sketches can be put together to form a comprehensive personal history. The data gathering, interviewing of parents, forming personal insights, and self-reflection that occur as a result of this process will make historians out of all your students. Don't be surprised if they start the lifelong habit of keeping a personal journal. You never know what influence you might have!

Students can keep journals that document events across the year, or they can write about specific aspects of their lives. For example, Figure 9.5 shows Rhonda's chronological essay about her changing hairstyles, with photos to illustrate! Students can also take oral histories from one another, pretending to be television interviewers asking about the events of the past summer or the past week at school.

One interesting type of personal history has each student research the day he or she was born. In most cases, the local library will have copies (or microfilm) of daily newspapers, or students can use the Internet to find interesting events that took place on their special days. (Simply type in the date on a search engine—Google or Yahoo,

figure 9.4 *An Autobiographical Sketch*

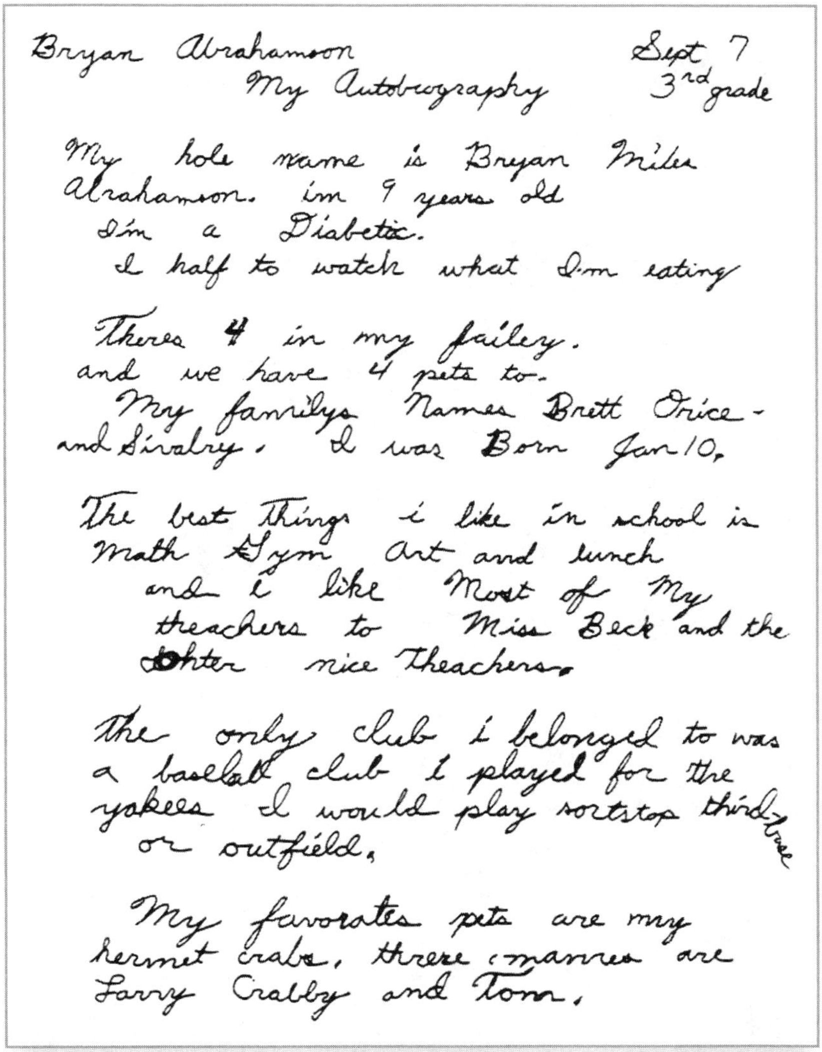

> Bryan Abrahamson   Sept 7
>   My Autobiography   3rd grade
>
> My hole name is Bryan Miller
> Abrahamson. im 9 years old
>   I'm a Diabetic.
>   I half to watch what I'm eating
>
> Theres 4 in my failey.
> and we have 4 pets to.
>   My familys Names Brett Orice
> and Siralry. I was Born Jan 10,
>
> The best Things i like in school is
> math Gym Art and lunch
>   and i like Most of My
>   theachers to Miss Beck and the
> Ohter nice Theachers.
>
> the only club i belonged to was
> a baseball club I played for the
> yakees I would play sortstop third
> or outfield.
>
> My favorates pets are my
> hermet crabs, threre names are
> Larry Crabby and Tom.

for example.) Students of almost any age will enjoy reading the newspaper for the day they entered the world. Things to look for might include the following:

- Headlines and big events
- News makers and important people
- Sports stories
- Advertisements
- Want ads
- Movies and television shows
- Fashions
- Comics

figure 9.5   *Rhonda's Essay: "My Hair Styles"*

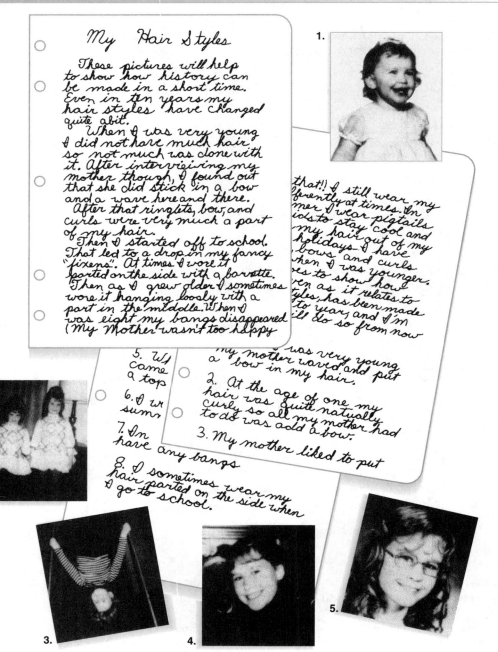

Rhonda illustrated her essay with photos of herself at various ages.

CURRENT EVENTS

Focus on Historical Inquiry

It has often been said that the newspaper (and we could now add the Internet) is "the first rough draft of history." This is actually a very exciting thought. Newspapers and news websites must meet daily and sometimes hourly deadlines. With the advent of the Internet, the flow of news changes by the minute. Twenty-four-hour-a-day cable news has also added to the speed with which the news is delivered. Take a few minutes to examine today's headlines and the stories behind them. Consider them as comprising the first rough draft of the history of our time. Eventually, scholars will sift through this information and revise it to form a second draft. But history is never final.

Here is one way to make historians out of your students: Have them examine history's first draft and evaluate it from the perspective of several years later, depending on their age. This activity is called "The Day You Were Born," and here is how it works.

Ask each student to go to the library (preferably, with a parent) and find a newspaper from the day he or she was born. Ask each student to write down answers to any or all of the following questions:

- What were the headlines and major stories on the day you were born? How do they differ from the headlines of today's papers?
- Which teams were winning in whatever sport was seasonal? Are they the same teams that usually win today?
- What comics were in the paper then? Are your favorites (if you have any) there?
- How much did a new car cost then? How much does a new car cost now?
- What movies were being advertised? Have you heard of any of them?
- In the want ads, what kinds of salaries were offered? What salaries are offered for comparable jobs today?
- How much did the newspaper cost then? How much does it cost now?
- What stories do you find most interesting in the paper from the day you were born? Why?

This project makes a wonderful way for a parent and child to spend a few hours together, working on a project that will almost inevitably engage both of them.

Time Lines

The concept of *chronology* is difficult for many children to acquire in a meaningful sense. Creating a time line can provide a clear graphic aid that enables students to think of the passage of time in a more concrete way. One useful assignment is to ask each student to prepare a personal time line, recording one or two significant events from each year of his or her life (see Figure 9.6). On a different scale, students can be asked to create time lines that include people and events from historical eras. Topics like the following are suitable for historical time lines:

- Women in American history
- Voyages of discovery
- Great African Americans
- American presidents
- Scientists and inventors
- Authors and artists
- Events of the American Revolution or the Civil War

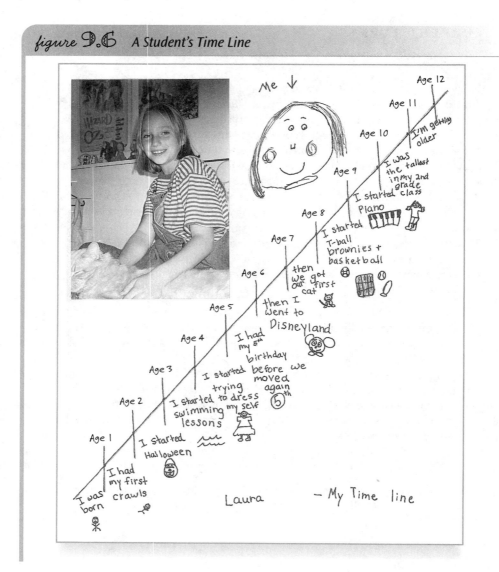

figure 9.6   A Student's Time Line

Experiential History Activities

Students can feel history come to life by replicating inquiries or testing possibilities from the past. For example, ancient Greek mathematician and philosopher Thales (sixth century B.C.) once journeyed to Egypt, where he was said to have used his knowledge of geometry to measure the height of the Great Pyramids and other structures. He is also said to have been able to calculate the distance from the shore to nearby ships at sea.

Young historians replicate Thales' experiment by calculating the height of the flagpole on the school grounds.

These kinds of measurements can be done easily today with technical instruments, but Thales had none available. All he needed was sunshine (to cast a shadow), knowledge of his own height, and a stick as long as he was tall. Ask your students: With just this much information, do you think you could calculate the height of the flagpole outside our school? Or the football goalposts? See if your students can figure out how Thales managed to make sophisticated calculations with only himself, a stick, and the sun as resources. Also see Sample Lesson 9.2 for an example of an experiential lesson.

Solving riddles of the past by interpreting stories and myths can be a fascinating experience for students. Try the following investigation with your students as an exercise in developing a hypothesis.

in the classroom Did the Chinese Discover America?

Some historians believe that in 458 A.D., five men set sail from China and, following the Japan current, traveled 20,000 li eastward (20,000 li equals about 7,000 miles). They reached a land that they called *Fusang* and stayed there for about 40 years. They returned to China in 499 A.D., where one of them, Hwui Shan, reported to the emperor about their adventures. He also presented the emperor with a stone, almost transparent, about a foot in diameter and shaped like a mirror. A servant wrote down the story, and some scholars believe that it proves that Hwui Shan and his countrymen discovered the New World more than a thousand years before Columbus did.

As you read the following part of Hwui Shan's story, ask yourself if you agree with those scholars.

Hwui Shan's Claims	Archeological Evidence
1. Hwui Shan said he traveled east 20,000 li from China.	1,000 li = about 333 miles 20,000 li = about 7,000 miles Mexico via the Japan Current is about 7,000 miles from China.
2. The Land of Marked Bodies was 7,000 li from Japan.	Marked women lived at Point Barrow, Alaska, about 2,400 miles from Japan.
3. Fusang has copper but no iron. The people there also have a system of writing.	Archeologists have found that Mexican Indians used copper by 400 A.D. Spanish explorers discovered iron in Mexico after 1500 A.D. By 400 A.D., some Indians in Mexico had a system of writing.
4. The people of Fusang use large cattle horns as containers.	Scholars knew that Montezuma, the Aztec chief of Mexico, showed Cortez, the Spanish explorer, some large bison horns after 1500 A.D.
5. The Land of Women is 1,000 li beyond Fusang.	Central American monkeys live about 300 miles south of Mexico. These monkeys are shy, chattering, and hairy.
6. The Land of Fusang is named after the Fusang trees, which have reddish, pearlike fruit. Sprouts of the Fusang trees look like bamboo.	Mexico means land of the century plant. The century plant's sprouts look like bamboo. Some people call it a tree. The Mexican century plant grows to a height of about thirty feet. The plant does not have reddish, pearlike fruit. The prickly pear or cactus apple is reddish and grows on a cactus, which looks like a century plant.
7. Fusang people make thread and paper from Fusang trees.	Archeologists have found that Mexican Indians made thread from century plants, and a form of paper can also be made from them.
8. Fusang has no forts or armies.	Archeologists have found that around 400 A.D., the Mexican Indians were at peace.
9. Hwui Shan gave the emperor of China a mirrorlike object from Fusang.	Archeologists have found that some Mexican Indians used mirrors made of polished stone.
10. Fusang has carts pulled by horses, cattle, and reindeer.	Archeologists have found that the Mexican Indians put wheels on their toys. There is no evidence as yet to show that Indian adults made use of the wheel. Spaniards brought the first horses and cattle to the Americas after 1500 A.D. The reindeer nearest to Mexico are found in Norway and Siberia. Hwui Shan probably stopped over in Siberia.

Source: Adapted from Fielder, 1972, pp. 23–27.

Try to decide whether it was possible or probable that the Chinese reached the Americas before the Vikings or Columbus.

Hwui Shan's Story

Fusang is located twenty thousand li east of the country of Ta Han in China. The Land of Marked Bodies is seven thousand li northwest of Japan. Its people have marks or stripes on their bodies like wild animals. In front they have three marks. If the marks are large and straight, they belong to the upper class, but if the marks are small and crooked, they belong to the lower class.

The land of Fusang has many Fusang trees, which give it its name. The Fusang tree's leaves look like those of the T'ung tree in China. Its first sprouts are like bamboo shoots. The people of the country eat these sprouts. Their fruit is like a pear but reddish.

The people also spin thread from the bark. They use the thread to make coarse cloth from which they make their clothing. They also make a finer fabric from this thread. The wood of the

Knowledge

1. Where were the explorers in the story from?
2. _____
3. _____

Comprehension

1. Give a brief summary of the story.
2. _____
3. _____

Application

1. Can you give the names and circumstances of other explorers who might have "discovered" America?
2. _____
3. _____

Analysis

1. Why don't all historians reach the same decision after they've seen the same evidence?
2. _____
3. _____

Synthesis

1. What are some reasons either for or against accepting this story?
2. _____
3. _____

Fusang tree is used to build houses, and the bark is used to make paper.

The people of Fusang have a system of writing. But they have no forts or walled cities, no military weapons or soldiers. They do not wage war.

Their ground has no iron, but it has copper. They have large cattle horns which they use as containers. The largest horns hold about five gallons. They have carts drawn by horses, cattle, and deer.

The Land of Women is about one thousand li beyond the Land of Fusang. Its women are completely covered with hair. They walk standing up straight and chatter a lot among themselves. They are shy when they see ordinary people. Their babies are able to walk when they are one-hundred days old, and they are fully grown in three or four years. (Fielder, 1972)

After your students have all read this story, ask them to respond to this question: Did the Chinese really discover America? Encourage them to share their hypotheses with each other. Help them understand that even though they may have devoted a substantial amount of time and thought to answering the question, their conclusions must still be seen as hypotheses because so little information is presented for them to interpret.

Next, divide the students into small groups, and provide them with the chart below. Ask each group to build a database of information, based on the content of the chart, from which they can revise or refine their earlier hypotheses.

Older students might want to explore this issue further through Internet research. Younger ones might hone their map skills by studying the possible routes that the Chinese explorers might have taken. Students of all ages will learn about the hierarchy or taxonomy of interpreting information. The guide below shows how you might emphasize what kinds of knowledge students can gain from studying this kind of historical riddle.

Summary

Several issues are involved in bringing history to life for children. One matter of concern is for them to see themselves as part of history. The family is the key to this. Every family has a history, a heritage—one that children should feel good about. This means exploring their own pasts and the pasts of their parents, grandparents, and ancestors. Researching the newspaper from the day each child was born provides a sense of what was happening in the world when he or she arrived as a newborn baby. Time lines of significant events in children's own lives can provide a graphic sense of history, and once they have the idea of time lines, they can apply it to larger-scale events, such as the history of their community or state.

Another way to bring history to life is through the medium of storytelling. Finding out about the lives of parents and grandparents when they were children helps build continuity across generations, giving students a sense of what went before them. The good thing about such historical inquiry is that it takes advantage of the stories already being told in families, with the added value of making the child a recorder of history. This is consciousness raising in action.

Your classroom itself is a good indicator of the level of interest you and your students have in history. If I could visit your class, I would look for time lines, bulletin boards, posters, photographs, maps, dioramas, drama, music, and art that speaks to a study of history. Fortunately, you don't have to do this by yourself. The children will be as helpful and creative as you allow them to be.

Finally, your task is to bring a sense of excitement and enthusiasm to the study of history. Enthusiasm, like the common cold, is catching. Just try it! If you talk to your students about books you're reading, read stories to them, recite stirring passages from inspirational moments in history, role-play historical characters, and generally extol the pleasures of historical inquiry, then magic will happen in your classroom.

Explorations

Reflect On . . .

1. Why should we study history? Write down three reasons that come to mind. Which of these do you think is most important? Why?
2. The National Council for the Social Studies (1994) says that "the primary purpose of social studies is to help young people develop the ability to make informed and reasoned decisions for the public good as citizens of a culturally diverse, democratic society in an interdependent world" (p. 2). How do you think the study of history fulfills this purpose?

In the Field

3. Celebrate a History Day in your classroom, either the class where you are student teaching or the class where this textbook is being used. Select a time period, such as the American colonial era, and then develop an entire day's set of school lessons from that time—for example, colonial mathematics, history, geography, spelling, reading, games, and so on. Dress in period costume and role-play a colonial teacher. Ask your students to dress up, as well. Share a colonial meal and play colonial games. All this will take planning and research. A helpful website to get you started is www2.lhric.org/kat/wq/colonial.htm.
4. Every town or city has one or more cemeteries. On your own or with other students, arrange to visit a nearby cemetery as a means of reconstructing some of the history of your local region. Record the birth and death dates from various

tombstones and markers, with special attention to those that are the oldest. Write the first names given to people of various eras to determine any trends. If you can, do a rubbing of an old tombstone with butcher paper and charcoal.

For Your Portfolio

5. Add some of your own history to your portfolio. Create a brief but creative résumé that shows your educational record, your work history, your travels, your hobbies and interests, samples of lessons, your motivation, a narrative that explains why you have chosen the teaching field, and a list of strengths.

Continuing the Journey: Suggested Readings

Alleman, J., & Brophy, J. (2003). History is alive: Teaching young children about changes over time. *Social Studies, 94*(3), 107–111.
A useful primer on the important concepts of change and chronology.

Barton, K., McCully, A., & Marks, M. (2004). Reflecting on elementary children's understanding of history and social studies. *Journal of Teacher Education, 55*(1), 70–91.
Insights to what children do and do not know about the past.

Collison, D., & Sanders-Brunner, M. (2004). Primary sources. *School Library Media Activities Monthly, 20*(10), 29–33.
A practical guide to involving students in the use of original source materials.

Fertig, G. (2005). Teaching elementary students how to interpret the past. *Social Studies, 96*(1) 2–9.
This article places emphasis on the higher-level thinking skills needed to go beyond facts and information.

Fox, J. (2004). Standards and testing: Obstacles for elementary history education. *Organization of American Historians Newsletter, 32*(1), 3.
An analysis of the dilemma posed for inquiry and reflective thinking by the current testing movement.

Kellett, M. (2005). *How to develop children as researchers.* Thousand Oaks, CA: Sage.
A remarkably good source for teachers who desire to make historians, geographers, and social scientific inquirers out of their elementary-age students. The book is filled with practical examples.

Morris, R. (2003). The nation's capital and first graders. *Social Studies, 94*(6), 265–270.
This article acquaints primary age children with Washington, D.C. in an appealing way.

Stearns, P. (1998). Why study history? American Historical Association. Retrieved April 2005 from www.historians.org/pubs/Free/WhyStudyHistory.htm.
This article provides any teacher with several convincing arguments for studying history. The arguments range from the practical to the aesthetic to the academic.

Stephens, J. (2005). Social studies connections: Making history, geography, economics, civics, and ethics come alive. *Library Media Connection, 23*(7), 98, 107.
The author gives important insights and suggestions for connecting the social studies curriculum to the real world. Any teacher interested in interdisciplinary studies will find this a valuable resource.

The International Reading Association (IRA) has three excellent websites for quality children's books:
    www.reading.org
    www.readingonline.org
    www.rwtc.org

For quality reading material for at-risk children, please see www.hoopoekids.com.

For authors and illustrators on the web, please see www.ucalgary.ca/~dkbrown/authors.html.

SAMPLE LESSON 9.1   *Role-Playing about the Civil War*

GRADE LEVEL: Appropriate for grades 5–7.

PURPOSE: To provide a frame for the students to use in evaluating both points of view in the Civil War.

OBJECTIVES: Students will be able to do the following:

1. Identify which states belonged to the Union and which states belonged to the Confederacy.
2. Identify three reasons articulated by the North and three reasons articulated by the South for the Civil War.
3. Identify and comprehend some of the feelings experienced by both Northern and Southern states.
4. Identify the qualities of exceptional leaders, regardless of their patriotic affiliation.
5. Feel compassion for participants in the Civil War, regardless of the side they fought on.

RESOURCES/MATERIALS NEEDED: Books on Civil War history; perhaps all or part of the PBS Ken Burns documentary on the Civil War; poster board and markers.

PROCEDURE:

1. Using the outline map on the board, remove the states from the map in the order they seceded from the Union.
2. Divide students into two groups: Union and Confederacy. From this point on, the two sides should not interact during the activity.
3. Have each side choose political and military leaders, draw their flags, and learn the background that supports their historical position. Students should, if possible, read primary source material—speeches by Abraham Lin-

coln, Robert E. Lee, Ulysses S. Grant, Jefferson Davis, and others; letters home from soldiers; and newspaper accounts of the war. Show students some of the photographs taken by Matthew Brady.
4. Have students create recruitment posters to encourage enlistment and support for their side.
5. Have each side make a presentation to the whole class, arguing their position in the war. Students might role-play Abraham Lincoln for the Union, Jefferson Davis for the Confederacy, or other leaders, or they may simply present a speech making their argument. Students from the opposing side may ask questions and discuss, but try to prevent anyone from arguing or haranguing without supporting his or her arguments.
6. Have students vote on which way they feel the Civil War should end, based on the arguments presented.

CLOSURE: Compare the results of your class vote with the real outcome of the Civil War. Are wars always decided based on rational argument?

EXTENSION: Let your class improve on history by having a reuniting ceremony, as Abraham Lincoln likely would have done had he lived. Have students research Lincoln's plans for Reconstruction, and note the differences between what he had hoped for and what actually happened. Why were his plans not implemented?

Source: Adapted from a lesson plan submitted by Carol Strickler (Grass Valley, Winnemucca, NM) to OFCN's Academy Curricular Exchange, Columbia Education Center, Social Studies.

SAMPLE LESSON 9.2   *Nevada Trek*

GRADE LEVEL: 6–7. Nevada history or U.S. history, westward expansion.

PURPOSE: To give students a greater appreciation of what hardships the early emigrant parties were faced with in the movement westward and what accomplishments they achieved. To give students a better understanding of the geographical region of the Great Basin while gaining insights on what a trip like that might have been like.

OBJECTIVES: The learner will demonstrate the ability to make decisions that will benefit his or her party as they cross this country moving west, using skills including estimation, mapping, problem solving, and other appropriate social studies skills and strategies.

RESOURCES/MATERIALS: Pens, pencils, colored pencils, drawing paper, some basic information provided by the teacher, and a good imagination.

PROCEDURE:

1. Have students count off to create five teams or parties.
2. Provide each team with information sheets telling them the following: the dimensions of the wagon (4 feet by 10 feet), how much each wagon can hold (15,000 pounds), and the fact that the wagons have no brakes; what kind of animals are available (mules, which are the most reliable and sure footed but also are very expensive; horses, which pull the fastest and cost less than mules but more than oxen; and oxen, which are the slowest but also the cheap-

est to buy and feed); and how much each kind of animal eats per day.
3. Provide each team with a map of the terrain they must cover, with the start and end points and various routes marked.
4. Have each team create a list of what they will take as provisions for the long trip, including food, clothing, ammunition, spare wagon parts, and so on.
5. Have each team decide what route to take, choose a departure date, and use estimation to determine the length of time they will be on the trail. They should take into account the terrain, weather, and need to feed and water the animals.
6. Have each team draw and label a map showing the route that they intend to take from St. Louis to their destination arrival in the Sacramento Valley.

CLOSURE: Have each team share their route and provisions list with the rest of the class and explain why they made the decisions they did.

REFLECTION: Let students discuss the process they went through in making decisions. Demonstrate that sometimes different paths can accomplish the same goal.

Source: Adapted from a lesson submitted by Sandy Kellogg (Churchill County Junior High School, Fallon, NV) to OFCN's Academy Curricular Exchange, Columbia Education Center, Social Studies.

chapter 10

Exploring Our Geographic World

Maps, Globes, and Graphics

In this chapter, we will explore these themes:

key concepts

- The tools of geography
- The five themes of geography
- Helping students learn to make and read maps
- Helping students learn to use maps

Geography is about maps.
—Edwin Bentley
*When it comes to the fusion of visual beauty and useful information,
is there anything as glorious as a map?*
—Roberta Smith

The world of maps, globes, graphs, and time lines is a fascinating world of signs and symbols, lines and space. These symbolic representations are meant to represent reality. Maps and globes are literally "earth writing," which is the meaning of the word *geography*. The key to inititating children into this world is to approach it in developmentally appropriate, experiential ways. This chapter will focus on strategies for teaching the concepts of geography in just these ways.

When visitors to the Washington state capitol in Olympia enter its massive front doors, one of the first sights they see is a statue of nineteenth-century pioneer Marcus Whitman, with this quote from him inscribed at the bottom: "My plans require time and distance." How remarkably apt these words are for those of us who teach elementary social studies. In fact, *time* and *distance* are two of the most crucial concepts in the social studies curriculum: Time is the key to history, and space, or distance, to geography. An integrated social studies curriculum brings the two together.

Children's sense of time—past, present, and future—develops gradually and experientially through the elementary years. So, too, does their sense of distance—far away, nearby, exact, and approximate. In everyday speech, we often fuse these two concepts: "How far is it from your home to your office?" "Oh, about half an hour, unless there's heavy traffic." Or "What's the distance from

Denver to Minneapolis?" "About two hours by plane—about a day and a half if you drive it." Indeed, in traditional desert cultures, time and space are intertwined, as people think of a certain distance as being so many days' ride by camel or horse.

Maps and globes are spatial essays. They tell stories about location, direction, area, distance, scale, and proportion. They convey information primarily in graphic and symbolic terms. Maps are graphic representations of space. In this sense, they are qualitatively different from the reading and writing that dominate the school day. Reading a map is different from reading a story. Making a map is different from writing a paragaraph. Don't be surprised if some of your best map makers and map readers are children who do less well with typical reading and writing activities. Different children have different gifts.

Experience, as always, is important. It has been noted, for example, that children who play a great deal with Lego blocks and other building materials often develop remarkable spatial-reasoning abilities. This should serve as a reminder to all teachers that concrete activities are especially important for elementary-age children. Playing with blocks is a developmentally appropriate precursor to map making, as is playing board games like checkers and chess. Playing with blocks and board games enhances spatial reasoning.

Understanding the Tools of Geography

The earth is a sphere, but most maps are flat. Thus, it's important to keep in mind that any map, of any portion of the earth, represents an attempt to show part of a sphere on a flat surface. This cannot be done without compromising something—size, distance, proportion—which means every map contains distortions.

The distortions are not particularly important if we are attempting to show a relatively small area, as we do in a treasure map, a map of a park, or even a map of one of our states. Problems arise, however, when we attempt to show a whole continent, and things become even more troublesome when we attempt to show the entire earth (a sphere) on a flat map. You may have grown up thinking that Greenland is larger than South America, for example. After all, it appears to be larger on many world maps, especially those based on the familiar *Mercator projection.* But, in fact, it would take more than seven Greenlands to equal the size of South America.

All this is merely a way of saying that for children, maps take some getting used to. Children (and adults) live in a three-dimensional world, and maps portray that world graphically in two dimensions. That's why good map making and map reading by children begins with observation, discussion, drawing, photograhy, and other more concrete means of representing the space around us.

Maps and globes are universal means of expression in geography, history, and the social sciences (and for teachers—see, for example, Figure 10.1). They provide to the geographer, historian, political scientist, and anthropologist graphic portrayals of great economy. In the social sciences, maps are intended as selective and abstracted representations of reality. In contrast to a photograph, which is nonselective (that is, it shows everything seen by the camera's eye), a good map portrays only what is central to the message of the researcher (such as the locations of cities and states, reconstructed bat-

figure **10.1**   *An Aerial View of an Ideal Classroom Learning Environment, as Conceived by an Elementary Teacher*

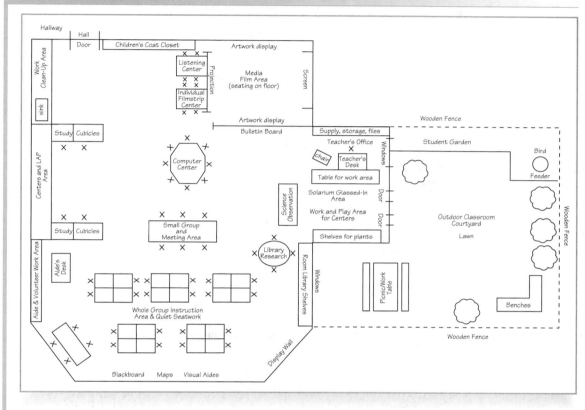

Source: Dy Ann Dennie.

tle lines from military engagements, results of voting by states in a presidential election, the hunting and gathering territory of a tribal group) and factors out the details not essential to the researcher's message.

At its most basic, a map shows one variable. The map in Figure 10.2, for example, offers the map reader nothing more than the spatial distribution of tropical rain forests throughout the world. Most maps illustrate a number of variables, but for young learners, a one-variable map is often a good starting place.

A map, then, is a basic communication tool that represents reality in an arbitrary and selective way. In creating Figure 10.2, we arbitrarily decided to select tropical rain forests for illustration. We could just as well have shown river systems, mountain ranges, or major cities. Keep this idea in mind when you are working with students of elementary school age. The selectivity that makes a map a powerful means of communicating spatial relationships renders that same map potentially confusing to the child

figure 10.2 Tropical Rain Forest Map

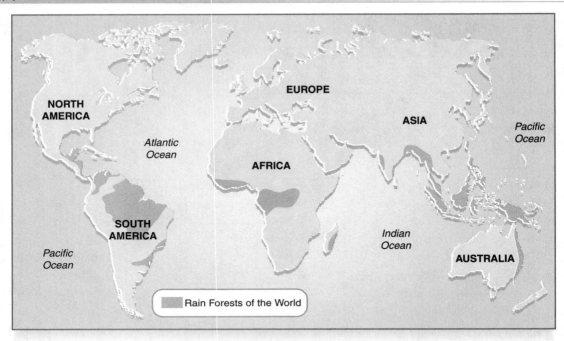

NORTH
AMERICA

Atlantic
Ocean

EUROPE

ASIA

Pacific
Ocean

AFRICA

SOUTH
AMERICA

Indian
Ocean

Pacific
Ocean

AUSTRALIA

Rain Forests of the World

figure 10.3 A Map of a Bedroom Drawn by a 6-Year-Old

CLOSET

Door

JOHN's
BeD

NIGHT
Stand

Dresser

Rocker

CLOCK

MY BeD

who has not had experience in making the developmental transition from real and pictorial representations to abstract representations.

A child's ability to conceptualize space develops with age and experience. For example, compare the bedroom map drawn by a 6-year-old (Figure 10.3) with that drawn by an 11-year-old (Figure 10.4). What differences can you see between the younger and the older child's conception of space?

With regard to map making and map interpretation, in particular, experiential approaches to teaching the underlying concepts and skills are much more effective than are traditional textbook approaches. The younger the children, the more hands-on (and feet-on!) experiences are needed to allow them to make the connection between the landscape and its graphic representation. Sample Lesson 10.1 provides a wonderful introductory experience with maps for children who are new to a school. Famous educator Maria Montessori once noted that children actually learn to write before they learn to read. This may seem backward, but she was right. Children's scribbling often represents their early attempts to put their thoughts on paper.

figure **10.4**   *A Map of a Bedroom Drawn by an 11-Year-Old*

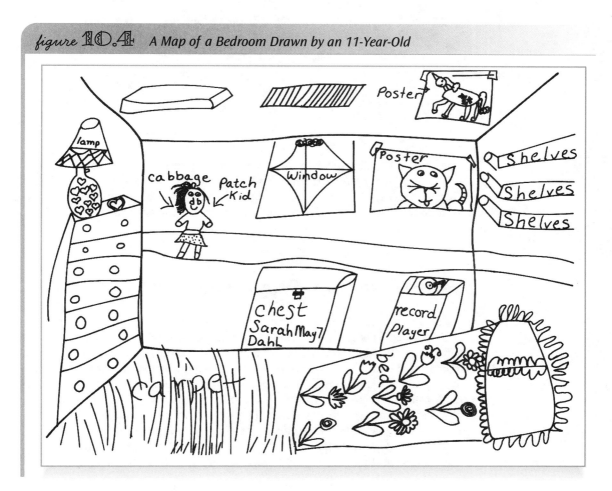

figure **10.5**   *A Child's Drawing of a Sheep Pasture*

Montessori's insight is especially appropriate to map reading. Children begin making maps—in the form of the drawings and pictures they create—before they begin reading maps. They are, in fact, natural map makers. Consider the child's drawing in Figure 10.5. It demonstrates perfect readiness for map making and map interpretation. The child has developed a sense of perspective, distance, and scale, all of which are basic elements of cartography.

The Five Themes of Geography

Before we begin thinking about specific techniques for making and interpreting maps and globes, let's step back and look at the larger picture. In 1984, the National Council for Geographic Education (NCGE) and the Association of American Geographers (AAG) cooperated in the development of five themes on which to base the curriculum of geographic education. Those five themes—location, place, human/environment interaction, movement, regions—provide a conceptual foundation on which to build appropriate learning experiences for children. The themes can provide points of reference for all the activities you undertake related to geographic learning (see Figure 10.6).

You can begin with the world around you and your students. Your school, for example, has an *absolute* location. It is located at a particular intersect of longitude and

figure **10.6**   *The Five Themes of Geography*

The five themes of geography were presented in 1984 by the Joint Committee on Geographic Education of the National Council for Geographic Education (NCGE) and the Association of American Geographers (AAG).

Theme 1: Location. Geographers use latitude and longitude to identify a place's absolute or precise location. Relative location means the location of one place on the Earth's surface relative to other places.

Theme 2: Place. A particular place on the Earth's surface can be described in terms of its human and physical features and characteristics.

Theme 3: Interaction. Human beings interact with their environments by changing them, using them for various purposes, and so on.

Theme 4: Movement. People change their locations, move across the landscape, and migrate from one place to another. Goods and services are transported from certain locations to other sites.

Theme 5: Region. A region is an area that displays physical, political, or cultural unity. There are three types of regions: (1) formal regions defined by political boundaries; (2) functional regions defined by a specific purpose such as trade, distribution, or service; and (3) vernacular regions defined generally by people's perceptions, such as New England or Southeast Asia.

Source: Adapted from the National Geographic Society. www.nationalgeographic.com.

latitude on the Earth's surface. It has an address that locates it within the city or town. Your school also is located *relative* to other places, such as stores, houses, parks, churches, and the like. So, your school, like all places, has both a particular absolute location (longitude and latitude) and a particular relative location (proximity to other places). Your school can also be described in terms of *place*—that is, the characteristics of its setting, whether hilly or flat, and so on. And your school represents a human modification of the environment from its natural state. Perhaps a century ago, the very place on which the school stands was used for some other purpose.

Then, there is *movement*. People move in and out of your school every day. Students and teachers come in the morning and leave in the afternoon. Visitors also arrive and leave. In addition to people, communication goes in and out: Mail and e-mail are sent and received at your school. And finally, your school is located in a particular *region* of the state and country. That region might be described as suburban, industrial, middle class, rainy, western, or whatever.

The five themes of geography should be used by childen as tools for investigation and as ways of thinking about the earth and how we occupy it. The themes are inherently interdisciplinary. They can form the conceptual point of reference for studying the environment, literature, art, music, history, health, and practically any topic you and your students decide to investigate. Geography may, in fact, be the most integrative subject in the curriculum. The study of geography involves not only the other areas of social studies education—history, economics, sociology, and so on—but also the skills and strategies of other disciplines: math, language arts, and even science. Geography is not merely the centerpiece of social studies; it goes beyond that, offering the possibility to connect well with every subject you teach.

Helping Students Learn to Make and Read Maps

To help students participate in the transition from reality to abstraction in representing space—that is, making maps and understanding how to read them—encourage them to develop the basic skills of the geographer: observing and recording. You can do a number of activities to move students forward in this process. An ideal way to lead students from a realistic understanding of an area to an abstract one is to use your school as a starting point. Follow these eight steps:

1. Have your students take a walking tour of the area surrounding the school. Note the various landmarks, such as streets, businesses, houses, parks, and so on.
2. Using a digital camera to record the sights, work with your students to put together a "slide show" of the area surrounding the school, in which various landmarks are portrayed.
3. View the school area from some elevated perspective, such as a hill or a tall building. Take some pictures and review them in class.
4. Have the class or several small groups do murals depicting the school and the surrounding area. Teams can illustrate the playground, the cafeteria, gym, and the like.
5. Make a model of the area from cardboard, wooden blocks, and paper. This can be done by the entire class or even better by small groups.
6. Borrow an aerial photograph of the area around the school from the local office of the U.S. Department of Agriculture or the local public library. Pick up a map of your city or area. Locate the school. Let the students compare the aerial photograph with the map.
7. Make an enlargement of the portion of a map that shows the area around the school, and give each student a copy. Compare this map to the aerial photograph, the model, the map mural, and the photos you and your students took of the area.
8. Take another walk around the area. Have each student bring along his or her copy of the map from step 7. As students see landmarks, have them point to them on their maps. Be sure to bring along sketch pads so students can draw items of interest.

This activity uses a series of developmental steps to take students from the concrete experience of walking through and observing an area to understanding its eventual abstract representation. The steps could be used in a daily sequence of eight lessons or scattered over a longer time period.

Mental Maps

Making and interpeting so-called mental maps ranks high on the list of national geography standards. All of us carry images, or *mental maps*, of spaces and places in our heads. Take a moment to refer to your own "atlas" of mental maps. Can you visualize your bedroom? (I hope you remembered to make the bed!) Can you visualize the route from your home to the grocery store? Can you imagine a tropical island paradise that you would love to visit? Can you see your fourth-grade classroom in your mind's eye? The fact is that you have literally thousands of mental maps stored in the atlas of your mind and memory.

Mental maps are more or less accurate, depending on a number of factors, including the reliability of one's memory, how often one visits a place or traverses a certain distance, and how important it is for one to know how to get someplace. For example, even very young children have pretty good mental maps of the rooms in their houses or apartments. They typically have little trouble navigating from one area to another. But if a very young child lives in a house with a basement that he or she never or seldom ventures into, then the mental map of that basement may be quite inaccurate. In fact, the basement may seem like a mysterious and frightening place.

On a different scale, the mental map of western North America contained about as much fiction as fact for many years. In fact, in 1804, President Thomas Jefferson sent Meriwether Lewis and William Clark from the Missouri River to the Pacific Ocean across North America for the purpose of finding the so-called Northwest Passage, an imagined water route from the Great Plains to the Pacific. Many maps of the day already showed the Northwest Passage in one location or another (see Figure 10.7). The only trouble was that it never existed except in people's imaginations. The mental map of the West changed dramatically as the vast region was explored over time. Map making has become much more scientific in modern times, but looking at certain maps from ancient times will tell you that imagination played as great a part in creating them as did surveying and cartography.

An individual has literally dozens of mental maps stored in his or her mind. Many of them are so accurate that the person navigates flawlessly, perhaps from his or her residence to the shopping mall or grocery store or Aunt Margaret's house. Certain other maps may be a bit on the hazy side, especially if the person is the type to get lost occasionally. Some mental maps cover small distances; others cover great distances. We are all map makers and navigators—some, better than others.

Generally, a mental map is retrieved only when the person needs it to go somewhere or to explain to someone how to get somewhere. In this sense, mental maps are quite functional. However, they have other uses, as well. Sometimes, people just like to think about places that they've been to and even places they've never visited. Other times, we may use mental maps to respond to requests for directions ("How do you get from here to the aquarium?") or rely on the mental maps of others when we need directions ourselves. It is always a good idea to bear in mind that mental maps are not necessarily *accurate* maps; they just represent the maps we have in our heads.

figure **10.7**   *Map of Northwest Passage*

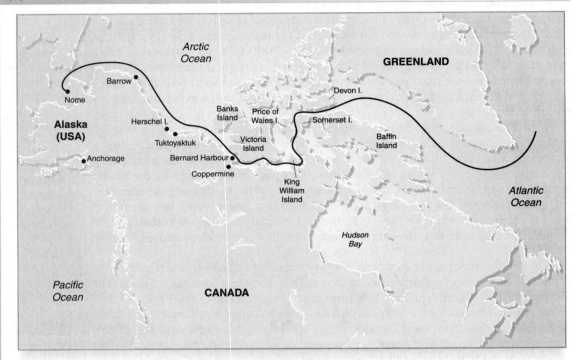

CURRENT EVENTS

Focus on the Weather Page

Every major newspaper carries a complete weather page each day, providing an incredible almanac of information. Here are two map-making activities in which to engage your students:

- Assign each student a city in the United States, and have him or her record the high and low temperatures for that city as reported daily on the weather page of the newspaper. Do this for a period of at least two weeks. Have each student create a line graph of the daily high (in red) and low (in blue) temperatures for this time period.
- Repeat this process using international city temperatures.

In each case, the work that results makes a wonderful display in your classroom. A bulletin board map should be posted during each activity that shows the cities for which records are being kept.

in the classroom **Drawing from a Mental Map**

Provide your students with opportunities to get their mental maps out of their heads and onto paper. Ask each student to think about a place not far from home that he or she enjoys visiting. For each student it may be a different place. That's good, because you will have more variety when the children put their maps up for display. (On the other hand, if you want to start with a place students have in common, have them make mental maps of the playground or how to get from their room to the principal's office.) Then have the students do the following:

1. Make a list of landmarks along the way—things that stand out in their minds. Younger children can tell you what landmarks they intend to include when they draw their maps, and older children can make a written list.
2. Draw their maps as they see them in their minds.

3. Take their maps home and verify them against reality—that is, check to see if their maps are more or less accurate. The process of verification is a very important skill that children need to learn.
4. Make new maps based on the knowledge gained in the verification process. This is a good time to reflect with students on the idea of making errors, because their first maps may have contained some. Point out that errors are not bad, as some children and adults think, but merely items to be corrected. Error analysis is used a great deal in problem solving, especially in the form of a technique called *reverse engineering,* where one takes a look at some product he or she has constructed and works backwards to see what needs to be improved.

Traverse Maps

One of the simplest map forms for children to understand is the traverse map. A *traverse map* represents a line or linear path through an area—usually an obvious one, such as a street, a lakeshore, a river, or a boundary of some sort. Traverse maps are very easy to make, and I encourage you to have even the youngest children construct them.

To do a traverse, begin with observation and recording, the two most basic skills of the investigator. For example, if you wish to map a single block of a city street, simply walk along the block, recording everything on either side—storefronts, signposts, and so on. Similarly, to map a brook or creek for, say, 200 feet, merely walk along the side of it and record the significant things you see along the way (trees, docks, bridges, houses, and so on).

These activities are called *fieldwork*. When your fieldwork has been completed, you are ready to make your traverse map. Figure 10.8 shows the development of a child's traverse map.

figure **10.8**   *A Child's Traverse Map of the Fremont Neighborhood*

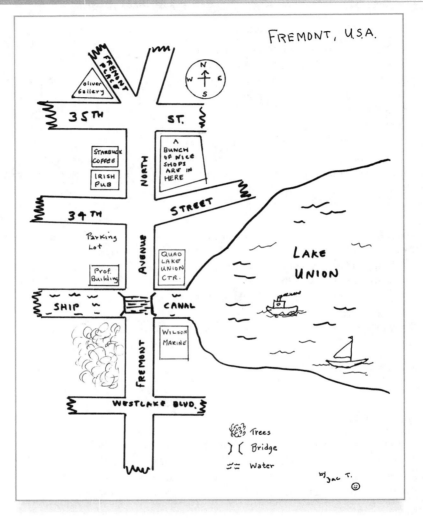

in the classroom   Conceptualizing a Common Traverse

Constructing a map of the route from home to school affords children an excellent opportunity to conceptualize a common spatial traverse. It's more complicated, of course, if students ride a bus to school over some distance than if they live

a block or two away. The assignment progresses like this:

1. For several days, have the children observe carefully as they walk or ride to and from

school. They should notice the street names and other important landmarks. This period of incubation and reflection about the landscape is crucial. Don't hurry the children into making a finished product. Instead, at this point, stress the skills of observation and mental recording.

2. Encourage older children to learn the particular cardinal directions they travel. For example, a child might walk two blocks south before turning east and so on.

3. Have the children begin taking field notes. They should write down street names, draw rough sketches, and so forth.

4. Have the students use their field notes to draw maps during class time. Be sure that several city maps are available, so students can refer to them as they construct their own maps.

5. Have the students give brief oral reports, in which they show the class their maps and verbalize the way they come to school.

6. Display the maps on the wall of the classroom. Encourage students to study them and make comparisons of the various routes used to get to school.

Visualizing Space

Visualizing space is a useful intellectual exercise for children. At the primary level, you can challenge students by asking them to verbalize the directions for getting from their homes to school. At the intermediate level, you might want to assign students the task of giving directions for getting from the school to certain landmarks, such as the city center, airport, zoo, park, or athletic stadium. Children can use their mental maps to help with this task.

Children also enjoy visualizing imaginary space. Instead of doing a standard book report, ask students to map the location in which a story takes place, or read a story aloud and have them note the landmarks mentioned and then draw maps. Figure 10.9 shows a map of Narnia, the setting for C. S. Lewis's popular tale *The Lion, the Witch, and the Wardrobe*. Other children's books that provide a lot of mapping possibilities are J. R. R. Tolkein's *Hobbit* books (*The Hobbit* and the *Lord of the Rings* trilogy) and J. K. Rowling's *Harry Potter* books. For many children, such a project is a welcome relief from the usual book report.

Aerial Photographs and Maps

To give younger students some insight into the overhead vertical perspective generally portrayed by maps, let them use a camera to take pictures of a terrain model or a set of blocks laid out to simulate a village. By standing directly over the model while photographing it, the student achieves the physical perspective of the map maker. Such a perspective is known as a *bird's-eye view* of a landscape.

Aerial photographs are widely available from a variety of sources and can be used to help students construct their own maps. Students can produce original and very accurate large-scale maps by placing tracing paper over an aerial photograph and tracing the roads, cities, waterforms, wooded areas, farmland, and so on. Such a map is an interpreted form of the photograph, in which the child has made decisions about what to portray and what to leave out. Figures 10.10 A and B illustrate the translation of an aerial photograph into a base map.

figure 10.9   *A Child's Map of the Fictional Land of Narnia*

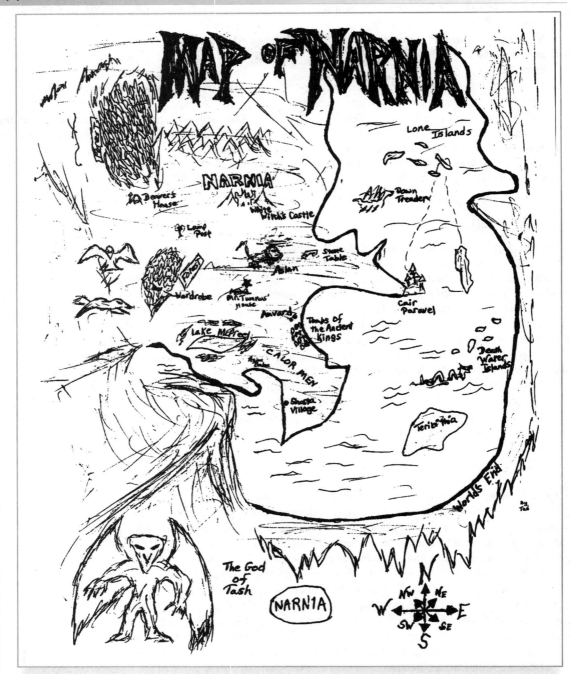

figure 10.10A   The Aerial Photograph Used to Construct the Base Map Below

figure 10.10B   The Base Map Drawn from the Aerial Photograph Above

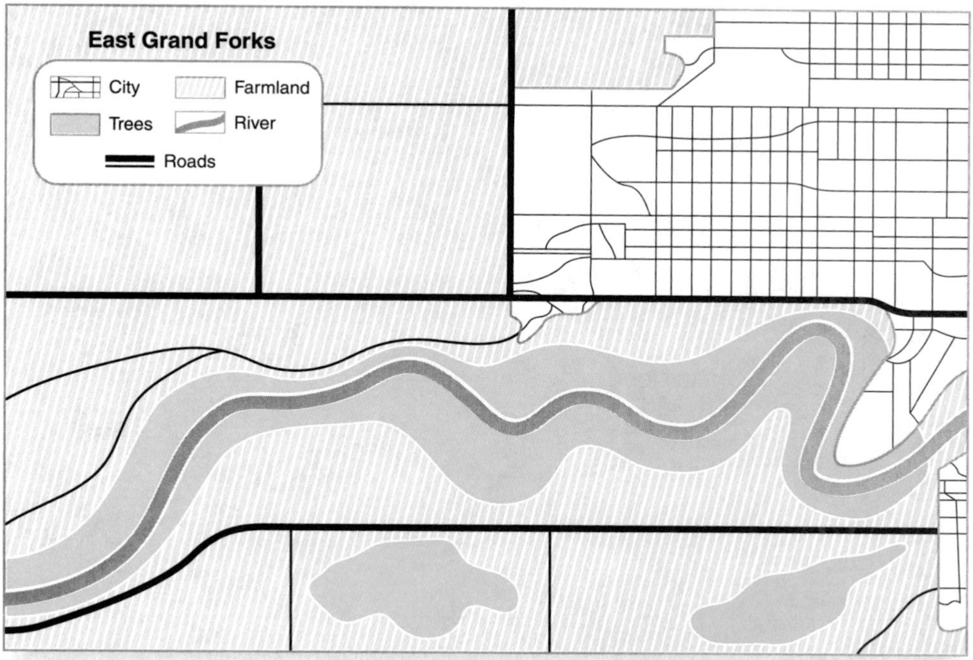

East Grand Forks

- City
- Trees
- Roads
- Farmland
- River

Changing the Scale of a Map

There are three basic techniques for changing the scale of a map: mechanical, optical, and mathematical.

- *Mechanical method.* The mechanical method uses a *pantograph*, which is an inexpensive instrument in the shape of a parallelogram. By using a pantograph, which may be set to various scale changes, the student can make a very accurate enlargement or reduction of an existing map. Also, junior cartographers can decide exactly what change of scale they want to make. You can order a pantograph from any school supply store.

- *Optical method.* The elementary school counterpart of the precision optical instruments available in certain cartography laboratories is the opaque projector. To use this method, place a map in the projector and show it on a wall; students can then trace the

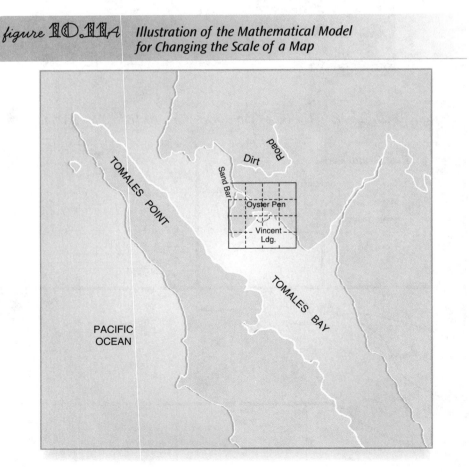

figure **10.11A**   *Illustration of the Mathematical Model for Changing the Scale of a Map*

enlarged map outline onto a sheet of paper taped to the wall. Although the opaque projector is probably the most commonly used scale-change instrument, it is the least satisfactory, for several reasons. First, it is not possible to reduce a map with an opaque projector. Second, students using this method do not really know what the change of scale is; they only know that the new map is larger. Third, distortions often occur because the book page does not lie flat in the projector or because the instrument is projecting at a slight angle to the wall.

- *Mathematical method.* The mathematical method, which is also called the *method of similar squares,* is useful for making both enlargements and reductions. After plotting points on a grid of larger or smaller dimension than a grid superimposed on an existing map, the student can then connect the points in a line to construct a new outline. Points for cities, mountains, and other features can also be plotted. Figures 10.11 A and B illustrate this method.

figure **10.11B**   *Illustration of the Mathematical Model for Changing the Scale of a Map*

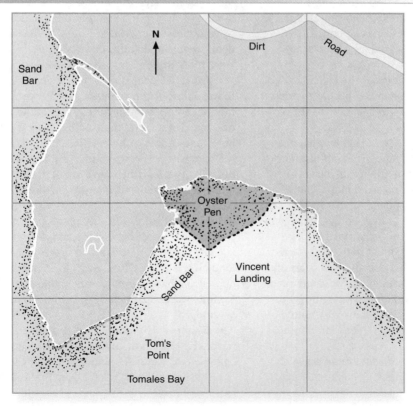

Keys to Understanding the Language of Maps

The following terms will help you and your students understand the vocabulary of maps.

- *Absolute and relative location.* *Absolute location* refers to a particular point on the earth's surface. Absolute location is fixed by longitude and latitude. For example, Cairo, Egypt, is located at 30 degrees east longitude and 30 degrees north latitude. *Relative location* refers to a particular place and its relation and access to other places. For example, Greybull and Cody, Wyoming, are located not far from each other in the same county. However, the summit of the Rocky Mountains lies between the two towns, making travel difficult in winter.

- *Symbols.* *Symbols* are used on maps to represent both natural features (such as mountains, rivers, forests, lakes, deserts) and constructed features (such as roads, bridges, schools, airports, towns). Most maps have a *key* or *legend* that explains the meanings of the symbols used. Symbols allow map makers to display a variety of information. (See Figure 10.12 for a list of common map symbols.)

- *Projection.* The globe is a sphere that accurately represents the shape, size, and distance of the earth's features. An attempt to show the earth's curved surface on a flat map is called a *projection*. Small areas of the earth's surface can be portrayed more accurately on flat maps than large areas. When the entire surface of the globe is projected onto a flat map, distortions always occur. (As noted elsewhere, the familiar Mercator projection, used to create many maps of the world, makes land areas near the poles seem larger than they are. That's why many people think Greenland is larger than South America.)

- *Scale.* *Scale* is used to determine size and distance on a map or globe. A large-scale map

shows a close-up representation of space (for example, a neighborhood), while a small-scale map may show the entire earth. A map's key usually contains a scale of feet or miles, centimeters or kilometers. Scale on a map describes the proportion of the size of the map to the reality it represents (for instance, 1 inch = 1 mile). Map scale makes it possible to determine real distances (for instance, if 1 inch = 1 mile, then cities shown 3 inches apart are actually 3 miles apart). Maps are nearly always smaller than the realities they represent: The larger the scale, the smaller the area depicted on a map (for example, a map of your bedroom is large scale; a map of the world is small scale). Conversely, the smaller the scale, the larger the area depicted on a map (a map of the United States is small scale; a map of your classroom is large scale). To help students understand scale and how to use mileage keys, try Sample Lesson 10.2.

- *Direction.* Map directions are generally set to the points of the compass. It is a common misconception that north is always at the top of a map (or up) and that south is always at the bottom (or down). The *cardinal directions* of the compass are north, south, east, and west, but a *compass rose* (the map symbol that indicates direction) can show as many as 32 directions on a map.

- *Lines and space.* On a map, lines define the boundaries of space. For example, a river is a line that separates land on one side from land on the other. Often, rivers form political as well as physical boundaries; Indiana and Kentucky are separated by the Ohio River, for example.

- *Elevation.* Elevation is the extent to which a particular place is at, above, or below sea level. In the Netherlands (Holland), much of the land is below sea level and is kept from flooding by dikes. Nepal is often referred to as the "roof of the world" because the Himalayan Mountains, and in particular Mount Everest, the world's highest peak, are located there. California contains rugged mountains, land below sea level, the great flat Central Valley, and just about every kind of landform imaginable. Elevation is typically shown on maps by using either shading or color gradations.

- *Areal association.* Areal association indicates the relationship of one area to another and can refer to both natural and humanmade associations. For example, cities are often located on major rivers and harbors. Shopping malls are located regionally to accommodate large numbers of residents in a local area. Schools and shops are located in neighborhoods to facilitate walking or short rides. Hotels are located near beautiful beaches and other sites of interest. Athletic facilities are located on the grounds of high schools and universities.

figure 10.12   *Map Symbols*

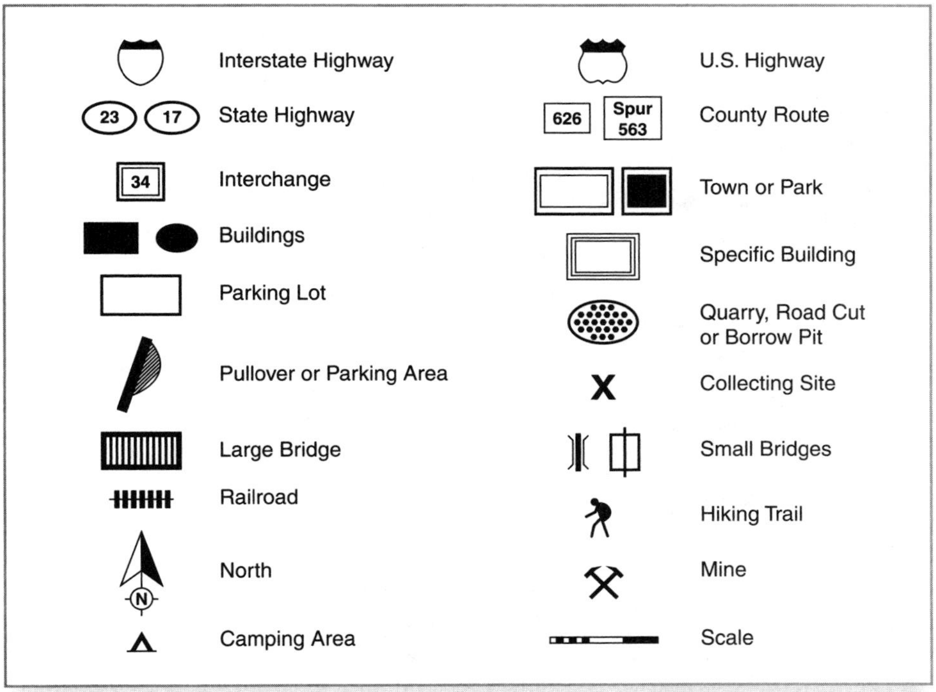

Symbol	Description	Symbol	Description
	Interstate Highway		U.S. Highway
23 17	State Highway	626 Spur 563	County Route
34	Interchange		Town or Park
	Buildings		Specific Building
	Parking Lot		Quarry, Road Cut or Borrow Pit
	Pullover or Parking Area	X	Collecting Site
	Large Bridge		Small Bridges
	Railroad		Hiking Trail
N	North		Mine
	Camping Area		Scale

Note that these symbols represent features of both natural and constructed environments.

Understanding Map Projections and Globes

I am convinced that it is difficult for most children to understand that maps are, in fact, projections of the earth's curved surface onto a flat piece of paper (see Figure 10.13). That is why the *constructivity principle*, which states that activity must precede analysis, is so crucial. In other words, *drawing* maps should come before *studying* maps, especially maps drawn by someone other than the child.

Any attempt to portray a sphere (the earth) onto a flat surface meets with difficulty. Nevertheless, it is necessary to do so, simply because we can't use a globe as efficiently as a flat map that's posted on a wall or bound up in a book. A map can also portray details and show particular regions using different scales.

When the round earth is portrayed on flat paper, the result is called a *map projection* because the sphere is projected onto a flat surface. There are many map projections of the earth, but they all have one thing in common: They distort something. As noted

figure **10.13** *An Illustration of a Projection*

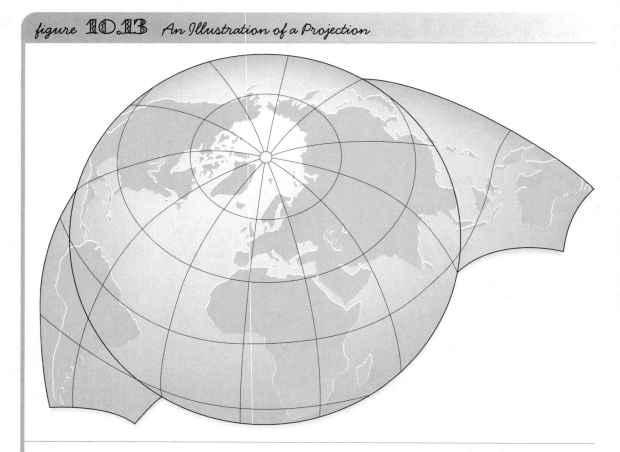

Attempts to portray a sphere (the earth) on a flat surface are called map projections.

earlier in this chapter, the most well recognized case of distortion is that of Greenland. Many children (and some adults) assume that Greenland is larger than it is. In fact, Greenland is about one-seventh the size of South America. The most common source of distortion arises from the attempt to portray lines of longitude and the spaces between them. As you know, lines of *longitude* converge at the earth's poles; they have to, since the earth is shaped like a ball, not a table top. But when they are shown on a flat map, the lines of longitude are often shown as straight vertical lines running from the North Pole to the South Pole, thereby distorting the sizes of land masses in the far north and south. To help your students understand the difficulties of making flat maps, see Sample Lesson 10.3.

The three most common projections of the round earth onto a flat surface are the following:

- The cylindrical projection
- The conic projection
- The plane surface projection

These three projections are illustrated in Figure 10.14. I suggest that you demonstrate them to your students and let them practice the activity, as well. It's a hands-on way of experiencing the difficulties of representing a sphere on a flat surface. In Figure 10.15, we see the different results of attempts to project the globe onto flat surfaces. In each case, something is sacrificed. Notice that the three main distortions are size, shape, and the sense of what the map should really look like.

in the classroom **A World Globe Activity**

To help students understand the relationship between maps and globes and the relative sizes and locations of continents on the globe, have them do the following activity.

Simply photocopy Figure 10.16, which includes outlines of the six settled continents. Divide the class into pairs, and give each pair a photocopy. Have them cut out the individual continents. Then provide each pair of students with a blue balloon, and have them glue the continents onto the balloon. Make sure they consult a map of the world before trying to do this, so they have a clear idea of each continent's location.

The students—and perhaps you!—will be surprised at the amount of blue still showing and the way the continents fit together.

Helping Students Learn to Use Maps

Obviously, one of the main purposes of a map is to help a person find his or her way from one place to another. Children benefit greatly from practice games, in which they are challenged to tell how they would go from point A to point B. For example, on the map of Lancaster, England (Figure 10.17), how would you explain to someone how to

figure 10.14 *Examples of Portraying the Round Earth on Flat Paper*

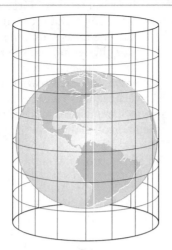
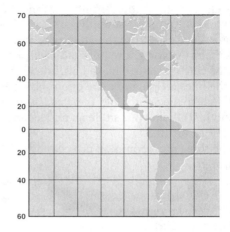

A cylindrical projection is based upon the projection of the globe onto a cylinder.

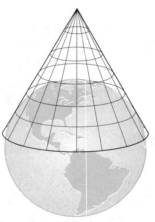
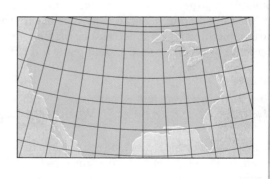

Projection of the globe onto a cone becomes a conic projection.

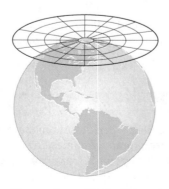
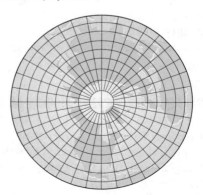

Plane-surface projection is based upon the projection of the globe onto a disc.

figure 10.15   *Various Portrayals of a Globe*

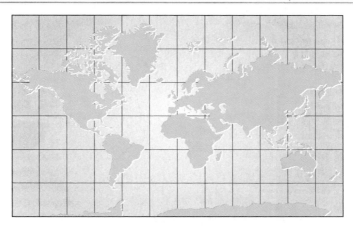

When the globe is portrayed as a rectangle the correct shapes are shown, but notice how large Greenland and Antarctica appear to be.

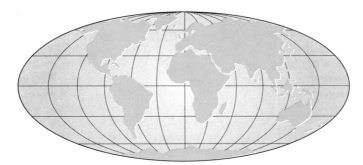

When the globe is portrayed as an oval, the sizes are shown correctly but the shapes are distorted.

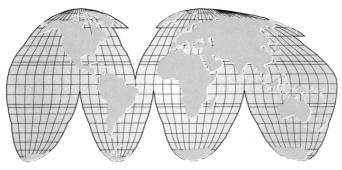

When the globe is portrayed as an orange peel both size and shape are accurate, but notice what happens to Antarctica.

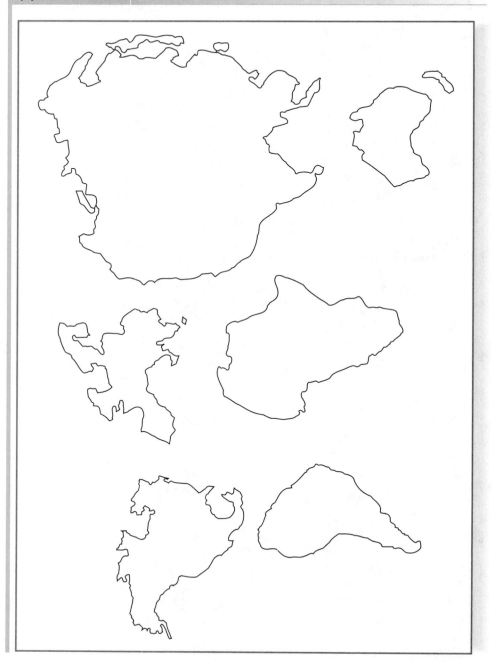

figure 10.16   *The Six Continents*

figure 10.17 *A Map of Historic Sites in Lancaster, England*

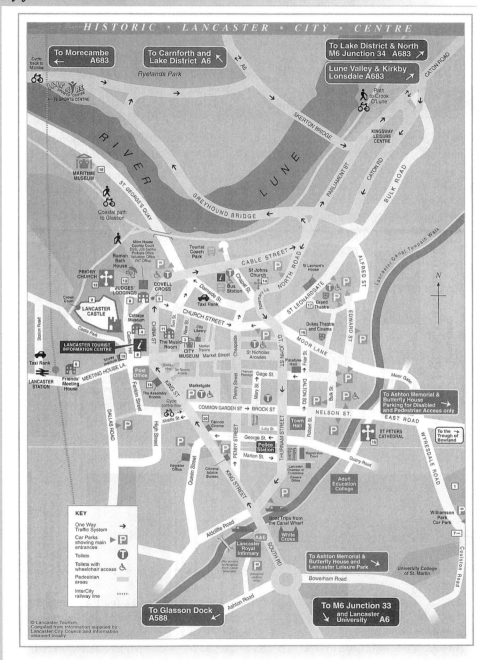

get from St. Peter's Cathedral to the Maritime Museum? From Town Hall to the Grand Theatre? From the City Library to the Roman Bath House? From the Police Station to the Sports Centre? Encourage your students to use maps to understand locations in relation to one another and ways to get from here to there.

in the classroom Mapping Directions

This activity is designed to help students visualize oral or written information spatially. Any story or written information that includes directions for traveling around a given space will do. Here is one example. You and your students can develop others.

Read your students the following story, and have them draw maps of the places involved. (One such map is shown in Figure 10.18.)

One morning, Little Red Riding Hood decided to visit her sick grandmother. After she left her house,

she went to the Muffin Man's to get some muffins for Grandmother. Then she went to the Flower Lady's for some nice fresh flowers to take to Grandmother. Next, Little Red Riding Hood entered the south entrance to the woods and walked along the path toward the Woodcutter's house, which was west of her house. When she reached the Woodcutter's house, she stopped for a drink of water. She then walked north to feed some squirrels, and from there, she went by the most direct path to Grandmother's house.

Considering Variables in Finding Your Way

People spend much of their time going from one place to another. Sometimes they go on foot, and sometimes by bicycle, and sometimes by bus or subway or car. Rarely is there only one way to go from one place to another. When a person decides to go from point A to point B, he or she usually considers the purpose of the trip, how much time there is to accomplish it, what means of transportation are available, and so on. All these things are called *variables*. Thus, a child walking to school must consider several variables: time, safety, friends, and perhaps scenery.

in the classroom Mapping Variables

Here is a problem-solving challenge for you to present to your students. Have them work in pairs for this exercise in cartography. Choose any two points in the local environment. The challenge is for students to illustrate three routes on a single map: (1) the fastest route; (2) the safest route; and (3) the most scenic route.

Such an activity does several things. First of all, it encourages careful observation and exploration. Second, it creates a situation where the junior map makers must plot three variables on a single map. And third, it requires decision making on the part of the participants. See Figure 10.19 for an example of a child's map showing three routes.

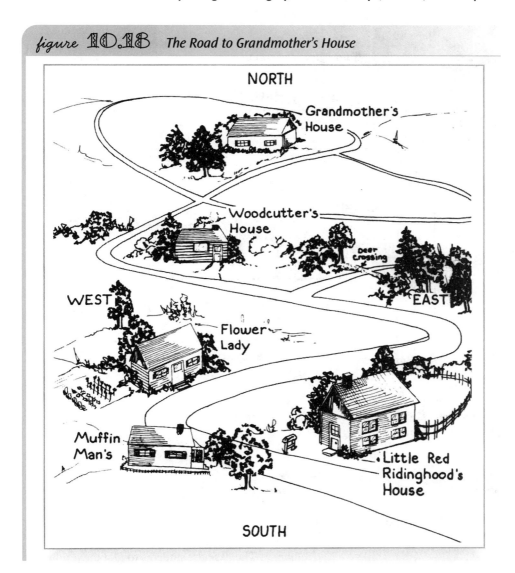

figure **10.18**   *The Road to Grandmother's House*

Studying Changes in Land Use

Maps and other spatial depictions, such as aerial photographs, can illustrate clearly the changes that people and nature have made to particular areas over time. Figure 10.20, for example, shows two aerial photographs taken about 30 years apart of basically the same site. Using photographs like these or historical maps, have students study two depictions of the same site and then document as many changes in the landscape as they can. You can use the two photos here for this task, but you may want to obtain two such photos of your school site or of the landscape in your local community. Aerial

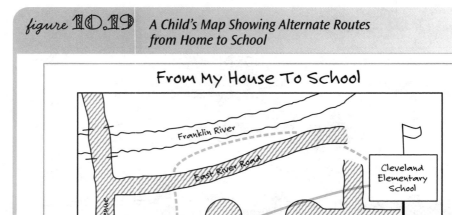

figure **10.19**   *A Child's Map Showing Alternate Routes from Home to School*

photographs are available from the Department of Agriculture and may also be available from local real estate agencies.

---

in the classroom   Learning Geography from Chocolate Bars

A typical chocolate bar contains the following ingredients:

Sugar	Milk
Chocolate	Soybeans
Cocoa butter	Almonds
Cacao	Vanilla

Where do these ingredients come from? The answer is that it takes many places from around the world to put together a chocolate candy bar.

Give the children a world map, and challenge them to discover where each ingredient comes from. (Don't forget the wrapper—it's probably made of paper and metal foil.) Let them use the Internet for research or look things up in the library. Then ask the students to plot the products on the map, encouraging them to make a pictorial representation of each product. Next, committees can report on each of the various products, as well as on how the products get from field to factory and how the candy bars are made at the factory. And finally, how do the candy bars get to the store so that we can buy them?

This activity will provide learning in a wide range of areas—beginning with map making but including history, nutrition, and economics.

figure **10.20**   *Aerial Photographs of a Site Taken 30 Years Apart*

Understanding Perspective

There is nothing like a map to teach children the concept of *perspective*. The best way to use maps, of course, is developmentally. By that, I mean that lessons should come from direct experiences, which are then thoughtfully considered and discussed.

For example, to help students understand how perspectives may differ, find a picture of a bird in flight—a magazine photograph, for example. Ask the students to talk about what the bird would see from its vantage point in the sky. Perhaps students who have flown in an airplane can describe the perspective as they recall it. Next, have the students draw maps using a bird's-eye view. To do this, have each student create a model of a small village from construction paper, complete with streams, forests, roads, houses, and so on. When the villages are done, ask each student to place his or her village on the floor, so that he or she can look straight down on it. Then have each student draw a sketch, or map, of what he or she sees.

Following this activity (perhaps the next day), take the class outside to an elevated place (if there is one) on the playground. Have them draw maps of what they see. Now you are ready to have a good discussion of the differences in perspective between an aerial view and a view from the ground.

The map in Figure 10.21 is a good example of perspective taking. Notice that the centerpiece of the map is the North Pole; therefore, this map is called a *polar projection*. The

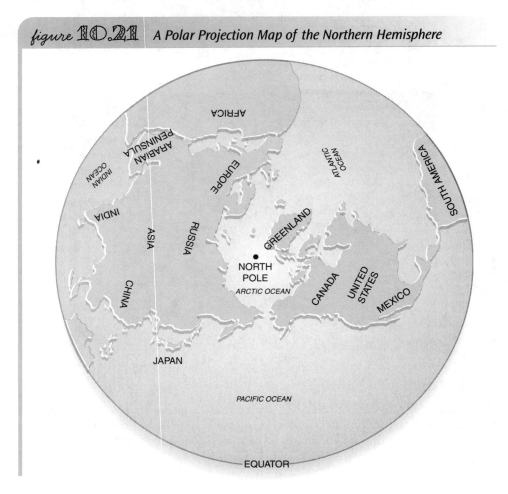

figure **10.21**   *A Polar Projection Map of the Northern Hemisphere*

space shown on the map is projected out from the North Pole. In this case, the horizon of the map is the equator, so we are looking at half the world's surface. This map makes it apparent that the vast majority of the earth's land surface is in the Northern Hemisphere.

Make copies of this map (one for each student), and have the students cut it out along the equator. Then ask them to rotate the map and examine it from Africa, Asia, North America, and so on. Ask students to express their thoughts about how the earth appears from these various vantage points. Ask them if they have ever considered looking at North America from such a perspective. Next, have each student draw the map. This enables them to let the perspective sink in. North America may appear upside down in their drawings, but that's only because they are used to a different perspective (see Figure 10.22).

Of course, the concept of *perspective* is pervasive. Even the perspective on a classroom lesson will be different for a child sitting in the back versus the front of the room or near a window.

in the classroom Four-Color Mapping Theory

Your students can have fun exploring the theory of *four-color mapping,* which allows them to differentiate all bordering areas from one another by means of color. This technique is used by professional cartographers, or map makers, to make borders clear. Intermediate-age children can quickly learn the idea and use it in their own map making.

Four-color map theory is based on a mathematical theorem that allows any series of bordering areas to be differentiated by color, using only four colors and without ever duplicating colors along any given border. A key for the United States is provided in Figure 10.23, but let your students try to figure this out themselves. It will take many tries!

Students may find four-color mapping relatively easy in the western United States, where most states have regular geometric shapes. There are two reasons for this regularity, by the way: (1) There are fewer major rivers to create natural boundaries, although there are exceptions (like the Columbia River, which forms the Washington–Oregon boundary); and (2) the boundaries for these states were mostly created long after the territories had been settled by map makers sitting in offices in Washington, DC, who seemed to love drawing long, straight lines!

But just notice the squiggly lines created by the Mississippi and Ohio Rivers! These two mighty rivers create the boundary lines between more than a dozen states. The Mississippi creates a natural boundary all the way from Minnesota to Louisiana, where the river runs into the Gulf of Mexico. Trace it with your finger from north to south. Notice how the Ohio River forms the entire northern boundary of Kentucky. Trace the Ohio from its origin in Pennsylvania, where it begins at the junction of the Allegheny and Monongahela Rivers, all the way to where it joins the Mississippi in southern Illinois.

The four-color theory is really put to the test by such states as Tennessee and Kentucky. Just count their neighbors! But still, it works. Maine has only one neighbor, so it's easy.

I suggest that you create an inductive lesson for your students. Give them each an outline map of the United States. Challenge them to color the map using only four colors, without ever duplicating colors along any state boundary line. Have a few extra maps on hand, just in case the trial-and-error process doesn't work at first.

Activities such as this are powerful ways of anchoring the concepts of space and place in the minds of children. A map begins to take meaningful form, it begins to make sense, and it takes its place in the memory when a person engages in activities such as these.

figure 10.22 A World Map Based on the Mercator Projection

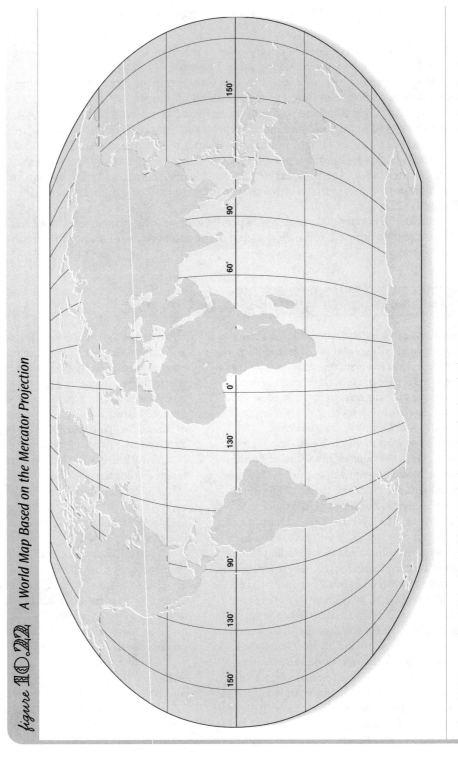

Compare this perspective of the world with the polar projection perspective shown in Figure 10.21.

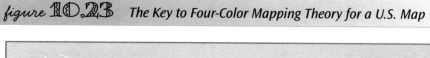

figure **10.23**   *The Key to Four-Color Mapping Theory for a U.S. Map*

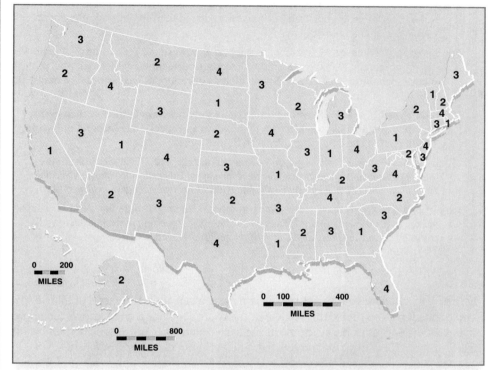

Estimating Distances

The ability to estimate distance is a very valuable skill (e.g., in driving). The National Council of Teachers of Mathematics (NCTM) lists estimation as one of its 10 goals for learning mathematics. You can do many things to develop this skill; here are two suggestions:

• Take the class out on the playground (or into a long hallway), and set two markers a certain distance apart. Have everyone write down or tell his or her best guess about the distance between the markers. Then measure the distance between the two markers with a tape measure, like the kind used for measuring distances in track meets. (Your school probably has one.) Measuring is an important skill, and in this instance, it allows students to employ yet another skill: that of verifying their guesses. With repeated practice, students will become quite skilled at estimating distances.

• Have your students work in cooperative groups of two and use a yardstick or meterstick to measure each other's typical stride. The best thing to do is to work in a little math

figure **10.24** *Useful Geographic Education Websites*

U.S. Geological Survey (USGS)   www.education.usgs.gov   Provides map collections, resources for meeting social studies standards, digital libraries, information about Earth Week, and a host of links.

For Geography Teachers   www.members.aol.com/bowermanb/teach.html   Provides links to more than 30,000 social studies lessons, information about geographic professional associations (such as NCSS) and global education, as well as puzzles, maps, and games.

Education World   www.education-world.com   Provides links to the five themes of geography and lessons to achieve them, holidays and special days around the world, a lesson plan of the day, geography A to Z, and more.

Global Issues Gateway   www.gig.org/departments/gig_k12   Provides links to the National Geographic Education Guide, Newsweek Education Program, Discovery Channel School, PBS, and other valuable sources for bringing geography to life.

City of San Antonio Library   www.sanantonio.gov/library/geography   Provides links to country profiles, currencies, flags, weather, maps, teaching materials, lesson plans, activities, curriculum resources, and other geography web resources.

here. If you measure your stride, say, five times, you can add up the total of all five strides and divide it by 5 to derive the average or mean stride. Once a child knows the approximate distance of his or her stride, he or she can use it to pace off distances. This becomes a built-in tool for estimating, measuring, and verifying distances anywhere.

The Internet and Maps

The explosion of electronic information has made maps and other geographic information readily accessible for both students and teachers. Figure 10.24 provides a list of websites that you may find worth exploring.

Summary

Maps are abstract representations of the surface of the earth or some other sphere that help people see certain spatial relationships. Maps are particularly useful to social scientists as a means of illustrating spatial data, such as political boundaries, population distributions, the relative locations of goods and services, and the distribution of land and water forms. The interpretation and development of maps by elementary-age students gives them a clearer picture of spatial phenomena. Using aerial and satellite photographs can help students view the earth's surface features more concretely.

The ability to interpret and develop maps is most effectively taught through experiential approaches. This chapter described a wide range of strategies and activities to help students learn map concepts and skills.

Maps and globes are iconic representations of the earth's surface. In a sense, they are word pictures that enable us to see spatial relationships such as distance, scale, size, and location. They are communication tools that are illustrative, rather than alphabetical. A map is different from a photograph, however, in that a map is a selective representation of space, whereas a photograph includes everything the camera sees. Using aerial and satellite photographs provides a useful foundation for understanding maps because children can make maps from them (by tracing or copying).

In this chapter, we focused mainly on the developmental processes of making maps. Children begin by sketching and drawing, tracing and copying, and gradually make the transition from seeing a concrete representation of the earth's surface to understanding the abstract representation shown on a map or globe.

The five themes of geography provide a conceptual point of reference for understanding the spatial world. Using a spiral approach, in which the same themes are revisited each year at an increasing level of sophistication, we set in motion a process of geographic literacy. Children at the primary level are introduced to these themes through reading stories, making drawings, and investigating the world around them. This sets the stage for acquiring the increasingly complex knowledge of location, place, interaction, movement, and region in the intermediate grades.

Explorations

Reflect On . . .

1. Take a few moments to reflect on your own thoughts about how children learn. Address the following issues: interest, motivation, activity, exploration, and collaboration. Write a brief paragraph about each topic.

In the Field

2. Become a social scientist for a brief period of time. Find an appropriate time and place to observe a group of children who are engaged in an activity. The size of the group can vary from two to many. Take notes as you observe. What conclusions do you reach about childhood learning on the basis of your systematic observation?

3. Ask the weather bureau or your local television station for satellite images of your area. Trace one of these images to make a map. What skills do you think your students might learn from doing this activity? What did you learn?

4. Go to a local playground and take photographs or make sketches of the equipment and the setting. What do you think this area looked like before the playground was built? What changes were made (in addition to simply installing equipment) to make the area "friendly" to children? What can you and your students learn about the relationships of natural and humanmade phenomena from this activity?

For Your Portfolio

5. Using the imaginary map on the next page, create a lesson plan for students that will help them understand one of the five themes of geography: location, place, human/nature interaction, movement, and region.

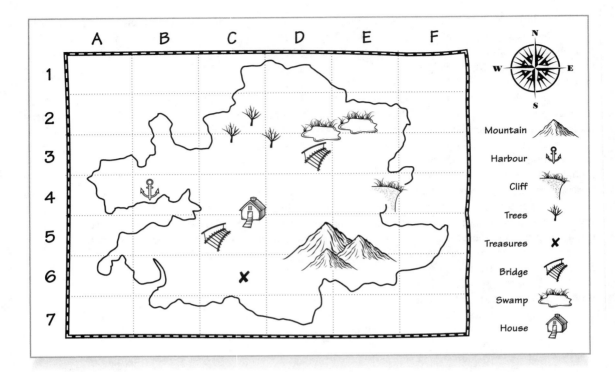

Continuing the Journey: Suggested Readings

Alibrandi, M. (2005). Online interactive mapping. *Social Studies and the Young Learner, 17*(3), 8, 16. *Offers techniques for using the Internet as geographic resource.*

Dill, B. (2003). *Teaching the five themes of geography.* New York: Frank Schaffer. *A very practical book that provides teachers with a host of ideas at various levels for teaching the five themes. Activities range from group to individual, with plenty of hands-on experiences.*

Haas, M. (2000). A street through time used with powerful instructional strategies. *Social Studies and the Young Learner, 13*(8), 20–23. *A delightful article that shows land use change over time, thereby integrating history and geography. It could provide a useful starting point for having your students interview neighborhood residents and examine old photographs to document changes in your school's location.*

Murphey, C. (1998). Using the five themes of geography to explore a school site. *Social Studies Review,* Spring/Summer, 45–48. *Local studies at its best. The author involves students as investigators using their own school site.*

Nagel, P. (2003). Applying the geography standards. *Social Studies and the Young Learner, 15*(4), 30–31. *A useful overview of the standards and how elementary teachers can put them into practice with children whose background in geography is limited.*

Ness, D. et al. (2005). Mapping your way to geographic awareness: Part II. *Science Scope, 28*(4), 59–63. *Illustrates ways in which teachers and students can become cartographers as a means of learning geography.*

Pearson, J., & Wright, D. (1994). First maps. *Childhood Education,* May, 31–38. *A useful primer for introducing young children to the world of maps and spatial relationships.*

SAMPLE LESSON 10.1 *Learning a New Environment*

GRADE LEVEL: Appropriate for grades K–2.

PURPOSE: To orient students to their surroundings.

OBJECTIVES: As a result of this activity, the students will:

1. Locate specific places in the school on a map.
2. Visit specific places in the school setting, such as the principal's office, restrooms, lunchroom, and playground.
3. Learn the rules and responsibilities associated with specific settings, including places within the school that are off limits.

RESOURCES/MATERIALS: Butcher paper, markers, maps of the building (one per student), crayons, construction paper, scissors, storybook.

PROCEDURE:

1. Make a large wall map of the school and its grounds on butcher paper, identifying specific places with different colors (classrooms, hallways, bathrooms, the gym, the lunchroom, etc.). Doors, water fountains, and the like can be cut from construction paper that's the same color as the specific place shown on the classroom map.
2. Give students small outline maps of the school (one map per student). Have them locate the specific areas and color them to match the large wall map.
3. Take the students on a building tour. Let each student bring his or her map and a marker. As you visit each area, tell students the rules of the area. Have them mark on their maps any special features that they want to remember, such as water fountains, outside doors or exits, and so on.
4. If possible, arrange to have the students make a special trip to the principal's office, and as a special treat, ask the principal to read a story to them. Similarly, visit the school nurse, the librarian, and other special people in the school.
5. On returning to the classroom, have the students cut their maps into pieces, creating jigsaw puzzles, and reassemble them to learn the relationship of one area to another.

CLOSURE: Use this unit at the beginning of the year for students who are new to the school building. Not only will they learn the layout of the building, but they will also begin to learn mapping skills. Doing this activity will help students feel comfortable and welcome, and that will enhance the learning process. When they know and respect the rules of the school setting, the environment becomes a better place for everyone involved.

Source: Adapted from a lesson plan submitted by Dianne Elaine Hill (West Junior High School, Muskogee, OK) to OFCN's Academy Curricular Exchange, Columbia Education Center, Social Studies.

SAMPLE LESSON 10.2 *Map Mileage*

GRADE LEVEL/SUBJECT: Grades 3–6.

PURPOSE: To give students experience in using the mileage key on a map.

OBJECTIVE(S): The students will be able to use the mileage key of a map to plan a trip and keep within a set amount of miles given by the teacher.

RESOURCES/MATERIALS: A map with a mileage key for each team of students; rulers, pencils, paper; small inexpensive plastic cars; and certificates.

PROCEDURE:

1. Announce that everyone in the class has the chance to win a brand-new car by doing one simple thing: planning a vacation.
2. Divide students into teams of three, and give each team a small toy car and a map of one state. It can be your state or a vacation state (like Florida, New York, or California), or it can be a region (like New England or the Southwest). Tell each team that their car is brand new and has 0 miles on its odometer.
3. Tell each team to plan a trip of not less than 1,000 miles and not more than 1,200 miles that includes at least three places of interest. If when they "return" from the trip, their odometer reads between 1,000 and 1,200, the car is theirs to keep.
4. Each team should plot their trip on their map and make a chart of the legs of the trip with the mileage noted. They must begin and end in the same place but cannot visit any place along the route more than once.

5. To add an element of history and culture to the activity, students can use the Internet, an atlas, or tourist brochures provided by the teacher to get information about things to see and do and to decide which places to visit. Teams should also try to find interesting routes with interesting scenery, which doesn't necessarily mean following interstate highways.
6. Have teams check one another's mileage totals. All teams who plot trips of the correct mileage win their cars.

CLOSURE: Have each team present their trip to the class orally, as though they are travel agents. They should talk about the places they visited and the routes they took. The class can vote on which is the most interesting route.

EXTENSION: For homework, have students use maps and mileage keys to plot their own dream vacations anywhere in the world.

Source: Adapted from a lesson plan submitted by Faun White to OFCN's Academy Curricular Exchange, Columbia Education Center, Social Studies.

SAMPLE LESSON 10.3 *Map Making*

GRADE LEVEL/SUBJECT: Grades 4–6; Map Skills.

PURPOSE: To help students understand that a map is a representation of all or part of the surface of the earth on a plane. To acquaint students with some of the problems associated with map making. This is a very effective first-day activity, not only to introduce a map unit but also to set the class tone for emphasizing problem solving as a way of addressing learning.

OBJECTIVES:

1. Students will identify the placement of the continents and the oceans by drawing them on a handmade globe.

2. Students will identify the placement of the equator, the Tropic of Cancer and the Tropic of Capricorn, and the North Pole and the South Pole by drawing them on a handmade globe.

RESOURCES/MATERIALS: One-half sheet of 8½" × 11" paper for each student (scrap paper is good); one tennis ball (or soft ball) for each student; scissors, tape, pencils.

PROCEDURE:

1. Ask each student to use the paper to wrap the tennis ball, without leaving wrinkles or overlapping the paper. Students may cut the paper,

if they feel that will help. This is not an easy task. You should be a facilitator in this activity; it is important to emphasize that each student will find her or his own solution. There is no one right answer. Stress that each student can develop his or her own strategy but also that students are free to get ideas by looking around the room.

2. Have each student tape the wrapping in place.
3. Ask each student to sketch the continent on his or her globe, using a classroom map as a guide. For older children, add the North and South Poles, the equator, and the Tropics of Cancer and Capricorn.
4. As students finish, have them bring their globes to the front of the room and compare them to a commercial globe. They can make adjustments to their own globes as necessary.
5. When each student has completed the drawing, have him or her remove the covering from the tennis ball, lay it flat on the desk, and study the map of the world that he or she created.
6. Have students compare their maps to the flat map of the world that they used initially.

CLOSURE: Have students discuss the ways they approached the problem of wrapping a round object with a flat piece of paper. Underscore in the discussion that students may have developed a variety of strategies.

REFLECTION: Use this activity as a springboard to introduce the problems of early cartography, the various flat map designs, the voyages of early explorers, and so on.

Source: Adapted from a lesson plan submitted by Linda Bauck (Wallowa Elementary, OR) to OFCN's Academy Curricular Exchange, Columbia Education Center, Social Studies.

chapter 11

Teaching and Learning Values, Character Education, and Moral Development

In this chapter, we will explore these themes:

key concepts

- The meaning of values, character education, and moral development in elementary school learning
- Teaching values, character, and morality
- Models of character education, values realization, and moral development

We passed the School, where Children strove
At Recess—in the Ring—
> —Emily Dickinson

If someone thinks honesty, cooperation, compassion, and discipline are important, we can say that person *values* those qualities. If someone behaves toward others in honest ways, gets along well with others, shows empathy, and works hard, we can say that person has certain desirable *character* traits. And if someone knows right from wrong and is a principled individual, then we can describe that person's *morals*. Obviously, values, character, and morals are closely related and intertwined.

All aspects of a social studies curriculum have their foundation in values, character, and moral issues. Regardless of how you teach, you convey your values, your character, and your moral judgment to your students. There is truth in the old expression that "Values are as often caught as taught." In recent years, a number of options have become available to teachers who are interested in teaching and exploring values issues with children.

Questions of value, character, and morality are among the most basic of social studies issues. Our behaviors—whether we are children or adults—put our character on display. For the teacher, these issues create both an awesome responsibility and a great opportunity. One thing you can count on is that your students will be aware of how you act toward them and others. Every act of kindness, every challenge to do better, every attempt at fairness, every moment of genuine caring on your part will exert some influence. As stated by writer Henry Adams, "A teacher effects eternity." He went on to say that you never know where your influence will stop.

In fact, one of our great rewards as teachers is *knowing* that we can indeed make a difference. The promise is there. I just know that you want to be the kind of teacher whose positive influence is such that your students will remember you the rest of their lives. Does this seem farfetched? I don't think so. I have talked with many an elderly person who clearly and fondly remembers the name of a teacher from elementary school. We live and teach in the present, but the present has a way of becoming the past. With each day of the school year, you are helping to create memories. At the same time, by molding the present in which you and your students live, you are shaping the future. The children you teach will in time become adults, and the adults they become will be, in some measure, the products of your influence. There are other influences in their lives, to be sure, but don't underestimate your own potential for good as you contribute to children's growth and development.

All this is merely a way of saying that every teacher teaches values, consciously or unconsciously. Every teacher shapes character, one way or another. And every teacher models morality every day of the school year. Most of the modeling, shaping, and teaching you do is made of little things that happen along the way. A reassuring word at the right time, a pat on the back for a job well done, or some encouragement in a time of difficulty—are all part of the process. Honesty, integrity, caring, collaboration, fairness, openness, and courage are merely vocabulary words at one level. But when they are lived, taught, acted out, and reflected on, they become a powerful reality. There is an old saying that "Children learn what they live." What will they live and what will they learn in your classroom?

The Meaning of Values, Character, and Morality in Elementary School Learning

In this book, we are focusing on teaching and learning social studies at the elementary level. What do values, character, and moral education have to contribute to the social studies curriculum?

I suppose if we were to pose this question to a wide range of people, we would receive answers ranging from "Nothing—social studies is about history, geography, and civics as academic subjects" to "Everything—social studies becomes an empty subject if it does not offer a vision of the good life." Well, let me be clear about my own position. I'll put it to you in the form of a position statement: Social studies has to be *social* in order to be meaningful. Keep in mind that this subject is not called *isolated* studies. The very word *social* implies groups, gatherings, community, teams, friendship, and people working and playing and learning together. But *social* also implies *moral*. Social settings are where we test our morality, our character, our values.

Psychologist Jean Piaget used the term *social knowledge* to mean the kind of knowledge people need to work with others, to be part of a community, and to understand the give and take that inevitably occurs when people find themselves in group settings. Piaget noted that the social setting provides us with moral issues that arise in the context of daily school life. When children disagree or when matters of cheating or misbehavior arise, they provide real-life issues about which to talk and reflect, about which to learn from and to grow socially and morally. This is experiential teaching and learning at its best. In an atmosphere of openness, honesty, and opportunity, the life experience of the school becomes integrated into the curriculum. How ironic it would be to teach about communities, cultures, and citizens without *applying* the skills, content, and concepts learned to our own community, our own culture, and the citizens of our own miniature democracy—the classroom and school.

Procedural Values: The Strategies of Inquiry and Reflection

In addition to such *substantive values* as tolerance, honesty, integrity, and fairness, to name a few, there are also *procedural values* to be taught in social studies. Procedural values are rooted in the methods of inquiry used by social scientists. The very use of such inquiry procedures as data gathering and inference making to determine relationships and provide descriptions and explanations of human behavior indicates a values position—one that favors the use of empirical evidence to answer questions.

Yet not even these activities always lead people to similar judgments on given issues. One could, for example, investigate which combination of attributes makes the best teachers. Taking a survey could help determine which attributes are most often favored, but the results—no matter how clearly they favored certain attributes—would not necessarily make those teachers who have those attributes the best. *Best* is a matter of individual judgment and thus a question of value.

Procedural values include observing, recording, classifying, hypothesizing, and making inferences. Why are these *values?* They are values because we can say that a person who uses systematic inquiry to answer questions *values* these procedural methods. You can readily see how substantive and procedural values are interwoven. Here is an example: Imagine that you find yourself as a teacher in a situation where fairness is at stake. Perhaps two children have quarreled over using a playground ball. After allowing some time for emotions to subside, you will examine both sides of the issue, ask questions, and reach some reasonable conclusion based on your evidence gathering. If you handle it sensitively, the entire class can be involved. So, you will have invoked the substantive value of fairness and modeled procedural values to achieve fairness.

This could be a very valuable lesson, probably more valuable than the one you had carefully planned. That would especially be true if later on, you were to hold a reflective-thinking session with your class and go back over the matter with them. That would be true experiential learning.

Considering the Social Context

Values represent both the ideal and the real dimensions of our feelings as individuals and as a culture. Every individual possesses a set of values, and except in extreme cases, those values are primarily mirrored on a larger level by the culture and by its history. Our ideal values are represented by our beliefs, our real values by our actions. For individuals to function successfully within their societal context, they must recognize and

The school day provides many opportunities, mostly unplanned, to explore social knowledge and moral growth experientially.

abide by the values of the larger society. That, of course, is why society has laws (and, on occasion, hermits) and why laws and rules often change over time.

Not too many years ago, persons of color were required by local laws in certain cities to sit in the backs of buses. Schools, restaurants, and hotels were all legally segregated by race. To young children who may not even be aware of this, it could seem like ancient history. As leaders such as Martin Luther King Jr. in the U.S. and Mohandas Gandhi in India helped show the citzens of their countries that such laws were inherently unfair, the laws were changed. These changes allowed whole groups of people to begin the long, slow march toward equality of opportunity. The U.S. Declaration of Independence had proclaimed equality for all, but in fact, that was not the case. The lesson for children is that it is important to know our history—the good and the not so good—and to know that in a democratic society, there is always hope for positive change.

Consider another example: In the 1960s, cars were allowed to travel at 70 miles per hour on interstate highways. Then in the 1970s, the speed limit was lowered to 55 because of a worldwide shortage of petroleum-based fuels. That phenomenon became known as the "energy crisis." By changing the law, Americans not only saved billions of gallons of gasoline each year but also an estimated 6,000 lives, because the reduced speed limits meant fewer accidents. So, the new law had one intentional good effect and one totally unintentional good effect. In recent years, however, the speed limit has been raised again, representing yet another shift in values and thus laws. Does the world today have more petroleum reserves than it had in the 1970s? Clearly, the answer is no; it does not. We have simply decided that we are not concerned about using oil responsibly.

We Americans have made much progress toward racial equality, but we have a long way to go in terms of our wise use of the earth's resources. Perhaps in the future, Congress will pass laws requiring us to use resources other than fossil fuels to operate our cars and trucks. Or maybe new legislation will require creation of more reasonable mass transit. Here is the exciting thing for the teacher of elementary social studies: These new laws and ideas may someday come about in part because you created in some young girl or boy a sense of the power that people in a democracy have to change the world. Never underestimate the power of a teacher to inspire, to show the possible, and to start a generation of young people on the road to accomplishing what we haven't even dreamt of.

Researcher Lawrence Kohlberg (1983) suggests that a *just* classroom environment (one where justice prevails) provides a remarkable medium for enhancing the moral development of students. The classroom, with its potential to mirror democracy, is the perfect place in which to resolve the great and abiding issues of the tensions between rights and responsibilities. Kohlberg has a vision of a just society. Are elementary-age children too young to understand all the ramifications of that idea? Perhaps. But if they experience openness, fairness, and civility in your classroom and if they are given opportunities to reflect on what they experience, they will surprise you with their insight.

What Really Matters?

Few questions are more basic in life than those about values. This became particularly significant for me as a classroom teacher. You know as well as I do that any good classroom teacher is remarkably busy with the details of the day. But at some point, being busy isn't the issue. Having priorities is the issue. There comes a time when all reflective people ask themselves, "What really matters?" I finally made myself a sign out of cardboard—one that said "WHAT REALLY MATTERS?" I hung the sign on my desk so I couldn't avoid it. That sign helped me a great deal in my work with children.

The fact that you are a teacher is a major statement of your values and what really matters to you. You have chosen a profession of service. You have said, in effect, that you want to work with children and to help them grow. Economist E. F. Schumacher (1973) spoke to the values issue in his book *Small Is Beautiful* when he said that nothing is more important than education because it answers the question of what to do with our lives.

The classroom has the potential for being a powerful forum for values. The proof of Schumacher's statement is provided by the occasional great teacher that everyone has along the way. A great teacher always lives and teaches a set of positive values. Think about your own best teachers. They taught you much more than content. They taught you about lasting ideas—integrity, compassion, self-discipline, and dignity—and they managed to do it without your knowing it at the time. They did it through a process of modeling the high-level, abstract concepts just mentioned. Somehow, they were able to make each concept real, concrete, experiential—something you could put into practice in your everyday life.

You bring your own values to the classroom every day. You are on display. Young children will be your witnesses. Occasionally, they will wonder why you are the way you are, but mostly, they will accept your behavior as natural for a teacher. In their naïve and unsophisticated way, they may characterize you to their parents and friends as

Values such as participation, freedom, and excellence are best learned through experience.

being "nice" or "mean" or "friendly." To a greater extent than perhaps you and they know, your students will be internalizing or rejecting your values as you model them. The students, of course, will also bring their own values to the classroom. Interest inventories and class discussions provide useful ways for students to reflect on and share their own values.

The Moral Life of Schools

Including moral education in public classrooms in the United States can be a challenge because of the legal separation of church and state in this country and the strong feelings that revolve around that issue. In an important book titled *The Moral Life of Schools,* however, Philip Jackson and his colleagues (1993) make an essential contribution to our knowledge of the social/moral fabric of school life. Using an ethnographic approach in their research, they furnish readers with unusually helpful glimpses of everyday life in classrooms and schools. They analyze a range of events that take place in the routine of school life, including interaction between teachers and their students, how students spend their time, the content and procedures of the school curriculum, attempts by teachers to instruct students in matters of morality, and the general social/moral ethos of the school. As a result of their exhaustive fieldwork, Jackson and his colleagues have identified eight categories of *moral activity* that take place at school. The first five categories represent deliberate attempts by the school to promote moral consciousness and to encourage positive behaviors. The last three categories consist of "activities that embody the moral" and are hence considerably more subtle.

The following accounts of these eight categories are brief, but I hope that they will give you food for thought—that reflecting on them will deepen your own awareness of the implications of this important topic for bettering the lives of children. The proof that you have internalized them will be found in your day-to-day behaviors as you work with children.

- *Moral instruction.* Many countries—Japan, for example—include an actual course of study in the basic school curriculum called *moral instruction.* In the United States, separate courses on this topic are found more commonly in private schools, especially those operated by particular religious denominations. Such a course may take the form of attending chapel, or it may be a course in religion or perhaps character education. Public schools rarely offer such courses because the lines between religion and moral education can be difficult to draw. But some basic principles of moral behavior are common to all religions and indeed should be common to humanity. These can and perhaps should be taught.

- *Intervention programs.* Intervention programs are special course offerings that teach a specific point of moral choice or behavior, generally about a topic of great societal concern. Often, these courses are taught by resource people, and each student receives a certificate on completion of the course. The most prominent of these programs in recent times has been the DARE program, a special course aimed at children in fifth grade. DARE is a drug awareness course, typically taught by a representative of the local police department. Children pledge to refuse to become involved with drugs as a result of their heightened awareness. Other programs focus on such topics as sex education, smoking and alcohol, and even self-esteem. While the actual effectiveness of many of these programs, including DARE, has been questioned, it seems that the public looks increasingly to the schools to address these troubling societal problems.

- *Moral instruction within the curriculum.* Teachers can make conscious use of examples from history, civics, biographies, drama, music, art, and stories to draw out acts of courage, loyalty, perseverance, dedication, helping, and determination. These virtues are abundantly found in good source material, and many teachers make it a point to build discussions and lessons around them. The learning derived from such instruction is vicarious, and the intent is to inspire by showing the possible. I well recall reading a children's biography of Chief Black Hawk when I was in fourth grade; it was full of stories of bravery, kindness, and courage. I wish the teacher had read it to the entire class and discussed it with us.

- *Rituals and ceremonies.* School is a place filled with rituals that would interest any anthropologist. Most of these rituals are simply taken for granted and go unquestioned. Even so, rituals and routines give a kind of rhythm and punctuation to the school day or year. Included in this category are saying the Pledge of Allegiance to the flag, playing and singing patriotic music, having show and tell, celebrating holidays such as Thanksgiving and Martin Luther King Jr.'s birthday, and having pageants, heritage celebrations, seasonal festivals, ethnic celebrations, assemblies, and school elections. All represent attempts to create community at school. Adults sometimes overlook how important these rituals and routines are in the lives of children. Children look forward to many of them with great anticipation and wonder, and they find security in the day-to-day patterns and routines that lend a sense of predictability to their lives.

• *Visuals and displays with moral content.* Foreign visitors are often surprised at the sheer number of flags on display in a typical American elementary school, from the school yard to the gym to nearly every classroom. The flag is the single most visible symbol in American schools, and in its function as a symbol, it is a nonverbal communication tool serving to remind us that we are united as a people. Other visual displays include portraits of famous Americans, exhibits and showcases with trophies, and hallways lined with children's work. Other displays are more subtle, but they are nonetheless reminders that this is a school, not anything else. Examples of these include the clock on the wall (you know, the one that never seemed to move when you were a kid) and the ever-present alphabet above the chalkboard. These visuals and displays serve as reminders that this is a school and that every school has its own distinctive characteristics. Just the other day when I visited a school, I was overwhelmed the moment I walked in the door with displays of children's work on hallway tables, the walls themselves, classroom doors, and certainly in the classrooms. It was a wonderful visit.

These first five categories are rather obvious, and they stand out in sharp relief to the observer. The next three are more elusive, but the careful investigator will find them.

• *Spontaneous commentary.* In the social fabric of school life, with its crowded conditions and problematic contexts, troublesome things as well as delightful things will happen from time to time. Sensitive teachers use these examples from school life to draw out and develop ideas of morality. Fights, cruelty, cheating, tattling, bullying, vandalism, and other antisocial behaviors inevitably occur, but they need not occur totally in vain. A teacher may use such situations to great advantage if he or she can lead students to deeper insights into human behavior. Of course, it's a wonderful thing to recognize situations where children have behaved with honesty, kindness, or helpfulness. Use these situations, as well. The power of learning from day-to-day experience has been extolled by such educational giants as John Dewey, Maria Montessori, and Jean Piaget.

• *Rules and regulations.* A classroom is a small, often crowded society that needs to function as smoothly and purposefully as possible. Thus, every classroom has rules and norms designed to make it work. In this realm, fairness, justice, and freedom are put to the test. To the extent that children can be included in making and reviewing rules, they will become participants in a democratic society. To the extent that you invite them to review, discuss, assess, and otherwise reflect on how the classroom functions as a miniature community and a microcosm of society, you enable children to grow and develop socially, morally, and intellectually.

• *Morality of the curriculum.* Get ready for this one! Textbooks and other materials, experiences themselves, exams and assignments, and opportunities to work together all speak to some moral point. How good are they? How honest? How purposeful? Who gains from the experience? Of course, there is the published and obvious curriculum. But how good is it, really? Does it inspire? Does it treat content sensitively and honestly? So, we should raise questions of morality about the published curriculum of textbooks and so on. But we must also address the more subtle level of life in the classroom—that of the so-called hidden curriculum. It doesn't take very much to learn, for example, that first-graders are studying families or that fourth-graders are studying regions in their social studies classes. It is with the *moral quality* of the experience that teachers must be ultimately concerned.

Jackson and colleagues (1993) have given us a framework within which to reflect on the fabric of school life. As a teacher, you have great discretionary power to make life challenging, purposeful, engaging, rewarding, and socially and morally uplifting. Your room needs to be one of those places where children genuinely desire to come and participate, for all the right reasons.

Teaching Values, Character, and Moral Education

What is teachable and what is learnable has long been a matter of debate. As mentioned before, no teacher teaches anything in a vacuum. Students bring with them to every situation certain abilities, interests, aptitudes, readinesses, and sources of outside support from parents and others. Therefore, teaching anything is always more complex than the content itself might suggest. This is particularly true of attempts to teach values to students.

Teaching values presents several problems. First, whose values will you teach? In an integrated, homogeneous society, we might have little trouble agreeing on a list of important values. But in a diverse, pluralistic society, the task becomes more difficult. Second, how will you teach values: by indoctrination? By example? With a workbook? Third, why bother when so many other value-laden forces—such as the home, the street, and the peer group—might contradict your efforts?

To answer the first question, ask yourself this question: Is our society so pluralistic that people cannot agree on any values? I think we can find areas of common value. (I'll give you a list in a moment.) The answer to the second question is that you should provide examples of certain values, and you should also provide some formal instruction in them. Third, a teacher's job will always be influenced by outside forces, but you still need to be optimistic that you can make a difference.

Let's look at some values I think you ought to teach. I'll say more about how to teach them in due course.

- *Participation.* Society needs participants to function. The town meeting, the voting booth, the PTA, and the many public and private organizations are symbols of this participation. At the classroom level, students must be given opportunities to participate in active learning, developing rules, functioning as groups, and anything else you can think of to get them off the sidelines. Active participation encourages feelings of affiliation and serves to combat apathy.

• *Cooperation.* A classroom is a crowded place. Why not encourage your students to share it in an atmosphere of cooperation? People need each other and can come to be freely interdependent in a classroom that fosters group projects, helping, and common goals.

• *Self-discipline.* True discipline comes from within; it is self-directed. This is a powerful idea that sets people free to learn on their own and to get along without being forced to get along. Self-discipline is a good topic to bring up from time to time with your students.

• *Pluralism.* It is one thing to have a different set of values from your neighbor, but it's another thing to respect your neighbor's right to have those personal values. Tolerance and appreciation for people who are different is fundamental to the maintenance of a free society.

• *Responsibility.* Aristotle pointed out that virtuous habits are best learned in childhood. That way, they become patterns of behavior. The child who has learned responsibility has acquired one of life's most important skills.

• *Dignity.* Every child's sense of dignity is a precious commodity that can be easily destroyed by sarcastic comments, embarrassment, and humiliation. Personal dignity is enhanced when you show respect for each student and when you expect your students to show respect for each other.

• *Freedom.* Above all, a classroom ought to be a place where minds are set free. Ironically, this is seldom the case. How can we expect students who are given little or no freedom to understand it and to eventually take their places in a democratic society? Risk taking, curiosity, creativity, and outlandish ideas are integral components of a classroom in which freedom is being taught.

• *Excellence.* Why expect less? Children quickly come to respect a teacher who cares enough to ask great things of them, saying in effect, "I know your abilities differ greatly, but I want the personal best from each of you."

• *Integrity.* The dictionary lists several synonyms for the word *integrity:* honesty, sincerity, wholeness, completeness. You could develop an entire curriculum from just these values! You need to tell the children that integrity includes trying their best, becoming a person and not just a number, and reaching toward their unique potential.

• *Joy.* We need more joy in our classrooms. Childhood is a brief season. Why not celebrate it? Rejoice when a student learns something. Laugh when something is funny. Set free, don't destroy, the natural spirit of the young.

There are other values, but I hope you get the idea from this sampling of which ones can be taught and how. These are not controversial values. They represent the building blocks of a free society. Tear them down or refuse to acknowledge them, and society will become the poorer for it. Discuss them, build them up, and model them, and we will all gain from your efforts.

Strategies for Teaching Values

Now that we have established some values worth teaching and learning (my list can certainly be added to), the next step is to examine what you can do to actively teach a set of positive values to your students. The extent to which your students will embrace those values is difficult to predict when we take into account the many variables in any given child's life. The influences are many, and they are often far from positive. Some children are given moral and spiritual training at home, and some are not. Some are the products of homes where generosity and compassion are practiced on a daily basis, and some are the products of homes where looking out for yourself and doing anything you can in order to get ahead are modeled.

   Sadly, many of the children you will teach over the years are neglected in the most fundamental sense of the word. They may really believe that no one cares about them. But when these children end up in your classroom, you have the opportunity to be positive and to take positive action. For things you can do to enhance the values in your classroom, see the Keys to Effective Values Education.

Keys to Effective Values Education

- *Hold regularly scheduled class meetings.* Students should feel free to share their feelings in a supportive atmosphere. If you are willing to do this and are consistent about it, your efforts will be paid back many times over. Once your students realize that they can trust you and that they are free to speak their minds during these meetings, they will begin to open up.
- *Be sure that each of the children you teach understands that you care.* Call each student by name. Every child has a name, and that name is important. Try to find time to talk with each child privately at some point during the week, if not each day. Let the child know that you've been thinking about him or her. Ask the child if there is anything you can do to help with schoolwork or other matters. Sometimes, maybe you and the child will just talk about little things for a moment. It's worth doing.
- *Provide opportunities for students to practice cooperative learning and shared responsibility in day-to-day assignments.* Individual accountability is important, and you will have to ensure that it occurs in your class. Even so, there are so many things students can and should do together. Working together builds a sense of esprit de corps. In addition, children need to learn early in life that people need each other and can help each other. Team building has been shown to work well in the worlds of sports and business. It works well in the classroom, as well.

Invite guests of diverse racial, ethnic, and national backgrounds to your classroom. Allow them to share their stories, insights, and experiences with your students. Prejudice and stereotyping are often the result of wrong ideas and lack of familiarity with the unknown. Responsible role models are very influential; you can play a key role by bringing in business people, artists, and others who represent varying ethnicities and racial backgrounds. If you are near a college or university, contact its foreign student association to see who might be available to visit your class. Don't wait for the world to come to you and your students. Make it happen!

Allow your students to help you develop a few simple rules of classroom and school conduct and see that they are enforced. As noted elsewhere, John Dewey thought of the ideal classroom as a miniature democracy, in which students actually became involved in the processes of citizenship. Begin to develop a democratic flavor in your class by inviting the students to help you govern it. A simple rule in teaching is to allow your children to decide all the things that they are capable of deciding for themselves. There will be some things that they cannot and should not decide, and that is where your decision-making skills come into play.

Expect a lot from all your students. Having high expectations communicates a caring, believing attitude on your part. Students respond when they know that you expect the best from them. You need to convince each of your students that you believe in his or her ability to work productively. Once students see you are sincere, they will help you with this. High expectations depend on high nurturing to be successful. One year, my class and I adopted the motto "Always the best." We lived by it. We worked and played in ways to consciously live up to our motto. It was a wonderful year.

Give your students opportunities. Allow them to take risks with ideas, to be creative, and to experiment with learning. Don't force everyone to respond to every assignment in the same way. There are so many ways to show that you are learning. The best social studies experiences happen when students find themselves in a stimulating environment where multiple options exist within a thoughtful structure. Getting to choose is a liberating experience, and it is especially instructive when you help children to think reflectively about their choices.

Model the behaviors you seek from your students. As you model crucial attributes such as openness, courtesy, tolerance, kindness, curiosity, and scholarship, be sure to discuss them with your students. They need to have these values laid on the table for exploration and thoughtful analysis. They need to hear stories about people who have set positive examples for others. But above all, your students need to have daily encounters with you as you model desirable behaviors. You have been placed in a position of great trust. It is an honor and a privilege.

Use good children's literature to explore positive values. Stories from *Aesop's Fables* provide a great place to begin. Each fable explores a virtue without being too heavy handed and is timeless in its ability to fascinate both children and adults. Ask your school librarian to recommend age-appropriate titles for your class. Use classics like *The Clown of God,* by Tomie de Paola, and *Little House in the Big Woods,* by Laura Ingalls Wilder. For middle-graders, try *Good Morning, Miss Dove,* by Francis Gray Patton; *Sounder,* by W. H. Armstrong; and *The Secret Garden,* by Frances Hodgson Burnett. Don't ignore contemporary books; there are many worth reading.

Using Moral Dilemmas

Moral dilemmas are useful to the social studies teacher as a means of giving students presumably real-life situations in which their thoughts and judgments come into play. Let's look at two moral dilemmas that have potential to stimulate children's thinking and perspective taking.

DOES THE INTENT OF AN ACTION MATTER?   The first dilemma was suggested by Jean Piaget. In the story, two boys act quite differently, but the results of their actions are similar. I told this story to three children, each one separately.

> This is a story about two boys, Larry and Henry. First, I'll tell you about Larry. Then, I'll tell you about Henry. Once, when Larry's mother was out of the kitchen, Larry decided he would help clean up. As he was taking some plates from the table to be washed, he dropped them and five plates broke. Now, I'll tell you about Henry. Once, when Henry's mother was out of the kitchen, Henry decided he would sneak a cookie. When Henry reached for a cookie, he knocked a plate off the shelf and it broke. Which boy do you think was naughtier?

Here are the three children's discussions with me:

John (age 5): Larry was.
Me: Why?
John: Because he broke five plates and Henry only broke one.
Me: Does it matter what they were trying to do?
John: Five plates made a big mess.

Kenny (age 7): They both were.
Me: Why?
Kenny: Because they both should have been more careful, that's why.
Me: Does it matter what they were trying to do?
Kenny: Yes, but neither one was very careful.

Julie (age 8): Henry was.
Me: Why?
Julie: Well, Larry was trying to help. And Henry was trying to sneak a cookie.
    It was an accident, but one boy was trying to help.

You can see in the responses of these three children a noticeable progression in moral development, particularly from John, the 5-year-old, to Julie, the 8-year-old. For John, the issue is the number of plates that were broken. Perhaps his clearly pragmatic view has a point if you have to clean up the plates or if you have to set the table that evening and there aren't enough plates to go around. For Julie, the matter is more complex. She takes into account each boy's motivation. In other words, she considers the extenuating circumstances before she reaches a decision. Thus, on the basis of intent, she decides that Henry's action was naughtier. In fact, she gives us no hint that Larry's action was naughty at all: "Larry was trying to help." In Julie's response, we see glimpses of Anglo–Saxon common law theory and the basis of our own judicial system, which take into account *why* somebody behaved in a certain way. Kenny, the 7-year-old, appears to be in a stage of transition and refuses to give a decision. In a way, his judgment is the most puzzling of all. His point is that folks ought to be careful when they're handling breakable objects, such as dinner plates. Well, he does have a certain point! But these were real kids, at different stages of development, and this is what they told me in answer to the problem.

Think about the possibilities for fruitful discussions with children using moral dilemmas. Many children never get the opportunity to discuss such issues. As a result, their judgment is impaired. Most dilemmas involve complex issues, and the best way to gain insight to those issues is to discuss them with others.

The teacher's role here is crucial. A good teacher will probe, suggest alternate decisions and reasons for decisions, listen, and help children think about the consequences of decisions. Moral judgment researcher Lawrence Kohlberg (1983) (and Jean Piaget before him) warned of attempts to speed up the process by getting children to agree to solutions that are beyond their understanding. Keep in mind that your modeling of appropriate moral behaviors will always be more powerful than your exhortations.

HOW SHOULD WE REACT TO THE IMMORALITY OF OTHERS—ESPECIALLY FRIENDS?
Another moral dilemma for your consideration is one that deals with a topic familiar to many children: shoplifting.

> Shawn and Morgan go shopping. While they are shopping, Shawn takes an item of jewelry and slips it into a pocket. Morgan sees Shawn take the item. What should Morgan do?

I asked a boy named Ian what he would do in such a situation. Here's our discussion:

Ian: I'd probably tell my friend I saw him take it.
Me: Do you have any other choices?
Ian: Yeah, I could tell the manager and get him in trouble.
Me: What else could you do?
Ian: I could just tell him to put it back before he gets in trouble.
Me: What if he refuses?
Ian: I could just ignore it. I didn't take anything.
Me: Do you feel you have any responsibility in this situation?
Ian: No, I mean, maybe if he's my friend I do.
Me: Why does it matter if he is your friend?
Ian: Well, friends should care about each other, even if they do something wrong.

In this hypothetical case, we have a child thinking about a serious issue: stealing. The job of the questioner is to mediate the child's thinking by posing questions that reveal the complexity of the issue. It is tempting to tell the child what to do, but what will he or she learn if you do that? By asking probing questions, you can help the child search through the many dimensions of such a situation. In this case, the purpose is to find out how the child thinks, not how the child *should* think. Of course, that is important, but it is all too easy to skip this important stage before going on to a teaching episode.

Imagine if you would tell this hypothetical story to your class. You would receive a range of responses. One valuable technique would be to have the class list as many possible courses of action they can think of. This would open a world of possibilities that many children might never consider on their own.

in the classroom Role-Playing a Moral Dilemma

Role-playing, or acting out a situation such as the shoplifting episode, can provide a more animated portrayal. Students can help each other probe issues when one person is given a script of questions while the other is left to think through and express his or her answers. This is typical of the kind of analytical-thinking session in which students can provide insights to each other. A group discussion following the student role-play will foster the opportunity for a variety of viewpoints to flower. Again, the teacher must exercise patience and tolerance and allow students to speak their thoughts. Even in a whole-class or group discussion, the teacher's role remains that of questioner and mediator.

For this role-play, divide students into groups of three and give each student in the group a role: a dog owner who wants to use a stadium; a jogger who fears being bitten by dogs; and a grounds-keeper who takes care of the stadium. Each group should consider this scenario:

> Queens High School, a private institution located in an urban setting, has a stadium with a football field and running track on its campus. The facility is enclosed by fences, and there are several gates by which people can enter.
>
> The relationship between the school and the surrounding community is a good one, and the school has always allowed people from the community to use the track for jogging and walking. Certain entrances are typically left unlocked year round to accommodate them.
>
> Recently, the school posted new signs at the entrances that listed the rules for using the track. In general, the rules are typical of those found at any track, but one of the newly posted rules states that dogs are prohibited from the grounds. In the past, people often brought their dogs to run there, but the school board decided to post the ban because a number of joggers had complained of being attacked or bothered by dogs and because some senior citizens from a nearby retirement home mentioned that the dogs intimidated them when they used the track for walking.

> People living in the area in apartments and in houses with small yards have complained that they have nowhere else to run their dogs. One person said that her dog would not bite anyone. Others have made the case that they have small dogs, friendly dogs, dogs kept on leashes, dogs that have been trained to obey, and so on. Some dog owners have refused to obey the rule banning dogs from the track.

Ask each group to think about the following questions:

- How would you state the nature of the problem?
- What questions would you want to ask the others in your group about this problem?
- What solutions (identify at least two) might there be to this problem?
- What do you think the best solution would be? Why?

Obviously, a number of points of view can be taken on this issue. People can disagree without becoming intolerant or rude. This itself is a value to be taught and learned in social studies classrooms. Often, individuals will attempt to move toward a solution without having taken the time to be certain that everyone involved has the same understanding of the problem. It is a good use of students' time to seek some common ground on the definition of a problem before moving ahead to solutions. Asking questions about a problem or dilemma brings out nuances that might well be overlooked. Certain extenuating circumstances may actually exist, and questions can draw them out. By asking students to identify more than one possible solution, we take them a little way toward the idea that almost any societal problem has more than one solution, none of which is probably perfect. Having covered this preliminary ground, we are in a much better position to voice our opinions about what finally ought to be done.

One last point is in order: You, the teacher, need to stand for something. Children desperately need positive role models. Even so, there's a huge difference between standing up for your values and attempting to shove them down children's throats. Students will want to know what you think, and you ought to feel free to tell them. But remember that the *process* of allowing them to discuss, to argue, to decide, and to reflect in a free, open, and supportive environment is crucial to their moral development. If each student is given a voice and that voice is listened to with respect, you might be surprised at the wisdom of childhood.

To give yourself a better idea of what is important to you—what your values are—try the activity in Figure 11.1.

Models of Character Education, Values Realization, and Moral Development

Let's look now at three different classroom models: (1) character education, (2) values realization, and (3) moral development. All of them have something to offer, and although you may find one most to your liking, you need to be aware of the nature and purpose of each. No doubt, you will find attractive elements in each model.

Character Education

Sometimes called *character training, character education* is focused on traditional values, sometimes known as *virtues* or *character traits*. When someone notes that a person is of good character, it is to these virtues that he or she typically refers. The greatly increased interest in character education on the part of professionals and the lay public alike can no doubt be traced to the many problems besetting society, including substance abuse, teen pregnancies, declining respect for authority, and so on. Of the three models presented here, character education is the most dominant in schools today.

Character education is based on a simple premise: "Always think of others." Known as the "golden rule," this premise has its roots in virtually all world religions, as well as the writings of such thinkers as Aristotle (*Ethics*), and Confucius (*Analects*) (see Figure 11.2). The guiding concept is that young children need to be schooled in appropriate behaviors even before they have developed the rational ability to examine the full meanings and implications of those behaviors. To wait until a person has reached the age of reason, say character educators, is too late. Thus, those who instruct the young (parents, teachers, coaches, clergy, etc.) are faced with the paradox of trying to teach children to be good before these children can fully understand why. Sample Lesson 11.1 is an interdisciplinary lesson that helps students understand commonly held values and morality.

Of course, there are many such paradoxes in life. Adults teach children not to run into the street, to brush their teeth, and to pick up their toys. These become habits. One could say much the same about such character traits as honesty, respect, kindness, willingness to work, and so on. To train young children in this manner strikes some people as manipulative; others applaud it, however, saying it is about time that adults assumed their responsibility to the young. In fact, recent brain research (Medina, 2003) indicates

figure **11.1**   *What Do I Believe?*

The following statements represent values positions regarding how an elementary social studies classroom should be operated. Circle the response that most closely fits your attitude toward each statement.

1. I think such values as honesty, cooperation, and civility can be taught by exposing children to examples set by people we read about and study but that such values need to be developed experientially, as well.   **Yes   No**
2. I think an important reason for studying other cultures is to expose children to alternative ways of organizing societies and to teach children respect for differences without disrespecting their own culture.   **Yes   No**
3. I think children need to learn from study, experience, and reflection how our democratic system works so they will be able to use it effectively as citizens.   **Yes   No**
4. I think teachers need to provide opportunities for children to clarify their values and that they must be accepting of children who differ from themselves, no matter how divergent those differences might seem.   **Yes   No**
5. I think a high priority should be placed on developing children's skills of critical thinking and investigation because a primary purpose of education is the development of effective decision makers.   **Yes   No**
6. I think history and literature can make an important contribution in social studies because they can give children a sense of time-honored human values.   **Yes   No**
7. I think that there is no one right set of values that children should learn in school and that even the term *right* is sometimes a matter of perspective.   **Yes   No**
8. I think the teacher should operate as a facilitator who has a mature, adult perspective and who is willing to share his or her values with the students but who realizes and respects that ultimately students will develop their own ideas of right and wrong.   **Yes   No**
9. I think environmental education is an important aspect of social studies because it can provide insight to the quality of life for humans, animals, and all living things.   **Yes   No**
10. I think that for children to become effective thinkers, they must conduct their own investigations by posing questions, gathering and sorting evidence, and reaching conclusions.   **Yes   No**

Now go back to the statements to which you responded yes and rank them in terms of your priorities. Place a 1 beside the statement you think is most important, a 2 beside the next most important, and so on. Having done this, you have begun to articulate a values position for your social studies teaching.

I am not suggesting what you should think; I am merely attempting to draw you out on a range of issues. But I can tell you this: It is better to think about and discuss values issues because all of us will surely act on them, consciously or unconsciously.

that most of life's character patterns are set by about age 11, offering a powerful argument for training young children in virtuous habits.

Character education places great responsibility in the teacher's hands. Serious proponents of character training believe that the most fundamental responsibilities are with the home, but the familiar question inevitably arises: What if the home is negligent?

figure **11.2**	Forms of the Golden Rule
Baha'i	He should not wish for others that which he doth not wish for himself. —*From writings of Baha u'llah 1870 CE*
Christianity	Treat others as you would like them to treat you. —*From Luke: Revised Standard Version of the New Testament c 90 CE*
Confucianism	Do not do to others what you would not like for yourself. —*From The Analects of Confucius c 500 BCE*
Epictetus	What you would avoid suffering yourself, seek not to impose on others. —*The Greek philosopher, Epictetus c 90 CE*
Hinduism	This is the sum of duty: Do naught to others which, if done to thee, could cause thee pain. —*From The Mahabharata c 150 BCE*
Islam	None of you "truly" believe, until he wishes for his brothers what he wishes for himself. —*A saying of Prophet Muhammad recorded by accepted narrators al-Bukari and Muslim 7th century CE*
Jainism	He should treat all beings as he himself should be treated. The essence of right conduct is not to injure anyone. —*From the Sutra Kritanga c 550 BCE*
Judaism	What is harmful to yourself do not to your fellow men. That is the whole of the law and the remainder is but commentary. —*From Hillel: The Talmud c 10 CE*
Sikhism	As thou deemest thyself, so deem others. —*From Guru Granth Sahib 1604 CE* Treat others as thou wouldst be treated thyself. —*Adi Granth*
Taoism	Regard your neighbour's gain as your own gain and your neighbour's loss as your own loss. —*T'ai Shang Kan Ying P'ien*
The Buddha	I will act towards others exactly as I would act towards myself. —*From The Siglo-Vada Sutta c 500 BCE*
Zoroastrianism	Do not unto others all that is not well for oneself. —*Shayast-na-shayast*

Source: Adapted from Alex Rodger, *Developing Moral Community in a Pluralist School Setting* (Aberdeen, Scotland: Gordon Cook Foundation, 1996).

Regardless of the home situation, everyone agrees that the school experience plays a key role in shaping children. In school-based character education, it is the teacher's responsibility to model and teach virtuous habits. Teachers who take character education seriously know that they must first serve as models for the character traits they wish to instill in the young. The guiding idea is that children will respond positively to kindness, honesty, courtesy, fairness, the work ethic, and other virtues when they see them lived by a respected authority figure in the form of their teacher.

A host of organizations for character education have sprung up in recent times, most notably the Center for the Advancement of Ethics and Character (605 Commonwealth Ave., Boston, MA 02215); the Character Counts Coalition (4640 Admiralty Way, Marina del Ray, CA 90292); and the Character Education Partnership (1250 N. Pitt St., Alexandria, VA 22315). Each of these organizations is an extremely valuable source of materials, ideas, and support for those teachers who would like to include character education in their curriculum.

Is character education controversial? As previously mentioned, many people are bothered by the notion of teaching values to young children who do not really understand what they are being taught. More serious objections are raised by those who find it difficult to agree on what values to teach and who question whether public school is the appropriate setting for such instruction. Both of these objections are reminders of the diverse, pluralistic nature of our society. For example, some may feel that punctuality is a virtue; others may not. The work ethic is seen by some as the foundation of American society, whereas others view it as based in greed, guilt, and material desire. Does wearing a baseball cap turned backwards indoors constitute rebellion against authority, or is it merely a harmless fad? It is easier than we think to confuse virtues with cultural norms, which are intrinsically neither virtuous nor lacking in virtue.

Is there such a thing as a universal set of values that ought to guide all human experience, regardless of culture? Is there a set of values that are based on natural law in somewhat the same way that there are natural laws of physics—for example, gravity or motion? In the 1940s, Cambridge University professor and noted writer C. S. Lewis (1947) set out in search of just such a thing. He reasoned that if certain laws of right conduct could be found in all or nearly all cultures, that would strengthen the claim that those laws are universal. Lewis found that certain values were indeed universal, and he called these values *natural law,* or the *Tao.* Lewis noted that he was not trying to prove the validity of the Tao as universal, even on the basis of common consent. As he said, its validity cannot be deduced. Nevertheless, the fact that the values found in the Tao are universally subscribed to by serious thinkers in all cultures does represent a significant finding for those who would teach traditional values to the young.

Among the universal values Lewis found were beneficence, or kindness toward others; duties to parents and elders; duties to children and posterity; justice; truthfulness and sincerity; mercy or compassion; and magnanimity, or forgiveness. All major religions and world views have taught these values as guides to right conduct. Perhaps this list developed by Lewis is a place to start.

Given the perception of the need to do something, the question remains: Does character education work? That is, do children's behaviors change in a positive direction as a direct result of instruction? Actually, there is very little empirical evidence showing that it does. Although character education is experiencing a revival, it is not new. A series of famous studies by Hartshorne and May in the 1920s showed no evidence that character education produced better behaviors in children. The studies have been criticized, and rightly so, for their lack of scientific rigor, but they did have a real impact at the time.

What does this mean to teachers who are conscientiously looking for ways to improve the individual and social lives of the children they teach? I think it is worthwhile to try to teach about character building. I would remind you that teaching is primarily about *trying.* We try to do our best. We want to do what is right. We are caring people. Many children have little to count on when it comes to finding a caring, responsible adult in their lives, who wants to point them in the right direction. I think it's worth a try.

Values Realization

Values realization, formerly known as *values clarification,* was a very popular phenomenon in American education during the 1970s. Leaders in the movement, such as Sidney Simon and Howard Kirschenbaum (Simon, Kirschenbaum, & Lowe, 1973), were in great demand as workshop leaders, writers, and gurus. Like many educational innovations, this one swept the country by storm and disappeared almost as quickly amid a raging controversy over its perceived harmful effects. What is values realization, and why does it have such strong advocates and detractors?

The guiding premise of the values realization model is that each individual has vague feelings about what is right, what he or she might become, how to relate to others, and so on, but that these feelings are seldom clear. Much of the reason for this, advocates maintain, is that too few forums exist in which people might express themselves and listen reciprocally to others. Thus, the values realization model is one in which discussion and activities are employed to draw out feelings and thoughts on various important issues.

The teacher's role in values realization is to facilitate the child's quest for clarification by supporting, questioning (although not in an aggressive way), and listening. A typical activity would be to present a situation involving moral judgment and then ask students how they feel about it. This is not a model based on traditional values or virtues, although it is not necessarily opposed to them. Rather, the equation is turned around, in that one starts with what students think instead of with the weight of authority and tradition. So, in discussing a story about shoplifting, the moral would not necessarily be "Honesty is the best policy." Instead, the question would be asked, "What could and would you have done in similar circumstances?" Students are encouraged to speak their real opinions, while the teacher attempts to remain neutral and to facilitate any discussion. The focus is on the student, and the teacher's role is to allow a student to say what he or she really feels.

The obvious criticism is: How will children learn what is right in life if responsible adults do not point the way? The answer given by advocates of values realization is that adults should tell children what they *think* is right (as opposed to what *is* right) but should leave room for dissenting opinions. Further, say supporters, suppose a young person has an opinion on a matter that is at odds with what you think is appropriate. Wouldn't you rather know that than remain ignorant of it?

Not all aspects of values realization are so controversial. Much of the time spent focuses on goal setting, social skills, and decision making. Goal setting enables a young person to think about his or her future and what he or she wants to make of it, to consider alternatives, and to choose from a range of possibilities. Social skills are necessary in order for people to get along, to work together, and to tolerate and appreciate others. In recent times, much emphasis has been placed on the social skills basic to conflict resolution, given that some children do not seem to realize they have options other than

A child's self-image is a fragile thing that must be given love and kindness in order to blossom.

force or withdrawal when differences arise. Decision-making skills enable young people to set priorities, develop strategies, and make the necessary links between thought and action in leading productive lives.

One of the key concepts in values realization is that of *self-esteem*. Teachers who use values realization strategies will often comment that they consider it one of their most important duties to enhance the self-esteem of every child. A wide range of self-esteem programs are available, and most of them focus on learning to accept oneself, to prize oneself, and to feel worthy.

Unfortunately, the research on efforts to raise self-esteem is not particularly encouraging. The work of psychologist Albert Bandura (1997) and others has pointed to *self-efficacy* as a more realistic idea for teachers to entertain. Bandura defines self-efficacy as a person's beliefs about his or her capabilities to learn or perform actions at certain levels. In other words, a person with self-efficacy in social studies believes he or she can learn the material, contribute to individual and group efforts, and have a successful experience. Regardless, Kirschenbaum (1996) continues to extol self-esteem as a concept, in spite of the lack of research evidence to support its validity. As Kirschenbaum writes,

> The connection of self-esteem with values education and moral education may initially not be apparent, but it is important. The lower a person's self-esteem, the less worthy a person feels, and therefore, the less likely a person will be to take charge of his life, set appropriate goals, or get out of an abusive situation. If we devalue ourselves, the less likely we will be to realize our values and find satisfaction and meaning in our lives.

Do values realization programs work? Apparently, enough people thought they did to become upset with their use in the 1970s. But in fact, there is not much empirical evidence of their effectiveness one way or the other. One of the problems with values realization, unlike the other two models examined in this section, is that it lacks a solid theoretical framework. Thus, it falls into a category that people either like or dislike, based more on intuition than anything else.

I do find it necessary to say that in its more extreme applications, it can be counterproductive and even dangerous. One such application is in an activity titled "The Lifeboat," in which students are asked to decide which members of an overcrowded lifeboat should get to live. Asking students to determine the value of one life over another can lead to nothing good. On the other hand, when teachers have the common sense to use activities that draw out children's dreams, that teach children to listen peaceably to and value others' comments, that enable them to predict from an array of alternative decisions the consequences of each, then it seems to me to be a valuable part of a teacher's repertoire.

Moral Development

Moral development is based on concepts of justice, ethical behavior, and fairness. This model, which has much of its foundation in law, represents an attempt to lead students to think rationally about what is right and wrong. Whereas character education is based on adult authority and the teaching of right and wrong to the young and values realization is based primarily on affective and experiential considerations, moral development takes a reasoned, analytical approach to exploring beliefs, rules, and values.

Of course, any time we encounter the word *development* in connection with teaching and learning, we can be quite certain that it involves stage theory. *Stage theory* implies that people progress through a hierarchy or set of levels, from more concrete to more abstract. Prominent among stage theorists of moral development is Lawrence Kohlberg (1983), who based his ideas that people progress through developmental stages of moral reasoning on the prior work of Jean Piaget (1965).

How does a child's moral sense develop? How capable are elementary-age children of reasoning about questions of morality? To what extent does a child's ability to reason through an issue affect his or her receptivity to adult values of right and wrong? Piaget (1965) writes, "Most of the moral rules which the child learns to respect he receives from adults, which means that he receives them after they have been fully elaborated, and often elaborated, not in relation to him as they are needed, but once and for all and through an uninterrupted succession of earlier adult generations" (p. 37). This statement furnishes a clue to the source of children's values, but we must look further to determine how and when values are acquired.

The development of a moral sense is something that has intrigued a number of philosophers and researchers over the years. Jean-Jacques Rousseau developed a stage theory in the eighteenth century, one that led him to the conclusion that children should not be coerced into behaving as though they were miniature adults. John Dewey was convinced that childhood is marked by stages of development, and of course, Jean Piaget, that most famous of stage theorists, wrote with great insight into the moral judgment of the child.

Again, psychologist Lawrence Kohlberg (1983) has developed the most widely studied and used stage theory of moral development. His research began nearly half a century ago with a longitudinal study of a cohort group of boys, whom he subsequently studied into their adult years. Kohlberg's research resulted in a hierarchical model of levels of moral development. He concluded that the levels and the stages within levels through which a person passes are sequentially ordered, from stage 1, a kind of primitive level of moral development based in rewards and punishments, to stage 6, a rarified level of universal ethical-principle orientation. Kohlberg's work is summarized in Figure 11.3.

Kohlberg and Whitten (1972) write,

> Given that moral development passes through a set of six distinct stages, what can the educator do to foster it in his students?
>
> First, and fundamentally, if you want to develop morality or a sense of justice in kids, you have to create a just school, a just classroom environment and atmosphere that you establish in your classroom—your *hidden curriculum.*
>
> In setting up a moral educational environment, the teacher does not relinquish his authority. Rather, the source of that authority is changed: instead of deriving from the role of teacher and being backed up by threat, punishment, reward and sanctions, the authority comes from being a mediator in the conflicts between children. A teacher using this approach would say, "Look, you're not going to solve your conflicts by force or trickery. You're going to solve them by talking—by trying to agree on something you and the other kids consider fair." Moral development, we have found, is facilitated in open, informal classrooms where there is a great deal of interaction among children and where the teacher is concerned with developing patterns of cooperation among the children. (p. 14)

Of course, the question of how and at what level you treat values issues with elementary students persists. How you deal with values issues (or refuse to deal with them) is something you have to come to grips with for yourself. It is a philosophical matter that you alone can decide.

The levels of moral development of students within a classroom will vary; although they are to some extent age related, they are not necessarily age determined. Evidence exists that parents are a powerful factor in their children's moral development, and as Paul Brandwein once suggested, "Not all children choose their parents wisely." Your own observation of students' comments as you deal with moral dilemmas can help to determine their levels of moral development. Kohlberg's research indicates that moral messages aimed at more than one stage above a child are seldom understood and that messages aimed at too low a level are demeaning to him or her.

Gender and Moral Development

The work of Harvard psychologist Carol Gilligan (1982) offers several contrasts to Kohlberg's (1983) theory. For instance, she challenges Kohlberg's idea that the sequence of stages is fixed and universal. Kohlberg's claim that his stages are universal is doubtful, Gilligan points out, if for no other reason than that the original research sample on

figure **11.3**   *Kohlberg's Model of Moral Development*

Preconventional Level

The child is responsive to such rules and labels as *good* and *bad* and *right* and *wrong*. He or she interprets these labels in purely physical or hedonistic terms: If the child is bad, he or she is punished; if the child is good, he or she is rewarded. The child also interprets the labels in terms of the physical power of those who enunciate them—parents, teachers, and other adults. This level has two stages:

Stage 1: Punishment and Obedience Orientation. The physical consequences of an action determine its goodness or badness, regardless of the human meaning or value of those consequences. Avoiding punishment and showing unquestioning deference to power are valued in their own right, not in terms of having respect for an underlying moral order supported by punishment and authority.

Stage 2: Instrumental Relativist Orientation. Right action consists of actions that instrumentally satisfy one's own needs and occasionally satisfy the needs of others. Human relations are viewed in terms similar to those of the marketplace. Elements of fairness, reciprocity, and equal sharing are present, but they are always interpreted in a pragmatic way. Reciprocity is a matter of "You scratch my back and I'll scratch yours," not one of loyalty, gratitude, or justice.

Conventional Level

Maintaining the expectations of the individual's family, group, or nation is perceived as valuable in its own right, regardless of the immediate and obvious consequences. The attitude is one not only of conforming to the social order but also of being loyal to it; of actively maintaining, supporting, and justifying it; and of identifying with the persons or group involved in it. This level also has two stages:

Stage 3: Interpersonal Concordance or "Good Boy–Nice Girl" Orientation. Good behavior is that which pleases or helps others and is approved by

them. There is much conformity to stereotypical images of what is the majority or so-called natural behavior. Behavior is frequently judged by intention: "Meaning well" becomes important, and one earns approval by "being nice."

Stage 4: "Law and Order" Orientation. Authority, fixed rules, and the maintenance of the social order are valued. Right behavior consists of doing one's duty, showing respect for authority, and maintaining the social order for its own sake.

Postconventional Level

There is a clear effort to reach a personal definition of moral values—to define principles that have validity and application apart from the authority of groups or persons and apart from the individual's own identification with these groups. This level has two stages:

Stage 5: Social–Contract Legalistic Orientation. Generally, this stage has utilitarian overtones. Right action tends to be defined in terms of general individual rights and standards that have been critically examined and agreed on by the whole society. There is a clear awareness of the importance of personal values and opinions and a corresponding emphasis on procedural rules for reaching consensus. Other than what is constitutionally and democratically agreed on, right is a matter of personal values and opinions. The result is an emphasis on procedural rules for reaching consensus. Outside the legal realm, free agreement is the binding element of obligation. This is the official morality of the U.S. government and the Constitution.

Stage 6: Universal Ethical–Principle Orientation. This stage, where right is defined by the conscience in accord with self-chosen ethical principles (which, in turn, are based on logical comprehensiveness, universality, and consistency), was eventually dropped from Kohlberg's model because no one in his sample of respondents reached it.

Source: Based on Kohlberg, 1983.

which the stages were based was composed exclusively of boys. Gilligan hypothesizes that females conceive of morality in interpersonal terms. Thus, for many females, moral goodness involves helping others and working cooperatively with others.

Gilligan suggests that a higher stage of morality exists than that postulated by Kohlberg. She calls this advanced level of moral development a *love ethic*. The love ethic is based on the assumption that meeting mutual needs, loving meaningfully, and being willing to make sacrifices for others are the fabric of advanced morality. Gilligan also notes that early in life, females learn to play nurturing roles, while males learn to be competitive and aggressive. This, of course, represents sex-role typing because these characteristics are learned by expectation and example. Young boys could just as well be taught to be more cooperative and supportive of the feelings and needs of others.

Not everyone agrees with Gilligan's assessment of the differences between boys and girls. Christina Hoff Sommers (2000) has been particularly critical of Gilligan's conclusions as well as her research. Sommers has concluded that differences in moral reasoning and judgment between boys and girls are greatly exaggerated. She cites a number of studies that point to no significant differences in moral reasoning. Further, she notes that the so-called achievement gap between boys and girls, if indeed it does exist, actually favors girls, who not only receive higher school grades but who also continue on to higher education in greater numbers than boys.

Gilligan (1982) has called for fundamental changes in childrearing practices that would develop the more sensitive, feminine side of boys' behavior. She has concluded that the very nature of childhood must be changed in order to keep boys more closely bonded with their mothers. Doing so, she thinks, would promote a more nurturing, caring, and supportive nature in boys than they typically exhibit. The debate continues.

The exploration of values is an integral part of the elementary social studies curriculum. The manner in which content, concepts, and processes are taught is itself a question of value. Your own values position is something you need to consider seriously because your work with children in this sensitive area will serve little purpose unless you have clarified your values. Whatever values position you assume as a teacher of children, your actions will speak more loudly and clearly than your words.

Posing and discussing moral dilemmas is one strategy for actively exploring values in the classroom. Discussion of controversial issues should not be avoided, although the stage of your students' moral development will affect your values teaching.

Summary

In this chapter, we have examined both the theories and the practice of teaching values, character education, and moral development. Young children are in the formative stages of the development of their world view, their character, their morality. By the time they reach elementary school, much of this will have been formed but much will remain unformed. For teachers, the challenge is to guide, direct, and most significantly, to model socially redeeming behaviors. For students, they have ongoing opportunities to test their values and to participate in clarifying them in a social setting with a mature adult present.

It has been noted many times that children learn what they live. If the classroom and the school represent a civil society—a place where integrity is a daily practice and where experiences are provided to promote growth and development—then positive things will happen. This is particularly so when children are engaged by sensitive teachers in reflective practice. It is good for young people to participate in team building; it is better yet for them to participate in team building and to reflect on that experience. The old adage of experience, reflection, and insight comes to mind.

Positive moral growth comes about as a result of bringing instruction and experience together. Teachers should capitalize on the day-to-day happenings at school, using them as grist for discussion and reflection. Such teachers will take students to the next level by conceptually expanding experience through stories, lessons, and activities designed to deepen

such concepts as conflict resolution, integrity, civility, respect for knowledge, team building, justice, compassion, and courage.

Certainly, some feel that teaching values, character, and morality is so problematic that it is largely a waste of time to try. They point to the futility of trying to convince children to be civil in light of the cross-currents and contradictions offered up by television, the street, and other influences. They point to the lack of leadership in the home. Indeed, you could just as well list these issues as reasons for not trying to teach children how to read or to do mathematics. After all, even given our best efforts to teach decimals, we can point to the child who doesn't remember much about them at all even after years of instruction. You and I went into teaching because we thought we could make a difference in the lives of children. Let us never forget that value.

Explorations

Reflect On . . .

1. Take a minute to list five qualities that you think are important in a good teacher. Why do you believe each is important? What you say will provide an initial look at your system of values. When you have completed your list and have given your reasons, join a group of others who have done the same thing and share your thoughts.

Some Important Qualities of a Good Teacher

Quality	*Why It Is Important*
(1) _____	_____
(2) _____	_____
(3) _____	_____
(4) _____	_____
(5) _____	_____

2. It has often been said that no teacher can escape teaching values to his or her students. Do you agree? Why or why not?
3. Make a list of 20 ideas or things that you value highly. Ask yourself: What effect will these priorities have on the children I teach?

In the Field

4. Visit an elementary school classroom and review a copy of the social studies textbook. Try to determine what values the authors of that book are trying to promote. How easy or difficult is it to make this determination? Would you want to use this book in your classroom? Why or why not?
5. The elementary social studies program *Man: A Course of Study* became controversial over questions of value. Research the arguments on both sides, and decide where you stand.

For Your Portfolio

6. Learn more about the building self-efficacy versus the building self-esteem approach in the classroom. Which do you think has more potential? Why? Develop a lesson plan on a social studies topic that encourages self-efficacy or self-esteem building.

Continuing the Journey: Suggested Readings

Allen, D. (2005). Daniel Allen thinks we are losing our way with raising children. *Nursing Standard, 19*(28), 20.
Allen provides a clarion call for the restoration of adult responsibility.

Christie, K. (2005). Changing the nature of parent involvement. *Phi Delta Kappan, 86*(9), 645–646.
A call for more proactive, engaged, and supportive parenting.

Forsyth, S., & Gilligan, C. (1998). *Girls seen and heard: Lessons for our daughters.* New York: Ms. Foundation for Women.
Time to question the old adage "seen but not heard."

Hill, B. (2004). Values education in schools: Issues and challenges. *Primary and Middle Years Education, 2*(2), 20–28.
Of course values must be taught at school. The question is, whose and what kind?

Joseph, P., & Efron, S. (2005). Seven worlds of moral education. *Phi Delta Kappan, 86*(7), 525–534.
An excellent analysis of different perspectives.

Kohn, A. (2004). Challenging students—And how to have more of them. *Phi Delta Kappan, 86*(3), 184–190.
Alfie Kohn, in true progressive tradition, speaks up on behalf of the abilities of all learners.

Lewis, C. S. (1947). *The abolition of man: How education develops man's sense of morality.* New York: Collier Books.
The great children's author searches for common values across cultures.

Sizer, T., & Sizer, N. (2000). *The students are watching: Schools and the moral contract.* New York: Beacon Press.
This work emphasizes the role modeling of adults and the obligations of each generation to the next.

Sommers, C. H. (2000). *The war against boys: How misguided feminism is harming our young men.* New York: Simon & Schuster.
Sommers continues her battle over the feminist critique.

SAMPLE LESSON 11.1 *Writing Fables*

AGE LEVEL: Appropriate for grades 3–8.

PURPOSE:

1. To teach character education through the use of children's literature.
2. To introduce social science concepts in psychology, sociology, and geography through an interdisciplinary approach.

OBJECTIVES: Students will be able to:

1. Produce a research paper.
2. Recognize the elements of a fable.
3. Write an original fable story.
4. Make connections with morals and other law-related concepts.

PROCEDURE:

1. Have students read (or read to them) a variety of animal fables by different authors (e.g., Jack Kent's *Fables of Aesop,* Arnold Lobel, Jean de la Fontaine, etc.). Filmstrips are also good resources. After having been exposed to many fables, have students discuss the elements of a fable.

Elements of a Fable
- *Characters:* Usually animal characters with human qualities, a wise or foolish story, a moral.
- *Beginning:* Setting, characters in situation.
- *Middle:* Explanation of what the problem is and how characters attempt to solve it.
- *End:* The moral or lesson to be learned.

2. Have each student select an animal as the central character for his or her fable and do a brief research project to discover the unique characteristics, habits, movements, likes and dislikes, and so on of that animal. As noted, fables are typically stories about animals that are often behaving as though they were human. To be able to write a fable effectively, the student needs to understand the uniqueness of the character he or she selects.
3. The research project can be initially conducted as class research (whole group), and each skill can be introduced and practiced with direct instructions. Allow library or computer time for students to gather information.

Research Steps
- Choose an animal.
- Write and group questions.
- Collect information (take notes).
- Evaluate information and source material.
- Organize information (sort note cards into categories).
- Communicate information—write a rough draft.
- Share information—edit with peer review.
- Write a final report.

4. When their research projects have been completed, review what the children learned earlier about fables. Talk about *morals*, the lessons often stated at the ends of fables. Share a list of common sayings or have children offer these, and then discuss them (e.g., "A stitch in time saves nine"; "A watched pot never boils"; and so on). Or have students discuss common problems and the reasons for them—for example:

Homework

Problem	Possible Reason
Never have enough time to finish.	Not on task or focused—TV on!
Don't understand it.	Didn't ask questions in class—afraid to.
Did wrong assignment.	Didn't listen in class.

Possible Lessons to Be Learned
- "Always get the information from the horse's mouth!"
- "He who plays while others work works while others play."

5. With new knowledge about their animals, gained through researching and having a deeper understanding of the structure of fables and what morals are, the students are ready to become authors and illustrators in creating their own original fables. Encourage students to create "real" books, with title pages, illustrations, and covers. Older children can use computers to create professional-looking published products.
6. While the students are doing the illustrations for the pages of their books, you may want to review the geography themes of location, place, movement, region and human–environment interaction so students can apply these themes to the settings of their artistic compositions.

CLOSURE: Have students share their fables with the class, and ask the class to discuss whether the morals that students have created are apt and follow from the fables. The most effective learning takes place when students can communicate their ideas and share their products with others. A feeling of ownership and pride in their work is enhanced when there is this sharing purpose to projects.

Research papers, art projects, and fable stories can be put on display at the school or community libraries, educational fairs, PTA meetings, and so on. The stories can also be published in newsletters or community papers. Do puppet shows and plays as part of the school assembly. The most significant result of this lesson, however, is the significant increase of a more responsible and ethical student citizenry.

EXTENSIONS: To develop communications skills, have students select a few fables written by their classmates and rewrite them into a children's theatre play form. Have groups of students put on a play or puppet show for other students. Videotape the performance and share it with the school's library-lending resources.

Share other stories that depict ethical issues, such as "The Boy Who Cried Wolf" (lying), "Jack and the Beanstalk" (stealing), "Goldilocks and the Three Bears" (trespassing), and "Pinocchio" (lying). Use lessons on morals and values to introduce other law-related concepts, like responsibility, privacy, justice, authority, freedom, and diversity.

Source: Adapted from a lesson plan submitted by Lynn F. Muraoka (Central Oahu School District, Wahiawa, HI) to OFCN's Academy Curricular Exchange, Columbia Education Center, Social Studies.

chapter 12

Social Studies and Curriculum Connections

Integrated Studies

In this chapter, we will explore these themes:

key concepts

- Projects as the building blocks of integrated study
- Significant themes for integration

All things are connected.
　　　　—Chief Seattle

Young children don't think in terms of separate subjects, academic disciplines, or a world fragmented by specialists. They inhabit a seamless world of daily adventure and discovery. That is their nature. They ask questions, take risks, make mistakes, and attempt to fit what is new (to them) into what they already know. In a sense, they are conducting an ongoing experiment about how things are, how they turn into other things, and why things are the way they are. By adult standards, their methods may seem clumsy, repetitive, and inefficient. But actually, children are incredibly effective learners. Some experts suggest that half of what a person will know in the course of a lifetime has been learned by the age of 5. It takes all the other succeeding years to learn the other half.

One aspect of children's efficiency is their ability and tendency to see everything as being connected. The separate subjects that we are taught in the name of learning come along the way, as we work our way through our school years. Ironically, these divisions are introduced in the name of efficiency. It is efficient to separate reading from writing, mathematics from geography, and so on. In time (predictably), children stop seeing things as connected, and they enter a world in which school subjects are routinely separated from one another. But what if they are intuitively right about learning, and we are mainly wrong? How might the curriculum be different? Well, in a single word, it would be *integrated*.

I n his insightful book *The Schools Our Children Deserve,* Alfie Kohn (1999) writes that often he will ask teachers which of two fractions is larger: 4/11 or 5/13? He writes that nearly everyone he asks gives the wrong answer, especially mathematics teachers. The right answer, according to Kohn, is "Who cares?" His point is that isolated facts and skills are not particularly important in the greater scheme of things.

This brings us quickly to a deeply imbedded problem in the school experience. The problem is that bits and pieces of information are all too often taught to children outside any meaningful frame of reference or context. The stuff literally goes in one ear and out the other. All of us were taught at some point in our school days (probably around fifth or sixth grade) how to compare the sizes of fractions by dividing the numerator by the denominator. It isn't difficult, so why don't we remember that particular skill or others? I'll let you answer that.

Integrated studies represent a kind of seamless whole in learning. Children see the world as a whole. They don't think in terms of separate disciplines. Incidentally, so do great philosophers and other profound thinkers. Leo Tolstoy, author of *War and Peace* and other great novels, was himself deeply interested in childhood education. He even started his own school for poor children. Tolstoy observed that children, unlike most adults, are drawn to and enjoy complex themes. He also noted that unfortunately, most teachers are not drawn to complex themes; they prefer the oversimplified world of textbooks, separate subjects, facts, skills, and so on.

Of course, the secret is to see the world as children see it. The purpose of this chapter is to stimulate your thoughts about the possibilities inherent in integrated teaching and learning.

Projects: The Building Blocks of Integrated Study

Integrated studies in the form of great projects have an energizing quality about them. At their best, they are what psychologists call *flow experiences*. When people are "in the flow," they tend to lose track of time, want to keep going, and feel engaged in something personally meaningful and rewarding. You'll know your kids are in a flow activity when they say, "Can't we just work on this a little longer?" or something to that effect.

Psychologists today say that human beings are "wired" to do projects. Some have gone so far as to say that projects are the single most purely human activity. I think there is much to this; for example, how often do people think, "One of these days I've got to spend a day getting all my stuff in order" or "Let's plan a trip to the mountains" or "Maybe we can organize a neighborhood cleanup campaign." Actually, something as simple as a trip to the grocery store is, in fact, a project. We may not call it that, but that's what it is. Some projects, of course, are greater than others.

Characteristics of Good Projects

Projects, whether they are ours alone or something we try with a class or even a whole school, have several interesting characteristics. First of all, a good project is a *defining activity*. If a project is about reconstructing Native American life in your area from 200 years ago, then it is clear what you are doing. You are not studying history or anthropology; rather, you are using both to help you complete your project.

The second characteristic of a good project is that it is *interdisciplinary*. A project on "Activities of the Night" will use music, art, mathematics, language, science, and, most of all, social studies. Projects have what can be called *syntactic complexity.* A project really is more complex than reading a text and answering questions. One truly needs all the help one can get from the various areas of the curriculum. The difference is that textbooks and questions are contributors to, not controllers of, the curriculum.

A third characteristic of a good project is that it allows a person the luxury of setting *boundaries*. A project has a beginning, a middle, and an end. If students in your class decide to create an art museum, then they must go through the stages of purpose, planning, development, exhibition, and evaluation. That's pretty straightforward compared to the seemingly endless voyage through a textbook. Most projects have a definite time frame; otherwise, students couldn't accomplish their goals.

The fourth and perhaps most significant characteristic of a project is that it has an *outcome*. A good project is undertaken with a clear purpose of achieving something. If your class decides to build a greenbelt along the edge of the school grounds, then you all know what needs to be done. You may not initially know *how* to do it or even what it will look like, but you know you are heading toward a culminating event—that of a finished greenbelt. An outcome is important, because it addresses the much-needed aspect of reality in learning and gives one a sense of closure.

Group versus Individual Projects

Projects can be done alone or with others; indeed, this is true of all learning. My position on working together or alone is that students must learn to do both. But in social studies, let's not forget that most of what a class does should be *social,* and that argues for group projects whenever possible. People need to cooperate with each other in life for a variety of reasons. One of those reasons is that many of the worthwhile things in life (a play or pageant, for example) are simply too complex and demanding to orchestrate alone. Another reason for working together on projects is that it gives children a chance to actually practice citizenship. So, a few projects can and should be done alone, but most projects should be group enterprises (see Figure 12.1).

The advantages to group projects are that they allow children to experience the give-and-take of community life and that they create a much more process-centered learning environment. The first advantage is pretty straightforward; working together comes closer to mirroring real life in a democracy than does working alone. The second advantage takes some explaining. To miss the underlying point is to miss something extremely important in learning theory.

When learners work together, a more complex learning environment is established. This is so because there is less opportunity for teacher control of intellectual and social forces. Although this may seem like a drawback at first glance, it is actually a step in the right direction. Learning becomes more process centered simply because students get to share their thoughts and feelings with each other. More conversation means more complexity; more complexity means more opportunity for language development, for perspective taking, and for moral development.

figure **12.1**   *Ideas for Individual and Group Projects*

Individual Projects	Group Projects
• Role-playing a famous person in history • Constructing a model of a ship, clothing, or village from another time or culture—specifically, its architecture, food, festivals, and such • Reporting on another culture—specifically, its architecture, food, festivals, and such • Conducting an investigation or neighborhood survey • Building a kite after the fashion of Japanese kites • Making a musical instrument from another culture	• Putting on a pageant of pioneer or Native American life • Creating a museum in the classroom • Investigating different brands of the same product • Producing a weekly "radio" news program to be broadcast over the school intercom • Conducting a schoolwide effort to improve safety conditions • Creating displays or exhibits of schoolwork • Issuing a class challenge to read a certain number of books • Putting on a schoolwide social studies fair • Mapping the local environment

The best way for language development to proceed for children is to put them into social situations with their peers and allow them to solve problems together. They learn to express themselves, to find their own voices, to listen to others, and to decide things together. Thus, the social and intellectual aspects of learning become intertwined, rather than separated.

The ability to see something from more than one perspective is useful whether one is viewing the Grand Canyon (it looks rather different from the top of the canyon than it does from the bottom) or finding ways to solve a problem. Weighing different perspectives on an issue is something one can learn from practice. Group projects afford children the opportunity to see things from other points of view. For example, if children want to build a greenbelt on the school grounds, they need to learn that their own viewpoint may be somewhat different from that of the school board or even from the viewpoints of students in other classrooms.

The richly textured environment that arises when children work together on projects is filled with opportunities for the thoughtful examination of moral issues. For example, children working together will have more disagreements than children working alone, but this is good in an atmosphere where people are free to express their thoughts and feelings. Such conditions help students confront real moral issues, such as sharing, reaching consensus, doing one's fair share, and learning through experience that different people have different innate gifts in life. In short, group work makes it clear that people need each other and that there is no room for condescension toward another if anything is to be accomplished.

Kinds of Projects

Four distinctly different kinds of projects will be discussed here: service-learning projects, production projects, problem-solving projects, and schoolwide projects.

Keys to Creating Effective Projects

- *Clear tasks.* Be as clear as possible about what students will be doing and about the purpose of the experience.
- *Common experiences.* As you begin the challenge, ensure that the whole class has a set of common experiences. This will enable the groups that emerge to share a knowledge base so that communication will be meaningful.
- *Content versus process.* One of the problems in curriculum development is that developers give undue emphasis to process and little emphasis to content. You want to be able to say at the conclusion of the project that your students have a body of knowledge, as well as an array of skills and values.
- *Focus groups.* Once you have established a common body of knowledge, you will be ready to move ahead with smaller groups that will work on subchallenges of the larger challenge. Assume that you will have three or four groups, and identify specifically what each group will be doing.
- *Seminars, class meetings.* The groups will need to keep each other informed. Create some kind of checkpoint to ensure that this happens.

- *Presentation.* Once the groups have completed their work and the efforts have been synthesized, to make a presentation to parents, the principal, the school board, or other interested parties. A second presentation will come when the students have actually finished the project.
- *Reflection.* Some ways of providing both formative and summative reflective thinking must be built into the process. Journals and informal assessment strategies seem to work best.
- *Connections.* A legitimate criticism of schoolwork is that it is often unconnected. Identify connections with literature (specific titles), science, geography, history, language, the arts, mechanical drawing, or landscape architecture.
- *Skills.* What specific skills will be employed and where?
- *Concepts.* What key ideas or generalizations should students learn?
- *Flowchart or webbing.* Provide some sort of diagram to show how the unit works. The webbing shown in Figure 12.2 is an example of how you might proceed.

SERVICE-LEARNING PROJECTS Service-learning projects, as the name implies, are about contributing to community, school, and family life. The purpose of such a project is to provide services or goods to others who can benefit from your work. An example of this would be a project where children become involved with the residents of a retirement home, attempting to include them in their lives. Many teachers have commented on the beneficial effects of such a service-learning project, both to the children and to the residents of the retirement home. The singing, artwork, plays, and reports bring joy to the residents and fulfillment to the children.

One service-learning project done by elementary school children that especially impressed me was at a school that had a considerable turnover of enrollment. New children were continually enrolling in the school. The students entered into a service project that involved making "Welcome to Our School" kits, which were given to new children when they enrolled during the school year. The kits were shoeboxes that

figure **12.2**   *The Tasks Needed to Complete a Project*

Greenbelt Project
- Committees
- Surveys
- Reading
- Field Trips
- Resource People
- Fund-Raising
- Films
- Photographs
- Maps
- Models

contained names of friendly children to meet, a map of the school, a letter from the principal, a free lunch ticket, and activities and puzzles. The students who did that project learned about moral development and caring for others who might be scared, anxious, or just plain feeling alone, and that was worth a lot more than some abstract discussion of fairness, caring, and other virtues. But more than that, when teachers get the children involved in such projects, they have concrete experiences to enhance the discussions.

Many children today do not even know elderly people. They are denied the wisdom and comfort that older people can share with the young. Others may never have considered what it would be like to be a new student in an unknown environment. The beautiful thing about service-learning projects is that they are truly win/win situations in which it is difficult to know who gains the most.

PRODUCTION PROJECTS   Anyone who has ever been in a play, helped to set up a school carnival, or participated in any equally ambitious project knows how much fun and how much work it can be. The key to production projects is that the focus is on *producing* something. The event itself represents only the outcome. It's what happens along the way that is so great: the rehearsals, the late-night hammering and sawing, the camaraderie, the worry over whether things will ever come together, and so on.

One of the best tests of school experience comes when one looks back from a perspective of time. In fact, Aristotle noted that such things as happiness are best defined in retrospect. Some of the great memories of school experience are created by production projects. To this day, one of my clearest, best memories of school comes from third

Teachers and students bring history alive through socio-drama and role-play.

grade (in my case, about a million years ago), when our class did a production of the play *The Shoemaker and the Elves,* which was broadcast over a local radio station. What a great teacher Mrs. Knott was to do that with us. Another great production that I recall was in fourth grade, when our class made a huge wrap-around-the-room mural of life in ancient Egypt, Greece, and Rome. Thanks to Mrs. Emery for making social studies come alive. Oh, what vision teachers have who get their students involved in group productions!

PROBLEM-SOLVING PROJECTS Solving problems using the project approach is great because it gets you and the students into the business of *applying* ideas and skills, rather than merely learning them for their own sake. A problem-solving project is best organized around an empirical question, one that can be answered by gathering information and reaching a solution on the basis of an analysis and synthesis of the information. Problem-solving projects use methods and ideas from every discipline, combining mathematics, language, science, music, art, social studies, and anything else that might be helpful.

Problem-solving projects are experiences with real problems that have real solutions. For example, if your class wants to improve communication in the school, you might begin with the question: How can we improve communication in our school? Once the question is framed to everyone's satisfaction, you are ready to go. The class will have to do surveys, experiments, and whatever it takes to solve the problem.

Here are some other examples of questions that can result in problem-solving projects:

- How can we make the pedestrian crossing near our school safer?
- How can we determine which of several brands of a product is the best buy?

- How can we establish ways for kids of different grades/ages in this school to work together?
- How can we find out about different ways to learn?
- How can we create a schoolwide celebration of Arbor Day?
- How can we redesign our classroom to make it a better place to learn?
- How can we get a schoolwide literacy campaign going?

SCHOOLWIDE PROJECTS   It is great to involve all the students in a classroom, or even all the students at a grade level, in projects of one kind or another. But schoolwide projects are particularly wonderful because they have the potential to bring the whole student body, faculty, and staff together to focus on a common topic. It takes energy and leadership to mobilize a whole school, but when it is done well, a different ethos will prevail.

Schoolwide projects create an esprit de corps that you can't achieve any other way. It is indeed heartwarming to see children of different ages working together, sharing, teaching, and learning from each other. School assemblies take on new meaning as the entire K–6 student body gathers to hear the outcome of a school project on helping the homeless, the elderly, or the needy; to present the culminating activities of a schoolwide fitness and nutrition project; or to present awards and certificates to the children who have taken part in a literacy campaign.

in the classroom Constructing a Greenbelt

Many school environments are dominated by pavement and noise. In recent years, *greenbelt theory,* first developed in England and Australia by urban geographers, has led to ecologically sound, aesthetically pleasing, and economically feasible ways to bring about positive change in even the most paved-over, congested areas. People around the globe have responded to the need to maintain places of beauty, animal habitats, and areas to play and relax.

People have developed the capacity to dominate most plant and animal species. For better or worse, human beings have become the main stewards of the planet. We need to teach our children positive stewardship in order to ensure a productive ecological balance of nature.

In the Greenbelt Design Project (Sharp & Ellis, 1994), students are challenged to explore the possibilities of designing and developing a greenbelt. The students take part in all facets of the project, from gathering information, doing feasibility studies, creating models, planning, and convincing

others of the need to the final stage, the actual construction of a greenbelt.

The purpose is clear: to design and construct a functional and beautiful greenbelt at the school. The greenbelt, no matter how small or large, must be something the children can themselves produce. The design considerations are beauty, cost, animal habitat, plant choice, safety, and low maintenance. The students will need to take into account ecological factors, such as growing conditions, soil, climate, and so on. This will demand a good deal of research. They will also need to study elements of design, architecture, and safety.

Here is how one primary teacher approached the project with her class (see Figure 12.3):

In creating our greenbelt, it was important for us to know all the basic needs of the plants we wanted in our little park, and how we could supply those needs. It was a small, bare lifeless corner of the school yard. What a challenge we faced if we wanted it to be beautiful! We learned all about the

figure **12.3**   *Constructing a Greenbelt*

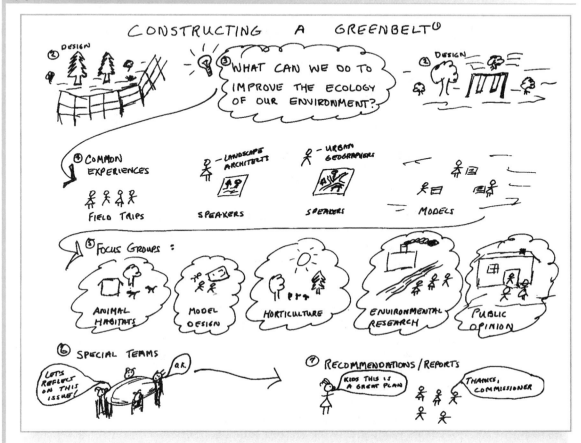

plants and animals (everything from dogs and rabbits to earthworms and bugs) that might inhabit the area. We learned how to test soil and how to enrich it. We studied the weather and climate patterns. Each day, we took temperature readings, checked sun angles, shade, and so on. We measured the rainfall faithfully. We took pictures, we drew maps, we interviewed kids, citizens, and experts. We watched films about parks and greenbelts, looking for ideas. We even figured out fund-raising ideas to pay for the plants and other work related to planting. We made designs, drew pictures, built models, had landscapers come to class—whatever it took!

Every day, committees met. They discussed, they argued, they listened to experts—they were be-

coming experts themselves. I was really proud of the kids. At *long* last, we presented our model to the school board, complete with drawings, sketches, and even cost estimates. They were surprised when we told them we had developed a budget and had raised the money to pay for the project. I wish you could have been there on the beautiful spring morning when we dedicated the greenbelt. What a crowd! And such beautiful music and dancing. Everyone was excited. I just watched from the side while the kids gave speeches and graciously accepted the praises of the Parks Commissioner, the principal, and the chairman of the school board. Those kids and I know what it means to be a citizen!

Significant Themes for Integration

The search for significant common themes is at the heart of integrated studies. Once established, themes become the rallying point of the curriculum, the place to go when you want to be sure that the pursuit is meaningful and excellent. Themes provide a means for the various contributing disciplines to be different, showcasing their unique properties yet at the same time carrying out a similar conceptual purpose. The liberating aspect of a carefully chosen, content-enriching theme is that it is supportive of connected, integrated experiences across the disciplines. Moreover, it prohibits a superficial tyranny of integration for its own sake from taking over the curriculum.

Of course, there are many significant themes that teachers and children might pursue. I will suggest here eight broad themes that have the potential to be encountered and reencountered in spiral fashion at gradually increasing levels of sophistication and complexity. Each theme, in order to qualify, must meet several important tests:

1. Is the theme truly conceptual—that is, is it representative of ideas that transcend place and time? If so, it has the potential for transfer and utility beyond the bounds of specific subject matter.
2. Does the theme lend itself to all three knowledge modes—that is, knowledge received, knowledge discovered, and knowledge constructed? If so, then the theme is suited to knowledge acquisition, cultural literacy, problem solving, experiential learning, and constructivist thinking and doing.
3. Is the theme fundamentally worth pursuing in each of the separate content areas—that is, social studies, science, arts, humanities, mathematics? If so, then the integrity of the curriculum can be ensured. After all, if a theme cannot be pursued within any given discipline, then it is not actually interdisciplinary but in fact peculiar to certain subject matter.
4. Does the theme have the potential to enrich the curriculum and therefore the lives of students and teachers? If so, then the theme is useful, beautiful, and truthful and it addresses an underlying sense of moral goodness.

There are many interesting and possibly worthwhile themes that teachers can use to integrate the curriculum. By applying this fourfold test, we can reduce the list to manageable, meaningful proportions. I do not mean to suggest that I have developed the one magic list; other themes no doubt could be readily added. The following themes, however, will do for purposes of illustration.

Cause and Effect

Children and adults, amateurs and professionals, and young and old notice effects all around them. Any given effect assumes one or more causes. Leaves fall from the trees in October. Someone is in a happy mood. War breaks out in a region of the world. People speak the same language but with different accents. These are all outcomes—that is, they are the effects of certain causes. How do things come to be the way they are? Why do things sometimes turn out differently from the way one had hoped they would?

What are the causative agents? How can one know? It seems to be in people's nature to want to identify the cause or causes of the effects they perceive. What were the causes of the Civil War? Why did the cake taste differently this time when you thought you followed the same recipe? What were the lasting effects of Lewis and Clark's epic trek to the West?

Sometimes, people use rational explanations to determine cause-and-effect relationships; sometimes they use other means. The linkage between cause and effect is always explanation. An explanation, however, is only as good as one's information, and one's information is only as good as one's ability to apply insight to it; otherwise, it's just information. Investigation, experience, and reflection are among the most useful tools in the search for explanation. History, science, literature, religion, the arts, myth, and folk wisdom all take their place as explainers in the search for cause and effect.

It is seldom a simple process. More often than not, causes are both multiple and complex, especially about worthwhile issues. Just as causes are usually multiple, so are effects. Often, one effect causes another to happen. At some point, teachers and students must acquire a high tolerance for ambiguity. Effects, like causes, are not necessarily what they appear to be. The role of individual or group perception looms large in this business. Astronomy started out as a serious cause and effect "science." The idea held by the ancients (and by many who take astrology seriously today) was that the movement and placement of the stars has serious effects on our daily lives and fortunes. So the next time you're walking down the sidewalk, watch out for that crack, because who knows what effect stepping on it might cause!

Commonality and Diversity

One of the hallmarks of investigation is the attempt to document similarities and differences. People ask themselves how they are like their parents and how they are different from them. They explore the similarities and differences between the travels of Marco Polo and those of Francis Drake. They wonder, if reading and writing are both branches of language arts and therefore similar, how then are they different? They contemplate how students studying such similar material at school can be so different in their learning preferences and learning styles. They ask how history and historical fiction are as different as a factual and make-believe account of something, yet at the same time, both can move one nearer to the truth about the past.

Three of the most basic processes of the arts and sciences are at the heart of exploring commonality and diversity. Observation, description, and classification are excellent points of departure. Young children notice differences and similarities in the patterns and shapes of leaves. Flowers are alike and different, beginning with simple and composite blossoms. Foods fit into different groups. Paintings can be classified by schools, time periods, and means of expression. Separate subjects or disciplines arose over time because enough perceived difference developed between and among them. Interdisciplinary teaching and learning turns the equation around and asks: What are the similarities?

People observe how things are alike and different. They begin to describe those properties through drawings, maps, words, diagrams, equations, and other means.

Classifications emerge on the basis of observations and descriptions. In time, taxonomies are built. In the eighteenth century, Swedish scientist Linneaus developed whole taxonomies for plants and animals based on differences and similarities. He began with a binomial classification that sorted living things into the kingdoms of plants and animals. From there, the classifications were refined into phylums, families, orders, varieties, and so on. Such a taxonomy allows one to categorize a hummingbird and a bumble bee as being both alike and different. Also, people tend to classify paintings according to such different schools as realism, impressionism, cubism, surrealism, and so on. Thus, Leonardo da Vinci's *Mona Lisa* and Pablo Picasso's *Guernica* are alike yet different.

Systems and Patterns

Children learn early in their lives to think and feel in terms of the patterns of holidays, birthdays, and special events. They intuitively perceive a system of special days and times of the year that take on a rhythm. The start of school in the fall, along with Halloween, Thanksgiving, Christmas, New Year's Day, Valentine's Day, spring break, and summer vacation, are all touch points in the elaborate culture of childhood. As students grow older, many of them relate to the patterns of the sports calendar of the school: football, followed by basketball, followed by baseball, and so on. For teachers, the system is often divided into reporting periods of three or four per school year. Units of study begin and culminate following a pattern. The school itself is a complex social/academic system, complete with roles, expectations, rules, checkpoints, diplomas, and so on.

As part of the solar system (see Figure 12.4), Earth is itself a system of water, land, creatures, plants, and atmosphere. Earth's system has an established pattern of seasons, with a time to sow and a time to harvest, a time to work and a time to rest. Within fam-

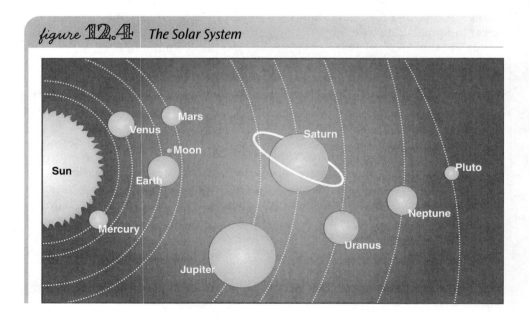

figure **12.4** *The Solar System*

ilies, patterns of behavior and traditions are established, complete with histories and mythologies. People search for patterns in their ancestry. Geneticists look for patterns in the work of such scientific undertakings as the human genome project, an intricate mapping of the the the DNA structure of human beings. Each atom of each element is itself a system with certain valences that place it in a family of similar elements.

Patterns of courage and decency, love and war emerge from the pages of literature and history. Art and music are the continuous assembling and reassembling of pigment or notes into new and varied patterns of expression. When a pattern is broken, a whole new field of expression emerges; for example, in the nineteenth century, a shift occurred away from landscape and portrait painting to impressionism.

Paradigm shifts in science represent fundamental reappraisals of systems. Isaac Newton showed that gravitational pull is a universal force; that is, gravity exists everywhere. In doing so, he altered people's sense of why an object in space behaves as it does. When Copernicus removed the earth from the center of the cosmos, he caused people to change their patterns of thought about the earth's (and therefore humans') place in the universe. Today, in the midst of the electronic revolution, changing patterns of how people communicate abound in the form of the Internet, faxes, e-mail, and so on.

Cycles and Change

The life cycle of the monarch butterfly illustrates four major changes in the growth and development of that beautiful creature: from egg, to larva, to pupa, to adult. The idea of a *cycle* is that of an interval of time during which a sequence of a recurring succession of events or phenomena is completed. Thus, the life cycle of the monarch butterfly has a sense of predictability in terms of time and form.

A cycle not only has a theme of recurrence but also a theme of circularity that makes it different from a pattern of linear development. The classic Greek sense of time and history was cyclical—that is, no beginning and no end—as opposed to the Hebrew sense of time and history, which was set more to a vector with a beginning point (creation), direction, and end time (judgment).

Cycles vary greatly in scale so that some are more immediately distinguishable as cycles—for instance, the cycle of day and night or of the seasons. Others—for example, the recurrence of ice ages that appear at least to have some cyclical pattern—are known only on the basis of serious scientific investigation. Comet Halley, which will reappear in the skies in the year 2061, has a cycle of 76 years, so some people are able to see the recurrence of the cycle in their lifetimes.

In astronomy, a period of time required to bring about the recurrence of certain relative positions (for example, Earth to Sun) or aspects of the heavenly bodies is known as a cycle. The earth orbits the sun every 365+ days, completing a cycle that takes it through its four seasons. In literature, a group of prose or poetic narratives, usually of different authorship, centering on a legendary hero and his or her associates is known as a cycle. Thus, there is the Arthurian cycle chronicling the noble deeds of King Arthur and his Knights of the Round Table. The Arthurian cycle is often referred to in medieval romance as the "matter of Britain." The term *cyclic poems* was first used in late

Historical change often occurs in cycles, just as change occurs cyclically in the lives of living things.

classical times to refer to the independent poems that appeared after Homer to supplement his account of the Trojan War and the homecomings of the heroes.

In music, any compositional form characterized by repetition from an earlier movement in order to unify the structure is called a cycle. The familiar children's tune "Row, Row, Row Your Boat" is a simple example. The need for cyclic devices became crucial during the times of Mozart and Haydn, when the romantic novel took the place of classical drama and narrative poems as the basic model for instrumental music. Thus, the idea of the cycle in music took on somewhat new meaning as changes in forms of expression happened in literature and other arts. The relationship between cycles and change, then, can also be seen between and among different art forms.

Historians search the events of the past in an attempt to identify cyclical patterns, often with little result. American historian Arthur Schlessinger Jr. wrote a book in which his thesis was that American political leadership in the twentieth century proceeded in cyclic form from conservative to liberal and back again. These cycles, according to Schlessinger, provided a kind of equilibrium, giving Americans a conservative president for a while followed by a more liberal one.

Economists document cycles of prosperity and hard times in the country's financial/industrial/commercial system. They point to panics, depressions, and recessions, followed by booms, expansions, and good times. Nations try, more or less, depending on the form of government, to intervene with programs during difficult economic times in order to control the cycles artificially. Nonetheless, no one seems to know for sure what causes these cycles, even though the effects are evident to the most casual observer.

The rate of change and therefore the recurring patterns of certain cycles vary greatly. Weather changes often within minutes from fair to foul. A person's mood may change abruptly on the basis of some new information. A rousing speech or sermon can change people's opinions in the space of an hour, although the long-term effects may be different. A child watching a pot on the stove wonders if the water will ever boil. Iron rusts quickly in a rain forest environment but slowly in desert conditions. People change: They grow and develop quickly in childhood, more slowly in adulthood, and ultimately decline in old age.

Maps change when an empire such as the Soviet Union collapses. The changed map, with its new and unfamiliar borders, confuses people as they try to learn different place names. However, the changed map is merely symbolic of the change after change brought about so rapidly when a seemingly invincible empire dissolves, not on the basis of outside attack, but from decay within. Futurist Alvin Toffler called too much change in too short a time "future shock." The people of Eastern Europe and Russia have seen vast changes in business and commerce, in the availability of consumer goods, and in the breakdown of an existing order in the space of just a few years.

Anyone who contemplates buying a personal computer understands the rapidity with which change occurs on the frontiers of technology. A great fear felt by ordinary people (like me!) is that whatever computer they buy, it will be obsolete by the time they get it set up at home and learn how to use it. Merchandisers play to these fears by exhorting would-be consumers not to be left behind in the wake of new "breakthroughs." Perhaps one of the most worthwhile pursuits for young learners is to study change and to learn to think about it and act on it responsibly and rationally.

One of the obvious lines of inquiry in a theme-driven curriculum is how exploration and investigation change the world. The Lewis and Clark expedition (1804–1806) changed the very idea of the United States in terms of its size, its grasp of a continent, and its place in the world as an ocean-to-ocean country in the making. Within a scant 50 years of this epic trek, the United States sent a seagoing expedition to Japan, a foreshadowing of Americans' perception of themselves as a global presence and the beginning of a tenuous, sometimes difficult relationship with that great nation.

The travels of Captain James Cook in the late eighteenth century set in place not only the vast holdings of the British empire but also a secure niche for navigational and astronomical science in the realms of exploration. Children who compare the voyages of Captain Cook with those of Christopher Columbus will become more fully aware of the rapid development of science and technology that took place in the intervening three centuries.

The travels of Italian teenager Marco Polo and of the more sophisticated African traveler Ibn Batuta in the late Middle Ages, on the cusp of the Renaissance, brought about a sense of Eurasia as opposed to a separate Europe and Asia. Coming from the east, the Mongol invasion of Russia and Eastern Europe also changed people's sense of distance, space, and time.

Some things change slowly, almost glacially, such as the weathering away of the earth's surface resulting in bizarre rock formations. Some changes appear to be isolated and not susceptible to repetition, and others appear to be perhaps cyclical, as the warming and cooling of the earth's atmosphere seems to suggest. Some changes are peaceful and tranquil, such as the gently falling snow on soft green grass, the maturing of a rosebud, and the rising of the moon on a summer night; other changes, such as earthquakes, tornadoes, and volcanic eruptions, showcase nature's violent side. Certain changes are inevitable, and others are ours to control.

Scale and Symmetry

Human beings are bilaterally symmetrical; that is, one side of the body is nearly a mirror image of the other, which could be demonstrated by drawing an axis from the top of the head to the place between the two feet. A hen's egg would be shown to be bilaterally symmetrical if an axis were drawn on it longitudinally but not if it were drawn around the middle of the egg, as if the line were an equator. A circle, no matter where one draws a line from one side to the other through the center, is biradially symmetrical.

Forms of symmetry, more or less, are found everywhere in nature and in the constructed environment. One finds forms of symmetry in a daffodil; in the Parthenon of ancient Athens; in the shell of a chambered nautilus; in Jane Austen's book *Pride and Prejudice* in the yin and yang of Eastern philosophy; and in Beethoven's symphonies. One also finds a certain symmetry in the seasons, in day and night, and in the configuration of the solar system. Symmetry is found in the leaves of a tree, in the three branches of U.S. government, in the design of the space shuttle, in the balance a teacher brings to the curriculum, in the need for both work and play, and in the graceful contours of a Grecian urn.

The converse of symmetry, *asymmetry,* also exists in the world. The external symmetry of the human is not necessarily found in the placement of the internal organs. No such symmetry can be found in the placement of the heart, liver, appendix, and so on, although one does find symmetry in the placement of the lungs and kidneys. Certain animals, notably sponges and ameboid protozoans, are asymmetrical in their design. Their shapes are irregular, different for each individual, or constantly changing. In the constructed environment, asymmetry is often sought by the designer, either for aesthetic purposes or because it suits a certain function.

In cartography, scale is represented by the ratio between distances on a map and distances on the earth's surface. A scale drawing showing the floorplan of a classroom is an attempt to illustrate the relative size and distances of objects from each other as they exist in the actual classroom. The more closely the size of features on a map or sketch approaches actual size, the larger is the scale. Thus, a map showing the whole earth is considered small scale, whereas a map showing a backyard would probably be considered large scale (see Figures 12.5 and 12.6).

In music, a scale is any series of tones arranged in rising or falling order of pitch, or vibrations (cycles) per second. The fewer the vibrations per second, the lower the note; the more vibrations per second, the higher the note. On a familiar instrument such as the piano, the white keys represent the diatonic scale of seven notes, five of which are whole tones and two of which are half-tones. The cycle begins anew with each succeeding octave. This repeating seven-note scale can be assembled by a composer in a seemingly infinite variety of combinations to make the many tunes, melodies, and so forth that have been written over the years. Of course, the black keys, or sharp notes, each of which is a half-step between two given white keys, add to the

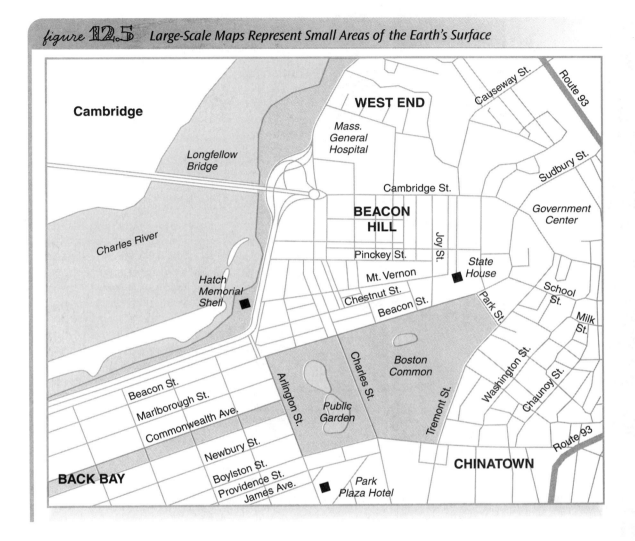

figure 12.5   *Large-Scale Maps Represent Small Areas of the Earth's Surface*

possibility for variety. Other scales are also possible, as shown in Hindu and Arabian music.

Athletic fields and gymnasiums are built to certain scales and symmetries. A football field must be built to an exact size, as must a tennis court, but a baseball field or a basketball court can vary in size. A basketball court must be a true rectangle, even though it may be somewhat different in size from one court to another. A baseball field, on the other hand, must be regular only in its infield proportions (i.e., from one base to another). The outfield may be allowed to vary so that the distances from home plate to the right-, center-, and left-field walls are quite different within a given park as well as from park to park. Thus, a baseball field has qualities of symmetry as well as of asymmetry.

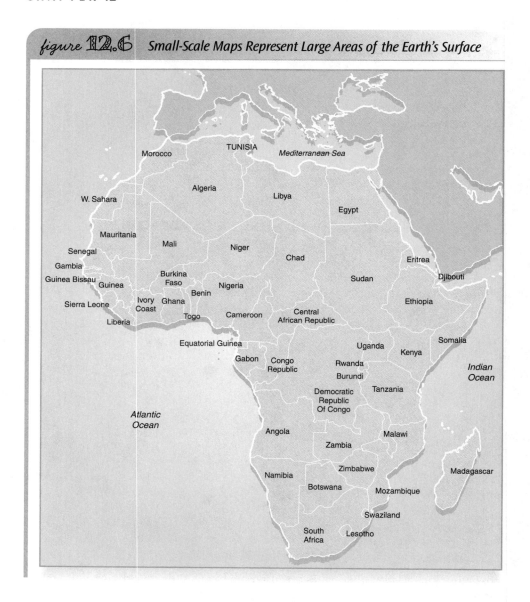

figure **12.6**   *Small-Scale Maps Represent Large Areas of the Earth's Surface*

Children, by nature, are marvelous sketch artists and map makers. As they begin to learn about scale and symmetry, they need to be encouraged to observe, draw, sketch, map, chart, talk, and sing and dance about what they see. Observing and recording are the two most basic skills of science, both social and natural. When a child begins to observe carefully and to record in some way what he or she sees, subtleties begin to emerge. Elements of color, line, texture, size, distance, symmetry, and scale become clearer, and the child's sense of consciousness is heightened. The doors leading to a world of real learning begin to open.

Interaction and Relationships

In a classroom of 25 people, the number of paired person-to-person combinations is 300! Assuming that you and a fellow teacher's classes have 25 students apiece for a total of 50, the three-to-a-group combinations of students the two of you could put together numbers 19,600! Just imagine the possibilities you have to allow your students to really get to know each other.

Of course, people interact not only with people but also with nature, the built environment, texts, films, and so on. A child's relationship with others is very different in a classroom where each student works alone at his or her desk versus a room where group projects and collaborative learning are emphasized. A child's relationship with the teacher is very different in a warm, supportive, caring, challenging environment versus an autocratic, aloof, and unfair environment.

School subjects can themselves be related and allowed to interact, or they can be isolated, unrelated, and unconnected. Whether there is interaction among people or school subjects in the teaching/learning equation is a fundamental pedagogical question. Where school life is dominated by what German philosopher Jürgen Habermas (1968) calls *technical interests,* then predictability and control become paramount pedagogical concerns. The technical interest focuses primarily on means–ends questions. Examples of this are the use of behavioral objectives and a tightly scripted lesson plan. In other words, any attempt to predict and therefore control the behavior of students toward a predetermined outcome is indicative of the technical interest at work. The result of such a preoccupation is a socially, morally, and intellectually simplified syntax of classroom life.

Habermas (1968) also identifies the *practical interest,* which in school life, calls for students and teachers to search for understanding and meaning in what is being learned. The practical interest encourages relationships and relational learning, conversation, working and getting along together, and a sense of integration of people and their experiences. The practical interest is at work when students and teachers engage in project learning, in shared activities, and in the constructivist enterprise. The constructivity principle—that experience precedes analysis—is basic to the practical interest.

Habermas (1968) identifies a third interest, one that calls on powers of *reflection* and *insight.* Here, the questions for a thoughtful consideration of school life take one to deeper levels. These reflective issues are developed in the patterns of classroom life through such recurring questions of utility (Is this useful?), aesthetics (Is this beautiful?), truth (Is this meaningful?), and morality (Is this right?). When those who join the teaching/learning enterprise begin to carry out a process of reflection around these key questions, a different sense of curriculum comes forth: Hope emerges. That is an empowering curriculum.

Time and Space

History and literature provide insights to time. Geography, art, and geometry illustrate space. Studied in integrated fashion, these disciplines bring time and space together as powerful themes for orienting oneself to one's place in the world. To a child, an hour can seem a long time. Adults often think in terms of projects of several years.

Nineteenth-century pioneer Marcus Whitman who together with his wife, Narcissa, founded a mission settlement near present-day Walla Walla, Washington, once wrote, "My plans require time and distance." Today, someone flies from New York to San Francisco in a matter of hours.

Although modern conveniences such as jet planes, telephones, fax machines, and the Internet are wonderful devices, they tend to distort our sense of time and space. In this limited sense, the people of the past had a deeper understanding of these concepts than we do today. For instance, if you've walked or hiked somewhere, you have a different sense of time and space than you do if you've gone to the same place in an air-conditioned car.

In modern life, things take on a sense of immediacy. A friend of mine once told me of his nightmarish experience on an overseas trip of being cooped up in a plane on a runway for six hours (with no food), being taken off the plane, being bused into the city and put into a hotel for two hours of sleep, and then being taken back to the airport for take-off at 3:00 in the morning, only to wait until after 9:00 A.M., again with no meal served, to take off. Sounds awful, doesn't it? Relative to most airplane flights, it really was a tough experience and one my friend does not wish to repeat. Mainly, however, it was an inconvenience. He still made it from Tokyo to Seattle in a time frame measured in hours, not days or weeks. Just imagine the inconveniences experienced by Marco Polo, the pioneers of the Oregon Trail, James Cook, and other travelers of the past.

Today's students are on the receiving end of these distortions of the realities of time and space. Somehow, the curricular experience must transcend these limitations. This is not a plea to return to those thrilling days of yesteryear. We live in this day and age, and that is our reality. The fact is, however, that most students today have little knowledge of the backcloth of their own existence. In other words, they apparently know little of history, literary portrayals of life in the past, the emergence of artistic and musical forms, and so on. Even the brief history of the United States is a blank slate to many students. Sadly, this can be said of some teachers as well.

Your job as an elementary social studies teacher, must, among other things, include an attempt to recapture with your students a sense of space and time and place. One of the great wonders of childhood is the innate sense of wonder. It's easy for a teacher to forget that very simple thought in the rush to cover all the things that need to be taught in school. For a student to join in, to become a participant on a journey of discovery, is far more than an academic study of some epic voyage taken by some heroes from the distant past. It is a coming together of a young person's desire to learn about his or her world with an invitation to participate in the journey itself.

Time and space are crucial to the musician. Not merely the musical sounds themselves but the space between the sounds and the timing of the sounds contribute to a symphony. The composer Hadyn, for example, made remarkable use of the empty space between notes, giving his music a nearly unequaled lightness. Space is also precious to the artist and sculptor. The painter decides how to arrange pigment on the space of a canvas. The sculptor decides how to chip and chisel away space from a block of stone in order to arrive at a finished work. Thus, one creates through addition of color while the other creates through the subtraction of stone.

To the map maker, lines organize space. Lines form the boundaries and points of demarcation that separate or denote one area from another. The beauty of a good map lies not only in its accuracy but also in its elegance as a portrayal of space and place. A child discovers that she can create a lake on a piece of paper by drawing an enclosed line. The child looks at it and decides the lake should be colored blue. The child thinks there should be a road leading to the lake and some mountains in the distance. These lines, drawn by the child, organize and give meaningful shape to space. By drawing a modern-looking boat on the lake, the child also orients the reader to a certain time period. The child's teacher asks the child to tell about the map. The child, referring to the map she created, cheerfully explains her thoughts.

Equilibrium and Disequilibrium

When disequilibrium occurs—for example, in war or in family problems—disorder follows close behind. When feelings, thoughts, and actions are harmonious, equilibrium and order result. Young people desperately need balance (equilibrium) and predictability (order) in their lives. Teachers know this better than anyone. They work daily with students who bring with them equilibrium and order as well as its opposite.

The idea of equilibrium applies well to systems theory. For instance, a traffic system maintains much of its equilibrium by balancing the rate and flow of traffic with a network of lights, signs, patrols, and the like. When the system is in a state of equilibrium and good order, traffic flows smoothly. Untoward events (e.g., a rush-hour pile up), however, can quickly throw the smoothest system out of balance. In the balance of nature, disequilibrium can occur in an ecosystem when previously outside elements are introduced. An example of this is the introduction of rabbits to the Australian ecosystem. The system, in its more natural state of balance, was not equipped to accommodate the influx of the fast-breeding and wide-ranging animals. Many attempts have been made to restore balance to the system, with mainly limited results.

In the Pacific Northwest of the United States, the building of several large dams (Grand Coulee, Bonneville, and others) has made the Columbia River system far more orderly and therefore more predictable than it was in its natural state. For purposes of flood control, hydroelectricity, irrigation, and recreation, the system of dams has been a considerable success. On the other hand, the equilibrium of elements of the system has been thrown into disorder. Two examples of this are the greatly diminished salmon run on the Columbia and the displaced river-dwelling Native Americans who, for centuries, had caught fish at such sites as Celilo Falls, which is now submerged beneath the waters of the reservoir created by one of the dams. Other more subtle changes may not be accurately assessed for years to come.

The warming and cooling cycles of the earth's atmosphere have a long-term scale of order and an equilibrium not easily determined in the short run. Recent scientific evidence points to a warming effect and a diminishment of the ozone layer. Whether this is part of a long-term change of equilibrium is not known. The earth, as part of the solar system, is situated at a point of delicate balance in its distance from the sun. This balance is necessary in order to maintain temperature conditions conducive to life forms as we know them. When the quality of the earth's atmosphere changes because of increased cattle grazing and increased automobile exhaust, the system is altered. The system's ability to restore itself is problematic.

It took human beings thousands of years to discern the order of the seasons and the attendant implications to the point that they could make the change from hunting and gathering to agriculture. Once systems of agriculture were established in place of systems of hunting and gathering, the need for order in architecture, laws, roads, and the many shared functions of permanently settled people emerged.

Each of these foregoing themes is connected to the others in ways that make the continual revisiting of them all necessary. Thus, the content may change from unit to unit and from year to year in the curriculum, but the themes remain as conceptual points of reference. The themes have the power of ideas, and ideas are the mortar that holds together the curricular building blocks of knowledge, insight, and wisdom.

Summary

The project approach to social studies is an effective way to create an integrated studies learning model. Projects have a real-world flavor to them, and that makes them appealing to children. They also have a beginning and an end, which allows students and teachers a better sense of what they are accomplishing. Projects offer splendid opportunities for children to work together, experiencing the give-and-take, shared decision making, and camaraderie that happens only in group activity.

There are four different but related kinds of social studies projects: (1) service-learning projects, (2) production projects, (3) problem-solving projects, and (4) schoolwide projects. Each is necessary along the road to childhood growth and development. Group projects put the *social* back in social studies, and they provide the syntactic complexities needed to enhance moral development, language development, perspective taking, problem-solving ability, and citizenship.

Explorations

Reflect On . . .

1. Some people feel that social studies becomes watered down when it is incorporated into integrated teaching and learning. Do you agree? Why or why not?

2. How are service-learning projects beneficial to students? Production projects? Problem-solving projects? Schoolwide projects? What are the essential differences among these?

In the Field

3. Observe a classroom where students are doing a project and one where students are doing more traditional school work. Do you see any differences between the two? If so, what kinds of differences?

4. Recall a project from your own days in elementary school. Describe it to a fellow student. Have that colleague describe a favorite project to you. Discuss what made these projects enjoyable.

For Your Portfolio

5. Make two lists of projects students could do: one for primary-grade students and one for intermediate-grade students. Note objectives for each project.

Continuing the Journey: Suggested Readings

Ellis, A. (2001). *Teaching, learning, and assessment together: The reflective classroom.* Larchmont, NY: Eye on Education.
This book includes more than twenty practical strategies (with underlying theories) for implementing reflective thinking with children.

Johnson, D., & Johnson, R. (1999). *Learning together and alone.* Boston: Allyn & Bacon.
The authors provide the reader with the purpose, goals, and means of implementing cooperative learning in classrooms.

Katz, L., & Chand, S. (1999). *Engaging children's minds: The project approach.* Norwood, NJ: Ablex.
This book is the single best source for teachers who wish to implement projects and project methods in their classrooms.

Kohn, A. (1999). *The schools our children deserve: Moving beyond traditional classrooms and "tougher standards."* Boston: Houghton Mifflin.
Alfie Kohn provides a stinging critque of back to basics, the standards movement, and our seeming desire to test every child.

Social Studies and the Literacy Connection

In this chapter, we will explore the following themes:

key concepts

- Reading and classroom life
- Literacy and democracy
- Social studies and language development
- The spoken word
- Electronic literacy

There is an art of reading, as well as an art of thinking and an art of writing.
　　　—Isaac D'Israeli

Literacy and democracy are inseparable. As John Jay, one of the founders of our republic, wrote, "Education is the soul of a republic." A democratic society cannot function without a literate citizenry.

One of your many tasks as a teacher is to ensure that the children you teach will become proficient readers and writers. Every worthwhile book that your students read will take them further down the road to becoming informed citizens. Your school librarian and your local public library are invaluable resources in this quest. In both cases, the librarians have access to lists of books that are age and content appropriate for your students.

We live in an age of electronic literacy, as well. Your students need not only to be able to read and write effectively but also to understand and function within the context of electronic images and text. Of course, we will probably never reach the point where books and the print medium, in general, are completely obsolete (at least, I hope not—since I write books!). In today's world, *literacy* means being able to process information from a variety of sources.

In recent years, people have witnessed a phenomenon characterized by two divergent outcomes. On the one hand, the amount of good literature related to social studies topics for children has reached an all-time high. Each year, *Social Education,* the official journal of the National Council for the Social Studies, publishes an annotated list of new books that have great promise. On the

figure 13.1 *Declining Literacy Rates*

The National Adult Literacy Survey (1993) tested 26,000 adults 16 or older in three skill areas. Few excelled. Many did poorly. Another survey, taken in 2003, has not yet released results.

Examples (Level 1):
Find a country in a short newspaper article; sign your name; total a bank deposit.

Examples (Level 3):
Find an interpretive sentence in a news article; use a bus schedule to find the right route; use a calculator to figure the discount on a bill.

Examples (Level 5):
Interpret a phrase taken from a long article; explain in writing a simple statistical table; use a calculator to figure the cost of carpeting a room.

How People Fared

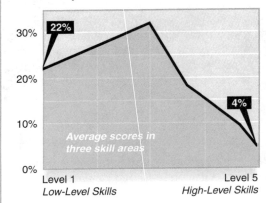

Average scores in three skill areas

Level 1 — Low-Level Skills
Level 5 — High-Level Skills

Types of Literacy

The tests measured skills in three areas:

Prose: Understand basic written information such as editorials, news stories, poems, and fiction.

Document: Use materials such as job applications, payroll forms, transportation schedules, maps, tables, and graphs.

Quantitative: Use numbers for such tasks as balancing a checkbook, figuring out a tip, and calculating interest from a loan advertisement.

According to the U.S. Department of Education, only 47 percent of adult Americans can function at even the lowest level of literacy (Level 1).

Source: National Adult Literacy Survey, 1993.

other hand, teachers report that many students are less and less interested in reading and writing.

The corresponding decline in literacy is to the point where U.S. government figures show that nearly half of adult Americans are functionally illiterate (see Figure 13.1). The term *functionally illiterate* means that people cannot read the label on a medicine bottle or they cannot write a coherent paragraph describing even the most basic things. The term has nothing to say about who reads the classics or who writes timeless essays. A rather new term, *aliterate,* has emerged to describe a related problem; an aliterate person is someone who *can* read but *doesn't.* There is, in fact, evidence to suggest that literacy rates today are actually lower in some cases than they were in the Middle Ages (U.S. Department of Education, 1993).

Reading and writing are related pursuits. They support each other. They supply energy to each other. In this chapter, we will search for ways to increase both the amount and quality of students' efforts in these two very important areas of learning.

Reading and Classroom Life

One year, in the course of my career as an elementary teacher, I found myself wondering about two teaching and learning issues that I was sure were closely connected. The first issue was how to make real readers out of my students, and the second was how to improve my students' knowledge of social studies content, especially biography, history, and geography.

It was not that my students never read anything; each week during library period, many of them would check out several books to read, and, of course, I required the obligatory one-written-book-report-per-term from each student. Still, I wasn't satisfied with the way things were going, so I tried two ideas at once.

The first idea was to drop the written book-report requirement. That idea was received with great joy by students, some of whom mentioned that they didn't mind reading but that they disliked having to write book reports. Now, a teacher can't simply run a class just by asking the students their preference about whether to do something or not to do it. Still, it is important to listen to them and give them a feeling of some influence because it's their classroom. The reason their joy resonated with me was that I had bad memories of writing book reports myself. So, we agreed: no book reports.

The second idea I had was to develop a very simple (and that is the key) system of acknowledging and supporting students' reading habits. To kick off this phase of my plan, I gave every student in class a green bookmark made from construction paper. It was an inch wide and six inches long, with one end cut at an angle. That was it—no fancy designs or anything else. I told the students that when they had finished reading a book, they were to record the date, title, and author. They were to inform me when they had finished their first book, and I would then give them a red bookmark. After five books, they would be given a blue bookmark; after ten, a yellow bookmark; and so on, in increments of five.

The amount and quality of reading done by those students literally exploded. The growth was exponential. They liked keeping track of their reading, and they loved the paper bookmarks. Why, I asked myself, hadn't I come up with something like this sooner? Napoleon himself once noted that the greatest discovery of his life was that soldiers would die for ribbons. Maybe that was the beginning of behavior modification. At any rate, I learned that children would read for bookmarks. They loved to show me their growing lists, and it gave me a chance to listen to them tell me about their reading and to suggest biographies, historical fiction, histories, good fiction, and so on. Also, they were so proud of their bookmarks. It doesn't take much to make children happy if they know you care about them.

What happened that year was rather successful. I read more, the students read more, and even their parents started reading more. I got reports from parents who said their child used to watch television "all the time, but now he really wants to read." The nice thing about the bookmarks was that it gave every child his or her own measure of progress. It never became a competitive thing between students. Each child was able to compete against himself or herself and to improve the record. We had great class discussions about what it means to improve your own standards.

A child and his grandfather share a story. The home is a vital link to learning in a child's growth and development.

Through my individual discussions with students, I was able to get closer to them and, as a result, felt much more comfortable suggesting new books for them to read. It occurred to me that maybe I was really listening to them for the first time. The social fabric of the classroom was changing for the better. We were reaching toward one of those transcendent moments in teaching and learning that can only occur when people feel empowered to chart their educational destiny and to talk about it comfortably with others.

Soon, something unforeseen occurred. The much-hated book reports had become a thing of the past, but the children were actually reporting on their reading more than ever. The difference was that it had an easygoing informality about it; in other words, it was a much more natural process, and that was fine because we were getting at *why* someone might read, rather than merely to comply with assignments. This is where the students' creativity emerged. They began to produce skits from books, do role-plays of famous characters, read brief excerpts from good books to the class, build model scenes depicting themes from books, draw elaborate posters advertising books they thought others should read, make bulletin-board displays, and a number of other things to share their knowledge.

These students had crossed a frontier that is seldom crossed in the annals of classroom life. Bringing me with them, they had crossed the frontier from teaching to learning. You think it was tough for the pioneers to cross the Rocky Mountains with their covered wagons? Yes, it was. But just try crossing the high barriers that separate true learning from teacher-centered instruction! Yet, once you've done it (and believe me, even most university students haven't done it), you won't want to go back to the low, swampy moral ground of just doing assignments that someone in charge wants you to carry out. True learning means freedom, and these children experienced it.

I am convinced that becoming a reader takes a lot of practice. A few children do it without any outside help, but most do not. In fact, many who could have become readers give up. I think for most people, there is a threshhold that, once you cross it, you become a reader; no one has to tell you to read. I am also convinced that you and I and the textbook cannot "teach" students enough social studies to amount to very much. Jean Piaget made it clear that *telling* is not *teaching*. What we can do is support children's learning, which is a very different thing—as different as dependence is to independence.

A good book is the ultimate portable learning tool. It can be read in bed, in the bathtub, in a tree house, in the backseat of a car, and even in a chair. It can be set aside, picked up later, thrown in a backpack and carried to a park bench, and, best of all, it requires no batteries. The reader controls the pace. The great thing about it is that not only is it fun, but the reader can also learn about prehistoric times, pioneers, other cultures, other children, famous women and men, great adventures, and who knows what else along the way.

Keys to Early Literacy: Parents

For teachers of primary-age children, the challenge is especially fruitful. This is so because habits begin early in life, so it is easier to make reading, or anything else for that matter, a pattern if it is begun early.

The parents are the key here. Somehow, you are going to have to convince them to read to their children. In fact, research illustrates that parents reading to children is vital to their cognitive growth. This procedure is most effective when the parent does three things:

- *Elaborates on the text,* giving information and insight that might not be explicit
- *Refers to the child's own experiences,* drawing him or her into the reading by comparing and contrasting events in the story with things the child knows from experience
- *Pauses from time to time to ask questions* in order to actively involve the child, who may wish to guess what is going to happen next, compare this story with another one, or so on

Literacy and Democracy

Returning to my earlier experience, the fact that my students were reading more was obvious to me, to them, and to others. The bookmarks seemed a small reward for all the energy and goodwill, and I was quite pleased with that result. Dropping the dreaded book reports had left me with a sense of ambivalence, because book reports are, and always have been, a part of reading—a kind of external obligation that proves you read the book. On the other hand, it seemed to have a liberating effect that was all to the good.

I was getting to know the children better because we spent time talking about books they were reading, which would lead inevitably to discussions of their interests. It

A children's book club discussion.

became easier and more natural for me to suggest good books to them, and they seemed always to welcome the suggestions. I was gradually coming to realize that they *were* reporting on the books they read; it was just that the reporting was casual and informal, much the same way members of a book club might share their reading with one another.

The important thing was that the students were reading, and they wanted to communicate their reading—witness the skits, role-playing, and model making discussed earlier. We had somehow improved and expanded the whole theory of book reporting, at least for us, and the students had done much of it themselves. They had reached a stage of empowerment, and I began to understand what the term *facilitator* truly meant.

The level and quality of communication rose dramatically as the students shared their reading. The classroom was becoming one big book club that just happened to carry on some other business during the day as well—you know, stuff like spelling, math, science, and a few other subjects. But in time, those subjects followed social studies and were swallowed up by the book club as well. The psychological edge that we all enjoyed was based on the premise that we were reading, discussing, writing, and calculating, not because of a routine based on teacher-centered assignments but because of self-direction and a social fabric that had brought us together and made us a community of learners.

Reading and Writing

Writer John Gardner stated that the best way to learn to write well is to read good books. He's perfectly right, of course. Good writing, both its substance and its style, is the best model for anyone of any age who aspires to write. This is an important point for any teacher of children. In order to get them to read good literature and to want to express themselves clearly in writing, a teacher must develop positive relationships with them. The relationship aspect in teaching and learning is key.

Novelist John Fowles, author of *The French Lieutenant's Woman, Daniel Martin,* and many other wonderful books, makes a very interesting point about reading and its effect not only on one's writing but also on one's thinking. In *Daniel Martin,* Fowles suggests that reading frees the imagination, allowing it to roam creatively. This is so, he says, because the reader must supply his or her own images, thus creating an ongoing mental process of interaction with the written text. Older people who listened to radio adventures when they were children say much the same thing: They had to supply the images in their minds. Of course, if you read to the children from a good book for 15 minutes or so after lunch (the favorite part of the school day for many children), they will supply the images as they listen to you read. Fowles contrasts the image making of the reader with the captured imagination of the television viewer, who has both text and images supplied for him or her. There is little else to do in terms of mental construction.

Now, this is all very important when it comes to writing. The person who has read a great deal of good literature has been tutored in how to use words and craft sentences so that he or she becomes actively involved in image making. Reading and writing, then, are actually a seamless process, each one supporting the other. For the child who finds it difficult to write the words that convey exactly what he or she wants to say, a greater appreciation for good writing is possible.

Take a moment to read the few lines that follow from Ralph Waldo Emerson's poem "Concord Hymn," written to commemorate the beginning of the American Revolution. Allow yourself to create images of the scene.

> *By the rude bridge that arched the flood,*
> *Their flag to April's breeze unfurled,*
> *Here once the embattled farmers stood*
> *And fired the shot heard round the world.*

I suggest to you that any fifth-grade child who reads this poem, discusses it with a thoughtful teacher who supplies interesting historical information surrounding it, and draws pictures of the scene (see Figure 13.2) can probably write a description of the events that has more emotion and life in it than that found in the account in the social studies textbook.

Of course, the road to good writing and reading doesn't stop there. Children with whom you have a good relationship, who trust you and value your opinion, are ready and eager to take cues from you. So when you suggest to a fifth-grade child that he or she read *Johnny Tremain, Little Women,* or some other well-written, worthwhile book, you are suggesting more than a book title; you are bringing the wealth of your goodwill and trust to a child who wants your advice. Believe me, it's great to have wonderful authors such as Louisa May Alcott helping you teach a child to write well.

When considering writing and reading for children, it is important to relate it to modes of thought. The work of Benjamin Whorf illustrates rather well that the

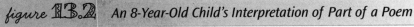

figure **13.2**   *An 8-Year-Old Child's Interpretation of Part of a Poem*

By the rude bridge that arched the flood...

Their flag to April's breeze unfurled...

Here once the embattled farmers stood...

And fired the shot heard round the world.

language people are exposed to (both written and oral) decides in great measure what thoughts are possible for them. They cannot escape from it into any other way of perceiving the world. Whorf's work was done with such culture groups as Inuits (Eskimos) and Native Americans, primarily Hopis. He showed that the rich vocabularies of these two groups in certain areas gave them an expressive ability that is indeed remarkable. For example, Inuits have an amazing number of words for snow, depending on the exact type of snow that might be falling at a given time. They can, therefore, think thoughts about snow that most English speakers cannot. The point of Whorf's research is that each individual can expand his or her vocabulary and, therefore, his or her range of thought and expression.

Keep in mind that what a person reads determines to a considerable extent what he or she becomes in life. Just recently, I talked with a teacher who told me that reading was her first love, and that was why she thought it was such an important subject in the school curriculum. When I asked her what she had read recently, she couldn't think of anything. I guess she meant it was important for children to read, but that she had already done that. This attitude simply will not work. If you want your students to read, you must model it. As you read, you will grow, and the students will sense the excitement and the growth.

Take a moment to consider the relationship between reading and writing as it is portrayed in the following example. A fourth-grade teacher read a descriptive paragraph from E. B. White's classic book *Charlotte's Web:*

The barn was very large. It was very old. It smelled of hay and it smelled of manure. It smelled of perspiration of tired horses and the wonderful sweet breath of patient cows. It often had a sort of peaceful smell—as though nothing bad could happen ever again in the world. It smelled of axle grease and of rubber boots and of new rope. And whenever the cat was given a fish head to eat, the barn would smell of fish. But mostly it smelled of hay, for there was always hay in the great loft up overhead.

Then the teacher asked the students to write a group composition describing their own classroom. Notice the learning effect that a piece of well-written prose had on the children:

The schoolroom was very large and old. It smelled of chalk dust and children's clothes. It often had a quiet smell—as if nothing bad could happen in school. It smelled of pencil lead, ink, ink paste, watercolor paints, and crayons. Whenever it rained or snowed, the wet coats and boots in the dressing room smelled like a skunk. When the children walked into the room, it smelled like potato chips, candy, nuts, and pumpkin seeds. Most of the time it smelled like smoke and dust. The dust came from the windows. The smoke came from the chimneys.

Experience and Discussion

In social studies, it is vital that children have direct experiences and vicarious experiences. Direct experiences build perceptions and ideas about reality. For example, a direct experience is taking primary-age children outside on a fall day to gather evidence of fall or allowing intermediate-level children to make a Native American meal with the guidance of a tribal member.

Vicarious experiences about human behavior and environments are often best supplied through print, film, or pictures. Of course, it would be fantastic to take your class to visit Japan or to travel backward through time to visit a colonial village, but in the absence of such possibilities, a teacher learns to use print and film strategically to build experience. Sample Lesson 13.1 allows students to combine emerging literacy skills with a lesson on cultural understanding.

Experience is necessary, but for it to become imbedded intellectually and emotionally, you must use your most characteristically human trait: *speech*. Schools will not improve until teachers are willing to give over vast amounts of time to both small-group and whole-class discussion. Too often, teachers fail to capitalize on the opportunity to really reflect and personalize experience. Talking about what they do, how they feel, how their perceptions change, and so on enables people to use their experiences as a springboard to deeper insight about themselves and others. Discussion also exposes people to the thinking of others who may have had the same experience yet whose perceptions of the experience are quite different. This adds a richness and a sense of quality possible only when people take the time to discuss things with others.

It sounds so simple, doesn't it? Unfortunately, research shows that student-initiated talk accounts for only about 7 minutes out of a typical 300-minute school day (Goodlad, 1984).

Social Studies and Language Development

The great Austrian philosopher Ludwig Wittgenstein offers a compelling argument linking language development to thinking and, therefore, to expression, both written and oral. Wittgenstein maintains that the limits of a person's language are the limits of that person's world. Thus, an individual's (or group's) world view is limited and determined by the language he or she commands.

The meaning of all this for classroom learning is that children need to read good material (unfortunately, the average elementary social studies textbook hardly qualifies), to write extensively, and to be given ample opportunity for oral discourse. The practice in recent years of journal writing is an excellent example of how children can be helped along the road to building up their talents for written expression.

In his book *Thought and Language,* Russian psychologist Lev Vygotsky (1986) examines the relationship between language and cognition. He comes to the conclusion that experience added to social interaction, or group sharing of written and oral language, is a key to language development. What is often overlooked or underestimated is that the expressive ability of children is an outcome of cognitive development, as well as an enhancer of cognitive development. In other words, you need to give your students as much practice as possible in reading, writing, and discussing.

Interpreting Text

A useful technique for combining reading and writing (and even oral discourse, for that matter) is called *interpreting text*. In a superficial sense, it looks like note taking as one reads, but it is far more than that.

Here's how it works: As a person reads a book, he or she actively interacts with the text. The interaction takes the form of responding to statements made by the author as well as adding the reader's knowledge, thoughts, feelings, impressions, questions, and insights. The purpose of interpreting text is to give the reader equal footing with the author, thereby giving the reader a participatory role. Thus, the role of the student is both reader and writer. Here is an example written by an 11-year-old student named Tony:

> I agree that the pioneers had to be tough and smart. Otherwise, they couldn't have made it with no roads and just covered wagons. So they are heroes for what they did. I never thought about it before, but maybe I get to live here because they settled our town. But I was just trying to think of how the Indians felt. Maybe they didn't know everything that happened. But they had lived there all their lives, and so had their grandparents back into history. It's hard for me to understand. Both the pioneers and the Indians had feelings. History is about the past, so when I read in this book everything I read about already happened. I still don't think the pioneers were wrong because they wanted to be farmers on different land. But I do think we should care about what happened to the Indians because they had a way of living that was good for them.

You can see in this child's writing a genuinely reflective viewpoint emerging. The child is bringing something to the text. The child has feelings of ambivalence that transcend

To record is to learn. Children acquire skills through experience.

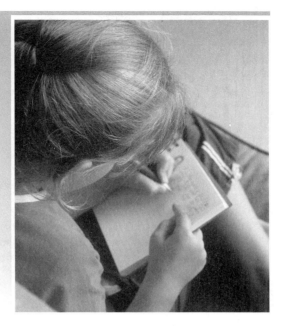

the reading of text merely for information. He is on the way to becoming an involved, critical reader.

Journal Writing

One of the more productive avenues toward improved thought and expression is journal writing. A journal encourages metacognition, or thinking reflectively about the experiences the writer has had. A good journal, like a good diary, includes thoughts, feelings, perspectives, insight, analyses, and other means of reflection. Some students like to imagine that their journals are ship's logs and that they are making entries each day as the ship sails from September to June.

In social studies, writing in a journal is useful as a way of reflecting on the ideas, skills, content, and values that are being considered. A journal should give a student a private avenue of expression for his or her personal growth. Take a moment to consider the journal entry written by a sixth-grade student:

February 17

I really enjoy sharing time when we get to tell about the biographies. Everybody tries to make it so interesting and it is so much fun that I never liked social studies as much as this year. Some days I look at the clock and wonder if it will ever turn two o'clock so we can get started, but today was the best of all when Maddie and Sean pretended they were Columbus and Chief Joseph who never really met but the way they did it made Columbus so surprised with the way things turned out. Now some of us are going to turn it into a play, I hope.

The Writing Process

In social studies, a useful place to begin the writing process is with descriptive writing. Remember that observing, recording, and explaining are three of the most basic social science processes. To make good descriptive writers of your students, you need to give them practice with the process itself. The writing process can be considered in four phases:

1. *Prewriting.* This is the initial, or warm-up, phase. In this phase, a young writer needs to consider the subject, think about who he or she is writing for, and create images of what he or she would like to say.
2. *Drafting.* The writer is ready to take the first written approach to the subject. At this stage, it is important that the writer says what he or she needs to say in rough form.
3. *Revising.* This is a good time to discuss the work with someone else, to get teacher comments, and to consider not merely *what* to say but *how* to say it.
4. *Editing.* This is the phase where the finished product will emerge. Spelling, punctuation, elements of style, and so on are important because others will read the product.

in the classroom Writing Descriptions

In a third-grade class, the teacher decided that she would give each child a chestnut and ask him or her to write a description of the chestnut. The children followed the four phases of the writing process, as follows.

In phase 1, the children looked up information on chestnuts, and the teacher read some background from a botany text she had obtained from the library. More important, the children drew several pictures of their chestnuts and chestnut trees. They worked with partners, telling them about their drawings and about their feelings as they drew their pictures.

In phase 2, each child began to write a description of his or her chestnut. These were rough drafts. The children shared their stories with their partners, and the teacher collected the rough drafts and made comments.

In phase 3, the children began helping each other with editing. They also considered the teacher's comments to help them with their expression.

In phase 4, each child wrote a finished paragraph about his or her chestnut and drew an accompanying illustration. The works were then displayed on the wall of the classroom.

Here is one child's finished paragraph:

Let me tell you about my chestnut. It is a kind of chestnut called a horse chestnut. People don't eat them, but squirrels like them. I know, because I have seen the squirrels eat them and bury them. The chestnut is brown with a smooth, shiny shell. It is about an inch wide. If you cut it open, you will see it is white, about the color of a piano key. The chestnut came from a blossom on the tree, and when it grew it had a green spiked cover. The spikes are sharp. The best time to find chestnuts is in the fall when they drop off the trees. If you study my drawings you will see the chestnut from beginning to end, even what a cut-open chestnut looks like. Good-bye.

The writing process served this child well. She learned about sequencing her ideas, about defining an object using words and pictures, and about conveying both form and function, in this case about chestnuts.

The great civil rights leader, Dr. Martin Luther King Jr., speaks to his fellow Americans about equality, compassion, and dignity.

Like anything else, it takes time and practice to become proficient as a writer. The earlier children begin the process, the more they will see it as a natural extension of their ability to communicate with others. They need to do a lot of writing, especially descriptive writing, and they need to read or listen to good writing.

The Spoken Word

In the first century A.D., Roman orator Quintilian noted that speech is our most purely human attribute. Nothing, he said, separates humans from other creatures more clearly than the ability to speak words and to listen to the spoken word.

One could argue the point, citing other characteristics of the human condition as equally or more significant, but Quintilian's meaning is still well taken. Sadly, many educators seem to have forgotten just how important it is for children to be given the opportunity to develop their speaking and listening skills. It is all too easy to overlook this form of literacy.

In ancient times, people had little choice but to communicate using the spoken word. Many culture groups did not even have written language; others did, but had little means of storing the written word in an age before books. Today, the situation is quite the opposite. There are so many means of preserving the record that people tend to undervalue the spoken word.

The poor speaking abilities of most politicians today serve as a reminder that no progress has been made in this area. In fact, great speakers in American history—such as Patrick Henry, Daniel Webster, Abraham Lincoln, and, more recently, Martin Luther King Jr.—seem no longer to be found.

Primary teachers usually do a better job than others in teaching speaking and listening skills, mainly because their students cannot write or read as well as they can speak and listen. Show and tell, dictating stories, and other oral moments of the curriculum are extremely useful in this regard. This is simply not enough, however. As children grow older and more self-conscious, it becomes crucial to encourage and nurture opportunities for oral discourse.

To illustrate how significant this topic is, consider that certain surveys of adults have shown that their number-one fear is speaking in front of a group. Four distinctly different strategies, effectively employed, will go a long way toward remedying this situation.

Public Speaking

It takes courage and skill to talk to a group, and like any other skill, it can only be improved with practice. It is useful to bear in mind John Dewey's idea of the classroom as a learning laboratory, where children are encouraged to take risks, to experiment, and to practice the skills that are needed in everyday life.

Like any other complex task, speaking to groups needs to be approached using developmentally appropriate practice. A good place to begin is to have your students give brief one- or two-minute descriptive speeches, in which they hold a prop and describe something (e.g., a chestnut, a baseball, a doll, or whatever). As success builds, as it will in a nurturing environment, students can be given more complex tasks, such as describing a certain river system, telling how to catch a ball, or explaining how to sew a particular stitch.

Small-Group Speaking

In real life, people often find themselves in relatively small groups, engaged in conversation with others. The art of speaking and listening in such a forum is perhaps best facilitated in school settings by having children work in collaborative groups. As they engage in answering questions, solving problems, and developing ideas, they will benefit from acquiring certain skills, such as showing courtesy to others, speaking in turn, talking quietly, asking questions, agreeing and disagreeing civilly, participating actively, encouraging others, contributing their share, being open to different perspectives, and so on. These skills need to be pointed out by you and discussed reflectively by the class. *Circles of Learning,* by David and Roger Johnson (1994), is an excellent source of ideas and skills for promoting small-group learning.

Informal Talks

Contrary to the opinion of those who think classrooms should always be so quiet that one can hear a pin drop, they should, in fact, be places of conversation. Of course, there is a time for quiet, but students should be encouraged to talk with each other as they work together on projects. For one thing, it encourages both language development and social intelligence. For another, it is natural behavior for human beings. Children benefit greatly from expressing themselves to each other as they build a colonial village, draw a mural, rehearse a play, organize a game, prepare a meal, and so forth.

A young speaker shares a book with the class. Public speaking is a cornerstone of social studies learning.

Ironically, there is far too little of this kind of shared activity in elementary school life, and your job is to make sure it happens. Social skills can be learned in such settings, especially if you and the class take the time to discuss appropriate behaviors for informal talk. In fact, the children will help you come up with rules governing their own behavior during these times.

Group Presentations

You need to be sure that your students engage in presentations in which they are part of a group. Examples of this are panel discussions, demonstrations, pageants, dramatizations, musical productions, debates, and such video productions as "newscasts" and "feature shows." The spoken word is invoked doubly with this procedure. First is the informal talk that goes along with planning, getting prepared, attending to details, orchestrating, and otherwise making sure things are ready. Second is the presentation itself, in which an audience is addressed. Presenting involves deciding on roles, determining who speaks when and how much, fielding questions from the audience, and other problematic issues.

These four strategies will go a long way toward putting the *social* back in social studies. They are aimed directly at the development of thought and language, especially at its public expression.

Constructivist approaches take a clear view on the distinction between *information* and *knowledge* and the need for public expression of ideas. If a teacher employs only silent reading, worksheets, and paper and pencil tests, then *information* will serve the student well, at least until it's forgotten. But *knowledge,* which implies the construction of meaning by learners—an activity that uses information as a way to build more complex social and intellectual structures—depends heavily on interaction, exchange, articulation, sharing of thoughts, reflection, and public expression of ideas.

Electronic Literacy

The invention of the printing press and movable type by German inventor Johannes Gutenberg in the fifteenth century brought about the most profound revolution ever in the advancement of literacy. Everything changed as a result. Books became available to ordinary people, and stored knowledge became decentralized for the first time in history.

Now we are in the midst of another revolution in the annals of literacy. This revolution has been brought about by electronic technology, especially in the form of the Internet, which provides a means of communication that affords people access to databases and online information systems of an incredible range. In less than 15 years, the Internet has become an indispensable tool for everyone from stockbrokers to school children.

Using the Internet in the form of the World Wide Web, children in remote sites of Alaska and in crowded urban centers can connect to classrooms in other countries, access the Library of Congress, and examine news reports from around the globe. For social studies teachers, the Internet can create a kind of global village, allowing them and their students to exchange pen-pal letters, stories, weather data, geography, history, and anything else of mutual interest. Useful websites for school purposes include the following:

- *The Globe Program* at www.globe.gov is a wonderful interdisciplinary source for teachers who wish to combine social studies, science, and related environmental issues. Some 3,000 classes around the world are collecting and posting environmental data to the site. Research scientists actually use the student data and offer feedback.
- *C-Span* at www.c-span.org gives you and your students access to the U.S. House of Representatives, allowing you to watch the actual process of debate, voting, and so on in the halls of Congress. C-Span also covers other political events and serious items in the news.
- *NCSSonline* at www.ncss.org gives you access to the National Council for the Social Studies, the largest organization in the country devoted solely to social studies education. NCSS provides members with networks for all the social science disciplines and for special topics as well, including law education, moral education, multicultural education, and others.
- *Maps.com,* at www.maps.com, and its educational sibling, maps101.com, provide access to thousands of maps and mapping software, as well as lesson plans and activities.

These are but a few of the thousands of electronic addresses available, and the list grows every day. The educational challenge of the Internet and the World Wide Web is one of the most exciting events of our lifetimes. I hope you will take advantage of the possibilities.

Remember, Jean Piaget wrote that teaching is about possibilities, and the World Wide Web has created a new horizon of the possible. By the way, I'd love to hear from you. You can contact me at aellis@spu.com.

Summary

The key to this chapter is the interdependent relationship among reading, writing, and the spoken word as ways to communicate thoughts and feelings in social studies. Each of us constructs our own knowledge, but we do it best in social and intellectual contexts that provide access to productive ideas and that allow us, in turn, to build structures of meaning. Children who become avid readers, willing writers, and confident public speakers are on the way to lifelong learning.

Just imagine what a gift it is to a child to have a teacher who creates a learning landscape that offers nurture, support, and encouragement toward those ends. It is through the medium of language that people are able to define and express their hopes, fears, dreams, insights, and ambitions. Please make reading, writing, and the spoken word an integral part of your social studies curriculum.

Explorations

Reflect On . . .

1. Does *literacy* mean more than reading and writing competently? What other skills are needed to be truly literate?
2. What qualities does a teacher need to create an environment in which children feel they can express themselves openly?

In the Field

3. Create a webbing with a central theme. Then complete the webbing with some partners by brainstorming about what reading, writing, and speaking activities students could do. Try these activities with fellow students.
4. Observe a class where students are giving oral reports. Do the students seem comfortable speaking in front of the class? What does the teacher do—or not do—to make them more comfortable?

For Your Portfolio

5. Select a good primary-level picture book with a social studies theme. Then develop a lesson around it—one that emphasizes discussion and reflection.

Continuing the Journey: Suggested Readings

Allen, J. (2004). *Read-aloud anthology: 35 short, riveting read alouds.* New York: Teaching Resources.
A wonderful source for teaching listening and higher-level thinking through discussions.

Gregory, C. (2000). *Jeeves, I'm bored: 25 Internet adventures for children.* Minneapolis, MN: Sagebrush/ Econ-Clad Books.
How to make time capsules, celebrate international holidays, travel the oceans, and other stimulating adventures in learning.

National Council for the Social Studies. (2005). "Notable tradebooks for young people." *Social Education* (April/May). Available at www.socialstudies. org/resources/notable.

Each year the official journal of the National Council for the Social Studies publishes it's April/May edition containing worthwhile children's trade books for social studies. Be sure to check the website for back years.

Silney, A. (2002). *The essential guide to children's books.* New York: Houghton Mifflin.
This book has received critical acclaim for its careful selection of good books for children.

SAMPLE LESSON 13.1 *Comparing Cultures*

GRADE LEVEL/SUBJECT: Appropriate for grades 1–5. Subject areas include language arts and social studies.

PURPOSE: Using literature to encourage students to use higher-level thinking skills, to help them cooperate more sensitively with their peers, and to develop respect for cultures different from their own.

OBJECTIVE(S): As a result of this activity, the children will be able to:

1. Work with a partner to answer questions in a cooperative manner.
2. Compare two stories/cultures and point out how they are alike and different.
3. Share their own version of a well-known story and adapt it to another culture, elaborating on why they made certain adaptations.

RESOURCES/MATERIALS: A copy of Shirley Climo's *The Egyptian Cinderella.* (Any version of the Cinderella story from another culture may be used here. The idea is to help children find comparisons and contrasts between two versions from different cultures.)

PROCEDURE:

1. Review the Cinderella story with students. Write an outline on the board that reflects the agreed-upon storyline, characters, and important points.
2. Ask students to find partners (or assign partners), and explain that they should watch you for visual cues during the remainder of the lesson. Use any agreed-upon hand signals for cueing:

- Putting a finger to your head indicating "think time," when everyone should be silently thinking about the best answer to the question
- Holding up two fingers to indicate that students should whisper answers to their partners
- Holding up a hand to call for silence again

3. Once the strategy of hand signals has been explained, read the story *The Egyptian Cinderella* to the class. Pause to ask questions that will guide students to compare and contrast this story to the version of the story that you discussed earlier. Here are some examples of appropriate questions:

- How is the dress of Rhodopis (the Egyptian Cinderella) different from the one worn by the Cinderella you have previously read about? Why do you think they dress differently? Can anyone tell us how the climate of Egypt compares with the climate of the United States? (You may want to show the students Egypt and the United States on the globe and on a map to integrate geography into the lesson.)
- How are Kipa and the other two servant girls like or different from Cinderella's stepsisters? Do they treat Rhodopis fairly? Tell why you think they do or don't.
- Does this story have a happy ending? Compare the way this story ends with the ending of the Cinderella we know.

The questions should be varied and geared toward the age level of your class. Point out that similar stories often arise in different cultures, and identifying the differences and similarities between the versions can help us understand differences in cultures and values.

CLOSURE: Have students listen to or read a folktale from another culture that does not have a familiar equivalent in English. Then ask them to write an American version.

EXTENSION: As homework, ask students to have their parents or grandparents tell them or write down folktales or children's stories from their own cultures. If the students are all from a homogeneous background, ask them to find stories from other cultures in the library or on the Internet. Have students share these stories with the class, and talk about any themes that seem to keep recurring.

REFLECTION: Encourage students to see that different cultures often see things slightly differently and that we all need to be tolerant of one another's values.

Source: Adapted from a lesson plan submitted by Mychael Willon (Unified School District #259, Wichita, KS) to OFCN's Academy Curricular Exchange, Columbia Education Center, Social Studies.

chapter 14

Children in a Democracy

Teaching and Learning Responsible Citizenship

In this chapter, we will explore the following themes:

key concepts

- The citizen's role in American democracy
- What children need to know to be active citizens
- How to help students become active citizens
- Effective citizenship education
- The meaning of citizenship: a global perspective
- A citizenship test

We have physiocrats, geometricians, chemists, astronomers, poets, musicians, and painters aplenty, but we have no longer a citizen among us.
          —Jean-Jacques Rousseau

What is the appropriate role of citizens in American democracy, and what conditions are needed to provide students with opportunities to become good citizens? I believe that schools—and social studies education—are critical in educating students to become thoughtful, responsible citizens. The emphasis in this chapter is not on creating passive conformists but on creating citizens who will challenge policy and participate actively in the democratic process.

itizenship is at the heart of the social studies curriculum. Nearly two centuries after Rousseau lamented that "we have no longer a citizen among us," Adlai Stevenson, who twice was a candidate for president, wrote that "as a citizen of this democracy, you are the rulers and the ruled, the lawgivers and the law-abiding, the beginning and the end." It is a beautiful thought, and it represents a great challenge to teachers of elementary social studies.

What does *citizenship* mean to children? How can they grasp this seemingly abstract concept? The answer is found in experience. Always remember that children learn what they live. If your classroom is a miniature democracy—where students are expected to participate in decisions, work and play together, share their thoughts and dreams, and become involved in school and community—I think they will begin to understand what it means to be a citizen.

If being a citizen is the beginning and the end, the alpha and the omega, then citizenship education is a necessity, not a luxury we can do without. Each of us, as a citizen of the United States of America, Canada, or any other democracy, for that matter, has certain rights and responsibilities. This is what is meant by *the beginning and the end:* Our rights are the beginning and our responsibilities are the end. We cannot have one without the other, if democratic citizenship is to have meaning. Just imagine what a position of trust this places you in as a teacher of tomorrow's citizens.

What Is the Citizen's Role in American Democracy?

It is always useful to approach teaching and learning as problem solving. Don't worry if you can't answer the question just posed now or if you and your students can't solve it completely, even in a year's time. It takes a lifetime of learning to be a good citizen. Your job is to get children started in the right direction.

Figure 14.1 identifies the roles of a citizen according to the *National Standards for Teaching Citizenship and Civics,* developed by the Center for Civic Education. Note the spiraling effect of a single important question throughout the K–12 curriculum. The question remains the same throughout the entire school experience, but the response deepens with each grade level. The contexts change. The experiences take on greater sophistication as students move from elementary to middle to senior high school.

Young children learn about individual responsibility by helping to make classroom rules and learning to follow them. They also learn that people must take responsibility for their actions. These early experiences serve as the foundation for increasingly sophisticated experiences throughout the succeeding school years.

Citizenship Is Participating in Society

At its best, a school is a community of learners. This implies that the children and teachers, administrators, and support staff who go there will find themselves in a communal setting. A true community is a relational place where people work together, play together, and share their thoughts, feelings, and dreams. School is a socially contrived environment. This means that society has determined that academic learning should take place in social settings.

The term *public school* originally meant that students learned in each other's company rather than privately from a tutor. In the first century A.D., Roman orator Quintilian advocated public schools over private instruction because, he argued, in public settings, children have the benefit of friendships, examples, and associations. In other words, Quintilian felt that the school environment would make children better Roman citizens. Like Plato before him, Quintilian thought that group play was especially productive for children. Games, activities, and free play put children in situations where moral issues, differences of opinion, camaraderie, sharing, and give-and-take inevitably arise.

In more recent times, such theorists as Jean Piaget and Lev Vygotsky have addressed the idea of *social knowledge.* Social knowledge arises from shared group experience. When children and teachers play and work together on projects, activities, and other aspects of school life, they become bonded through their commonly held knowledge and

figure **14.1**   *Standards for Teaching Citizenship and Civics: The Roles of the Citizen*

K–4	5–8	9–12
What Are the Roles of the Citizen in American Democracy?	**What Are the Roles of the Citizen in American Democracy?**	**What Are the Roles of the Citizen in American Democracy?**
The meaning of citizenship	The meaning of citizenship	The meaning of citizenship in the United States
Becoming a citizen	Becoming a citizen	Becoming a citizen
Rights of individuals	Personal rights	Personal rights
Responsibilities of individuals	Political rights	Political rights
Dispositions that enhance citizen effectiveness and promote the healthy functioning of American democracy	Economic rights	Economic rights
	Scope and limits of rights	Relationships among personal, political, and economic rights
	Personal responsibilities	Scope and limits of rights
Forms of participation	Civic responsibilities	Personal responsibilities
Political leadership and public service	Dispositions that enhance citizen effectiveness and promote the healthy functioning of American constitutional democracy	Civic responsibilities
Selecting leaders	Participation in civic and political life and the attainment of individual and public goals	Dispositions that lead the citizen to be an independent member of society
	The difference between political and social participation	Dispositions that foster respect for individual worth and human dignity
	Forms of political participation	Dispositions that incline the citizen to public affairs
	Political leadership and public service	Dispositions that facilitate thoughtful and effective participation in public affairs
	Knowledge and participation	The relationship between politics and the attainment of individual and public goals
		The difference between political and social participation
		Forms of political participation
		Political leadership and careers in public service
		Knowledge and participation

Source: Adapted from *National Standard for Civics and Government* (Calabasas, CA: Center for Civic Education, 1997).

collective memory. This leads to a sense of community, a sense of belonging—the beginning of citizenship. Just how this happens is captured by Don Rowe (1992), who writes:

> Schools are highly complex communities [with] value systems linked to their purpose and role, power structures, and rules enforced by a justice system. The "citizens" (or "subjects") of school communities can exhibit widely differing degrees of loyalty to the community. Pupils who feel disregarded by a school (or at odds with its aims) will have little reason to feel a sense of obligation to uphold its values or rules. (p. 160)

Two young Americans display their "good citizenship" awards.

The power of the school's social system to make a child feel part of things (or alienated) is enormous. Therefore, the social studies teacher's role is crucial. You must take seriously the social aspects of the school curriculum. How a child feels about being included or excluded will go a long way toward determining his or her lifelong view of the value of participating in society.

Oh, the responsibilities of an elementary teacher are never ending! But it's worth it, because you have the opportunity to do such important work. Just imagine: Your job is about improving people's lives. What could be more significant?

Citizenship Is Serving the Community

To be a citizen means many things. We are citizens of the world, citizens of our country, citizens of our state or province, citizens of our school and classroom, and citizens of our family. One of the arenas of citizenship that children need to experience is citizenship in the local community. The community affords opportunities for participation at many levels; children can be helpful citizens by picking up litter, planting trees, helping elderly people, and undertaking service-learning projects.

One group of primary school children studied a crosswalk near their school with the idea of making it safer. Their work was very important because it probably prevented injuries or loss of life. A class of middle school children were successful in having chlorofluorocarbon-containing styrofoam cups removed from the school district's purchasing list. A third-grade class studied their school's playground equipment and were successful in having dangerous equipment replaced. An intermediate-level class decided to "adopt" a retirement home near their school; they were successful in making ties and friendships between themselves and the elderly. As Martin Luther King Jr. once said, "Everyone can be great, because everyone can serve."

Anderson and associates (Anderson, 1993) report on a community service program implemented in the Springfield, Massachusetts, schools. They describe a program built around the following components:

1. Establish a schoolwide service-learning theme.
2. Determine the objectives.
3. Meet with community representatives.
4. Build a repertoire of activities.
5. Develop learning experiences.
6. Establish a time line.
7. Reflect on the experience.
8. Celebrate.

One of the Springfield schools, Lincoln School, adopted a citizenship theme to help develop a sense of community within the school. The guiding idea was, "If children are exposed in their formative years to the values of participation in the community, they will internalize those values. . . . The climate of the school is orderly, friendly, open and warm. Negative behavior is rare, and children routinely choose to be helpful, kind, and caring" (Anderson, 1993, p. 162).

Children live what they learn. If you give your students love, kindness, fairness, consideration, politeness, and warmth, they will reflect it. I can remember in my own elementary teaching experience that I routinely thanked a child every time he or she handed me a paper. It became a matter of course that students would always thank me or others when we handed out papers. Courtesy—in an age where drivers show extreme anger toward one another on the streets of our cities and rudeness is displayed in a dozen different ways—is something that must become natural behavior when a child is young.

Citizenship Is Understanding Conflict

Rowe (1992) describes a conflict model of citizenship education designed in Britain. The model is designed to stimulate critical and reflective thought built around key questions such as the following:

- What rules are needed for people to live together?
- Why do people break rules, and what should happen to them?
- What makes a rule or a law fair?
- Who has rights, and what are they?
- What responsibilities arise from these rights?
- What happens when our rights conflict with the rights of others?
- Who can tell you what to do and on what basis?
- What makes a good or fair leader?
- What is meant by fairness or justice?

To have meaning, these questions must be considered in context and posed in appropriate ways for children of different ages; nevertheless, they are at the very heart of what it means to be a citizen. Teachers can apply these questions to the ordinary routines of schoolwork and play. As Rowe notes, "Posed at an appropriate level, these questions are as interesting and relevant to pupils of seven as they are to moral and political philosophers" (p. 162).

The appealing thing about a conflict model of citizenship is that it addresses the points of tension that arise naturally when people work and play together. To deny that conflicts exist in the lives of children is to limit their moral horizon. Conflict resolution is an ongoing process in a democratic society. Children need to learn at an early age that they can talk about their feelings, share their points of view, and learn to appreciate the fact that others may see things differently from time to time. It's part of a functional, healthy social environment to have a certain amount of conflict.

I would go so far as to say that you should set time aside each day for you and your class to talk about classroom and playground life. Your young citizens should be given ample opportunity to express themselves in an open forum. This is the essence of democracy: to hear and to be heard. If you take this idea seriously and stay with it, you will see considerable advance in your students' insights, openness, reflective thinking, and willingness to participate in the fundamental processes of daily life. Note a child's attempt to articulate the meaning of citizenship, as illustrated in Figure 14.2.

figure **14.2**   *A Child's Essay on Citizenship*

> What is a good citizen?
>
> I think a good citizen is a person who does what he or she is asked to do and obeys the rules. Another thing a good citizen does is when he or she is nice to one another and helps someone out if somebody is hurt or needs help with schoolwork. That's what I think a good citizen is.
>
> Lauren Griffin
> Mr. Johnson's class Grade 5

Citizenship Education: An Interview with JoAnne Buggey

JoAnne Buggey is a nationally recognized authority on social studies and citizenship education. Her work represents some of the best text material on the subject available today. She is known by her students and by the educational community to be an outstanding educator. Following is an interview with Buggey concerning citizenship education.*

WHAT ARE THE IMPLICATIONS OF CITIZENSHIP EDUCATION FOR CHILDREN? Effective citizenship education has been a major concern of educators in the United States throughout our history. All that occurs in our schools each day can be broadly interpreted as citizenship education. In addition, it is a central focus of the social studies. The role of citizenship education in the elementary school is to prepare students for their roles as responsible decision makers and concerned citizens. The focus is on setting the stage for a life of meaningful participation for each and every learner.

WHAT CAN TEACHERS AND CHILDREN DO TO BRING CITIZENSHIP EDUCATION TO LIFE? Social studies textbooks continue to provide the firm foundation for meaningful citizenship education in most classrooms. Children's literature provides a valuable resource for building on the textbook. Extending activities beyond the classroom and into the community is the ultimate goal. In order for this to happen, a total community-involvement program must be developed. The teacher/school and parent/community must interact in a planned and meaningful way for citizenship education to come alive for students.

CAN YOU CITE SOME EXAMPLES OF CLASSES OR SCHOOLS THAT ARE DOING A GOOD JOB OF CITIZENSHIP EDUCATION? It is most effective when a school adopts *citizenship education* as its school theme. However, there are individual classrooms where citizenship is also a meaningful focus. The following are only a few examples:

- Kindergarten classes and the forestry department worked together during the year on a community reforestation project. Pictures were taken of each tree being planted. Students continued to observe the trees throughout their grade school experience.
- The parents and their first-graders organized a community cleanup campaign as a result of student interest in pollution. Teams worked several Saturdays cleaning up areas of their community. Posters were displayed to try to get others interested in keeping the community clean.
- Second-graders worked with the local police department on a bicycle safety program. The culmination of the program was a Bicycle Safety Day.

*This interview is reprinted with the permission of Dr. JoAnne Buggey.

- Third-graders took a survey of the community regarding the installation of street lights at an intersection near the school. Students devised the survey, and teams of students and parents collected the information. Results were sent to the city council.
- Fourth-graders subscribed to the local newspaper and several news magazines. They worked in teams, each of which focused on one problem. Once a month, they produced a class newspaper in which each group summarized its special problem area. They distributed the paper to each class in the school.
- Fifth-graders belonged to the Birthday Club at a nearby senior citizen residence. Each month, those students who had a birthday attended the party at the senior residence. Students participated in the entertainment and made cards for their birthday friends.
- Sixth-graders were in charge of organizing a mock election for the school. The election took place in November in conjunction with the local election. Everyone had a chance to vote. Students made posters and gave campaign speeches. Election results were reported and compared to local election results.

WHAT ARE THE KEY CONCEPTS OF CITIZENSHIP EDUCATION?   There are many key concepts relating to effective citizenship education. The following are only a few: patriotism, government, participation, caring, rights and responsibilities, and rules and laws. (Figure 14.3 illustrates the relationships between a citizen's rights and responsibilities.)

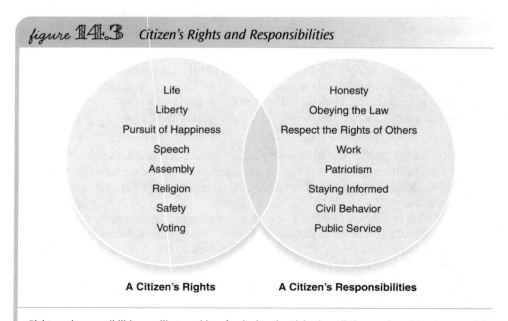

figure **14.3**   *Citizen's Rights and Responsibilities*

A Citizen's Rights	A Citizen's Responsibilities
Life	Honesty
Liberty	Obeying the Law
Pursuit of Happiness	Respect the Rights of Others
Speech	Work
Assembly	Patriotism
Religion	Staying Informed
Safety	Civil Behavior
Voting	Public Service

Rights and responsibilities are like two sides of a single coin. Rights have little meaning without responsibilities. Each gives meaning to the other.

What Do Children Need to Know to Be Active Citizens?

Much of what children are taught in school consists of *information*. They are told or they read about places, names, events, and dates. This is exactly what information is: unconnected bits and pieces that the learner is supposed to make sense of. Some children see or make their own connections, but most do not.

Social studies, especially with its bewildering array of facts, is difficult to understand and appreciate. The problem is quite simple: information overload. The solution is even simpler: Create meaningful experiences. But in spite of how easy it is to identify both problem and solution, few teachers seem to grasp the obvious.

Knowledge versus Information

For citizenship education to be effective, we must lead our students beyond the horizon of information. One can have information about the three branches of the government and not be a particularly good citizen. One can know that the United States consumes something close to 40 percent of the world's natural resources and do nothing about it. One can be aware about poverty in one's neighborhood and not try to help. Information in learning is like a spectator sport: Watching tennis on television won't make you physically fit or even sweaty.

Jean Piaget once noted that verbal knowledge is not real knowledge. By that, he meant that there are differences between *information* and *knowledge*. John Dewey noted that the abstract nature of the curriculum prevented it from having intellectual potential. He explained that most of what children are taught is merely abstract information from books or lectures. The principle of constructivism states that activity or experience must precede analysis. The point of all this is that you must seek ways to actively involve your students in learning, particularly in learning about what it means to be a citizen in a democratic society.

Let me give you an example of learning about citizenship through experience. An elementary school in Kingston, Washington, recently decided to study the Asian–Pacific Economic Cooperation (APEC) group of nations. The United States and Canada are member nations of APEC, as are Japan, China, South Korea, Australia, New Zealand, Singapore, Taiwan, and a few others. Led by the school principal, every teacher and student in the school studied about APEC. It was very much a hands-on study, with emphasis on letter writing, performances, speeches, maps, drawings, and construction.

This is very different from merely studying these countries from a text. The two basic differences between this experience and traditional instruction are (1) the study took place around a theme (APEC) involving the whole school and (2) the learning was active and experiential. Another example is reflected in Sample Lesson 14.1.

To learn to be a good citizen, a child must work with others, become actively involved, and somehow see himself or herself as contributing to knowledge as opposed to taking in information. The beneficial outcome of such an approach is that students enjoy learning more, retain more knowledge, and get to practice being a participating citizen.

Experiences in democracy should be an integral part of school life.

Keys to Being a Well-Prepared Citizen

Kathleen Cotton (1996) identifies these six key attributes:

- *Democratic values.* Prepared citizens understand and are committed to the values inherent in the U.S. Constitution and Bill of Rights: justice, freedom, equality, diversity, authority, privacy, due process, property, participation, truth, patriotism, human rights, rule of law, tolerance, mutual assistance, personal and civic responsibility, self-restraint, and self-respect.
- *Respect for the common good.* Citizens need to act from respect for the common good; that is, they need to be willing to deliberate about the nature of the public good and how to achieve it. They also need to possess

compassion, ethical commitment, social responsibility, and a sense of interdependence among people and between people and their environment. They need to express their commitment to the common good through their actions, such as voting, volunteering, serving on juries, petitioning the government for change, and so on.

- *Knowledge.* Effective civic education results in knowledge and understanding of our nation's founding documents, the structure of government, the political process, and the global context in which the United States functions.
- *Thinking skills.* Competent citizens require skills in higher-level thinking processes—critical reasoning, problem solving, decision

making, perspective taking, divergent thinking—as well as constructing hypotheses and evaluating evidence.

- *Social process skills.* Social skills identified as critical for high-functioning citizens include communication, conflict management, consensus building, and working in cooperative endeavors.

- *Appropriate attitudes.* Effective civic education influences students in such a way that they believe in the efficacy of civic participation, are interested in participating, and have a feeling of obligation to participate.

Source: Adapted from Cotton, 1996, pp. 6–7.

What Can You Do to Help Your Students Become Active Citizens?

Americans live in the world's oldest constitutional democracy. The U.S. Constitution was drafted and ratified in the period from 1787–1789, well before far older European nations began their march toward democracy and citizenship. And today, more than two centuries later, the Declaration of Independence and the American Revolution still serve as reminders that free institutions and individual freedoms are precious achievements. The road to freedom has not always been an easy one for many Americans. In 1863, black Americans were finally set free from the tyranny of slavery, and in 1918, women were at long last allowed to vote.

Believe me, teaching citizenship education to young children is one of the most important contributions you can make as a teacher. The children you teach will assume positions of leadership and responsibility well into the twenty-first century. More and more of them will have been born in this century, which means they will set the course for the twenty-second century. The trust and responsibility placed in your hands is one of destiny—certainly of this nation and perhaps even the world. It was noted by French statesman and author Alexis de Tocqueville, who made a thorough investigation of American life in the nineteenth century, that democracy is not a "machine that would go of itself." It is your task and mine to keep democracy alive by inspiring the young toward meaningful participatory citizenship.

Citizenship education at its best takes place at two separate but related levels that we can call the *formal* and the *informal*. Each is necessary, and each supports the other. *Formal citizenship education* involves the academic study of history, civics, literature, the arts, and other subjects. *Informal citizenship education* is experiential, often involving the life of the classroom, the playground, the community, and the home. The high art of teaching weaves the formal and the informal into a seamless whole.

Formal Strategies for Citizenship Education

As just noted, the formal curriculum involves the study of civics and government. Students need to learn the functions of political systems at the local, state, and national levels. They need to understand the relationship of the United States to other countries, many of which have quite different systems of governance.

Following is a sampling of specific strategies that can be used at the elementary level, each of which takes into account developmentally appropriate practice:

- Students should learn that in most cases, elections decide who will govern. They should know the basic responsibilities of their mayor and city council, their governor and state legislature, and their president and Congress. Every city and town has a charter; obtain a copy for your class to study.
- Students should learn that certain officials are appointed to office. This includes many officials who serve in the judicial branch of government, including the U.S. Supreme Court. A letter written by your class to a member of the judiciary is sure to bring a response.
- Students should become acquainted with the meanings of such documents of liberty as the Magna Carta, the Declaration of Independence, and the Constitution. Many children have never even been taught the meaning of the flag salute, even though they may go through the ritual daily.
- Students need to understand the rights and duties of citizens in a democracy. Reviewing the Bill of Rights is a good place to start. Your class can author its own Bill of Rights and Responsibilities. Sample Lesson 14.2 shows one way to introduce concepts of civic responsibility.
- Share the newspaper with your students. Every day, it contains articles about local, state, and national government; international affairs; and other issues of moral, social, and political significance.
- Students need to become familiar with the lives and contributions of outstanding citizens. No child should leave elementary school without formal knowledge of the work of Martin Luther King Jr., George Washington, Abraham Lincoln, and others who sacrificed much to make all Americans' lives better.

Informal Strategies for Citizenship Education

Formal citizenship education initiates the process by exposing children to ideas, but ideas take hold best when they are related to direct experience. That's the role of informal teaching and learning, and it's especially crucial at the elementary level. Experience is the key. As stated throughout this book, children learn what they live.

Here are some sample informal strategies:

- Create opportunities for service learning at all levels, K–12. All children need to become involved in community projects, and community members need to become involved in the life of the school. Your task is to determine and arrange age-appropriate opportunities for your students to serve.
- Make your classroom and school miniature democracies. The essence of democracy is citizens' engagement in decision making and conflict resolution, in working with others, in taking responsibility, and in practicing self-governance. Holding

class meetings, participating in school assemblies, and helping to make rules of conduct give students the practice they need to become responsible citizens.

- Be sure your students have opportunities to work with others beyond the classroom. Older students can pair with younger students for tutorial purposes, and volunteers from the community can be invited to work with students in school.
- Connect the classroom to the home. Assign topics for students to discuss with their families.
- Take advantage of the opportunities to reflect on the social/moral life of school. Issues related to fairness, sharing, cooperation, bullying, cheating, fighting, and the like occur quite naturally in classrooms and schools. They provide opportunities for reflection and action by students.
- Create a civil society. Manners are close to morality. Children need to experience a polite, concerned, and compassionate environment in the classroom. How they are treated there will be mirrored in how they treat others. Respect builds respect. Tolerance creates tolerance.

Research Findings on Civic Education

Citizenship and civic education are closely related. Together, they form a crucial cornerstone of the goal structure of elementary social studies. What should our young citizens know and be able to do as a result of their study of such topics in the social studies curriculum?

The National Assessment of Educational Progress (NAEP) (1998), an organization that measures achievement in a variety of academic disciplines, has identified three areas that should be the focus of social studies instruction in citizenship:

1. *Civic knowledge.* There are five categories of civic knowledge that every student should master:

- Civic life, politics, and government
- Foundations of the American political system
- How the government established by the Constitution represents the purposes, values, and principles of American society
- The relationship of the United States to other nations and to world affairs
- The roles of citizens in American democracy

Of course, this knowledge is developmental and to be gained over the entire span of the K–12 school experience. But keep in mind the necessity of developing the foundations of this knowledge at the elementary level. If this does not happen, the American high school graduate will be greatly diminished in his or her potential to contribute to civic life.

2. *Civic skills.* Students should be able to demonstrate both intellectual and participatory skills. *Intellectual skills* include the abilites to identify, describe, explain, and evaluate and to take and defend positions on public issues. *Participatory skills* include working with others, expressing ideas, and managing conflict.

3. *Civic dispositions.* Civic dispositions are the ideals held by citizens, including beliefs in the rights and responsibilities of individuals in society and in the advancement of the ideals of government in a democratic society. Such dispositions include participating in civic life through elections, community service, and personal, political, and economic responsibilities.

The NAEP test is administered to fourth-, eighth-, and twelfth-graders nationally. Typical NAEP questions for grades 4 and 8 are shown in Figure 14.4.

Research findings generated by the NAEP (1998) show that while there is some room for encouragement, we could be doing much better. This is the challenge for you as a teacher of elementary social studies. Here are selected findings in summary form, along with questions for you to think about:

1. Students in classrooms where civic education is taught for more than one hour per week tend to do much better on tests of civic knowledge, skills, and dispositions than their counterparts who receive less instruction. What conclusion do you draw from this finding?
2. Twenty-one percent of public school fourth-graders scored at the "proficient" level of achievement, while 35 percent of nonpublic school fourth-graders scored at the "proficient" level. What can you and I do to increase civics achievement for *all* children?
3. Students who discuss civic issues related to their school experience at home tend to score higher than those who do not. What can teachers do to make home discussions of civics more likely?
4. Fourth-grade students who use the Internet consistently in the classroom (at least once a week) have higher civics scores than those who do not. How can the Internet be used effectively as a teaching/learning tool?

You can make a difference by taking several positive practical steps. Let's turn to some strategies that you can implement along the pathway to better civic education and improved citizenship. As we do this, we will explore the natural link between civic education and character education.

Effective Citizenship Education

Effective citizenship education has been a major concern of educators in the United States throughout its history. Much of what occurs in our schools each day, including the teaching of the three Rs, can be interpreted as preparation of our citizens. James Madison identified the importance of citizenship education when he stated, "A people who mean to be their own governors must arm themselves with the power which knowledge gives." More than a hundred years ago, Herbert Spencer restated the importance of citizenship education when he wrote, "The need to function as effective citizens called for familiar school subjects: history, civics, economics, and politics. These subjects should stress practical application."

figure **14.4**   *NAEP Test Questions for Grades 4 and 8*

GRADE 4 SAMPLE QUESTIONS AND RESPONSES

Basic Level—Sample Question and Response

Scott wants to be a police officer when he grows up. He says the police get to wear fancy uniforms with badges, use hadcuffs, and drive cars as fast as they want. What is wrong with Scott's ideas about why he wants to be a police officer?

He thinks he gets to be big and powerful because he gets to brake the rules of others

Think about the things police officers do in rtheir work. What are two good reasons to be a police officer?

1) *You discipline people so they can learn from your mistakes.*

2) *Make peace between people that are fighting and fix the poroblem.*

67% of all 4th graders received a rating of "Acceptable" or better.*

Percentage of students at each achievement level who received a rating of "Acceptable" or better		
Basic	*Proficient*	*Advanced*
71%	87%	◆

* The percentage of all fourth graders includes those who were below *Basic*.
◆Too few fourth graders reached the *Advanced* level to report the results for this question.

This constructed-response question was designed to measure students' ability to tell the difference between power and authority. The response shown received a score of "3" ("Acceptable") on a four-point scale and represents the *Basic* level at grade 4. Although the first part of this response was not credited because its meaning was unclear, both reasons the student gave for being a police officer were credited.

Proficient Level—Sample Question

11. Which of the following is the most important reason why the United States trades with other countries?

   A   People get a chance to travel.

   (B)   It help people get the things they need.

   C   It helps us learn about other cultures.

   D   We can learn other languages.

49% of all 4th graders answered this question correctly.*

Percentage of students at each achievement level who answered correctly.		
Basic	*Proficient*	*Advanced*
49%	70%	◆

* The percentage of all fourth graders includes those who were below *Basic*.
◆Too few fourth graders reached the *Advanced* level to report the results for this question.

The multiple-choice question measured students' understanding of international trade. While reasons A, C, and D may result when the United States trades with other countries, reason B is clearly the most important. Fourth graders at the Proficient level were likely to choose the correct response.

GRADE 8 SAMPLE QUESTIONS AND RESPONSES

Proficient Level—Sample Question

Two countries both claim that an island in the Pacific Ocean belongs to them. The countries are preparing to go to war with each other over this issues.

What is the United Nations able to do to help end the conflict?

   A   Send weapons to both sides.

   B   Disarm the militaries of both countries.

   (C)   Arrange for diplomatic negotiations between the two countries.

   D   Force all other countries to stop trading with the two countries.

77% of all 8th graders answered this question correctly.*

Percentage of students at each achievement level who answered correctly.		
Basic	*Proficient*	*Advanced*
84%	94%	◆

* The percentage of all fourth graders includes those who were below *Basic*.
◆Too few fourth graders reached the *Advanced* level to report the results for this question.

This eight-grade question falls within the civics knowledge category of the United States and its relationship to other countries and to world affairs. It was designed to measure students' understanding of what the United Nations can do to help resolve international conflicts. Eight graders at the *Basic* level were likely to choose the correct response.

Source: NAEP, 1998.

Citizenship education was clearly to be a central focus of the social studies. Whether it should continue to be was asked many times in the twentieth century. This question has recently gained renewed emphasis. Current societal problems, a stress on back to basics, and an increased concern for patriotism and global education have all worked to renew interest in citizenship education. The National Council for the Social Studies has defined outcomes for citizenship education (see Figure 14.5). Researchers and writers in the area of citizenship education also have given us a clear picture of how schools can contribute to the goal of producing good citizens. They point to such factors as school and classroom climate, teaching practices, student experiences, and the content and materials taught and learned.

John Dewey's dream of school as a miniature democracy represents a school and classroom ideal. In fact, there are a number of ways in which a school *cannot* be a democracy, but it can be a place where certain democratic values can be lived and learned. For example, you can allow your students to participate in decisions that affect school and classroom life. It is easy for adults to overlook how meaningful it is for a child to choose among alternative possibilities in carrying out an assignment. Students can and should be encouraged to make classroom rules. They should have class government with elected officers. They should take responsibility for helping to decorate and keep the room orderly.

Beyond these matters, a more subtle issue of class climate emerges. It has to do with how open your classroom is. According to Angell's (1991) review of the research, an *open classroom* is characterized by democratic leadership behaviors, positive teacher verbal behaviors, respect for students, peer interaction, open discussion, student participation, and cooperation. Interestingly, another factor related to openness is the use by students of source materials other than textbooks. According to researcher Torney-Purta (1983), allowing students to express their opinions freely is the most positive contribution a teacher can make toward the acquisition of democratic values.

Teachers who are committed to citizenship education realize that good citizenship is an active role, and therefore the classroom must be a place dedicated to active learning. A great deal of support has already been given to active learning for other pedagogical reasons, so this only strengthens the case. Passively learning facts about citizenship will not do. Children must experience active learning in order to practice doing what involved citizens do. Nothing does this better than group projects that involve teamwork, decisions, investigation, and production.

A number of learning strategies are recommended to facilitate citizenship education, many of which are discussed in other chapters in this book. Those strategies include practice in class discussion, the use of open-ended and higher-level questions by teachers, research by children using sources other than textbooks, writing projects (including letter writing), cooperative group projects, brainstorming, role-play, simulations, field trips and onsite investigations, observation, class meetings, class and school government, community service projects, and interaction with guest speakers. Of particular importance is the much needed component of reflective thinking. The strategies enumerated in this paragraph have much deeper implications

figure **14.5**   *NCSS Expectations for Civic Education*

Social studies programs should include experiences that provide for the study of *the ideals, principles, and practices of citizenship in a democratic republic,* so that the learner can:

Early Grades

a. identify key ideals of the United States' democratic republican form of government, such as individual human dignity, liberty, justice, equality, and the rule of law, and discuss their application in specific situations;
b. identify examples of rights and responsibilities of citizens;
c. locate, access, organize, and apply information about an issue of public concern from multiple points of view;
d. identify and practice selected forms of civic discussion and participation consistent with the ideals of citizens in a democratic republic;
e. explain actions citizens can take to influence public policy decisions;
f. recognize that a variety of formal and informal actors influence and shape public policy;

g. examine the influence of public opinion on personal decision-making and government policy on public issues;
h. explain how public policies and citizen behaviors may or may nor reflect the stated ideals of a democratic republican form of government;
i. describe how public policies are used to address issues of public concern;

j. recognize and interpret how the "common good" can be strengthened through various forms of citizen action.

Middle Grades

a. examine the origins and continuing influence of key ideals of the democratic republican form of government, such as individual human dignity, liberty, justice. equality, and the rule of law;
b. identify and interpret sources and examples of the rights and responsibilities of citizens;
c. locate, access, analyze, organize, and apply information about selected public issues—recognizing and explaining multiple points of view;
d. practice forms of civic discussion and participation consistent with the ideals of citizens in a democratic republic;
e. explain and analyze various forms of citizen action that influence public policy decisions;
f. identify and explain the roles of formal and informal political actors in influencing and shaping public policy and decision-making;
g. analyze the influence of diverse forms of public opinion on the development of public policy and decision-making;
h. analyze the effectiveness of selected public policies and citizen behaviors in realizing the stated ideals of a democratic republican form of government;
i. explain the relationship between policy statements and action plans used to address issues of public concern;
j. examine strategies designed to strengthen the "common good," which consider a range of options for citizen action.

Source: Expectations of Excellence: Curriculum Standards for Social Studies (p. 44), Bulletin 89, Fall 1994, Washington, DC: NCSS. © National Council for the Social Studies. Reprinted by permission.

for learning and for application to life experiences when students are given ample opportunity to discuss, reflect, seek meaning, and employ a range of metacognitive techniques.

Keys to Effective Citizenship Education

The Carnegie Corporation and the Center for Information and Research on Civic Learning and Engagement (2005) commissioned a group of more than 50 distinguished scholars and practitioners to summarize the evidence in support of civic education in K–12 school settings. The group cited these six research-based recommendations for effective programs:

- *Study a wide range of topics.* Students perform better on tests of civic skills and knowledge if they have studied a range of relevant subjects, such as the Constitution, U.S. history, the structure of government and elections, and the legal system.
- *Use interactive lessons.* Students who participate in active debates related to current issues have greater interest in politics, improved critical-thinking and communication skills, and are more likely to say they will vote and volunteer as adults.
- *Include service learning.* Service learning provides students with applications of what they learn. Service learning can be more effective at installing civic skills and values among students than volunteer work that's not connected to the school curriculum.
- *Encourage student participation in school governance.* Research suggests that giving students more opportunities to help manage their own classrooms and schools builds civic skills and attitudes.
- *Encourage extracurricular participation.* Long-term studies show that students who participate in extracurricular activities remain more civically engaged than those who do not.
- *Consider using simulations.* Evidence indicates that simulations of voting, trials, legislative deliberations, and diplomacy can lead to students becoming more interested in and informed about politics and government.

Of course, these research findings need to be applied in developmentally appropriate ways for children to benefit from them. But notice that the common thread running throughout the findings is that classrooms and schools that practice democracy, active learning, and engagement in the community are making a difference.

Community Service

Community service-learning projects deserve additional mention here because they truly are at the heart of what it means to be a giving, participating person in one's school, neighborhood, larger community, and so on. To quote Berman (1990), "Community service efforts build self-esteem and allow students to experience themselves as part of the larger network of people who are helping to create a better world" (p. 76). A review of the writing and research on service-learning projects indicates that several variables, when present, enhance the effectiveness of such experiences.

Community service-learning projects should address real needs. Elementary school children are perfectly well equipped to take the age-old "Community Helpers" study to deeper levels by becoming community helpers themselves. Among the projects that work well are such involvements as an ongoing relationship with a nursing home near the school where the children touch the lives of elderly people, many of whom are lonely and whose days tend to be tedious; projects such as cleaning up a stream, pond, or field near the school; assembling published local histories and geographies in conjunction with the local historical society, museum, or library; the production of dramas or pageants to which community people are invited; volunteer efforts by older elementary-age students who are willing to read to young children; and even a school carnival experience, if the children can be meaningfully involved, is an excellent means of bringing community people to the school and creating a positive image. Take a moment to consider this child's experience as she reflected on her visits to a nearby nursing home:

> When our class went there first I didn't know what to think. The people were old and it smelled funy. But everyone was nice they were happy when we gave them the pictures. My frend Helen put my picture of my dog on her wall. His name is Tykey. Now she asks me about Tykey and I told her he took some meat off the table when my mom went outside. The we started lafing. Helen is hapy to see me I love her. Some of the people ded there to. Mrs Lowe tokked to us about it.

Among the other research-based recommendations (Cotton, 1996) for community service projects are that they should (1) incorporate academic skills, (2) provide opportunities for young people to be depended on, (3) encourage collaborative work, (4) give students responsibility for organizing and following through, and (5) produce a tangible product or evidence of accomplishment.

Decision Making

In a democratic society, citizens are expected to participate as fully as possible in the decision-making process. A citizen entering a voting booth keeps alive and passes on a centuries-old tradition of right and privilege.

Yet, one wonders how people learn (or are taught) to make wise and good decisions. Even though it is important to focus on political decision making, don't forget that people make hundreds of personal decisions every day. Those decisions range from whether to wear blue socks or white socks, whether to cook dinner or grab some hamburgers, whether to play outside or watch television, and so on, depending on the circumstances. Of course, if the person has only a pair of blue socks, little money, and no television, the choices are narrowed.

Decision making, therefore, is a function of the alternatives available to the individual. In a country offering only one political slate of candidates, no decision making is necessary. In a classroom in which the teacher makes all decisions, students have no opportunity to develop the skill. I argue that you should provide numerous opportunities for your students to make decisions, and in at least some cases, those decisions should be real and not merely part of a case study or a contrived activity.

As Kathleen Cotton (1996) has so correctly pointed out, "Nearly all writers on the subject of citizenship education agree that it is essential for preserving America's democratic way of life" (p. 1). Cotton reviewed some 93 articles and reports on citizenship education and developed a profile of the good citizen as a person who is informed, autonomous, respectful, participating, mindful of the common good, and committed to democratic values and principles.

In an educational experiment I helped conduct, a class of first-graders was given a half hour of free time each day. The children were told they could do whatever they chose during the free time. A few rules were agreed on, such as no leaving the room except by permission and being fairly quiet.

There were two reasons for giving the students this free time. One was to give them the opportunity to make real decisions about something important—their time and how to use it. The other reason was to see if the children could put the time to constructive use.

The teacher was instructed to develop a rich classroom environment, with games, interest centers, a small library, art materials, and science mate-

rials. The teacher was also instructed to interact with the students, not by telling them what to do but by talking personally to them, helping them with various tasks, and reviewing their free-time use.

The outcome was very gratifying. The children showed that they could make wise decisions about their use of free time. In fact, they invariably chose productive activities that permitted cooperative learning, language development, sharing, taking turns, peer teaching, and exploration. The free time provided a wonderful opportunity for growth in such areas as responsibility, organization, reflection, and planning. The experiment lasted the entire year and received many parental compliments.

Sadly, there is little evidence that social studies teachers take these attributes seriously in terms of the day-to-day experiences in classrooms. In fact, there is some reason to think that the way citizenship education is typically taught, mainly through textbooks, that those attributes are in fact not a high curricular priority.

I've laid out the problem pretty clearly: As teachers, you and I need to do a better job of educating for citizenship. I don't feel very good about giving you such bad news, but you are the country's best hope for turning things around. What can you do to improve the situation?

To begin, take a few minutes to study the Keys to Effective Citizenship Education on page 360 and the NCSS outcomes in Figure 14.5 (page 359). As you do, keep in mind that these are desired outcomes of the entire school experience, grades K–12. Thus, the attributes listed represent the profile we hope to produce over time, not overnight. Using the basic premise of the spiral curriculum—identifying important concepts and teaching them each year at increasing levels of sophistication—we can imagine that primary students can learn these attributes through simpler experiences that have meaning in their lives and that intermediate students will continue the journey.

The Meaning of Citizenship: A Global Perspective

No one can deny any longer that the world is interdependent. The global village predicted by Marshall McLuhan in the midtwentieth century has come to pass. Rather than live in a world of cold war, two superpowers, and a tense world peace based on the prospect of mutually assured nuclear destruction, we live in a world where global corporation often produces more than nations, where whole industries depend on workforces located across oceans, and where the prospect of war within nations, rather than between nations, is more real. International corporations know no borders—and neither do terrorist organizations. On September 11, 2001, the United States felt the reality of a foreign attack on its continental soil for the first time in its history.

Now more than ever, our children must learn to live together peacefully. Overarching organizations, such as the European Union, the Group of Eight, and the United Nations, struggle to bring collaboration to global efforts. The Charter of the United Nations, written in 1948, has seldom seemed more relevant (see Figure 14.6).

Much closer to home, we must find ways to help children understand their role as citizens of the world as well as their country. That's the idea underlying *global education,* which is discussed in the following section. Figure 14.7 identifies recommendations by the NCSS (1994) for how social studies programs can address the concepts of *global connections* and *interdependence* at the early and middle grades.

One simple yet effective approach to global education is illustrated by Figure 14.8, the drawing of a Lithuanian child who corresponds regularly with American pen pals.

figure **14.6**   *Preamble to the United Nations Charter*

UNITED NATIONS HIGH COMMISSIONER FOR HUMAN RIGHTS

Charter of the United Nations

Preamble

We the Peoples of the United Nations Determined

to save succeeding generations from the scourge of war, which twice in our lifetime has brought untold sorrow to mankind, and

to reaffirm faith in fundamental human rights, in the dignity and worth of the human person, in the equal rights of men and women and of nations large and small, and

to establish conditions under which justice and respect for the obligations arising from treaties and other sources of international law can be maintained, and

to promote social progress and better standards of life in larger freedom,

And for these Ends

to practice tolerance and live together in peace with one another as good neighbors, and

to unite our strength to maintain international peace and security, and

to ensure by the acceptance of principles and the institution of methods, that armed force shall not be used, save in the common interest, and

to employ international machinery for the promotion of the economic and social advancement of all peoples,

Have Resolved to Combine our Efforts to Accomplish these Aims

Accordingly, our respective Governments, through representatives assembled in the city of San Francisco, who have exhibited their full powers found to be in good and due form, have agreed to the present Charter of the United Nations and do hereby establish an international organization to be known as the United Nations.

figure **14.7** *NCSS Standards for Global Education*

Social studies programs should include experiences that provide for the study of *global connections and interdependence,* so that the learner can:

Early Grades

a. explore ways that language, art, music, belief systems, and other cultural elements may facilitate global understanding or lead to misunderstanding

b. give examples of conflict, cooperation, and interdependence among individuals, groups, and nations;

c. examine the effects of changing technologies on the global community;

d. explore causes, consequences, and possible solutions to persistent, contemporary, and emerging global issues, such as pollution and endangered species;

e. examine the relationships and tensions between personal wants and needs and various global concerns, such as use of imported oil, land use, and environmental protection;

f. investigate concerns, issues, standards, and conflicts related to universal human rights, such as the treatment of children, religious groups, and effects of war.

Middle Grades

a. describe instances in which language, art, music, belief systems, and other cultural elements can facilitate global understanding or cause misunderstanding;

b. analyze examples of conflict, cooperation, and interdependence among groups, societies, and nations;

c. describe and analyze the effects of changing technologies on the global community;

d. explore the causes, consequences, and possible solutions to persistent, contemporary, and emerging global issues, such as health, security, resource allocation, economic development, and environmental quality;

e. describe and explain the relationships and tensions between national sovereignty and global interests, in such matters as territory, natural resources, trade, use of technology, and welfare of people;

f. demonstrate understanding of concerns, standards, issues, and conflicts related to universal human rights,

g. identify and describe the roles of international and multinational organizations.

Source: Expectations of Excellence: Curriculum Standards for Social Studies (p. 45), Bulletin 89, Fall 1994, Washington, DC: NCSS. © National Council for the Social Studies. Reprinted by permission.

What a perfect way for children to make a global connection! Through this type of correspondence, children learn not only about one another as individuals but as members of other countries and cultures. Certainly, the experience of actually *knowing* someone from another country cannot be replicated by any amount of reading or research.

Global Education: An Interview with John J. Cogan

John J. Cogan is my colleague in elementary social studies education. He is widely known as an expert on global education. Following is an interview with Cogan concerning global education.*

*This interview is reprinted with the permission of John J. Cogan.

figure **14.8** *The Statue of Liberty Drawing of a Lithuanian Child Involved in Exchanging Letters with American Students*

WHAT IS GLOBAL EDUCATION? It is a way of viewing the world. Simply stated, global education is a systematic effort to communicate the awareness that the planet Earth and the people who live on it are increasingly *interdependent*—that is, we are all citizens of the world as well as of our respective nations. It is a way of viewing and thinking about the world that is quite different from traditional models. What one nation does

Today's students must prepare to be citizens of the world's "global village."

today greatly affects other nations. The day when each nation "does its own thing" is no longer applicable, if indeed, it ever was.

IS THIS JUST ONE MORE SPECIAL-INTEREST GROUP SEEKING A PLACE IN THE CURRICU-LUM?   No. People supportive of global education come from all walks of life. Although some see global education as the sole province of the social studies, most supporters believe strongly that global education should permeate *all* areas of the curriculum—that is, science, math, language, music, art, and so on. What is not needed is another course added to an already overcrowded curriculum. Rather, a global perspective should be woven into the very fabric of the elementary curriculum. We need to help in-service and prospective teachers see how they can highlight a global perspective in existing programs. This necessitates making them personally aware of just how interdependent the world in which they live is—for example, just bringing to their attention how many of the many products they use during any given day are from another country, or where products raised or manufactured in their communities are sent internationally. This is easy enough to do and yet doesn't overwhelm the teacher. If teachers begin slowly and do a little at a time, the overall picture will begin to develop.

WHAT ARE SOME POSITIVE OUTCOMES OF GLOBAL EDUCATION?   This, of course, rests in part on how one interprets *positive*. I would interpret it as "furthering the development of the human condition." In this context, there are several hoped-for outcomes as a result of global education programs:

- An increased ability to perceive the world in a more systematic manner.
- An increased awareness of the world as an ecosystem with finite resources that must be carefully managed.

- An increased ability to perceive alternative choices to problems and issues that face all humankind.
- An increased empathy for the worth, dignity, and uniqueness of all members of the human species. We really need to work very hard at breaking down ethnocentric attitudes that become major barriers to understanding one another—break down stereotyping.
- An increased recognition that *all* human beings contribute to the "world bank of culture."
- An increased recognition of the interdependent nature of the planet Earth.
- An increased awareness of one's own values and beliefs in relation to others.

WHAT CRITICISMS ARE TYPICALLY LEVELED AT GLOBAL EDUCATION? There are several criticisms often leveled at global education. They clearly reflect the value orientation of the individual and/or movement with whom they are associated.

One has already been referred to in your question about whether or not this was just a special-interest group trying to get space in the curriculum. Some educators believe that in spite of statements regarding the need to integrate a global perspective into the entire curriculum, what will really happen is that another new course will emerge. They cite their recent experiences with career education, environmental education, ethnic studies, and law education as examples. It's up to us to demonstrate *how* to integrate concepts into ongoing programs to dispel these fears.

Some educators, parents, and pressure groups view the achievements of the United States as demonstration of the fact that "we know best" and thus the rest of the world ought to be modeling us. They fear "basic American values" will be undermined or compromised via a global perspective.

Some people with fundamentalist religious backgrounds view development of a global perspective as a direct contradiction to Biblical teachings. And some people in the business community view the development of a global perspective as a direct threat upon the free enterprise system.

I believe the key factor in all of these criticisms is fear. What people don't understand scares them and thus they reject it. These are not "bad" people. Indeed, most are very well meaning. I think we have failed to communicate adequately the need for a global perspective, given the realities of the modern, technological world in which we live. This is a major task confronting proponents of global education.

AT WHAT AGE SHOULD GLOBAL EDUCATION BEGIN? One major obstacle to introducing global education content into the school curriculum is the belief that young children are not capable of learning the concepts of interdependence, change, and systems. However, available research indicates just the opposite—the primary and middle school years are perhaps the optimal time for introducing these concepts.

An extensive review of research by Judith Torney-Purta (1982) strongly suggests that the years of middle childhood, roughly the ages seven to twelve, may be the ideal period for developing a global perspective. Preconceptions about the world have not yet been formed, and the child may be more receptive to a broader international view than in the later years of schooling. During these early years of primary schooling, the child is moving from what Piaget terms "egocentric" thought, in which actions and attitudes are judged more in terms of the possible personal impact, to more "sociocentric" thought, in which the child considers the broader consequences, not only personally but also for others as well; the child becomes able to understand perspectives other than personal ones.

Torney-Purta summarizes the critical nature of the primary school years in the development of a global perspective:

> These five years, then, are unique. They come *before* too many stereotypic attitudes dominate the child's view of the world, and are *concurrent* with the period in which the child's cognitive development is sufficiently advanced to accept a diversity of viewpoints. This is the time in which learning about the larger world from a global vantage should begin. (p. 202)

WHAT ARE SOME OF THE KEY CONCEPTS OF GLOBAL EDUCATION?   Interdependence is the key concept in global education. This concept of mutual dependence stresses the interrelatedness of and the connections, consequences, and vulnerabilities among natural and social systems; it underlies all other concepts. Other closely related major concepts include change, systems, conflict, cooperation, tolerance, problem solving, cultural diversity, adaptation, modification, responsibility, distribution, pluralisms, and technology.

WHAT WOULD BE MISSING FROM CHILDHOOD EDUCATION IF CHILDREN DID NOT STUDY GLOBAL EDUCATION?   Students in schools today will live their adult lives in the twenty-first century in an increasingly complex and interrelated world. Preparing them to live as effective, responsible citizens has traditionally been a major goal of the social studies. This goal has become even more complex as new developments in scientific technology produce an expanding amount of data and problems, while at the same time developments in the areas of transportation and communication make the world smaller and smaller almost daily. The quality of life these students will experience, possibly their survival on this planet, will depend on the extent to which they develop the abilities to think, feel, and act from a global perspective. In addition to their roles as citizens in their local communities and nations, they will need to assume responsibilities at the global level.

In closing this chapter, think about your own role as an American citizen. Take the citizenship test in Figure 14.9 to see what you know about your country and how it's governed. How do you score?

figure **14.9** *A Citizenship Test*

What are some things every citizen of the United States should know? Immigrants to the United States are given an interview before they take the citizenship test. Following are some sample questions asked of them during the interview. I have turned them into multiple-choice items so that you can respond yourself. See how well you do.

1. What do the stars on the flag mean?
   a. Each star represents a state.
   b. Each star represents a region.
   c. Each star represents a nationality.
   d. Each star represents independence.
2. What are the three branches of the U.S. government?
   a. federal, democratic, republican
   b. metropolitan, regional, national
   c. executive, legislative, judicial
   d. presidential, gubernatorial, mayoral
3. What do we call changes to the Constitution?
   a. additions
   b. corrections
   c. amendments
   d. legislation
4. What is the duty of Congress?
   a. to direct the states
   b. to make the laws
   c. to organize government
   d. to elect governors
5. Which of the following rights is guaranteed by the First Amendment?
   a. the right to have a job
   b. the right to pay taxes
   c. the right to free speech
   d. the right to vote
6. Which of the following three rights is guaranteed by the Bill of Rights?
   a. free speech, freedom of the press, right to assemble
   b. free voting, freedom of liberty, right to celebrate
   c. free declaration, freedom of travel, right to a position
   d. free government, freedom of literacy, right to publish

7. Which of the following is a purpose of the United Nations?
   a. to reaffirm faith in fundamental human rights
   b. to redirect legal control of sovereign nations
   c. to abolish state and international borders
   d. to create new nations using scientific methods
8. Who is the commander of the U.S. military?
   a. the leader of the Joint Chiefs of Staff
   b. the president of the United States
   c. the director of the military command
   d. the general of the army
9. Which of the following is a benefit of being a citizen of the United States?
   a. A citizen has the right to vote in elections.
   b. A citizen has the right to a decent job.
   c. A citizen has the right to fair compensation.
   d. A citizen has the right to own a business.
10. Whose rights are guaranteed by the Constitution and the Bill of Rights?
    a. the rights of the elected
    b. the rights of the citizens
    c. the rights of the voters
    d. the rights of the people
11. What is the basic philosophy of the Declaration of Independence?
    a. All men are entitled to guaranteed jobs.
    b. All men are created equal.
    c. All men are entitled to passports.
    d. All men are created citizens.
12. What did the Emancipation Proclamation do?
    a. It gave citizens the right to vote.
    b. It proclaimed citizenship throughout the land.
    c. It abolished slavery in the United States.
    d. It gave women and children equal rights.

Answers: 1-a; 2-c; 3-c; 4-b; 5-c; 6-a; 7-a; 8-b; 9-a; 10-d; 11-b; 12-c

Summary

A child is a citizen of the family, classroom, school, community, state, country, and the world. Inevitably, our citizenship takes place within diverse and pluralistic environments. The abiding concepts of rights and responsibilities are found within this framework. The classroom and the school offer wonderful possibilities for participation, cooperation, team building, and esprit de corps. These are the building blocks of citizenship education.

Citizenship education is a part of every school activity, but it is especially central to the social studies experience. Elementary social studies stresses its importance at each grade level. Students learn the ideas of citizenship best when they are given the opportunities to experience it in the classroom, the school, and the community.

A classroom should be a miniature community, democratic in structure and experience, in which students participate actively and reflectively in decision-making processes and where they learn what it truly means to work and play together. As they mature, their horizons continue to expand and their sense of rights and responsibility deepens.

Here is a closing thought for your consideration: Philosopher Mortimer Adler has written that only in a democracy can a person be considered a citizen. In an autocracy, a person is not a citizen but a subject. Without freedom and the duties attendant to freedom, there is no citizenship in its deeper meaning.

With that thought in mind, I challenge you to make your classroom a place of opportunity rather than one of restraint. I challenge you to make your classroom a place where children are truly citizens.

Explorations

Reflect On . . .

1. Voting is considered both the right and the responsibility of a citizen, yet less than 50 percent of U.S. citizens typically vote in elections. Why do you think this percentage is so low?
2. What are the key differences between primary-grade and intermediate-grade experiences in citizenship education? What are the key similarities?

In the Field

3. What examples of community service-learning activities have you seen in the classrooms you have visited? How might you make these activities even more focused on citizenship?
4. Describe at least three activities you have observed in schools that taught lessons about citizenship. These don't have to be planned activities but can be the results of spontaneous interactions in the classroom, on the playground, or in the lunchroom.

For Your Portfolio

5. Research citizenship education on the web. Find at least three sample lessons on citizenship that are interactive and stress participation as an active citizen. Print these out and include them in your portfolio.

Continuing the Journey: Suggested Readings

Bennett, L. J. (2004). Classroom recitation of the Pledge of Allegiance and its education value: Analysis, review, proposal. *Journal of Curriculum and Supervision, 20*(1): 56–75.
The article provides opportunities for teachers to work with children in developing understanding and critical thinking skills.

Bickmore, K. (2001). Student conflict resolution, power sharing in schools, and citizenship education. *Curriculum Inquiry, 31*(2), 137–163.
Strategies for peacefully resolving differences and for empowering young people.

Bolen, J. (1999). Taking student government seriously. *Social Studies and the Young Learner, 11*(1), 6–8.
A plea for making student government meaningful and effective.

Carpenter, J. (2004). Jefferson's views on education: Implications for today's social studies. *Social Studies, 95*(4), 140–147.
A look back at Thomas Jefferson's enlightened ideas about education and their relevance for today.

Glover, R., & O'Donnel, B. (2003). Understanding human rights: The development of perspective taking and empathy. *Social Studies and the Young Learner, 15*(3), 15–18.
Ideas for helping children understand and appreciate the idea of the fundamental rights of all human beings.

Lee, W., & Fouts, J. (2005). *Education for social citizenship: Perceptions of teachers in the USA, Australia, England, Russia, and China.* Hong Kong: Hong Kong University Press.
A survey-research based book of teachers' perceptions of citizenship education in five countries.

MacEachron, G. (2005). The Great Depression: Character, citizenship, and history. *Social Studies and the Young Learner, 17*(3), 15–20.
This sensitive article is designed to help children understand the struggles of the Great Depression and its shaping role in today's society.

Nelson, P. (2005). Preparing students for citizenship: Literature and primary documents. *Social Studies and the Young Learner, 17*(3), 21–29.
The use and study of original source material by young historians.

Silva, D., & Mason, T. (2003). Developing pedagogical content knowledge for civics in elementary teacher education. *Theory and Practice in Social Education, 31*(3), 366–397.
This article stresses contextually based methods for studying citizenship.

Wenmik, S. (2004). Reporting on the process of legislation: A civics webquest. *Social Studies and the Young Learner, 17*(1), 11–14.
Insights to how legislation originates and how it becomes law.

SAMPLE LESSON 14.1 *Candidate Debate*

AGE LEVEL: Appropriate for grades 3–8.

PURPOSE: To stimulate a political debate based on issues relevant to third- to fifth-graders, their parents, and the community. To introduce and develop the concept that an informed voter uses his or her voting power to support issues that are important to him or her.

OBJECTIVES: Students will be able to:

1. Participate in a political debate by developing questions, listening, and analyzing responses.

2. Apply their knowledge of a candidate to make an informed choice.

PROCEDURES:

1. We invited the local campaign managers for the candidates for Alaska's one seat in the U.S. House of Representatives: Don Young, representing the Republican incumbent, and Peggy Begich, representing the Democratic challenger. We informed them that they would be representing their candidates in a 45-minute debate.

2. The students were divided into multigrade small groups and asked to list issues of concern at the local, state, and national levels.

3. The large group met and categorized the issues into five basic ones: the environment, natural resources, pollution, education, and the local employment.

4. The students read one to two pages of campaign literature on each candidate. Reading partners were used. Postreading literal and inferential comprehension questions were used to develop questions about the previously agreed on issues for each candidate. The questions were edited and submitted to the questioning panel.

5. The questioning panel was chosen from student volunteers.

6. All students voted on the candidates and filled out short questionnaires concerning the reasons for their choices.

7. Parents and community members were invited to the debate. (The debate proceeded without a hitch except that it was held on Halloween, so the campaign managers were questioned by a punk rocker, a gorilla, and a mummy!) At the end of the formal questioning, before the final comments, four questions were taken from the audience. The level and concerns of the questions showed that the students had listened to the responses and comments closely.

8. The students voted again. Then they were required to interview at least two classmates concerning how they voted and reasons for change or consistency with their previous vote. The students also wrote thank-you notes to the campaign managers, each citing at least one specific reaction or response to information revealed in the debate.

9. The students predicted statewide results using their knowledge of the issues.

10. The students monitored the statewide election results on election day and compared their predictions to the actual results.

CLOSURE: Our students were able to experience the fact-finding procedure of informed voters. We chose not to develop the concept of political parties beyond the introductory level, but many students visited the election headquarters of various candidates. Later that year, when a decrease in school population threatened the closure of our school, our students felt empowered to represent themselves at school board and city assembly meetings and to write letters to the newspaper editor. The feedback that we received from parents was an increase in newspaper reading and participation in political discussions. Our goal to give students methods for finding out about candidates was met, and we were encouraged by the students' choice to participate in other aspects of the political process.

Source: Adapted from a lesson plan submitted by Susan M. Baxter (Harborview School, Juneau, AK) to OFCN's Academy Curricular Exchange, Columbia Education Center, Social Studies.

SAMPLE LESSON 14.2 *A Classroom Civics Meeting*

PURPOSE: To teach students problem solving through the experience of classroom meetings.

CONCEPT: Students will learn the concept of *civic identity* by participating in classroom meetings designed to resolve problems that may arise from classroom and school life. This can be accomplished by focusing on the preconcept of *group membership.*

PROCEDURE: Students meet at regularly scheduled times (e.g., once a week) in order to discuss any problems or issues that may have arisen. The problems/issues may come from the students or may be suggested by the teacher.

The students take responsibility for calling the meeting to order and are expected to carry out the meeting in a polite and orderly fashion. Rules must be established to avoid name calling and bad language and to provide for turn taking and the like.

When everyone has had a turn to speak and the issue has been clarified, an appropriate plan of action should be made.

REFLECTION: Students should be given opportunities to discuss and/or write about their insights or feelings regarding the success of the meeting and the success of the action plan.

CONNECTING: How are classroom meetings like and different from the meetings held by our city council?

ASSESSMENT: Because this procedure involves real problem solving, the measure(s) of success should be taken in the following ways: (1) Did all students have ample opportunity to participate? (2) Did each student feel included in the meeting? (3) Was the decision reached fair and resonable? (4) Was the action plan implemented and evaluated?

chapter 15

Reflective Thinking

The Essence of Social Studies

In this chapter, we will explore the following themes:

key concepts

- How reflective thought develops
- Constructivist thought and social studies
- Social studies strategies for reflection
- Active reflective learning
- The emotional and intellectual landscape

We had the experience but missed the meaning.
            —T. S. Eliot

Cognitive psychology, in general, and the constructivist movement, in particular, have given us major insights into how children learn and how they construct knowledge. Put simply, we know that children learn best in a supportive, active, engaging environment. We also know that human beings construct knowledge both individually and socially on the basis of their experiences. And finally, we know that experience itself is not enough: Human beings also need to reflect on their experiences in order to build meaningful knowledge.

We've been down a long road together. We've taken elementary social studies from theory to practice, from philosophy to application. Now, I'd like to ask you to reflect on what you've learned. How will you synthesize theory and practice into your own model of teaching and learning? What steps will you take to ensure that social studies is engaging, collaborative, enjoyable, and meaningful for you and your students? To help you in your thinking, I will devote some pages to the critical issues of experience, knowledge construction, and reflective thinking.

When you have read this concluding chapter, you should be able to call on the theoretical and practical dimensions covered previously to help you reach some conclusions of your own about how to be a good teacher, and about children as learners. Teaching and learning are practical pursuits, but for the professional, good practice is based on good theory.

It has been noted that "You can have experience without reflection, but you cannot have reflection without experience." After all, you have to have something to reflect about! This is a very important axiom of learning. We want the children we teach to become good citizens, capable scholars, and fulfilled persons. The dreams we have for our students (and our children) become reality as we nurture and support their inquiry and discovery, their teamwork and collaboration, and their growing sense of self and others.

The Importance of Experiential Learning

Teachers today have access to a variety of active teaching and learning strategies, including discovery, inquiry, cooperative learning, simulation, group investigation, and projects. These strategies have made it possible to create attractive, engaging, and potentially productive learning landscapes. Taken together and thoughtfully applied, they have the potential to remove textbooks and workbooks from their position of dominance in the social studies curriculum. These learning strategies have a common property in that they invite learners to share in active experiences, thereby creating a communal frame of reference that emanates from the investigation of an idea or problem.

For children, experience is the port of entry to reflective thinking. Without experience, students are relegated to a school life of verbal knowledge, which is, as Jean Piaget noted, not *real* knowledge. For example, read the article below:

England Fights Back in Tense Test

LONDON—Pace bowler Angus Fraser, not always the first choice of selectors' chairman Ray Illingworth, inspired an England fightback against West Indies in the second test at Lord's on Friday.

Fraser captured his 100th test wicket by removing Brian Lara for six and later produced a burst of two for one to cut short a recovery by Jimmy Adams (54) and captain Richie Richardson (49).

West Indies, replying to England's first innings of 283, were 209 for six at the close of a tense and absorbing second day watched by another capacity 28,000 crowd under cloudless skies.

Fraser, originally overlooked for the 1994–95 tour of Australia before being called up in an injury crisis, and left out of the team who lost the first test to West Indies by nine wickets, ended the day with three for 37 from 20 overs.

Playing on his Middlesex home ground, Fraser set the tone for a much-needed disciplined performance by England's pace bowlers on a dry pitch showing signs of disconcerting bounce.

But for four missed chances in the final session, three from Adams, England might have taken a firm grip.

After England's largely disappointing batting, the need for their bowlers to strike early was answered initially by Darren Gough and Fraser.

Gough struck with the fifth delivery off the West Indian innings, getting opener Sherwin Campbell caught behind for five by Alec Stewart with one that left the batsman a shade.

Now, answer these questions:

- Did you have trouble pronouncing the words? Probably not.
- Did you understand what you read? Probably not.

When I read it, I found that I could barely figure out even the simplest sense of what took place, even which side won. Unless you have a background in the sport of cricket, you probably lack the schema necessary for an understanding of the story.

You and I need to remind ourselves that some children go down this road every day. We tend to confuse *ability* with *prior knowledge.* This is why experiential learning is so important in childhood. The words printed on the page are useful, but only if one's frame of reference can accommodate them.

How Reflective Thought Develops

John Dewey (1916) addressed the crucial nature of experience in learning when he wrote, "The fundamental fallacy in methods of instruction lies in supposing that experience on the part of pupils may be assumed." Dewey went on to say that "ready-made" subject matter and delivery systems in their variety of artificial forms (textbooks, workbooks, lesson plans, etc.) are a "waste of time." That's a pretty strong statement. He stated further that experience with ideas should begin in the most concrete forms and that it should be as "unscholastic" as possible. He advised teachers who wished to involve their students in experience "to call to mind the sort of situation that presents itself outside of school."

Dewey suggested that the most productive ways to engage students involve real problems and social issues. He said that students should begin their inquiry by poking around at a trial-and-error level. The important thing, he said, is the ultimate quality of a problem to be investigated because good problems "give the pupils something to do, not something to learn and the doing is of such a nature as to demand thinking, or the intentional noting of connections; learning naturally results."

Dewey (1916) was convinced that much of what comprises the official learning environment is hostile to reflective thinking. He decried the "great premium put upon listening, reading, and the reproduction of what is told and read." This statement is filled with irony when one considers the potential of social studies to create a sense of community. No wonder, Dewey claimed, that when children go to school, they might as well leave their minds at home, for they cannot use their minds in the abstract curriculum that prevails.

Dewey's observations separate the terms *abstract* and *intellect* with surprising clarity, given the criticism of his writing as conceptually dense and often obtuse. He offers no radical argument against reading or listening as avenues to understanding. Rather, his point is that when these processes are devoid of an experiential backcloth, the learner is left with emptiness, not insight.

Dewey (1916) wrote in the second decade of the twentieth century. One might suppose that learning environments have improved considerably since then. In fact, they have at the level of educational theory, in the realms of research in learning and teaching, and among a relatively small but growing number of informed teachers. Reference to systematic observation in schools, however, reveals less improvement than one might imagine.

The realities of school life changed very little in the twentieth century. John Goodlad (1984) notes that the most predictable event in secondary classrooms is the lecture and in elementary classrooms, seat work. Both are passive, abstract pursuits that offer little hope of intellectual or moral stimulation. Goodlad writes, "Three categories of student activity marked by passivity—written work, listening, and preparing for assignments—dominate in the likelihood of their occurring at any given time at all three levels of schooling. The chances are better than 50–50 that if you were to walk into any of the classrooms of our sample, you would see one of these three activities under way" (p. 105).

In a similar vein, William Glasser (1990) notes that "students in school . . . are asked to learn well enough to remember for important tests innumerable facts that both they and their teachers know are of no use except to pass the tests" (p. 7). Glasser calls this stuff "throwaway information" because it is unconnected to experience and, by inference, to the real lives of students. Even students who receive good grades will often remark that they do not remember much of anything about a particular subject or teacher. Glasser goes on to say that a majority of students, even good ones, believe that much of the present academic curriculum is not worth the effort it takes to learn it. No matter how well teachers manage them, he suggests, if students do not find *quality* in what they are asked to do, they will not work hard enough to learn the material.

Keys to Reflective Thinking

- Reflective thinking takes *time*.
- Reflective thinking requires *strategy*.
- Reflective thinking assumes *trust*.
- Reflective thinking requires *discipline*.

- Reflective thinking is *social and moral*.
- Reflective thinking assumes *experience*.

Source: Adapted from Ellis, 2001.

Constructivist Thought and Social Studies

With the emergence of constructivist thought as a pervasive force in curriculum theory, it is once again becoming easier to find teaching and learning ideas that are based on meaningful experience and that offer the promise of quality. *Constructivism* is a theory of knowledge with roots in philosophy, art and architecture, psychology, and cybernetics. It asserts two main principles:

1. Knowledge is not passively received but actively built up by the cognizing subject.
2. The function of cognition is adaptive and serves the organization of the experiential world, not the discovery of ontological reality (i.e., having to do with the nature of being, existence).

The first principle represents trivial constructivism, a principle known since Socrates. The second principle suggests that knowledge cannot and need not be true in the sense that it matches ontological reality. It only has to be viable in the sense that it fits within the experiential constraints that limit the cognizing organism's possibilities of acting and thinking.

The greatest impact of constructivist theory to date has been in psychotherapy and in the empirical study of literature. In literature reading, meaning is supplied by the reader from his or her own store of experiential abstractions—thus, the subjective interpretation of text.

The teacher will realize that knowledge cannot be transferred to the student by linguistic communication but that language can be used as a tool in a process of guiding a student's construction. Student's need experiences of high quality that are at once engaging and intellectually demanding are needed. Reflective thinking, especially in regard to a search for meaning, and personal, social applications are crucial.

Thus, the basis of constructivity is that *experience precedes analysis.* The decade or more spent on such quests as time on task, behavioral objectives, and other teacher-centered instructional protocols proved to be a cul-de-sac along the road to inspiration in childhood learning, especially after the promise provided by the many learner-referenced social studies curriculum projects of a generation ago.

Constructivist thought, which invests learners in a search for their own sense of meaning based on many of the active teaching and learning strategies mentioned earlier, meets the conditions of what could be called an *experiential focus* in teaching and learning. Dewey (1916) himself foreshadowed the constructivist movement when he wrote that a person's ability to think about or apply reason to a given situation has a constructive function. He used the term *constructive* because a person constructs an idea or plan of action "which could not be produced otherwise." Social studies learning that is informal, exploratory, and interdisciplinary provides the needed conditions.

Yet engaging students *actively* is only half the battle. Active student engagement in a meaningful situation, problem, or issue makes it possible to create the conditions for reflective thinking because the students are bonded by a common experience. The experience becomes the focal point of reflective thought. Students reconstruct, evaluate, debrief, second-guess, and otherwise mentally reorganize what they did or what they are doing. It is from that concrete, common experience that students and teachers together can build the intellectual scaffolding necessary for the creation of ideas or concepts.

This is not easy to do. Goodlad (1984) said that in his seven-state study, he saw virtually no evidence of teachers teaching concepts. He concluded that either they felt concepts were unimportant or that they themselves did not think conceptually. However, concept teaching through reflective thinking is, in fact, the key to the saying "Less is more." This is because a few concepts carefully considered are worth far more as intellectual currency than the great amounts of information students are typically asked to cover. Teachers and learners must deliberately slow down, cover less, and think at length about what they are learning. Philosopher Jean-Jacques Rousseau knew this, and that is why he advised teachers to teach less and teach it well. In this same spirit, Alfred North Whitehead (1929) wrote, "What you teach, teach thoroughly" (p. 2).

Although it is imperative to include firsthand experience as an integral part of social studies learning, there should be no bias against abstract thought in constructivist classrooms. In fact, it is needed desperately. The abstract thought that one seeks, however, must be rooted in a meaningful frame of reference called experience. This was Francis Bacon's intent when he said that learning ought to be about facts—one's *own* facts and not someone else's. Bacon's Experience → Mind → Meaning model is much the same as that of Dewey:

Constructivist learning theory states that each of us must construct our own knowledge; others cannot give it to us. The role of experience and reflection in learning has been explored at length in the annals of cognitive research. Experience and reflection are, for example, the twin pillars of significance in constructivist learning theories. But one finds similar thinking in structuralist, developmental, and information-processing literature.

Robert Karplus, the director of the Science Curriculum Improvement Study (SCIS), developed a three-phase learning model consisting of preliminary exploration, invention, and discovery. Karplus notes that students need to start by exploring a concept using concrete materials. By starting an investigation in this manner, Karplus argues, a learner has a direct experience from which to begin processes of abstract thought. But to be meaningful, the learning cycle must continue beyond the direct experience.

Jerome Bruner (1963) makes a clear distinction between learning *by* experience and learning *from* experience, and the distinction lies not so much with the experience itself as with how one reflects back on the experience. Bruner notes that animals typically learn by experience. A dog that burns its paw on the stove will not repeat such a mistake. The dog is too intelligent for that. But the dog is incapable of reflecting on such ideas as heat transfer or thermodynamics as a result of its experience. So experience, as valuable as it is, is not enough. A search for meaning must accompany the experience.

These are the dual imperatives of constructivism. This is to say that in order for learners to think reflectively about important things, they must have direct experience. Equally important, they must also have opportunities to reconstruct their experience. The implication is that a given activity must be extended beyond the experiential phase into a time of reflection and knowledge construction.

To those who point out that there seems little new in these lines of argument, I advise a careful reading of the research-based policy guidelines that have appeared in leading educational journals and government publications over the last decade. The persuasive efforts aimed at school personnel to keep students focused on reductionist, teacher-centered, direct-instruction tasks have been legion.

Social Studies Strategies for Reflection

Attempts to redirect social studies toward a sense of greater activity and accompanying reflective thought inevitably bring up the element of time. Ask any teacher to name sources of frustration in his or her work, and the time factor invariably appears, usually in connection with having too little of it against too much material to cover.

John Carroll (1963) suggests that time is the most problematic variable in the curriculum. Most of what students are expected to learn in school settings is configured by class periods of an hour or less. This is obviously true at secondary levels, where separate subjects are assigned their own time slots, but it is more true than most care to admit at elementary levels. In addition, most social studies curriculums are set on time vectors from the first day of the school year forward. Teachers feel the need to forge ahead in order to provide the coverage demanded by the textbook or the district guide. This is particularly true of basic subjects such as social studies. It is less true of so-called soft subjects such as art, physical education, and music.

Carroll implies that if educators would slow down the curriculum, most students would actually learn more. His proposition is that the curriculum favors only those who learn quickly. The problem, he believes, is that most students never have the opportunity to process or to reflect on what they are learning—in essence, what is taught never gets internalized or connected to other learning. This problem is especially vexing in social studies, where so much new content involving place names, dates, and events washes over learners daily.

It has been noted that average and below-average learners often leave out steps when they try to solve problems. Apparently, they go too fast in their efforts to keep up, taking mental shortcuts. An example of this would be a child playing, say, checkers who rather impulsively makes what seem on the surface to him or her to be reasonable moves. Often, the moves this young checker player makes are poorly thought out and could be vastly improved by talking through a move with another person, in which case certain lapses in logic might be confronted. To those who might think that such a procedure in checkers would be unfair, it is well to keep in mind that our teaching and learning objective is not to win against an opponent but to become better at what we do.

Thinking Strategies

Robert Sternberg (1986) and others suggest that students should be encouraged to think aloud with a partner in order to slow themselves down. Such a strategy allows the learner to find out how well developed his or her ideas really are. Thinking aloud brings the process of coming to thought to the surface, giving learners an opportunity to compare and contrast their ideas with those of others. In other words, it provides students with the opportunity to think reflectively.

Jean Piaget (1965) wrote about the social knowledge that develops from working and interacting with others. He was convinced that the linguistic compatibility found within the peer group enables students to teach each other quite effectively, perhaps more effectively than an adult teacher, whose language structure is quite different from that of students. Russian psychologist Lev Vygotsky (1986) wrote about the community of knowledge and insight that the members of a community must share in order for learning to come to life. These insights point to the need for major restructuring of social studies learning and teaching.

Problem-Solving Strategies

Here is a rather simple example of how we might develop strategies for slowing down and making our thoughts more explicit in order to make them more productive. Imagine that there are 10 apples in a sack in a ratio of 3 red apples to 2 yellow apples. How many apples would you have to take out of the sack to be certain of having a matched pair either red or yellow?

This is a difficult problem for many children partly because it purposely contains some extraneous information. But is the problem inherently difficult or is it difficult because we expect students to solve it with paper and pencil after reading it from a page? Imagine two alternative methods of trying to solve the problem: (1) talking about it while drawing diagrams with a partner and (2) simply reaching into a container that held the apples several times and trying to construct with a partner why you got the results you did. Both of these methods take considerably more time than we generally allow for such problems, and both yield better results.

Some teachers, apparently satisfied with the results they are getting, simply do not see how we could possibly slow down the curriculum. They know they must cover a great deal of information to comply with the social studies agenda. One possible means of accommodation is for teachers to talk less. Research shows that teachers talk three times as much as their students (Goodlad, 1984). Since students outnumber teachers by about 27 to 1, it doesn't take a mathematics genius to figure out that students are allowed very little time to practice reflective thought.

A remedy for this situation, of course, is to use cooperative learning of some sort, where students are expected to share their thoughts and to listen to the thoughts of others. Cooperative learning not only changes the amount of student-to-student interaction so desperately needed for reflective thinking to occur, but it also changes the very social fabric of the classroom. Students are given far more control over their time, and teachers are able to shift from teaching as telling to allowing learning to take place.

Crossing the Frontier to Active Reflective Learning

Of course, much of this is already known by well-informed teachers. The problem lies with their many colleagues who are less informed about how to create the proper conditions for learning. Even among those who promote active learning, however, there is a reluctance to build in the extra time needed for genuine reflection by both students and teachers. Such a need is obviously not perceived by administrators as being necessary for teachers, who have little or no time to reflect alone or with fellow teachers. Therefore, it is little wonder that teachers often neglect reflective thinking with their students.

Economist Peter Drucker (1990) states in his provocative book *The New Realities* that schools will never improve until classrooms become places where people have crossed the frontier from teaching to learning. When the primary focus in a classroom is on *teaching,* a teacher-centered curriculum results. Teacher-centered instruction is the stuff of lesson plans, scripted activities, behavioral objectives, and predictable outcomes. When the focus in social studies is on *learning,* a constructivist curriculum emerges. Student-centered, constructivisit learning allows students the latitude to make choices, to play to their strengths, to work at length on projects, to develop ideas, to cooperate with other students, and to reflect on the quality and meaning of their work.

Instances of crossing the frontier from teaching to learning abound, but rarely in classrooms. Rather, they are found in the real world, where learners make their own connections, do their own investigations, and continuously process what they are learning.

Recently, I asked a colleague for some help with a problem I was having with a computer. He patiently walked me through a series of steps that got me on the right track. I asked him how he had learned so much about computers. He replied that he had learned what he knew by hanging around, using computers, and talking to other interested people. He explained that when he was in high school, there was a computer hooked up through a terminal to a mainframe and he used to go down to the little room where it was housed, close the door, and get online. He said he had never taken a computer class.

What my friend had done unwittingly was to follow John Dewey's prescription for learning: Make it experiential, make it as unscholastic as you can, and reflect on what you do with other interested people. This is how many children are learning on their own, outside school, when they play and discuss with friends the various video games, simulations, and so on. The success of Lego blocks in actually raising children's spatial intelligence is an example.

Perhaps you could cite similar examples of real learning from your own experience. In fact, you ought to write down and share with a friend a time when you were involved in *real* learning. The point is that such examples have significance because they have the power to redirect one's sense of teaching and learning away from formal, bookish procedures to the creation of learning environments that approximate real-world learning.

The Emotional/Intellectual Landscape

One other condition essential to creating classrooms where students and teachers think reflectively is that of a healthy emotional/intellectual landscape. Not long ago, I observed in a third-grade class where the teacher was doing an inquiry social studies lesson. The approach was inductive: Artifacts were available for the students to examine, the students were working in teams, and they were encouraged to make inferences from their observations and recordings. This was all to the good.

Unfortunately, the atmosphere was tense and rigid. The teacher kept interrupting the students to remind them to "stay on task," even though there was no evidence of misbehavior. Additionally, it became clear that the teacher was looking for right answers, and the students found themselves trying to please her or second-guess her wishes. None of the spontaneity that Piaget said must be present was there. Risk taking, outlandish ideas, a sense of humor, a relaxed and friendly pace—all were lacking.

In this case, what might have been a good formal curriculum was unraveled by a bad hidden curriculum. The possibility of one of those transcendent moments in teaching and learning that occur when a good experience is wedded to a good discussion was lost.

Keys to Teacher Beliefs

Following are a couple of simple but powerful tasks that involve writing statements of belief. First, write down several statements of belief about good teachers—in other words, some traits of good teachers. Then write down several things you believe about children. Create your own list of Keys.

Some Things I Believe about Good Teachers:

1. _____
2. _____
3. _____
4. _____
5. _____

Some Things I Believe about Children:

1. _____
2. _____
3. _____
4. _____
5. _____

Take some time to share your thoughts with someone else. How are his or her statements similar to or different from yours?

Summary

The proper conditions for reflective thinking in social studies derive from a complex set of strategies developed by teachers and students. Learning by doing is simply not sufficient in itself, and neither is direct experience—although both are important. You must be a guide, a fellow inquirer, an organizer of the environment, and a mediator of your students' thinking. You must establish a new set of priorities that run counter to the prevailing modes of instruction and classroom management. You must be committed to increasing the amount of student-to-student interaction, the number of decisions made by students, the amount of time given to reconstructing learning experiences, and the freedom given to your students to speak their minds and to take intellectual and emotional risks. When these conditions are met, the term *paradigm shift*—a term used so often to signal a basic transformation in what we do and what we expect to happen as a result—moves beyond the realm of cliché and into the realm of reality.

Explorations

Reflect On . . .

1. Discuss with a partner how you think classrooms would have to change in order for reflective thinking to become a reality.
2. Some people might argue that children are not capable of reflective thought. Do you agree? Why or why not?

In the Field

3. Many educators over the years have suggested that we teach less and teach it well. What are the implications for social studies of teaching less?

4. How can a teacher know if his or her students are thinking reflectively? What strategies are necessary to ensure that it will happen?

For Your Portfolio

5. Identify at least three differences you might expect to see between a constructivist classroom and a traditional classroom.

Continuing the Journey: Suggested Readings

Broadwater, K. (2005). Museum field trips. *School Arts, 104*(7), 6.
A useful article on purposes, procedures, and reflection for field trips.

Dewey, J. (1938). *Experience and education.* New York: Collier.
Written late in his career, this readable book sets the record straight on the balance between progressive and traditional teaching and learning.

Ellis, A. (2001). *Teaching, learning, and assessment together: The reflective classroom.* Larchmont, NY: Eye on Education.
This book includes twenty strategies for promoting reflective thinking while integrating it into ongoing assessment.

Ellis, A. (2005). *Research in educational innovations* (3rd ed.). Larchmont, NY: Eye on Education.
A review and critique of twelve educational innovations, including cooperative learning, brain science, multiple intelligences, etc.

Gordinier, C., Moberly, D., & Conway, K. (2004). Scaffolding enables reflective thinking to become a disposition. *Childhood Education, 80*(3), 146.
A useful article that illustrates ways to make children habitual reflective thinkers.

Hmelo-Silver, C. (2004). Problem-based learning: What and how do students learn? *Educational Psychology Review, 16*(3), 235–257.
A research-based review of problem-based learning.

Rogers, C. (2004). Defining reflection: Another look at John Dewey and reflective thinking. *Teachers College Record, 104*(4), 842–867.
A thoughtful account of the meaning and purpose of reflective thinking by teachers and students.

Sharp, K. (2003). Teacher reflection: A perspective from the trenches. *Theory into Practice, 42*(3), 243–248.
A practical look at reflective thinking by teachers.

Appendix

Standards Sampler

More and more, students must demonstrate mastery of standards set by national educational organizations or professional organizations in various disciplines, and the social studies are no exception. The following pages provide a brief overview of the standards created for both students and teachers by three groups: the National Council for the Social Studies, the National Center for History in the Schools, and the National Council for Geography Education.

*National Council for the Social Studies Thematic Standards**

Teachers of social studies at all school levels should provide developmentally appropriate experiences as they guide learners in the study of the following topics.

Culture and Cultural Diversity

Teachers should

- Enable learners to analyze and explain the ways groups, societies, and cultures address human needs and concerns.

- Guide learners as they predict how data and experiences may be interpreted by people from diverse cultural perspectives and frames of references.

- Assist learners to apply an understanding as an integrated whole that explains the functions and interactions of language, literature, the arts, traditions, beliefs and values, and behavior patterns.

- Encourage learners to compare and analyze societal patterns for preserving and transmitting culture while adapting to environmental and social change.

• Ask learners to give examples and describe the importance of cultural unity and diversity within and across groups.

• Have learners interpret patterns of behavior reflecting values and attitudes that contribute or pose obstacles to cross-cultural understanding.

• Guide learners as they construct reasoned judgments about specific cultural responses to persistent human issues.

• Have learners explain and apply ideas, theories, and modes of inquiry drawn from anthropology and sociology in the examination of persistent issues and social problems.

Time, Continuity, and Change

Teachers should

• Assist learners in understanding that historical knowledge and the concept of time are socially influenced constructions that lead historians to be selective in the questions they seek to answer and the evidence they use.

• Have learners apply key concepts from the study of history—such as time, chronology, causality, change, conflict, and complexity—to explain, analyze, and show connections among patterns of historical change and continuity.

• Ask learners to identify and describe significant historical periods and patterns of change within and across cultures, such as the development of ancient cultures and civilizations, the rise of nation-states, and social, economic, and political revolutions.

• Guide learners as they systematically employ processes of critical historical inquiry to reconstruct and reinterpret the past, such as using a variety of sources and checking their credibility, validating and weighing evidence for claims, and searching for causality.

• Provide learners with opportunities to investigate, interpret, and analyze multiple historical and contemporary viewpoints within and across cultures related to important events, recurring dilemmas, and persistent issues, while employing empathy, skepticism, and critical judgment.

• Enable learners to apply ideas, theories, and modes of historical inquiry to analyze historical and contemporary developments, and to inform and evaluate actions concerning public policy issues.

People, Places, and Environments

Teachers should

• Enable learners to construct, use, and refine mental maps of locales, regions, and the world that demonstrate their understanding of relative location, direction, size, and shape.

● Have learners create, interpret, use, and distinguish various representations of Earth, such as maps, globes, and photographs, and use appropriate geographic tools such as atlases, databases, systems, charts, graphs, and maps to generate, manipulate, and interpret information.

● Teach students to estimate and calculate distance, scale, area, and density, and to distinguish spatial distribution patterns.

● Help learners locate, distinguish, and describe the relationships among varying regional and global patterns of geographic phenomena such as landforms, climate, and natural resources.

● Challenge learners to speculate about and explain physical system changes, such as seasons, climate, and weather.

● Ask learners to describe how people create places that reflect culture, human needs, current values and ideals, and government policies.

● Challenge learners to examine, interpret, and analyze the interactions of human beings and their physical environments.

● Have learners explore the ways Earth's physical features have changed over time, and describe and assess the ways historical events have influenced and have been influenced by physical and human geographic features.

● Provide learners with opportunities to observe and analyze social and economic effects of environmental changes and crises.

● Challenge learners to consider, compare, and evaluate existing alternative uses of resources and land in communities, regions, nations, and the world.

Individual Human Development and Identity

Teachers should

● Assist learners in articulating personal connections to time, place, and social/cultural systems.

● Help learners identify, describe, and express appreciation for the influences of various historical and contemporary cultures on their daily lives.

● Assist learners in describing the ways family, religion, gender, ethnicity, nationality, socioeconomic status, and other group and cultural influences contribute to the development of a sense of self.

● Have learners apply concepts, methods, and theories about the study of human growth and development, such as physical endowment, learning, motivation, behavior, perception, and personality.

● Guide learners as they examine the interactions of ethnic, national, or cultural influences in specific situations or events.

- Enable learners to analyze the role of perceptions, attitudes, values, and beliefs in the development of personal identity.

- Have learners compare and evaluate the impact of stereotyping, conformity, acts of altruism, and other behaviors on individuals and groups.

- Assist learners as they work independently and cooperatively within groups and institutions to accomplish goals.

- Enable learners to examine factors that contribute to and damage one's mental health and analyze issues related to mental health and behavioral disorders in contemporary society.

Individuals, Groups, and Institutions

Teachers should

- Help learners understand the concepts of role, status, and social class and use them in describing the connections and interactions of individuals, groups, and institutions in society.

- Help learners analyze group and institutional influences on people, events, and elements of culture in both historical and contemporary settings.

- Explain to learners the various forms institutions take, and explain how they develop and change over time.

- Assist learners in identifying and analyzing examples of tensions between expressions of individuality and efforts used to promote social conformity by groups and institutions.

- Ask learners to describe and examine belief systems basic to specific traditions and laws in contemporary and historical movements.

- Challenge learners to evaluate the role of institutions in furthering both continuity and change.

- Guide learner analysis of the extent to which groups and institutions meet individual needs and promote the common good in contemporary and historical settings.

- Assist learners as they explain and apply ideas and modes of inquiry drawn from behavioral science and social theory in the examination of persistent issues and social problems.

Power, Authority, and Governance

Teachers should

- Enable learners to examine the rights and responsibilities of the individual in relation to his or her family, social groups, community, and nation.

• Help students to explain the purpose of government and how its powers are acquired, used, and justified.

• Provide opportunities for learners to examine issues involving the rights, roles, and status of individuals in relation to the general welfare.

• Ask learners to describe the way nations and organizations respond to forces of unity and diversity affecting order and security.

• Have learners explain conditions, actions, and motivations that contribute to conflict and cooperation within and among nations.

• Help learners identify and describe the basic features of the U.S. political system, and identify representative leaders from various levels and branches of government.

• Challenge learners to apply concepts such as power, role, status, justice, and influence to the examination of persistent issues and social problems.

• Guide learners to explain how governments attempt to achieve their stated ideals at home and abroad.

Production, Distribution, and Consumption of Goods and Services

Teachers should

• Enable learners to explain how the scarcity of productive resources (human, capital, technological, and natural) requires the development of economic systems to make decisions about how goods and services are to be produced and distributed.

• Help learners analyze the role that supply and demand, prices, incentives, and profits play in determining what is produced and distributed in a competitive market system.

• Help learners compare the costs and benefits to society of allocating goods and services through private and public sectors.

• Explain to learners the relationships among the various economic institutions that comprise economic systems such as households, businesses, banks, government agencies, labor unions, and corporations.

• Guide learner analysis of the role of specialization and exchange in economic processes.

• Provide opportunities for learners to assess how values and beliefs influence economic decisions in different societies.

• Have learners compare basic economic systems according to how rules and procedures deal with demand, supply, prices, the role of government, banks, labor and labor unions, savings and investments, and capital.

- Challenge learners to apply economic concepts and reasoning when evaluating historical and contemporary social developments and issues.

- Ask learners to distinguish between the domestic and global economic systems, and explain how the two interact.

- Guide learners in the application of knowledge of production, distribution, and consumption in the analysis of public issues such as the allocation of health care or the consumption of energy, and in devising economic plans for accomplishing socially desirable outcomes related to such issues.

- Help learners distinguish between economics as a field of inquiry and the economy.

Science and Technology

Teachers should

- Enable learners to identify, describe, and examine both current and historical examples of the interaction and interdependence of science, technology, and society in a variety of cultural settings.

- Provide opportunities for learners to make judgments about how science and technology have transformed the physical world and human society and our understanding of time, space, place, and human–environment interactions.

- Have learners analyze the way in which science and technology influence core societal values, beliefs, and attitudes and how societal attitudes shape scientific and technological change.

- Prompt learners to evaluate various policies proposed to deal with social changes resulting from new technologies.

- Help learners to identify and interpret various perspectives about human societies and the physical world using scientific knowledge, technologies, and ethical standards from diverse world cultures.

- Encourage learners to formulate strategies and develop policy proposals for influencing public discussions associated with science, technology, and society issues.

Global Connections and Interdependence

Teachers should

- Enable learners to explain how language, art, music, belief systems, and other cultural elements can facilitate global understanding or cause misunderstanding.

- Help learners explain conditions and motivations that contribute to conflict, cooperation, and interdependence among groups, societies, and nations.

● Provide opportunities for learners to analyze and evaluate the effects of changing technologies on the global community.

● Challenge learners to analyze the causes, consequences, and possible solutions to persistent, contemporary, and emerging global issues, such as health care, security, resource allocation, economic development, and environmental quality.

● Guide learner analysis of the relationships and tensions between national sovereignty and global interests in such matters as territorial disputes, economic development, nuclear and other weapons deployment, use of natural resources, and human rights concerns.

● Have learners analyze or formulate policy statements in such ways that they demonstrate an understanding of concerns, standards, issues, and conflicts related to universal human rights.

● Help learners to describe and evaluate the role of international and multinational organizations in the global arena.

● Have learners illustrate how individual behaviors and decisions connect with global systems.

Civic Ideals and Practices

Teachers should

● Assist learners to understand the origins and interpret the continuing influence of key ideals of the democratic form of government, such as individual human dignity, liberty, justice, equality, and the rule of law.

● Guide learner efforts to identify, analyze, interpret, and evaluate sources and examples of citizens' rights and responsibilities.

● Facilitate learner efforts to locate, access, analyze, organize, synthesize, evaluate, and apply information about selected public issues identifying, describing, and evaluating multiple points of view.

● Provide opportunities for learners to practice forms of civic discussion and participation consistent with the ideals of citizens in a democratic republic.

● Help learners analyze and evaluate the influence of various forms of citizen action on public policy.

● Prepare learners to analyze a variety of public policies and issues from the perspective of formal and informal political actors.

● Guide learners as they evaluate the effectiveness of public opinion in influencing and shaping public policy development and decision making.

● Encourage learner efforts to evaluate the degree to which public policies and citizen behaviors reflect or foster the stated ideals of a democratic form of government.

● Support learner efforts to construct policy statements and action plans to achieve goals related to issues of public concern.

• Create opportunities for learner participation in activities to strengthen the "common good," based on careful evaluation of possible options for citizen action.

The National Center for History in the Schools

Overview of K–4 Content Standards in History

Topic 1: Living and working together in families and communities, now and long ago

> Standard 1: Family life now and in the recent past; family life in various places long ago
> Standard 2: History of students' local community and how communities in North America varied long ago

Topic 2: The history of the students' own state or region

> Standard 3: The people, events, problems, and ideas that created the history of their state

Topic 3: The history of the United States: Democratic principles and values and the peoples from many cultures who contributed to its cultural, economic, and political heritage

> Standard 4: How democratic values came to be, and how they have been exemplified by people, events, and symbols
> Standard 5: The causes and nature of various movements of large groups of people into and within the United States, now and long ago
> Standard 6: Regional folklore and cultural contributions that helped to form our national heritage

Topic 4: The history of peoples of many cultures around the world

> Standard 7: Selected attributes and historical developments of various societies in Africa, the Americas, Asia, and Europe
> Standard 8: Major discoveries in science and technology, their social and economic effects, and the scientists and inventors responsible for them

National Council for Geography Education

The geographically informed person knows and understands the following.

The World in Spatial Terms

> Standard 1: How to use maps and other geographic representations, tools, and technologies to acquire, process, and report information

Standard 2: How to use mental maps to organize information about people, places, and environments

Standard 3: How to analyze the spatial organization of people, places, and environments on the Earth's surface

Places and Regions

Standard 4: The physical and human characteristics of places

Standard 5: That people create regions to interpret the Earth's complexity

Standard 6: How culture and experience influence people's perception of places and regions

Physical Systems

Standard 7: The physical processes that shape the patterns of the Earth's surface

Standard 8: The characteristics and spatial distribution of ecosystems on the Earth's surface

Human Systems

Standard 9: The characteristics, distribution, and migration of human populations on the Earth's surface

Standard 10: The characteristics, distributions, and complexity of the Earth's cultural mosaics

Standard 11: The patterns and networks of economic interdependence on the Earth's surface

Standard 12: The process, patterns, and functions of human settlement

Standard 13: How forces of cooperation and conflict among people influence the division and control of the Earth's surface

Environment and Society

Standard 14: How human actions modify the physical environment

Standard 15: How physical systems affect human systems

Standard 16: The changes that occur in the meaning, use, distribution, and importance of resources

The Uses of Geography

Standard 17: How to apply geography to interpret the past

Standard 18: How to apply geography to interpret the present and plan for the future

References

Adler, M. (1982). *The paideia proposal.* New York: Macmillan.

Anderson, C. (1993, April). The context of civic competence and education. *Social Education,* 160–164.

Angell, A. V. (1991, Summer). Democratic climates in elementary classrooms: A review of theory and research. *Theory and Research in Social Education,* 241–266.

Aronson, E., & Patnoe, S. (1997). *The jigsaw classroom.* New York: Longman.

Bales, R. (1957). *Effects of size of problem-solving groups on the system of interaction.* Report to the American Psychological Association. Washington, DC: APA.

Bandura, A. (1997). *Self-efficacy: The exercise of control.* New York: W. H. Freeman.

Banks, J. A., & Banks, C. A. M. (2001). *Multicultural education: Issues and perspectives* (4th ed.). New York: John Wiley & Sons.

Berliner, D., & Biddle, B. (1997). *The manufactured crisis.* White Plains, NY: Longman.

Berman, S. (1990, November). Educating for social responsibility. *Educational Leadership,* 75–80.

Bloom, B. S. (1984). *Taxonomy of educational objectives.* Boston: Allyn & Bacon.

Bruner, J. (1963). *The process of education.* New York: Vintage Books.

Calderwood, J. D., Lawrence, J. D., & Maher, J. E. (1970). *Economics in the curriculum.* New York: John Wiley & Sons.

Carroll, J. (1963). A model of school learning. *Teachers College Record, 64,* 722–733.

Center for Information and Research on Civic Learning and Engagement. (2005). Civics education: What students are learning. In *Campaign for the civic mission of schools: Educating for democracy.* College Park: University of Maryland School of Public Policy.

Collingwood, R. G. (1946). In T. M. Knox (Ed.), *The idea of history.* London: Oxford University Press.

Cotton, K. (1996). *Educating for citizenship.* Portland, OR: Northwest Regional Educational Laboratory.

Deutsch, M. (1949). A theory of cooperation and competition. *Human Relations, 2,* 129–152.

Devlin, S., & Freeney, A. (1973). *The design of surveys and samples.* Newton, MA: Education Development Center.

Dewey, J. (1899). *The school and society.* Boston: Houghton Mifflin.

Dewey, J. (1916). *Democracy and education.* New York: Macmillan.

Diller, J., & Moule, J. (2005). *Cultural competence: A primer for educators.* Belmont, CA: Wadsworth.

Drucker, P. (1990). *The new realities.* New York: Perennial Library.

Easton, D. (1966). *A systems approach to political life.* Boulder, CO: Social Science Education Consortium.

Ebel, R. (1971). *Measuring educational achievement.* Englewood Cliffs, NJ: Prentice-Hall.

Eggen, P., & Kauchak, D. (1996). *Strategies for teachers: Teaching content and thinking skills.* Boston: Allyn & Bacon.

Ellis, A. (2001). *Teaching, learning, and assessment together: The reflective classroom.* Larchmont, NY: Eye on Education.

Ellis, A. (2006). *Research on educational innovations.* Larchmont, NY: Eye on Education.

Ellis, A., & Fouts, J. (1997). *Research on educational innovations* (2nd ed.). Princeton, NJ: Eye on Education.

Fenton, E. (1967). *The new social studies.* New York: Holt, Rinehart, & Winston.

Fielder, W. (Ed.). (1972). *Inquiring about American history.* New York: Holt, Rinehart, & Winston.

Fouts, J. (1989, Spring). Classroom environments and student views of social studies: A replication study. *Theory and Research in Social Education,* 136–147.

Gardner, H. (1983). *Frames of mind: The theory of multiple intelligences.* New York: Basic Books.

Gardner, H. (1991). *The unschooled mind.* New York: Basic Books.

Gilligan, C. (1982). *In a different voice: Psychological theory and women's development.* Cambridge, MA: Harvard University Press.

Glasser, W. (1990). *The quality school.* New York: Harper & Row.

Goodlad, J. (1984). *A place called school.* New York: McGraw-Hill.

Greco, P. (1966). *Geography.* Boulder, CO: Social Science Education Consortium.

Haberman, M. (1996). Selecting and preparing culturally competent teachers for urban schools. In J. Sikula, T. Buttery, & H. Guyon (Eds.), *Handbook of research on teacher education* (2nd ed.). New York: Macmillan.

Habermas, J. (1968). *Knowledge and human interest.* Cambridge, UK: Polity Press.

Hamilton, M. H. (2000). Creating a culturally responsive learning environment for African American students. In M. Magolda (Ed.), *Teaching to promote intellectual and personal maturity: Incorporating students' worldviews and identities into the learning process* (pp. 45–54). San Francisco: Jossey-Bass.

Hamilton, M. H. (2004). *Meeting the needs of African American women: New directions for student services.* San Francisco: Jossey-Bass.

Harper, R., & Schmudde, T. (1973). *Between two worlds: A new introduction to geography.* Boston: Houghton Mifflin.

Heidel, J., Lyman-Mersereau, M., & Janke, J. E. (Eds.). (1999). *Character education: Grades K–6.* Nashville, TN: Incentive Publications.

Hirsch, E. D. (1987). *Cultural literacy.* Boston: Houghton Mifflin.

Hirsch, E. D. (1991–2005). *The core knowledge series K–8.* New York: Delta.

Jackson, P., Boostrom, R., & Hansen, D. (1993). *The moral life of schools.* San Francisco: Jossey-Bass.

Johnson, D., & Johnson, R. (1974, April). Instructional goal structure: Cooperative, competitive, or individualistic. *Review of Educational Research, 213.*

Johnson, D., & Johnson, R. (1988). *Cooperation and competition: Theory and research.* Edina, MN: Interaction Book Company.

Johnson, D., & Johnson, R. (2004). *Assessing students in groups: Promoting group responsibility and individual accountability.* Thousand Oaks, CA: Corwin.

Johnson, D., Johnson, R., & Holubec, E. (2002). *Circles of learning.* Edina, MN: Interaction Book Company.

Johnston, J. H. (1995, November/December). Climate: Building a culture of achievement. *Schools in the Middle,* 10–15.

Kaye, E. (1974). *The family guide to children's television.* New York: Random House.

Kinch, J. (1971). *Introductory sociology: The individual in society.* San Rafael, CA: Individual Learning Systems.

Kirschenbaum, H. (1996). *100 ways to enhance values and morality in schools and youth settings.* Boston: Allyn & Bacon.

Kohlberg, L. (1983). *The psychology of moral development.* New York: Harper & Row.

Kohlberg, L., & Whitten, P. (1972, December). Understanding the hidden curriculum. *Learning, 14.*

Kohn, A. (1999). *The schools our children deserve: Moving beyond traditional classrooms and "tougher standards."* Boston: Houghton Mifflin.

Krug, M. (1967). *History and the social sciences.* Waltham, MA: Blaisdell.

Lewis, C. S. (1947). *The abolition of man: How education develops man's sense of morality.* New York: Collier Books.

Maher, J. E. (1969). *What is economics?* New York: John Wiley & Sons.

Marzano, R., & Arredondo, D. (1986). *Tactics for thinking.* Aurora, CO: Mid-Continent Regional Laboratory.

McCombs, B., & Whisler, J. (1997). *The learner-centered classroom and school.* San Francisco: Jossey-Bass.

Medina, J. (2003). "Brainchild: Stress and the human brain." *Brain Science and Human Learning, 26*(4), 24–26.

Michigan Department of Education. (2001). *What research says about parent involvement in children's education.* Lansing, MI: Author.

National adult literacy survey. (1993). Washington, DC: National Center for Education Statistics.

National Assessment Governing Board. (1994, 2001). *Geography Framework for the 1994 and 2001 National Assessment of Educational Progress.* Washington, DC: U.S. Department of Education.

National Assessment of Educational Progress (NAEP). (1998). *Report card on civics education.* Washington, DC: U.S. Department of Education.

National Center for Education Statistics (NCES). (1994, 2001). *National Assessment of Educational Progress: History Standards.* Washington, DC: U.S. Department of Education.

National Council for the Social Studies. (1994). *Curriculum standards for social studies: Expectations of excellence.* Washington, DC: Author.

Oliver, D. (1964). *Invitation to anthropology.* Garden City, NY: Natural History Press.

Onosko, J., & Newmann, F. (1994). Creating more thoughtful learning environments. In J. Mangieri & C. Block (Eds.), *Creating powerful thinking in teachers and students.* Fort Worth, TX: Harcourt Brace.

Papert, S. (1984). *Mindstorms.* New York: Basic Books.

Perrucci, R. (1966). *Sociology.* Boulder, CO: Social Science Education Consortium.

Piaget, J. (1965). *The moral development of the child.* New York: Free Press.

Rest, J., Narváez, M., Bebeau, M. J., & Thoma, S. J. (1999). *Postconventional moral thinking: A neo-Kohlbergian approach.* New York: Erlbaum.

Rogers, C., & Frieberg, J. (1994). *Freedom to learn* (3rd ed.). New York: Macmillan.

Rose, C. (1965). *Sociology: The study of man in society.* Columbus, OH: Merrill.

Rowe, D. (1992, Winter). A conflict model of citizenship education. *Curriculum.*

Scheuerman, R., & Ellis, A. (Eds.). (2003). *North American journeys of discovery: The expedition of Lewis & Clark.* Madison, WI: DEMCO.

Scheuerman, R., & Ellis, A. (Eds.). (2004). *The expeditions of Lewis and Clark and Zebulon Pike.* Madison, WI: DEMCO.

Schug, M., et al. (1984). Why don't kids like social studies? *Social Studies Education, 48,* 382–387.

Schumacher, E. F. (1973). *Small is beautiful.* New York: Harper & Row.

Senn, P. (1971). *Social science and its methods.* Boston: Holbrook Press.

Sharp, R., & Ellis, A. (1994). *Greenbelt design.* Unpublished paper, Project 2061, American Association for the Advancement of Science.

Sheindlin, J. (2000). *Win or lose by how you choose.* New York: HarperCollins.

Simon, S., Kirschenbaum, H., & Howe, L. (1973). *Values clarification.* New York: Hart.

Sommer, C. H. (2000). *The war against boys: How misguided feminism is harming our young men.* New York: Simon & Schuster.

Stearns, P. (1993). *Why study history?* Washington, DC: The American Historical Society.

Stearns, P. (2006). *Childhood in world history.* New York: Routledge.

Sternberg, R. (1986). *Intelligence applied: Understanding and increasing your intellectual skills.* San Diego: Harcourt Brace Jovanovich.

Torney-Purta, J. (1982, Summer). Global awareness survey: Implications for teacher education. *Theory into Practice, 200–205.*

Torney-Purta, J. (1983, November/December). Psychological perspectives on enhancing civic education through the education of teachers. *Journal of Teacher Education, 30–34.*

Vygotsky, L. (1986). *Thought and language* (A. Kozulin, Trans.). Cambridge, MA: MIT Press.

Wadsworth, B. (2004). *Piaget's theory of cognitive and affective development* (5th ed.). Boston: Allyn & Bacon.

Ward, P. (1971). The awkward social science: History. In I. Morrissett & W. Stevens (Eds.), *Social science in the schools.* New York: Holt, Rinehart, & Winston.

Watkins, F. (1960). In V. Van Dyke (Ed.), *Political science: A philosophical analysis.* Stanford, CA: Stanford University Press.

Watson, G., & Johnson, D. (1972). *Social psychology: Issues and insights.* Philadelphia: Lippincott.

Whitehead, A. (1929). *Aims of education.* New York: Free Press.

Index

Credits